For linear regression line TI-82
(line of best fit)

C. KOSTAL
B-2

Y=

VARS

#5 → →

#7

to change from degrees to radians or vice versa, the calculator has to be in Radian Mode, then proceed

The University of Chicago School Mathematics Project

Precalculus and Discrete Mathematics

Second Edition

Teacher's Edition

Part 1, Chapters 1-6

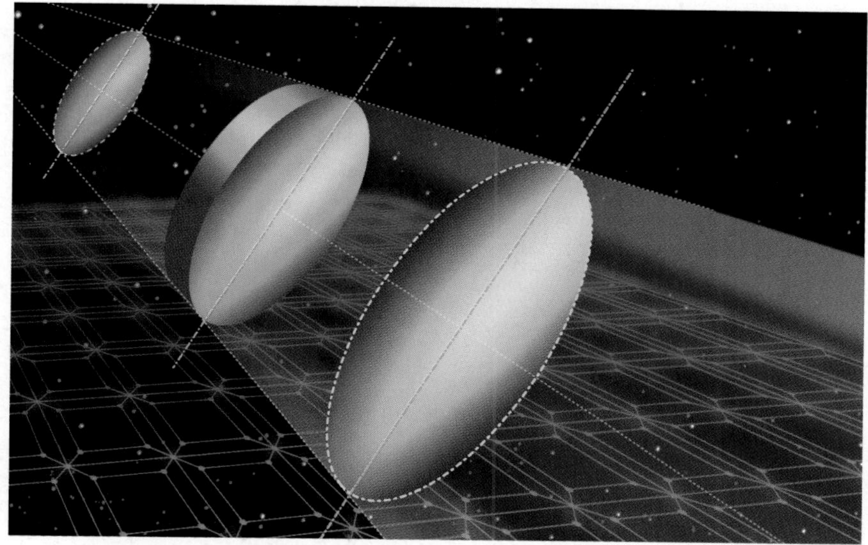

About the Cover In *Precalculus and Discrete Mathematics,* we prepare for calculus and preview the concepts of derivative and integral which are related to area and volume. The background contains a tessellation based on a network, a discrete graph, which represents the vertices of a rectangular solid.

Authors

Anthony L. Peressini John W. McConnell Zalman Usiskin
Susanna S. Epp Nils P. Ahbel David Witonsky
Kathleen A. Hollowell Susan Brown Wade Ellis, Jr.
John Sorteberg Denisse R. Thompson Dora Aksoy
Geoffrey D. Birky Greg A. McRill

Scott Foresman
Addison Wesley

Editorial Offices: Glenview, Illinois • Menlo Park, California
Sales Offices: Reading, Massachusetts • Atlanta, Georgia • Glenview, Illinois
Carrollton, Texas • Menlo Park, California
http://www.sf.aw.com

ACKNOWLEDGMENTS

Authors

Anthony L. Peressini
Professor Emeritus of Mathematics, University of Illinois, Urbana

John W. McConnell
Instructional Supervisor of Mathematics, Glenbrook South H.S., Glenview, IL

Zalman Usiskin
Professor of Education, The University of Chicago

Susanna S. Epp
Professor of Mathematics, DePaul University, Chicago, IL (First Edition only)

Nils P. Ahbel
Mathematics Teacher, Deerfield Academy, Deerfield, MA (Second Edition only)

David Witonsky
UCSMP (Second Edition only)

Kathleen A. Hollowell
Coordinator of Secondary Mathematics Inservice Programs, University of Delaware, Newark, DE (First Edition only)

Susan Brown
Mathematics Department Chair, York H.S., Elmhurst, IL (First Edition only)

Wade Ellis, Jr.
Mathematics Instructor, West Valley College, Saratoga, CA (First Edition only)

Jack Sorteberg
Mathematics Teacher, Burnsville H.S., Burnsville, MN (First Edition only)

Denisse R. Thompson
Associate Professor of Mathematics Education, University of South Florida, Tampa, FL (First Edition only)

Dora Aksoy
UCSMP (First Edition only)

Geoffrey D. Birky
UCSMP (First Edition only)

Greg McRill
UCSMP (First Edition only)

UCSMP Production and Evaluation

Series Editors: Zalman Usiskin, Sharon L. Senk

Technical Coordinator: Susan Chang

Managing Editor: David Witonsky

Director of First Edition Study: Denisse Thompson

We wish also to acknowledge the generous support of the **Amoco Foundation** and the **Carnegie Corporation of New York** for the development, testing, and distribution of the First Edition of these materials.

We wish to thank the many editors, production personnel, and design personnel at Scott Foresman Addison Wesley for their magnificent assistance.

Design Development

Steven Curtis Design, Inc.

ISBN: 0-673-45915-2

Printed in the United States of America

123456789—WO—01009998

Contents
of Teacher's Edition

The complete Table of Contents for the Student Edition begins on page *vi*.

Your UCSMP Professional Sourcebook is found at the back of this book, starting on page T20.

UCSMP Precalculus and Discrete Mathematics

SECOND EDITION

"We are entering an age where our students will be asked to complete thought-provoking tasks and perform jobs which do not yet exist. Our students deserve an education which enables and requires them to reflect, to discover their own learning, and to connect all subject matter. These goals are inherent in UCSMP."

Rodney V. De Jarnett
Concord, New Hampshire

The University of Chicago School Mathematics Project

It works

Carefully developed by a prestigious team of authors in full accordance with the goals of the NCTM Standards, UCSMP has been refined through field testing and feedback from users. Millions of successful students and an ever-growing network of enthusiastic teachers have proven that UCSMP is a program that works.

Why it works as today's curriculum

UCSMP's flexible six-year curriculum emphasizes connections within mathematics and to other disciplines, develops concepts through real-world applications, implements the latest technology, and encourages independent learning.

How it works for today's students

Clear and inviting, UCSMP *Precalculus and Discrete Mathematics* offers continual opportunities for problem solving, practice and review, and end-of-chapter mastery. Attention to individual needs and a broad approach to assessment help you offer success to all students.

The following section provides an overview of UCSMP *Precalculus and Discrete Mathematics.* For more detailed information, see the Professional Sourcebook at the back of this book (page T20).

WHAT'S NEW in the Second Edition

In the Student Edition:

- Appealing, student-friendly layout
- Reading Organizers to outline each lesson
- In-class and In-lesson Activities
- More extensive use of latest technology
- Current statistical data integrated throughout

In the Teacher's Edition:

- Warm-up ideas for introducing each lesson
- Enhanced integration and connections
- Optional activities to reinforce and extend topics
- Frequent suggestions for adapting to individual needs
- Ideas for setting up the next lesson

PLUS—

In the support package:

- An enhanced Assessment Sourcebook
- Study Skills Handbook
- Implementing UCSMP: A User's Handbook
- Visual Aids
- Explorations Software
- Teacher's Resource File CD-ROM Version

UCSMP — It works

The U.S. Department of Education has granted UCSMP its "A+ Award" for helping the nation work toward the six National Education Goals.

Program development

The UCSMP Secondary Component Materials have been developed with extensive input from classroom teachers and a special advisory board. The project has been funded by several major corporations that recognize the need for exciting new materials for mathematics education.

An innovative approach

UCSMP is the first full mathematics curriculum to implement the NCTM Standards by teaching concepts *through* their applications, emphasizing the reading and writing of mathematics, providing a wide variety of meaningful problem-solving opportunities, and incorporating the latest technology.

"Our math enrollment is up; even seniors, who don't have to take math to graduate, are taking math courses."

Tom Postema
Tokyo, Japan

Proven success

The UCSMP materials have been carefully refined through years of field testing and feedback from users of the First Edition. Teachers throughout the country have discovered that UCSMP is the way to offer success to the greatest number of students.

The **best** book to help students learn precalculus and discrete mathematics has gotten even better!

First Edition Study

The first edition of *Precalculus and Discrete Mathematics* was piloted for two consecutive years beginning in 1987. Extensive revisions were made based on teacher feedback. A formative evaluation began in 1989. Students were tested prior to using the materials and then tested at the end of the school year. Based on posttest student performance, changes were again made to improve the text prior to publication.

Second Edition Study

To prepare for the second edition of *Precalculus and Discrete Mathematics*, teachers using the text were invited to evaluate each lesson and provide feedback on other aspects of the course; seventeen teachers participated. Users' comments gathered over the years by UCSMP and Scott Foresman Addison Wesley were also considered. Some second-edition authors are experienced teachers of *Precalculus and Discrete Mathematics*. All of this information factored into the changes made in the second edition.

For a complete discussion of the research and development of UCSMP *Precalculus and Discrete Mathematics*, please see the Professional Sourcebook, Section 4, in the Teacher's Edition.

"With UCSMP, our students have grown in personal maturity and have learned more mathematics. UCSMP is beautifully organized, constantly reviewing for depth and integrating for breadth. It is student-centered, and our students using UCSMP are demonstrating a high degree of confidence and competence."

Barry Walker
Birmingham, Alabama

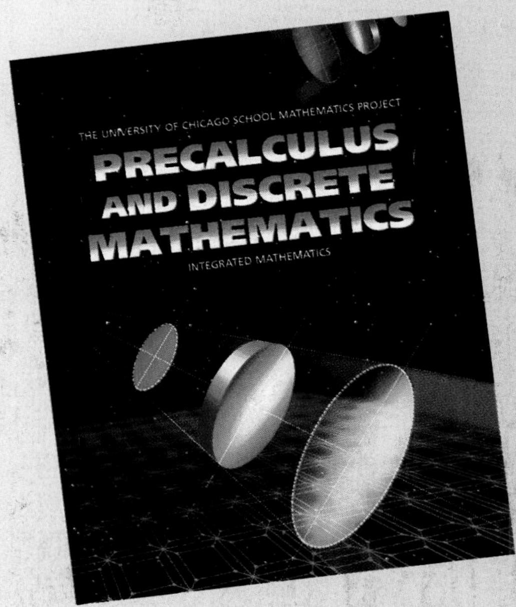

Why it works as today's curriculum

Grades	Top 10% of 5th graders	50th-90th percentile of 6th graders	30th-70th percentile of 7th graders	15th-50th percentile of 8th graders
6	Transition Mathematics			
7	Algebra	Transition Mathematics		
8	Geometry	Algebra	Transition Mathematics	
9	Advanced Algebra	Geometry	Algebra	Transition Mathematics
10	Functions, Statistics, and Trigonometry	Advanced Algebra	Geometry	Algebra
11	Precalculus and Discrete Mathematics	Functions, Statistics, and Trigonometry	Advanced Algebra	Geometry
12	Calculus (Not part of UCSMP)	Precalculus and Discrete Mathematics	Functions, Statistics, and Trigonometry	Advanced Algebra

A flexible curriculum

UCSMP provides a complete program for students in middle school and high school. It spreads the usual secondary mathematics content over six years, allowing students to both broaden and deepen their understanding of each topic.

"I have taught advanced math-precalculus-math analysis (it has gone by all these names) for a lot of years with a lot of different books. The UCSMP PDM book is far and away the best book ever written for this level."

Jerry Detweiler
Goshen, Indiana

Real-world applications

By constantly answering the question "When are we ever going to have to use this?" UCSMP *Precalculus and Discrete Mathematics* develops lessons more meaningfully and motivates students to learn. *See pages 27, 86–88, 253–254, 560, 660–661, and 721 for further examples.*

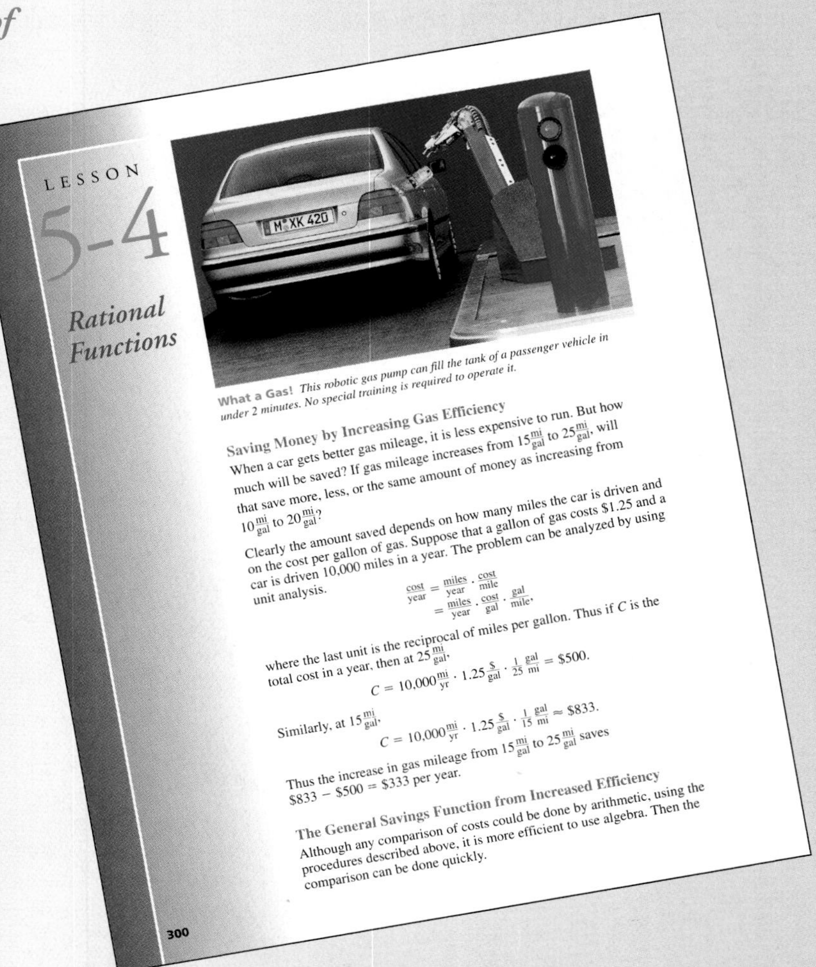

LESSON 5-4

Rational Functions

What a Gas! *This robotic gas pump can fill the tank of a passenger vehicle in under 2 minutes. No special training is required to operate it.*

Saving Money by Increasing Gas Efficiency

When a car gets better gas mileage, it is less expensive to run. But how much will be saved? If gas mileage increases from $15\frac{\text{mi}}{\text{gal}}$ to $25\frac{\text{mi}}{\text{gal}}$, will that save more, less, or the same amount of money as increasing from $10\frac{\text{mi}}{\text{gal}}$ to $20\frac{\text{mi}}{\text{gal}}$?

Clearly the amount saved depends on how many miles the car is driven and on the cost per gallon of gas. Suppose that a gallon of gas costs \$1.25 and a car is driven 10,000 miles in a year. The problem can be analyzed by using unit analysis.

$$\frac{\text{cost}}{\text{year}} = \frac{\text{miles}}{\text{year}} \cdot \frac{\text{cost}}{\text{mile}} = \frac{\text{miles}}{\text{year}} \cdot \frac{\text{cost}}{\text{gal}} \cdot \frac{\text{gal}}{\text{mile}},$$

where the last unit is the reciprocal of miles per gallon. Thus if C is the total cost in a year, then at $25\frac{\text{mi}}{\text{gal}}$,

$$C = 10{,}000\frac{\text{mi}}{\text{yr}} \cdot 1.25\frac{\$}{\text{gal}} \cdot \frac{1}{25}\frac{\text{gal}}{\text{mi}} = \$500.$$

Similarly, at $15\frac{\text{mi}}{\text{gal}}$,

$$C = 10{,}000\frac{\text{mi}}{\text{yr}} \cdot 1.25\frac{\$}{\text{gal}} \cdot \frac{1}{15}\frac{\text{gal}}{\text{mi}} \approx \$833.$$

Thus the increase in gas mileage from $15\frac{\text{mi}}{\text{gal}}$ to $25\frac{\text{mi}}{\text{gal}}$ saves \$833 − \$500 = \$333 per year.

The General Savings Function from Increased Efficiency

Although any comparison of costs could be done by arithmetic, using the procedures described above, it is more efficient to use algebra. Then the comparison can be done quickly.

300

Integration and connections

UCSMP *Precalculus and Discrete Mathematics* thoroughly integrates and makes connections to other areas of mathematics, to other disciplines, and to the real world. Students see how each mathematical idea fits into a larger context. *See pages 130, 363, 539, 624, 693, and 785 for further examples.*

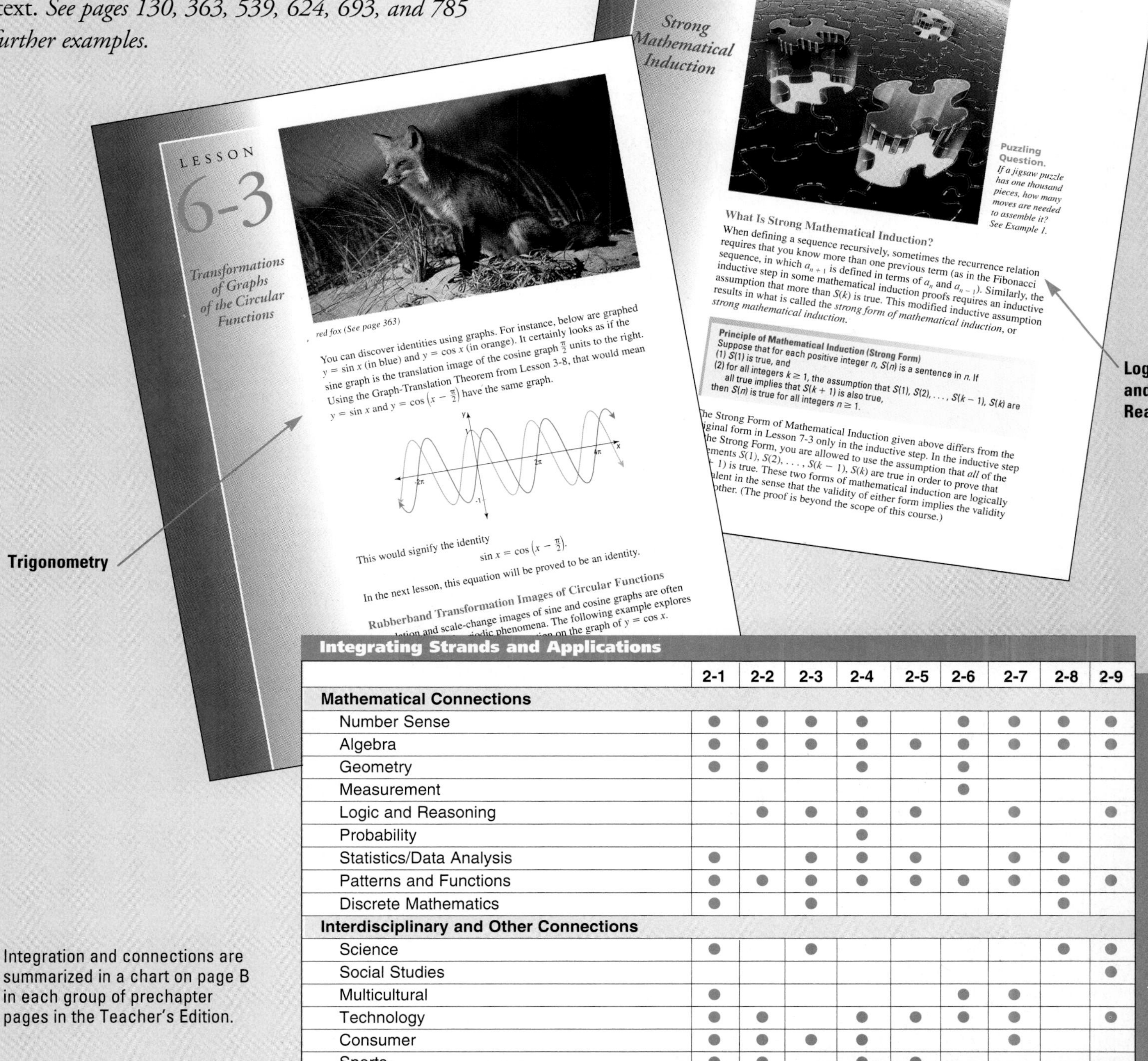

LESSON 7-7

Strong Mathematical Induction

Puzzling Question. *If a jigsaw puzzle has one thousand pieces, how many moves are needed to assemble it? See Example 1.*

What Is Strong Mathematical Induction?

When defining a sequence recursively, sometimes the recurrence relation requires that you know more than one previous term (as in the Fibonacci sequence, in which a_{n+1} is defined in terms of a_n and a_{n-1}). Similarly, the inductive step in some mathematical induction proofs requires an inductive assumption that more than $S(k)$ is true. This modified inductive assumption results in what is called the *strong form of mathematical induction*, or *strong mathematical induction*.

Principle of Mathematical Induction (Strong Form)
Suppose that for each positive integer n, $S(n)$ is a sentence in n. If
(1) $S(1)$ is true, and
(2) for all integers $k \geq 1$, the assumption that $S(1), S(2), \ldots, S(k-1), S(k)$ are all true implies that $S(k+1)$ is also true,
then $S(n)$ is true for all integers $n \geq 1$.

The Strong Form of Mathematical Induction given above differs from the original form in Lesson 7-3 only in the inductive step. In the inductive step of the Strong Form, you are allowed to use the assumption that *all* of the statements $S(1), S(2), \ldots, S(k-1), S(k)$ are true in order to prove that $S(k+1)$ is true. These two forms of mathematical induction are logically equivalent in the sense that the validity of either form implies the validity of the other. (The proof is beyond the scope of this course.)

Logic and Reasoning

LESSON 6-3

Transformations of Graphs of the Circular Functions

red fox (See page 363)

You can discover identities using graphs. For instance, below are graphed $y = \sin x$ (in blue) and $y = \cos x$ (in orange). It certainly looks as if the sine graph is the translation image of the cosine graph $\frac{\pi}{2}$ units to the right. Using the Graph-Translation Theorem from Lesson 3-8, that would mean $y = \sin x$ and $y = \cos\left(x - \frac{\pi}{2}\right)$ have the same graph.

This would signify the identity

$$\sin x = \cos\left(x - \frac{\pi}{2}\right).$$

In the next lesson, this equation will be proved to be an identity.

Rubberband Transformation Images of Circular Functions ... and scale-change images of sine and cosine graphs are often ... periodic phenomena. The following example explores ... on the graph of $y = \cos x$.

Trigonometry

Integrating Strands and Applications

	2-1	2-2	2-3	2-4	2-5	2-6	2-7	2-8	2-9
Mathematical Connections									
Number Sense	●	●	●	●		●	●	●	●
Algebra	●	●	●	●	●	●	●	●	●
Geometry	●	●		●		●			
Measurement						●			
Logic and Reasoning		●	●	●	●		●		●
Probability				●					
Statistics/Data Analysis	●		●	●	●		●	●	
Patterns and Functions	●	●	●	●	●	●	●	●	●
Discrete Mathematics	●		●					●	
Interdisciplinary and Other Connections									
Science	●		●					●	●
Social Studies									●
Multicultural	●					●	●		
Technology	●	●		●	●	●	●		●
Consumer	●	●	●	●			●		
Sports	●	●		●	●				

Sample from Chapter 2

Integration and connections are summarized in a chart on page B in each group of prechapter pages in the Teacher's Edition.

Why it works

Technology

State-of-the-art technology enhances mathematical understanding and strengthens problem-solving skills. Applications using calculators, graphics calculators, computers, and the Internet are incorporated throughout the text. The Explorations CD-ROM provides 40 easy-to-use interactive computer explorations for teacher demonstrations or student activities. *See pages 85, 183–184, 497, and 639 for further examples.*

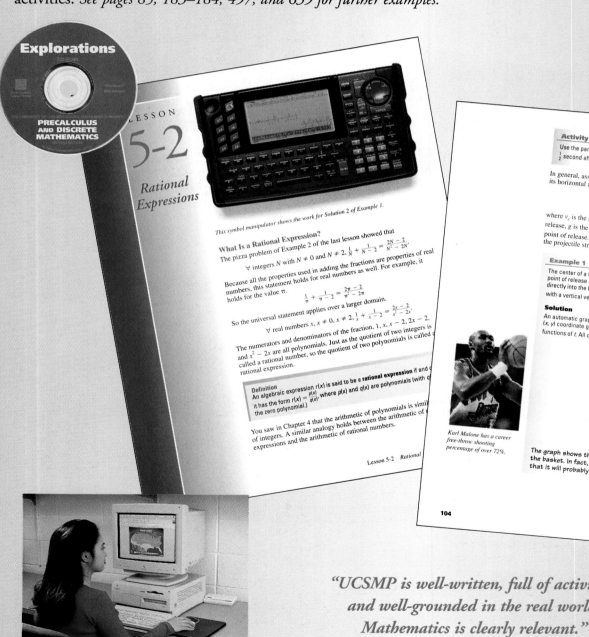

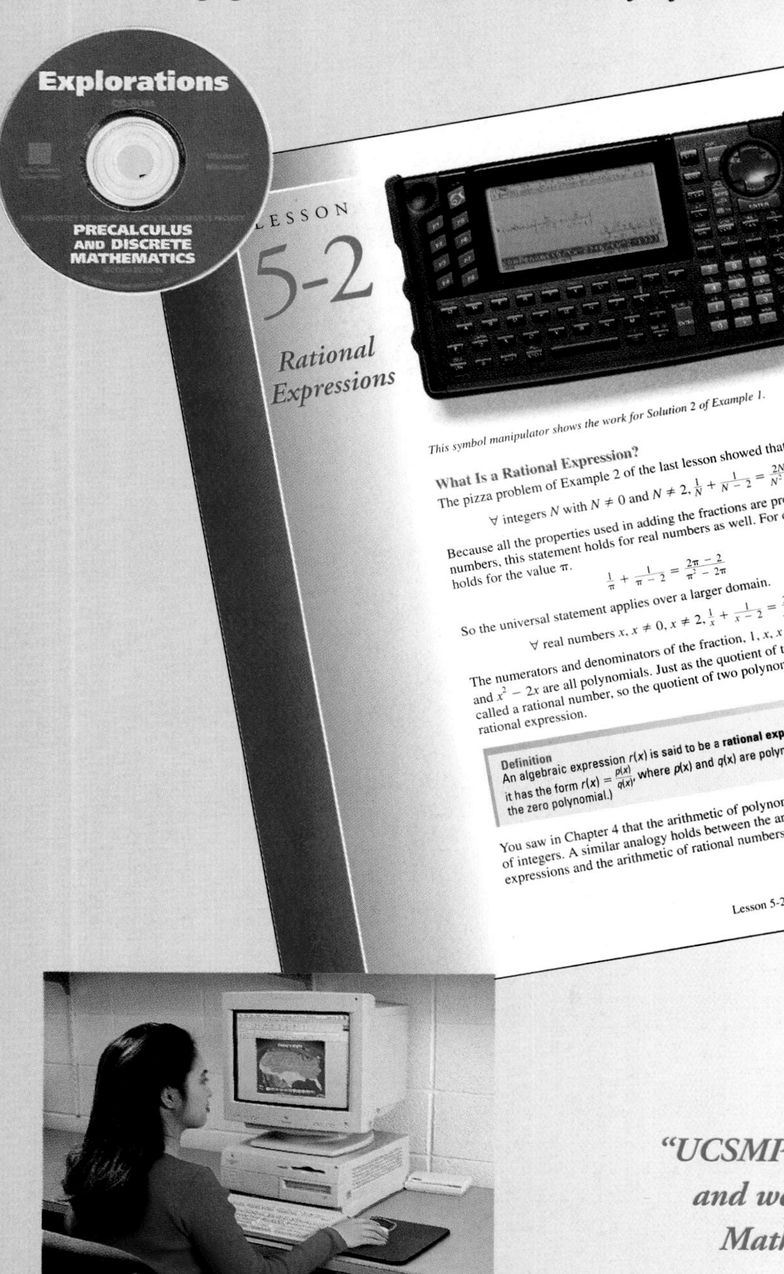

LESSON 5-2

Rational Expressions

This symbol manipulator shows the work for Solution 2 of Example 1.

What Is a Rational Expression?

The pizza problem of Example 2 of the last lesson showed that $\frac{1}{N} + \frac{1}{N-2} = \frac{2N-2}{N^2-2N}$ $\forall$ integers N with $N \neq 0$ and $N \neq 2$.

Because all the properties used in adding the fractions are properties of real numbers, this statement holds for real numbers as well. For example, it holds for the value π.

$$\frac{1}{\pi} + \frac{1}{\pi - 2} = \frac{2\pi - 2}{\pi^2 - 2\pi}$$

So the universal statement applies over a larger domain.

$$\forall \text{ real numbers } x, x \neq 0, x \neq 2, \frac{1}{x} + \frac{1}{x-2} = \frac{2x-2}{x^2-2x}.$$

The numerators and denominators of the fraction, 1, x, $x - 2$, $2x - 2$, and $x^2 - 2x$ are all polynomials. Just as the quotient of two integers is called a rational number, so the quotient of two polynomials is called a rational expression.

Definition
An algebraic expression $r(x)$ is said to be a **rational expression** if and o… it has the form $r(x) = \frac{p(x)}{q(x)}$, where $p(x)$ and $q(x)$ are polynomials (with q… the zero polynomial.)

You saw in Chapter 4 that the arithmetic of polynomials is simil… of integers. A similar analogy holds between the arithmetic of r… expressions and the arithmetic of rational numbers.

Lesson 5-2 Rational…

Activity
Use the parametric equations to determine the location of the basketball $\frac{1}{2}$ second after release.

In general, assuming that a projectile is unhindered by forces such as wind, its horizontal and vertical distances x and y from the origin are given by

$$x = v_x t + d_0$$
$$y = -\tfrac{1}{2}gt^2 + v_y t + h_0 \quad 0 \le t \le T$$

where v_x is the horizontal velocity at release, v_y is the vertical velocity at release, g is the gravitational constant $\left(32\frac{\text{ft}}{\text{sec}^2} \text{ or } 9.8\frac{\text{m}}{\text{sec}^2}\right)$, and (d_0, h_0) is the point of release. The time of release is $t = 0$, and $t = T$ is the time when the projectile strikes an object in its path.

Example 1
The center of a basket in basketball is 10 ft high and about 14 ft from the point of release of a free throw. Will a basketball player shoot a free throw directly into the basket if it is released from the same point as earlier but with a vertical velocity of $22\frac{\text{ft}}{\text{sec}}$?

Solution
An automatic grapher can be used to plot the parametric equations as an (x, y) coordinate graph. The symbols $x(t)$ and $y(t)$ emphasize that x and y are functions of t. All coefficients are the same as above except $v_y = 22\frac{\text{ft}}{\text{sec}}$.

$$x(t) = 13.78t + 1.06$$
$$y(t) = -\tfrac{1}{2} \cdot 32t^2 + 22t + 6.51$$

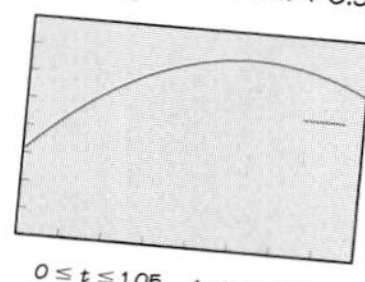

$0 \le t \le 1.05$, t-step = 0.05
$0 \le x \le 16$, x-scale = 2
$0 \le y \le 16$, y-scale = 2

Karl Malone has a career free-throw shooting percentage of over 72%.

The graph shows that the ball is too high to go directly through the basket. In fact, it seems so high when it hits the backboard that it will probably bounce back over the basket.

104

"UCSMP is well-written, full of activities, and well-grounded in the real world. Mathematics is clearly relevant."

Caren B. Bradshaw
Austin, Texas

Activities and Projects

Activities and Projects in each chapter provide engaging ways for students to work individually or in groups to explore and extend their knowledge. Your Teacher's Edition also includes additional Optional Activities. *See pages 327, 500, 568, 639, and 819 for further examples of Activities. See pages 5 (Teacher's Edition), 67, 273–274, and 397–398 for further examples of Projects.*

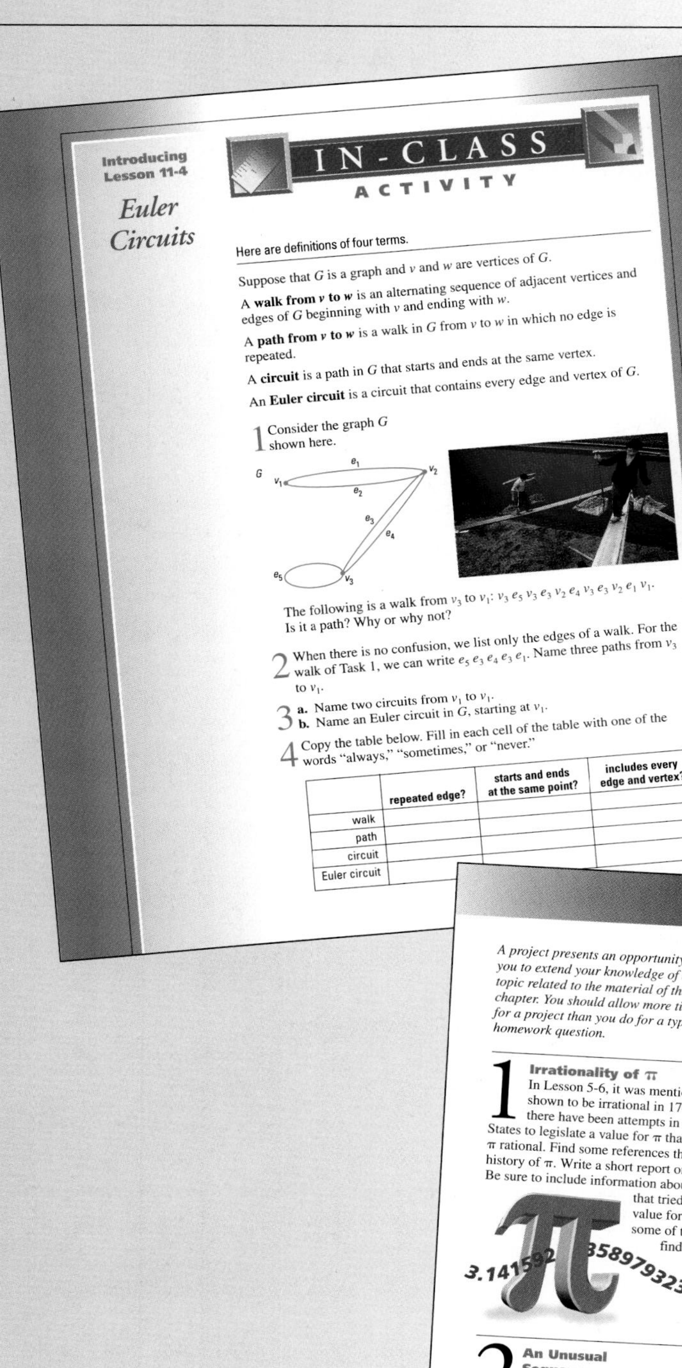

Introducing Lesson 11-4

Euler Circuits

IN-CLASS ACTIVITY

Here are definitions of four terms.

Suppose that G is a graph and v and w are vertices of G.

A **walk from v to w** is an alternating sequence of adjacent vertices and edges of G beginning with v and ending with w.

A **path from v to w** is a walk in G from v to w in which no edge is repeated.

A **circuit** is a path in G that starts and ends at the same vertex.

An **Euler circuit** is a circuit that contains every edge and vertex of G.

1 Consider the graph G shown here.

The following is a walk from v_3 to v_1: $v_3\ e_5\ v_3\ e_3\ v_2\ e_4\ v_3\ e_3\ v_2\ e_1\ v_1$. Is it a path? Why or why not?

2 When there is no confusion, we list only the edges of a walk. For the walk of Task 1, we can write $e_5\ e_3\ e_4\ e_3\ e_1$. Name three paths from v_3 to v_1.

3 a. Name two circuits from v_1 to v_1.
b. Name an Euler circuit in G, starting at v_1.

4 Copy the table below. Fill in each cell of the table with one of the words "always," "sometimes," or "never."

	repeated edge?	starts and ends at the same point?	includes every edge and vertex?
walk			
path			
circuit			
Euler circuit			

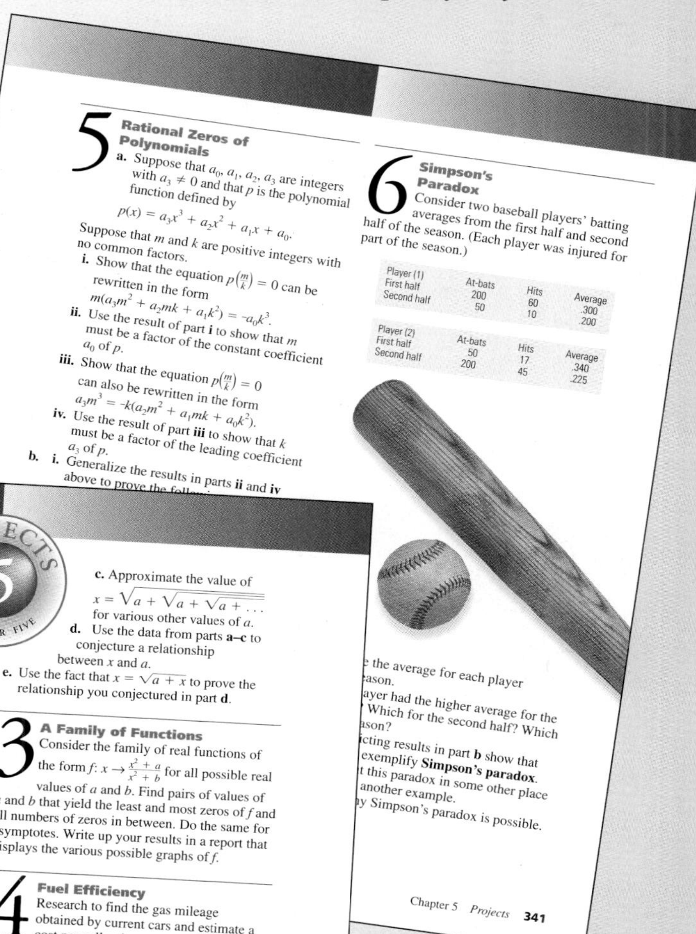

5 Rational Zeros of Polynomials

a. Suppose that a_0, a_1, a_2, a_3 are integers with $a_3 \neq 0$ and that p is the polynomial function defined by

$$p(x) = a_3x^3 + a_2x^2 + a_1x + a_0.$$

Suppose that m and k are positive integers with no common factors.

i. Show that the equation $p\left(\frac{m}{k}\right) = 0$ can be rewritten in the form $m(a_3m^2 + a_2mk + a_1k^2) = -a_0k^3$.

ii. Use the result of part **i** to show that m must be a factor of the constant coefficient a_0 of p.

iii. Show that the equation $p\left(\frac{m}{k}\right) = 0$ can also be rewritten in the form $a_3m^3 = -k(a_2m^2 + a_1mk + a_0k^2)$.

iv. Use the result of part **iii** to show that k must be a factor of the leading coefficient a_3 of p.

b. i. Generalize the results in parts **ii** and **iv** above to prove the follo...

6 Simpson's Paradox

Consider two baseball players' batting averages from the first half and second half of the season. (Each player was injured for part of the season.)

Player (1)	At-bats	Hits	Average
First half	200	60	.300
Second half	50	10	.200

Player (2)	At-bats	Hits	Average
First half	50	17	.340
Second half	200	45	.225

...e the average for each player ...ason.
...ayer had the higher average for the ... Which for the second half? Which ...son?
...cting results in part **b** show that ... exemplify **Simpson's paradox**. ...t this paradox in some other place ... another example.
...y Simpson's paradox is possible.

Chapter 5 *Projects* 341

PROJECTS 5 CHAPTER FIVE

A project presents an opportunity for you to extend your knowledge of a topic related to the material of this chapter. You should allow more time for a project than you do for a typical homework question.

1 Irrationality of π

In Lesson 5-6, it was mentioned that π was shown to be irrational in 1761. However, there have been attempts in the United States to legislate a value for π that would make π rational. Find some references that review the history of π. Write a short report on π's history. Be sure to include information about the state(s) that tried to legislate a value for π and about some of the attempts to find π's decimal expansion.

3.141592 ...358979323846...

2 An Unusual Sequence

a. Approximate the value of:

i. $\sqrt{2 + \sqrt{2}}$

ii. $\sqrt{2 + \sqrt{2 + \sqrt{2}}}$

iii. $\sqrt{2 + \sqrt{2 + \sqrt{2 + \ldots}}}$

b. Approximate the value of $\sqrt{6 + \sqrt{6 + \sqrt{6 + \ldots}}}$

c. Approximate the value of $x = \sqrt{a + \sqrt{a + \sqrt{a + \ldots}}}$ for various other values of a.

d. Use the data from parts **a–c** to conjecture a relationship between x and a.

e. Use the fact that $x = \sqrt{a + x}$ to prove the relationship you conjectured in part **d**.

3 A Family of Functions

Consider the family of real functions of the form $f: x \rightarrow \frac{x^2 + a}{x^2 + b}$ for all possible real values of a and b. Find pairs of values of a and b that yield the least and most zeros of f and all numbers of zeros in between. Do the same for asymptotes. Write up your results in a report that displays the various possible graphs of f.

4 Fuel Efficiency

Research to find the gas mileage obtained by current cars and estimate a cost per gallon in your area. Make a table of amounts a person could save in a year in gas costs by driving some particular cars over others; have the table include a variety of miles driven in a year.

340

How it works for today's students

Inviting design

The text's appealing and functional format and unique lesson development make concepts easy to follow and comprehend. Colorful pages and a wealth of contemporary visuals — including greatly enhanced graphs — help stimulate students' interest throughout the course.

"UCSMP is not the traditional 'crank and grind' math program which produces students who can manipulate symbols but have little or no understanding of how mathematics is used. UCSMP delivers a program in which students see the development of mathematics and learn to use it as a tool."

Michael Lambe
Spring Valley, California

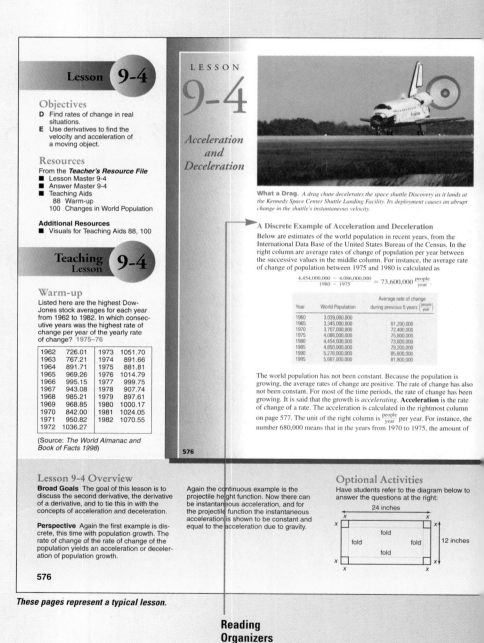

Lesson 9-4

Objectives

D Find rates of change in real situations.
E Use derivatives to find the velocity and acceleration of a moving object.

Resources

From the ***Teacher's Resource File***
- Lesson Master 9-4
- Answer Master 9-4
- Teaching Aids
  88 Warm-up
  100 Changes in World Population

Additional Resources
- Visuals for Teaching Aids 88, 100

Teaching Lesson 9-4

Warm-up

Listed here are the highest Dow-Jones stock averages for each year from 1962 to 1982. In which consecutive years was the highest rate of change per year of the yearly rate of change? 1975–76

1962	726.01	1973	1051.70
1963	767.21	1974	891.66
1964	891.71	1975	881.81
1965	969.26	1976	1014.79
1966	995.15	1977	999.75
1967	943.08	1978	907.74
1968	985.21	1979	897.61
1969	968.85	1980	1000.17
1970	842.00	1981	1024.05
1971	950.82	1982	1070.55
1972	1036.27		

(Source: *The World Almanac and Book of Facts 1998*)

LESSON 9-4

Acceleration and Deceleration

What a Drag. *A drag chute decelerates the space shuttle Discovery as it lands at the Kennedy Space Center Shuttle Landing Facility. Its deployment causes an abrupt change in the shuttle's instantaneous velocity.*

A Discrete Example of Acceleration and Deceleration

Below are estimates of the world population in recent years, from the International Data Base of the United States Bureau of the Census. In the right column are average rates of change of population per year between the successive values in the middle column. For instance, the average rate of change of population between 1975 and 1980 is calculated as

$$\frac{4{,}454{,}000{,}000 - 4{,}086{,}000{,}000}{1980 - 1975} = 73{,}600{,}000\ \frac{\text{people}}{\text{year}}.$$

Year	World Population	Average rate of change during previous 5 years $\left(\frac{\text{people}}{\text{year}}\right)$
1960	3,039,000,000	
1965	3,345,000,000	61,200,000
1970	3,707,000,000	72,400,000
1975	4,086,000,000	75,800,000
1980	4,454,000,000	73,600,000
1985	4,850,000,000	79,200,000
1990	5,278,000,000	85,600,000
1995	5,687,000,000	81,800,000

The world population has not been constant. Because the population is growing, the average rates of change are positive. The rate of change has also not been constant. For most of the time periods, the rate of change has been growing. It is said that the growth is *accelerating*. **Acceleration** is the rate of change of a rate. The acceleration is calculated in the rightmost column on page 577. The unit of the right column is $\frac{\text{people}}{\text{year}}$ per year. For instance, the number 680,000 means that in the years from 1970 to 1975, the amount of

576

Lesson 9-4 Overview

Broad Goals The goal of this lesson is to discuss the second derivative, the derivative of a derivative, and to tie this in with the concepts of acceleration and deceleration.

Perspective Again the first example is discrete, this time with population growth. The rate of change of the rate of change of the population yields an acceleration or deceleration of population growth.

Again the continuous example is the projectile height function. Now there can be instantaneous acceleration, and for the projectile function the instantaneous acceleration is shown to be constant and equal to the acceleration due to gravity.

Optional Activities

Have students refer to the diagram below to answer the questions at the right:

24 inches
x x
x fold x
fold fold 12 inches
fold
x x
x x

576

These pages represent a typical lesson.

Reading Organizers

Communication

Instead of spending valuable time explaining the textbook, you can devote more time each day to exploring additional examples and applications. Students learn to read and understand mathematics on their own, and to express this understanding both orally and in writing. Reading Organizers in each lesson help direct students' attention to key ideas in the reading.

population increase per year itself increased by about 680,000 each year. It was calculated using the average rate of change numbers for 1970 and 1975.

$$\frac{75{,}800{,}000 \frac{\text{people}}{\text{year}} - 72{,}400{,}000 \frac{\text{people}}{\text{year}}}{(1975 - 1970) \text{ years}} = 680{,}000 \frac{\frac{\text{people}}{\text{year}}}{\text{year}}$$

Year	World Population	Average rate of change	Average rate of change of average of rate of change
1960	3,039,000,000		
1965	3,345,000,000	61,200,000	
1970	3,707,000,000	72,400,000	2,240,000
1975	4,086,000,000	75,800,000	680,000
1980	4,454,000,000	73,600,000	-440,000
1985	4,850,000,000	79,200,000	1,120,000
1990	5,278,000,000	85,600,000	1,280,000
1995	5,687,000,000	81,800,000	-760,000

From 1975 to 1980, the population change per year lessened. It had been 75,800,000 people per year from 1970 to 1975; it became 73,600,000 people per year from 1975 to 1980. It is said that the population increase *decelerated*. When acceleration is negative, it is called **deceleration**.

You are, of course, familiar with the terms acceleration and deceleration as they pertain to buses or cars. These words have a similar meaning to that in the population growth example above. A car accelerates when its velocity (rate of change of position) increases. That is, the rate of change of velocity is what is called acceleration. For instance, if a car goes from 20 mph to 60 mph in 5 seconds, then its average acceleration—its average rate of change of velocity—is $\frac{40 \text{ mph}}{5 \text{ sec}}$ or 8 mph per second. A car is said to decelerate when its velocity decreases.

However, there is a difference between the world population and car acceleration examples. Population data are discrete whereas the positions of a car are thought of as being continuous. So the instantaneous acceleration for population cannot be defined, but instantaneous acceleration for the motion of an object can be defined.

Instantaneous Acceleration

The **instantaneous acceleration** $a(t)$ of a projectile or other object at time t is defined to be the instantaneous rate of change of its velocity with respect to time at time t. To compute it, take the derivative of the velocity function v at t:

$$a(t) = v'(t) = \lim_{\Delta t \to 0} \frac{v(t + \Delta t) - v(t)}{\Delta t}.$$

The units for acceleration are $\frac{\text{ft/sec}}{\text{sec}}$, the same as the units of the difference quotient $\frac{v(t + \Delta t) - v(t)}{\Delta t}$. This is written as feet per second per second or $\frac{\text{ft}}{\text{sec}^2}$.

In 1975–76, the Dow-Jones stock average increased by 143 points per year more than it had increased the previous year, the largest acceleration in growth of the average in this time period. (Note: Old data has purposely been used here because, in recent years, the changes have been so great that any one could tell when the change was greatest. This data also illustrates that there was a 20-year period in which the Dow-Jones average did not change that much. This may come as a surprise to some students.)

Notes on Reading

This lesson applies the ideas of the first three lessons to the first derivative itself. The discussion on page 577 shows that there is meaning for taking the rate of change of a rate of change. **Teaching Aid 100** shows the changes in world population.

Students may be familiar with the ideas of acceleration and with the fact that acceleration tells how fast the velocity is changing. Thus, it is natural that the acceleration is just the derivative of the velocity. This discussion provides a natural lead-in to acceleration as being the second derivative of distance from a starting point.

You might extend the graph-sketching activities of the first three lessons in this chapter. Give students a time versus distance graph of a car trip. Ask them to sketch plausible corresponding velocity and acceleration graphs. How is a slowdown in velocity reflected in the acceleration graph?

1. Find a formula $V(x)$ for the volume of a box in terms of x.
[$V(x) = 4x^3 - 72x^2 + 288x$]
2. Given that $V'(x) = 12x^2 - 144x + 288$, find a formula for the acceleration of volume as a function of x.
[$V''(x) = 24x - 144$]
3. What is the rate of change of volume expansion at $x = 1$?
[$V''(1) = -120$ in^3 per in^2]
4. What is the "acceleration" at $x = 5$? What does this negative acceleration imply? [$V''(5) = -24$ in^3 per in^2; the volume is decreasing at a slower rate.]

Adapting to Individual Needs

Extra Help
Emphasize that we can speak of *average acceleration* whether the function is continuous or discrete; but we can only speak of *instantaneous acceleration* for a continuous function with first and second derivatives.

"We are enthusiastic users of UCSMP and are pleased with the success we are experiencing in our classrooms. Your program has given us a beginning look at the changing role of the teacher and student in the mathematics classroom."

Denise E. Keltz
Springfield, Pennsylvania

How it works

Problem solving

Students learn to use mathematics effectively through problem-solving experiences that include use of higher-order thinking skills in daily assignments, a wide variety of problem types in the questions, and open-ended problems. *See pages 126–127, 194, 363, 450–453, and 602 for further examples.*

The **Example** finishes off the explanation for how the height of a projectile is modeled by a quadratic polynomial. Here we see that the coefficient of the square term is half of the acceleration.

Additional Examples

1. a. Suppose a projectile has height $h(t) = 960t - 16t^2$. Find the acceleration $a(t)$ of the projectile at any time t. $a(t) = -32$ ft/sec^2
   b. Determine the acceleration of the projectile at time $t = 4$ seconds. $a(4) = -32$ ft/sec^2; These answers could be expected since the only force acting on the projectile is gravity.
2. When an object moves so that its position at time t seconds is given by $s(t) = \frac{2}{3}t^3 - 8t^2 + 5t + 7$ m/sec, then the velocity of the object is given by $v(t) = 2t^2 - 16t + 5$.
   a. Find a formula for the acceleration of the object. $a(t) = 4t - 16$
   b. At time $t = 1$ minute, is the object speeding up or slowing down? Speeding up

Notes on Questions

Questions 5–6 Error Alert Be sure students understand the distinction between these two statements. The statement in **Question 6** is false because an object could have negative velocity but its acceleration could be positive; for instance, if an object was coming down to earth at a slower and slower pace.

Example

a. Find the instantaneous acceleration $a(t)$ of a projectile whose position at time t is given by $h(t) = 800t - 16t^2$.
b. Determine the instantaneous acceleration of the projectile at $t = 20$ sec.

Solution

a. By definition, the acceleration $a(t)$ is the derivative of the velocity function.

Since	$v(t) = 800 - 32t$,	From Lesson 9-3, Example 1
then	$v'(t) = -32$.	Derivative of a Linear Function Theorem
$\therefore$	for all t, $a(t) = -32 \frac{ft}{sec^2}$.	

b. Since $a(t) = -32$ for *all* values of t, the acceleration at $t = 20$ sec is $-32 \frac{ft}{sec^2}$.

Acceleration and Derivatives

In general, position, velocity, and acceleration are related as follows:

acceleration = derivative of velocity
acceleration = derivative of (derivative of position).

Another way to state the relationship between position and acceleration is to say the following:

Let $s(t)$ represent the position of an object at time t. Then instantaneous velocity at time $t = v(t) = s'(t)$, and instantaneous acceleration at time $t = a(t) = v'(t) = (s')'(t)$.

Because acceleration is a derivative of a derivative, acceleration is said to be the *second derivative* of position with respect to time, written $a(t) = s''(t)$.

Given an arbitrary function f, the derivative function f' of f is called the **first derivative** of f. The **second derivative** of f is the derivative of the first derivative and is denoted f''.

The functions h, v, and a of the Example are graphed below.

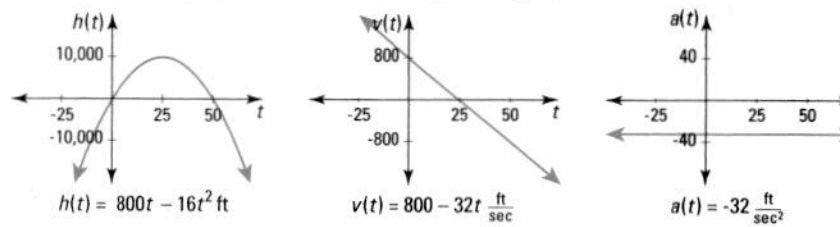

$h(t) = 800t - 16t^2$ ft $v(t) = 800 - 32t \frac{ft}{sec}$ $a(t) = -32 \frac{ft}{sec^2}$

The equation $h(t) = 800t - 16t^2$ is of the form $h(t) = v_0t - \frac{1}{2}gt^2$, the equation for the height of a projectile at time t if v_0 is the initial velocity and g is the acceleration due to gravity. You can see that v_0 is, in fact, the value of the first derivative $v(t)$ when $t = 0$, and g is -32 ft/sec^2, the second derivative of $v(t)$ for all t. This is the constant acceleration due to the gravity of Earth. When the acceleration is constant, people usually do not speak of the *instantaneous acceleration at time t*, but simply *the acceleration*.

QUESTIONS

Covering the Reading

In 1–3, use the world population data in this lesson.

1. What does the number 61,200,000 in the third column mean, and how it calculated? See margin.
2. What is the average rate of change of the average rate of change of population from 1975 to 1980? $-440{,}000 \frac{\text{people}}{\text{year}}$ per year
3. If the average acceleration of the world population had remained the same from 1990 to 1995 as it was from 1985 to 1990, what would the population have been in 1995? 5,363,600,000 people
4. A car went from 0 to 60 mph in 6 seconds. What was its average acceleration during this time interval? 10 mph/sec
5. *True or false.* If the acceleration of a moving object is negative, then velocity is decreasing. True
6. *True or false.* If the velocity of a moving object is negative, then the acceleration of the object is negative. False
7. a. Is the height of the projectile in the Example increasing or is it decreasing at time $t = 3$ seconds? increasing
   b. Is its velocity increasing or is it decreasing at this time? decreasin
   c. Is its acceleration increasing or is it decreasing at this time? Neither; it is always -32 ft/sec^2
8. Let $s(t) = 10 + 15t - 4.9t^2$ be the height (in meters) of an object at ti
   a. Find the velocity $v(t)$ at time t. $v(t) = s'(t) = 15 - 9.8t$ m/sec
   b. Find the acceleration $a(t)$ at time t. $a(t) = v'(t) = s''(t) = -9.8$ m/sec^2

Applying the Mathematics

In 9 and 10, a hot object is placed on a table to cool. The temperature (in degrees Fahrenheit) of the object after x minutes is given by

$$f(x) = 80e^{-0.555x} + 70.$$

9) $\frac{\text{degree Fahrenheit}}{\text{min}}$ per minute or degrees Fahrenheit/min^2

9. What units should be used to measure the second derivative of f? See left.
10. For this function, the first derivative is $f'(x) = -44.4e^{-0.555x}$ and the sec derivative of f is $f''(x) = 24.642e^{-0.555x}$. Use an automatic grapher to g f, f', and f'' over the interval $0 \le x \le 10$. (Use a separate set of axes f each function.) See margin.
    a. How fast is the rate of cooling changing at time $t = 2$ minutes?
    b. How fast is the temperature changing at time $t = 2$ minutes?
    c. At what time during the first 10 minutes is the rate of cooling char the fastest?
    d. At what time during the first 10 minutes is the rate of cooling char the slowest?

Adapting to Individual Needs

Challenge

Pose this problem: The height, in feet after t seconds, of a ball dropped from an initial height of 144 feet is $h(t) = -16t^2 + 144$.

1. How long does it take the ball to hit the ground? [3 seconds]
2. What is the ball's velocity at the time of impact? [-96 ft/sec]
3. What is the ball's average velocity? [-32 ft/sec]
4. At what time and height is the ball traveling at that velocity? [1 sec; 128 ft]

Additional Answers

1. 61,800,000 is the average rate of change in world population for the years 1960 to 1965. It is found by taking one-fifth of the difference between the 1965 and 1960 populations.

10. graph of f

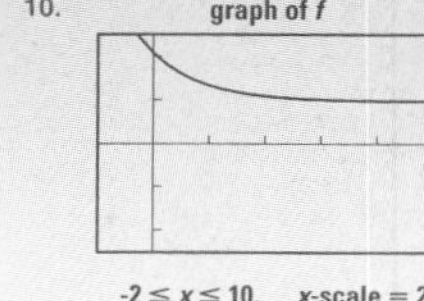

$-2 \le x \le 10$, x-scale = 2
$-180 \le y \le 180$, y-scale = 80

10. (continued)

graph of f'

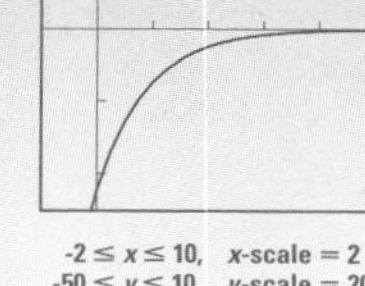

$-2 \le x \le 10$, x-scale = 2
$-50 \le y \le 10$, y-scale = 20

graph of f''

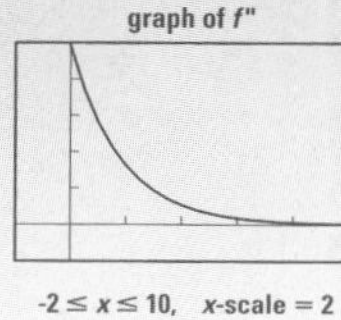

$-2 \le x \le 10$, x-scale = 2
$-5 \le y \le 25$, y-scale = 5

a. < 8.12 degrees/min
b. < -14.63 degrees/min^2
c. at the beginning; t 5 0
d. at the end; t 5 10

"Enrollment in courses is growing. This year enrollment is well over three times as much as last year."

Margaret Housinger
Calumet City, Illinois

Practice and review

Continual opportunities for practice and review throughout UCSMP *Precalculus and Discrete Mathematics* help students strengthen conceptual understanding and ensure optimum performance. *See pages 122–123, 152–153, 166–167, 236–237, 401–403, 566–567, 671–672 for further examples.*

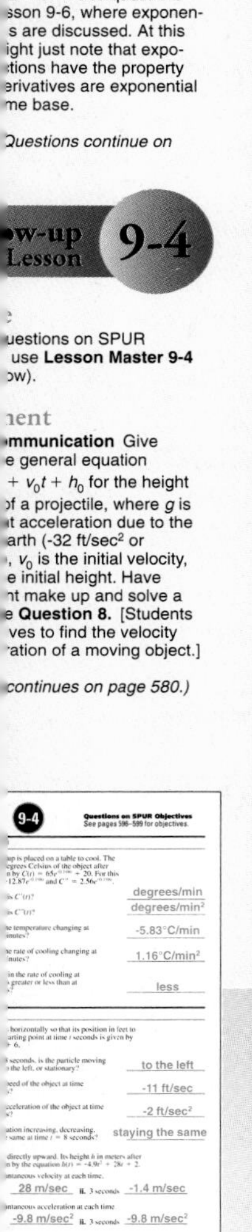
9–10 These questions
sson 9-6, where exponen-
s are discussed. At this
ight just note that expo-
tions have the property
erivatives are exponential
me base.

Questions continue on

w-up
Lesson 9-4

uestions on SPUR
use **Lesson Master 9-4**
ow).

ent
mmunication Give
e general equation
$+ v_0t + h_0$ for the height
of a projectile, where g is
t acceleration due to the
arth (-32 ft/sec² or
, v_0 is the initial velocity,
e initial height. Have
nt make up and solve a
e **Question 8.** [Students
ves to find the velocity
ation of a moving object.]

continues on page 580.)

9-4 **Questions on SPUR Objectives**
See pages 596–599 for objectives.

degrees/min
degrees/min²
-5.83°C/min
1.16°C/min²
less
to the left
-11 ft/sec
-2 ft/sec²
staying the same
28 m/sec — ii. 3 seconds -1.4 m/sec
-9.8 m/sec² — ii. 3 seconds -9.8 m/sec²

579

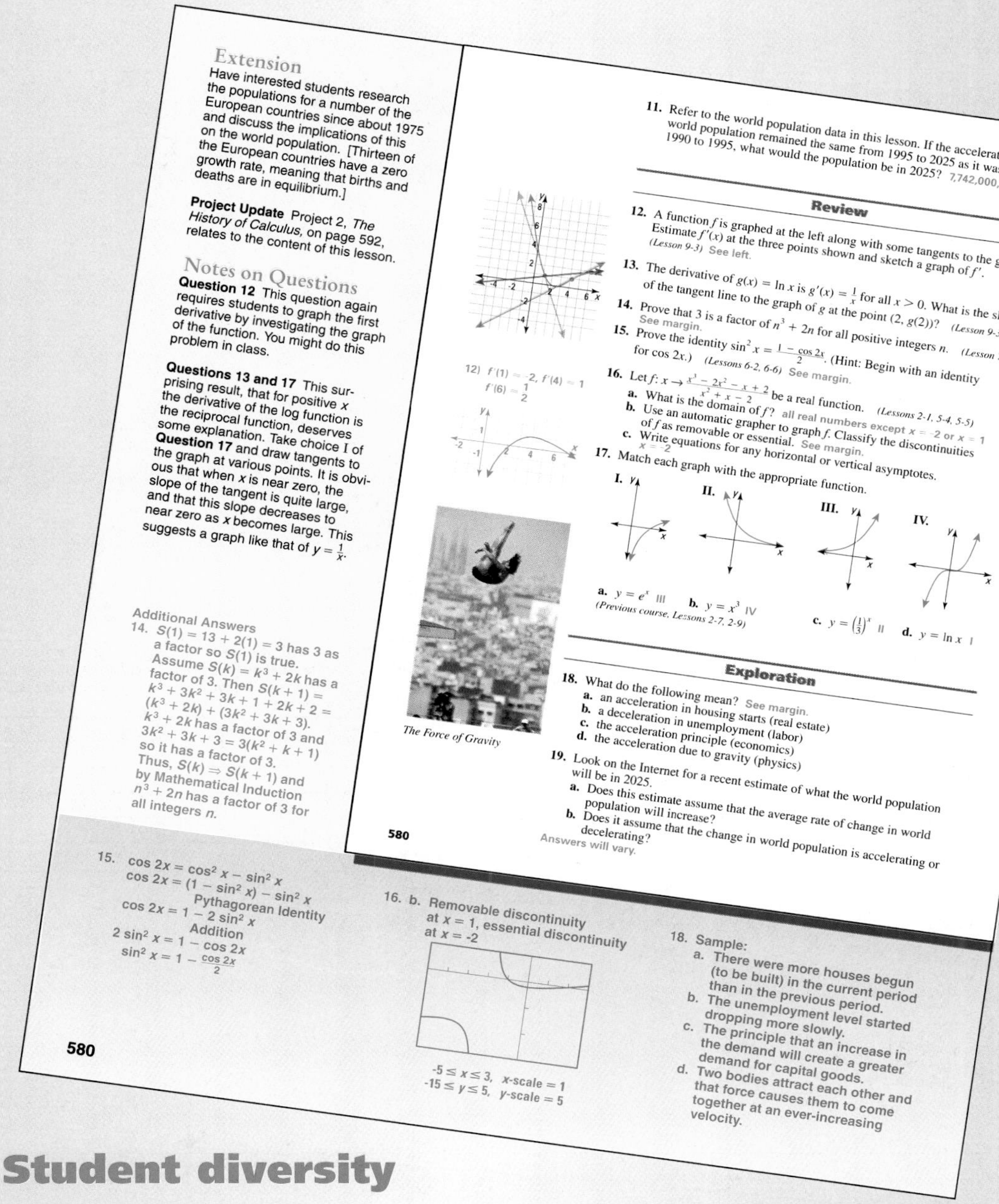

Extension

Have interested students research the populations for a number of the European countries since about 1975 and discuss the implications of this on the world population. [Thirteen of the European countries have a zero growth rate, meaning that births and deaths are in equilibrium.]

Project Update Project 2, *The History of Calculus,* on page 592, relates to the content of this lesson.

Notes on Questions

Question 12 This question again requires students to graph the first derivative by investigating the graph of the function. You might do this problem in class.

Questions 13 and 17 This surprising result, that for positive x the derivative of the log function is the reciprocal function, deserves some explanation. Take choice I of **Question 17** and draw tangents to the graph at various points. It is obvious that when x is near zero, the slope of the tangent is quite large, and that this slope decreases to near zero as x becomes large. This suggests a graph like that of $y = \frac{1}{x}$.

11. Refer to the world population data in this lesson. If the acceleration of the world population remained the same from 1995 to 2025 as it was from 1990 to 1995, what would the population be in 2025? 7,742,000,000

Review

12. A function f is graphed at the left along with some tangents to the graph. Estimate $f'(x)$ at the three points shown and sketch a graph of f'. *(Lesson 9-3)* See left.

13. The derivative of $g(x) = \ln x$ is $g'(x) = \frac{1}{x}$ for all $x > 0$. What is the slope of the tangent line to the graph of g at the point $(2, g(2))$? *(Lesson 9-3)* $\frac{1}{2}$

14. Prove that 3 is a factor of $n^3 + 2n$ for all positive integers n. *(Lesson 7-4)* See margin.

15. Prove the identity $\sin^2 x = \frac{1 - \cos 2x}{2}$. (Hint: Begin with an identity for $\cos 2x$.) *(Lessons 6-2, 6-6)* See margin.

16. Let $f: x \rightarrow \frac{x^3 - 2x^2 - x + 2}{x^2 + x - 2}$ be a real function. *(Lessons 2-1, 5-4, 5-5)*

a. What is the domain of f? all real numbers except $x = -2$ or $x = 1$

b. Use an automatic grapher to graph f. Classify the discontinuities of f as removable or essential. See margin.

c. Write equations for any horizontal or vertical asymptotes. $x = -2$

17. Match each graph with the appropriate function.

I. II. III. IV.

a. $y = e^x$ III b. $y = x^3$ IV c. $y = \left(\frac{1}{3}\right)^x$ II d. $y = \ln x$ I

(Previous course, Lessons 2-7, 2-9)

12) $f'(1) \approx -2$, $f'(4) \approx 1$, $f'(6) \approx \frac{1}{2}$

The Force of Gravity

Exploration

18. What do the following mean? See margin.

a. an acceleration in housing starts (real estate)

b. a deceleration in unemployment (labor)

c. the acceleration principle (economics)

d. the acceleration due to gravity (physics)

19. Look on the Internet for a recent estimate of what the world population will be in 2025.

a. Does this estimate assume that the average rate of change in world population will increase?

b. Does it assume that the change in world population is accelerating or decelerating?

Answers will vary.

580

Additional Answers

14. $S(1) = 1^3 + 2(1) = 3$ has 3 as a factor so $S(1)$ is true. Assume $S(k) = k^3 + 2k$ has a factor of 3. Then $S(k + 1) = k^3 + 3k^2 + 3k + 1 + 2k + 2 = (k^3 + 2k) + (3k^2 + 3k + 3)$. $k^3 + 2k$ has a factor of 3 and $3k^2 + 3k + 3 = 3(k^2 + k + 1)$ so it has a factor of 3. Thus, $S(k) \Rightarrow S(k + 1)$ and by Mathematical Induction $n^3 + 2n$ has a factor of 3 for all integers n.

15.
$\cos 2x = \cos^2 x - \sin^2 x$
$\cos 2x = (1 - \sin^2 x) - \sin^2 x$ Pythagorean Identity
$\cos 2x = 1 - 2 \sin^2 x$ Addition
$2 \sin^2 x = 1 - \cos 2x$
$\sin^2 x = 1 - \frac{\cos 2x}{2}$

16. b. Removable discontinuity at $x = 1$, essential discontinuity at $x = -2$

$-5 \le x \le 3$, x-scale = 1
$-15 \le y \le 5$, y-scale = 5

18. Sample:

a. There were more houses begun (to be built) in the current period than in the previous period.

b. The unemployment level started dropping more slowly.

c. The principle that an increase in the demand will create a greater demand for capital goods.

d. Two bodies attract each other and that force causes them to come together at an ever-increasing velocity.

580

Student diversity

UCSMP materials have been carefully designed to accommodate the full range of today's diverse student population. Your Teacher's Edition is full of ideas for addressing the needs of each student. *See pages 16–18, 172, 184, 226–227, 415, and 458 for further examples.*

How it works

Progress checks for students

A Progress Self-Test at the end of each chapter helps students determine how well they've assimilated chapter concepts. Various types of problems, keyed to chapter objectives, provide ideal preparation for chapter tests and teach study skills.

PROGRESS SELF-TEST

Take this test as you would take a test in class. Then check the test yourself using the solutions at the end of this volume.

In 1 and 2, a problem is given. **a.** Describe the essential features of each problem. **b.** Solve the problem.

1. You wish to know how many different outcomes are possible when five identical dice are rolled.

2. A pizza parlor has the following toppings available: anchovy, pepperoni, sausage, black olive, double cheese, green pepper, mushroom, and onion. Thick or thin crust is offered. The problem is to determine the number of different 4-topping pizzas available.

3. A red die and a white die are rolled. Use a possibility tree to determine the number of rolls possible in which the red die is a five or six and the total showing on the two dice is less than ten.

4. Consider the computer program below.

```
10 FOR I = 1 TO 2
20   FOR J = 3 TO 8
30     FOR K = 10 TO 20
40       PRINT I+J+K
50     NEXT K
60   NEXT J
70 NEXT I
80 END
```

When the program is run, how many times is line 40 executed?

5. In how many ways can you answer a ten-question multiple-choice test if each question has four possible answers?

In 6 and 7, evaluate the expression.

6. $P(18, 4)$ **7.** $\binom{8}{4}$

8. A committee of twelve people is to choose a chairperson, assistant chairperson, and secretary from among the members of the committee. In how many ways can the selection be made?

9. The alphabet has 21 consonants and 5 vowels. Suppose five-letter strings are to be created in which the first letter is a vowel.
a. How many such strings are there if the same letter can occur more than once?
b. How many are there if a letter can only occur once?

10. A caterer must choose three vegetable dishes from nine vegetable dishes which are available. In how many ways can this be done?

11. Find the fourth term in the expansion of $(2x - y)^9$.

12. A coin is flipped seven times. How many of the possible sequences of heads ... exactly 4 tails?

13. How many subsets of a set with ... are there that contain 3 or fewer ... that set?

14. A soda machine offers a choice ... cola, lemon-lime soda, and gra... 7 cans are to be purchased, in ... different ways can this be don...

15. Prove that for positive integer... $r \le n$, $P(n + 1, r + 1) = (n$ ...

16. Suppose that the probability is ... does not have enough cream filling. If a box of 10 Snackos is purchased, what is the probability that two Snackos are inadequately filled?

The chart below keys the **Progress Self-Test** questions to the objectives in the **Chapter Review** on pages 653–655 or to the **Vocabulary** (Voc.) on page 651. This will enable you to locate those **Chapter Review** questions that correspond to questions missed on the **Progress Self-Test.** The lesson where the material is covered is also indicated on the chart.

Question	**1**	**2**	**3**	**4**	**5**	**6**	**7**	**8**
Objective	A, G	A, G	I	F	F	B	B	F
Lesson	10-1, 10-7	10-1, 10-4	10-2	10-2	10-2	10-3	10-4	10-2
Question	**9**	**10**	**11**	**12**	**13**	**14**	**15**	**16**
Objective	F	G	C	H	E	G	D	H
Lesson	10-2	10-4	10-5	10-6	10-6	10-7	10-3	10-6

A chart for each Progress Self-Test (at the back of the Student Edition) keys test questions to chapter objectives.

End-of-chapter mastery

Comprehensive chapter reviews based on SPUR objectives — Skills, Properties, Uses, and Representations — ensure a multidimensional understanding of key concepts.

Skills

Uses

CHAPTER TEN CHAPTER TEN

USES DEAL WITH APPLICATIONS OF MATHEMATICS IN REAL SITUATIONS.

Objective F: *Use the Multiplication Counting Principle and permutations to solve counting problems.* *(Lessons 10-2, 10-3)*

20. a. How many 6-letter strings can be created from the 26 letters of the English alphabet?

b. How many 6-letter strings are possible if the first letter must be *d* and the last letter must be *r*?

21. At a ceremony, seven people are to be seated on the podium. How many different seatings are possible?

22. A combination lock on a briefcase has three dials with the digits from 0 through 9 on each dial. How many different possible combinations are there for this lock?

In 23–25, 15 old books and 4 old bookmarks are to be displayed in a row at an art exhibit.

23. How many different displays are possible?

24. How many displays are possible if the 4 bookmarks must be displayed together?

25. How many displays are possible if only 7 of the books and 2 of the bookmarks are displa

26. How many integers from
99,999 have at least one

27. Consider the computer pro

```
10 FOR I = 3 TO 5
15   FOR J = 6 TO 10
20     FOR K = 4 TO 11
25       B = I * J * K
30       PRINT B
35     NEXT K
40   NEXT J
50 NEXT I
60 END
```

How many numbers does line 30

28. Consider the computer program below.

```
10 FOR I = 1 TO 4
20   FOR J = 2 TO 7
30     PRINT I, J
40   NEXT J
50   FOR K = 1 TO 3
60     PRINT I, K
70   NEXT K
80 NEXT I
90 END
```

How many lines of data are printed?

Objective G: *Use combinations and the Binomial Theorem to solve counting problems.* *(Lessons 10-4, 10-6, 10-7)*

29. An ice cream shop has 20 flavors.

a. How many triple cones (3 dips) are possible if no flavor can be repeated? (Do not count different arrangements of the same flavors as different.)

b. How many triple cones are possible if flavors can be repeated?

30. Solve the problem in Question 4.

31. For a literature class, a teacher must choose four novels from a list of ten. In how
ways can this choice be

32. A dan

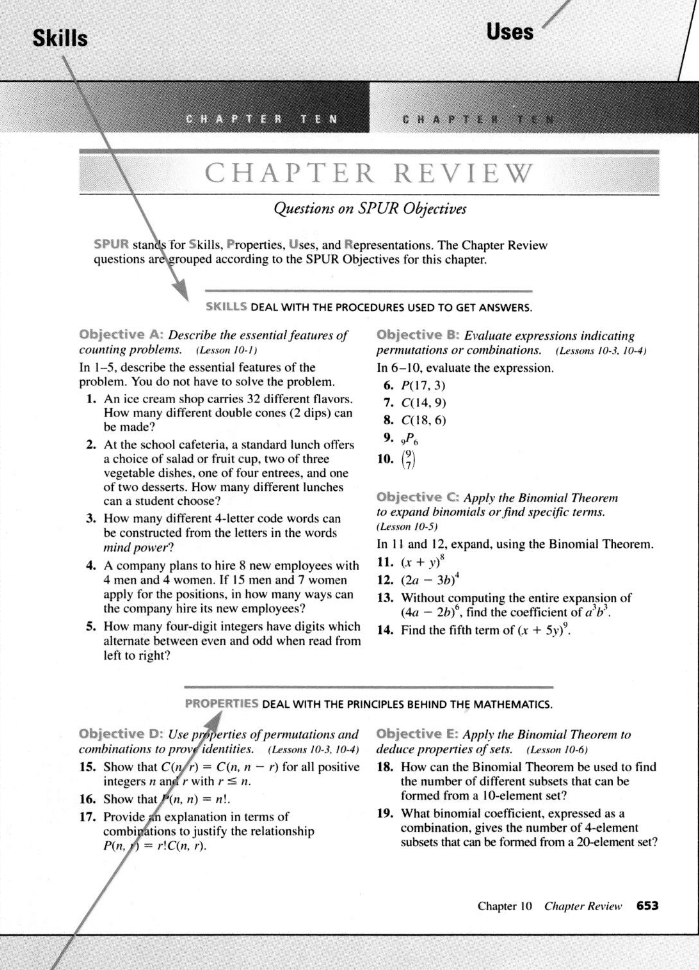

CHAPTER TEN CHAPTER TEN

CHAPTER REVIEW

Questions on SPUR Objectives

SPUR stands for Skills, Properties, Uses, and Representations. The Chapter Review questions are grouped according to the SPUR Objectives for this chapter.

SKILLS DEAL WITH THE PROCEDURES USED TO GET ANSWERS.

Objective A: *Describe the essential features of counting problems.* *(Lesson 10-1)*

In 1–5, describe the essential features of the problem. You do not have to solve the problem.

1. An ice cream shop carries 32 different flavors. How many different double cones (2 dips) can be made?

2. At the school cafeteria, a standard lunch offers a choice of salad or fruit cup, two of three vegetable dishes, one of four entrees, and one of two desserts. How many different lunches can a student choose?

3. How many different 4-letter code words can be constructed from the letters in the words *mind power*?

4. A company plans to hire 8 new employees with 4 men and 4 women. If 15 men and 7 women apply for the positions, in how many ways can the company hire its new employees?

5. How many four-digit integers have digits which alternate between even and odd when read from left to right?

Objective B: *Evaluate expressions indicating permutations or combinations.* *(Lessons 10-3, 10-4)*

In 6–10, evaluate the expression.

6. $P(17, 3)$

7. $C(14, 9)$

8. $C(18, 6)$

9. ${}_9P_6$

10. $\binom{9}{7}$

Objective C: *Apply the Binomial Theorem to expand binomials or find specific terms.* *(Lesson 10-5)*

In 11 and 12, expand, using the Binomial Theorem.

11. $(x + y)^8$

12. $(2a - 3b)^4$

13. Without computing the entire expansion of $(4a - 2b)^6$, find the coefficient of a^3b^3.

14. Find the fifth term of $(x + 5y)^9$.

PROPERTIES DEAL WITH THE PRINCIPLES BEHIND THE MATHEMATICS.

Objective D: *Use properties of permutations and combinations to prove identities.* *(Lessons 10-3, 10-4)*

15. Show that $C(n, r) = C(n, n - r)$ for all positive integers n and r with $r \le n$.

16. Show that $P(n, n) = n!$.

17. Provide an explanation in terms of combinations to justify the relationship $P(n, r) = r!C(n, r)$.

Objective E: *Apply the Binomial Theorem to deduce properties of sets.* *(Lesson 10-6)*

18. How can the Binomial Theorem be used to find the number of different subsets that can be formed from a 10-element set?

19. What binomial coefficient, expressed as a combination, gives the number of 4-element subsets that can be formed from a 20-element set?

Chapter 10 *Chapter Review* **653**

CHAPTER TEN CHAPTER TEN

33. In how many ways is it possible to obtain at least two heads in a sequence of five coin tosses?

34. Student council members are to be selected from the general student body. Suppose a high school has 2000 students: 620 freshmen, 580 sophomores, 450 juniors, and 350 seniors. Leave your answers to the following questions in $C(n, r)$ form.

a. How many 50-member councils can be formed from the whole student body?

b. How many 50-member councils can be formed if there must be 12 freshmen, 12 sophomores, 13 juniors, and 13 seniors in the council?

35. A Mix-n-Match selection of 10 cookies is to be made from three varieties: oatmeal, peanut butter, and sugar. How many different selections are possible?

Objective H: *Find binomial probabilities in realistic situations.* *(Lesson 10-6)*

36. A jar contains purple jelly beans and green jelly beans. There are three times as many purple ones as green ones. If an individual chooses 5 beans from the jar, what is the probability that 3 of the beans will be green?

37. Suppose the probability is 0.2% that a pencil sharpener produced at a factory is defective.

a. If the quality control department randomly selects 100 sharpeners for testing, find the probability that two of those sharpeners are defective.

b. Find the probability that at least one sharpener is defective.

c. If the quality control department selects 500 sharpeners, find the probability that at least one of those sharpeners is defective.

REPRESENTATIONS DEAL WITH PICTURES, GRAPHS, OR OBJECTS THAT ILLUSTRATE CONCEPTS.

Objective I: *Use a possibility tree to determine the number of outcomes in a given situation.* *(Lesson 10-2)*

38. Make a possibility tree to determine the number of two-letter strings that can be created from the letters *d, e, f,* and *g* if *d* and *e* can be repeated but *f* and *g* cannot.

39. Three-digit numbers are to be made from the digits 1, 2, 3, and 4. Use a possibility tree to count the number of three-digit numbers that can be made if digits must alternate even-odd-even or odd-even-odd.

40. In a tournament, two teams play each other until one team wins two in a row or a total of four games. Use a possibility tree to count the number of different possible outcomes of this tournament.

Chapter 10 *Chapter Review* **655**

Properties

Representations

"The homework questions are beautifully designed to reinforce the material and explore its possibilities. Few students fail and all students learn."

Mary Evelyn Klingenberg
Erlanger, Kentucky

How it works

Multiple forms of assessment

Your *Assessment Sourcebook* includes quizzes, test forms A and B, performance tests C and D, and a cumulative test for each chapter, and comprehensive tests after Chapters 3, 6, 9, and 13. Plus, TestWorks CD-ROM software enables you to adapt existing tests or create your own in various forms. Your *Assessment Sourcebook* also includes abundant resources for providing portfolio, problem-solving, cooperative-group, and self-assessment materials.

"More than two-thirds of the A.P. calculus students (all of whom had the UCSMP curriculum prior to calculus) passed the A.P. exam."

Gail O. Sutton
Grand Rapids, Michigan

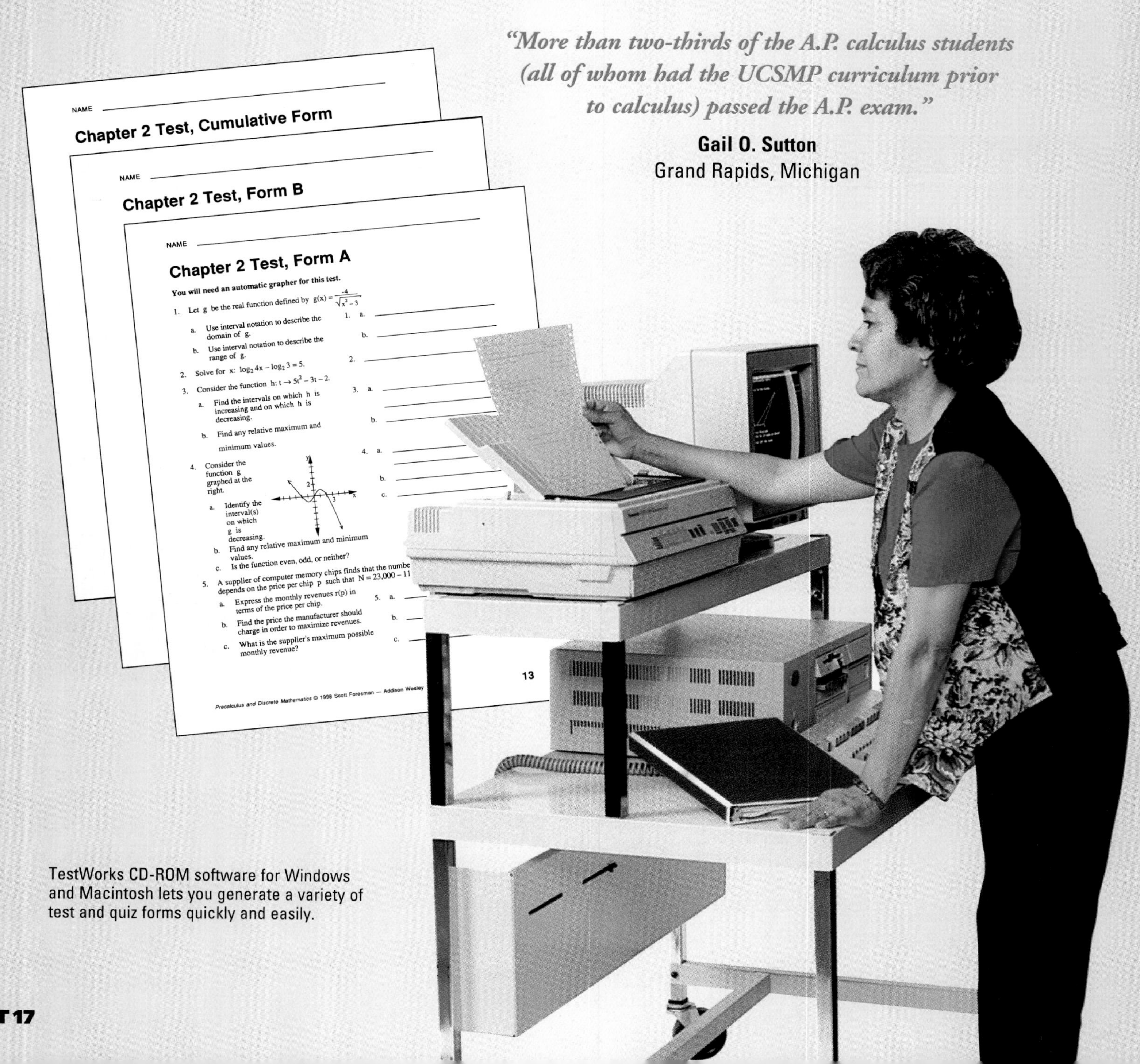

TestWorks CD-ROM software for Windows and Macintosh lets you generate a variety of test and quiz forms quickly and easily.

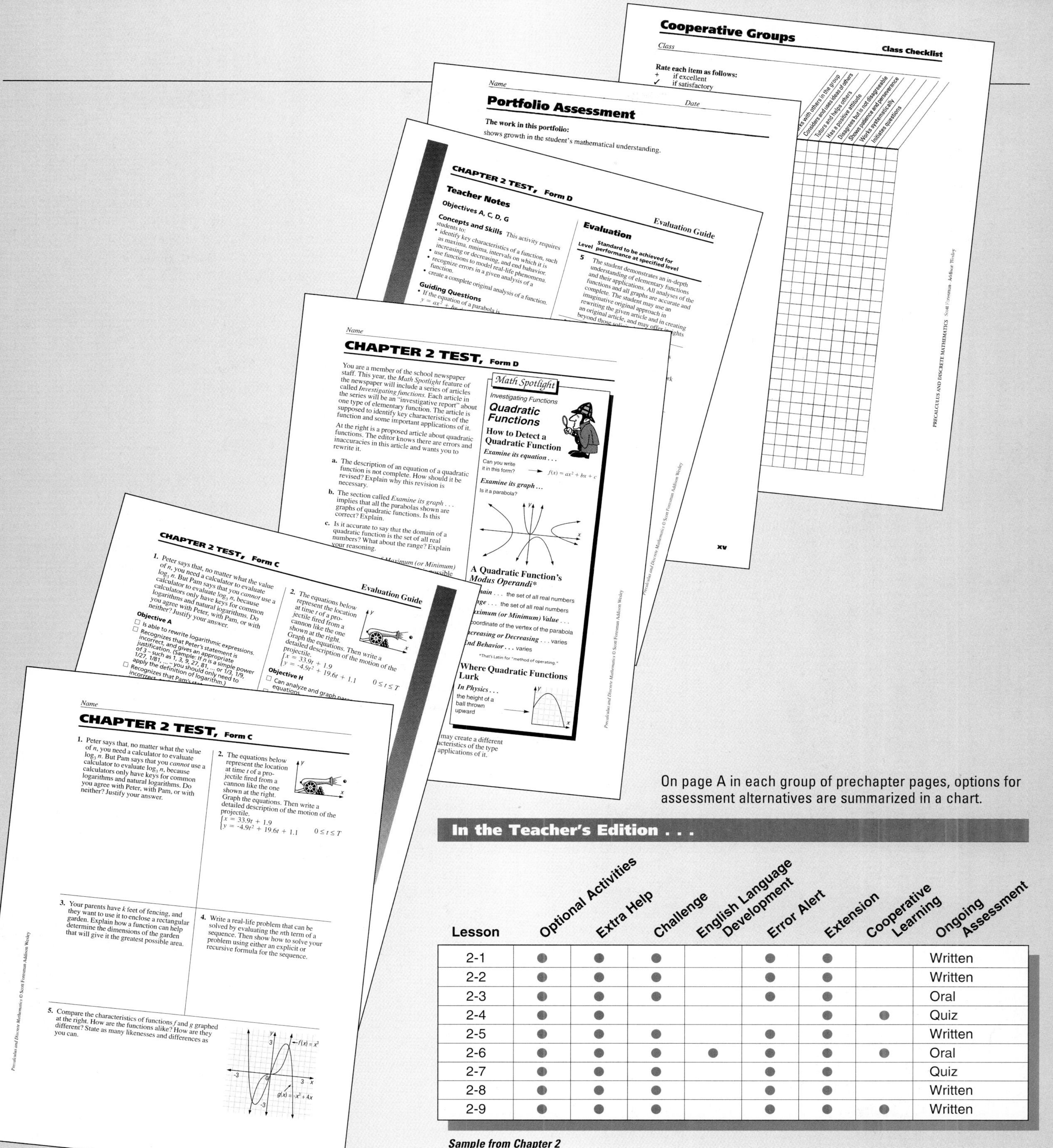

Cooperative Groups
Class Checklist
Portfolio Assessment
The work in this portfolio:
shows growth in the student's mathematical understanding.
CHAPTER 2 TEST, Form D
Teacher Notes
Evaluation Guide
CHAPTER 2 TEST, Form D
Math Spotlight
Quadratic Functions
How to Detect a Quadratic Function
A Quadratic Function's Modus Operandi*
Where Quadratic Functions Lurk
CHAPTER 2 TEST, Form C
Evaluation Guide
CHAPTER 2 TEST, Form C
1. Peter says that, no matter what the value of n, you need a calculator to evaluate $\log_3 n$. But Pam says that you *cannot* use a calculator to evaluate $\log_3 n$, because calculators only have keys for common logarithms and natural logarithms. Do you agree with Peter, with Pam, or with neither? Justify your answer.
2. The equations below represent the location at time t of a projectile fired from a cannon like the one shown at the right. Graph the equations. Then write a detailed description of the motion of the projectile.
$\begin{cases} x = 33.9t + 1.9 \\ y = -4.9t^2 + 19.6t + 1.1 \end{cases} \quad 0 \le t \le T$
3. Your parents have k feet of fencing, and they want to use it to enclose a rectangular garden. Explain how a function can help determine the dimensions of the garden that will give it the greatest possible area.
4. Write a real-life problem that can be solved by evaluating the nth term of a sequence. Then show how to solve your problem using either an explicit or recursive formula for the sequence.
5. Compare the characteristics of functions f and g graphed at the right. How are the functions alike? How are they different? State as many likenesses and differences as you can.
$f(x) = x^3$
$g(x) = -x^3 + 4x$

On page A in each group of prechapter pages, options for assessment alternatives are summarized in a chart.

In the Teacher's Edition . . .

Lesson	Optional Activities	Extra Help	Challenge	English Language Development	Error Alert	Extension	Cooperative Learning	Ongoing Assessment
2-1	●	●	●		●	●		Written
2-2	●	●	●		●	●		Written
2-3	●	●	●		●	●		Oral
2-4	●	●				●	●	Quiz
2-5	●	●	●		●	●		Written
2-6	●	●	●	●	●	●	●	Oral
2-7	●	●	●		●	●		Quiz
2-8	●	●	●		●	●		Written
2-9	●	●	●		●	●	●	Written

Sample from Chapter 2

The works

Components of UCSMP *Precalculus and Discrete Mathematics, Second Edition*

Student Edition
0-673-45914-4.

Teacher's Edition (in two parts)
Includes Teacher's Resource File CD-ROM Version. 0-673-45917-9.

Teacher's Resource File
Contains hundreds of blackline masters and a Solution Manual correlated to the Student Edition. Booklets are also available separately. 0-673-45918-7.

- ☐ **Lesson Masters.** Single-page blackline masters correlated to each lesson in the Student Edition—ideal for extra practice. 0-673-45919-5.
- ☐ **Teaching Aid Masters.** All Warm-ups and many Additional Examples from the Teacher's Edition margin notes, tables, graphs, drawings, and more. 0-673-45920-9.
- ☐ **Assessment Sourcebook.** Quizzes, standard tests, performance assessment, and cumulative tests for each chapter, plus comprehensive tests and guidelines for portfolio materials, problem-solving and cooperative-group activities, and self-assessment. 0-673-45921-7.
- ☐ **Technology Sourcebook.** Blackline master activities for use with both calculators and computers. Helps students explore and extend concepts through the latest technologies. 0-673-45922-5.
- ☐ **Answer Masters.** Answers for all questions in the Student Edition. 0-673-45923-3.
- ☐ **Solution Manual.** Complete step-by-step solutions to all questions in the Student Edition. 0-673-45924-1.
- ☐ **Implementing UCSMP: A User's Handbook.** An overview of block-scheduling suggestions, a plan for teaching *Transition Mathematics* and UCSMP *Algebra* as two-year courses, strategies from classroom teachers, and more. 0-673-45938-1.

Visual Aids
Overhead transparencies of all Answer Masters and Teaching Aids, including Warm-ups and many Additional Examples from the Teacher's Edition margin notes, to enhance your classroom presentations. 0-673-45925-X.

Study Skills Handbook
A UCSMP exclusive containing tips and models to help students develop study skills. 0-673-45823-7.

Explorer Series Software
Includes a Reference Guide and blackline master activities.

- ☐ **GraphExplorer**
  IBM: 0-673-44304-3; Macintosh: 0-673-44305-1.
- ☐ **StatExplorer**
  IBM: 0-673-44302-7; Macintosh: 0-673-44303-5.

TestWorks CD-ROM (Windows and Macintosh)
Create a wealth of custom quizzes and tests quickly and easily, with a minimum of computer expertise. Includes extra challenge problems. 0-673-57551-9

Explorations CD-ROM
Offers interactive explorations involving functions, graphs, statistical analysis, modeling, and more. Users can manipulate variables and study the changes to graphs and other displays. Activities are tied directly to lessons in the Student Edition. 0-673-45912-8.

Scott Foresman
Addison Wesley

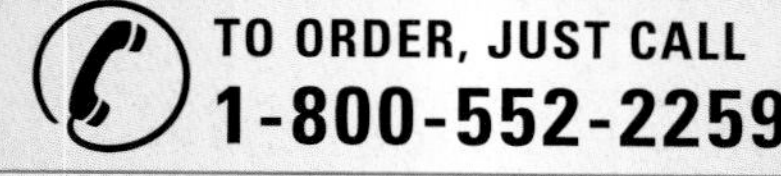

The University of Chicago School Mathematics Project

Precalculus and Discrete Mathematics

Second Edition

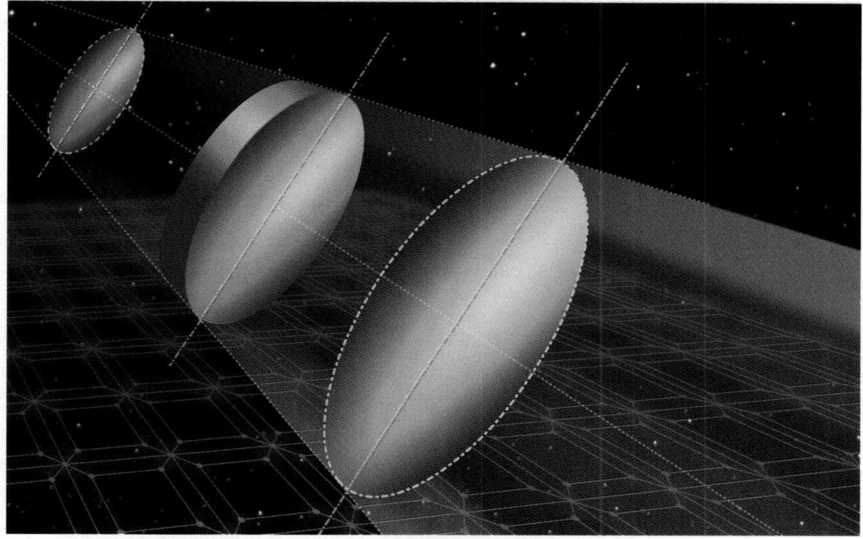

About the Cover In *Precalculus and Discrete Mathematics,* we prepare for calculus and preview the concepts of derivative and integral which are related to area and volume. The background contains a tessellation based on a network, a discrete graph, which represents the vertices of a rectangular solid.

Authors

Anthony L. Peressini John W. McConnell Zalman Usiskin
Susanna S. Epp Nils P. Ahbel David Witonsky
Kathleen A. Hollowell Susan Brown Wade Ellis, Jr.
John Sorteberg Denisse R. Thompson Dora Aksoy
Geoffrey D. Birky Greg A. McRill

Scott Foresman
Addison Wesley

Editorial Offices: Glenview, Illinois • Menlo Park, California
Sales Offices: Reading, Massachusetts • Atlanta, Georgia • Glenview, Illinois
Carrollton, Texas • Menlo Park, California
http://www.sf.aw.com

ACKNOWLEDGMENTS

Authors

Anthony L. Peressini
Professor Emeritus of Mathematics,
University of Illinois, Urbana

John W. McConnell
Instructional Supervisor of Mathematics,
Glenbrook South H.S., Glenview, IL

Zalman Usiskin
Professor of Education,
The University of Chicago

Susanna S. Epp
Professor of Mathematics, DePaul University,
Chicago, IL (First Edition only)

Nils P. Ahbel
Mathematics Teacher, Deerfield Academy,
Deerfield, MA (Second Edition only)

David Witonsky
UCSMP (Second Edition only)

Kathleen A. Hollowell
Coordinator of Secondary Mathematics Inservice
Programs, University of Delaware, Newark, DE
(First Edition only)

Susan Brown
Mathematics Department Chair, York H.S.,
Elmhurst, IL (First Edition only)

Wade Ellis, Jr.
Mathematics Instructor, West Valley College,
Saratoga, CA (First Edition only)

Jack Sorteberg
Mathematics Teacher, Burnsville H.S., Burnsville,
MN (First Edition only)

Denisse R. Thompson
Associate Professor of Mathematics Education,
University of South Florida, Tampa, FL
(First Edition only)

Dora Aksoy
UCSMP (First Edition only)

Geoffrey D. Birky
UCSMP (First Edition only)

Greg McRill
UCSMP (First Edition only)

UCSMP Production and Evaluation

Series Editors: Zalman Usiskin,
Sharon L. Senk

Technical Coordinator: Susan Chang

Managing Editor: David Witonsky

Director of First Edition Study:
Denisse Thompson

We wish also to acknowledge the generous support of the **Amoco Foundation** and the **Carnegie Corporation of New York** for the development, testing, and distribution of the First Edition of these materials.

We wish to thank the many editors, production personnel, and design personnel at Scott Foresman Addison Wesley for their magnificent assistance.

Design Development

Steven Curtis Design, Inc.

It is impossible for UCSMP to thank all the people who have helped create and test these books. We wish particularly to thank Carol Siegel, who heads our office staff; Chad Dau, Alfred Estberg, Lianghuo Fan, Robert Hallman, Noel Le, and Ralph Schwartz of our editorial staff; and Christopher Naud and Christopher Lee of our technical staff.

We wish to acknowledge and give thanks to the following teachers who taught preliminary versions of the first edition of this text, participated in the field testing or formative evaluations, and contributed ideas to help improve this text.

John Adkinson
Thornton Fractional High School South
Lansing, IL

Cynthia Crenshaw
University School of Nashville
Nashville, TN

Ronald Godar
San Marcos High School
Santa Barbara, CA

Deborah Klipp
Mainland Regional High School
Linwood, NJ

Rheta Rubenstein
Professor of Education
University of Windsor, Windsor, Ontario

David Tyson
Mercersburg Academy
Mercersburg, PA

Michael Bowers
Churchill High School
Eugene, OR

Joyce Evans
Breck School
Minneapolis, MN

Mary Hahn
Woodward High School
Cincinnati, OH

Mercedes McGowen
William Rainey Harper College
Palatine, IL

Martin Sanford
Renaissance High School
Detroit, MI

We also wish to express our thanks and appreciation to the other schools and students who have used earlier versions of these materials and informally given us comments.

THE UNIVERSITY OF CHICAGO SCHOOL MATHEMATICS PROJECT

The University of Chicago School Mathematics Project (UCSMP) is a long-term project designed to improve school mathematics in grades K–12. UCSMP began in 1983 with a six-year grant from the Amoco Foundation. Additional funding has come from the National Science Foundation, the Ford Motor Company, the Carnegie Corporation of New York, the General Electric Foundation, GTE, Citibank/Citicorp, and the Exxon Education Foundation, and from royalties from the sales of UCSMP materials by Scott Foresman Addison Wesley.

The project is centered in the Departments of Education and Mathematics of the University of Chicago. The project has translated dozens of mathematics textbooks from other countries, held three international conferences, developed curricular materials for elementary and secondary schools, formulated models for teacher training and retraining, conducted a large number of large and small conferences, engaged in evaluations of many of its activities, and through its royalties has supported a wide variety of research projects in mathematics education at the University. UCSMP currently has the following components and directors.

Resources	Izaak Wirszup, Professor Emeritus of Mathematics
Elementary Materials	Max Bell, Professor Emeritus of Education
Secondary	Sharon L. Senk, Professor of Mathematics, Michigan State University Zalman Usiskin, Professor of Education
Evaluation Consultant	Larry Hedges, Professor of Education

From 1983–1987, the overall director of UCSMP was Paul Sally, Professor of Mathematics. Since 1987, the overall director has been Zalman Usiskin.

Precalculus and Discrete Mathematics

The text *Precalculus and Discrete Mathematics* was developed by the Secondary Component (grades 7–12) of the project, and constitutes the core of the final year in a six-year mathematics curriculum devised by that component. The names of the six texts around which these years are built are:

Transition Mathematics
Algebra
Geometry
Advanced Algebra
Functions, Statistics, and Trigonometry
Precalculus and Discrete Mathematics

The content and questions of this book integrate the major ideas of mathematics needed for calculus (elementary functions—with special attention to polynomial, rational, and trigonometric functions, polar coordinates, and complex numbers) with the fundamental notions of discrete mathematics (recursion, mathematical induction, combinatorics, graphs, vectors, matrices, and circuits).

Mathematical thinking, including specific attention to formal logic and proof and comparing structures, is a unifying theme. The algebra, geometry, and function ideas studied in previous years are applied throughout in the solution of equations and inequalities, in graphing, and in proofs.

The first edition of *Precalculus and Discrete Mathematics* included many features that have been retained in this edition. The value of some of these features has influenced other mathematics courses as well. As the content described in the preceding paragraph indicates, there is **wider scope** than is normally found in senior level courses. These topics are not isolated as separate units of study or enrichment. They are employed to motivate, justify, extend, and otherwise enhance the important ideas of precalculus and discrete mathematics. A **real-world orientation** has guided both the selection of content and the approaches allowed the student in working out exercises and problems, because being able to do mathematics is of little use to an individual unless he or she can apply that content. We require **reading mathematics,** because students must read to understand mathematics in later courses and must learn to read technical matter in the world at large. The use of **up-to-date technology** is integrated throughout, with *automatic graphers* assumed available at all times and occasional reference to *symbol manipulators.*

Four dimensions of understanding are emphasized: skill in carrying out various algorithms; developing and using mathematics properties and relationships; applying mathematics in realistic situations; and representing or picturing mathematical concepts. We call this the **SPUR** approach: **S**kills, **P**roperties, **U**ses, **R**epresentations.

The **book organization** is designed to maximize the acquisition of both skills and concepts. Ideas introduced in a lesson are reinforced through Review questions in the immediately succeeding lessons. This daily review feature allows students several nights to learn and practice important concepts and skills. Then, at the end of each chapter, a carefully focused Progress Self-Test and a Chapter Review, each keyed to objectives in all the dimensions of understanding, are used to solidify performance of skills and concepts from the chapter so that they may be applied later with confidence. Finally, to increase retention, important ideas are reviewed in later chapters.

There are **projects** at the end of each chapter because in the real world much of the mathematics done requires a longer period of time than is customarily available to students in daily assignments, and because teachers who have tried projects in the first edition of these materials have been enthusiastic about them.

The first edition of *Precalculus and Discrete Mathematics* was published in 1992 and has been used in thousands of classes. Some of the teachers who used the first edition have made suggestions for improvements and there have been advances in technology and in thinking about how students learn. We have attempted to utilize these ideas in the development of the second edition. Every bit of text and every question has been examined, and many revisions have been made to improve the materials. We have moved a number of lessons and reorganized others. We have added many new applications and updated others.

Those familiar with the first edition will notice the following significant changes. A number of reading lessons have been dropped. This is because most teachers did not find them useful and many teachers did not complete as much of the text as they would like. Material on parametric equations has been added because of the importance of this material in all of mathematics and the ease of graphing such equations with automatic graphers. Chapter 3, considered by some to be the most difficult chapter in the book, has been reorganized.

There are also a number of features new to this edition, including the following: **In-class activities** have been incorporated between lessons to help students develop concepts before they read. **Activities** are also included within the lessons to help students understand as they read. There are many more questions requiring **writing** and a special writing font, because writing helps students clarify their own thinking, and writing is an important aspect of communicating mathematical ideas to others.

Comments about these materials are welcomed. Please address comments to:
UCSMP, The University of Chicago,
5835 S. Kimbark, Chicago, IL 60637.

CONTENTS

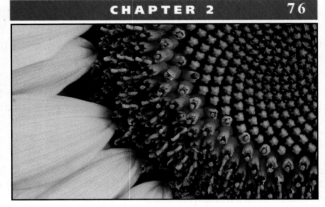

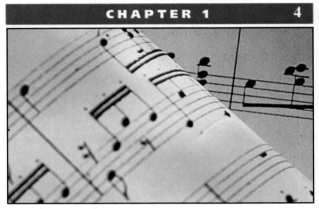

FUNCTIONS, EQUATIONS, AND INEQUALITIES

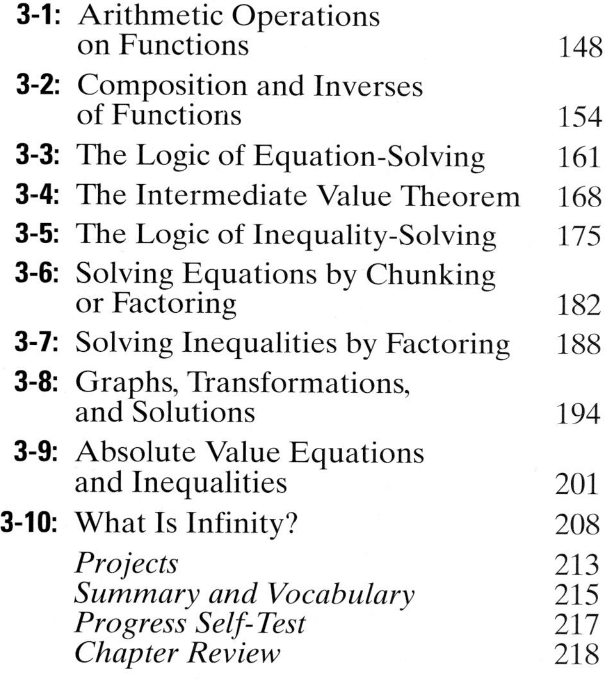

INTEGERS AND POLYNOMIALS

vii

CHAPTER 8 470

POLAR COORDINATES AND COMPLEX NUMBERS

CHAPTER 9 550

THE DERIVATIVE IN CALCULUS

CHAPTER 10 600

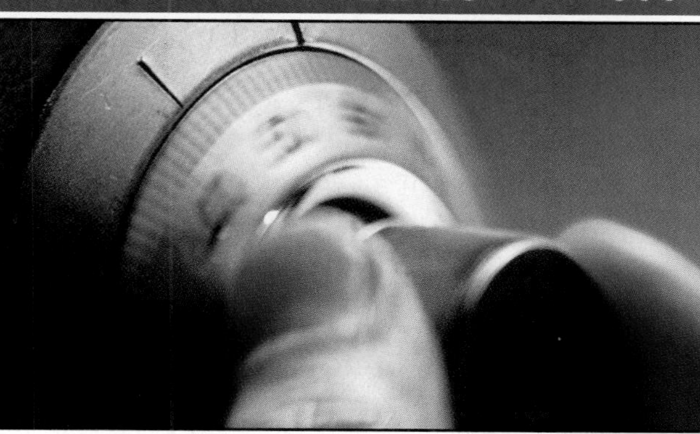

COMBINATORICS

6206
6206

To the Student

Getting Started

Welcome to Precalculus and Discrete Mathematics.
We hope you enjoy this book—it was written for you.

What is This Book About?

Regardless of what mathematics you might use or study in college, it is very likely that you will use the mathematics in this book.

Precalculus is a phrase that describes the mathematics that calculus teachers feel students should know before they take a calculus course. Precalculus includes:

the properties of linear, quadratic, polynomial, exponential, logarithmic, and trigonometric functions;

sequences and limits ;

manipulation of algebraic expressions and the solution of equations and inequalities;

formulas for slope and distance in the coordinate plane, and for areas and volumes of figures both with and without coordinates;

certain other special topics such as absolute value, polar coordinates, and vectors.

You can see that most of the mathematics you have been studying the past few years involves precalculus topics!

Discrete mathematics refers to a collection of topics that are important for computer science. The word "discrete" (not to be used with its homonym "discreet") means separate, in contrast to the word "continuous", which applies to the basic functions of calculus. Discrete mathematics is about sets that are akin to the integers, with space between consecutive elements, whereas the mathematics of calculus is about sets like the set of real numbers, with no such thing as consecutive elements.

The topics of discrete mathematics include logic, recursion, mathematical induction, combinatorics, graphs, and circuits. Some people also include vectors and matrices under discrete mathematics.

Equipment Needed for this Course

To be a successful student in this course, you will need notebook paper, sharpened pencils, erasers, a ruler, and graph paper. It is best if the ruler is made of transparent plastic, and marked in both centimeters and inches.

You will need technology throughout the course for use in class, for homework, and on tests. The technology must include:

(1) a *scientific calculator* with keys such as those for exponents and powering logarithms and trigonometric functions.
(2) an *automatic grapher*, that is, a calculator, or computer software that is capable of drawing graphs of equations; and
(3) a *table-generator*, that is, a calculator, a spreadsheet, or a programming language such as BASIC, that enables you to make tables of values for equations.

Notes on Reading

The reading abilities of students who use UCSMP *Precalculus and Discrete Mathematics* will differ. One way to find out who may have trouble reading is to have students read the pages on their own, and then ask them questions about what they have read.

Cooperative Learning Emphasize the cooperative nature of learning as stated in point 4 on page 2. Encourage students to discuss questions with each other in school or call each other at home if they have difficulty with a problem or idea. You might want to make sure that each student in your class has the phone numbers of at least two other students. However, be sure to distinguish the difference between *cooperation* and *copying.*

If you plan to use cooperative groups often during the year, you might divide the class into groups of four and arrange the desks or tables to form rectangles. After students have read a section, each group should go through the questions; instruct one of the students to write the answers on a sheet of paper. You might want to walk around the room to monitor the groups, to keep them on task, and to help groups that are floundering.

Overview

These pages contain four important types of information about this book:

1. a description of the terms *precalculus* and *discrete mathematics*;
2. a list of the equipment needed for the book;
3. a description of the expectations related to the active learning approach of the book, including participation, reading, writing, and problem solving;
4. a set of questions designed to familiarize students with the locations of various features in the book.

Before beginning this chapter, make sure that students have read the section entitled *Getting Started* so they know what materials they are expected to have in class and at home.

It is assumed throughout this book that students have access to a graphing calculator. Throughout the book they will need its capabilities of graphing functions. It helps if the calculator can graph quadratic relations and can graph polar coordinates. If you expect your students to purchase their own graphing calculators, show them one that is similar to the kind you expect them to purchase.

Reading Mathematics Reading a mathematics textbook will be a new expectation to those students who are not familiar with UCSMP texts. To read well, students must read carefully and watch for important terms and symbols. Encourage students to use the headline phrases that identify some of the key ideas taught in the lessons. Point out that these headlines can help students organize their thoughts, preview the reading, and locate answers to questions about the lesson.

For more information on reading skills, see *General Teaching Suggestions: Reading* in the *Professional Sourcebook,* which begins on page T20 in Part 1 of the Teacher's Edition.

Also point out that as students read, they should stop to examine any graphs or charts and to study all computations that might be in examples. Looking at pictures and photographs and reading captions are also considered part of the lesson. Point out that important terms are printed in boldface type throughout this book.

✎ **Writing** Writing is an important aspect of this course. When students are expected to give a response by writing a sentence or paragraph, the pencil logo (shown at the beginning of this paragraph) will appear in the Teacher's Edition notes.

It must also be able to operate on matrices (multiply, find the inverse); and *iterate functions*, that is, use the output of a function as the input of that same function repeatedly.

Many graphing calculators have all of the above features in one hand-held machine. Thus, we urge you to buy a graphing calculator, even if your school provides such calculators for use during class.

Occasionally there is discussion of a *symbol manipulator*. This is a calculator or computer that is capable of working with algebraic expressions symbolically. If you can, obtain a symbol manipulator because it will serve you well not only for this course but also for future mathematics courses.

Studying Mathematics

An important goal of this book is to continue to help you learn mathematics on your own, so that you will be able to deal with the mathematics you see in newspapers, magazines, on television, on any job, and in school. The authors offer the following advice.

1 You can watch basketball hundreds of times on television. Still, to learn how to play basketball, you must have a ball in your hand and actually dribble, shoot, and pass it.

Mathematics is no different. You cannot learn much mathematics just by watching other people do it. You must participate. You must think through and work problems.
Some teachers have a slogan:

Mathematics is not a spectator sport.

2 You are expected to read each lesson, and it is vital for you to understand what you have read. In *Precalculus and Discrete Mathematics*, there are also graphs and new symbols that you must understand. Here are some ways to improve your reading comprehension.

Read slowly and thoughtfully, paying attention to each word, graph, and symbol.

Look up the meaning of any word you do not understand.

Work examples yourself as you follow the steps in the text.

Draw graphs by hand or on your automatic grapher when following a complicated example.

Reread sections that are unclear to you.

Discuss difficult ideas with a fellow student or your teacher.

3 Writing is a tool for communicating your solutions and thoughts to others, and can help you understand mathematics, too. In *Precalculus and Discrete Mathematics* you will often be asked to justify your solution to a problem, to write a formal argument, or to make up your own example to illustrate an idea. Writing good explanations takes practice. You should use solutions to the examples in each lesson to guide your writing.

4 If you cannot answer a question immediately, don't give up! Read the lesson again. Read the question again. Look for examples. If you can, go away from the problem and come back to it a little later. Do not be afraid to ask questions in class or to talk to others when you do not understand something. School is designed so that you do not have to learn everything by yourself.

At times we want students to have access to a symbol manipulator such as the one pictured by Question 3 on page 3.

Please stress that students will not be told when to use a calculator. However, they should be instructed to use calculators *when appropriate*. We expect that students will use calculators in class, for homework, with projects, and on tests. We have deliberately not included "use a calculator" even when calculators are needed because we want students to consider these tools as naturally as they view paper and pencils.

Students are expected to read this book; those students who have used previous books in this series will be accustomed to reading mathematics. Other students will have to adjust to this expectation.

Getting Acquainted with *Precalculus and Discrete Mathematics*

It is always helpful to spend some time getting acquainted with your textbook. The questions that follow are an activity designed to help you become familiar with this book. The first set of questions is called Covering the Reading. You will find this type of question in every lesson in this book. The second set of questions will help you become more familiar with special features of *Precalculus and Discrete Mathematics*.

We hope you join the thousands of students who have enjoyed this book. We wish you much success.

QUESTIONS

Covering the Reading

1. Name four topics that discrete mathematics includes. logic, recursion, mathematical induction, graphs
2. What tools other than paper and pencil are needed for this course? scientific calculator, automatic grapher, table generator
3. What is meant by the term *automatic grapher*? calculator or computer software that is capable of drawing graphs of equations

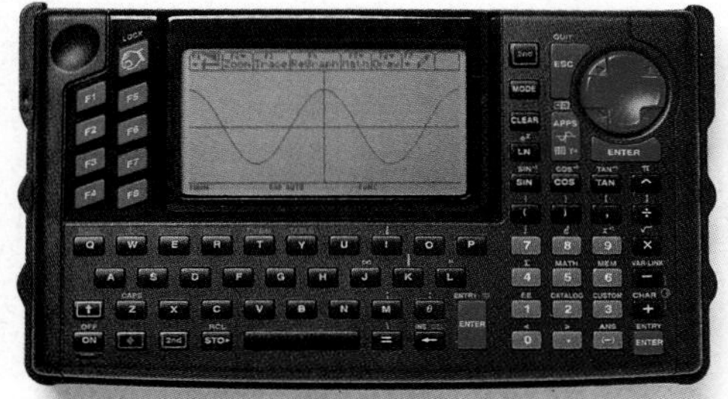

4. How can the statement "Mathematics is not a spectator sport" be applied to the study of precalculus topics? See margin.
5. Name the reading comprehension strategy mentioned in this lesson that you think is the most helpful. Sample: Reread sections that are unclear to you.

10) You should be able to give a definition of the terms marked with an asterisk.

12) SPUR stands for the four types of objectives: Skills, Properties, Uses, and Representations.

Knowing Your Textbook

In 6–13, answer the questions by looking at the Table of Contents, the lessons and chapters of the textbook, or material at the end of the book.

6. Refer to the Table of Contents. What lesson would you read to learn about algorithms for sorting? Lesson 7–8
7. What are the four categories of questions at the end of each lesson? Covering the Reading, Applying the Mathematics, Review, Exploration
8. Suppose you just finished the questions in Lesson 1-1.
   a. On what page can you find answers to check your work? page 852
   b. Which answers are given? odd numbered questions in Applying the Math and Review
9. At the end of Question 20 in Lesson 3-2, you see *(Lesson 1-6, 1-7)*. What does this mean? An idea that might help with Question 20 is in Lesson 1–6 or 1–7.
10. In the vocabulary sections at the end of each chapter, why are some terms marked with an asterisk? See left.
11. Look at a Progress Self-Test at the end of a chapter. What should you do after taking the Self-Test? Check your work with the solutions in the Selected Answer Section.
12. Refer to the Objectives and Review at the end of each chapter. What does SPUR mean? See left.
13. This book has some Appendices. How many are there and what do they cover? 2: List of Theorems and Properties; Parent Functions and their graphs

Notes on Questions

If students are not in groups, we suggest that you have the class answer only the questions in *Questions Covering the Reading* (**Questions 1–5**), and then have students work on **Questions 6–13** on their own or with a partner.

Questions 1–5 Point out that, except for statements of definitions, students should try to put their answers in their own words, even though answers to *Questions Covering the Reading* are sometimes found word for word in the lesson.

Question 3 This question provides an opportunity to discuss the types of calculators that students should have and those (if any) that will be available in class for student use. Pictured here is a TI-92, the most commonly used symbol manipulating calculator in schools at the time this book went to press.

Question 5 Students differ; what is helpful to one student may not be helpful to another student.

Additional Answers

4. Sample: Precalculus cannot be learned by watching other people do it. This involves thinking through and working problems, reading each lesson, and not giving up if you cannot answer a question immediately.

Setting Up Lesson 1-1

Homework If you have a short class period (15–25 minutes) the next day, or if your students have not studied from a UCSMP text before, assign the reading and **Questions 1–14** in Lesson 1-1. Otherwise, assign the reading and all the Questions in Lesson 1-1.

For more information on homework, see *General Teaching Suggestions: Homework* in the *Professional Sourcebook,* which begins on page T20 in Part 1 of the Teacher's Edition.

Error Alert Some students may feel that they can skip the Chapter 1 Opener on pages 4–5. Tell them that they should read all chapter openers along with the first lessons of each chapter because there may be questions within the chapter that refer to the opener.

Chapter 1 Planner

Adapting to Individual Needs

The student text is written for the vast majority of students. The chart at the right suggests two pacing plans to accommodate the needs of your students. Students in the Full Course should complete the entire text by the end of the year. Students in the Minimal Course will spend more time when there are quizzes and more time on the Chapter Review. Therefore, these students may not complete all of the chapters in the text.

Options are also presented to meet the needs of a variety of teaching and learning styles. For each lesson, the Teacher's Edition provides a section entitled *Adapting to Individual Needs.* This section regularly includes **Optional Activities, Challenge** problems, **English Language Development** suggestions, and suggestions for providing **Extra Help.** The Teacher's Edition also frequently includes an **Error Alert,** an **Extension,** and an **Assessment** alternative. The options available in Chapter 1 are summarized in the chart below.

Chapter 1 Pacing Chart

Day	Full Course	Minimal Course
1	1-1	1-1
2	1-2	1-2
3	1-3	1-3
4	1-4	1-4
5	Quiz*; 1-5	Quiz*; begin 1-5.
6	1-6	Finish 1-5.
7	1-7	1-6
8	Quiz*; 1-8.	1-7
9	Self-Test	Quiz*; begin 1-8.
10	Test*	Finish 1-8.
11		Self-Test
12		Review
13		Review
14		Test*

*in the Teacher's Resource File

In the Teacher's Edition...

Lesson	Optional Activities	Extra Help	Challenge	English Language Development	Error Alert	Extension	Cooperative Learning	Ongoing Assessment
1-1	●	●	●	●	●	●	●	Written
1-2	●	●	●	●	●	●		Written
1-3	●	●	●		●	●		Written
1-4	●	●	●		●	●		Quiz
1-5	●	●	●		●	●	●	Written
1-6	●	●	●	●	●	●	●	Oral
1-7	●	●			●		●	Quiz
1-8	●	●	●		●	●		Oral

In the Additional Resources...

	In the Teacher's Resource File							
Lesson	Lesson Masters	Teaching Aids*	Answer Masters	Technology Sourcebook	Assessment Sourcebook	Visual Aids**	Technology	Explorations Software
1-1	1-1	1, 5	1-1			1, 5, AM		
1-2	1-2	1, 6, 7	1-2			1, 6, 7, AM		
1-3	1-3	2, 6, 8	1-3	Comp 1		2, 6, 8, AM	Spreadsheet	
1-4	1-4	2, 9, 10	1-4		Quiz	2, 9, 10, AM		1-4
1-5	1-5	3, 6	1-5			3, 6, AM		1-5
1-6	1-6	3, 11	1-6			3, 11, AM		
1-7	1-7	4	1-7		Quiz	4, AM		1-7
1-8		4	1-8			4, AM		
End of chapter					Tests			

*Teaching Aids are pictured on pages 4C and 4D.

**Visual Aids provide transparencies for all Teaching Aids and all Answer Masters.

Also available is the Study Skills Handbook which includes study-skill tips related to reading, note-taking, and comprehension.

Integrating Strands and Applications

	1-1	1-2	1-3	1-4	1-5	1-6	1-7	1-8
Mathematical Connections								
Number Sense	●	●	●	●	●	●	●	●
Algebra	●	●	●	●	●	●	●	●
Geometry	●	●	●		●	●	●	●
Measurement	●	●				●		
Logic and Reasoning	●	●	●	●	●	●	●	●
Patterns and Functions	●	●	●	●	●		●	
Discrete Mathematics							●	
Interdisciplinary and Other Connections								
Art							●	
Music				●	●		●	
Literature					●	●	●	
Science	●			●	●		●	●
Social Studies	●	●	●			●		
Multicultural						●	●	
Technology			●	●	●	●		●
Career				●		●		●
Consumer				●				
Sports	●				●	●		●

Teaching and Assessing the Chapter Objectives

Chapter 1 Objectives (Organized into the SPUR catetgories—Skills, Properties, Uses, and Representations)	Lessons	Progress Self-Test Questions	Chapter Review Questions	In the Teacher's Resource File: Chapter Test, Forms A and B	Chapter Test, Forms C	Chapter Test, Forms D
Skills						
A: Identify forms of logical statements.	1-1, 1-5	1, 2, 14	1–4	1, 9	1, 4	X
B: Write equivalent forms of logical statements.	1-1, 1-3, 1-5	4, 8, 10, 11, 15	5–14	8, 10	2	X
C: Write the negation of a logical statement.	1-2, 1-3, 1-5	6, 9	15–21	7	1	X
D: Determine the truth value of a logical statement.	1-1, 1-2, 1-3, 1-5	5	22–26	6	1	
Properties						
E: Identify properties of logical statements.	1-1, 1-2, 1-3, 1-5	1, 12, 13	27–32	2, 11	1	X
F: Use the Law of Substitution to verify specific statements.	1-1	7, 24	33–34	3		
G: Determine whether arguments are valid or invalid.	1-6, 1-7	16, 17	35–39	4, 5	3	X
H: Use logic to prove or disprove statements.	1-1, 1-3, 1-6, 1-8	19, 20, 24	40–46	15, 20	4	
Uses						
I: Determine the truth of quantified statements outside of mathematics.	1-1, 1-2, 1-3, 1-5	3	47–53	17, 18, 19	2	
J: Determine whether or not a logical argument outside of mathematics is valid.	1-6, 1-7, 1-8	18	54–57	16		
Representations						
K: Translate logic networks into logical expressions and determine output signals.	1-4	21, 22	58–60	12, 13		
L: Write truth tables for logical expressions.	1-3, 1-5	23	61–65	14	2	

Assessment Sourcebook
Quiz for Lessons 1-1 through 1-4
Quiz for Lessons 1-5 through 1-7
Chapter 1 Test, Forms A–D

TestWorks CD-ROM

Teaching Aids

TEACHING AID 1

Warm-up
Lesson 1-1

Let $p(x)$ be $3x + 5 \geq 8x - 2$.

1. Is $p(x)$ a statement?
2. Give the value of $p(1)$.
3. Find a value of x for which $p(x)$ is not true.
4. Describe the set of all values of x for which $p(x)$ is true.
5. Describe the set of all values of x for which $p(x)$ is false.

Warm-up
Lesson 1-2

1. Give the opposite of each term.
   a. black
   b. large
   c. positive
   d. 11
   e. wrong
2. Give the negation of each statement.
   a. The color of that car is black.
   b. That is a large triangle.
   c. The solution to the sentence is a positive number.
   d. $x = 11$
   e. You answered all of the questions wrong.

TEACHING AID 2

Warm-up
Lesson 1-3

In 1–6, tell whether the sentence is true or false when $x = 30$.

1. $x \geq 30$
2. $x > 30$ and $x = 30$.
3. $x > -31$ and $x < 31$.
4. $x < -31$ and $x > 31$.
5. $x^2 > 900$
6. $x^2 \leq 30x$
7. Give the negation of each sentence in 1–6 and tell whether the negation is true or false when $x = 30$.

Warm-up
Lesson 1-4

1. Make a table showing all possibilities for opening or not opening a door with two locks that are unlocked or locked.
2. Relate the situation in *Warm-up* Question 1 to a truth table.

TEACHING AID 3

Warm-up
Lesson 1-5

First determine whether the sentence is a statement. If so, tell whether it is true or false.

1. If $3 > 2$, then $5 > 4$.
2. If $x > 3$, then $x > 4$.
3. For all x, if $x > 3$, then $x > 4$.

Warm-up
Lesson 1-6

Order these statements to put together a logical argument and state its conclusion.

A. If a convex polygon has seven sides, then it is a heptagon.

B. If the sum of the measures of the interior angles of a convex polygon is 900°, then the polygon must have at least 4 obtuse angles.

C. If a convex polygon has seven vertices, then it has 7 sides.

D. If a convex polygon is a heptagon, then the sum of the measures of its interior angles is 900°.

TEACHING AID 4

Warm-up
Lesson 1-7

Consider these statements:

All *A*s are *B*s.

Some *B*s are *C*s.

All *C*s are *D*s.

Is it valid to conclude Some *A*s are *D*s? Why or why not?

Warm-up
Lesson 1-8

Let line segments $\overline{AB}$ and $\overline{CD}$ intersect at point E.

1. Prove: If E is the midpoint of both $\overline{AB}$ and $\overline{CD}$, then lines AC and BD are parallel.
2. Express the statement to be proved in *Warm-up* Question 1 as a universal conditional.

TEACHING AID 5
Lesson 1-1

Definitions from the Lesson

Definition

Let S be a set and $p(x)$ a property that may or may not hold for any element x of S. A **universal statement** is a statement of the form

For all x in S, p(x).

or symbolically

$\forall$ *x in S, p(x).*

A universal statement is true if and only if $p(x)$ is true for every element x in S; otherwise, it is **false.**

Definition

Given a universal statement

$\forall$ *x in S, p(x),*

a value of x in S for which $p(x)$ is false is called a **counterexample** to the statement.

Definition

Suppose that S is a set and that $p(x)$ is a property that may or may not hold for elements x of S. An **existential statement** is a statement of the form

There exists x in S such that p(x).

or, symbolically,

$\exists$ *x in S such that p(x).*

An existential statement is true if and only if $p(x)$ is true for at least one element x in S, otherwise, it is **false.**

TEACHING AID 6
Lessons 1-2, 1-3, 1-5

Truth Tables

Truth Table for Negation

p	$\sim p$
T	F
F	T

Truth Table for *and*

p	q	p and q
T	T	T
T	F	F
F	T	F
F	F	F

Truth Table for *or*

p	q	p or q
T	T	T
T	F	T
F	T	T
F	F	F

Truth Table for Conditional

p	q	if p, then q $p \Rightarrow q$
T	T	T
T	F	F
F	T	T
F	F	T

TEACHING AID 7
Lesson 1-2

Question 22

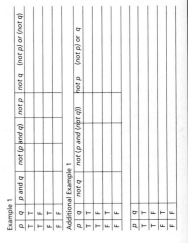

	academic club			fine arts club			foreign language club				sports teams					
	science	debate	math	band	chorus	drama	Spanish	Russian	German	French	swimming	track	soccer	baseball	basketball	football
Dominique			✓						✓		✓					
Raul		✓	✓			✓							✓			✓
Karen			✓	✓						✓		✓				
Tom	✓	✓	✓					✓						✓		

TEACHING AID 8
Lesson 1-3

Example 1 and Additional Example 1

Example 1

p	q	p and q	not (p and q)	not p	not q	(not p) or (not q)
T	T					
T	F					
F	T					
F	F					

Additional Example 1

p	q	not q	not (p and (not q))	not p	(not p) or q
T	T				
T	F				
F	T				
F	F				

p	q					
T	T					
T	F					
F	T					
F	F					

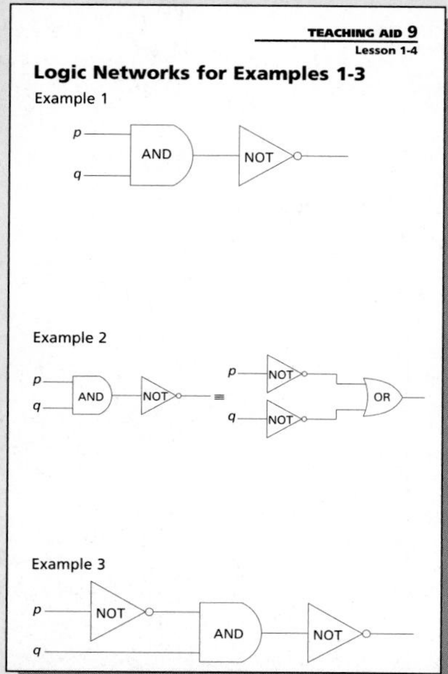
TEACHING AID 9
Lesson 1-4

Logic Networks for Examples 1-3

Example 1

Example 2

Example 3

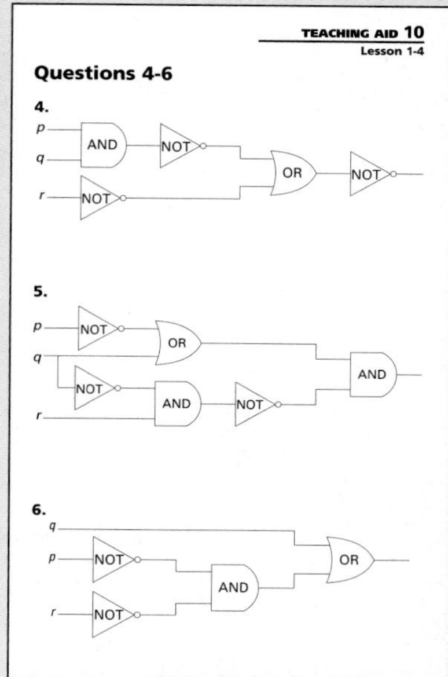
TEACHING AID 10
Lesson 1-4

Questions 4-6

4.

5.

6.

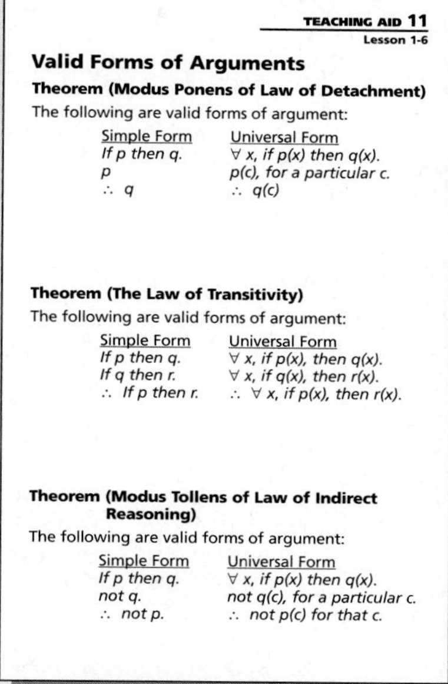
TEACHING AID 11
Lesson 1-6

Valid Forms of Arguments

Theorem (Modus Ponens of Law of Detachment)

The following are valid forms of argument:

Simple Form	Universal Form
If p then q.	*∀ x, if p(x) then q(x).*
p	*p(c), for a particular c.*
∴ q	*∴ q(c)*

Theorem (The Law of Transitivity)

The following are valid forms of argument:

Simple Form	Universal Form
If p then q.	*∀ x, if p(x), then q(x).*
If q then r.	*∀ x, if q(x), then r(x).*
∴ If p then r.	*∴ ∀ x, if p(x), then r(x).*

Theorem (Modus Tollens of Law of Indirect Reasoning)

The following are valid forms of argument:

Simple Form	Universal Form
If p then q.	*∀ x, if p(x) then q(x).*
not q.	*not q(c), for a particular c.*
∴ not p.	*∴ not p(c) for that c.*

Chapter Opener

Pacing

All lessons in this chapter are designed to be covered in one day. At the end of the chapter, you should plan to spend 1 day to review the Progress Self-Test, 1–2 days for the Chapter Review, and 1 day for a test. You may wish to spend a day on projects, and possibly a day is needed for quizzes. This chapter should therefore take 11–14 days. Spending more than 15 days on this chapter is not recommended; there is ample opportunity to review ideas in later chapters.

Using Pages 4–5

From their study of geometry, students should know that a mathematical system consists of defined and undefined terms, postulates, and a system of logic that allows for the development and proof of theorems. The logic of mathematics is precise and demanding. The error in the proof on page 5 is subtle; it is identified and explained in Lesson 1-1. You may wish to ask students in class to try to find the error before they read that lesson.

Make certain that students have read the "To the Student" pages and know what supplies they are expected to have for this class.

CHAPTER 1

4

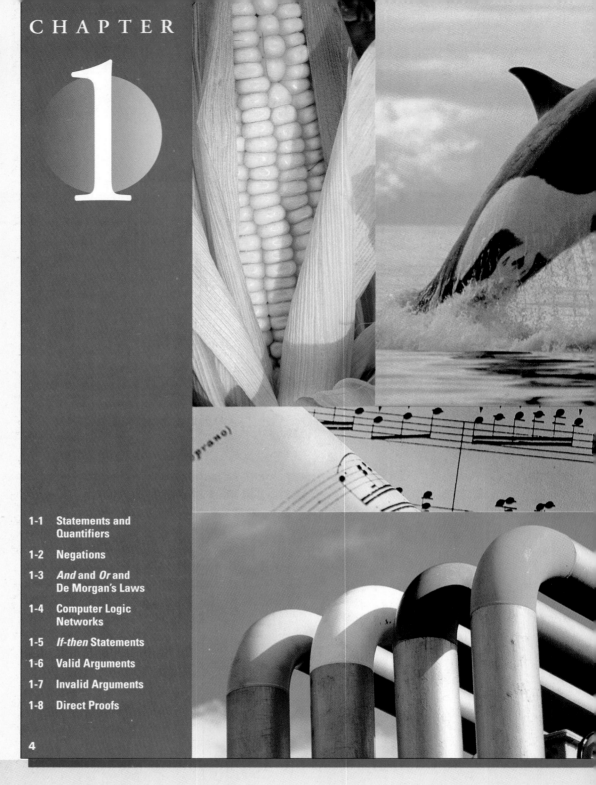

Chapter 1 Overview

Before proceeding with this chapter, you should read the *Professional Sourcebook* beginning on page T20 of Part 1 of the Teacher's Edition. This will help you know what your students are expected to learn from it. Also, if you have not done so before, you will probably want to read the introduction for an overview of the UCSMP program and its scope.

The content of Chapter 1 is a blend of both new and familiar material. The formalization of logic probably will be new for most students. In geometry, students dealt with *if-then* statements and the contrapositive, inverse, and converse of such statements. However, they probably have not dealt with universal or existential statements and the relationship of these statements to conditionals. Nor have they applied these ideas to examine computer logic networks.

Throughout the chapter, students will need to pay great attention to detail; such attention is critical to success in all advanced mathematics courses.

Both English sentences and mathematical sentences are used to illustrate the logic. The mathematical sentences are taken from geometry and from such standard precalculus topics as properties of exponents, logarithms, and trigonometric functions. As such,

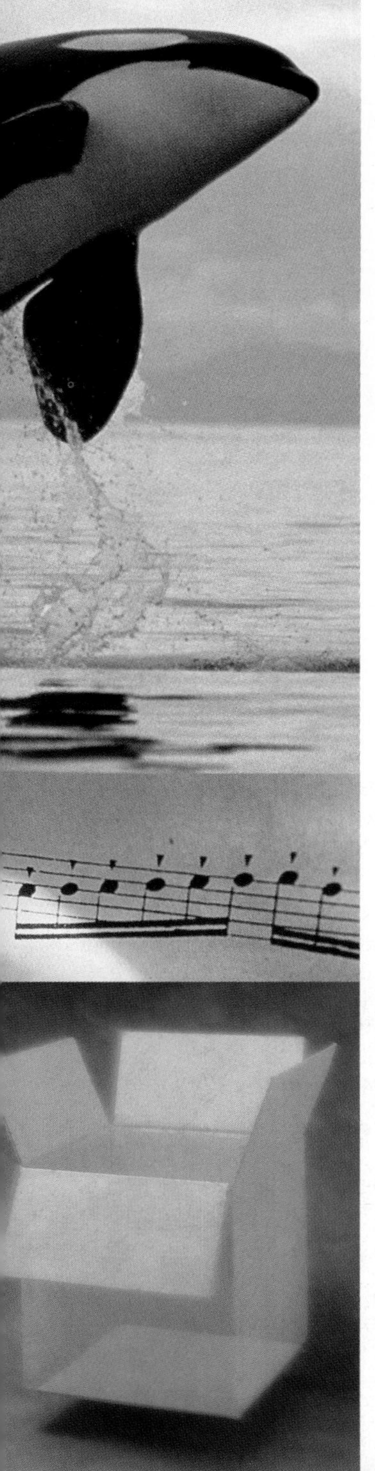

Mathematical Logic and Reasoning

Mathematics is a beautiful subject whose results provide help in clear thinking. Yet, occasionally, something occurs that seems to violate this beauty and clear thinking. Consider the following "proof" that $1 + 1 = 1$.

Let $x = 1$ and $y = 1$. Then	$y = x.$
Multiply by $-y$.	$-y^2 = -xy$
Add x^2.	$x^2 - y^2 = x^2 - xy$
Factor.	$(x + y)(x - y) = x(x - y)$
Divide by $x - y$.	$x + y = x$
Substitute back.	$1 + 1 = 1$
Add.	$2 = 1$

Either something is wrong or mathematics has failed! Finding the cause of the problem requires the examination of mathematical arguments and logic.

Distinguishing valid from invalid conclusions sometimes requires careful logical analysis. From the statement

There is a risk of an accident if nuclear power is used.

it is correct to conclude

To have no risk, you cannot use nuclear power.

but incorrect to conclude

There is no risk if you use a power source other than nuclear power.

In this chapter on logic, you will touch upon many of the components of mathematical reasoning: the use of careful language, the meaning of a generalization, and the criteria for a valid proof. You will also see how mathematical reasoning is employed in computer logic networks and everyday thinking.

Photo Connections

The photo collage makes real-world connections to the content of the chapter: logic and reasoning.

Corn: In Lesson 1-6, **Question 11** deals with an argument about drought and the corn crop. Students write the form of the argument and determine if it is valid.

Whales: In Lesson 1-7, **Question 4,** students are given a statement about whales and mammals. They write and determine the validity of the converse and the inverse of the statement.

Music: An invalid argument in the introduction of Lesson 1-7 deals with the relationship between band members and persons that play musical instruments.

Power Plants: On this page, students see correct and incorrect conclusions that can be made from a statement about risks of accidents and nuclear power.

Box: The U.S. Post Office has specific regulations concerning the size of items that are mailed. **Question 18** in Lesson 1-3 asks students to use De Morgan's Laws to describe an item that cannot be mailed.

Chapter 1 Projects

At the end of each chapter, you will find projects related to the chapter. The projects provide an opportunity to extend the work on topics related to the content of the chapter and are meant to be equivalent to one or two night's full homework assignment.

At this time, you might want to have students look over the projects on page 67. Have each student tentatively select a project on which to work. As students read and progress into the chapter, they can finalize their project choices.

Some teachers wait until Chapter 2 or 3 to have students do projects and give their students options from all the chapters. For more information on projects, see *General Teaching Suggestions: Projects* in the *Professional Sourcebook,* which begins on page T20 in Part 1 of the Teacher's Edition.

students begin an implicit process of review that will be made explicit in Chapter 2. Do not take time to discuss the exponential, logarithmic, and trigonometric functions at this point. Simply assign the questions containing these ideas and go over them.

Pacing Although in many schools the first week contains many shortened periods, it is important to try to adhere to a lesson-a-day pace, if it is at all reasonable. The beginning of the year establishes the routines that will exist throughout the year. Going too slowly now will probably cause problems later in the year. Rather than spending more than one day on a lesson in this chapter, move at the suggested pace and then spend two or three days at the end of the chapter on the Progress Self-Test and the Chapter Review. At that point, students will have an overall picture of the goals of the chapter.

Lesson 1-1

Objectives

A Identify forms of logical statements.
B Write equivalent forms of logical statements.
D Determine the truth value of a logical statement.
E Identify properties of logical statements.
F Use the Law of Substitution to verify specific statements.
H Use logic to prove or disprove statements.
I Determine the truth of quantified statements outside of mathematics.

Resources

From the ***Teacher's Resource File***
- Lesson Master 1-1
- Answer Master 1-1
- Teaching Aids
  1 Warm-up
  5 Definitions From the Lesson

Additional Resources
- Visuals for Teaching Aids 1, 5

Teaching Lesson 1-1

Warm-up

You can use the *Warm-up* or the *Additional Examples* on page 10 as questions for students to work on as you begin class.

Let $p(x)$ be $3x + 5 \geq 8x - 2$.
1. Is $p(x)$ a statement? No
2. Give the value of $p(1)$. $8 \geq 6$

LESSON

1-1 Statements and Quantifiers

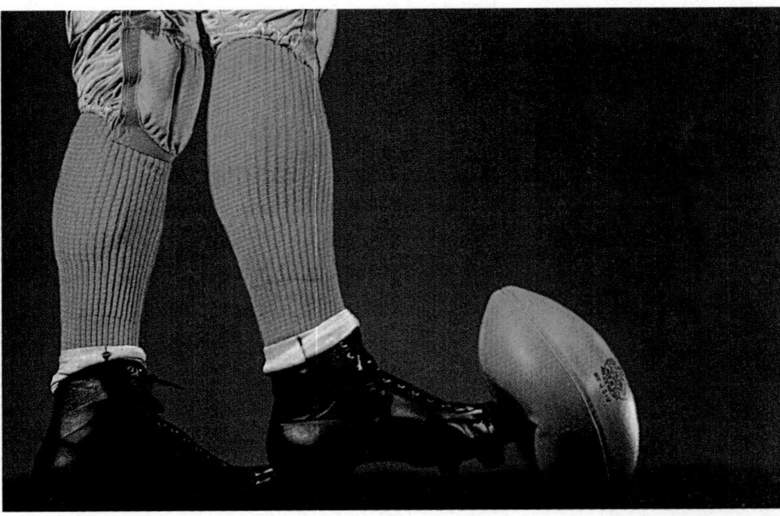

❶ **Just for Kicks.** *This is one of the first stop-motion color photos ever taken (1934). It demonstrates Newton's Third Law. (See Question 22.) Just as the foot pushes against the ball, the ball pushes against the foot.*

What Is a Statement?

The logic of *statements* helps to find and explain the mathematical problem on the previous page. In logic and mathematics, a **statement** is a sentence that is true or false but not both.

The sentence $1 + 1 = 2$ is a statement because it is true.
The sentence $1 + 1 = 1$ is a statement because it is false.
The sentence $x + 1 = 5x$ is not a statement because it is true for some values of x and false for others.

❷ In this book when a sentence is being discussed for its logical properties, it is written in *italics*. Any sentence may be represented by a single letter such as p. If the sentence contains a variable such as x, then it may be represented by a symbol such as $p(x)$. For instance, let $p(x)$ be the sentence *x + 1 is an integer.* Notice that $p(x)$ is not a statement, because it might be true and it might be false:

p(3): 3 + 1 is an integer.

is true while *p(0.5): 0.5 + 1 is an integer.*

is false.

If the words *for all integers x* are put at the beginning of the sentence $p(x)$, the result

For all integers x, x + 1 is an integer.

is a statement because it has a truth value (true). The phrase "for all" is called a **quantifier** and is represented in logic by the symbol $\forall$. With this symbol, the statement can be written

∀ integers x, x + 1 is an integer.

Lesson 1-1 Overview

Broad Goals This lesson covers the distinction between a *statement* and a *sentence,* and introduces the terminology and symbolism of *universal statement* and *existential statement*.

The lesson has pedagogical objectives as well: (1) to ease the student into the book with content that is new yet somewhat familiar; (2) to encourage the student to read the lessons; and (3) to introduce some rigor by means of questions that require attention to detail.

Perspective In mathematics, we make a distinction between a *statement*, which must be true or false, and other types of sentences. For instance, $3 + 2 = 5$ is a (true) statement, and $6 + 2 = 5$ is a (false) statement; $x + 2 = 5$ is not a statement. However, $x + 2 = 5$ can be made into a statement by specifying the value of x or by affixing appropriate quantification: *For all integers x, x + 2 = 5* is a (false) statement; *There exists an integer x such that x + 2 = 5* is a (true) statement.

The previous UCSMP courses discuss counterexamples, so this term should not be new to students. Notice that a universal statement lends itself to the question of whether there is a counterexample,

Letting I stand for the set of integers, the statement can be rewritten even more briefly:

$$\forall\ x \text{ in } I,\ x + 1 \text{ is an integer.}$$

This statement is true.

Universal Statements

Statements asserting that a certain property holds for all elements in some set—such as the set of all triangles or the set of all integers—are called *universal statements.*

Definitions

Let S be a set and $p(x)$ a property that may or may not hold for any element x of S. A **universal statement** is a statement of the form

For all x in S, p(x).

or, symbolically,

$$\forall\ x \text{ in } S,\ p(x).$$

A universal statement is true if and only if $p(x)$ is true for every element x in S; otherwise, it is **false**.

Universal statements are powerful because they assert that a certain property holds for *every* element in a set. Thus, if you are given any particular element of the set, you can deduce that the property holds for that element. In formal logic, this is known as the **Law of Substitution**. For instance, because the sum of the measures of the angles of *any* triangle equals 180°, then the sum of the measures of the angles of the particular triangle ABC shown below is 180°.

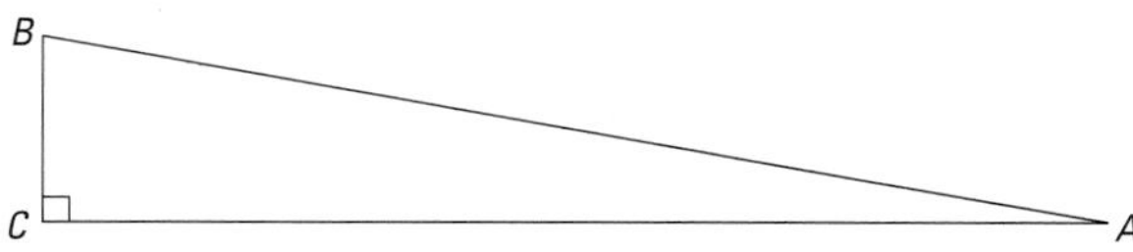

❸ With these ideas, the fallacy in the "proof" that $1 + 1 = 1$ can be explained. The argument began with statements assumed to be true: $x = 1$ and $y = 1$. From these statements, the following four statements can be deduced. (You can verify by substituting 1 for x and 1 for y.)

$$y = x$$
$$-y^2 = -xy$$
$$x^2 - y^2 = x^2 - xy$$
$$(x + y)(x - y) = x(x - y)$$

The next step is where the mistake arises. It assumes the justification: $\forall$ *real numbers d, if both sides of an equation are divided by d, then the quotients are equal.* But this universal statement is not true for all real numbers because it is not true when $d = 0$. When both sides are divided by $x - y$, it may not look like division by 0, but $x - y = 1 - 1 = 0$. The result

$$x + y = x$$

is seen to be false when the number 1 is substituted back for x and y.

3. Find a value of x for which $p(x)$ is not true. **Sample: 10**

4. Describe the set of all values of x for which $p(x)$ is true. **$\{x: x \leq 1.4\}$**

5. Describe the set of all values of x for which $p(x)$ is false. **$\{x: x > 1.4\}$**

Notes on Reading

Reading Mathematics Students should be aware that they are expected to read the text. This lesson has a little more reading than most, but the reading is not as dense. As you discuss the reading, you might want to use **Teaching Aid 5,** which contains all of the definitions found in the lesson.

❶ **Sports Connection** At the end of the 1997–1998 U.S. professional football season, the record for the longest field goal kick is 63 yards, made on November 8, 1970, by Tom Dempsey of the New Orleans Saints. The record for the longest punt is 98 yards, kicked on September 21, 1969, by Steve O'Neal of the New York Jets.

❷ Students may wonder why we use the notation $p(x)$ to represent a property that may or may not be true for any element x in some set. The letter p is used often because $p(x)$ is a "proposition in x." You may compare the $p(x)$ notation with the $f(x)$ notation common to functions. Strictly speaking, p is a statement-valued function. For instance, just as replacing x with 7 in the function $f(x) = x^2 - 3x + 7$ gives $f(7) = 35$, replacing x with 7 in the sentence $p(x)$: $x^2 > x + 1$ yields the statement $p(7)$: $7^2 > 7 + 1$. In this way, the use of variables in logic parallels the use of variables in algebra.

❸ In the "proof" that $1 + 1 = 1$, you may wish to go through the justification for each step. First, both sides of the original equation are multiplied by $-y$ (Multiplication Property of Equality). Then, x^2 is added to both sides (Addition Property of Equality). Each side is factored (Distributive Property). Next, both sides are divided by $x - y$ (or multiplied by $\frac{1}{x - y}$). Then the Law of Substitution is used.

whereas the idea of counterexample is inappropriate for an existential statement.

Optional Activities

Cooperative Learning After discussing the reading, you might have students work together to suggest as many different ways as possible to state the property "The square of a real number is nonnegative."

❹ Emphasize that it takes only one example to show that an existential statement is true. A universal statement can be shown to be true by example if the set S over which the statement is defined is finite and the statement is verified for all elements of S. The proof is then called a *proof by exhaustion*.

The set S is critical to determining the truth or falsity of a universal statement. This bears emphasis. Consider the inequality $x^2 \geq x$. The universal statement

$\forall$ *natural numbers* x, $x^2 \geq x$ is true, whereas

$\forall$ *real numbers* x, $x^2 \geq x$ *is false*, with infinitely many counterexamples (for any real x such that $0 \leq x \leq 1$).

A universal statement may involve more than one variable. For instance, let $p(a, b)$ be the sentence $(a - b)(a + b) = a^2 - b^2$ and let R be the set of real numbers. Then the universal statement

For all real numbers a and b, $(a - b)(a + b) = a^2 - b^2$.

can be written symbolically as

$$\forall \text{ a and b in } R,\ p(a, b).$$

Using the Law of Substitution, you can deduce $p(100, 3)$, which is

$$(100 - 3)(100 + 3) = 100^2 - 3^2.$$

You can also deduce $p(x, y)$, which is

$$\forall \text{ x and y in } R,\ (x - y)(x + y) = x^2 - y^2.$$

You can also deduce other statements.

Example 1

Suppose $k \geq 0$. Use substitution to show that

$$\left(\sqrt{k+1} - \sqrt{k}\right)\left(\sqrt{k+1} + \sqrt{k}\right) = 1.$$

Solution

The sentence

$$(a - b)(a + b) = a^2 - b^2$$

holds for all real numbers a and b. Hence, in particular, it holds when $a = \sqrt{k+1}$ and $b = \sqrt{k}$ because when $k \geq 0$, both $\sqrt{k}$ and $\sqrt{k+1}$ are real numbers. Substituting $\sqrt{k+1}$ for a and $\sqrt{k}$ for b yields

$$\left(\sqrt{k+1} - \sqrt{k}\right)\left(\sqrt{k+1} + \sqrt{k}\right) = \left(\sqrt{k+1}\right)^2 - \left(\sqrt{k}\right)^2$$
$$= (k + 1) - k.$$

Thus, when $k \geq 0$,

$$\left(\sqrt{k+1} - \sqrt{k}\right)\left(\sqrt{k+1} + \sqrt{k}\right) = 1.$$

In English it is possible to say one thing in several different ways. Let S be the set of all triangles and $p(x)$ be the sentence *the sum of the measures of the angles of x is 180°*, then the universal statement

$$\forall x \text{ in } S,\ p(x).$$

can be phrased in many ways, including the following:

For all triangles x, the sum of the measures of the angles of x is 180°.
For every triangle x, the sum of the measures of the angles of x is 180°.
The sum of the measures of the angles of any triangle is 180°.
If x, y, and z are the measures of the angles of a triangle, then
$x + y + z = 180°$.

LESSON MASTER 1-1 — Questions on SPUR Objectives
See pages 71–75 for objectives.

Skills Objective A

1. Is the following statement universal, existential, or neither? *Some integers are prime.* — existential

Skills Objective B

2. Rewrite the following statement using universal and existential quantifiers.
Every number is greater than some number.
$\forall x$ in R, $\exists y$ such that $x > y$

Skills Objective D

In 3–6, let $p(x)$ be the sentence $6x^2 - 7x + 2 \leq 0$. Determine whether the given statement is true or false.

3. $p(0.68)$ — False
4. $\exists$ *an integer x such that* $p(x)$. — False
5. $\exists$ *a rational number x such that* $p(x)$. — True
6. $\forall$ *real numbers x such that* $0.58 \leq x \leq 0.62$, $p(x)$. — True

Properties Objective E

In 7 and 8, determine whether the given sentence is a statement. If it is a statement, determine whether it is true or false.

7. $\frac{x}{x} = 1$ — not a statement
8. $\forall x, \frac{x}{x} = 1$ — statement, false

Properties Objective F

9. Given $\forall x, x \neq 1$, $1 + x^1 + x^2 + x^3 + \ldots + x^n = \frac{1 - x^{n+1}}{1 - x}$, use the Law of Substitution to prove that $\forall k$, $k \neq 1$ and $k \neq 0$, $1 + k^{-1} + k^{-2} + k^{-3} + \ldots + k^{-n} = \frac{k - k^{-n}}{k - 1}$.
Substitute k^{-1} for x. Then, if $k^{-1} \neq x$, $x \neq 1$ and $1 + (k^{-1})^1 + (k^{-1})^2 + (k^{-1})^3 + \ldots + (k^{-1})^n =$ $1 + k^{-1} + k^{-2} + k^{-3} + \ldots + k^{-n} =$ $\frac{1 - (k^{-1})^{n+1}}{1 - k^{-1}} = \frac{1 - k^{-n-1}}{1 - k^{-1}} \cdot \frac{k}{k} = \frac{k - k^{-n}}{k - 1}$

Adapting to Individual Needs

Extra Help
You might want to have students work in small groups to practice writing universal and existential statements. Refer to **Questions 12** and **13.** Have students work together to generate statements similar to those given at the beginning of each question. Then have the group rewrite the statements in all of the forms shown in the questions.

English Language Development
Note that the symbols $\forall$ and $\exists$ are not letters in the alphabet. They are the upside-down first letters of "all" and "exist," and they are read as "for all" and "there exists."

Often, when a sentence of the form *If p(x) then q(x)* contains a variable *x*, the sentence is understood to be a claim about all values of *x* in some set *S* (which is determined by the context of the situation). For example, a sentence such as

$$\textit{If } \tfrac{x}{3} > 5, \textit{ then } x > 15.$$

is often intended to mean

$$\textit{For all real numbers } x, \textit{ if } \tfrac{x}{3} > 5, \textit{ then } x > 15.$$

Counterexamples

There is an English saying that "the exception proves the rule." This is not true for most rules and certainly not true in mathematics. One exception, or *counterexample*, to a universal statement, however, proves that the universal statement is false.

Definition
Given a universal statement

$$\forall\ x \text{ in } S,\ p(x),$$

a value of *x* in *S* for which *p(x)* is false is called a **counterexample** to the statement.

Example 2

Is the following statement true or false?

For all real numbers x, $x^4 \geq 1$.

Solution

Let p(x) be the sentence $x^4 \geq 1$ and S be the set of real numbers.

As a counterexample, let $x = \frac{1}{2}$.

$p\left(\frac{1}{2}\right)$ is the statement $\left(\frac{1}{2}\right)^4 \geq 1$. Because $\frac{1}{16} < 1$, $p\left(\frac{1}{2}\right)$ is false and so the given statement is false.

❹ Existential Statements

Example 2 illustrates the following fact: saying that the universal statement

$$\forall \textit{ real numbers } x,\ x^4 \geq 1.$$

is false is equivalent to saying that the following statement is true:

There is at least one real number x such that $x^4 < 1$.

The phrase "there is" or "there exists" is another quantifier and is represented by the symbol ∃, read "there exists." The above statement can be written

$$\exists \textit{ a real number } x \textit{ such that } x^4 < 1.$$

Statements asserting that there exists at least one element of a set for which a certain property holds are called *existential statements*.

If this is a student's first UCSMP course, note the following characteristics of *Questions*. The questions in *Covering the Reading* take the students through the lesson in order; if students have difficulty with any of these questions, they should return to the lesson to find help. The *Applying the Mathematics* questions require students to extend the content of the lesson or to put ideas together in new ways. It is important that students understand the function of the *Review*. Review questions provide a continual review of material so that students continue to work on ideas after they have been presented. Continued work on the ideas of Chapter 1 occurs through the later chapters.

Answers to all odd-numbered questions are found in the back of the student text, except for (1) those *Covering the Reading* questions whose answers are literally contained in the lesson, (2) questions that ask for an opinion (and thus have no correct answer) and, (3) Exploration questions.

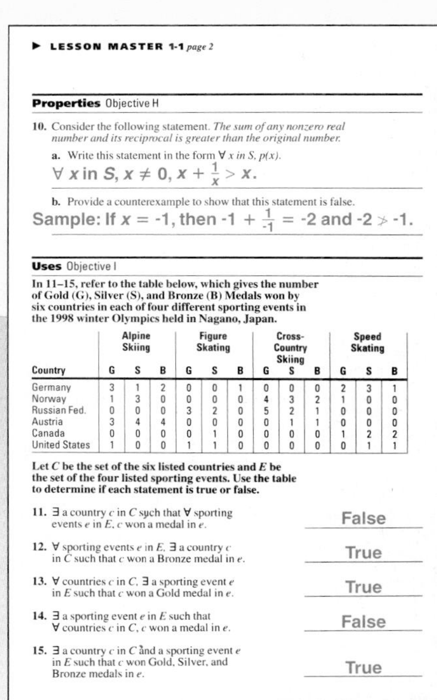

▶ **LESSON MASTER 1-1** *page 2*

Properties Objective H

10. Consider the following statement. *The sum of any nonzero real number and its reciprocal is greater than the original number.*

a. Write this statement in the form ∀ *x in S, p(x).*

$\forall\ x \text{ in } S,\ x \neq 0,\ x + \frac{1}{x} > x.$

b. Provide a counterexample to show that this statement is false.

Sample: If $x = -1$, then $-1 + \frac{1}{-1} = -2$ and $-2 \not> -1$.

Uses Objective I

In 11–15, refer to the table below, which gives the number of Gold (G), Silver (S), and Bronze (B) Medals won by six countries in each of four different sporting events in the 1998 winter Olympics held in Nagano, Japan.

	Alpine Skiing			Figure Skating			Cross-Country Skiing			Speed Skating		
Country	G	S	B	G	S	B	G	S	B	G	S	B
Germany	3	1	2	0	0	1	0	0	0	2	3	1
Norway	1	3	0	0	0	0	4	3	2	1	0	0
Russian Fed.	0	0	0	3	2	0	5	2	1	0	0	0
Austria	3	4	4	0	0	0	0	1	1	0	0	0
Canada	0	0	0	0	1	0	0	0	0	1	2	2
United States	1	0	0	1	1	0	0	0	0	0	1	1

Let *C* be the set of the six listed countries and *E* be the set of the four listed sporting events. Use the table to determine if each statement is true or false.

11. ∃ a country *c* in *C* such that ∀ sporting events *e* in *E*, *c* won a medal in *e*. False

12. ∀ sporting events *e* in *E*, ∃ a country *c* in *C* such that *c* won a Bronze medal in *e*. True

13. ∀ countries *c* in *C*, ∃ a sporting event *e* in *E* such that *c* won a Gold medal in *e*. True

14. ∃ a sporting event *e* in *E* such that ∀ countries *c* in *C*, *c* won a medal in *e*. False

15. ∃ a country *c* in *C* and a sporting event *e* in *E* such that *c* won Gold, Silver, and Bronze medals in *e*. True

Adapting to Individual Needs

Challenge

Have students find the error in the proof that 4 = -4.

$4 = \sqrt{16} = \sqrt{(-4)(-4)} = \sqrt{-4} \cdot \sqrt{-4} = 2i \cdot 2i = 4i^2 = -4$

[$\sqrt{A \cdot B} = \sqrt{A} \cdot \sqrt{B}$, a universal property that is used in the third step, requires *A* and *B* to be nonnegative.]

Additional Examples

Cooperative Learning You may want to have students work in **small groups** for many of the additional examples given throughout this text.

1. Use substitution into a known true universal statement to show that for any real numbers x and y, $(x^2 - y^2)(x^2 + y^2) = x^4 - y^4$. **The sentence $(a - b) \cdot (a + b) = a^2 - b^2$ is true for all real numbers a and b. Hence, in particular, it is true when $a = x^2$ and $b = y^2$ for any real numbers x and y, since if x and y are real numbers, so are x^2 and y^2. Substituting for a and b yields $(x^2 - y^2)(x^2 + y^2) = (x^2)^2 - (y^2)^2 = x^4 - y^4$. Thus $(x^2 - y^2)(x^2 + y^2) = x^4 - y^4$.**
2. Is the following statement true or false? *For all real numbers y, $y^2 > y$.* **False: 0.5 is a counterexample.**
3. Is this statement true or false? *∃ a real number y such that $y^2 > y$.* **True. One such real number is 2.**

Definitions

Suppose that S is a set and that $p(x)$ is a property that may or may not hold for elements x of S. An **existential statement** is a statement of the form

There exists x in S such that p(x).

or, symbolically,

∃ x in S such that p(x).

An existential statement is true if and only if $p(x)$ is true for at least one element x in S; otherwise, it is **false**.

Example 3

Is this statement true or false?

∃ an integer n such that $n^2 = 2$.

Solution

The statement is: *There is an integer n such that $n^2 = 2$.* **But the only solutions to $n^2 = 2$ are $\sqrt{2}$ and $-\sqrt{2}$. These are not integers. So there is no integer n such that $n^2 = 2$. Thus the statement is false.**

To prove the truth of a universal statement, you must show that the statement is true for all members of the appropriate set S. However, to prove the truth of an existential statement, you need to find only one member of the appropriate set S for which the statement is true. For instance, the statement ∃ *a real number n such that $n^2 = 2$.* is true because $\sqrt{2}$ is a real number. (Of course, so is $-\sqrt{2}$.)

Existential statements may also be written in a variety of ways. Let S be the set of all real numbers and $p(x)$ be the sentence $x^2 = x$. The existential statement ∃ *x in S such that p(x)* can be written in the following equivalent ways.

There exists a real number x such that $x^2 = x$.
There is at least one real number x for which $x^2 = x$.
For some real number x, $x^2 = x$.
For some real numbers x, $x^2 = x$.
There is a real number which is equal to its square.

Some statements contain both "for all" and "there exists." For instance, the Additive Identity Property of Zero can be written

∃ a real number n such that ∀ real numbers x, $x + n = x$.

The number n is, of course, 0. The existence of additive inverses uses the quantifiers in reverse order:

∀ real numbers x, ∃ a real number y such that $x + y = 0$.

You know that $y = -x$.

Here is a summary of the properties of universal and existential statements.

statement:	universal	existential
form:	*For all x in S, p(x).*	*There exists an x in S such that p(x).*
quantifier:	for all	there exists
symbol:	$\forall$	$\exists$
true:	if true for all values of x in S	if true for at least one value of x in S

QUESTIONS

Covering the Reading

10) $(a + b)^2 = a^2 + 2ab + b^2$ holds for all real numbers a and b. Because $\sqrt{75}$ and $\sqrt{12}$ are real, the relation holds when $a = \sqrt{75}$ and $b = \sqrt{12}$. Hence, $(\sqrt{75} + \sqrt{12})^2 = \sqrt{75}^2 + 2\sqrt{75} \cdot \sqrt{12} + (\sqrt{12})^2 = 75 + 60 + 12 = 147$.

These questions check your understanding of the reading. If you cannot answer a question, you should go back to the reading to help you find an answer.

In 1–3, tell whether the sentence is a statement.

1. *There is exactly one solution to the equation* $2x = 5$. statement

2. *The equation* $x^2 = 1$ *has three solutions.* statement

3. $6x^2 = 7x - 1$. not a statement

4. *Multiple choice.* Which is the true statement? b
(a) $\forall x, x^9 = x$.
(b) $\exists x$ *such that* $x^9 = x$.

5. Suppose $p(x)$ is the sentence $x^3 - 1 = (x - 1)(x^2 + x + 1)$.
a. State $p(4)$ and tell whether $p(4)$ is true. $p(4) = 4^3 - 1 = (4 - 1)(4^2 + 4 + 1)$; true
b. Write $p(\sqrt{a})$. $p(\sqrt{a}) = (\sqrt{a})^3 - 1 = (\sqrt{a} - 1)(a + \sqrt{a} + 1)$
c. Is this sentence $\forall$ *real numbers* $x, x^3 - 1 = (x - 1)(x^2 + x + 1)$. a statement? yes

In 6–8, identify the statement as a universal statement, existential statement, or neither.

6. *There exists a bird b such that b cannot fly.* existential

7. *For all rivers r in North America, r flows into the Mississippi.* universal

8. *Chicago is the capital of Illinois.* neither

9. Name the two quantifiers introduced in this lesson. for all, $\forall$; there exists, $\exists$

10. The following statement is true:

$$\forall \text{ real numbers } a \text{ and } b, (a + b)^2 = a^2 + 2ab + b^2.$$

If $a = \sqrt{75}$ and $b = \sqrt{12}$, use the Law of Substitution to deduce that

$$(\sqrt{75} + \sqrt{12})^2 = 147.$$ See above left.

Ground bound. *The ostrich is the largest living bird. It cannot fly, but it can run over 64 km/ h.*

11. Find a counterexample to show that the following statement is false:

$$\forall \text{ real numbers } x, x^3 > x^2.$$

Sample: $x = 1$

Notes on Questions

Question 10 Students should use **Example 1** as a model for answering this question.

Question 11 Encourage students to describe, when possible, the set of all counterexamples to a false universal statement. At this point in this course, students may not be able to do so for this question. In Lesson 3-5, we study in detail those operations on sides of an inequality that yield equivalent inequalities. One of them is division by a positive number. When $x \neq 0$, dividing both sides by x^2 yields $x > 1$, which is false for all real numbers $x \leq 1$. The Test-Point method for solving this inequality is given in Lesson 3-7. For that method, one could add $-x^2$ to each side to achieve the equivalent inequality $x^3 - x^2 > 0$. Then factor $x^2(x - 1) > 0$, which shows that 0 and 1 are endpoints of key intervals. Trying values in these intervals yields the solutions $x > 1$.

Notes on Questions

Question 15c Error Alert Students will gain better understanding of this question if they make a table of values or graph $y = 2^x$ and $y = x^2$.

Questions 24–26 These questions help students prepare for analyzing functions in Chapter 2.

Question 27 This *Exploration* question may lead to lively class discussion. Here is a similar paradox: The male barber in a town shaves all the men and only those men in the town who do not shave themselves. Is the sentence *The barber shaves himself* true or false? [If the barber shaves himself, then he does not belong to the group of men he shaves, and so he does not shave himself. If he does not shave himself, then he belongs to the group of men he shaves, and so he shaves himself. The contradictions obtained in each case show that this sentence is neither true nor false and hence is not a statement.

History Connection Questions of the type in the paradox above were first put forth by Bertrand Russell about a century ago, and they challenged the foundations of the mathematical logic of the time. The result was to make people much more careful about using self-referential sentences.

12. Consider the statement

For all squares x, x is a rectangle.

Rewrite this statement in each form by filling in the blanks below.

a. ∀ __?__ x, __?__. squares; x is a rectangle
b. *All* __?__ *are* __?__. squares; rectangles
c. *Each* __?__ *is a* __?__. square; rectangle
d. *If* __?__ *then* __?__. x is a square; x is a rectangle

13. Consider the statement

There exists an even integer that is prime.

Write the statement in each form.

a. ∃ __?__ *x such that* __?__. an even integer; x is prime
b. *Some* __?__ *is* __?__. even integer; prime
c. *At least one* __?__ *is* __?__. even integer; prime

14. The Multiplicative Identity Property of One states that any real number times 1 equals that number. Write this property using the symbols ∀ and ∃.

∃ a real number x such that ∀ real numbers y, $y \cdot x = y$.

Applying the Mathematics

These questions extend the content of the lesson. You should take your time, study the examples and explanations, and try a variety of methods. Check your answers to odd-numbered questions with the ones in the back of the book.

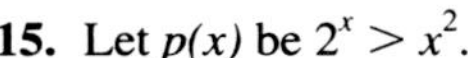

15. Let $p(x)$ be $2^x > x^2$.
a. Is $p(x)$ true when $x = 5$? yes
b. Is $p(-1)$ true? no
c. For what integer values of x is $p(x)$ true? (You do not have to prove your answer is correct.)
for 0, 1, and all integers greater than or equal to 5

16. Identify a property that is true for all students in your math class. Write this as a universal statement.
Sample: All students in my math class are teenagers.

17. Identify a property that is true for some, but not all, students in your math class. Write this as an existential statement.
Sample: There exists a student in my math class who owns a car.

18. *True or false.* ∀ *real numbers a, b, and x, the equation* $ax = b$ *has exactly one solution.* If false, find a counterexample.
False; Samples: $a = 0, b = 1$; $a = 0, b = 0$

19. *True or false.* Justify your answer. See left.

∀ *positive real numbers x,* $\log x > 0$.

19) False; Sample: $\log\left(\frac{1}{10}\right) = -1$ and $-1 < 0$

20. Consider the statement

Everybody can fool somebody.

Rewrite this statement by filling in the blank below:

∀ *people x,* ∃ *a person y such that* __?__.

x can fool y

Setting Up Lesson 1-2

As a preview of Lesson 1-2, students might try to add a row to the table at the top of page 11 with the heading "false: if there is a single x in S for which $p(x)$ is false; if there is no x in S for which $p(x)$ is true."

Homework
1. If you have assigned all the Questions in Lesson 1-1, ask students to read and do all the Questions in Lesson 1-2.
2. If you have not assigned all the Questions in Lesson 1-1, assign them and ask students to read and do the Questions Covering the Reading in Lesson 1-2.

For more information on homework, see *General Teaching Suggestions: Homework* in the *Professional Sourcebook,* which begins on page T20 of Part 1 of the Teacher's Edition.

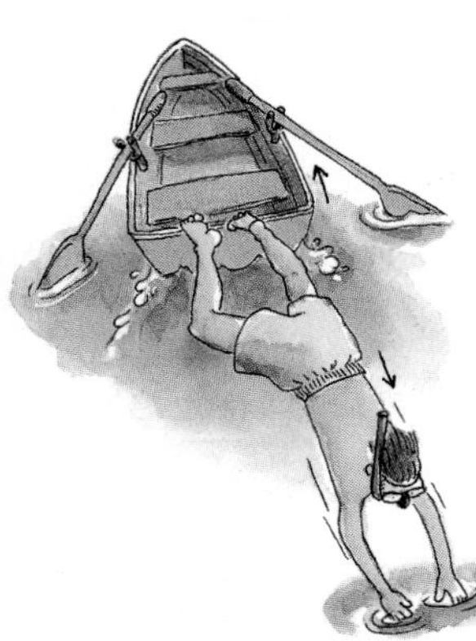

21. Find a counterexample to show that the following statement is false:

For all real numbers x there exists a real number y such that $x \cdot y = 1$.
Sample: Let $x = 0$, $\forall$ real numbers y, $0 \cdot y = 0 \neq 1$.

22. Newton's Third Law of Motion states that every action has an equal and opposite reaction. Write this law in the form

$$\forall \underline{\ ?\ }\ x, \exists \underline{\ ?\ }\ y \text{ such that } \underline{\ ?\ }.$$

$\forall$ actions x, $\exists$ a reaction y such that $x = -y$

23. The statement *No dogs have fleas.* can be written $\forall$ *dogs x, x does not have fleas*. Write the statement *No circles are parabolas.* in the form $\forall \underline{\ ?\ }\ x, \underline{\ ?\ }$.

$\forall$ circles x, x is not a parabola.

Review

Each lesson in this book contains review questions to give you practice using ideas you have studied earlier. In this lesson all review questions are from previous courses.

24. **a.** Solve $x^2 + 2x - 8 = 0$. $x = -4$, or $x = 2$
b. Graph $y = x^2 + 2x - 8$. *(Previous course)* See left.

25. Let $f(x) = x^2 - x + 1$. Evaluate each of the following. *(Previous course)*
a. $f(2)$ 3 **b.** $f(c)$ $c^2 - c + 1$ **c.** $f(a - b)$
c) $a^2 - 2ab + b^2 - a + b + 1$

26. Evaluate without using a calculator. *(Previous course)*
a. $\sin \frac{\pi}{2}$ 1 **b.** $\cos 180°$ -1 **c.** $\tan \frac{3\pi}{4}$ -1

Exploration

These questions ask you to explore ideas related to the lesson. Sometimes they require that you use reference books or other sources. Frequently, they have many possible answers.

27. Consider the sentence

This sentence is false.

a. Suppose it is true that *This sentence is false*. What can you deduce?
b. Suppose it is false that *This sentence is false*. What can you deduce?
c. Is *This sentence is false.* a statement? Why or why not?
d. Parts **a–c** exemplify a paradox known as *Russell's paradox*. Use another source to determine what this paradox is and who Russell was.

a) The sentence is false.
b) The sentence is true.
c) No, it is neither true nor false.
d) See left.

24b)

$y = x^2 + 2x - 8$

27d) Bertrand Russell (1872-1970) was a mathematician of many talents and wrote books on mathematics, philosophy, logic, sociology, and education. The paradox is: Let B be the set of all sets that are not members of themselves. If X is any set, then $X \in B \leftrightarrow X \notin X$. Now if X is B, then $B \in B \leftrightarrow B \notin B$. Thus, there is a contradiction.

Follow-up for Lesson 1-1

Practice

For more questions on SPUR Objectives, use **Lesson Master 1-1** (shown on pages 8–9).

Assessment

Written Communication Provide a universal statement such as *For all real numbers x,* $x^3 \geq 0$. Then have students (1) write the statement symbolically, (2) write an existential statement in English that would have to be true in order for the universal statement to be false, and (3) write the existential statement symbolically. [Students write statements symbolically and show the relationship between universal and existential statements.]

Extension

Have students look in a newspaper for examples of universal and existential statements. Warn them that the statements will probably not be quite as obvious as they appear in the lesson! Have them rewrite the sentences they found using the notation in the lesson and attach the article(s) with the original sentences highlighted. [For example, the statement: *Law schools don't offer courses on "Defending the Difficult, Delusional, or Mentally Ill,"* can be rewritten as $\forall$ *law school x, x does not offer courses on "Defending the Difficult, Delusional, or Mentally Ill."* Also, the statement *But research that I did yesterday suggests that many jurisdictions and many people disagree with me,* can be rewritten as *The research I did yesterday suggests* $\exists$ *a person x or jurisdiction y such that x or y disagree with me.*]

Project Update Project 1, *Russell's Paradox,* on page 67, relates to the content of this lesson.

Lesson 1-2

Objectives

C Write the negation of a logical statement.
D Determine the truth value of a logical statement.
E Identify properties of logical statements.
I Determine the truth of quantified statements outside of mathematics.

Resources

From the ***Teacher's Resource File***
- Lesson Master 1-2
- Answer Master 1-2
- Teaching Aids
  1 Warm-up
  6 Truth Tables
  7 Question 22

Additional Resources
- Visuals for Teaching Aids 1, 6, 7

Teaching Lesson 1-2

Warm-up

You can use the *Warm-up* or the *Additional Examples* on pages 16–17 as questions for students to work on as you begin class.

1. Give the opposite of each term.
   a. black **white**
   b. large **small**
   c. positive **negative**
   d. 11 **-11**
   e. wrong **right**

LESSON

1-2 Negations

The Negation of a Statement

You know that a statement must be either true or false. Every statement has a negation which is also a statement.

Definition
The **negation** of a given statement *p* is a statement, called **not *p***, that, if true, exactly expresses what it would mean for *p* to be false.

This definition can be summarized in a **truth table** that gives the truth values for *not p* that correspond to the two possible truth values for *p*. In the table, T stands for *true* and F stands for *false*. The symbol **~*p*** is used for *not p*. The table shows: when *p* is true, ~*p* is false; when *p* is false, ~*p* is true.

Truth Table for Negation

p	~*p*
T	F
F	T

The negation of any statement can be formed simply by inserting the phrase *It is not the case that* at the beginning of the statement. For example, the negation of the false statement

s: Earth is farther from the Sun than Mars.

is the true statement

~s: It is not the case that Earth is farther from the Sun than Mars.

The Negation of a Universal Statement

Consider the statement

p: All teenagers have jobs.

Its negation is the statement

~p: It is not the case that all teenagers have jobs.

Some people think that a way to write ~*p* is *No teenagers have jobs.* But this is incorrect. Observe that both statements *All teenagers have jobs.* and *No teenagers have jobs.* are false. If one were the negation of the other, one would have to be true and the other false.

Lesson 1-2 Overview

Broad Goals In this lesson, negations of simple statements, universal statements, existential statements, and combinations of these statements are considered.

Perspective The ideas in this lesson are critical in determining the truth or falsity of statements and for an understanding of indirect reasoning. Students should be familiar with negations of statements from their study of geometry, but they may not have seen the others.

It is natural to confuse opposites with negations, because of the everyday use of the term "opposite." The purpose of the *Warm-up* is to emphasize the difference between these ideas.

Life Savers? *Unlike some jobs that teenagers hold, being a certified lifeguard requires over 30 hours of training, including CPR and water rescue.*

There are other ways of phrasing the negation of a universal statement. Notice that p is a sweeping statement that asserts a property of every single teenager. If this property fails to hold even for one teenager, then the statement is false. Thus, other correct negations are

$\sim p$: *At least one teenager does not have a job.*

or

$\sim p$: *Some teenager does not have a job.*

or

$\sim p$: *$\exists$ a teenager who does not have a job.*

Using the definition of the truth and falsity of a universal statement, the idea behind this example can be generalized to yield the following theorem.

Theorem (The Negation of a Universal Statement)
Let S be a set and $p(x)$ be a property that may or may not be true for elements x in S. The negation of

$\forall$ *x in S, p(x).*

is

$\exists$ *x in S such that not p(x).*

Example 1

Write the negation of

All prime numbers are odd.

You can take either a formal or an informal approach to solving this problem.

Solution 1
In the formal approach, you would rewrite the given statement as

p: $\forall$ prime numbers x, x is odd.

According to the theorem, the negation is

not p: $\exists$ a prime number x such that x is not odd.

Solution 2
To find the negation in an informal way, use reasoning similar to the reasoning that preceded the theorem. Note that the universal statement *All prime numbers are odd* is false as long as there is one prime number that is not odd. This would lead you to write the negation as

At least one prime number is not odd.

or you could write

Some prime number is not odd.

or

There is a prime number that is not odd.

Optional Activities

You might use this activity to extend the discussion of **Questions 4–6.** Ask students whether the statement or its negation is true. This emphasizes that exactly one of them is true. [**Question 4** is false. Students can name a person they know who cannot drive a car. Such a person is a counterexample. For **Question 5,** the statement is false. $\frac{\pi}{2}$ is a counterexample. For **Question 6**, the statement is true; x can be any number of the form $\frac{\pi}{4} + n\pi$, where n is an integer.]

2. Give the negation of each statement. **Sample responses are given.**
   a. The color of that car is black. **The color of that car is not black.**
   b. That is a large triangle. **That is not a large triangle.**
   c. The solution to the sentence is a positive number. **The solution to the sentence is not a positive number.**
   d. $x = 11$ $x \neq 11$.
   e. You answered all of the questions wrong. **There exists a question that you answered correctly.**

Notes on Reading

This lesson considers the negations of four types of statements: simple statements in which the verb is changed to its opposite; universal statements whose negations are existential; existential statements whose negations are universal; and statements involving both a universal and an existential quantifier.

❶ **Reading Mathematics** Truth tables will be new to most students. Advise them to read the table across each row, noting the top of each column as they read. This truth table is shown on **Teaching Aid 6.**

If a student is having difficulty forming the negation of a statement, tell the student to think of the truth value of the statement and what it would mean for the statement to have the opposite truth value.

Example 1 Ask students whether p or *not* p is true and why. This question will help you learn what students know about primes. Further treatment of prime numbers is found in Chapter 4.

Error Alert The purpose of **Example 1** is to show that the negation of a *for all* statement is a *there exists* statement. This idea can be troublesome to students. For instance, consider the statement *All prime numbers are odd.* Some students will write the negation as *All prime numbers are not odd*, a statement that can be interpreted in two different ways. To explain this, read the statement aloud emphasizing the word *not*: All prime numbers are *not* odd. When read in this way, the sentence means that there is a prime number that is not odd. This is the correct negation. Then try

The Negation of an Existential Statement

The previous theorem states that the negation of a *for all* statement is a *there exists* statement. Because *not (not p)* is equivalent to *p*, the negation of a *there exists* statement is a *for all* statement. Consider the statement

q: There exists a real number x for which $|x| = -3$.

In order for this statement to be true, there must exist at least one real number whose absolute value equals -3. But there is no such number because $|x| \geq 0$ for all real numbers *x*. Thus, the statement that, if true, exactly expresses what it would mean for the given statement to be false is

~q: For all real numbers x, $|x| \neq -3$.

This negation *~q* is true; the original statement *q* is thus false. In general, from the definition of the truth and falsity of an existential statement, this theorem follows.

Theorem (The Negation of an Existential Statement)
Let *S* be a set and *p(x)* be a property that may or may not be true for elements *x* in *S*. The negation of

$\exists$ *x in S such that p(x).*

is

$\forall$ *x in S, not p(x).*

Example 2

Write the negation of

p: Some triangles are isosceles.

Solution

Some people think that the negation is *Some triangles are not isosceles,* but this is not the case, as a careful analysis shows.

p: Some triangles are isosceles.

is equivalent to

p: $\exists$ *a triangle x such that x is isosceles.*

Hence, the negation is

~p: $\forall$ triangles x, x is not isosceles.

which means that there is not a single isosceles triangle. In other words,

~p: No triangles are isosceles.

Notice that the statement *Some triangles are not isosceles.* just means that it is possible to find at least one triangle that is not isosceles, which is quite different in meaning from *No triangles are isosceles.*

reading the sentence aloud emphasizing the word *all*. In this case, the sentence means that every prime number has the property of not being odd—that is, no prime numbers are odd. This is not the correct negation. Because of this possible ambiguity, students should be advised to avoid statements of the form *All ____ are not ____.*

In the solution of **Example 2**, a *for all* statement has been rewritten as a *no* statement. As another example, *All Romans are honorable* can be written as *No Romans are dishonorable.* The form that is used depends upon personal preference and ease of understanding.

Students may need some help with the negation of statements containing both *for all* and *there exists*. We have provided both a formal technique (before and in **Example 3**) and an informal technique (after **Example 3**) for determining the negation. Initially students may need to rewrite a statement formally to help them transform *for all* to *there exists* when forming negations. This formalism is helpful for negating statements with more than one quantifier.

Additional Examples

1. Write the negation of *All composite numbers are greater than 3.* **Formal approach: p: $\forall$ composite numbers *x*, $x > 3$. By the Negation of a Universal Statement theorem, the negation is *~p*: $\exists$ a composite number *x* such that $x \not> 3$ ($x \leq 3$). Informal approach: The statement *All composite numbers are greater than 3* is false if there exists at least one composite number that is less than or equal to 3. Thus some forms of the negation are *At least one composite number is not greater than 3* or *Some composite number is not greater than 3* or *There is a composite number that is not greater than 3.* (Note: The original statement is true, so its negation is false.)**

Adapting to Individual Needs

Extra Help
You might want to use the chart at the right to summarize how to write the negation of *for all* statements, *there exists* statements, and statements that contain both *for all* and *there exists.* Then as you discuss various examples and questions, have students identify the correct form of the original statement and verify that its negation fits the form given in the following chart.

Original Statement	Negation
$\forall$ *x in S, p(x)*	$\exists$ *x in S such that not p(x)*
$\exists$ *x in S such that p(x)*	$\forall$ *x in S, not p(x)*
$\forall$ *x in S,* $\exists$ *y in T such that p(x, y)*	$\exists$ *x in S such that* $\forall$ *y in T not p(x, y)*
$\exists$ *x in S such that* $\forall$ *y in T p(x, y)*	$\forall$ *x in S,* $\exists$ *y in T such that not p(x, y)*

The Negation of a Complex Statement

Now consider the question of writing the negation of a statement that contains both *for all* and *there exists*. For instance, consider the statement

p: $\forall$ *real numbers x*, $\exists$ *a real number y such that xy* = *1*.

According to the Negation of a Universal Statement Theorem, the negation is

~*p*: $\exists$ *a real number x such that not* ($\exists$ *a real number y such that xy* = *1*).

By the Negation of an Existential Statement Theorem, *not* ($\exists$ *a real number y such that xy* = *1*). is equivalent to $\forall$ *real numbers y*, *xy* $\neq$ *1*.

Therefore, the negation of *p* is

~*p*: $\exists$ *a real number x such that* $\forall$ *real numbers y*, *xy* $\neq$ *1*.

In general, if *S* and *T* are sets and *p*(*x*, *y*) is a property that may or may not be true for elements *x* in *S* and *y* in *T*, then the negation of

$\forall$ *x in S*, $\exists$ *y in T such that p*(*x*, *y*).

is $\exists$ *x in S such that* $\forall$ *y in T*, *not p*(*x*, *y*).

and vice versa.

Example 3

Negate the statement *Everyone trusts someone.*

Solution 1

Here is a solution in words.

p: Everyone trusts someone.
~p: There is someone who does not trust anyone.

Solution 2

Here is a more formal analysis.

p: $\forall$ people x, $\exists$ a person y such that x trusts y.
~p: $\exists$ a person x such that $\forall$ people y, x does not trust y.

Observe that, in general, the negation of a statement can be generated by reading the statement from left to right and changing $\forall$ to $\exists$, changing $\exists$ to $\forall$, and changing *p*(*x*, *y*) to *not p*(*x*, *y*). The words *such that* are deleted when $\exists$ is changed to $\forall$ and are added when $\forall$ is changed to $\exists$.

QUESTIONS

Covering the Reading

1. If a given statement is true, then its negation is __?__. false

2. *True or false.* The negation of a universal statement is another universal statement. False

2. Write the negation of the statement *Some rectangles are squares.* *p: Some rectangles are squares* is equivalent to *p*: $\exists$ *a rectangle x, such that x is a square*. Thus, the negation is *~p*: $\forall$ *rectangles x, x is not a square* which means that there is no rectangle that is also a square. Thus *~p: No rectangle is a square.*

3. Negate the statement *Everybody loves something.*
   Solution 1: In the vernacular:
   p: Everybody loves something.
   ~p: There is someone who does not love anything.
   Solution 2: More formally:
   p: $\forall$ *people x*, $\exists$ *a thing y such that x loves y.* *~p*: $\exists$ *a person x such that* $\forall$ *things y, x does not love y.*

Adapting to Individual Needs

English Language Development

Emphasize the difference between the words "opposite" and "negation." In everyday use, "opposite" means "the other end of the spectrum." In mathematical use, "negation" means "everything else but."

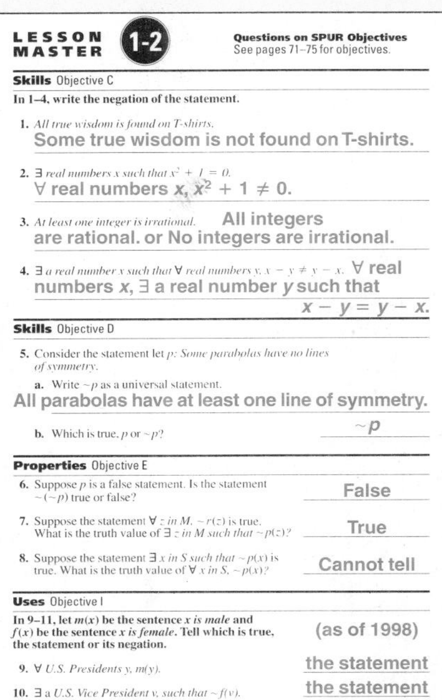

LESSON MASTER 1-2

Questions on SPUR Objectives
See pages 71–75 for objectives.

Skills Objective C

In 1–4, write the negation of the statement.

1. *All true wisdom is found on T-shirts.*
   Some true wisdom is not found on T-shirts.

2. $\exists$ *real numbers x such that* $x^2 + 1 = 0$.
   $\forall$ real numbers *x*, $x^2 + 1 \neq 0$.

3. *At least one integer is irrational.* All integers are rational. or No integers are irrational.

4. $\exists$ *a real number x such that* $\forall$ *real numbers y*, $x - y \neq y - x$. $\forall$ real numbers *x*, $\exists$ a real number *y* such that $x - y = y - x$.

Skills Objective D

5. Consider the statement let *p: Some parabolas have no lines of symmetry.*
   a. Write ~*p* as a universal statement.
   All parabolas have at least one line of symmetry.
   b. Which is true, *p* or ~*p*? ~*p*

Properties Objective E

6. Suppose *p* is a false statement. Is the statement ~(~*p*) true or false? False

7. Suppose the statement $\forall$ *z in M*, ~*r*(*z*) is true. What is the truth value of $\exists$ *z in M such that* ~*p*(*z*)? True

8. Suppose the statement $\exists$ *x in S such that* ~*p*(*x*) is true. What is the truth value of $\forall$ *x in S*, ~*p*(*x*)? Cannot tell

Uses Objective I

In 9–11, let *m*(*x*) be the sentence *x is male* and *f*(*x*) be the sentence *x is female*. Tell which is true, the statement or its negation. (as of 1998)

9. $\forall$ *U.S. Presidents y*, *m*(*y*). the statement

10. $\exists$ a *U.S. Vice President v, such that* ~*f*(*v*). the statement

11. $\forall$ *U.S. Secretaries of State z*, ~*f*(*z*). the negation

Notes on Questions

Questions 4–6 *Optional Activities* on page 15 relate to these questions.

Question 11 The given statement is true. One such function has the rule $f(x) = 3x$. Consequently, the negation is false. See the Challenge in *Adapting to Individual Needs* below.

Question 15 Error Alert Some students may say that the negation of $n < 11$ is $n > 11$, ignoring $n = 11$. You may wish to write on the board $n < 11$ *or* $n = 11$ *or* $n > 11$ *by the Law of Trichotomy* and say that to find the negation of $n < 11$, cover $n < 11$ with your hand. The negation is what remains: $n = 11$ or $n > 11$, which may be written as $n \geq 11$.

Question 20 Choices (a) and (b) are negations of each other, so one of them must be true.

(Notes on Questions continue on page 20.)

3. *True or false.* The negation of

For all states s, s requires a driver to have a valid driver's license

is

There exists a state s such that s requires a driver to have a valid driver's license. False

In 4–6, write a negation for the statement.

4. *Every person can drive a car.*
There exists a person who cannot drive a car.

5. *All fractions are rational numbers.*
There exists a fraction which is not a rational number.

6. $\exists$ *a real number x such that* $\sin x = \cos x$.
$\forall$ *real numbers x,* $\sin x \neq \cos x$.

7. For any statement p, *not (not p)* is equivalent to _?_. p

8. *Multiple choice.* Give the negation of c

Some quadratic equations have three solutions.

(a) *Some quadratic equations do not have three solutions.*
(b) *All quadratic equations have three solutions.*
(c) *No quadratic equations have three solutions.*
(d) *There exists a quadratic equation with three solutions.*

9. Consider the statement

Everybody loves somebody.

a. Write this statement in the form
$\forall$ _?_ , $\exists$ _?_ such that _?_. people x; a person y; x loves y

b. Write the negation of this statement.
$\exists$ *a person x such that* $\forall$ *people y, x does not love y.*

10. To negate the existential statement $\exists$ *x in S and y in T such that p(x, y)*, change $\exists$ to _?_ , delete the words *such that*, and change *p(x, y)* to _?_.
$\forall$; *not p(x, y)*

11. Write the negation of the following statement:
$\exists$ *a function f such that* $\forall$ *real numbers a and b,* $f(a + b) = f(a) + f(b)$.
$\forall$ *functions f,* $\exists$ *real numbers a and b such that* $f(a + b) \neq f(a) + f(b)$.

Socrates (459?–399 B.C.)

Applying the Mathematics

In 12 and 13, a statement is given.

a. Write the negation of the statement.
b. Which is true: the given statement or its negation?

12. *p: For all real numbers x,* $2x + 4 > 0$.
a) $\exists$ *a real number x such that* $2x + 4 \leq 0$. b) the negation

13. *q: All men are mortal.* (Socrates)
a) *There is a man who is not mortal.* b) the given statement

14. *Multiple choice.* Give the negation of

No one under 21 can legally buy alcohol in Illinois. d

(a) *All people under 21 cannot legally buy alcohol in Illinois.*
(b) *All people under 21 can legally buy alcohol in Illinois.*
(c) *Some people under 21 cannot legally buy alcohol in Illinois.*
(d) *Some people under 21 can legally buy alcohol in Illinois.*
(e) *No one under 21 cannot legally buy alcohol in Illinois.*

Adapting to Individual Needs

Challenge

Have students examine **Question 11** and answer the following questions.

1. If a function f has the property that $\forall a$ and $\forall b$, $f(a + b) = f(a) + f(b)$, prove that $f(0) = 0$. [Proof: Since the property is true for all a and b, it is true when $a = b = 0$. Thus $f(0 + 0) = f(0) + f(0)$. Thus $f(0) = f(0) + f(0)$. Subtracting $f(0)$ from each side, $f(0) = 0$.]

2. Which is true, the statement or its negation, and why? [The statement is true; one such function is defined by $f(x) = 3x$.]

15a) $\exists$ *n in S such that* $n \geq 11$.
b) the negation; 11 is in *S* and 11 = 11.

16a) $\forall$ *even integers m, m is not in S.*
b) the negation; *S* contains no even integers.

17a) $\exists$ *a real number x such that* $\forall$ *real numbers y,* $\tan x \neq y$.
b) the negation; For $x = \frac{\pi}{2}$, $\tan \frac{\pi}{2}$ is undefined so $\forall$ *real numbers y,* $\tan \frac{\pi}{2} \neq y$.

19) The flaw occurs after the fourth line. Since $x - y = 0$, one cannot divide both sides of the equation by $(x - y)$.

In 15 and 16, let *S* be the set $S = \{1, 3, 5, 7, 9, 11\}$. A statement is given.

a. Write the negation of the statement.

b. Which is true: the given statement or its negation? Justify your answer.

15. *r: For all n in S,* $n < 11$. See left.

16. *s: There exists an even integer m such that m is in S.*

17. Consider the statement

$\forall$ *real numbers x,* $\exists$ *a real number y such that* $\tan x = y$.

a. Write the negation of this statement.

b. Which is true: the statement or its negation? Justify your answer.

18. *Multiple choice.* Consider the statement

$\triangle ABC$ *is isosceles.*

Which of the following is the negation of this statement? b

(a) $\triangle ABC$ *is a right triangle.*
(b) $\triangle ABC$ *is a scalene triangle.*
(c) $\triangle ABC$ *is an equilateral triangle.*
(d) $\triangle ABC$ *is an obtuse triangle.*

Review

19. Find the flaw in the following argument. See left.

Let	$x = 2$ and $y = 2$.
Then	$x^2 + y = y^2 + x$.
So	$x^2 - y^2 = x - y$.
So	$(x + y)(x - y) = x - y$.
So	$x + y = 1$.
But because	$x = y = 2, x + y = 4$.
Thus	$1 = 4$. *(Lesson 1-1)*

20. *Multiple choice.* If *t* is a real number, which of the following statements is true? *(Lesson 1-1)* b

(a) $\forall t, \cos t = 0$.
(b) $\exists t$ *such that* $\cos t = 0$.

21. *Multiple choice.* You learned in geometry that

The measure of an angle inscribed in a semicircle is 90°.

Which of the following statements is not equivalent to the one above? *(Lesson 1-1)* e

(a) *All angles which are inscribed in a semicircle have a measure of 90°.*
(b) *If* $\angle A$ *is an angle inscribed in a semicircle, then* $m\angle A = 90°$.
(c) *For all angles* $\angle A$, *if* $\angle A$ *is inscribed in a semicircle, then* $m\angle A = 90°$.
(d) *Every angle which is inscribed in a semicircle has a measure of 90°.*
(e) All of the above are equivalent.

SAT

Follow-up for Lesson 1-2

Practice

For more questions on SPUR Objectives, use **Lesson Master 1-2** (shown on page 17).

Assessment

Written Communication Have students work with a partner. Ask each student to write a *for all* statement, a *there exists* statement, and a statement that contains both *for all* and *there exists*. Students should write the negations of their partner's statements and check their work together by determining the truth value of each original statement and the truth value of its negation. [Students write negations and determine truth values of statements.]

Extension

Have students answer the following questions.

1. Is the following true or false? *This statement is true.* [Most will probably say true.]
2. Give the negation of the statement in Question 1. [*This statement is false.*]
3. Is this negation true or false? [Neither; this is an instance of Russell's paradox referred to in Lesson 1-1.]
4. How do you explain this result, since the negation of a true statement should be false? [The original sentence is not a statement, since its negation cannot be said to be either true or false.]

Setting Up Lesson 1-3

Homework

1. If you have assigned all the Questions in Lesson 1-2, ask students to read and do all the Questions in Lesson 1-3.
2. If you have not assigned all the Questions in Lesson 1-2, assign the rest and ask students to read and do the Questions Covering the Reading in Lesson 1-3.

For more information on homework, see *General Teaching Suggestions: Homework* in the *Professional Sourcebook,* which begins on page T20 of Part 1 of the Teacher's Edition.

Notes on Questions

Question 22 This question will take some time but is worth it. It is shown on **Teaching Aid 7.**

Question 25 You may need to remind students of the basic definition for converting from logarithmic form to exponential form: $\log_b x = y \Leftrightarrow x = b^y$. Note that this definition is implicitly universal. It is a shorthand form of $\forall$ *positive real numbers x and* $\forall$ *real numbers y,* $\log_b x = y \Leftrightarrow x = b^y$.

Question 26 Remind students that while it would take only one example to show Mr. Mailer's claim is false, examples themselves are not sufficient to show it is true. A major challenge is to generalize this question: Suppose you have unlimited quantities of stamps of two integer denominations *a* and *b*, where *a* and *b* have no common factor other than 1. What is the largest postage that cannot be exactly covered by these stamps? [$ab - a - b$]

History Connection In 1840, in an attempt to create uniform postal rates, Britain introduced the first postage stamp. The stamps cost one penny and were printed in black, hence they got the name "penny black." Soon after the stamps appeared it became apparent that a more attractive stamp should be created. As a result, one-penny red stamps and two-pence blue stamps were issued.

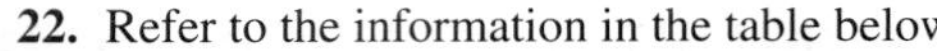

22a) True. Every student is on at least one sports team.
b) True. No one is in the Spanish club.
c) True. Every student is in the math club.
d) False. Each academic club has at least one member in the sample.
e) False. Raul is not in a foreign language club.

22. Refer to the information in the table below.
At King High School, extracurricular activities are offered in four categories: sports teams, foreign language clubs, fine arts clubs, and academic clubs. The activities of a sample of four students are described below.

	sports teams						foreign language clubs				fine arts clubs			academic clubs		
	football	basketball	baseball	soccer	track	swimming	French	German	Russian	Spanish	drama	chorus	band	math	debate	science
Dominique						✓		✓						✓		
Raul	✓			✓							✓			✓	✓	
Karen					✓		✓						✓	✓		
Tom			✓						✓					✓	✓	✓

Determine whether each of the following statements is true or false for the students in this sample. Justify your answer. See left.

a. $\forall$ *students s in the sample, s participates on some sports team.*
b. *Some foreign language club has no members from the sample.*
c. $\exists$ *an academic club c such that* $\forall$ *students s in the sample, s is a member of c.*
d. *For every category there is some club which has no members in the sample.*
e. *Every student in the sample is a member of some club in each category.* *(Lesson 1-1)*

23. Consider the true statement

$$\forall \text{ nonnegative real numbers } x, \sqrt{x^2} = x.$$

Find a counterexample to show that the given statement is false if the condition that *x* is nonnegative is removed. *(Previous course, Lesson 1-1)*
Sample: $\sqrt{(-1)^2} = 1 \neq -1$

24. Consider the expression $(2x + 3)^2$. See margin.
a. What universal statement could you use to expand it?
b. Expand the expression. *(Previous course, Lesson 1-1)*

25. Evaluate without using a calculator. *(Previous course)*
a. $\log_3 81$ 4 **b.** $\log_5 \frac{1}{125}$ -3 **c.** $\log 1$ 0

Exploration

26. Mr. Mailer claims he can put postage on any letter requiring 88 cents or more postage using a combination of 23-cent and 5-cent stamps. See margin.
a. Write his claim in the form
$\forall$ _?_, $\exists$ _?_ *such that* _?_.
b. Check that Mr. Mailer's claim is correct for mail requiring 88¢, 89¢, 90¢, and 91¢.
c. Explore the validity of Mr. Mailer's claim by checking it for other postal charges. Write a convincing argument to show that his claim is either true or false.

Additional Answers

24. a. $\forall$ real numbers *a* and *b*, $(a + b)^2 = a^2 + 2ab + b^2$.
b. $(2x + 3^2) = 4x^2 + 12x + 9$
26. a. $\forall$ *postal charges* $P \geq 88¢$, $\exists$ *n and m nonnegative integers such that* $23n + 5m = P$.
b. $88 = 23 + 13 \cdot 5$; $89 = 3 \cdot 23 + 4 \cdot 5$; $90 = 18 \cdot 5$; $91 = 2 \cdot 23 + 9 \cdot 5$.
c. It is true. You can get 92¢ with four 23¢ stamps. By adding a 5¢ stamp to 88, 89, 90, 91, and 92 cents, you can get all charges over 88¢.

LESSON

1-3

And *and* Or *and* De Morgan's Laws

Not so fast. *Posted speed limits on the 42,800 miles of the Interstate Highway System vary depending on the character of the route. See Example 3.*

And

The words *and* and *or* can combine two or more statements, both in everyday language and in mathematics. You are familiar with the mathematical use of these words to explain inequalities. For instance, consider the sentence $s(z)$: $-3 < z < 4$. $s(z)$ means $-3 < z$ *and* $z < 4$.

In order for $s(z)$ to be true, z must satisfy both inequalities above. In general, we define the truth value of the statement *p and q* following this example.

Definition
The statement *p and q* is true when, and only when, both *p* and *q* are true.

Or

In contrast, consider the use of the word "or." Let $t(x)$ be as follows:

$t(x)$: *x is a rectangle or x is a rhombus.*

In order for $t(x)$ to be true, x needs to satisfy only one (either one or both) of the conditions. That is, $t(x)$ is true when x is a rectangle, x is a rhombus, or x is both (a square). This is called the **inclusive or**, because it includes the possibility that both might be true. In mathematics, *or* is always the inclusive or.

Definition
The statement *p or q* is true when *p* is true, *q* is true, or both are true.

Lesson 1-3

Objectives

B Write equivalent forms of logical statements.
C Write the negation of a logical statement.
D Determine the truth value of a logical statement.
E Identify properties of logical statements.
H Use logic to prove or disprove statements.
I Determine the truth of quantified statements outside of mathematics.
L Write truth tables for logical expressions.

Resources

From the ***Teacher's Resource File***
- Lesson Master 1-3
- Answer Master 1-3
- Teaching Aids
  - 2 Warm-up
  - 6 Truth Tables
  - 8 Example 1 and Additional Example 1
- Technology Sourcebook Computer Master 1

Additional Resources
- Visuals for Teaching Aids 2, 6, 8
- Spreadsheet

Teaching Lesson 1-3

Warm-up

In 1–6, tell whether the sentence is true or false when $x = 30$.
1. $x \geq 30$ True

(Warm-up continues on page 22.)

Lesson 1-3 Overview

Broad Goals De Morgan's Laws state that for all statements *p* and *q:*
$\sim(p \text{ and } q) \equiv (\sim p) \text{ or } (\sim q)$;
$\sim(p \text{ or } q) \equiv (\sim p) \text{ and } (\sim q)$.
These laws are applied in the next lessons and have surprising application to a variety of topics in the book. The laws are deduced from definitions of *and* and *or* and *not* using truth tables.

Perspective Just as two algebraic expressions are equivalent if they yield the same values for all values of the variables, logical expressions are equivalent if and only if they have the same truth values for all values of their statement variables. No matter what specific statements are substituted for the statement variables in equivalent expressions, the resulting statements will either both be true or they will both be false. The recognition of equivalent expressions is not only useful in making some complicated expressions more understandable, it is also vital in the design of computer logic networks (see Lesson 1-4).

In symbolic logic the symbol $\wedge$ denotes *and* and $\vee$ denotes *or*. We have not introduced these symbols because we do not use them later in the book, but you may wish to introduce them as a convenience.
(Overview continues on page 22.)

2. $x > 30$ and $x = 30$. False
3. $x > -31$ and $x < 31$. True
4. $x < -31$ and $x > 31$. False
5. $x^2 > 900$ False
6. $x^2 \leq 30x$ True
7. For 1–6, give the negation. Tell whether the negation is true or false when $x = 30$.
   1. $x < 30$, False
   2. $x \leq 30$ or $x \neq 30$, True
   3. $x \leq -31$ or $x \geq 31$, False
   4. $x \geq -31$ or $x \leq 31$, True
   5. $x^2 \leq 900$, True
   6. $x^2 > 30x$, False

Notes on Reading

The truth tables for *and* and *or* are shown on **Teaching Aid 6**. The *not* truth table of Lesson 1-2 uses one statement variable *p* and requires 2 lines of T/F values. The truth tables for *and* and *or* use two statement variables *p, q* and require 4 lines of T/F values. In **Question 25,** the truth table using three statement variables *p, q, r* requires 8 lines of T/F values. Elicit from your students a generalization that a complete truth table with *n* statement variables requires 2^n lines of T/F. Emphasize that every possible combination of T/F values for the variables must be represented in a truth table. A tree diagram, such as the following, may be helpful to show this.

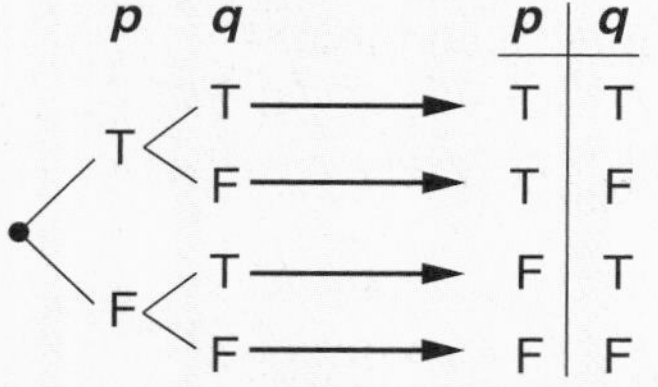

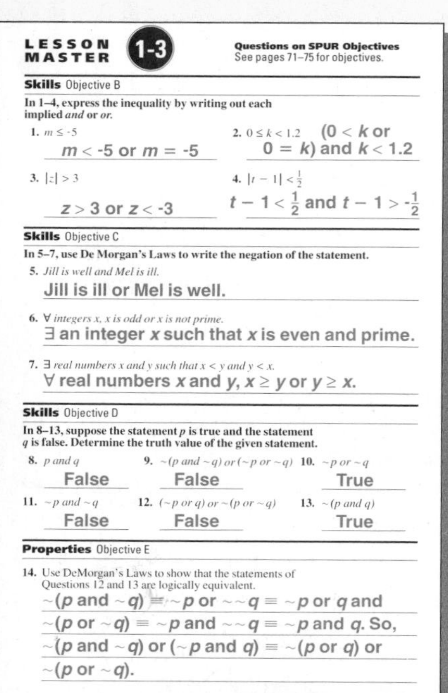

LESSON MASTER 1-3

Questions on SPUR Objectives
See pages 71–75 for objectives.

Skills Objective B

In 1–4, express the inequality by writing out each implied *and* or *or*.

1. $m \leq -5$ — $m < -5$ or $m = -5$
2. $0 \leq k < 1.2$ — ($0 < k$ or $0 = k$) and $k < 1.2$
3. $|z| > 3$ — $z > 3$ or $z < -3$
4. $|t - 1| < \frac{1}{2}$ — $t - 1 < \frac{1}{2}$ and $t - 1 > -\frac{1}{2}$

Skills Objective C

In 5–7, use De Morgan's Laws to write the negation of the statement.

5. *Jill is well and Mel is ill.* — Jill is ill or Mel is well.
6. ∀ *integers x, x is odd or x is not prime.* — ∃ an integer *x* such that *x* is even and prime.
7. ∃ *real numbers x and y such that $x < y$ and $y < x$.* — ∀ real numbers *x* and *y*, $x \geq y$ or $y \geq x$.

Skills Objective D

In 8–13, suppose the statement *p* is true and the statement *q* is false. Determine the truth value of the given statement.

8. *p and q* — False
9. $\sim$(*p and* $\sim q$) *or* ($\sim p$ *or* $\sim q$) — False
10. $\sim p$ *or* $\sim q$ — True
11. $\sim p$ *and* $\sim q$ — False
12. ($\sim p$ *or q*) *or* $\sim$(*p or* $\sim q$) — False
13. $\sim$(*p and q*) — True

Properties Objective E

14. Use DeMorgan's Laws to show that the statements of Questions 12 and 13 are logically equivalent.
$\sim$(*p* and $\sim q$) $\equiv$ $\sim p$ or $\sim\sim q$ $\equiv$ $\sim p$ or *q* and $\sim$(*p* or $\sim q$) $\equiv$ $\sim p$ and $\sim\sim q$ $\equiv$ $\sim p$ and *q*. So, $\sim$(*p* and $\sim q$) or ($\sim p$ and *q*) $\equiv$ $\sim$(*p* or *q*) or $\sim$(*p* or $\sim q$).

The truth values in the definitions of **and** and **or** are summarized in the following truth tables.

Truth Table for *and*

p	*q*	*p and q*
T	T	T
T	F	F
F	T	F
F	F	F

Truth Table for *or*

p	*q*	*p or q*
T	T	T
T	F	T
F	T	T
F	F	F

In ordinary language, we sometimes use the **exclusive or** (one or the other but not both) and sometimes the inclusive or (one or the other or both). For example, if a restaurant menu stated, "Coffee or tea is free with any sandwich order," you should probably interpret that to mean you can have either coffee or tea free with your sandwich, but you would pay extra if you wanted both. That is the *exclusive or*. In contrast, if your waiter asked "Cream or sugar?" you would normally take that to mean that he is offering cream, sugar, or both. That is the *inclusive or*.

Logically Equivalent Expressions

A **logical expression** is a formula in which variables representing statements are combined in an unambiguous way with *and*, *or*, *not*, or *if-then*. For example,

not (p and q) and *(not p) or q*

are logical expressions. On the other hand, the formula

not p and q

is not a logical expression because it is not clear whether it means

not (p and q) or *(not p) and q*.

If two logical expressions have the same truth values for all substitutions of statements for their statement variables, we say that the two expressions are **logically equivalent**. The symbol ≡ is sometimes used to denote logical equivalence. For example, $\sim(\sim p) \equiv p$. Logical equivalence can be deduced using truth tables.

Example 1

Use a truth table to prove that *not (p and q)* ≡ *(not p) or (not q)*.

Solution

Set up a truth table in which the first two columns list the truth values for *p* and *q* and the remaining columns give the truth values for *p and q*, *not (p and q)*, *not p*, *not q*, and *(not p) or (not q)*. We show how to fill in the columns in several steps.

p	q	p and q	not (p and q)	not p	not q	(not p) or (not q)
T	T					
T	F					
F	T					
F	F					

▶

Lesson 1-3 Overview, continued

The distinction between the *inclusive or* and the *exclusive or* may motivate discussion. In ordinary language, the context assists in deciding which use of *or* is intended. In mathematics, ambiguity needs to be avoided and we must state which use of *or* is meant. **Question 17** discusses the *exclusive or*. Some calculators have both an *or* and an *xor* key.

Optional Activities

Technology Connection
In *Technology Sourcebook, Computer Master 1,* students apply rules of logic to the AND and OR functions used in spreadsheet formulas.

Now, using the truth tables for *and* and *not*, fill in three more columns.

p	q	p and q	not (p and q)	not p	not q	(not p) or (not q)
T	T	T		F	F	
T	F	F		F	T	
F	T	F		T	F	
F	F	F		T	T	

From these columns, the two remaining columns can be filled.

p	q	p and q	not (p and q)	not p	not q	(not p) or (not q)
T	T	T	F	F	F	F
T	F	F	T	F	T	T
F	T	F	T	T	F	T
F	F	F	T	T	T	T

same truth values

Because the corresponding truth values in the [not (p and q)] and the [(not p) or (not q)] columns of the table are the same, these two logical expressions are logically equivalent.

De Morgan's Laws

An important point about the truth table proof of Example 1 is that it does not depend on the specific statements substituted in place of p and q. The truth table exhibits the proof of the first of two results known as *De Morgan's Laws*.

Augustus Louis De Morgan

Theorem (De Morgan's Laws)
For all statements p and q:
1. $\sim(p \text{ and } q) \equiv (\sim p) \text{ or } (\sim q)$
2. $\sim(p \text{ or } q) \equiv (\sim p) \text{ and } (\sim q)$

We have mentioned that the everyday expression *either a or b* often means the *exclusive or*, that is,

(a or b) and not (a and b).

To avoid ambiguity, for the *exclusive or* we say *either a or b but not both*. Note that in ordinary language, the phrase "neither *a* nor *b*" means "not *a* and not *b*." This logical equivalence is the second of De Morgan's Laws. You are asked to prove this in the Questions.

Augustus Louis De Morgan (1806–1871) was a distinguished mathematician and logician. Verbal statements of the logical principles expressed by laws (1) and (2) were known at least as early as the fourteenth century. However, De Morgan was the first to state them symbolically in his book *Formal Logic*, which was published in 1847.

You may wish to make an analogy between algebraic and logical expressions. Variables, numbers, and operation symbols are used in algebraic expressions. When you replace variables with numbers, algebraic expressions yield numerical values.

Similarly, logical expressions use statement variables and operation symbols. The statement variables of logic can have only true statements or false statements as their values. Replacing the variables in a logical expression with true or false statements yields the value of the expression: a true or false statement. In Lesson 3-9 De Morgan's Laws are used to help solve absolute value inequalities.

Teaching Aid 8 can be used to complete the truth table for **Example 1**. When explaining the process of filling in the truth table columns, point out that, for instance, because an *or* statement is false only when both components are false, the only F in the rightmost column will occur in the first row; all other rows will be filled in with a T. Similarly for an expression involving *and*: Given an expression *A and B* where the truth values of *A* are given in column a and those for *B* in column b, just check the rows in a and b where both entries are T. Enter a T in that row for *A and B*. In all other rows, enter an F.

Adapting to Individual Needs

Extra Help

Some students might benefit from illustrating De Morgan's laws with simple language statements. For example, let

p: The light is on.
q: The door is open.

Lead students to form the following:

First law

$\sim(p \text{ and } q)$: It is not the case that the light is on and the door is open.

$(\sim p)$ or $(\sim q)$: The light is off or the door is closed.

Second law

$\sim(p \text{ or } q)$: It is not the case that the light is on or the door is open.

$(\sim p)$ and $(\sim q)$: The light is off and the door is closed.

Have students discuss, possibly with illustrations, how the equivalent forms have the same truth value.

LESSON MASTER 1-3 *page 2*

Properties Objective H

15. Show that the following statement is false. $\forall$ *real numbers x, $x \geq 0$ or $\sin x \leq 0$.*
$x = -\frac{3\pi}{2}$ is a real number and the statements $-\frac{3\pi}{2} > 0$ and $\sin -\frac{3\pi}{2} \leq 0$ are both false

Uses Objective I

In 16–18, refer to the table below, which lists the amenities available at five hotels with rooms reserved for an upcoming convention. H = Handicapped Access; FC = Fitness Center; IP = Indoor Pool; L = Lounge; R = Restaurant; D = Distance to Convention Center; S = Single Price

Hotel	H	FC	IP	L	R	D	S
1	*	*	*	*	*	15 blocks	\$180
2	*				*	6 blocks	\$100
3	*					4 miles	\$146
4	*	*		*	*	12 blocks	\$175
5		*		*	*	15 blocks	\$109

Use the table to determine whether the given statement is true or false.

16. $\exists$ *a hotel h such that h has an indoor pool and S < \$180.* False
17. $\forall$ *hotels h, h has a restaurant or D > 3 miles.* True
18. $\forall$ *hotels h, h has a restaurant and lounge or h has handicapped access.* True

Representations Objective L

19. Use a truth table to show that *p and (q or r) ≡ (p and q) or (p and r).*

p	q	r	q or r	p and (q or r)	p and q	p and r	(p and q) or (p and r)
F	F	F	F	F	F	F	F
F	F	T	T	F	F	F	F
F	T	F	T	F	F	F	F
F	T	T	T	F	F	F	F
T	F	F	F	F	F	F	F
T	F	T	T	T	F	T	T
T	T	F	T	T	T	F	T
T	T	T	T	T	T	T	T

The result of **Example 1** provides the basis for negating statements containing *and* or *or*. Each such statement is negated by changing *and* to *or* and vice versa, and negating the components of the statement.

Error Alert Caution students to take care when reading or writing sentences that contain the mathematical *and* or *or* as well as ordinary language usage of these terms. Remind them that in this text, the mathematical *and* and *or* are always given in italics.

Example 3 Geography Connection More than 45,000 miles of the almost 4 million miles of roads in the United States are part of the interstate highway system, whose official name is the *Dwight D. Eisenhower System of Interstate and Defense Highways.*

Additional Examples

Additional Example 1 is shown on **Teaching Aid 8.**

1. Use a truth table to prove that *not(p and (not q)) ≡ (not p) or q.*

p	*q*	*not q*
T	T	F
T	F	T
F	T	F
F	F	T

not (p and (not q))	*not p*	*(not p) or q*
T	F	T
F	F	F
T	T	T
T	T	T

***not (p and (not q))* and *(not p) or q* have the same truth values and are thus equivalent. (In Lesson 1-5 it will be found that these logical expressions are also equivalent to *if p, then q*.)**

Example 2

Use De Morgan's Laws to give an expression logically equivalent to $y \not\leq -1$.

Solution

$y \not\leq -1 \equiv$ not ($y \leq -1$)

$\equiv$ not ($y < -1$ or $y = -1$).

By the second of De Morgan's Laws,

$\equiv$ not ($y < -1$) and not ($y = -1$).

Since y cannot be less than -1 and cannot be equal to -1, it must be greater. So the original statement is logically equivalent to $y > -1$.

$\equiv y > -1$

Example 3 uses De Morgan's Laws to analyze a double inequality.

Example 3

Legal speeds L (in mph) on a particular interstate highway are those for which $45 \leq L \leq 65$. Use De Morgan's Laws to describe the illegal speeds.

Solution

The illegal speeds are those values of L for which

$$\sim (45 \leq L \leq 65)$$
$$\equiv \sim (45 \leq L \text{ and } L \leq 65).$$

Think of $45 \leq L$ as p, and $L \leq 65$ as q. Applying the first of De Morgan's Laws:

$$\equiv \sim (45 \leq L) \text{ or } \sim (L \leq 65)$$
$$\equiv 45 > L \text{ or } L > 65.$$

So you are breaking the law if your speed is under 45 or if it is over 65.

QUESTIONS

Covering the Reading

In 1 and 2, express the following inequalities by writing out each implied *and* and *or*. **See left.**

1. $L \geq 12$ **2.** $3 < x \leq 4$

3. Give the truth value of *p and q* if *p* is true and *q* is false. **False**

4. For what truth values of *p* and *q* is the statement *p or q* true? **See left.**

5. a. Complete the truth table at the right.

b. Two of the columns should be the same in your answer to part **a.** What does this mean? **$p \equiv p$ or (p and q)**

p	*q*	*p and q*	*p or (p and q)*
T	T	T	T
T	F	F	T
F	T	F	F
F	F	F	F

1) *L* is greater than 12 or *L* equals 12.

2) *x* is greater than 3 and *x* is less than or equal to 4.

4) When *p* is true and *q* is false, or when *p* is false and *q* is true, or when both *p* and *q* are true.

Adapting to Individual Needs

Challenge

Have students solve this De Morgan puzzle: "I was x years old in the year x^2." Determine what year to which De Morgan was referring. [He was 43 in the year 1849, which is 43^2.]

Additional Answers, page 25

9.

p	*q*	*p or q*	*not (p or q)*	*not p*	*not q*	*(not p) and (not q)*
T	T	T	F	F	F	F
T	F	T	F	F	T	F
F	T	T	F	T	F	F
F	F	F	T	T	T	T

same truth values

In 6–8, *true or false.*

6. In mathematics, the word *or* is always used in the exclusive sense. False
7. The negation of an *and* statement is an *or* statement in which each component is negated. True
8. The negation of an *or* statement is an *and* statement in which each component is negated. True
9. Use the method of Example 1 to prove the second of De Morgan's Laws:

$$not\ (p\ or\ q) \equiv (not\ p)\ and\ (not\ q).$$

See margin.

10. Use one of De Morgan's Laws to express the negation of the sentence of Question 1. $\sim(L \geq 12) \equiv \sim(L > 12 \text{ or } L = 12) \equiv \sim(L > 12) \text{ and } \sim(L = 12) \equiv L \leq 12 \text{ and } L \neq 12 \equiv L < 12$
11. Use one of De Morgan's Laws to express the negation of the sentence of Question 2. $\sim(3 < x \leq 4) \equiv \sim(3 < x \text{ and } x \leq 4) \equiv \sim(3 < x) \text{ or } \sim(x \leq 4) \equiv x \leq 3 \text{ or } x > 4$

Applying the Mathematics

In 12–14, let x be a real number. Let $p(x)$, $q(x)$, and $r(x)$ be the following sentences.

$$p(x)\text{: } x > 5 \quad q(x)\text{: } x > 11 \quad r(x)\text{: } x \leq 7$$

Write an expression for the following.

12. $p(x)$ *or* $r(x)$ — $x > 5$ or $x \leq 7$
13. $p(x)$ *and* (*not* $q(x)$) — $5 < x \leq 11$
14. *not* $r(x)$ *and* (*not* $q(x)$) — $7 < x \leq 11$
15. Is the exclusive or inclusive *or* intended in this quotation of Harriet Tubman? exclusive

There's two things I've got a right to . . . death or liberty.

Harriet Tubman

16. *Multiple choice.* Give the negation of

You are driving over the speed limit, and you get a ticket. c

(a) *You are not driving over the speed limit, and you do not get a ticket.*
(b) *You are driving over the speed limit, and you do not get a ticket.*
(c) *You are not driving over the speed limit, or you do not get a ticket.*
(d) *You are driving over the speed limit, or you get a ticket.*

17. The symbol *xor* is sometimes used to denote "exclusive or." That is, if p and q are statements, then p *xor* q is defined to be the statement that is true if and only if p is true or q is true but not both are true.
    a. Construct a truth table for *xor* using the definition of *xor* given above.
    b. Use a truth table to prove that

$$p\ xor\ q \equiv (p\ or\ q)\ and\ (not\ (p\ and\ q)).$$

See margin.

18. Post office regulations used in 1998 indicate that all pieces which are to be mailed to U.S. residents and are $\frac{1}{4}$ inch or less thick must be rectangular in shape, at least $3\frac{1}{2}$ inches high, and at least 5 inches long. Use one of De Morgan's Laws to describe pieces which are $\frac{1}{8}$ inch thick but cannot be mailed.
They are not rectangular, or are less than $3\frac{1}{2}$ inches high, or are less than 5 inches long.

2. Express the following inequalities by writing out each implied *and*, *or*, and *not*.
   a. $x \geq -2$ — $x > -2$ *or* $x = -2$
   b. $y \not\geq 7$ — *not* $(y \geq 7)$, which is equivalent either to *not* $(y > 7$ or $y = 7)$ or to $y < 7$.
   c. $-8 < x \leq 5$ — $-8 < x$ *and* $(x < 5$ *or* $x = 5)$
3. Negate the following statement: *Superman is faster than a speeding bullet, more powerful than a locomotive, and able to leap tall buildings in a single bound.*
   Superman is not faster than a speeding bullet or he is not more powerful than a locomotive or he is not able to leap tall buildings in a single bound.
4. The therapeutic range for the dosage L of a high blood pressure medication is given by $1.45 \leq L \leq 2.65$. Describe the range for which the medication dosage is not therapeutic.
   The non-therapeutic range consists of those values of L for which $\sim(1.45 \leq L \leq 2.65)$
   $\equiv \sim(1.45 \leq L \text{ and } L \leq 2.65)$
   $\equiv \sim(1.45 \leq L) \text{ or } \sim(L \leq 2.65)$
   $\equiv 1.45 > L \text{ or } L > 2.65$.
   The medication dosage is not therapeutic if its level is less than 1.45 or greater than 2.65.

Notes on Questions

Questions 9 and 17 Emphasize that to prove logical equivalence with a truth table, one analyzes the truth values of each expression by working from the inside out. Each step adds columns to the table, so the more complicated the expression, the greater the likelihood that there will be more columns.

Question 15 The exclusive *or* is rather obvious here, as it is in many real situations. It is also obvious when a parent says, "Finish your meal or you will not get dessert." Contrast these situations with those in mathematics, in which the exclusive *or* can never be assumed.

Social Studies Connection After escaping from slavery in 1849, Harriet Tubman became one of the most famous leaders of the underground railroad.

Additional Answers

17. a.

p	q	p xor q
T	T	F
T	F	T
F	T	T
F	F	F

b.

p	q	p xor q	not p	not q	(not p) and q	p and (not q)	((not p) and q) or (p and (not q))
T	T	F	F	F	F	F	F
T	F	T	F	T	F	T	T
F	T	T	T	F	T	F	T
F	F	F	T	T	F	F	F

same truth values

Notes on Questions

Question 21 Students are assumed to have encountered circular functions previously. This question provides an opportunity to review the values of sin θ and cos θ for $\theta = \frac{\pi}{3}$ and $\theta = \frac{\pi}{4}$.

Follow-up for Lesson 1-3

Practice

For more questions on SPUR Objectives, use **Lesson Master 1-3** (shown on pages 22–23).

Assessment

Written Communication Have students make a truth table to verify that *~(~p and q) ≡ p or ~q.* [Students use truth tables to prove the equivalence of logical expressions.]

Extension

The Absorption Property of Boolean algebra states:
p or (p and q) ≡ p and
p and (p or q) ≡ p.
Have students prove this property using the method of **Example 1.**

[The truth table is:

p	*q*	*p and q*	*p or (p and q)*
T	T	T	T
T	F	F	T
F	T	F	F
F	F	F	F

p or (p and q) has the same truth values as *p*, so they are equivalent.

p	*q*	*p or q*	*p and (p or q)*
T	T	T	T
T	F	T	T
F	T	T	F
F	F	F	F

p and (p or q) has the same truth values as *p*, so they are equivalent.]

Project Update Project 4, *Logic and Programming,* on page 67, relates to the content of this lesson.

SAT II's

21) $\sin\left(\frac{7\pi}{12}\right) =$
$\sin\left(\frac{\pi}{3} + \frac{\pi}{4}\right) =$
$\sin\frac{\pi}{3} \cdot \cos\frac{\pi}{4} +$
$\cos\frac{\pi}{3} \cdot \sin\frac{\pi}{4} =$
$\frac{\sqrt{3}}{2} \cdot \frac{\sqrt{2}}{2} + \frac{1}{2} \cdot \frac{\sqrt{2}}{2} =$
$\frac{\sqrt{6} + \sqrt{2}}{4}$

23)

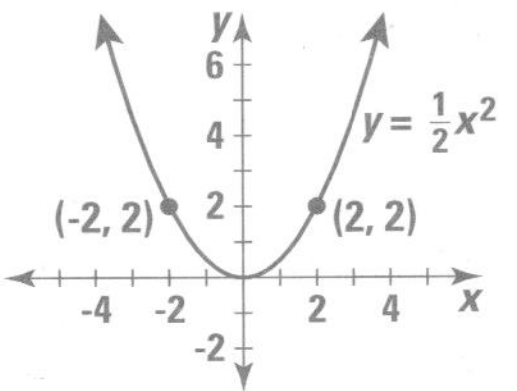

25a) Sample: the waiter gives you a choice of coffee, tea, or milk. He then comes back to tell you that he has run out of all three. Therefore, you can't have coffee and you can't have tea and you can't have milk.

Review

19. Given the statement
∃ a positive real number x such that $\log_{10} x = 0$.
a. Write the negation. *∀ real numbers x < 0, $\log_{10} x \neq 0$.*
b. Which is true: the statement or its negation? The statement is true.
(Previous course, Lessons 1-1, 1-2)

20. *Multiple choice.* Identify the negation of
∀ integers n ∃ integers a and b such that $n = \frac{a}{b}$. c
(a) *∀ integers n ∃ integers a and b such that $n \neq \frac{a}{b}$.*
(b) *∃ an integer n such that ∀ integers a and b, $n = \frac{a}{b}$.*
(c) *∃ an integer n such that ∀ integers a and b, $n \neq \frac{a}{b}$.*
(d) *∀ integers n and ∀ integers a and b, $n \neq \frac{a}{b}$.* *(Lesson 1-2)*

21. Use the Law of Substitution with the true statement
∀ real numbers x and y, sin (x + y) = sin x cos y + cos x sin y.
to show that $\sin\frac{7\pi}{12} = \frac{\sqrt{6} + \sqrt{2}}{4}$. (Hint: Let $x = \frac{\pi}{3}$ and $y = \frac{\pi}{4}$.) *(Lesson 1-1)*
See left.

22. *True or false.*
a. *∀ rectangles r, r is a square.* False
b. *∃ a rectangle r such that r is a square.* *(Lesson 1-1)* True

23. Graph the set of points (*x*, *y*) such that $y = \frac{1}{2}x^2$. *(Previous course)*
See left.

24. Identify the slope, the *y*-intercept, and the *x*-intercept of the line with equation $3x + 2y = 5$. *(Previous course)*
slope $= -\frac{3}{2}$, y-intercept $= \frac{5}{2}$, x-intercept $= \frac{5}{3}$

Exploration

25. An extension of De Morgan's second law is
~(p or (q or r)) ≡ (~p) and ((~q) and (~r)).
a. Give a nonmathematical example of this extension. See left.
b. Append more columns, and fill in the truth table to prove this extension.
See margin.

p	*q*	*r*	*~p*	*~q*	*~r*
T	T	T			
T	T	F			
T	F	T			
T	F	F			
F	T	T			
F	T	F			
F	F	T			
F	F	F			

Additional Answers
25. b.

p	*q*	*r*	*~p*	*~q*	*~r*	*(p or q or r)*	*~(p or q or r)*	*~p and ~q and ~r*
T	T	T	F	F	F	T	F	F
T	T	F	F	F	T	T	F	F
T	F	T	F	T	F	T	F	F
T	F	F	F	T	T	T	F	F
F	T	T	T	F	F	T	F	F
F	T	F	T	F	T	T	F	F
F	F	T	T	T	F	T	F	F
F	F	F	T	T	T	F	T	T

same truth values

LESSON

1-4 Computer Logic Networks

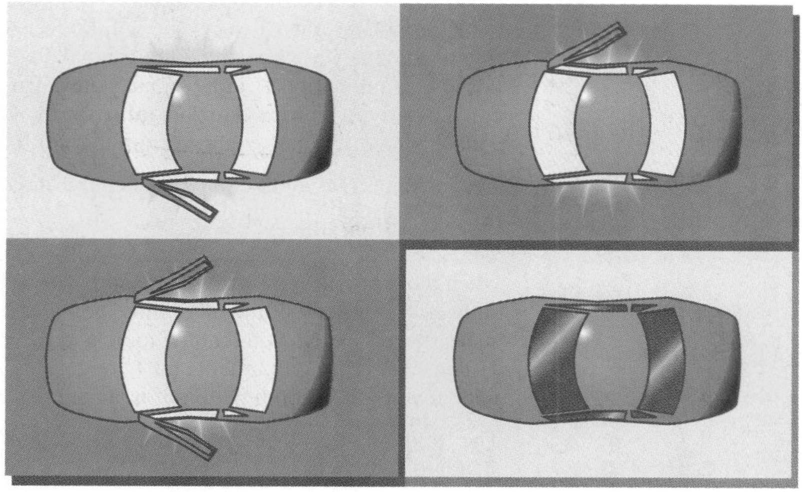

Think of the light in the ceiling of a 2-door car. Unless you have done something with an inside switch, that light will be on when either or both doors are open, and off when both are closed. The table at the right tells whether the light is on or off by the positions of the doors.

door 1	door 2	light
open	open	on
open	closed	on
closed	open	on
closed	closed	off

Does this table look familiar? It may, for it has the same structure as the truth table for *or*, with the words *open* and *on* replacing T and the words *closed* and *off* replacing F. This suggests that logic and electronics are intimately related, and they are. Every time that you press a button on a calculator, or type in a command to a computer, or flip a light switch, you are activating the first *logic gate* in an electronic system. Microprocessors may contain millions of logic gates. These gates are interconnected so that they transmit electrical current to produce outputs such as the displays you see after inputting various keystrokes on a calculator.

As pieces of computer hardware, logic gates can take a variety of forms. It is not necessary for you to know how these gates are physically constructed in order to understand how they function. Instead, you can think of logic gates as electrical devices with input and output wires. A model of a logic gate is illustrated below.

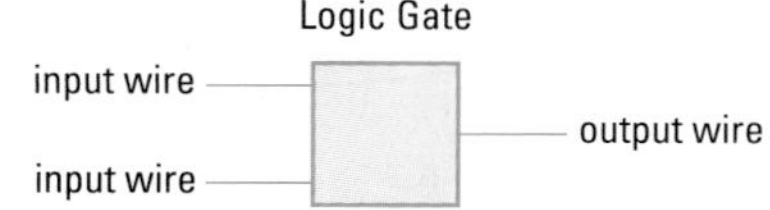

The input and output wires carry electrical signals that are in one of two mutually exclusive states. You can think of these two states as *current ON* or *current OFF* or as *high voltage* or *low voltage*. For convenience, we will refer to these signal states as **1** or **0**. They correspond to *True* and *False*, respectively, in logic. *True* is *1* or ON; *False* is *0* or OFF.

Lesson 1-4

Objectives

K Translate logic networks into logical expressions and determine output signals.

Resources

From the ***Teacher's Resource File***
- Lesson Master 1-4
- Answer Master 1-4
- Assessment Sourcebook: Quiz for Lessons 1-1 through 1-4
- Teaching Aids
  - 2 Warm-up
  - 9 Logic Networks for Examples 1–3
  - 10 Questions 4–6

Additional Resources
- Visuals for Teaching Aids 2, 9, 10
- Exploration 1-4

Teaching Lesson 1-4

Warm-up

1. Make a table showing all possibilities for opening or not opening a door with two locks that are unlocked or locked.

Lock 1	Lock 2	Door
unlocked	unlocked	unlocked
unlocked	locked	locked
locked	unlocked	locked
locked	locked	locked

2. Relate the situation In Warm-up question 1 to a truth table. **It relates to the truth table for *and*: The door will open when and only when both locks are open.**

Lesson 1-4 Overview

Broad Goals This lesson applies *and*, *or*, and *not* statements to the study of computer logic networks. Students are expected to construct an input-output table for a given network and to determine the logical expression corresponding to a particular network. However, students are not expected to construct a logical network for a particular logical expression.

Perspective Students can see that the input-output tables for the AND, OR, and NOT logic gates are identical to the truth tables for *and*, *or*, and *not*, except that T has been replaced by 1 and F by 0. The truth tables for studying logical expressions are structurally equivalent to input-output tables for studying networks of gates.

The kind of analysis introduced in this lesson is used in the construction of electrical circuits of all kinds, from those in large installations to those on computer chips.

Notes on Reading

The logic networks in **Examples 1–3** are shown on **Teaching Aid 9.**

The symbolic shapes used for the *AND*, *OR*, and *NOT* logic gates are standard in computer science, and in practice the words inside the shapes are often omitted.

Consumer Connection Students may wonder why there is concern with determining whether or not two networks are functionally equivalent. Explain that cost concerns usually require that a network be built for as low a cost as possible while still performing a specific function. For example, the absorption law states *p or (p and q)* ≡ *p*. This law permits the replacement of a part of the network represented by *p or (p and q)* by the single gate *p*. Such a replacement decreases both network cost and size. The process of reducing networks is studied by computer design engineers.

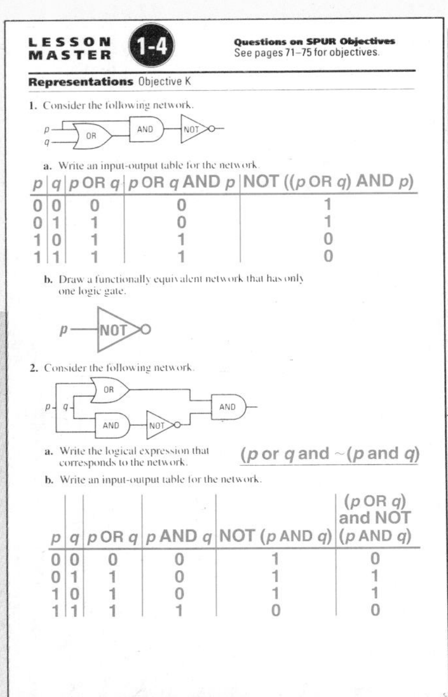

LESSON MASTER 1-4 — Questions on SPUR Objectives. See pages 71–75 for objectives.

Representations Objective K

1. Consider the following network.

a. Write an input-output table for the network.

p	q	p OR q	p OR q AND p	NOT ((p OR q) AND p)
0	0	0	0	1
0	1	1	0	1
1	0	1	1	0
1	1	1	1	0

b. Draw a functionally equivalent network that has only one logic gate.

2. Consider the following network.

a. Write the logical expression that corresponds to the network. (p or q and ~(p and q)

b. Write an input-output table for the network.

p	q	p OR q	p AND q	NOT (p AND q)	(p OR q) and NOT (p AND q)
0	0	0	0	1	0
0	1	1	0	1	1
1	0	1	0	1	1
1	1	1	1	0	0

Input		Output
p	q	
1	1	0
1	0	1
0	1	1
0	0	1

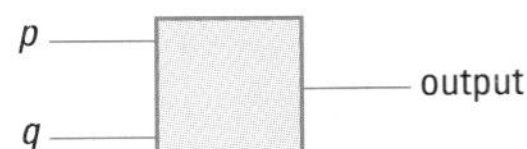

A logic gate acts on the input signals that it receives to produce an output signal (1 or 0). Consequently, you will know exactly how a logic gate functions once you know the output signal state that is produced for every possible combination of input signal states. This information can be listed conveniently in an **input-output table** for the logic gate. At the left is such a table for a different logic gate from that for the car-door situation.

The table has two input columns labeled *p* and *q*, so you can picture the logic gate as shown at the left.

The table tells you that the logic gate will produce an output signal of 0 when the input wire *p* carries a signal of 1 and the input wire *q* carries a signal of 1. For any of the other three possible combinations of input signal states, the table tells you that the logic gate will produce an output signal of 1. Thus, the input-output table tells you exactly what the logic gate will do with any possible combination of input signals.

The following three logic gates are so basic that they are given special standard symbols.

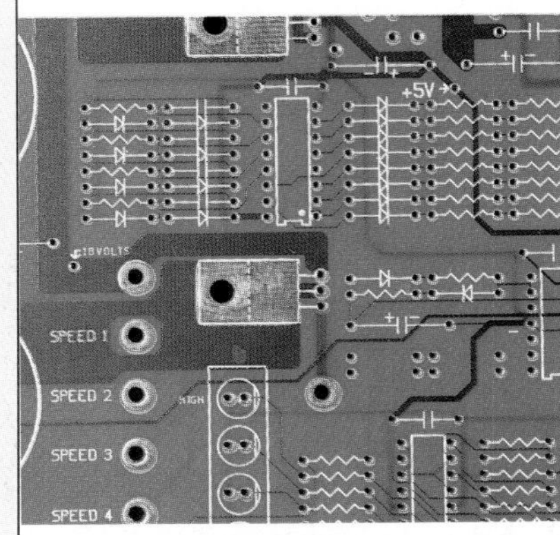

Chip Off the Old Board.
The computer chips on a logic board contain thousands of electronic logic gates.

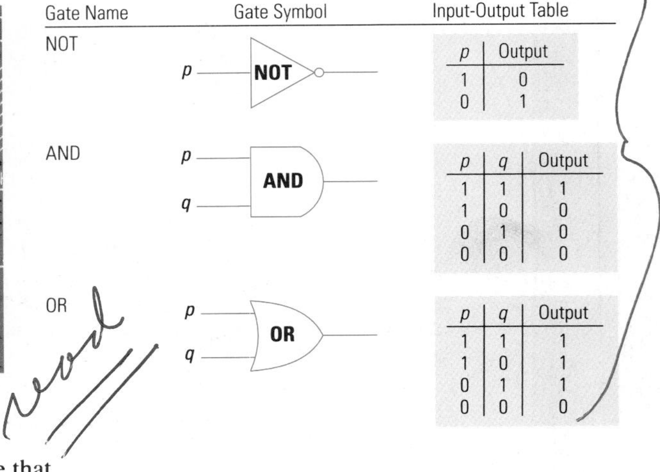

Gate Name	Gate Symbol	Input-Output Table
NOT	p → NOT →	
AND	p, q → AND →	
OR	p, q → OR →	

NOT:

p	Output
1	0
0	1

AND:

p	q	Output
1	1	1
1	0	0
0	1	0
0	0	0

OR:

p	q	Output
1	1	1
1	0	1
0	1	1
0	0	0

Notice that

a. the NOT gate output signal is 0 if the input signal is 1, and that the output signal is 1 if the input signal is 0;

b. the AND gate output signal is 1 if the input wire *p and* the input wire *q* carry a signal of 1. Otherwise, the output signal is 0;

c. the OR gate output signal is 1 if the input wire *p or* the input wire *q* (or both) carries a signal of 1. Otherwise, the output signal is 0.

If you have not noticed already, you should see that the input-output tables for the NOT, AND, and OR logic gates are essentially the same as the truth tables for *not p*, *p and q*, and *p or q*. The only differences are notational: 1 and 0 are used in place of T and F, respectively, and the last column is labeled with the word *output* instead of with the appropriate logical expression.

Optional Activities

Activity 1 Technology Connection
Materials: Explorations software

Students may use *Exploration 1-4, Logic Networks,* to explore logic networks and truth tables. Students choose from a list of logic sentences. The program displays the corresponding network and an incomplete truth table. Students can predict results for the table and check their predictions by choosing appropriate values.

Activity 2 After completing the lesson, you may want to discuss the axioms for Boolean algebra. In such an algebra defined on a set *S*, there are three operations, denoted by $\wedge$, $\vee$, and ′ that satisfy the following conditions:

For all a, b, and c in S:

Closure $a \wedge b$, $a \vee b$, and a' are in *S*.

Associativity

$a \wedge (b \wedge c) = (a \wedge b) \wedge c$

$a \vee (b \vee c) = (a \vee b) \vee c$

NOT, AND, and OR gates are usually connected in such a way that the output signals from some of the gates become input signals for other gates. This is called a *network* of logic gates. The relationship between the input-output tables for NOT, AND, and OR gates and the truth tables for *not p*, *p and q*, and *p or q* means that for each network of logic gates, you can construct a corresponding logical expression. Also, you can use logic to determine the action of any network.

Example 1

Construct an input-output table that corresponds to the following network.

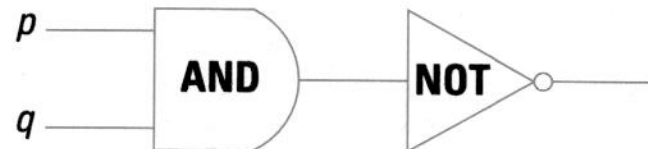

Solution

Because the network has an input wire labeled *p* and an input wire labeled *q*, the input-output table should list all possible combinations of signal states for *p*, *q*.

p	q	
1	1	
1	0	
0	1	
0	0	

Input signals first go to an AND gate whose output goes to a NOT gate. Tracking each pair of input signals through the network allows you to determine the appropriate output signal. If *p* is 1 and *q* is 1, then the output from the AND gate is also 1. The NOT gate reverses this value and gives a final output of 0. The other rows of the table are completed in a similar manner.

p	q	p AND q	output of network NOT (p AND q)
1	1	1	0
1	0	0	1
0	1	0	1
0	0	0	1

Check

The circuit should represent the truth table for *not (p and q)*.

p	*q*	*p and q*	*not (p and q)*
T	T	T	F
T	F	F	T
F	T	F	T
F	F	F	T

LESSON MASTER 1-4 *page 2*

3. Are the two networks shown below, each with four inputs *p*, *q*, *r*, and *s*, functionally equivalent? Justify your answer.

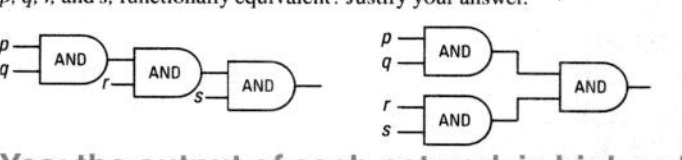

Yes; the output of each network is high only when all four inputs are high.

4. Consider the following network.

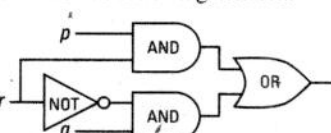

a. Fill in the input-output table below for this network.

p	*q*	*r*	NOT *r*	*p* AND *r*	*q* AND NOT *r*	(*p* AND *r*) OR (*q* AND NOT *r*)
0	0	0	1	0	0	0
0	1	0	1	0	1	1
1	0	0	1	0	0	0
1	1	0	1	0	1	1
0	0	1	0	0	0	0
0	1	1	0	0	0	0
1	0	1	0	1	0	1
1	1	1	0	1	0	1

b. What effect does input *r* have on the output?

When *r* is 0, the final output is equal to the input for *q*. When *r* is 1, the final output is equal to the input for *p*.

Commutativity
$a \wedge b = b \wedge a$ $\quad$ $a \vee b = b \vee a$

Distributivity
$a \wedge (b \vee c) = (a \wedge b) \vee (a \wedge c)$
$a \vee (b \wedge c) = (a \vee b) \wedge (a \vee c)$

Identities There are distinct and unique elements 0 and 1 in *S* such that
$a \wedge 1 = a$ $\quad$ $a \vee 0 = a$

Complements For each *a* in *S* there exists one and only one *a′* in *S* such that
$a \wedge a' = 0$ $\quad$ $a \vee a' = 1$

The correspondences shown below can be made between general Boolean algebra and the specific Boolean algebra of statements.

general	specific
elements in *S*	statements
$\wedge$	and
$\vee$	or
$'$	not

(Activity 2 continues on page 30.)

Recall that two logical expressions are logically equivalent if their truth values are always the same. Similarly, if the output columns of the input-output tables for two networks are identical, then the networks produce the same output for each combination of input signals, and so the networks are **functionally equivalent**. The symbol ≡ can be used between functionally equivalent networks just as it can be used between logically equivalent expressions.

Example 2 illustrates the use of functionally equivalent networks to represent one of De Morgan's Laws in network terms:

$$not\ (p\ and\ q) \equiv (not\ p)\ or\ (not\ q).$$

Example 2

Verify this network version of the first Law of De Morgan:

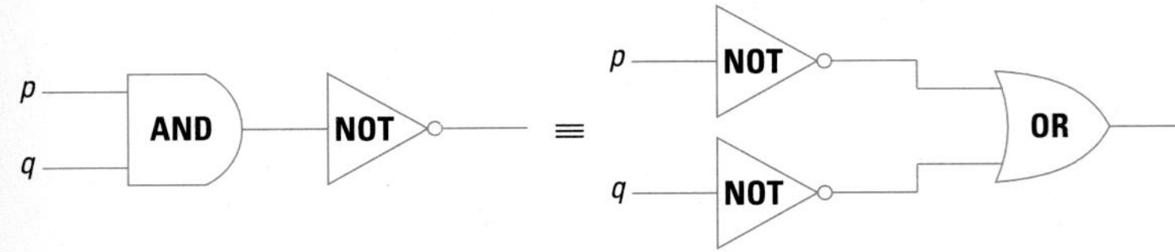

Solution

Build the input-output table for each side of the equivalence to show that each possible combination of input signals gives the same output. Here is the table for the right side.

p	q	NOT p	NOT q	(NOT p) OR (NOT q)
1	1	0	0	0
1	0	0	1	1
0	1	1	0	1
0	0	1	1	1

The values in the rightmost column are identical to those computed in Example 1 for the network on the left.

In Examples 1 and 2, we started with a network and constructed the corresponding input-output table. It is also possible to start with a network and find the corresponding logical expression. Some people do this by tracing the network backwards from output to input rather than working from input to output.

Additional Examples

1. Construct an input-output table that corresponds to the following network.

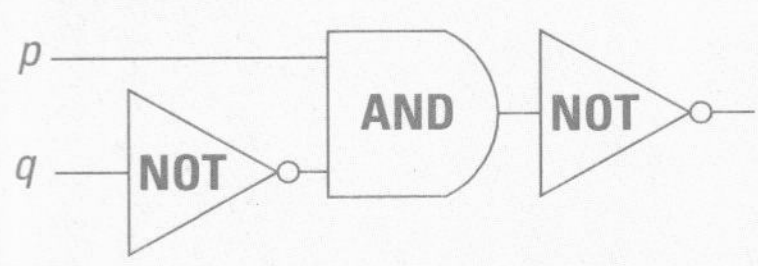

Because the network has two input wires labeled *p* and *q*, the input-output table lists all possible combinations of signal states for *p* and *q*.

p	*q*	*not q*	*p and (not q)*	*not (p and (not q))*
1	1	0	0	1
1	0	1	1	0
0	1	0	0	1
0	0	1	0	1

2. Verify that the two networks of Lesson 1-3, Additional Example 1, are equivalent.

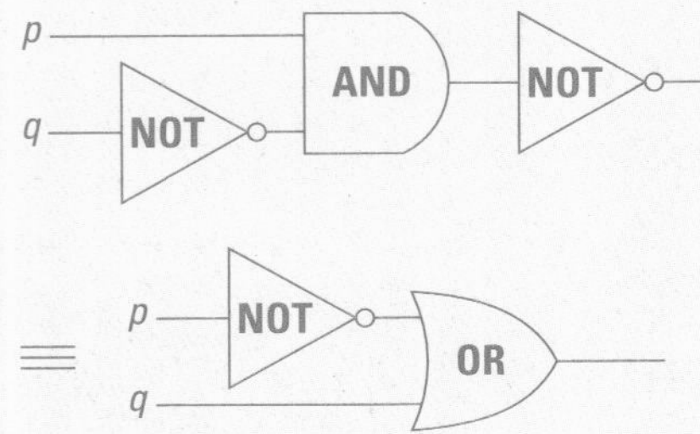

One consequence of the above axioms is the **Idempotent Theorem:** (only the first identity is proved below) For all elements *a* in a Boolean algebra, $a \wedge a = a$; $a \vee a = a$.

$a = a \wedge 1$	Identity
$= a \wedge (a \vee a')$	Comp. Prop.
$= (a \wedge a) \vee (a \wedge a')$	Distrib. Prop.
$= (a \wedge a) \vee 0$	Comp. Prop.
$= a \wedge a$	Identity

Adapting to Individual Needs

Extra Help

To reinforce the AND logic gate with an illustration similar to the one about the car at the beginning of the lesson, point out that AND requires a situation in which two or more operations must both be completed before the desired output occurs. Most electrical appliances work under this principle. The appliance must be plugged in and the appliance must be turned on before the appliance can be operated.

Example 3

Find the logical expression that corresponds to the following network.

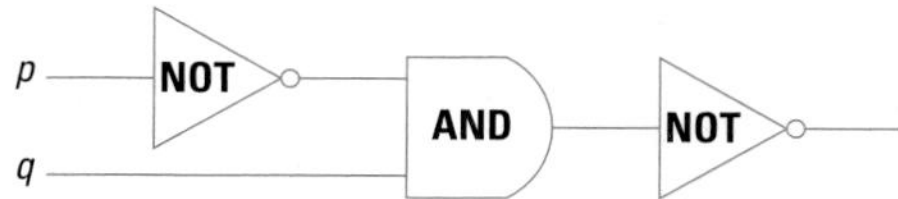

Solution 1

Read the network from right to left and build the expression as you go. The last NOT gate reverses the output of the part prior to it. So,

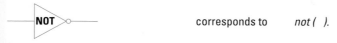

Also,

Thus, the entire network corresponds to not ((not p) and q).

Solution 2

Read the network from left to right, putting each previous step in parentheses.

The first component is	not p.
The second is	(not p) and q.
The last is	not ((not p) and q).

George Boole

The algebraic properties of *and*, *or*, and *not* were first studied by George Boole (1815–1864) in his book *An Investigation of the Laws of Thought*, which was published in 1854. Though Boole came from a poor family and had only three years of formal education, he went on to become a brilliant scholar who not only contributed new knowledge to several fields in mathematics but also taught Latin and Greek.

Boole discovered that the logical operations of *and*, *or*, and *not* can form an algebraic system. This discovery has been applied to other situations involving two values like ON-OFF, YES-NO, 1-0. If the values can be combined using operations similar to *and*, *or*, and *not*, then the system is called a **Boolean algebra**.

The first applications of Boolean algebra to the analysis of networks were by A. Nakashima in 1937 and Claude Shannon in 1938. Today the Boolean algebra of electronics is an important application of mathematics. One of its uses is in the design of systems of microprocessors, a focus of very active research by engineers, computer scientists, and mathematicians.

Additional Example 1 shows the input-output table for the first network. The table for the equivalent network appears below.

p	*q*	*not p*	*(not p) or q*
1	1	0	1
1	0	0	0
0	1	1	1
0	0	1	1

Because both networks have the same outputs for the given inputs (last columns are identical), the networks are equivalent.

3. Find the logical expression that corresponds to the following network.

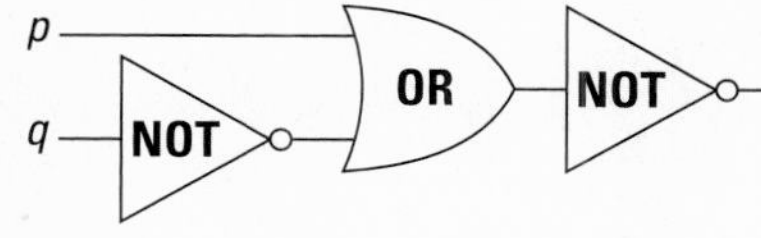

not (*p or* (*not q*))

Adapting to Individual Needs

Challenge

Have students answer the following questions.

1. Write an input-output table for:

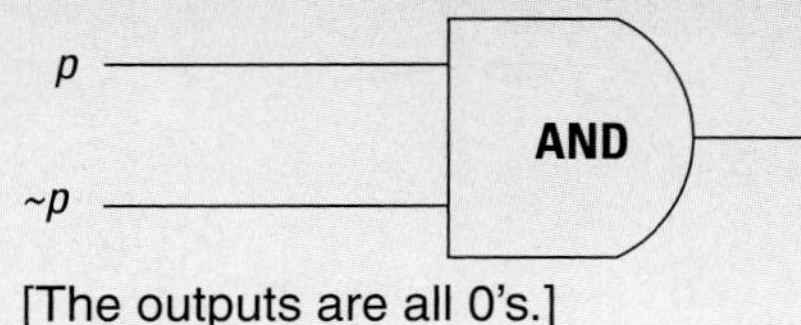

[The outputs are all 0's.]

2. Write an input-output table for:

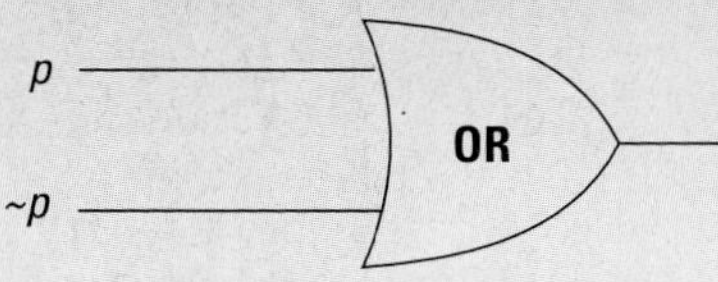

[The outputs are all 1's.]

3. The two logic networks in the preceding two questions relate to what logic statement results? [The statement *p and* ~*p* is always false. The statement *p or* ~*p* is always true.]

Notes on Questions

Questions 1 and 6 Error Alert If some students have trouble completing input/output (or truth) tables, which are required in these questions, a discussion on column headings may help.

Questions 2, 4, and 5 While we ask students to write a logical expression that corresponds to a network, we do not ask them to do the reverse. You may wish to challenge them with a logical expression that they are to convert to the corresponding network.

Questions 4–6 Teaching Aid 10 is provided to make it easier to discuss these questions.

QUESTIONS

Covering the Reading

1. Use the circuit network version below of De Morgan's Law *not (p or q)* ≡ *(not p) and (not q)*. **a, b) See margin.**

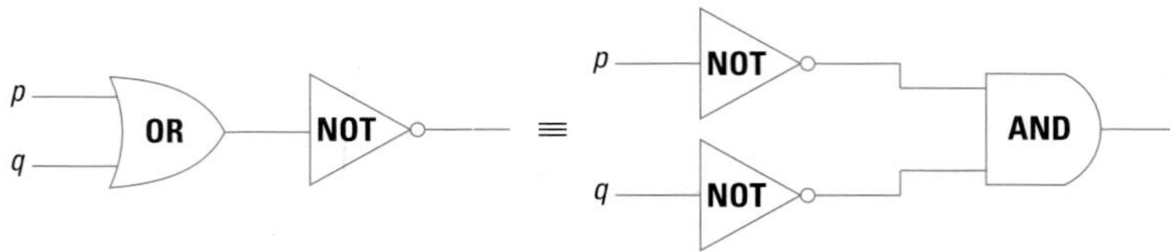

a. Write an input-output table for the left side of the ≡ sign.
b. Write an input-output table for the right side of the ≡ sign.
c. Why do your answers in parts **a** and **b** establish that the two networks are functionally equivalent?
The output columns for each network are identical.

2. Write a logical expression that corresponds to the network below.
(*p* or (not *q*)) and *r*

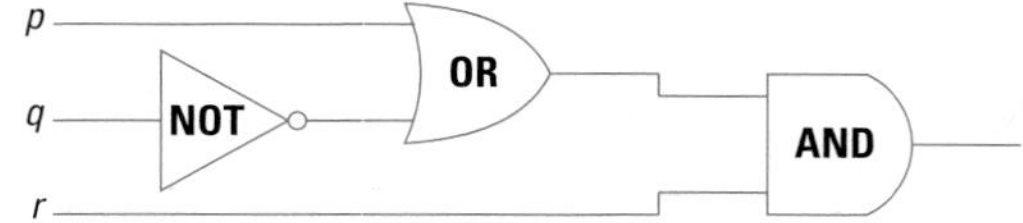

3. a. How long ago were the algebraic properties of *and*, *or*, and *not* first studied? **In 1999, it was 146 years ago.**
b. How long ago were these properties first applied to electronic networks? **In 1999, it was 62 years ago.**

Applying the Mathematics

In 4 and 5, write a logical expression to describe each network.

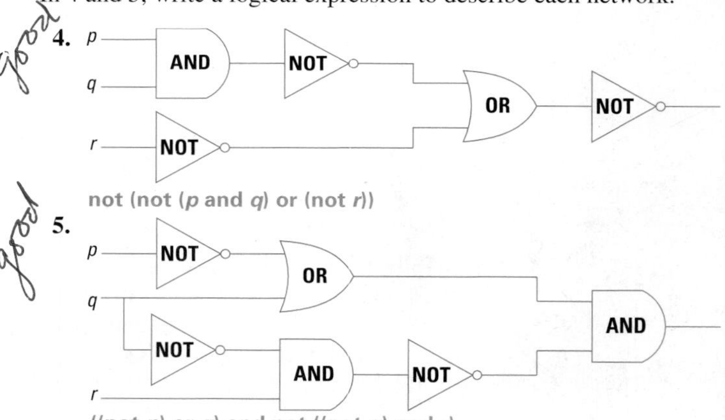

Additional Answers, pages 32–33

1. a.

p	q	p OR q	NOT (p OR q)
1	1	1	0
1	0	1	0
0	1	1	0
0	0	0	1

b.

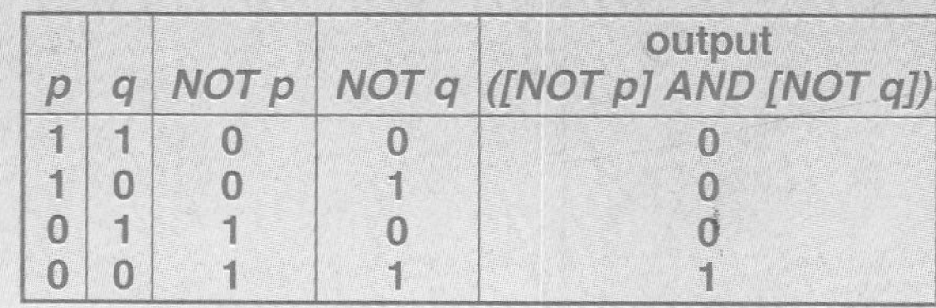

p	q	NOT p	NOT q	output ([NOT p] AND [NOT q])
1	1	0	0	0
1	0	0	1	0
0	1	1	0	0
0	0	1	1	1

6. The network in Question 6 corresponds to the logical expression *q or ((not p) and (not r))*. Then the input/output table for the networks of Questions 5 and 6 is shown at the right.

6. Show that the following network is functionally equivalent to the network of Question 5. See margin.

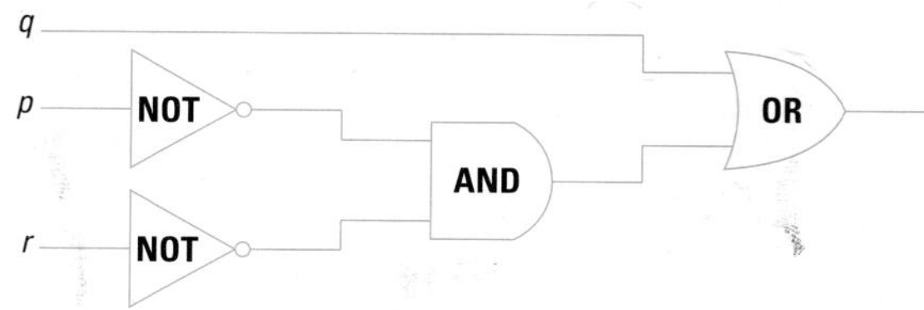

7. Suppose that an AND gate costs 3¢, an OR gate 2¢, and a NOT gate 1¢.

a. What is the cost of the network in Question 5? 11¢

b. What is the cost of the network in Question 6? 7¢

c. Which network would be preferred in an electronic application? the network in Question 6

8. The living room in a particular house can be entered from the front door *F*, the dining room *D*, and the family room *M*. At each entrance there is a switch for the ceiling light in the room. The front door switch *F* is a master switch; when it is down, the ceiling light cannot be turned on from switches *D* and *M*. When the master switch is up, the ceiling light will be turned on if switches *D* and *M* are in the same position; otherwise it will be off. If 1 = up and 0 = down, complete this input-output table for the ceiling light. The first row has been filled in. See margin.

input *F*	input *D*	input *M*	output (ON or OFF)
1	0	0	ON

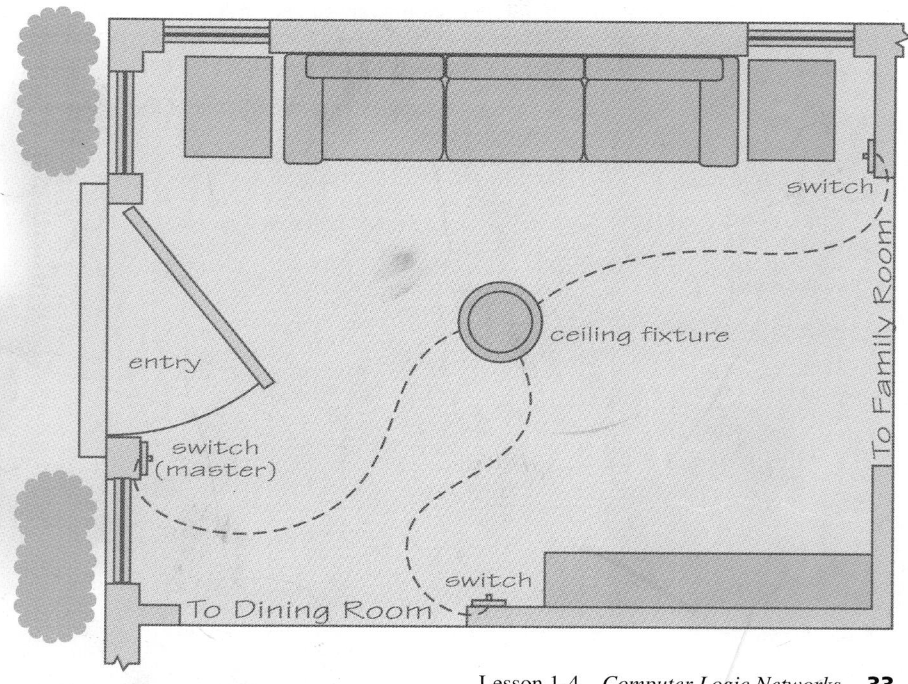

Follow-up for Lesson 1-4

Practice

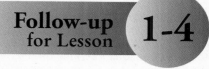

For more questions on SPUR Objectives, use **Lesson Master 1-4** (shown on page 28–29).

Assessment

Quiz A quiz covering Lessons 1-1 through 1-4 is provided in the *Assessment Sourcebook.*

(Follow-up continues on page 34.)

Additional Answers

8.

input F	input D	input M	output (ON or OFF)
1	0	0	ON
1	0	1	OFF
1	1	1	ON
1	1	0	OFF
0	0	0	OFF
0	0	1	OFF
0	1	1	OFF
0	1	0	OFF

p	q	r	NOT p	(NOT p) OR q	NOT q	(NOT q) AND r	NOT((NOT q) AND r)	output for Question 5	NOT r	(NOT p) AND (NOT r)	ouput for Question 6
1	1	1	0	1	0	0	1	1	0	0	1
1	1	0	0	1	0	0	1	1	1	0	1
1	0	1	0	0	1	1	0	0	0	0	0
1	0	0	0	0	1	0	1	0	1	0	0
0	1	1	1	1	0	0	1	1	0	0	1
0	1	0	1	1	0	0	1	1	1	1	1
0	0	1	1	1	1	1	0	0	0	0	0
0	0	0	1	1	1	0	1	1	1	1	1

same truth values

Thus, they have the same output.

Extension

The following exercises extend Activity 2 in *Optional Activities* that begin on page 28. You might ask students to supply reasons for these proofs.

1. **Theorem of 0:** For all elements a of a Boolean algebra, $a \wedge 0 = 0$.
   Proof: Suppose a is an element of a Boolean algebra.
   $a \wedge 0$
   $= a \wedge (a \wedge a')$ [Comp. Prop.]
   $= (a \wedge a) \wedge a'$ [Assoc. Prop.]
   $= a \wedge a'$ [Idemp. Thm.]
   $= 0$ [Comp. Prop.]
2. **Theorem of 1:** For all elements a of a Boolean algebra, $a \vee 1 = 1$.
   Proof: Suppose a is an element of a Boolean algebra.
   $a \vee 1$
   $= a \vee (a \vee a')$ [Comp. Prop.]
   $= (a \vee a) \vee a'$ [Assoc. Prop.]
   $= a \vee a'$ [Idemp. Thm.]
   $= 1$ [Comp. Prop.]
3. **Absorption Law:** For all elements a and b of a Boolean algebra, $a \vee (a \wedge b) = a$; $a \wedge (a \vee b) = a$.
   Proof (Only the first identity is proved here.): Suppose a and b are elements of a Boolean algebra.
   $a \vee (a \wedge b)$
   $= (a \wedge 1) \vee (a \wedge b)$ [Identity]
   $= a \wedge (1 \vee b)$ [Dist. Prop.]
   $= a \wedge 1$ [Thm. of 1]
   $= a$ [Identity]
4. **Cancellation Theorem:** Suppose that a, b, and c are elements of a Boolean algebra. If $a \wedge c = b \wedge c$ and $a \vee c = b \vee c$, then $a = b$.
   Proof: Suppose a, b, and c are elements of a Boolean algebra, $a \wedge c = b \wedge c$ and $a \vee c = b \vee c$.
   Then a
   $= a \vee (a \wedge c)$ [Absorption]
   $= a \vee (b \wedge c)$ [Subs.]
   $= (a \vee b) \wedge (a \vee c)$ [Dist. Prop.]
   $= (a \vee b) \wedge (b \vee c)$ [Subs.]
   $= (b \vee a) \wedge (b \vee c)$ [Com. Prop.]
   $= b \vee (a \wedge c)$ [Dist. Prop.]
   $= b \vee (b \wedge c)$ [Subs.]
   $= b$ [Absorption]

Project Update Project 3, *Boolean Algebra*, and Project 4, *Logic and Programming,* on page 67, relate to the content of this lesson.

Review

9. Construct a truth table to show all possible truth values of the expression p *and* $\sim q$. Label the columns p, q, $\sim q$, and (p *and* $\sim q$). *(Lesson 1-3)* See below.

10. Write as an inequality: x is greater than -2 and less than or equal to 4. *(Lesson 1-3)* $-2 < x \leq 4$

In 11 and 12, write the negation. *(Lesson 1-2)*

11. *No symphony orchestra contains a full-time banjo player.*
There is a symphony orchestra with a full-time banjo player.

12. $\forall$ *real numbers* x *and* y, $x^2 + y^2 > 0$.
$\exists$ *real numbers* x *and* y *such that* $x^2 + y^2 \leq 0$.

13. Is this statement true or false? Explain your answer. *(Lesson 1-1)*

$\forall$ *integers* n $\exists$ *an integer* m *such that* $n = 2m$.

False; counterexample: Let n be 3.

14. Consider the true statement

$\forall$ *negative real numbers* y, $|y| = -y$.

a. Use the Law of Substitution to show that the statement is true for $y = -5$.
b. Show that the statement is false if the restriction on y is removed.
(Previous course, Lesson 1-1) See left.

15. Sketch the parabola $y = x^2 - 7x + 10$. Give values for the x- and y-intercepts, the axis of symmetry, and the coordinates of the vertex. *(Previous course)* See left.

Exploration

16. Claude Shannon was a student at the Massachusetts Institute of Technology when he did his pioneering work with the algebra of circuits. Find out more about this great applied mathematician. See left.

17. Write a paragraph linking the content of this lesson to the ideas of circuits in parallel and circuits in series.
Sample: For circuits in series, consider a string of lights. If one light fails, none of the lights will work. Each light must work for the string of lights to work. This is analogous to the AND gate. For circuits in parallel, consider the lights in a house. A light in one room may work regardless of whether any other lights in the house work or not. The house is completely dark only when all the lights are off. This is analogous to the OR gate.

9)

p	q	$\sim q$	(p and $\sim q$
T	T	F	F
T	F	T	T
F	T	F	F
F	F	T	F

14a) $|-5| = -(-5) = 5$
b) Sample: Let $y = 5$. Then $|5| = 5$, not -5.

15)

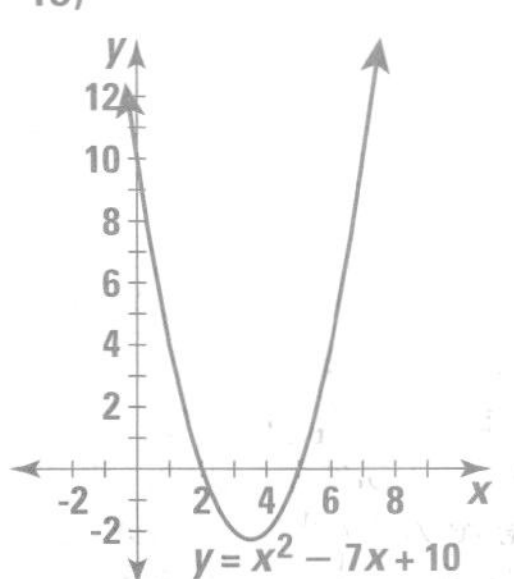

x-intercepts: 2 and 5
y-intercept: 10
The axis of symmetry: $x = 3.5$
vertex: (3.5, -2.25)

16) Sample: While working at Bell Laboratories (1941–1957), he developed a mathematical theory of communication known as "information theory."

LESSON

1-5

If-then *Statements*

Name that Tune. *One of the if-then song lines below comes from the musical* Carousel. *Gordon MacRae sang it to Shirley Jones in the 1956 movie made from the 1945 Rodgers and Hammerstein Broadway hit.*

(a) *If you knew Peggy Sue, then you'd know why I feel blue.* ©
(b) *If I loved you, time and again I would try to say all I want you to know.* ©
(c) *If I had a hammer, I'd hammer in the morning.* ©
(d) *If you want to make the world a better place, take a look at yourself and make that change.* ©

If-then statements are found everywhere. (Can you tell the origins of the four statements written above?) Both inside and outside mathematics, *if-then* statements are present whenever one statement is supposed to follow from another. Within mathematics they form the basis of the language of deduction and proof. In this lesson, we review the language of *if-then* statements that you have studied in previous years and apply the formal logic of the preceding lessons to these statements.

The Conditional $p \Rightarrow q$

A statement, such as any one of the four above, of the form

If p, then q.

is called a **conditional statement**, denoted $\boldsymbol{p \Rightarrow q}$, and read "$p$ implies q."

Statement p is called the **hypothesis** or **antecedent** and statement q is called the **conclusion** or **consequent**, as in this example.

If a quadrilateral is a rectangle, then its diagonals bisect each other.

hypothesis or antecedent	conclusion or consequent
If a quadrilateral is a rectangle,	*then its diagonals bisect each other.*

Lesson 1-5

Objectives

A Identify forms of logical statements.
B Write equivalent forms of logical statements.
C Write the negation of a logical statement.
D Determine the truth value of a logical statement.
E Identify properties of logical statements.
I Determine the truth of quantified statements outside of mathematics.
L Write truth tables for logical expressions.

Resources

From the ***Teacher's Resource File***
- Lesson Master 1-5
- Answer Master 1-5
- Teaching Aids
  - 3 Warm-up
  - 6 Truth Tables

Additional Resources
- Visuals for Teaching Aids 3, 6
- Exploration 1-5

Teaching Lesson 1-5

Warm-up

First determine whether the sentence is a statement. If so, tell whether it is true or false.

1. If $3 > 2$, then $5 > 4$. **A true statement, since both antecedent and consequent are true. Also, you can add 2**

(Warm-up continues on page 36.)

Lesson 1-5 Overview

Broad Goals The treatment of the truth values of a universal conditional and of its negation in this lesson applies many of the ideas of the previous lessons to an exceedingly important type of statement.

Perspective Students have studied *if-then* statements before, particularly in geometry. In the conditional $p \Rightarrow q$, many texts call p the *hypothesis* and q the *conclusion*. Here we usually refer to p as the *antecedent* and to q as the *consequent*, reserving the word conclusion for the result of a logical argument.

In the standard logic used to do mathematics, a statement must be either true or false. The only way for a sentence of the form *if p, then q* to be false is for p to be true and q to be false. It follows that for such a sentence to be a statement, it must be true in all other cases—including those for which p is false. Some people say that when p is false, the conditional *if p, then q* is "true by default."

We assume that students are familiar with the meaning of the contrapositive, converse, and inverse of a statement. You may want to illustrate the relationship of the conditional to these other statements by means of a Venn diagram. For instance, consider the conditional statement *If a car is a Taurus,*

(Overview continues on page 36.)

to both sides of the antecedent to get the consequent.

2. If $x > 3$, then $x > 4$.
Not a statement.
3. For all x, if $x > 3$, then $x > 4$.
A false statement, since 3.5 is a counterexample.

Notes on Reading

Music Connection The song at the beginning of the lesson is from the musical *Carousel.* This musical was an adaptation of *Liliom,* a play about a carnival barker. The play was written in 1909 by Hungarian dramatist Ferenc Molnár.

Error Alert Students often think (wrongly) that:

1. the truth value of $p \Rightarrow q$ depends upon the truth value of p alone, or
2. the truth value of $p \Rightarrow q$ depends upon the truth value of q alone, or
3. the truth value of $p \Rightarrow q$ depends upon the contexts of the statements that p and q represent (not merely their truth values).

Each of these beliefs has some justification in the way *if-then* is used formally in mathematics and logic. The discussion of the conditional *If* $x \geq 8$*, then* $x^2 \geq 64$ preceding **Example 1** and the example itself are meant to focus on this point.

Teaching Aid 6 shows the truth table for the conditional.

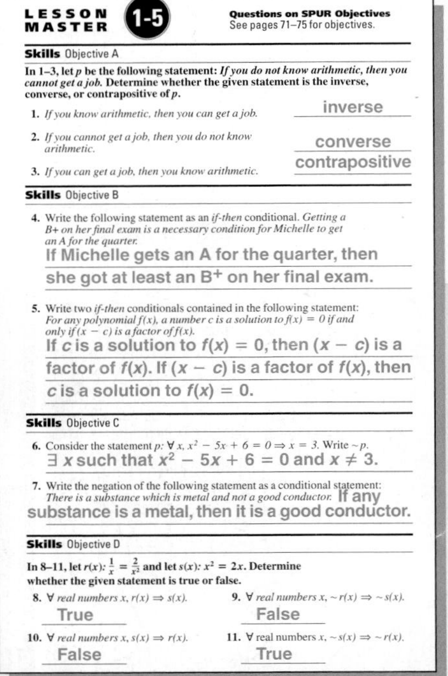

LESSON MASTER 1-5 — **Questions on SPUR Objectives**
See pages 71–75 for objectives.

Skills Objective A

In 1–3, let p be the following statement: *If you do not know arithmetic, then you cannot get a job.* Determine whether the given statement is the inverse, converse, or contrapositive of p.

1. *If you know arithmetic, then you can get a job.* inverse
2. *If you cannot get a job, then you do not know arithmetic.* converse
3. *If you can get a job, then you know arithmetic.* contrapositive

Skills Objective B

4. Write the following statement as an *if-then* conditional. *Getting a B+ on her final exam is a necessary condition for Michelle to get an A for the quarter.*
If Michelle gets an A for the quarter, then she got at least an B+ on her final exam.
5. Write two *if-then* conditionals contained in the following statement: *For any polynomial $f(x)$, a number c is a solution to $f(x) = 0$ if and only if $(x - c)$ is a factor of $f(x)$.*
If c is a solution to $f(x) = 0$, then $(x - c)$ is a factor of $f(x)$. If $(x - c)$ is a factor of $f(x)$, then c is a solution to $f(x) = 0$.

Skills Objective C

6. Consider the statement p: $\forall x, x^2 - 5x + 6 = 0 \Rightarrow x = 3$. Write $\sim p$.
$\exists x$ such that $x^2 - 5x + 6 = 0$ and $x \neq 3$.
7. Write the negation of the following statement as a conditional statement: *There is a substance which is metal and not a good conductor.* If any substance is a metal, then it is a good conductor.

Skills Objective D

In 8–11, let $r(x)$: $\frac{1}{x} = \frac{2}{x^2}$ and let $s(x)$: $x^2 = 2x$. Determine whether the given statement is true or false.

8. $\forall$ *real numbers* x, $r(x) \Rightarrow s(x)$. True
9. $\forall$ *real numbers* x, $\sim r(x) \Rightarrow \sim s(x)$. False
10. $\forall$ *real numbers* x, $s(x) \Rightarrow r(x)$. False
11. $\forall$ real numbers x, $\sim s(x) \Rightarrow \sim r(x)$. True

How is the truth value of $p \Rightarrow q$ determined by the truth values of p and q? The following example will help answer this question.

Suppose $p(x)$: $x \geq 8$ and $q(x)$: $x^2 \geq 64$. Then $p(x) \Rightarrow q(x)$ is the conditional

If $x \geq 8$*, then* $x^2 \geq 64$.

For all real numbers x, this conditional is a true statement. Now let us see what pairs of truth values are possible for $p(x)$ and $q(x)$.

The table below covers all possible values of x and the corresponding truth values for $p(x)$ and $q(x)$.

Interval	Test Point	$p(x)$: $x \geq 8$		$q(x)$: $x^2 \geq 64$	
$x \geq 8$	$x = 8$	$8 \geq 8$	T	$8^2 \geq 64$	T
$x \leq -8$	$x = -10$	$-10 \geq 8$	F	$(-10)^2 \geq 64$	T
$-8 < x < 8$	$x = 2\frac{1}{2}$	$2\frac{1}{2} \geq 8$	F	$\left(2\frac{1}{2}\right)^2 \geq 64$	F

Thus, in a true conditional it is possible to have the following truth values for the antecedent and the consequent:

antecedent	consequent
T	T
F	T
F	F

Note that a true conditional can have an antecedent which is false.

This reasoning shows that the only combination of truth values that a true conditional *cannot* have is a true antecedent and a false consequent.

Now consider the conditional

If $x \geq 8$*, then* $x^2 \geq 100$.

Are there any values of x for which this conditional is a false statement? Of course, the answer is Yes. For instance, if $x = 9$, the antecedent is $9 \geq 8$, which is true, and the consequent is $9^2 \geq 100$, which is false. The result of this analysis is the following definition of the truth value of $p \Rightarrow q$.

> **Definition**
> The statement $p \Rightarrow q$ is false whenever p is true and q is false, true in all other cases.

Just as with *not*, *and*, and *or*, this definition can be summarized in a truth table showing the truth values for *if p then q* that correspond to all possible assignments of truth values to p and q.

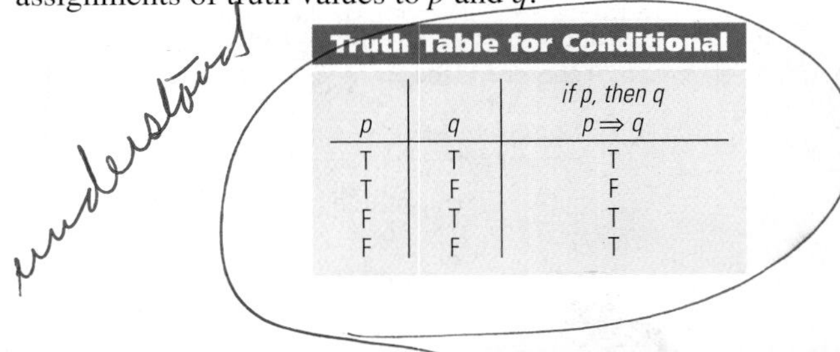

Truth Table for Conditional

p	q	if p, then q $p \Rightarrow q$
T	T	T
T	F	F
F	T	T
F	F	T

Lesson 1-5 Overview, continued

then it is a Ford. The truth of this statement can be shown by the Venn diagram below where car 1 is a Taurus. Its contrapositive, *If a car is not a Ford, then it is not a Taurus*, can also be shown to be true by via the same diagram by referring to car 2.

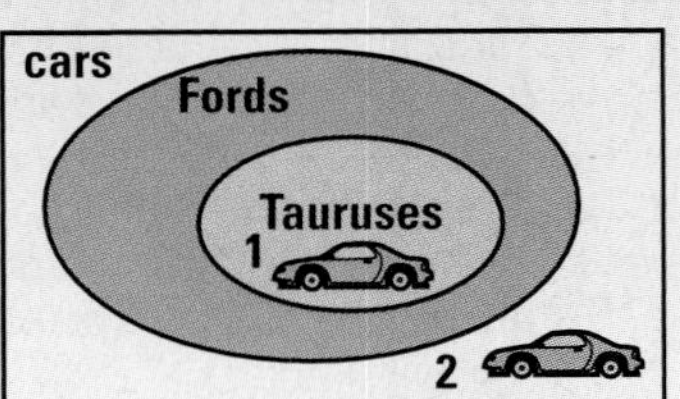

Venn diagrams can also be used to illustrate the converse and inverse. Consider the true statement *p: If a car is a Taurus, then it is a Ford.* The converse of this statement is: *If a car is a Ford, then it is a Taurus.* The diagram on page 37 helps illustrate the fact that a statement and its converse are not

Example 1

Your teacher makes you the following promise at the beginning of a course. "If your test scores total above 500, then you will get an *A* for this course." At the end of the course, your test scores total 485 and your teacher gives you an *A*. Has your teacher kept the promise? Explain why or why not.

Solution

The promise is a conditional statement. The antecedent is false (485 is not above 500) and the consequent is true (you got an A). With this combination, the conditional is true. Thus, the teacher did not break the promise, and accordingly, we could say that the teacher kept the promise.

The Negation of a Conditional

The negation of a conditional must be true exactly when the conditional is false and false when the conditional is true. Only when p is true and q is false is $p \Rightarrow q$ false. This suggests the following theorem, which can be proved using truth tables.

Theorem (Negation of a Simple Conditional)
The negation of the conditional statement

If p then q.

is

p and (not q).

Proof
Expressed symbolically, the theorem to be proved is $\sim(p \Rightarrow q) \equiv p \text{ and } (\sim q)$.

Activity

Copy the table below, complete it, and indicate what in the table proves the theorem. See Question 4 on page 41.

p	q	$p \Rightarrow q$	$\sim(p \Rightarrow q)$	$\sim q$	p and $(\sim q)$
T	T				
T	F				
F	T				
F	F				

Caution! The negation of a conditional statement is not another conditional statement. Rather, it is an *and* statement.

Students tend to have difficulty accepting the truth of a conditional statement with a false antecedent. This may be because in informal speech there are not very many instances of conditional statements with false antecedents. (Here are two: If the answer to this problem is 6, then I'm a monkey's uncle. If there were nothing in the world to eat but this, then I still would not eat this.) Students may feel that a conditional with a false antecedent should not be assigned a truth value at all—that if the antecedent is false, it does not make sense to call the conditional either true or false. Indeed, there are formalizations of logic where this possibility is explored. However, no one disputes that the only way for a sentence of the form *if p, then q* to be false is for p to be true and q to be false. It follows that for such a sentence to be a statement, it must be true in all other cases—including those for which p is false. Some people find comfort in saying that when p is false, the conditional *if p, then q* is "true by default."

equivalent. For car 1, both statement p and its converse are true. For car 2, statement p is true and its converse is false. Thus a statement may have a different truth value from its converse. Since the implication $p \Rightarrow q$ is logically equivalent to its contrapositive $\sim q \Rightarrow \sim p$, the proof of the latter implies the former is also true. This is the basis of most indirect proofs.

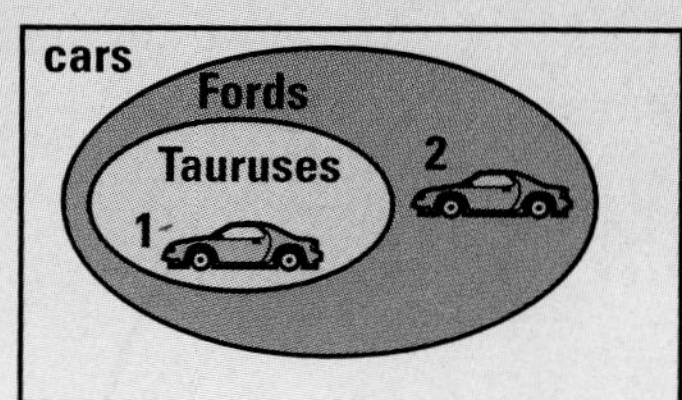

▶ LESSON MASTER 1-5 *page 2*

Properties Objective E

12. Suppose p and $p \Rightarrow q$ are both true statements. What is the truth value of q? True
13. Suppose q and $p \Rightarrow q$ are both true statements. What is the truth value of p? Cannot tell
14. *Multiple choice.* Which statement is logically equivalent to $\forall x$, *if* $p(x)$ *then* $q(x)$? c
    (a) $\exists x$ *such that* $p(x)$ *and* $\sim q(x)$. (b) $\forall x$, $p(x)$ *or* $\sim q(x)$.
    (c) $\forall x$, $\sim p(x)$ *or* $q(x)$. (d) $\forall x$, $p(x)$ *and* $q(x)$.

Uses Objective I

In 15–17, refer to the table below, which shows the types of paints that can be used on different exterior surfaces. Determine whether the given statement is true or false.

	Wood				Masonry			Metal			
	Clapboard	Shutters/trim	Window frames	Natural siding/trim	Brick	Cement/cinder block	Stucco	Metal siding	Copper surfaces	Galvanized surfaces	Iron surfaces
Latex house	✓	✓	✓		✓	✓	✓	✓		✓	✓
Alkyd house	✓	✓	✓		✓	✓	✓	✓		✓	✓
Cement powder					✓	✓	✓				
Trim		✓		✓				✓		✓	✓
Aluminum			✓		✓	✓	✓	✓		✓	✓

15. $\forall$ *paints p, if p can be used on brick then p can be used on metal siding.* False
16. $\forall$ *surfaces s, a latex paint can be used on s if and only if an alkyd paint can be used on s.* True

Representations Objective L

17. Complete the truth table for $p \Rightarrow (s \text{ or } r)$.

p	s	r	s or r	$p \Rightarrow (s \text{ or } r)$
F	F	F	F	T
F	F	T	T	T
F	T	F	T	T
F	T	T	T	T
T	F	F	F	F
T	F	T	T	T
T	T	F	T	T
T	T	T	T	T

If you wish huge groans from your class, you might ask your students the following rhetorical questions. Did you know that people who write *inverse* are poets? Or that poetry written by prisoners is called *converse*?

In the discussion of *if and only if* on page 40 stress the following: (1) *p if and only if q* is often expressed as *p is a necessary and sufficient condition for q.* (2) Two *if-then* statements are contained within this one compound statement.

The negation of a conditional is often confusing to students. It is important that they realize that the negation is not another conditional but is an *and* statement. Have students give the negations of several conditionals aloud, emphasizing the word *and.* Here is an additional example: *If Sara is taking this course, then Sara is a senior.* (negation: Sara is taking this course and is not a senior.)

You may wish to write the Negation of a Universal Conditional more symbolically:

$\sim(\forall\ x,\ p(x) \Rightarrow q(x)) \equiv \exists\ x$ such that $p(x)$ and $\sim q(x)$.

An example is: If a country has sent a person to the moon, then that country is the United States. Negation: There is a country that has sent a person to the moon and is not the United States. (The original statement is true; it's negation is consequently false.)

Example 2

Write the negation of the conditional statement

If Andrew lives in Springfield, then Andrew lives in Massachusetts.

Solution

Let *p: Andrew lives in Springfield.* and *q: Andrew lives in Massachusetts.* The given statement is a conditional of the form *if p then q.* Therefore, its negation has the form *p and (not q).*

Andrew lives in Springfield and Andrew does not live in Massachusetts.

One of the most important types of statements in mathematics is both conditional and universal. It has the form

$$\forall\ x \text{ in } S, \text{ if } p(x), \text{ then } q(x).$$

For instance, the following universal conditional statement is true.

$$\forall \text{ positive real numbers } x, \text{ if } x^2 > 9, \text{ then } x > 3.$$

But enlarge the domain of x to be the set of all real numbers, and the statement becomes false.

$$\forall \text{ real numbers } x, \text{ if } x^2 > 9, \text{ then } x > 3.$$

The reason that this second statement is false is that there are values of x (for example $x = -4$) for which the antecedent is true ($(-4)^2 > 9$ is true) and the consequent false ($-4 > 3$ is false). Because of the definition of truth and falsity of a conditional, the conditional is false, and so the conditional is not true $\forall$ real numbers x. As with simpler universal statements, -4 is called a *counterexample.*

The theorem below states this idea symbolically: a universal conditional is false if and only if a counterexample exists.

Theorem (Negation of a Universal Conditional)
Let S be a set and let $p(x)$ and $q(x)$ be statements that may or may not hold for elements x in S. The negation of

$$\forall\ x \text{ in } S, \text{ if } p(x) \text{ then } q(x).$$

is

$$\exists\ x \text{ in } S \text{ such that } p(x) \text{ and not } q(x).$$

Example 3

Consider the following statement

$$\forall \text{ real numbers } a \text{ and } b, \text{ if } a < b \text{ then } \cos a < \cos b.$$

a. Write the negation of this statement.
b. Is the given statement true or false? If false, give a counterexample.

Optional Activities

Activity 1 Technology Connection
Materials: Explorations software

You may use *Exploration 1-5, Equivalent Statements,* to introduce equivalency of logic statements. Students choose two statements to display. The program shows the related incomplete truth tables. Students test for equivalency by filling in the tables and comparing the final output of each case.

Activity 2 After discussing this lesson, and as a brief review of the previous lesson, have the class construct a logic network for *if p, then q,* based on its truth table.

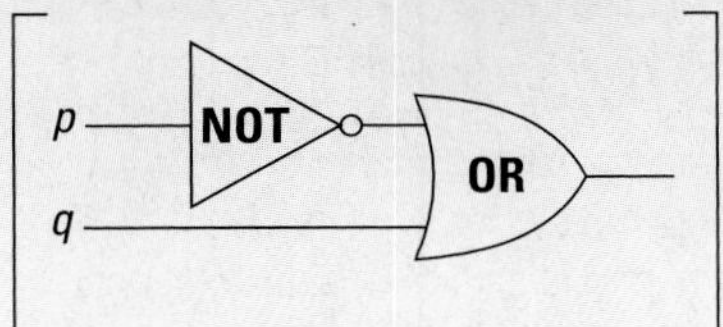

Activity 3 Cooperative Learning
You might have students **work in groups** to find a conditional statement whose converse, inverse, and contrapositive are all true. [Sample: If a triangle has three congruent sides, then it is equilateral. Converse: If a triangle is equilateral, then it has three congruent sides. Inverse: If a triangle does not have three congruent sides, then it is not equilateral.

Solution

a. The negation of the given statement is
∃ real numbers a and b such that $a < b$ and $\cos a \not< \cos b$.

b. The given statement is false. As a counterexample, let $a = 0$ and $b = \frac{\pi}{2}$. Then $a < b$ because $0 < \frac{\pi}{2}$, but $\cos a \not< \cos b$ because $\cos a = \cos 0 = 1$, $\cos b = \cos \frac{\pi}{2} = 0$, and $1 \not< 0$.

The Contrapositive of a Conditional

A conditional statement is sometimes proved by establishing its *contrapositive*.

Definitions
The **contrapositive** of $p \Rightarrow q$ is $\sim q \Rightarrow \sim p$.
The **contrapositive** of ∀ *x in S, if p(x) then q(x).*
is ∀ *x in S, if* $\sim q(x)$ *then* $\sim p(x)$.

The table below shows that the truth values of the conditional statement $p \Rightarrow q$ and its contrapositive $(\sim q) \Rightarrow (\sim p)$ are the same.

p	q	$p \Rightarrow q$	$\sim q$	$\sim p$	$(\sim q) \Rightarrow (\sim p)$
T	T	T	F	F	T
T	F	F	T	F	F
F	T	T	F	T	T
F	F	T	T	T	T

same truth values

The truth table above proves the following theorem.

Contrapositive Theorem
A conditional and its contrapositive are logically equivalent. That is, they always have the same truth values.

Example 4

State the contrapositive of the following statement and determine whether the contrapositive is true or false.

$$\forall \text{ real numbers } a, \text{ if } a^2 = 10, \text{ then } a^6 = 1000.$$

Solution

The contrapositive is

$$\forall \text{ real numbers } a, \text{ if } a^6 \neq 1000, \text{ then } a^2 \neq 10.$$

Because the original statement is true, the contrapositive is also true.

Additional Examples

1. Write the negation of the conditional statement: *If Tom is a Packers fan, then he loves the Bears.* **Tom is a Packers fan and he does not love the Bears.**
2. Consider the following statement ∀ *real numbers x and y, if* $x < y$, *then* $|x| < |y|$.
   a. Write the negation of this statement. **∃ *real numbers x and y such that*** $x < y$ ***and*** $|x| \geq |y|$.
   b. Is the given statement true or false? If false, give a counterexample. **The given statement is false. As a counterexample, let** $x = -10$ **and** $y = 1$. **Then** $x < y$ **because** $-10 < 1$, **but** $|x| \geq |y|$ **because** $|-10| \geq |1|$.
3. State the contrapositive of the statement and determine whether the contrapositive is true or false.
   a. ∀ real numbers a, if $a > 1$, then $a^2 > a$. **The contrapositive is ∀ real numbers** a, **if** $a^2 \leq a$, **then** $a \leq 1$. **Because the original statement is true, the contrapositive is also true.**
   b. ∀ real numbers b, if $\sqrt{b} = 3$, then $b^2 = 81$. **The contrapositive is ∀ real numbers** b, **if** $b^2 \neq 81$, **then** $\sqrt{b} \neq 3$. **Because the original statement is true, the contrapositive is also true.**

(Additional Examples continue on page 40.)

Contrapositive: If a triangle is not equilateral, then it does not have three congruent sides.]

Adapting to Individual Needs

Extra Help

If some students are having difficulty with the negation of a conditional, refer back to the conditional in **Example 1.** Let *p: Your test scores total above 500* and *q: You will get an A for the course.* The negation of if p then q is p and $(\sim q)$, which, in this case, is *Your test scores total over 500 and you will not get an A in the course.* Hence, the negation of the teacher's promise is a broken promise.

4. Give the converse and inverse of the universal conditional
∀ *functions f and real numbers x, if f(2x) = 2f(x), then f(4x) = 4f(x).*
Its converse is ∀ *functions f and real numbers x, if f(4x) = 4f(x), then f(2x) = 2f(x).* Its inverse is ∀ *functions f and real numbers x, if f(2x) ≠ 2f(x), then f(4x) ≠ 4f(x).*

5. Break the biconditional of the given definition into its two conditionals.
   a. ∀ functions *f* and real numbers *a*, *f*(*a*) = 0 if and only if *a* is a real zero of *f*.
   **∀ functions *f* and real numbers *a*, if *f*(*a*) = 0, then *a* is a real zero of *f*.
   ∀ functions *f* and real numbers *a*, if *a* is a real zero of *f*, then *f*(*a*) = 0.**
   b. ∀ angles *A* and *B*, *A* and *B* are complementary angles if and only if the sum of their measures is 90°. **∀ angles *A* and *B*, if *A* and *B* are complementary angles, then the sum of their measures is 90°. ∀ angles *A* and *B*, if the sum of their measures is 90°, then *A* and *B* are complementary angles.**

The Converse and the Inverse of a Conditional

By either negating or switching the antecedent and consequent of a conditional, but not doing both, two other conditionals are formed.

Definitions
Let $p \Rightarrow q$ be a conditional.
The **converse** of $p \Rightarrow q$ is $q \Rightarrow p$.
The **converse** of ∀ *x in S, if p(x) then q(x).*
is ∀ *x in S, if q(x) then p(x).*
The **inverse** of $p \Rightarrow q$ is $\sim p \Rightarrow \sim q$.
The **inverse** of ∀ *x in S, if p(x) then q(x).*
is ∀ *x in S, if ~p(x) then ~q(x).*

Converses and inverses of universal statements may seem to be similar to contrapositives. But, unlike the contrapositive, neither the converse nor the inverse of a true conditional needs to be true if the original conditional is true.

Example 5

Give the converse and inverse of the universal conditional

∀ *functions f, if f is the cosine function, then f(0) = 1.*

Solution

Its converse is

∀ functions f, if f(0) = 1, then f is the cosine function.

Its inverse is

∀ functions f, if f is not the cosine function, then f(0) ≠ 1.

The original conditional is true because cos 0 = 1. But the converse is not true. There are many functions f with $f(0) = 1$ that are not the cosine function. One is the function f defined by $f(x) = 3x + 1$ for all real numbers x. This same function is a counterexample that shows the inverse is not true either.

Biconditional Statements

Given statements p and q,

p if and only if q

means

(if p then q) and (if q then p)

or, symbolically,

$$p \Rightarrow q \text{ and } q \Rightarrow p.$$

This is naturally written

$$p \Leftrightarrow q$$

and is called a **biconditional**. All definitions are biconditionals.

Adapting to Individual Needs

Challenge
Have students read the programming chapter of the manual for a programmable calculator. Then have them write a program using computer conditional statements such as a program that would solve the quadratic equation: $ax^2 + bx + c = 0$. [Exact program notation will vary with calculator, but the program should input the values of a, b, and c. The conditional step should display the following if $b^2 - 4ac$ is nonnegative:
$\frac{-b + \sqrt{b^2 - 4ac}}{2a}$ and $\frac{-b - \sqrt{b^2 - 4ac}}{2a}$,
and the following if $b^2 - 4ac$ is negative:
$\frac{-b - \sqrt{4ac - b^2}\,i}{2a}$ and $\frac{-b + \sqrt{4ac - b^2}\,i}{2a}$.]

Example 6

Here is the definition of logarithm with base 2. Break this biconditional into its two conditionals.

$\forall$ *positive real numbers x,* $\log_2 x = y$ *if and only if* $2^y = x$.

Solution

$\forall$ positive real numbers x, if $\log_2 x = y$ then $2^y = x$.
$\forall$ positive real numbers x, if $2^y = x$ then $\log_2 x = y$.

Some additional language associated with conditionals and biconditionals is found in Questions 19–21.

QUESTIONS

Covering the Reading

1. Let x be a real number. Consider the following conditional:

   If $x > 1$ *then* $2x^2 + 3x^3 > 1$.

   a. Identify the antecedent, the conclusion, the consequent, and the hypothesis. **antecedent, hypothesis = $x > 1$; conclusion, consequent = $2x^2 + 3x^3 > 1$**

   b. Is the conditional true, or is it false? **True**

2. *Multiple choice.* Consider the statement

   If Sandra is on the swim team, then she swims every day. **b**

   Which would tell you that the statement is false?
   (a) *Sandra is not on the swim team and she swims every day.*
   (b) *Sandra is on the swim team and she does not swim every day.*
   (c) *Sandra is not on the swim team and she does not swim every day.*

3. *True or false.* The negation of

   $\forall$ *real numbers x, if* $2x - 1 > 5$ *then* $x > 2$.

   is

   $\exists$ *a real number x such that* $2x - 1 > 5$ *and* $x > 2$.

   False

4. Indicate what you wrote for the Activity in this lesson. **See margin.**

In 5 and 6, determine whether the conditional is true or false. If false, give a counterexample.

5. *If a quadrilateral is a square, then it is a parallelogram.* **True**

6. $\forall$ *real numbers x, if* $\frac{\pi}{2} < x$ *then* $\cos x$ *is negative.* **See left.**

7. Choose the correct word. The (contrapositive, inverse, converse) of

   If $e^x = e^y$ *then* $x = y$. is *If* $e^x \neq e^y$ *then* $x \neq y$.

   inverse

In 8 and 9, a conditional is given. **a.** Write its contrapositive. **b.** Determine whether or not the contrapositive is true. **See left.**

8. *If the graph of* $y = mx + b$ *is an oblique line, then* $m \neq 0$.

9. *If a quadrilateral has two sides of equal length, then the quadrilateral has two angles of equal measure.*

6) False. Counterexample: Let $x = 2\pi$; $\cos x = 1$, which is not negative.

8a) *If $m = 0$, the graph of $y = mx + b$ is not an oblique line.*
b) True

9a) *If a quadrilateral does not have two angles of equal measure, then the quadrilateral does not have two sides of equal length.*
b) False

Notes on Questions

Question 1a This question asks for the same information twice, in order to familiarize students with all four terms.

Additional Answers

4.

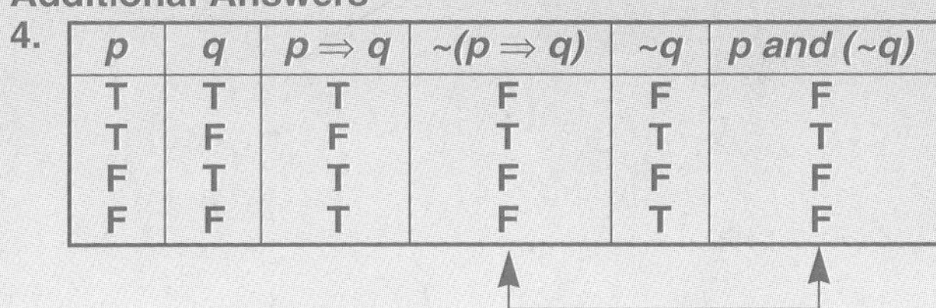

p	q	$p \Rightarrow q$	$\sim(p \Rightarrow q)$	$\sim q$	p and $(\sim q)$
T	T	T	F	F	F
T	F	F	T	T	T
F	T	T	F	F	F
F	F	T	F	T	F

same truth values

Notes on Questions

Question 10 Students may enjoy discussing the truth values of the converse and inverse of the statement *If it rains, then I carry an umbrella.*

Question 13 Some students will find that examining the truth or falsity of the negation of each statement is easier than looking at the original statement. Finding a counterexample to a false statement is often easier than proving a true statement.

Question 18 This question is the topic of the *Extension* on page 43.

Question 19 Use of the contrapositive may assist students in understanding why *p only if q* is equivalent to *if p then q*. It is usually not difficult to convince students that *p only if q* is equivalent to *if (not q) then (not p)*. For instance, *Hal can make the team only if he gains ten pounds* is equivalent to *If Hal does not gain ten pounds, then he cannot make the team. If (not q) then (not p)* is equivalent to its contrapositive *if p then q*. Thus *p only if q* is equivalent to *if p then q*.

Questions 20–21 Point out that to say that *p is a necessary and sufficient condition for q* is equivalent to saying *p if and only if q*. We expect students to learn the meanings of these terms.

Students might compare the condition in **Question 21** with the conditions in your school.

10) Converse: *If it will rain tomorrow, then it will rain today.* Inverse: *If it does not rain today, then it will not rain tomorrow.*

11) *If two supplementary angles are congruent, then they are right angles. If two supplementary angles are right angles, then they are congruent.*

15) *If one has been convicted of a felony, then that person is not allowed to vote.*

17a) *If Jon wasn't at the scene of the crime, then Jon didn't commit the crime.*
b) If one has a true alibi, then one is innocent.

Tracking Data and Relay Satellite (TDRS) as it is released from Discovery's cargo bay

10. Write the converse and inverse of

If it rains today, then it will rain tomorrow.

See left.

11. Given the statement

Two supplementary angles are congruent if and only if they are right angles.

Write two *if-then* conditionals contained in this statement.
See left.

12. Use the Law of Substitution and the definition of logarithm to complete this sentence:

If $2^5 = 32$, *then* ___?___. $\log_2 32 = 5$

Applying the Mathematics

13. Suppose that $p(n)$ and $q(n)$ are the sentences

$p(n)$: *n is a prime number.*

$q(n)$: *n is an odd number.*

Determine the truth or falsity of each statement.

a. $\forall$ *positive integers n*, $p(n) \Rightarrow q(n)$. False

b. $\forall$ *positive integers n*, $q(n) \Rightarrow p(n)$. False

14. Let $p(x)$ be *If* $|x| > 6$, *then* $x > 5$.

a. Is $p(7)$ true? yes **b.** Is $p(-7)$ true? no

c. Is $p(2)$ true? yes **d.** Is $p(x)$ true for all real numbers x? no

In 15 and 16, rewrite each statement in *if-then* form.

15. *No one who has been convicted of a felony is allowed to vote.* See left.

16. *Those who can, do.* If one can, then one does.

17. Consider the statement

If Jon committed the crime, then Jon was at the scene of the crime.

a. Write the contrapositive.

b. What is the legal significance of the contrapositive?

See left.

18. Show by a truth table that $p \Rightarrow q$ is not logically equivalent to $q \Rightarrow p$.
See margin.

19. The statement p **only if** q is logically equivalent to *if p then q*. Rewrite the following statement in *if-then* form:

A satellite can stay in orbit only if it is at a height of at least 200 miles above the earth.

See margin.

20. "p is a **sufficient condition** for q" is another way of saying $p \Rightarrow q$. Write the following statement in *if-then* form:

Having the form 2k for some integer k is a sufficient condition for an integer to be even.

See margin.

21. "p is a **necessary condition** for q" is another way of saying $q \Rightarrow p$. Consider the following rule:

Having a GPA of at least 3.5 is a necessary condition for being elected to the honor society.

Write this statement in *if-then* form.
See margin.

Additional Answers

18.

p	q	$p \Rightarrow q$	$q \Rightarrow p$
T	T	T	T
T	F	F	T
F	T	T	F
F	F	T	T

not equivalent

19. If a satellite can stay in orbit, then it is at a height of at least 200 miles above the earth.
20. If an integer is of the form $2k$ for some integer k, then it is even.
21. If one is elected to the honor society, then one's GPA is at least 3.5.

22. IF-THEN statements in computer programs have the form IF *condition* THEN *action*. If the condition is satisfied, then the action is performed. If the condition is not satisfied, then the execution of the program moves to the next statement following the IF-THEN statement. Consider the program below.

```
10 INPUT N
20 IF N > 0 THEN PRINT N, LOG(N)
30 IF N <= 0 THEN PRINT N, "THE LOG IS UNDEFINED"
40 STOP
```

Determine the output for each input value of N.

a. N = 1000 1000, 3 **b.** N = -50 -50 THE LOG IS UNDEFINED **c.** N = 0.1 0.1, -1

Review

23. Complete the input-output table for the logic network below. *(Lesson 1-4)*

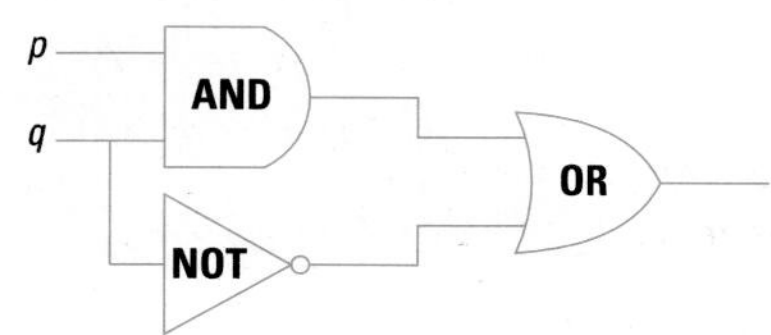

p	q	p AND q	NOT q	(p AND q) OR (NOT q)
1	1	1	0	1
1	0	0	1	1
0	1	0	0	0
0	0	0	1	1

24. Compute the output signal for the logic network below for each of the following input signals. *(Lesson 1-4)*

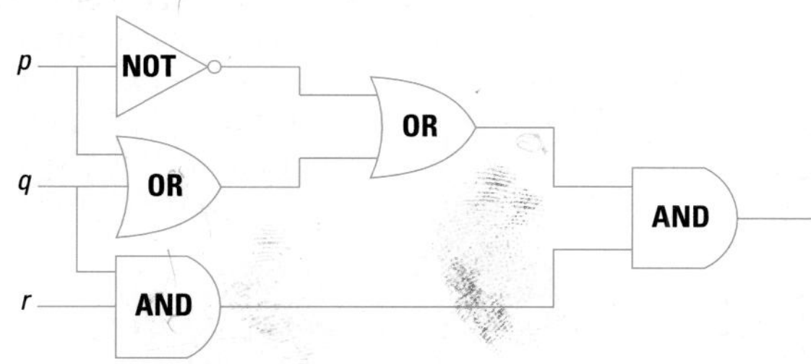

a. $p = 1, q = 1, r = 1$ 1 **b.** $p = 0, q = 1, r = 1$ 1 **c.** $p = 1, q = 0, r = 1$ 0

25. Let x be a real number. Given the double inequality $-5 < x \leq 2$.

a. Fill in the blank with *and*, *or*, or *not* to make the sentence equivalent to the given inequality.

$$-5 < x \;\underline{\ ?\ }\; x \leq 2$$ and

b. Write the negation of the sentence in part **a.** $-5 \geq x$ or $x > 2$

c. Graph on the number line the values of x which make the statement in part **b** true. *(Previous course, Lesson 1-3)*

-5 0 2 x

Exploration

26. Find a source for each of the four conditionals which begin this lesson. See margin.

Additional Answers

26. a. *Peggy Sue*, Buddy Holly
b. *If I Loved You*, from *Carousel*, Rodgers and Hammerstein
c. *If I Had a Hammer*, Peter, Paul and Mary
d. *Man in the Mirror*, Michael Jackson

Question 22 Some versions of BASIC have an IF...THEN...ELSE construct that would allow lines 20 and 30 to be combined into the one statement.

```
20 IF N > 0 THEN PRINT N, LOG(N)
   ELSE PRINT N, "THE LOG IS UNDEFINED"
```

Question 25 You might ask students to graph all solutions to the original compound inequality and compare the graph obtained with the graph of **part c.**

Follow-up for Lesson 1-5

Practice

For more questions on SPUR Objectives, use **Lesson Master 1-5** (shown on pages 36–37).

Assessment

Written Communication Have students work with a partner. Ask each student to write an *if-then* statement in ordinary language. Then ask students to write the negation, the inverse, the converse, and the contrapositive of their partner's statement. (Students write the negation, inverse, converse, and contrapositive of a conditional statement.)

Extension

Extend **Question 18** by asking students to show by truth tables that $p \Rightarrow q$ is not logically equivalent to $\sim p \Rightarrow \sim q$. Then have them compare their results with their results to **Question 18** and have them explain why $\sim p \Rightarrow \sim q$ is logically equivalent to $q \Rightarrow p$. [The contrapositive of $\sim p \Rightarrow \sim q$ is $q \Rightarrow p$, and vice-versa. So, the contrapositive of the inverse is the converse and vice-versa. As a result, there is a corollary to the Contrapositive Theorem on page 39: the converse and the inverse of a conditional are logically equivalent.]

Project Update Project 4, *Logic and Programming*, on page 67, relates to the content of this lesson.

Lesson 1-6

Objectives

G Determine whether arguments are valid or invalid.
H Use logic to prove or disprove statements.
J Determine whether or not a logical argument outside of mathematics is valid.

Resources

From the ***Teacher's Resource File***
- Lesson Master 1-6
- Answer Master 1-6
- Technology Sourcebook
- Teaching Aids
  3 Warm-up
  11 Valid Forms of Arguments

Additional Resources
- Visuals for Teaching Aids 3, 11

Teaching Lesson 1-6

Warm-up

Order these statements to put together a logical argument and state its conclusion.

A. If a convex polygon has seven sides, then it is a heptagon.
B. If the sum of the measures of the interior angles of a convex polygon is 900°, then the polygon must have at least 4 obtuse angles.
C. If a convex polygon has seven vertices, then it has 7 sides.
D. If a convex polygon is a heptagon, then the sum of the measures of its interior angles is 900°.

LESSON 1-6 *Valid Arguments*

A Great Catch. *Solving a Lewis Carroll puzzle is not as difficult as performing some acrobatic feats. See Question 14.*

❶ A major reason to study logic is to help you make correct inferences or deductions and to help you determine when others have made false deductions. Lewis Carroll (the pseudonym of Charles Lutwidge Dodgson, 1832–1898, an English mathematician, logician, and minister), who is best known as the author of *Alice in Wonderland*, also published two books of logical puzzles. The following problem is adapted from one of those books.

Consider the sentences:

(1) *When I work a logic example without grumbling, you may be sure it is one I can understand.*

(2) *This example is not arranged in regular order like the ones I am used to.*

(3) *No easy examples give me a headache.*

(4) *I can't understand an example that is not arranged in regular order like the ones I am used to.*

(5) *I grumble when I work an example only if I get a headache.*

Suppose each of sentences (1)–(5) is true. Must the following conclusion also be true?

(6) *This example is not easy.*

We will give the answer to this puzzle at the end of this lesson. But first we develop general methods to help solve it.

Lesson 1-6 Overview

Broad Goals Three valid argument forms are introduced in this lesson: Modus Ponens, or Law of Detachment; the Law of Transitivity; and Modus Tollens, or Law of Indirect Reasoning. (The principles behind the forms are more important than the names of the forms.) These three forms are the basis for most of the proofs students will encounter in this book. They are proved valid using truth tables.

Perspective Students who have studied from UCSMP *Geometry* or some other books will have seen the simple forms of the Law of Detachment and the Law of Transitivity.

In the lesson, we have chosen to demonstrate the validity of an argument form via truth tables. You may also want to use Venn diagrams to illustrate the validity of argument forms. For instance, consider the following argument:

If a pie contains apples, then it is a fruit pie.
This pie contains apples.
∴ *This pie is a fruit pie.*

Analysis of the Venn diagram at the right shows that if both premises are true, the conclusion must also be true.

❷ What Is an Argument?

In logic and mathematics, an argument is not a dispute. An **argument** is a sequence of statements in which all but the final statement are called **premises,** and the final statement is called the **conclusion.** Usually the word *therefore,* or some synonym, or the shorthand symbol ∴ (read "therefore"), is written just before the conclusion.

Consider the following two arguments:

(a) *If Jane solved the problem correctly, then Jane got the answer 10.*
Jane solved the problem correctly.
∴ *Jane got the answer 10.*

(b) *For all real numbers x, if* $x > 3$, *then* $2x^2 - x - 15 > 0$.
$\pi > 3$
∴ $2\pi^2 - \pi - 15 > 0$

Although the subject matters of arguments (a) and (b) are very different, the forms of the arguments are very similar. In each argument, one premise is a conditional statement and the other premise is its antecedent. The conclusion is the consequent. Here are the forms.

Argument (a)	Argument (b)
Simple Form	Universal Form
If p then q	$\forall$ *x, if p(x) then q(x).*
p	*p(c), for a particular c.*
∴ *q*	∴ *q(c).*

The Law of Detachment

The simple form has a very important property: no matter what statements are substituted in place of *p* and *q* in the premises, the truth value of the form is true. The universal form has a similar property: no matter what conditions are substituted in place of *p(x)* and *q(x)* in the premises, the truth value of the form is true. Any form of argument having such a property is called *valid.*

> **Definition**
> An argument form is **valid** if and only if the form is true regardless of the truth or falsity of the statements in it.

Another way of thinking of a valid argument is that in such an argument, if all premises are true, so is the conclusion. Otherwise we would have $p \Rightarrow q$ with *p* true and *q* false, so the form would be false.

The fact that forms (a) and (b) are valid is called the *Law of Detachment* (because the antecedent is detached from the conditional) or *modus ponens* (which is Latin for "method of affirming").

We prove the validity for the simple form of the Law of Detachment on page 46; proving the validity of the universal form requires a technique beyond the scope of this book.

Order: C, A, D, B: If a convex polygon has seven vertices, then the polygon must have at least 4 obtuse angles.

Notes on Reading

Valid forms of arguments (the three theorems of this lesson) are shown on **Teaching Aid 11**.

❶ **Literature Connection** Charles Lutwidge Dodgson published mathematical works under his real name, but he chose the pseudonym "Lewis Carroll" for less serious writings. "Lewis Carroll" came from *Carolus Ludovicus*, the Latin version of Charles Lutwidge.

❷ We begin this paragraph by saying "In logic and mathematics." Logic is often considered to be a branch of mathematics although it is also claimed as a branch of philosophy. Some of your students might be interested in investigating how different a college-level logic course in philosophy might be from a logic course in mathematics.

Students often equate valid arguments with true conclusions. Emphasize that the structure of an argument determines its validity. A valid argument with a false premise can have a false conclusion. See the *Overview* below.

You can use the truth table proof of Modus Ponens (the Law of Detachment) to emphasize that an argument is valid if whenever the premises are true, then the conclusion is also true. If the truth table for an argument contains a row of true premises followed by a false conclusion, then the argument is invalid.

Now consider the following argument.
If a pie is a fruit pie, then it contains apples.
A pie is a fruit pie.
∴ *The pie contains apples.*

This argument has the same form as the first one and is therefore also valid. However, while the conclusion of this argument is valid, it need not be true. There are many examples of fruit pies that do not contain apples. Of course, the reason that a false conclusion can be deduced from this valid argument is that the first premise of the argument is false. Consideration of these two arguments may help students distinguish between *valid* conclusions and *true* conclusions.

To help make Modus Tollens (the Law of Indirect Reasoning) reasonable to students who accept Modus Ponens, you may wish to make a connection between these forms of argument and the fact that *if p, then q* is equivalent to *if not q, then not p*. Students already know that a conditional and its contrapositive are equivalent. The validity of the Modus Tollens argument form can be deduced from Modus Ponens and the equivalence of a statement and its contrapositive, as follows:

Given $p \Rightarrow q$
$\sim q$

we can deduce
$\sim q \Rightarrow \sim p$
$\sim q$

by the equivalence between a conditional and its contrapositive. $\sim p$ follows by Modus Ponens.

You may wish to relate the Law of Transitivity to the transitive property of equality.

If $a = b$ and $b = c$, then $a = c$,

or to the transitive property of inequality:

If $a < b$ and $b < c$, then $a < c$.

Mathematics contains many examples of transitive properties.

Theorem (Modus Ponens or Law of Detachment)
The following are valid forms of argument:

Simple Form	Universal Form
If p then q.	*$\forall$ x, if p(x) then q(x).*
p	*p(c), for a particular c.*
$\therefore$ *q*	$\therefore$ *q(c)*

Proof
The premises are $(p \Rightarrow q)$ and p. To prove the Law of Detachment, we must show that the conditional

$$((p \Rightarrow q) \text{ and } p) \Rightarrow q$$

is always true. So we construct a truth table showing all possible truth values for p and q. Then we give truth values for the premises, the conclusion, and the argument form. Because all the rows in the form column are true, the argument is valid.

		premises	premises		conclusion	form
p	q	$p \Rightarrow q$	p	$(p \Rightarrow q)$ and p	q	$((p \Rightarrow q)$ and $p) \Rightarrow q$
T	T	T	T	T	T	T
T	F	F	T	F	F	T
F	T	T	F	F	T	T
F	F	T	F	F	F	T

Must the Result of a Valid Argument Be True?

The conclusion of a valid argument is called a **valid conclusion**. In a valid argument, the truth of the premises guarantees the truth of the conclusion. However, if one of the premises is false, then the conclusion, while valid, may be false. Thus, a *valid* conclusion is not necessarily a *true* conclusion.

Consider the following argument:

If a country has over 200 million people, then it imports more than it exports.
Japan has over 200 million people.
$\therefore$ *Japan imports more than it exports.*

The argument is valid (by the Law of Detachment), but the conclusion is false. In this case, neither premise is true. In general, even clear thinking from false premises is risky. Do not trust conclusions unless you are certain of the premises from which they are made.

The Law of Transitivity

The Law of Detachment enables you to make a single deduction. A second form of valid argument allows you to build chains of deductions. From the premises

If a figure is a square, then it is a parallelogram.
If a figure is a parallelogram, then its diagonals bisect each other.

you can deduce

If a figure is a square, then its diagonals bisect each other.

Optional Activities

Writing You might use this activity after students have completed the lesson. Have students write an explanation for why a conclusion to an argument can be valid but not necessarily true. They should produce other examples similar to the one on page 46 to support their explanation. [Most importantly, a valid argument depends on its structure. Three valid structures for arguments are shown in this lesson, all of which will produce valid conclusions. However, if one or more of the premises in the argument is false, the conclusion may be false even though the argument is still valid. Example: If a person lives on my block, then the person goes to my high school. Susan lives on my block. $\therefore$ She goes to my high school. The conclusion is valid by the Law of Detachment, but not necessarily true.]

This fact exemplifies the *Law of Transitivity*. The Law of Transitivity allows you to deduce an *if-then* statement.

Theorem (The Law of Transitivity)
The following are valid forms of argument:

Simple form	Universal form
If p then q.	*$\forall$ x, if p(x), then q(x).*
If q then r.	*$\forall$ x, if q(x), then r(x).*
$\therefore$ *If p then r.*	$\therefore$ *$\forall$ x, if p(x), then r(x).*

Again, the proof of this theorem is given only for the simple form.

Proof
First, write the argument form as a conditional.

$$((p \Rightarrow q) \text{ and } (q \Rightarrow r)) \Rightarrow (p \Rightarrow r)$$

Now construct a truth table and show that this conditional is always true. Because there are three statements *p*, *q*, and *r*, the table has 8 rows.

p	q	r	$p \Rightarrow q$	$q \Rightarrow r$	$(p \Rightarrow q)$ and $(q \Rightarrow r)$	$p \Rightarrow r$	$((p \Rightarrow q)$ and $(q \Rightarrow r)) \Rightarrow (p \Rightarrow r)$
T	T	T					
T	T	F					
T	F	T	F	T	F	T	T
T	F	F					
F	T	T					
F	T	F					
F	F	T					
F	F	F					

Activity

We leave it to you to complete this table and finish the proof.
See Question 8 on page 50.

Recognizing the form of an argument is an important step in determining whether an argument is valid or not.

Example 1

Write the form of the following argument:

$\forall$ polygons x, if x is a hexagon, then the sum of the measures of the interior angles of x is 720°.
A particular polygon c has an angle sum of 540°.
$\therefore$ *c is not a hexagon.*

Solution

Let *p*(*x*) and *q*(*x*) represent the following statements:

p(x): x is a hexagon.
q(x): the sum of the measures of the interior angles of x is 720°.

Error Alert Some students have difficulty labeling a statement of fact with *p* or *q*. Stress the relationship of a statement such as *Jane solved the problem correctly* to the property part in the definition of a universal statement on page 7.

Technology You can use a graphing calculator to demonstrate examples such as: *If a point (x, y) is in the third quadrant, then 3x + 2y < 5. (-2, -5) is in quadrant III. Hence, 3(-2) + 2(-5) < 5.*

LESSON MASTER 1-6
Questions on SPUR Objectives
See pages 71–75 for objectives.

Properties Objective G

In 1–3, supply the missing premise so that the argument is valid.

1. $s \Rightarrow t$
   $\sim t$
   $\therefore \sim s$

2. $n \Rightarrow q$
   $q \Rightarrow r$
   $\therefore n \Rightarrow r$

3. $a \Rightarrow b$
   a
   $\therefore b$

Properties Objective H

In 4–6, draw a valid conclusion from the given premises and state whether the conclusion is true or false. If the conclusion is false, circle the false premise or premises.

4. *$\forall$ integers $n \geq 1$, if n is not prime then n has a factor less than or equal to $\sqrt{n}$. 101 has no factor less than or equal to $\sqrt{101}$.*
   101 is prime; true

5. *If a quadrilateral's diagonals are not perpendicular, then it is not a kite. If a quadrilateral is not a kite, then it is not a rhombus.* If a quadrilateral's diagonals are not perpendicular, then it is not a rhombus. True

6. *$\forall$ x and y, if x and y are irrational numbers then their product is an irrational number. π and $\frac{1}{\pi}$ are irrational numbers.*
   $\pi \cdot \frac{1}{\pi} = 1$ is irrational; false.

Uses Objective J

In 7 and 8, tell whether the argument uses the Law of Detachment (modus ponens), the Law of Indirect Reasoning (modus tollens), or the Law of Transitivity.

7. *The movie that wins the Academy Award for "Best Picture" is the most critically acclaimed movie of the year.* Titanic *won the Academy Award for "Best Picture" of 1997. So* Titanic *was the most critically acclaimed movie for that year.*
   Law of Detachment

8. *If we do not increase federal funding for education, our nation's students will not be prepared for the jobs of the 21st century. And if they are not prepared for the jobs of the 21st century, America will not be able to compete in the global marketplace. America will not be able to compete in the global marketplace, if we do not increase federal funding for education.*
   Law of Transitivity

Adapting to Individual Needs

Extra Help
If students are confused about the entries in the first three columns of the truth table above the Activity on page 47, remind them that every possible combination of truth values for the three statements, *p*, *q*, and *r*, must be considered. In Lesson 1-3, you may have discussed that if there are *n* statements, there are 2^n possible combinations. Hence, in this case, there are $2^3 = 8$ possible combinations. Students can verify this with a tree diagram. The particular order of Ts and Fs used in these three columns follows convention: In column 1, the values alternate in groups of 4; in column 2 in groups of 2, and in column 1 in groups of 1. (Following this pattern, if there were 4 statements, column 1 would alternate in groups of 8, column 2, in groups of 4; column 3 in groups of 2, and column 4 in groups of 1.)

③ The solution to the Lewis Carroll puzzle on page 44 can be accomplished in two ways: (1) one conditional by using the Law of Transitivity and then applying the use of the Law of Detachment; or (2) repeated application of the Law of Detachment. Students need to realize that either way is acceptable; there is no one correct way to complete the problem.

Here is another Lewis Carroll puzzle that you might want to do with your class:

Babies are illogical.
Nobody is despised who can manage a crocodile.
Illogical persons are despised.
∴ *All babies are incapable of managing crocodiles.*

An alternative conclusion is
A person able to manage a crocodile is no baby.

Then the argument has the following form.

$\forall$ x, if p(x) then q(x).
not q(c), for a particular c.
∴ not p(c).

The form of the argument in Example 1 is called *modus tollens* (Latin for "method of denial") or the Law of Indirect Reasoning. This form is also valid.

Theorem (Modus Tollens or Law of Indirect Reasoning)
The following is a valid form of argument:

Simple form	Universal form
If p then q.	*$\forall$ x, if p(x) then q(x).*
not q.	*not q(c), for a particular c.*
∴ *not p.*	∴ *not p(c) for that c.*

The proof of this theorem is left as Question 9.

Example 2

Assume that premises (1) and (2) are both true:
(1) If Sylvia is sick, then she does not go to work.
(2) Sylvia goes to work.
What true conclusion can be deduced?

Solution

The premises fit the form of the premises of *modus tollens.* A true conclusion is

Sylvia is not sick.

Charles Dodgson (Lewis Carroll)

③ We are now ready to return to the Lewis Carroll puzzle. We want to decide if the conclusion *This example is not easy.* follows from the premises. In order to apply the theorems in this lesson, we have rewritten four of the premises in *if-then* form.

(1) *If I work a logic example without grumbling, then you may be sure it is one I can understand.*
(3) *If an example is easy, then it does not give me a headache.*
(4) *If an example is not arranged in regular order like the ones I am used to, then I cannot understand that example.*
(5) *If I grumble when I work an example, then the example gives me a headache.* (Recall the use of *only if* from Question 19 in Lesson 1-5.)

The other premise is the simple statement

(2) *This example is not arranged in regular order like the ones I am used to.*

and the conclusion is the simple statement

(6) *This example is not easy.*

Adapting to Individual Needs

English Language Development
Students may be familiar with the term "valid" as in "valid excuse" for an absence. This use is the same as is found in this lesson; a valid excuse is one that follows particular regulations.

To apply the three valid argument forms, it is useful to represent the statements symbolically as done below:

$\sim g$: *I work this logic example without grumbling.*
u: *This logic example is one I understand.*
e: *This example is easy.*
$\sim h$: *This example does not give me a headache.*
$\sim r$: *This example is not arranged in regular order like the ones I am used to.*

With these symbols, the given premises are:

(1) *If* $\sim g$ *then* u.
(2) $\sim r$
(3) *If* e *then* $\sim h$.
(4) *If* $\sim r$ *then* $\sim u$.
(5) *If* g *then* h.

We need to know whether we can conclude

(6) $\sim e$.

Now we reorder the premises. Starting with (2) (the only premise that cannot be put into *if-then* form), we build a chain of *if-then* statements in which the conclusion of each *if-then* statement is the premise of the next, ending with (6) (the conclusion). To do so, we need to use the Contrapositive Theorem from Lesson 1-5 to change statements (1) and (3) into equivalent forms (1') and (3').

(2) $\sim r$
(4) *If* $\sim r$ *then* $\sim u$.
(1') *If* $\sim u$ *then* g. contrapositive form
(5) *If* g *then* h.
(3') *If* h *then* $\sim e$. contrapositive form

Now applying the Law of Detachment four times shows that the conclusion is $\sim e$, or *This example is not easy*. Hence, the answer to the question at the beginning of this lesson is yes: the conclusion *This example is not easy.* follows from the premises.

QUESTIONS

Covering the Reading

1. Consider the following argument:
   For all integers n, if n is divisible by 3 then its square is divisible by 9.
   10 is divisible by 3.
   $\therefore$ *10^2 is divisible by 9.*
   a. Identify the premises of the argument. See left.
   b. Identify the conclusion of the argument. 10^2 is divisible by 9.
   c. Write the form of the argument. See left.
   d. Is the conclusion true? no
   e. Is the conclusion valid? yes

1a) If a number is divisible by 3, then its square is divisible by 9. 10 is divisible by 3.
c $\forall$ integers n, if $p(n)$, then $q(n)$; $p(c)$, for a particular c $\therefore$ $q(c)$.

Additional Examples

1. Write the form of the following argument: *$\forall$ angles x, if x is a right angle, then the degree measure of x is 90. A particular angle c has degree measure 88. $\therefore$ c is not a right angle.*
   Let $p(x)$ and $q(x)$ represent the following statements:
   $p(x)$: *x is a right angle.*
   $q(x)$: *the degree measure of x is 90.*
   Then the argument has the following form.
   $\forall$ x, if p(x), then q(x)
   not q(c) for a particular c
   $\therefore$ *not p(c).*
2. Assume that premises (1) and (2) are both true: (1) If my puppy Rover scratches, then Rover has fleas. (2) Rover does not have fleas. What conclusion can be deduced? The premises fit the form of the premises of modus tollens. A true conclusion is: My puppy Rover does not scratch.

Notes on Questions

Questions 1–2 The thrust of **Questions 1d, 1e,** and **2** is that a valid argument may have a false conclusion. Validity is a function of the structure of the argument form.

Adapting to Individual Needs

Challenge
Have students use truth tables to test the validity of the following argument forms.

1. *p or q*
   $\sim q$
   $\therefore p$
   [Valid]
2. $p \Leftrightarrow q$
   $\sim p$
   $\therefore \sim q$
   [Valid]
3. $p \Rightarrow \sim q$
   $\sim p$
   $\therefore q$
   [Invalid]
4. *p xor q*
   q
   $\therefore \sim p$
   [Valid]
5. *p or q*
   q
   $\therefore \sim p$
   [Invalid]

Notes on Questions

Questions 8–9 If you have introduced Venn diagrams as an alternative method for proving validity, you may want to have students apply that method to these problems.

2. *True or false.* The conclusion of a valid argument can be false. True

3. *Multiple choice.* Which of the following is *modus tollens*? c

(a) $p \Rightarrow q$
q
$\therefore\ p$

(b) $p \Rightarrow q$
p
$\therefore\ q$

(c) $p \Rightarrow q$
not q
$\therefore$ not p

(d) $p \Rightarrow q$
not p
$\therefore\ q$

(e) none of these

In 4–6, determine whether the argument is valid. If so, identify the valid argument form. If not, find a counterexample.

4. *If a person is at least 21 years old, then the person is eligible for a driver's license.*
Lucy is eligible for a driver's license.
$\therefore$ *Lucy is at least 21 years old.* Invalid; Sample: Any individual under 21 years old with a driver's license provides a counterexample.

5. $\forall$ *real numbers x, if* $x > 2$, *then* $x^2 > 4$.
$\forall$ *real numbers x, if* $x^2 > 4$, *then* $3x^2 - 9 > 3$.
$\therefore$ $\forall$ *real numbers x, if* $x > 2$, *then* $3x^2 - 9 > 3$.
Valid; Law of Transitivity

6. *If Ken wants to see the world, then Ken will join the Navy.*
Ken wants to see the world.
$\therefore$ *Ken will join the Navy.*
Valid; Law of Detachment

7. Which of the three laws in this lesson was not used in the resolution of the Lewis Carroll puzzle? Laws of Indirect Reasoning and Transitivity

8. Use your work on the Activity in this lesson to complete the proof of the Law of Transitivity. See margin.

9. **a.** Write the Law of Indirect Reasoning using the symbols ~ and $\Rightarrow$.
b. Prove the simple form of the Law of Indirect Reasoning. See margin.
a) $p \Rightarrow q$; $\sim q$; $\therefore \sim p$

Applying the Mathematics

10. You know that your friend Mary always answers the phone if she is home. You just called her and there was no answer.
a. What valid conclusion can you draw? *Mary is not home.*
b. Write the form of this argument. See left.
c. Name the law that guarantees the validity of this argument.
Law of Indirect Reasoning

10b) Let p and q be the statements:
p: Mary is at home.
q: Mary answers the phone.
Then the argument has the form
If p then q
not q
$\therefore$ not p

11. Consider the argument:
If the drought continues, then the corn crop will decline.
If the corn crop declines, then the price of corn will move higher.
Therefore, if the drought continues, then the price of corn will move higher.
a. Write the form of this argument. See below.
b. Is the above argument valid? Explain.
Yes, it follows from the Law of Transitivity.
a) If p then q; If q then r; $\therefore$ If p then r

Additional Answers

8.

p	q	r	$p \Rightarrow q$	$q \Rightarrow r$	$(p \Rightarrow q)$ and $(q \Rightarrow r)$	$p \Rightarrow r$	$((p \Rightarrow q)$ and $(q \Rightarrow r)) \Rightarrow (p \Rightarrow r)$
T	T	T	T	T	T	T	T
T	T	F	T	F	F	F	T
T	F	T	F	T	F	T	T
T	F	F	F	T	F	F	T
F	T	T	T	T	T	T	T
F	T	F	T	F	F	T	T
F	F	T	T	T	T	T	T
F	F	F	T	T	T	T	T

12. Faced with the task of determining if a crown made for the king of Syracuse contained anything other than gold, Archimedes (c. 287–212 B.C.) used the following principle:

If an object is made of pure gold, then its weight equals the product of its volume and the density of gold (19.3 g/cm³ in modern units).

Archimedes devised a method to measure the volume of the crown accurately. Then he calculated that the weight was less than it would be if the crown were made of pure gold. He concluded that the crown was not made of pure gold.

a. What form of argument was he using? Law of Indirect Reasoning

b. Is this a valid form? yes

13. Deduce a valid conclusion from these three true premises.

(1) *The diagonals of a parallelogram bisect each other.*

(2) *All rhombuses are parallelograms.*

(3) *ABCD is a rhombus.*

The diagonals of ABCD bisect each other.

14) Sample: *If an acrobat feat involves a quadruple somersault, then it is not attempted by the circus acrobats.*

14. Consider the statements in this adaptation of a Lewis Carroll puzzle.

(1) *If an acrobatic feat is possible, then it does not involve a quadruple somersault.*

(2) *If an acrobatic feat is impossible, it is not announced in the bills of a circus.*

(3) *If an acrobatic feat is not announced in the bills of a circus, then it is not attempted by the circus acrobats.*

Deduce a valid conclusion. (Hint: You may need to write the contrapositive of some of the statements.) See left.

15. Find the error that leads to the false conclusion.

$\forall$ positive real numbers s and t, if $s < t$ then $s^2 < t^2$.

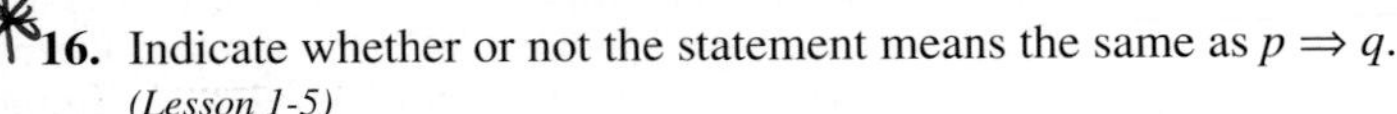

$-3 < -1$

$(-3)^2 < (-1)^2$

$\therefore\ 9 < 1$

-3 and -1 are not positive real numbers, so the universal statement does not apply.

Review

16. Indicate whether or not the statement means the same as $p \Rightarrow q$. *(Lesson 1-5)*

a. *p implies q* yes **b.** *q implies p* no

c. *q is implied by p* yes **d.** *p is sufficient for q* yes

e. *p is necessary for q* no **f.** *p only if q* yes

17. *Multiple choice.* Identify the contrapositive for

If a fruit is a kiwi, then it comes from New Zealand.

(a) *If a fruit is not a kiwi, then it does not come from New Zealand.*

(b) *If a fruit is a kiwi, then it does not come from New Zealand.*

(c) *If a fruit does not come from New Zealand, then it is not a kiwi.*

(d) *If a fruit comes from New Zealand, then it is a kiwi.*

(e) *There is a fruit that is not a kiwi and does not come from New Zealand.* *(Lesson 1-5)* c

New Zealand

Home of the Kiwi. *New Zealand is known for both its kiwis: the fruit with the bright green flesh and the nocturnal bird.*

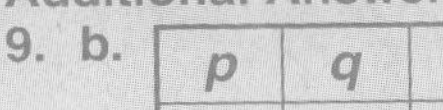

Additional Answers

9. b.

p	q	p ⇒ q	~q	((p ⇒ q) and ~q)	~p	((p ⇒ q) and ~q) ⇒ ~p
T	T	T	F	F	F	T
T	F	F	T	F	F	T
F	T	T	F	F	T	T
F	F	T	T	T	T	T

Notes on Questions

Question 24 Cooperative Learning If a limited number of Lewis Carroll's books are available, you might have students **work in groups** for this question.

Follow-up for Lesson 1-6

Practice

For more questions on SPUR Objectives, use **Lesson Master 1-6** (shown on page 47).

Assessment

Oral Communication Have students name a chain of three events in their daily lives and make them into a valid argument. For example: *If I get up in the morning, I will eat breakfast. If I eat breakfast, I will eat cereal. Hence, if I get up in the morning, I will eat cereal.*

Extension

Have students make up their own "Lewis Carroll" puzzle. Their final puzzle should have at least four premises, and require some rearrangement to solve. Tell students to use at least two of the forms of arguments from the lesson and give bonus points for using all three.

Project Update Project 2, *Lewis Carroll's Logic,* on page 67, relates to the content of this lesson.

22a) $\frac{x(x-2)+y(x+2)}{(x+2)(x-2)}$

23b)

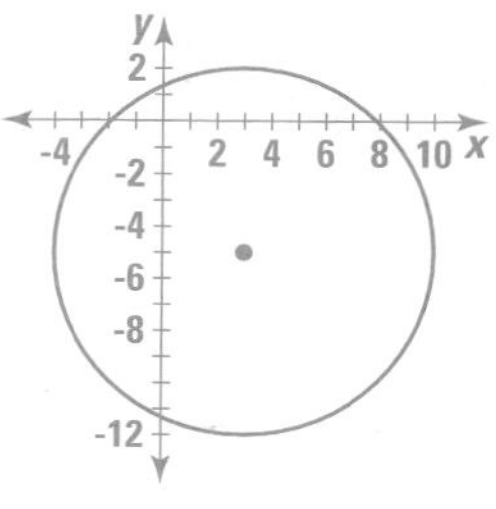

18. Use the choices of Question 17. Which is the inverse of the given statement? *(Lesson 1-5)* a

19. If p is *on*, q is *off*, and r is *off*, will the output be *on*? *(Lessons 1-3, 1-4)*

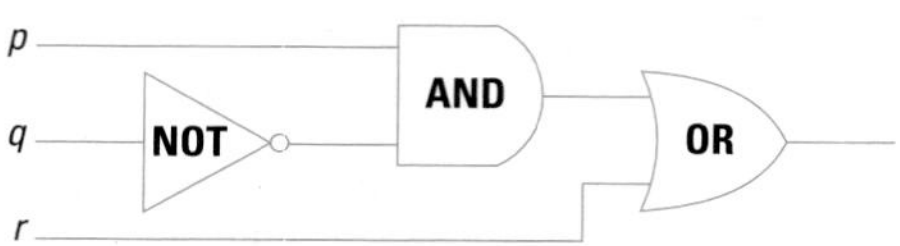

yes

20. Consider the statement

$\forall$ *real numbers y,* $y^2 + 3 \geq 3$.

a. Write the negation of this statement. See below.

b. Which is true: the statement or its negation? the statement *(Lessons 1-1, 1-2)*

a) $\exists$ a real number y, such that $y^2 + 3 \leq 3$.

21. *True or false.* The negation of

There exists an integer n such that $\frac{1}{n}$ *is not an integer.*

is

For all integers n, $\frac{1}{n}$ *is an integer.* *(Lesson 1-2)*

True

22. The following statement is true:

$\forall$ *real numbers a, b, c, d with* $b \neq 0$ *and* $d \neq 0$,

$$\frac{a}{b} + \frac{c}{d} = \frac{ad + bc}{bd}.$$

a. Use substitution to add $\frac{x}{x+2} + \frac{y}{x-2}$. See left.

b. For what values of x is the expression in part **a** undefined? *(Previous course, Lesson 1-1)* 2 or -2

23. a. Identify the center and the radius of the circle with equation $(x-3)^2 + (y+5)^2 = 49$. center (3, -5); radius 7

b. Sketch a graph. *(Previous course)* See left.

Exploration

24. The books *The Magic of Lewis Carroll* (edited by John Fisher) and *Symbolic Logic* by Lewis Carroll are two sources of logic puzzles by Lewis Carroll. Many of these puzzles are similar to the one presented in this lesson. Find one of these books or some other book containing puzzles by Lewis Carroll. Locate one or more of his puzzles and either determine a valid conclusion or show that the argument is valid. Answers may vary.

LESSON

1-7 Invalid Arguments

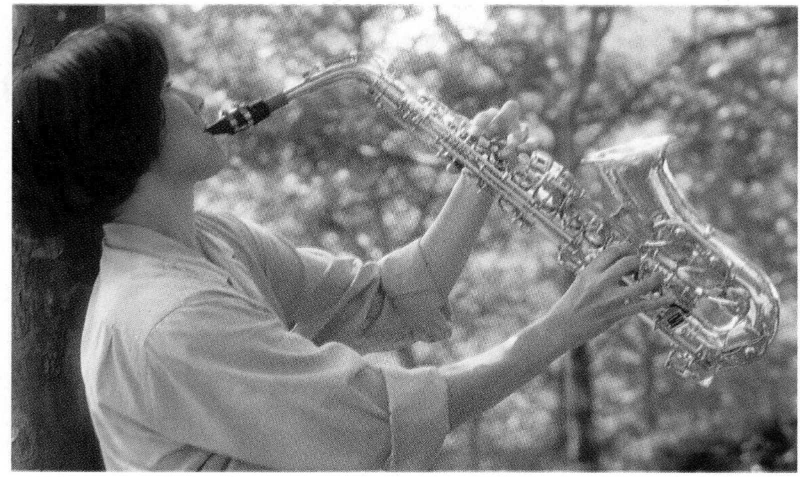

In Lesson 1-6 three valid forms of argument were presented. Some other forms of argument are often used by people but are, in fact, invalid.

Consider the following argument

If a person is a member of the band, then the person plays an instrument.
Natalie plays an instrument.
$\therefore$ *Natalie is a member of the band.*

This argument is of the form

$\forall$ *x, if p(x), then q(x).*
q(c), for a particular c.
$\therefore$ *p(c).*

where *p(x): x is a member of the band, q(x): x plays an instrument,* and *c = Natalie.*

While you might look at this argument and think that it is valid, it is actually invalid. The diagram at the right illustrates this possibility: all members of the band play instruments and Natalie plays an instrument, but Natalie is not a member of the band. Thus, it is possible for both premises to be true while the conclusion is false.

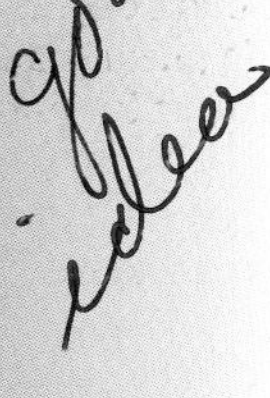

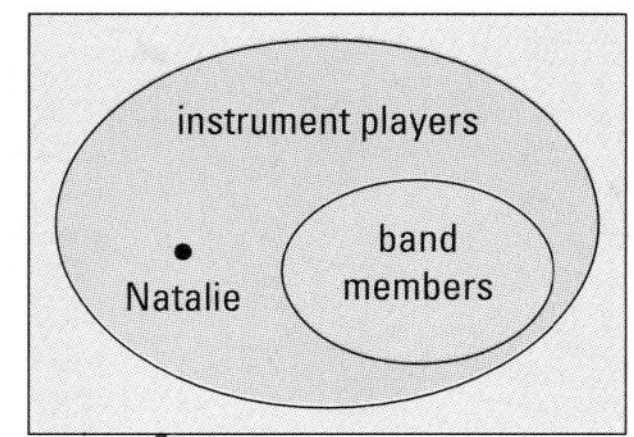

In general, an argument form is **invalid** if and only if it is not valid. That is, there are truth values for the premises that lead to a false truth value for that form. This happens when there are arguments of that form in which the premises are true and the conclusion is false.

SAT's

Lesson 1-7

Objectives

G Determine whether arguments are valid or invalid.
J Determine whether or not a logical argument outside of mathematics is valid.

Resources

From the ***Teacher's Resource File***
- Lesson Master 1-7
- Answer Master 1-7
- Assessment Sourcebook: Quiz for Lessons 1-5 through 1-7
- Teaching Aid 4: Warm-up

Additional Resources
- Visuals for Teaching Aid 4
- Exploration 1-7

Teaching Lesson 1-7

Warm-up

Consider these statements:
All As are Bs.
Some Bs are Cs.
All Cs are Ds.
Is it valid to conclude *Some As are Ds*? Why or why not?
No. The diagram shows a situation in which no *A*s are *D*s.

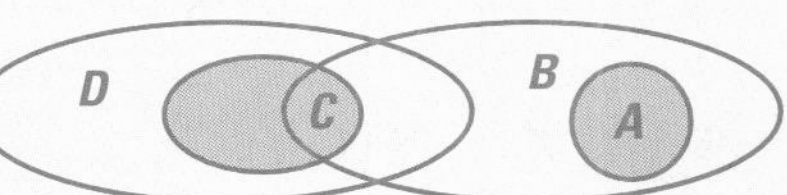

Lesson 1-7 Overview

Broad Goals Three kinds of invalid arguments are considered here: inverse error, converse error, and improper induction.

Perspective It is a generally accepted pedagogical principle that students will better comprehend an idea when they have seen both instances and noninstances of it. Valid arguments, then, are not really best understood until invalid arguments are discussed.

Notes on Reading

Alternate Approach The truth table of **Example 1** can be restructured in a different way to show that the converse error argument form is invalid.

conclusion ↓ (p) — premises (q, p ⇒ q)

p	q	p ⇒ q
[T]	(T	T)
T	F	F
[F]	(T	T)
F	F	T

The two highlighted rows illustrate the cases where the premises are all true. In one of these, the conclusion is false, which shows that an argument of this form can have true premises and a false conclusion. Therefore, the argument form is invalid. A similar discussion can be used with the argument form known as the inverse error.

Converse Error

Example 1 shows how to prove the invalidity of the simple form of the argument using a truth table.

Example 1

Show that the form

If p, then q.
q
$\therefore$ *p*

is invalid.

Solution

Construct a truth table. The table needs to finish with the form $((p \Rightarrow q)$ and $q) \Rightarrow p$.

premises: $p \Rightarrow q$, q; conclusion: p; form: $((p \Rightarrow q)$ and $q) \Rightarrow p$

p	q	$p \Rightarrow q$	$(p \Rightarrow q)$ and q	p	$((p \Rightarrow q)$ and $q) \Rightarrow p$
T	T	T	T	T	T
T	F	F	F	T	T
F	T	T	T	F	F
F	F	T	F	F	T

Examine the table closely. Notice that the form (in the right column) is not always true. In particular, **the third line represents a situation in which the form is false. This means that the argument form is invalid.**

This type of invalid argument is called the **converse error**, because it results from confusing the premise $p \Rightarrow q$ with its converse $q \Rightarrow p$. As you know, a true conditional can have a false converse.

Example 2

A person cleared of a crime argues as follows:

If a person has not done anything wrong, he is cleared at the end of the investigation into his activities. I was cleared at the end of the investigation into my activities. Therefore, I have not done anything wrong.

a. Write the form of this argument.
b. Is the person's argument valid or invalid? Justify your answer.

Solution

a. Let $p(x)$ and $q(x)$ represent the following statements in x:

p(x): x has not done anything wrong.
q(x): x is cleared at the end of the investigation into his activities.

Optional Activities

Activity 1 Technology Connection
Materials: Explorations software

Students may use *Exploration 1-7, Euler Circles* as an alternative to the exploration at the end of Lesson 1-7. Students can represent an argument using Euler circles and decide if the argument is valid or invalid.

Activity 2 You might use this activity after students have completed the lesson. Give each student in a small group a piece (or pieces) of an invalid proof. Do not number or order the pieces. Have students decide (1) the order in which the pieces should be placed; (2) the reason for each statement if mathematical properties are involved; (3) what the premises and the conclusion are; and (4) where the error occurred and what kind it was.

Let I be the particular person who is speaking. Then

p(I): I have not done anything wrong.
q(I): I am cleared at the end of the investigation into my activities.

Thus, the argument has the form:

For all people x, if p(x) then q(x).
q(I)
∴ p(I).

b. This is an invalid argument form; it is an example of the converse error.

Inverse Error

Recall that the inverse of a conditional statement *If p then q* is *If not p then not q*. The following argument illustrates a second type of invalid argument: the **inverse error**.

If a person is a member of the Spanish club, then the person speaks Spanish.
William is not a member of the Spanish club.
∴ *William does not speak Spanish.*

This argument is of the form

For all x, if p(x) then q(x).
not p(c), for a particular c.
∴ *not q(c).*

To see why this argument is invalid, notice that it is possible for the two premises to be true while the conclusion is false. So the form is false. The diagram at the right pictures a situation in which all Spanish club members speak Spanish and William is not a member of the Spanish club; however, William does speak Spanish.

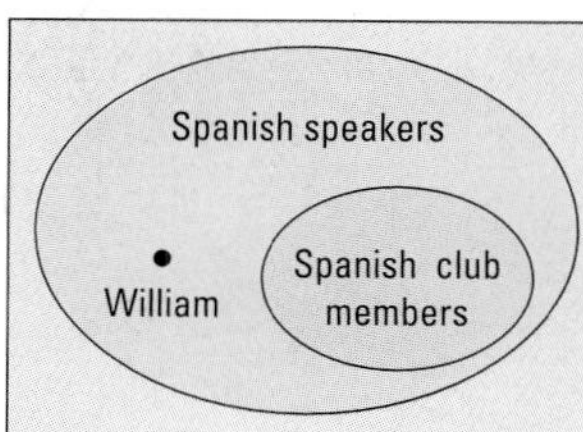

Improper Induction

A third type of invalid argument occurs when a generalization is made prematurely. For example, consider the argument

$$\forall x, f(x) = x^3 - 6x^2 + 12x - 6.$$
$$f(1) = 1$$
$$f(2) = 2$$
$$f(3) = 3$$
$$\therefore f(n) = n \text{ for all positive integers } n.$$

First, compute $f(4)$ and note that $f(4) \neq 4$. Therefore the conclusion is false. Because the premises are true but the conclusion is false, this argument is invalid. The error is called **improper induction**. In this type of invalid argument, the premises show that a property is true for some, but not all, elements in a set, and the conclusion asserts that the property is true

Here are three other arguments for class discussion. Students might be asked to write the form of the argument and determine whether it is valid or invalid.

1. If a number is divisible by 8, then it is divisible by 4.
   20 is not divisible by 8.
   ∴ 20 is not divisible by 4.
   [Inverse Error, invalid]
2. If a number is divisible by 8, then it is divisible by 4.
   20 is not divisible by 4.
   ∴ 20 is not divisible by 8.
   [Law of Indirect Reasoning, valid]
3. If a person without a handicap license is caught parking in a handicap space, the person will get a ticket.
   Jim does not have a handicap license and was caught parking in a handicap space.
   ∴ Jim got a ticket.
   [Law of Detachment, valid]
4. If it's Sunday, then Teri reads the comics.
   Teri reads the comics.
   ∴ It is Sunday.
   [Converse Error, invalid]

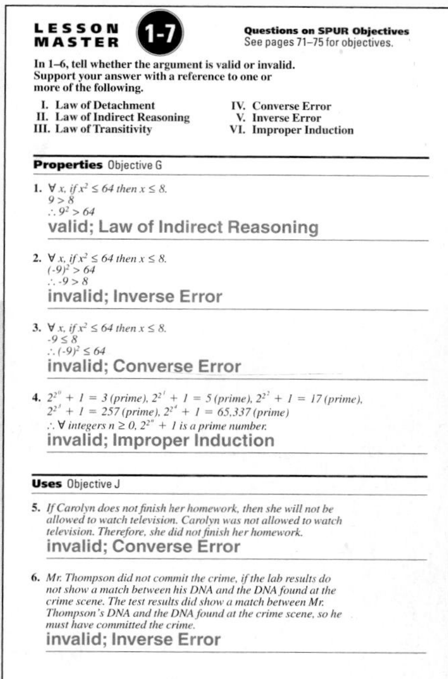

LESSON MASTER 1-7

Questions on SPUR Objectives
See pages 71–75 for objectives.

In 1–6, tell whether the argument is valid or invalid. Support your answer with a reference to one or more of the following.

I. Law of Detachment
II. Law of Indirect Reasoning
III. Law of Transitivity
IV. Converse Error
V. Inverse Error
VI. Improper Induction

Properties Objective G

1. $\forall x$, *if* $x^2 \le 64$ *then* $x \le 8$.
   $9 > 8$
   $\therefore 9^2 > 64$
   valid; Law of Indirect Reasoning
2. $\forall x$, *if* $x^2 \le 64$ *then* $x \le 8$.
   $(-9)^2 > 64$
   $\therefore -9 > 8$
   invalid; Inverse Error
3. $\forall x$, *if* $x^2 \le 64$ *then* $x \le 8$.
   $-9 \le 8$
   $\therefore (-9)^2 \le 64$
   invalid; Converse Error
4. $2^{2^0} + 1 = 3$ (prime), $2^{2^1} + 1 = 5$ (prime), $2^{2^2} + 1 = 17$ (prime), $2^{2^3} + 1 = 257$ (prime), $2^{2^4} + 1 = 65,337$ (prime)
   $\therefore \forall$ integers $n \ge 0$, $2^{2^n} + 1$ is a prime number.
   invalid; Improper Induction

Uses Objective J

5. *If Carolyn does not finish her homework, then she will not be allowed to watch television. Carolyn was not allowed to watch television. Therefore, she did not finish her homework.*
   invalid; Converse Error
6. *Mr. Thompson did not commit the crime, if the lab results do not show a match between his DNA and the DNA found at the crime scene. The test results did show a match between Mr. Thompson's DNA and the DNA found at the crime scene, so he must have committed the crime.*
   invalid; Inverse Error

Adapting to Individual Needs

Extra Help

Some students may need reminders that even if both the premises and the conclusion of an argument are true, the argument could be invalid. Relate invalid arguments to counterexamples. Stress that even if the conclusion in an argument with true premises can be verified to be true, if there is any other argument of the same form in which true premises lead to a false conclusion, that form of the argument is said to be invalid. This is similar to showing a statement is false by producing just a single counterexample. In the *converse error* discussion about the band, Natalie provides the counterexample. In the *inverse* discussion about Spanish Club, William provides the counterexample. And for the *improper induction* discussion about $f(x) = x^3 - 6x^2 + 12x - 6$, $f(4)$ provides the counterexample. These counterexamples correspond to those instances in the truth table where true premises lead to a false conclusion.

Additional Examples

1. Show that the following form of argument is invalid.

   If $\sim p$*, then* $\sim q$.
   p
   $\therefore\ q$

   Construct a truth table which has as its final column heading the form $((\sim p \Rightarrow \sim q)$ and $p) \Rightarrow q$. In the second row of the table, both the premises are true, but the conclusion is false. Thus, the argument form is invalid. (This is a variant of Inverse Error).

Premise ↓ (column p); Premise ↓ (column $\sim p \Rightarrow \sim q$)

p	q	$\sim p$	$\sim q$	$\sim p \Rightarrow \sim q$
T	T	F	F	T
T	F	F	T	T
F	T	T	F	F
F	F	T	T	T

Conclusion ↓ (column q); Form ↓ (column $((\sim p \Rightarrow \sim q)$ and $p) \Rightarrow q$)

$(\sim p \Rightarrow \sim q)$ and p	q	$((\sim p \Rightarrow \sim q)$ and $p) \Rightarrow q$
T	T	T
T	F	F
F	T	T
F	F	T

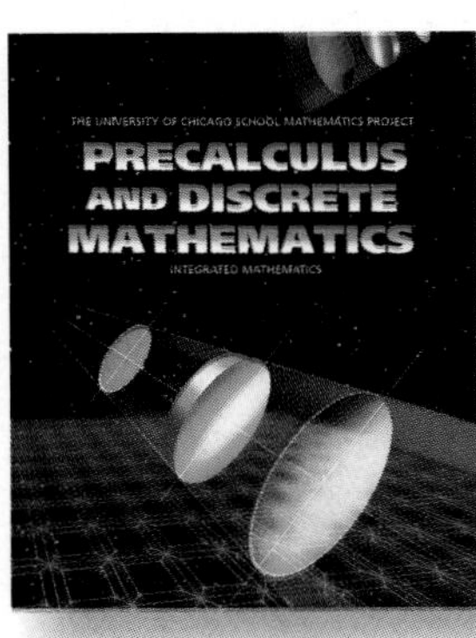

for all elements in a set. Although not a proof, the method of improper induction is often used by mathematicians to make *conjectures* which they then try to prove by other means. Recall that a **conjecture** is a statement believed to be true but whose truth has not been proved.

For instance, here is a conjecture that was made over 250 years ago by Christian Goldbach (1690–1764).

Premises: $2 = 0 + 2, 4 = 3 + 1, 6 = 3 + 3, 8 = 3 + 5, 10 = 3 + 7$
$\ldots 100 = 57 + 43$
$\ldots 980 = 489 + 491$
Conjecture: Every even number greater than 2 can be written as the sum of two primes.

Goldbach's conjecture is a famous unsolved problem.

It is important to note that an invalid argument may have a true conclusion. But invalid arguments may lead to false conclusions, even from true premises. Only in a valid argument with true premises is the conclusion guaranteed to be true.

Example 3

Identify the type of error in the argument.

All high school mathematics books have more than 500 pages.
This book has more than 500 pages.
$\therefore$ *This is a high school mathematics book.*

Solution

Let p be *x is a high school mathematics book.*
and q be *x has more than 500 pages.*
The argument is

$p \Rightarrow q$
q
$\therefore\ p$

This is the converse error. Even though the conclusion might be independently verified as true in one case, the general reasoning form is invalid.

QUESTIONS

Covering the Reading

In 1–3, indicate whether the statement is true or false.

1. An argument form is invalid if you find one argument of that form in which the premises are all true but the conclusion is false. **True**
2. If an argument is invalid, then it must have a false conclusion. **False**
3. If a given conditional statement is true, then its inverse must be false. **False**

Humpback whale

4a)

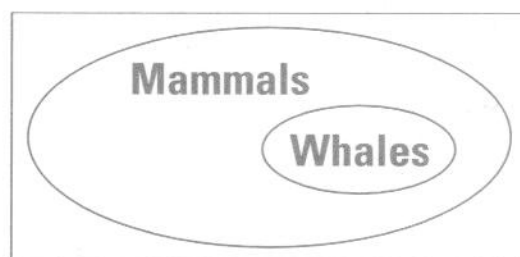

b) *If an animal is a mammal, then it is a whale.* False

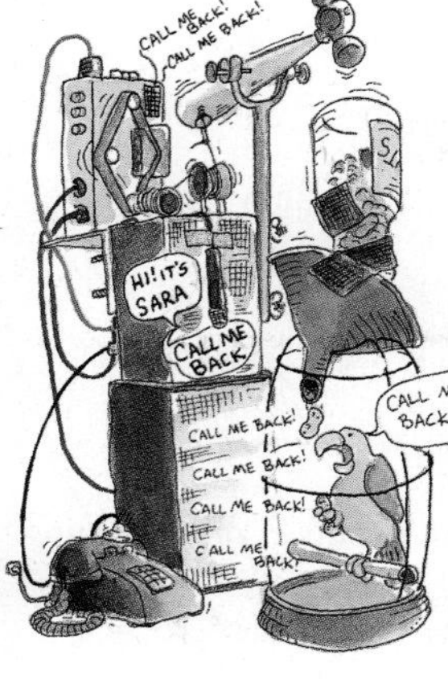

4. Given the statement:

If an animal is a whale, then it is a mammal.

a. Draw a diagram to illustrate the relationship between whales and mammals. a, b) See below left.
b. Write the converse and determine whether it is true or false.
c. Write the inverse and determine whether it is true or false.
c) *If an animal is not a whale, then it is not a mammal.* False

In 5–9, an argument is given. **a.** Identify the type of argument. **b.** Tell whether or not it is valid.

5. $\sin 30° = \frac{\sqrt{1}}{2}$ a) improper induction

$\sin 45° = \frac{\sqrt{2}}{2}$ b) invalid

$\sin 60° = \frac{\sqrt{3}}{2}$

$\therefore \quad \sin(15n)° = \frac{\sqrt{n-1}}{2}$ *for all integers* $n \geq 2$.

6. *If you buy a ticket to the concert, you will go.*
You don't buy a ticket to the concert.
∴ *You don't go.*
a) inverse error b) invalid

7. *If a person does not register to vote, then the person cannot vote.*
John can vote.
∴ *John has registered to vote.*
a) Law of Indirect Reasoning b) valid

8. *If this is a presidential race, education is a top issue.*
Education is a top issue.
∴ *This is a presidential race.*
a) converse error b) invalid

9. $\forall x$, *if* $x > 2$, *then* $x^2 > 4$.
$\forall x$, *if* $x > 3$, *then* $x^2 > 9$.
∴ $\forall x$, *if* $x > n$, *then* $x^2 > n^2$.
a) improper induction b) invalid

Applying the Mathematics

10. Given the conditional statement $p \Rightarrow q$.
a. Write the converse. $q \Rightarrow p$
b. Write the contrapositive of the converse. $\sim p \Rightarrow \sim q$
c. Identify your answer to part **b** as either the inverse, converse, or contrapositive of the original statement. inverse

11. Assume that Peter has an answering machine attached to his telephone. He turns it on whenever he is leaving home. When Sara called, she got the message on the answering machine. Sara concluded that Peter was not home. See below.
a. Write the form of argument Sara used to draw her conclusion.
b. Is it valid or invalid? Explain your answer. invalid, converse error

a) *p: Peter is not home.*
q: The answering machine is on.
$p \Rightarrow q$
q
$\therefore \ p$

2. Consider this argument :
The college said that if I got my application in by October 1st, then it would consider me for early admission. I got my application in by September 25th. Therefore, the college will consider me for early admission.
a. Write the form of the argument. Let *p*: I get my application in by October 1st. Let *q*: The college considers my application. The argument has the form: ($p \Rightarrow q$ and p), $\therefore q$.
b. Is the argument valid or invalid? Justify your answer. This is a valid argument form (modus ponens).

3. Identify the type of error in this argument:
If a person does not eat well, then the person will have health problems. Mrs. Jackson eats well. Therefore she will not have health problems.
Let $p(x)$: x does not eat well.
Let $q(x)$: x has health problems.
The argument has the form:
If not $p(x)$, then $q(x)$;
p(Mrs. Jackson).
∴ not q(Mrs. Jackson).
This is an example of inverse error.

Notes on Questions

Question 5 Error Alert The pattern shown may help people remember the sines of 30°, 45°, and 60°, but be sure students do not try to extend it to other numbers.

Notes on Questions

Question 14 Science Connection With most of Antarctica covered with an ice sheet averaging 6500 feet thick, it is hard to imagine that much of the continent is considered a desert. The desert classification comes from the fact that there is only about 2 inches of precipitation per year over the polar plateau.

Question 22 Cooperative Learning This question could be expanded and done as a **small group.** Mathematical or non-mathematical statements could be used. Results could be presented to the entire class as part of an assessment.

Additional Answers

14. *p*: the land is covered with ice.
    q: the land is Antarctica.
    r: there are research stations there.
    s: scientific study is being conducted.
    $p \Rightarrow q$
    $q \Rightarrow r$
    $r \Rightarrow s$
    s
    $\therefore p$
    Invalid; converse error
15. $p(x)$: x is a real number.
    $q(x)$: $x^2 \geq 0$
    $r(x)$: x is a pure imaginary number.
    Let $c = 2i$
    $\forall x, p(x) \Rightarrow q(x)$
    $\forall x, r(x) \Rightarrow \sim q(x)$
    $r(c)$
    $\therefore \sim p(c)$
    Valid; $r(c) \Rightarrow \sim q(c)$ by the Law of Detachment, and $\sim q(c) \Rightarrow \sim p(c)$ by the Law of Indirect Reasoning.
16. *p*: you send a minimum order of $10 to a mail order house.
    q: you can return a sweepstakes coupon enclosed with the catalog.
    r: your order is one of the first 1000 orders.
    s: you have a chance of winning $100.
    $p \Rightarrow q$
    $(q \text{ and } r) \Rightarrow s$
    s
    $\therefore p$
    invalid, converse error

13a) $p(x)$: *x is President of the United States.*
$q(x)$: *x is at least 35 years old.*
Let c be Queen Elizabeth.
$\forall x, p(x) \Rightarrow q(x)$
$q(c)$
$\therefore p(c)$

12. Given the following argument:

$$\forall x, x = 3 \Rightarrow x^2 = 9$$
$$x \neq 3$$
$$\therefore \quad x^2 \neq 9$$

a) p: $x = 3$
q: $x^2 = 9$
$p \Rightarrow q$
$\sim p$
$\therefore \sim q$

a. Write the form of the argument.
b. Is the argument valid or invalid? Justify your answer. invalid, inverse error

13. Given the following argument:

For all persons p, if p is President of the U.S., then p is at least 35 years old.
Queen Elizabeth II is at least 35 years old.
$\therefore$ *Queen Elizabeth II is President of the U.S.*

a. Write the form of this argument. See left.
b. Are the premises true? Is the conclusion true? yes, no
c. Is the argument valid or invalid? Justify your answer. invalid, converse error

In 14–16, write the form of the argument and determine whether the argument is valid or invalid. If the argument is invalid, identify the type of error made in the argument.

Cierva Bay, Antarctica

14. *If the land is covered with ice, then the land is Antarctica. If the land is Antarctica, then there are research stations there. If the land has research stations, then scientific study is being conducted. Scientific study is being conducted on the land. Therefore, the land is covered with ice.* See margin.

15. *If x is a real number, then* $x^2 \geq 0$. *If x is a pure imaginary number, then* $x^2 < 0$. *2i is a pure imaginary number. Therefore, 2i is not a real number.* See margin.

16. *If you send a minimum order of $10 to a mail order house, then you can return a sweepstakes entry coupon enclosed with the catalog. If you return the coupon and your order is one of the first 1000 orders, then you have a chance of winning $100. You win $100 in the sweepstakes. Therefore, you must have sent a minimum order of $10 to the mail order house.* See margin.

17. a. By considering all possible truth values that p and q may have, show that $((p \Rightarrow q) \text{ and } \sim p) \Rightarrow \sim q$ is not always true. See margin.
b. What type of error does the form in part **a** exemplify? inverse error

18. Refer to the two arguments below. (A trapezoid is a quadrilateral with *at least* one pair of parallel sides.)

I. *All squares are rectangles.*
All squares are trapezoids.
$\therefore$ *All rectangles are trapezoids.*

II. *All squares are rectangles.*
All squares are rhombuses.
$\therefore$ *All rectangles are rhombuses.*

a. For argument I, are the premises true? Is the conclusion true? yes; yes
b. For argument II, are the premises true? Is the conclusion true? yes; no
c. Write the form of each argument. See left.
d. Use your results from parts **a** and **b** to conjecture whether your argument form for part **c** is valid or invalid. invalid

18c) Arguments I and II have the form:
$p \Rightarrow q$
$p \Rightarrow r$
$\therefore q \Rightarrow r$

17. a.

p	q	$p \Rightarrow q$	$\sim p$	$(p \Rightarrow q)$ and $\sim p$	$\sim q$	$((p \Rightarrow q)$ and $\sim p) \Rightarrow \sim q$
T	T	T	F	F	F	T
T	F	F	F	F	T	T
F	T	T	T	T	F	F
F	F	T	T	T	T	T

19a) Let p: Devin is a boy.
Let q: Devin plays baseball.
Let r: Devin is a pitcher.
$p \Rightarrow q$
$q \Rightarrow r$
$\sim r$
$\therefore \sim p$
b) The argument correctly uses the Law of Indirect Reasoning and the Law of Transitivity.

Review

19. Consider the following argument: See left.

If Devin is a boy, then Devin plays baseball.
If Devin plays baseball, then Devin is a pitcher.
Devin is not a pitcher.
$\therefore$ *Devin is not a boy.*

a. Express the argument symbolically.
b. Show that the argument is valid. *(Lesson 1-6)*

Look at ans in book

20. Use the Law of Transitivity to explain why the following Law of Transitivity for biconditionals is a valid reasoning pattern. See margin.

$p \Leftrightarrow q$
$q \Leftrightarrow r$
$\therefore \quad p \Leftrightarrow r$ *(Lessons 1-5, 1-6)*

21. Deduce a valid conclusion from all of premises (1) to (5) and justify your reasoning. See margin.
(1) p
(2) $q \Rightarrow r$
(3) *not* $t \Rightarrow$ *not* s
(4) $p \Rightarrow q$
(5) *not* $s \Rightarrow$ *not* r *(Lesson 1-6)*

22) Sample: Let p: $2 < 1$. Let q: $3 < 2$. Both statements are false. (p and q) is false, but $p \Rightarrow q$ is true.

22. Give an example of two statements p and q such that p *and* q and $p \Rightarrow q$ have different truth values. *(Lessons 1-3, 1-5)* See left.

23. Write the following statement as an *if-then* statement.

$\forall$ *integers a and b*, $\frac{a}{b} = \sqrt{2}$ *only if* $\frac{a^2}{b^2} = 2$.

(Lesson 1-5) $\forall$ integers a and b, if $\frac{a}{b} = \sqrt{2}$ then $\frac{a^2}{b^2} = 2$.

24. Write the negation of the statement

If Vanna White is the hostess, then the show is Wheel of Fortune.

(Lessons 1-2, 1-5) Vanna White is the hostess and the show is not Wheel of Fortune.

25. a. Write a universal statement that could be used to factor the expression $x^2 - a^2$. $\forall$ real numbers x and a, $x^2 - a^2 = (x - a)(x + a)$.
b. Use the Law of Substitution with the statement from part **a** to factor each expression. See left.
i. $x^2 - 16$ **ii.** $9y^4 - z^2$
c. Use the Law of Substitution with the statement from part **a** to calculate the value of $48^2 - 52^2$ in your head. *(Previous course, Lesson 1-1)* -400

25b) i: Let $a = 4$. By substitution, $x^2 - 16 = (x - 4)(x + 4)$.
ii: Let $x = 3y^2$ and $a = z$. By substitution, $9y^4 - z^2 = (3y^2 - z)(3y^2 + z)$.

26. Match each property with its name. *(Previous course, Lesson 1-1)*

a. $\forall$ *x and y*, $xy = yx$ iii
b. $\forall$ *x and y, if x and y are integers, then* $x + y$ *is an integer.* v
c. $\forall$ *x, y, and z*, $z(x + y) = zx + zy$ iv
d. $\exists$ *y such that* $\forall$ *x*, $x + y = x$ ii
e. $\forall$ *x*, $\exists$ *y such that* $x + y = 0$ i

(i) Additive Inverse Property
(ii) Additive Identity Property
(iii) Commutativity of Multiplication
(iv) Distributivity of Multiplication over Addition
(v) Closure of Addition
(vi) Associativity of Addition

Additional Answers

20. $p \Rightarrow q$, $q \Rightarrow r$, hence: $p \Rightarrow r$.
$r \Rightarrow q$, $q \Rightarrow p$, hence: $r \Rightarrow p$.
$\therefore \ p \Leftrightarrow r$

21.
$p \Rightarrow q$ (4)
$q \Rightarrow r$ (2)
$r \Rightarrow s$ contrapositive of (5)
$s \Rightarrow t$ contrapositive of (3)
$\therefore p \Rightarrow t$ Law of Transitivity
p (1)
$\therefore t$ Law of Detachment

Follow-up for Lesson 1-7

Practice

For more questions on SPUR Objectives, use **Lesson Master 1-7** (shown on page 55).

Assessment

Quiz A quiz covering Lessons 1-5 through 1-7 is provided in the *Assessment Sourcebook.*

Extension

Cooperative Learning As a class, you might discuss the following well-known improper induction example from geometry. Begin with a circle, mark n points on it, connect the points with chords, and count the number of regions created.

Circle	Number of points	Number of regions
	2	2
	3	4
	4	8
	5	16

Students may conjecture that n points will result in 2^{n-1} regions. In fact, for $n = 6$, there are only 31 regions!

Exploration

27. In this lesson a circle diagram was used to represent premises in an argument. These diagrams are often called **Euler circles** or **Venn diagrams**. Here is how premises are represented by Euler circles.

All A are B.

No A are B.

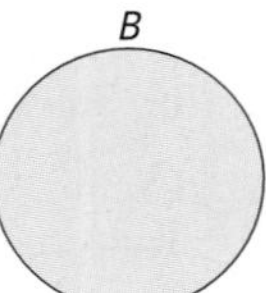

Some A are B.

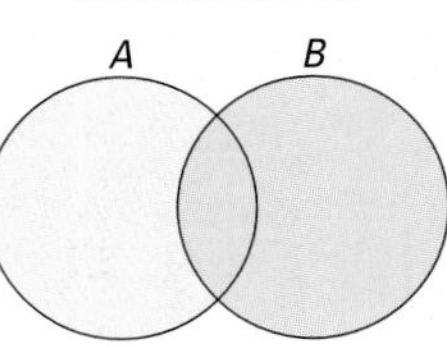

a. Represent each argument below using Euler circles and determine whether the argument is valid or invalid. See below.

i. *All treaties must be ratified by Congress.*
All things ratified by Congress become law.
$\therefore$ *All treaties become law.*

The Signing of the Treaty of Versailles, *an oil painting by John Christen Johansen*

ii. *Some artists paint in oil.*
Some artists paint with watercolors.
$\therefore$ *Some oil painters also paint with watercolors.*

iii. *All isosceles triangles have reflection symmetry.*
No triangle with reflection symmetry is scalene.
$\therefore$ *No isosceles triangle is scalene.*

b. Compose three arguments and represent their premises by Euler circles. Indicate how you can decide whether each argument is valid or invalid, using the method of Euler circles. Answers may vary.

a)

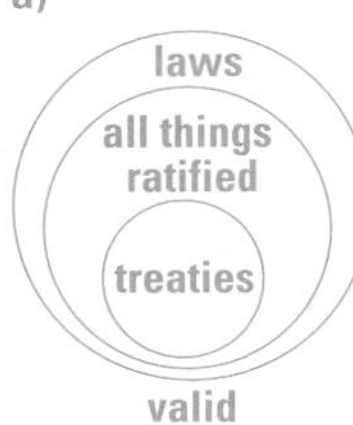

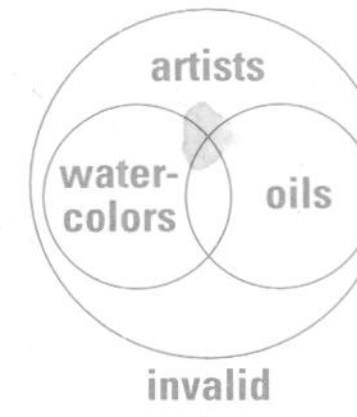

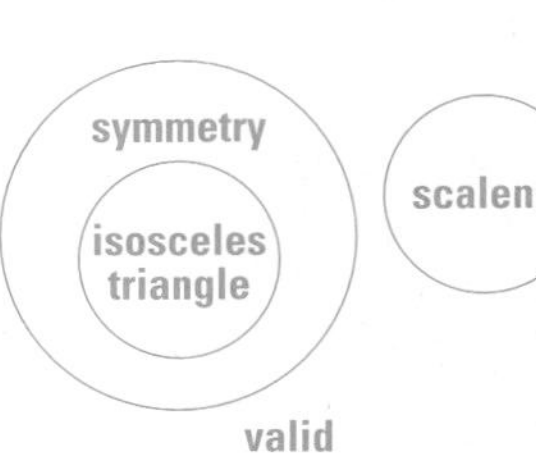

LESSON

1-8

Direct Proofs

Logical Links. *Both a chain of deductions and a metal chain are only as strong as their weakest links.*

A **mathematical proof** is a chain of logically valid deductions using agreed-upon assumptions, definitions, or previously proved statements. When you studied geometry, you were asked to prove statements, and you have proved statements in algebra even though the word "proof" might not have been used. So you have had a great deal of experience with mathematical proof.

A Proof Involving a Linear Equation

For example, consider the solving of the linear equation $8x + 500 = 740$. Here are steps you might write down. We name each step with a letter for further reference.

$$p\colon 8x + 500 = 740$$
$$q\colon 8x = 240$$
$$r\colon x = 30$$

The conditional $p \Rightarrow q$ is an instance of the universal conditional called the Addition Property of Equality: $\forall$ *real numbers a, b, and c, if* $a = b$*, then* $a + c = b + c$. In this case, $a = 8x + 500$, $b = 740$, and $c = -500$.

The conditional $q \Rightarrow r$ is an instance of the Multiplication Property of Equality: $\forall$ *real numbers a, b, and c, if* $a = b$*, then* $ac = bc$. (Do you see what a, b, and c are?) Because $p \Rightarrow q$ and $q \Rightarrow r$ are both true, you can conclude $p \Rightarrow r$ by using the Law of Transitivity. That is, you can conclude: *If* $8x + 500 = 740$*, then* $x = 30$. Now if you are given a situation in which you know that $8x + 500 = 740$ is true, you can repeatedly use the Law of Detachment to conclude that $x = 30$. Such a situation is in Example 1.

In a proof, generalizations like the Addition and Multiplication Properties of Equality are called **justifications**. Justifications are generally written when they are not obvious. Logical justifications, such as the Laws of Detachment and Transitivity, tend not to be written down.

Lesson 1-8

Objectives

H Use logic to prove or disprove statements.

J Determine whether or not a logical argument outside of mathematics is valid.

Resources

From the ***Teacher's Resource File***

- Lesson Master 1-8
- Answer Master 1-8
- Teaching Aid 4: Warm-up

Additional Resources

- Visual for Teaching Aid 4

Teaching Lesson 1-8

Warm-up

Let line segments $\overline{AB}$ and $\overline{CD}$ intersect at point E.

1. Prove: If E is the midpoint of both $\overline{AB}$ and $\overline{CD}$, then lines $\overleftrightarrow{AC}$ and $\overleftrightarrow{BD}$ are parallel.

(Warm-up continues on page 62.)

Lesson 1-8 Overview

Broad Goals A major objective of this book is to have students become proficient in writing proofs. This lesson relates the logic of the previous lessons to proofs students have seen in earlier courses.

Perspective In this book students are given experiences with a variety of types of proofs, starting with proofs of properties of equations, and including divisibility proofs in Chapter 4, indirect proofs with rational and irrational numbers in Chapter 5, proofs of trigonometric identities in Chapter 6, and proofs utilizing mathematical induction in Chapter 7. For each of these types of proofs, attention is given to the structure and words used in the proofs, because we feel that the *writing* of proofs is as much a difficulty as the *conceptualization.*

We try to keep the presentation of proof as simple as possible. For this reason, direct proofs often start with a sentence beginning "Suppose" and stating the full hypothesis of the theorem to be proved. Occasionally, this sentence is followed by one beginning "We must show that" and stating explicitly what must be shown to complete the proof of the theorem. In college mathematics courses, students are often expected to write proofs. The proofs in college tend to be algebraic,

(Overview continues on page 62.)

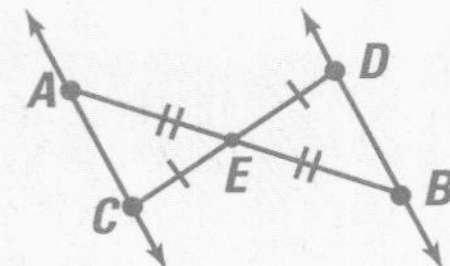

From the given, $\overline{AB}$ and $\overline{CD}$ intersect at point E. If E is the midpoint of both $\overline{AB}$ and $\overline{CD}$, then by the definition of midpoint, $\overline{AE} \cong \overline{BE}$ and $\overline{CE} \cong \overline{DE}$. Then, since vertical angles are congruent, $\angle AEC \cong \angle BED$. Then, $\triangle AEC \cong \triangle BED$ by the SAS Theorem. Since corresponding angles of congruent triangles are congruent, $\angle EAC \cong \angle EBD$.
$\therefore \overleftrightarrow{AC} \parallel \overleftrightarrow{BD}$ because if the alternate interior angles are congruent, the lines are parallel.

2. Express the statement to be proved in Warm-up Question 1 as a universal conditional.
If $\overline{AB}$ and $\overline{CD}$ intersect at point E and E is the midpoint of both $\overline{AB}$ and $\overline{CD}$, then $\overleftrightarrow{AC}$ and $\overleftrightarrow{BD}$ are parallel.

Example 1

Given: A person normally earns $500 a week on a job but earns $740 in a particular week working 8 hours of overtime.
To prove: The person has earned $30 per overtime hour.

Solution 1

Here is a proof argument written in paragraph form. Let x be the overtime hourly wage. From the given, 8x + 500 = 740. If 8x + 500 = 740, then by the Addition Property of Equality (adding -500 to each side), 8x = 240. Then, using the Multiplication Property of Equality (multiplying both sides by $\frac{1}{8}$), x = 30. So the person has earned $30 per overtime hour.

Solution 2

Here is a proof argument written in two-column form.
Let x be the person's overtime hourly wage.

Conclusions	Justifications
8x + 500 = 740	from the given information
8x = 240	Addition Property of Equality (add -500)
x = 30	Multiplication Property of Equality (mult. by $\frac{1}{8}$)

So the person has earned $30 per overtime hour.

Proofs Involving Quadratic Equations

A list of assumed properties of real and complex numbers is given in Appendix A of this book. Also included in Appendix A are theorems you are expected to know. Among these theorems is the Quadratic Formula. The Quadratic Formula follows from a theorem about the solution to the simplest quadratic equation $x^2 = k$. You have known this theorem for many years, but you may never have seen a proof of it.

Theorem
For all real numbers k, if $x^2 = k$, then $x = \sqrt{k}$ or $x = -\sqrt{k}$.

Proof
The proof relies on the Distributive Property and the definition of square root. Begin with the antecedent.

$$x^2 = k$$

Now add $-k$ to both sides, applying the Addition Property of Equality.

$$x^2 - k = 0$$

Factoring is an application of the Distributive Property. Factor the left side.

$$(x - \sqrt{k})(x + \sqrt{k}) = 0$$

Now apply the Zero Product Theorem: If $ab = 0$, then $a = 0$ or $b = 0$.

$$x - \sqrt{k} = 0 \quad \text{or} \quad x + \sqrt{k} = 0$$

Add $\sqrt{k}$ to both sides of the left equation, $-\sqrt{k}$ to both sides of the right equation.

$$x = \sqrt{k} \quad \text{or} \quad x = -\sqrt{k}$$

Lesson 1-8 Overview, continued

written in paragraphs, and do not have a formal "given" and "to prove" commonly found in geometry. Mathematicians often omit these phrases, but they are always implicitly contained in proofs.

The field testing of these materials has found that these proofs are accessible to students of all abilities. Even students who found geometry proofs to be difficult were able to do these proofs.

Optional Activities

After discussing the lesson you might explain that an integer k is even if and only if there exists an integer m such that $k = 2m$. An integer k is odd if and only if there exists an integer n such that $k = 2n + 1$. Have students use these definitions to prove the following: If two integers are even, so is their sum. [Suppose k and ℓ are even. Then $\exists m$ and $\exists n$ such that $k = 2m$ and $\ell = 2n$. Then $k + \ell = 2m + 2n = 2(m + n)$, which is even.]

What Is a Direct Proof?

The proof of the preceding theorem and the proof in Example 1 are known as **direct proofs** because they proceed directly from the antecedent (given) to the conclusion. (In Chapter 5, you will study *indirect proofs*, which are based on the Law of Indirect Reasoning.) The structure of a direct proof of a universal conditional is summarized here.

Structure of a Direct Proof of a Universal Conditional

1. Express the statement to be proved in the form

$$\forall \text{ } x \text{ in } S, \text{ if } p(x), \text{ then } q(x).$$

p(x) is the *given*; *q(x)* is the *to prove*.

2. Proof *argument*: Begin by assuming the antecedent *p(x)*. Use the Law of Detachment, the definitions of the terms that appear in *p(x)* and *q(x)*, and known properties of the ideas to make a chain of deductions leading to *q(x)*.
3. Use the Law of Transitivity to conclude the universal conditional.

In the proof of the previous theorem, S is the set of real numbers, $p(x)$ is $x^2 = k$ and $q(x)$ is $x = \sqrt{k}$ or $x = -\sqrt{k}$. To prove the Quadratic Formula, the idea is to work with the equation until it is in the form $x^2 = k$, and then to apply the previous theorem.

Theorem (Quadratic Formula)
For all real numbers a, b, and c,
if $ax^2 + bx + c = 0$ and $a \neq 0$, then $x = \frac{-b \pm \sqrt{b^2 - 4ac}}{2a}$.

Proof

Begin with the antecedent.

Suppose $\quad ax^2 + bx + c = 0 \quad$ and $a \neq 0$.

Multiply both sides by $4a$ (applying the Multiplication Property of Equality).

$$4a^2x^2 + 4abx + 4ac = 0$$

Now add $b^2 - 4ac$ to both sides (applying the Addition Property of Equality).

$$4a^2x^2 + 4abx + b^2 = b^2 - 4ac$$

Factoring is an application of the Distributive Property. Factor the left side.

$$(2ax + b)^2 = b^2 - 4ac$$

This equation is of the form $x^2 = k$, so the previous theorem can be applied.

$$2ax + b = \sqrt{b^2 - 4ac} \quad \text{or} \quad 2ax + b = -\sqrt{b^2 - 4ac}$$

Now add $-b$ to both sides.

$$2ax = -b + \sqrt{b^2 - 4ac} \quad \text{or} \quad 2ax = -b - \sqrt{b^2 - 4ac}$$

Divide both sides by $2a$. This can be done because $a \neq 0$.

$$x = \frac{-b + \sqrt{b^2 - 4ac}}{2a} \quad \text{or} \quad x = \frac{-b - \sqrt{b^2 - 4ac}}{2a}$$

By the Law of Transitivity, the desired statement is proved.

It is important to realize that a written proof is a *communication* that tries to express the most important steps in thinking. When writing a proof, you should try to show enough steps and justifications so that another person can understand the argument. In the following example, as in many proofs, the proof traces the steps of the thinking process that led to conclusion.

Notes on Reading

The word "proof" conveys auras of mystery and fear to many students. Yet, as an essential element of mathematical thought, we would like proof to be thought of as an exciting demonstration of how some knowledge gives rise to other knowledge.

There are four proofs in this lesson. Their subject matter is as follows:

1. the solving of a linear equation (specifically $8x + 500 = 740$) in **Example 1**;
2. the solving of the simplest quadratic $x^2 = k$;
3. the Quadratic Formula; and
4. the mean of the solutions to the quadratic equation $ax^2 + bx + c = 0$ is $\frac{-b}{2a}$.

The proofs (2) to (4) are obviously in a sequence where each is used in the proof of the next. Not so obvious is that the derivation of the Quadratic Formula in (3) requires the solving of a linear equation. This occurs in the last three steps of the proof. You might wish to point out to students that this kind of sequence in algebra, from simple theorems to the more complicated, is akin to the sequence of theorems in proofs in geometry.

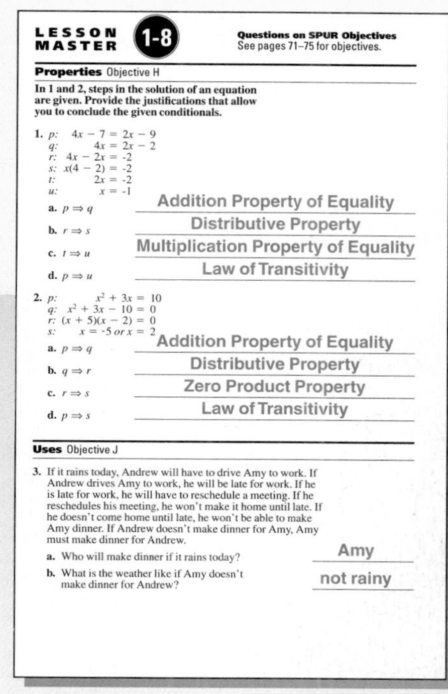

LESSON MASTER 1-8

Questions on SPUR Objectives
See pages 71–75 for objectives.

Properties Objective H

In 1 and 2, steps in the solution of an equation are given. Provide the justifications that allow you to conclude the given conditionals.

1. p: $4x - 7 = 2x - 9$
   q: $4x = 2x - 2$
   r: $4x - 2x = -2$
   s: $x(4 - 2) = -2$
   t: $2x = -2$
   u: $x = -1$
   a. $p \Rightarrow q$ Addition Property of Equality
   b. $r \Rightarrow s$ Distributive Property
   c. $t \Rightarrow u$ Multiplication Property of Equality
   d. $p \Rightarrow u$ Law of Transitivity

2. p: $x^2 + 3x = 10$
   q: $x^2 + 3x - 10 = 0$
   r: $(x + 5)(x - 2) = 0$
   s: $x = -5$ *or* $x = 2$
   a. $p \Rightarrow q$ Addition Property of Equality
   b. $q \Rightarrow r$ Distributive Property
   c. $r \Rightarrow s$ Zero Product Property
   d. $p \Rightarrow s$ Law of Transitivity

Uses Objective J

3. If it rains today, Andrew will have to drive Amy to work. If Andrew drives Amy to work, he will be late for work. If he is late for work, he will have to reschedule a meeting. If he reschedules his meeting, he won't make it home until late. If he doesn't come home until late, he won't be able to make Amy dinner. If Andrew doesn't make dinner for Amy, Amy must make dinner for Andrew.
   a. Who will make dinner if it rains today? Amy
   b. What is the weather like if Amy doesn't make dinner for Andrew? not rainy

Adapting to Individual Needs

Extra Help

You might compare the two different forms of the proof argument in **Example 1.** Some students may tend to skip important steps in their argument. If this happens, ask the students to write a complete proof in two-column form. It may be easier to discuss and prevent significant omissions in this format. Discuss which, if any, steps might be shortened or omitted in paragraph form. Then guide students to write the argument in paragraph form.

Challenge

Writing Have students do one of the following.

1. Find different proofs for the Pythagorean Theorem and write a report on the one that (they feel) is easiest to understand and the one that is most unusual.
2. Write a report about the famous Fermat's Last Theorem and how its proof has been approached.

Stress the need for the words in the proof of **Example 2,** what some might term the "non-mathematical part" of the written proof. If we only wrote the following

$$\frac{\frac{-b+\sqrt{b^2-4ac}}{2a}+\frac{-b-\sqrt{b^2-4ac}}{2a}}{2}=\frac{\frac{-2b}{2a}}{2}=\frac{-b}{2a},$$

we would have shown the computations, but not have told what is being done. So the reader would not be able to easily determine what was proved.

Additional Examples

1. Prove: If $3c > 5c$, then $c < 0$.
   By the Addition Property of Inequality, $3c - 5c > 5c - 5c$. By the Distributive Property, $-2c > 0$. (The Zero Product Property is also used here.) By the Multiplication Property of Inequality (multiply both sides by -0.5), $c < 0$.
2. Willie bought a shaver for $29.95. The total amount with sales tax was $31.90. Find the sales tax rate and prove your result. Let r = the sales tax rate. Then $29.95(1 + r) = 31.90$, by the definition of sales tax. Then, by the Multiplication Property of Equality (multiply by $\frac{1}{29.95}$, $1 + r \approx 1.06511...$Thus $r \approx 0.06511....$ Since sales taxes are usually a multiple of 0.25%, or 0.0025, the rate is 0.065. This checks. (An alternate proof might begin with $29.95 + 29.95r = 31.90$, from which students would solve the linear equation.)

Example 2

Find the mean of the solutions to the quadratic equation $ax^2 + bx + c = 0$, and prove your result.

Solution

To write the proof, first assert what you will prove.

To Prove: For all quadratic equations $ax^2 + bx + c = 0$, the mean of the solutions is $\frac{-b}{2a}$.

Proof: Proceed from the given. By the Quadratic Formula, the solutions to $ax^2 + bx + c = 0$ are

$$\frac{-b+\sqrt{b^2-4ac}}{2a} \quad \text{and} \quad \frac{-b-\sqrt{b^2-4ac}}{2a}.$$

Remind your reader of the definition of mean. To obtain the mean, I add the solutions and divide by 2. Their sum is $\frac{-2b}{2a}$, which reduces to $\frac{-b}{a}$. Divide the sum by 2 and the result is $\frac{-b}{2a}$.

Questions

Covering the Reading

1) A proof is a chain of logically valid deductions using agreed upon assumptions, definitions, or previously proved statements.

1. In mathematics, what is a *proof*? See below left.
2. In the proof in this lesson involving the equation $8x + 500 = 740$, the statement $q \Rightarrow r$ is justified by the Multiplication Property of Equality: If $a = b$, then $ac = bc$. Identify a, b, and c. $a = 8x$; $b = 240$; $c = \frac{1}{8}$
3. Write a proof of the following statement: *For all m, if $1000 = 30m - 80$, then $2m = 72$.* See margin.
4. Suppose a laborer normally earns $460 for a 5-day week and $598 for a 6-day week in which the worker earns time-and-a-half for the 8 hours of the sixth day. Write an argument deducing the normal hourly wage the worker earns. See margin.

In 5–7, solve the quadratic equation.

5. $120 = x^2$ $x = \pm 2\sqrt{30}$
6. $n^2 - n - 2162 = 0$ $n = -46$ or 47
7. $4y^2 + 2y = 17$ $y = \frac{-1 \pm \sqrt{69}}{4}$
8. You are asked to find the difference of the solutions to the quadratic equation $ax^2 + bx + c = 0$, and to prove your result. See margin.
   a. In this situation, if the universal conditional is $\forall$ *x in S, if p(x), then q(x)*, identify *p(x)* and *q(x)*.
   b. Write a proof following the form of Example 2.

Applying the Mathematics

9. Use the Addition and Multiplication Properties of Inequality (see Appendix A if you have forgotten what these are) to complete this sentence and prove your result is correct: *If* $\frac{1}{2}y - 5 < \frac{1}{3}y + 10$, *then* __?__. See margin.

Additional Answers

3.

Conclusions	Justifications
$1000 = 30m - 80$	Given
$1080 = 30m$	Add. Prop. of Equality (Add 80)
$72 = 2m$	Mult. Prop. of Equality (Multiply by $\frac{1}{15}$)
$2m = 72$	Reflective Prop of Equality

4. Let x be the regular hourly wage. From the given, $8(1.5x) + 460 = 598$. By the Addition Property of Equality (adding -460 to each side), $12x = 138$. Then, using the Multiplication Property of Equality (multiplying both sides by $\frac{1}{12}$), $x = 11.5$. So the worker earns $11.50 per hour.

8. a. $p(x)$: x is the difference in the two solutions to the quadratic equation $ax^2 + bx + c = 0$, $(a \neq 0)$. $q(x)$: the difference is $x = \frac{\sqrt{b^2-4ac}}{a}$ or $x = -\frac{\sqrt{b^2-4ac}}{a}$.

   b. By the Quadratic Formula, the solutions to the quadratic equation $ax^2 + bx + c = 0$ are $\frac{-b+\sqrt{b^2-4ac}}{2a}$ and $\frac{-b-\sqrt{b^2-4ac}}{2a}$. Let $x_1 = \frac{-b+\sqrt{b^2-4ac}}{2a}$ and $x_2 = \frac{-b-\sqrt{b^2-4ac}}{2a}$. Then $x = x_1 - x_2 = \frac{\sqrt{b^2-4ac}}{a}$.

10. A baseball was hit into the air and landed 300 feet from the batter. Use the result of Example 2 to estimate the distance from the plate when the ball was at its highest point. Explain your reasoning.
About 150 feet from the batter; it is the mean of $x_1 = 0$ and $x_2 = 300$.

Review

In 11 and 12, tell what kind of mathematically invalid argument is represented by the situation. *(Lesson 1-7)*

11. *If a person has heat exhaustion, he will have symptoms of headache, nausea, slow breathing, clammy skin, and cold sweat.*
On a warm summer day, a patient reports headache, vomiting, and cold skin. The doctor treats for heat exhaustion. converse error

12. $x^2 - x - 2 = (x - 2)(x + 1)$
$x^2 - 2x - 3 = (x - 3)(x + 1)$
$\therefore\ x^2 - nx - (n+1) = (x - (n + 1))(x + 1)\ \forall$ *positive integers n*
improper induction

13. Consider the following argument, based on a TV ad.

If you paid full price for a book, you did not buy it at Tiara's.
You did not pay full price for a certain book.
$\therefore$ *You bought the book at Tiara's.*

Is this argument valid or invalid? Justify your reasoning. *(Lessons 1-6, 1-7)*
invalid; inverse error

14. a. Suppose the following premises are true. Deduce a valid conclusion.

If you have outstanding school grades, you will be admitted to College Q.
If you are admitted to College Q, then you will receive financial aid.

b. What argument form did you use in answering part **a**? *(Lesson 1-6)*
a) See left. b) Law of Transitivity

15. Is the following conditional true or false? Explain your reasoning.

$\forall$ *real numbers x, if* $x^2 = 9$, *then* $x = 3$. *(Lesson 1-5)*

False. x could be -3.

16. Write the inverse, converse, and contrapositive of the following statement.

If the temperature inside a refrigerator is above 40°F, then the cooling system is activated. *(Lesson 1-5)*

See left.

17. Given the computer program

```
10 INPUT A, B
20 IF NOT (A = 7 AND B > 4) THEN PRINT "HELLO"
   ELSE PRINT "GOODBYE"
30 END
```

a. What will be printed if 7 is input for A, and 4 is input for B? HELLO

b. Use De Morgan's laws to create an equivalent computer program with a different version of line 20. See below.

c. Fill in the blank in the following program to create a computer program equivalent to the given one: (A = 7 and B > 4)

```
10 INPUT A, B
20 IF __?__ THEN PRINT "GOODBYE"
   ELSE PRINT "HELLO"
30 END
```

(Lessons 1-3, 1-5)

(b) IF (A ≠ 7) or (B ≤ 4) THEN PRINT "HELLO" ELSE PRINT "GOODBYE"

14a) Sample: *If you have outstanding school grades, then you will receive financial aid.*

16) Inverse: *If the temperature inside a refrigerator is not above 40°F, then the cooling system is not activated.*
Converse: *If a refrigerator's cooling system is activated, then the temperature inside is above 40°F.*
Contrapositive: *If a refrigerator's cooling system is not activated, then the temperature inside is not above 40°F.*

Notes on Questions

Question 10 Here we neglect air resistance, so the ball is found to reach its highest point at the midpoint of its path, that is, at about 150 feet from the batter. However, the movement of air can significantly affect the path of a ball, causing the actual highest point to be either before or after the middle of the path.

Question 15 Error Alert Some students may need to be reminded that a disproof of a statement requires only one example, but a proof requires a general argument.

(Notes on Questions continue on page 66.)

Follow-up for Lesson 1-8

Practice

For more questions on SPUR Objectives, use **Lesson Master 1-8** (shown on page 63).

Assessment

Oral Communication On the chalkboard write "If $11x - 32 = 133$, then $x = 15$." As students state the steps and justifications in a two-column proof, record these on the board. [Students write a direct proof of the solving of a linear equation.]

(Follow-up continues on page 66.)

If we let $x_1 = \frac{-b - \sqrt{b^2 - 4ac}}{2a}$

and $x_2 = \frac{-b + \sqrt{b^2 - 4ac}}{2a}$,

Then $x = x_1 - x_2 = \frac{-\sqrt{b^2 - 4ac}}{a}$.

9. $y < 90$;

Conclusions	Justifications
$\frac{1}{2}y - 5 < \frac{1}{3}y + 10$	Given
$\frac{1}{6}y < 15$	Addition Property of Inequality
$y < 90$	Multiplication Property of Inequality

Extension

Have students build off the proof in **Example 4** to prove that the vertex of any parabola, $y = ax^2 + bx + c$, is given by $(\frac{-b}{2a}, \frac{-b^2}{4a} + c)$. [The solutions to the quadratic equation $0 = ax^2 + bx + c$ are the *x*-intercepts of the graph of the function $y = ax^2 + bx + c$, since *x*-intercepts are by definition the point(s) where the *y*-coordinate is equal to zero. Since parabolas are symmetrical about the line through their vertex (the axis of symmetry), the vertex must be exactly midway between the two *x*-intercepts, or the mean of the two *x*-intercepts. It has been proven that $\frac{-b}{2a}$ is the mean of the two solutions to any quadratic equation in **Example 4.** Therefore, $\frac{-b}{2a}$ is the *x*-coordinate of the vertex of the parabola. To find the *y*-coordinate, substitute into the function: $y = a(\frac{-b}{2a})^2 + b(\frac{-b}{2a}) + c$. Simplifying, we find $y = \frac{-b^2}{4a} + c$. Therefore, the vertex of any parabola, $y = ax^2 + bx + c$, is given by $(\frac{-b}{2a}, \frac{-b^2}{4a} + c)$.]

Project Update Project 5, *Proof Styles,* on page 67, relates to the content of this lesson.

Notes on Questions

Question 24 The first thing that students should think is that only one of the students is correct. Then, to determine that student, the solution for student B might be checked in the original sentence. (It works.) Now try some other number to see whether student B or student C is correct. Once this is determined, examine the argument to find the error.

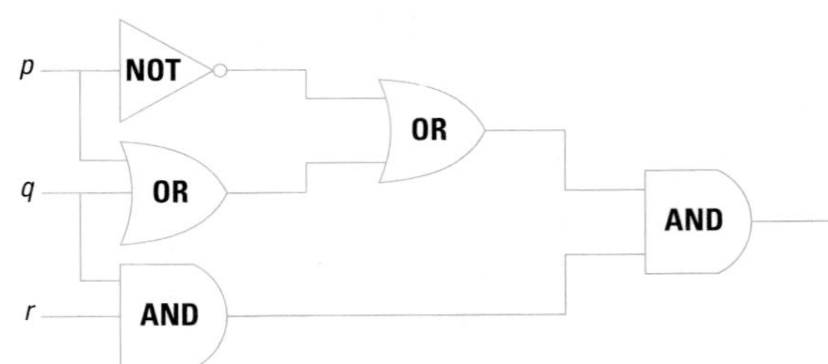

18. Compute the output signal for the logic network at the left for each of the following input signals. *(Lesson 1-4)*
a. $p = 1, q = 1, r = 0$ 1
b. $p = 0, q = 1, r = 0$ 1
c. $p = 0, q = 0, r = 1$ 0

19. Prove that for any pair of truth values of p and q, the converse and inverse of $p \Rightarrow q$ have the same truth value. *(Lesson 1-5)* See margin.

In 20 and 21, write the negation of the statement. *(Lesson 1-2)*

20. *$\forall$ real numbers x and y, xy = 2.*
$\exists$ real numbers x and y such that $xy \neq 2$.

21. *$\exists$ real numbers x and y such that xy = 0.*
$\forall$ real numbers x and y, $xy \neq 0$.

22. a. Rewrite the following statement using *there exists.* See left.

Some values of θ make cos θ = 0.

b. Is the statement a universal or an existential statement? *(Lesson 1-1)* existential

22a) *$\exists$ a real number value of θ such that cos θ = 0.*

23. Consider the universal statement

$\forall$ real numbers t, $f(t) = -4t^2 - 3t + 1$.

Use the Law of Substitution to calculate each.
a. $f(-5)$ -84 **b.** $f(2 + h)$ $-4h^2 - 19h - 21$ **c.** $f(t + 1)$ $-4t^2 - 11t - 6$
(Previous course, Lesson 1-1)

Exploration

24. Three students were asked to solve the equation $3 - 3t = 4(1 - t)$. Their work follows. Is any student correct? Is any student wrong? Why or why not? See left.

Student *A* wrote:
Given: $3 - 3t = 4(1 - t)$
Use the Distributive Property.
$3(1 - t) = 4(1 - t)$
Multiply both sides by $\frac{1}{1-t}$.
$3 = 4$
I have reached a false conclusion, so there is no solution.

Student *B* wrote:
Given: $3 - 3t = 4(1 - t)$
Use the Distributive Property.
$3 - 3t = 4 - 4t$
Add 4t to both sides.
$3 + t = 4$
$t = 1$

Student *C* wrote:

Conclusions	Justifications
$3 - 3t = 4(1 - t)$	Given
$0t = 4(1 - t)$	Arithmetic
$0 = 4(1 - t)$	Zero Product Property
$0 = 4 - 4t$	Distributive Property
$0 = 0t$	Arithmetic

t can be any number.

24) Student *B* is correct, because all steps he used are valid. Both students *A* and *C* are wrong. Student *A* multiplied both sides by $\frac{1}{1-t}$, which is invalid if $t = 1$. Student *C* made a mistake when he equated $3 - 3t$ to $0 \cdot t$.

Additional Answers

19.

p	q	p AND q	NOT q	(NOT q) OR (p AND q)
1	1	1	0	1
1	0	0	1	1
0	1	0	0	0
0	0	0	1	1

Possible Responses, page 67

1. The original version of this logical predicament is that of the village barber's boasting that of course he does not shave those people who shave themselves but does shave all those who do not shave themselves. Who shaves the barber? If he does not shave himself, then by his boast he must shave himself. If he does shave himself, then he cannot shave himself. Contradictions in set theory led mathematicians to question the validity of deductive mathematics. Russell and Whitehead attempted to derive mathematics from self-evident universal logical truths (logicism). Hilbert's formalism hoped to derive mathematics from a set of basic assumptions. Kronecker's intuitionism avoided all use of numbers which could not be constructed from natural numbers—it was free from contradiction because it was limited to constructive methods.

A project presents an opportunity for you to extend your knowledge of a topic related to the material of this chapter. You should allow more time for a project than you do for a typical homework question.

PROJECTS 1 CHAPTER ONE

1 Russell's Paradox
Question 27 of Lesson 1-1 refers to Russell's paradox. Report on other examples of this paradox, and how paradoxes of this type caused a crisis in the foundations of mathematics at the beginning of the twentieth century. Describe ways in which mathematicians have tried to deal with this crisis, including the development of new types of logic.

2 Lewis Carroll's Logic
Charles Dodgson (Lewis Carroll) developed a way of representing statements in logical arguments. Describe his method and indicate some problems to which he applied it.

3 Boolean Algebra
Look in a mathematics book to determine what are usually taken as postulates for a *Boolean* algebra. What are theorems that can be proved? Illustrate these postulates and theorems with logic networks.

4 Logic and Programming
Report on how logical variables, operators (AND, OR, and NOT), and statements (IF, IF-THEN, IF-THEN-ELSE, and CASE) work in two different computer or calculator languages. Describe both their syntax (format) and semantics (what they cause the computer or calculator to do).

5 Proof Styles
Search three or more geometry books for a theorem that is proved differently in the books. Compare and contrast the proofs on such characteristics as the justifications used, the amount of detail, and their length and clarity.

Chapter 1 Projects

Discuss Chapter 1 projects and what you expect students to do with them. For more information about how projects can be incorporated into this course, see *General Teaching Suggestions: Projects* in the *Professional Sourcebook* which begins on page T20 in Part 1 of the Teacher's Edition.

The projects in this book are meant to be equivalent to about a one night's full homework assignment. Normally you should allow students their choice of project.

Chapter 1 projects relate chiefly to the content of the lessons as shown below. They can, however, be used at any time after the lessons have been taught. Suggestions for using a project are given in the lesson notes under *Project Update*.

Project	Lesson(s)
1	1-1
2	1-6
3	1-4
4	1-3, 1-4, 1-5
5	1-8

1 Russell's Paradox Most books on the overall history of mathematics (e.g., *History of Mathematics —An Introduction,* by Victor Katz, or *An Introduction to the History of Mathematics*, by Howard Eves) will contain some material related to Russell's Paradox.

2 Lewis Carroll's Logic Dodgson's book *Symbolic Logic and the Game of Logic*, contains a detailed description of the method.

3 Boolean Algebra Books on abstract or higher algebra usually discuss Boolean algebras.

4 Logic and Programming This is an appropriate project for students who have already taken a course in computer programming.

5 Proof Styles You may wish to distinguish between different mathematical treatments and different ways of writing what are essentially the same mathematical arguments.

2. Charles Dodgson developed methods of expressing classical logic in terms of symbols. He dealt particularly with syllogisms and sorites. He also developed a diagrammatic method of drawing conclusions from propositions. Dodgson's favorite problems were thought-provoking puzzles. Sample problems students may use come from the book *Symbolic Logic and the Game of Logic* by Lewis Carroll, which also contains all the information needed to use Carroll's methods.
3. In the following theorems and postulates, the letters *A, B,* and *C* symbolize any subsets of any universe ℓ. The most important interpretations are binary Boolean Algebra where ℓ consists of a singular element.

(Responses continue on page 68.)

Summary

The Summary gives an overview of the entire chapter and provides an opportunity for students to consider the material as a whole. Thus, the Summary can be used to help students relate and unify the concepts presented in the chapter.

Vocabulary

Terms, symbols, and properties are listed by lesson to provide a checklist of concepts a student must know. Emphasize to students that they should read the vocabulary list carefully before starting the Progress Self-Test. If students do not understand the meaning of a term, they should refer back to the indicated lesson.

Additional Responses, page 67

3. (Project 3, continued) If a set contains the element, it can be represented by a 1; if it does not, the ∅ will be represented by a 0. ⊕ represents logical addition, and ⊗ represents logical multiplication.

Addition

⊕	0	1
0	0	1
1	1	1

Multiplication

⊗	0	1
0	0	0
1	0	1

Complementation

x	x'
0	1
1	0

Postulates

Commutative Laws
$A \oplus B = B \oplus A$ $\quad A \otimes B = B \otimes A$

Associative Laws
$A \oplus (B \oplus C) = (A \oplus B) \oplus C$
$A \otimes (B \otimes C) = (A \otimes B) \otimes C$

Distributive Laws
$A \otimes (B \oplus C) = (A \otimes B) \oplus (A \otimes C)$
$A \oplus (B \otimes C) = (A \oplus B) \otimes (B \oplus C)$

Idempotent Laws
$A \oplus A = A$ $\quad A \otimes A = A$

Complementation Laws
$A \oplus A' = 1$ $\quad A \otimes A' = 0$

De Morgan's Laws
$(A \oplus B)' = A' \otimes B'$
$(A \otimes B)' = A' \oplus B'$

Double Complementation
$(A')' = A$

Laws Involving ϕ and I
$A \oplus 1 = 1$ $\quad A \oplus 0 = A$
$A \otimes 0 = A$ $\quad A \otimes 1 = A$
$1' = 0$ $\quad 0' = 1$

Laws of Absorption
$A \otimes (A \oplus B) = A$
$A \oplus (A \otimes B) = A$

The following are the building blocks of logic networks.

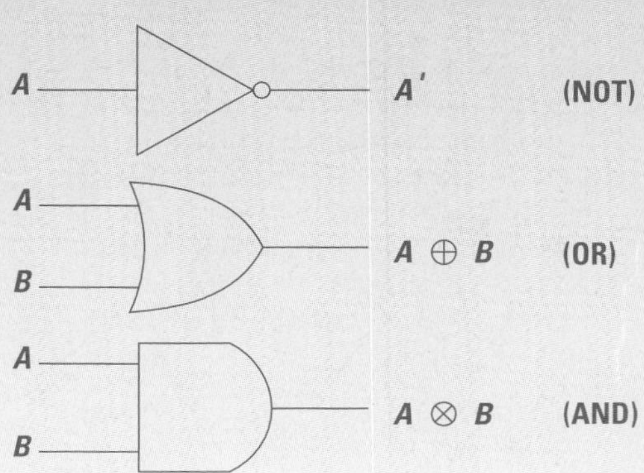

All the above theorems can be constructed by combining the gates above. For example:

Law of Absorption

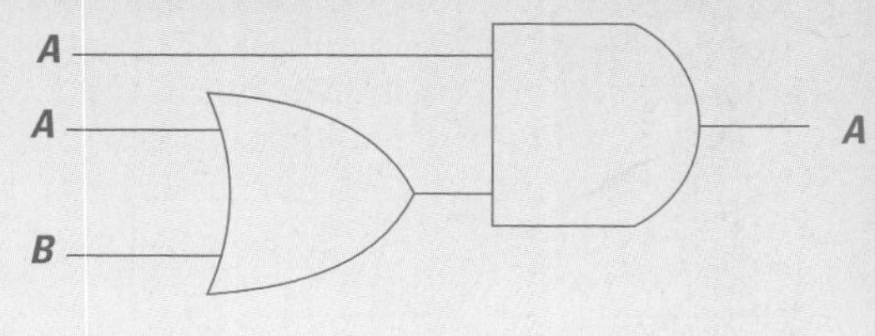

SUMMARY

In this chapter you have studied logic as well as the processes of reasoning used in mathematics and the everyday world. Universal statements assert that all members of a set have a certain property, and existential statements assert that at least one member of a set has a certain property. To write the negation of a statement, you express what it would mean for the statement to be false. The negation of a universal statement is an existential statement, and the negation of an existential statement is a universal statement.

The three words *and, or,* and *not* are important in the study of logic, and have applications to the design and evaluation of computer logic networks. De Morgan's Laws can be used to negate logical expressions containing *and* and *or.*

Conditional statements, symbolized $p \Rightarrow q$, are false under only one set of circumstances: when the antecedent is true and the consequent is false. As is the case with existential and universal statements, conditionals can be expressed in a variety of forms.

A conditional and its contrapositive are logically equivalent, that is, they always have the same truth values. However, a conditional and its converse may have different truth values, as may a conditional and its inverse.

An argument consists of premises and a conclusion. An argument is valid if no matter what the truth value of its statements, the truth value of the argument form is true. The Laws of Detachment (*modus ponens*), Indirect Reasoning (*modus tollens*), and Transitivity are valid forms of argument. Converse Error, Inverse Error, and Improper Induction are invalid forms of argument. The direct proof of a universal statement uses valid forms of argument to make a chain of deductions leading from the antecedent to the consequent of the conditional to be proved.

VOCABULARY

Below are the most important terms and phrases for this chapter. You should be able to give a general description and a specific example of each and a precise definition for those marked with an asterisk (*).

Lesson 1-1
statement
∀, ∃, quantifier
*universal statement
Law of Substitution
*existential statement
*counterexample

Lesson 1-2
*negation, *not p*
truth table

Lesson 1-3
**p or q*, **p and q*
exclusive *or*, inclusive *or*
logical expression
*logically equivalent expressions, ≡
De Morgan's Laws

Lesson 1-4
input-output table
network of logic gates
functionally equivalent networks
Boolean algebra

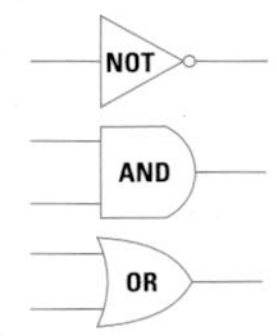

Lesson 1-5
*conditional statement, $p \Rightarrow q$
*antecedent, hypothesis
*consequent, conclusion
*negation of a simple conditional
*negation of a universal conditional
*contrapositive
Contrapositive Theorem
*converse, *inverse
**p* if and only if *q*, $p \Leftrightarrow q$
*biconditional
**p* only if *q*
sufficient condition
necessary condition

Lesson 1-6
argument, premises, ∴
conclusion of an argument
*valid argument
valid conclusion
*Law of Detachment, *modus ponens*
*Law of Indirect Reasoning, *modus tollens*
*Law of Transitivity

Lesson 1-7
invalid argument
converse error, inverse error
improper induction
Goldbach's conjecture
Euler circles, Venn diagrams

Lesson 1-8
mathematical proof
justification
direct proof

CHAPTER ONE

PROGRESS SELF-TEST

6–11) See margin.

Take this test as you would take a test in class. Then check the test yourself using the solutions at the back of the book.

In 1 and 2, match each sentence with the best description of it:

(a) statement
(b) universal statement
(c) existential statement
(d) none of these

1. *There is a condor that has been born in captivity.* c

2. $4 + x \geq 17$ d
3. *True or false.* True
   $\forall$ *mammals m, m is not a mosquito.*
4. Identify all statements logically equivalent to
   All Olympic medalists are tested for illegal drug use.
   (a) *No Olympic medalists are tested for illegal drug use.*
   (b) *There exists an Olympic medalist who is tested for illegal drug use.*
   (c) *Some Olympic medalist is tested for illegal drug use.*
   (d) *For all Olympic medalists m, m is tested for illegal drug use.*
   (e) *If an individual is an Olympic medalist, then the individual is tested for illegal drug use.*
   (f) *None of these sentences is equivalent to the original.*
   d, e

True

5. *True or false.* $\forall$ *real numbers y,* $0 + y = y$.
6. Write the negation of the statement in Question 5.
7. The following statement is true:
   $\forall$ *real numbers x,* $\sqrt{x^2} = |x|$.
   Use the Law of Substitution to simplify $\sqrt{(-7c)^2}$, where c is a real number.
8. Rewrite $-8 \leq x < 12$, spelling out the implied *and* and *or*.
9. Write the negation of
   The bald eagle is our national bird and "The Star-Spangled Banner" is our national anthem.
10. A researcher has collected information on courses taken by students in different parts of the country. Student computer records have been coded by a field called Location that has the values 1 to 6, as follows:
    1 Northeast
    2 Southeast
    3 Central
    4 Plains
    5 Southwest
    6 West
    The researcher wants to consider all but the Southwest and Central categories for parts of the study. Consider the following command:
    SELECT IF NOT (LOCATION = 2 OR LOCATION = 3).
    Use De Morgan's Laws to change this command without changing its output.
11. Write the following statement as an *if-then* statement:
    A person can be admitted to an R-rated movie only if the person is at least 17 years old.
12. Imagine that s is a particular real number. Consider the sentence
    If $s < 4$, *then* $|s| < 4$.
    Under what circumstances is this sentence false?
    $s \leq -4$

Progress Self-Test

For the development of mathematical competence, feedback and correction, along with the opportunity to practice, are necessary. The Progress Self-Test provides the opportunity for feedback and correction; the Chapter Review provides additional opportunities and practice. We cannot overemphasize the importance of these end-of-chapter materials. It is at this point that the material "gels" for many students, allowing them to solidify skills and understanding. In general, student performance should be markedly improved after these pages.

Assign the Progress Self-Test as a one-night assignment. Worked-out *solutions* for all questions are in the Selected Answers section of the student book. Encourage students to take the Progress Self-Test honestly, grade themselves, and then be prepared to discuss the test in class.

Advise students to pay special attention to those Chapter Review questions (pages 71–75) that correspond to questions missed on the Progress Self-Test.

Additional Answers

6. $\exists$ a real number y, such that $0 + y \neq y$.
7. $\sqrt{(-7c)^2} = |-7c| = |7c|$
8. ($x > -8$ or $x = -8$) and ($x < 12$).
9. *The bald eagle is not our national bird or "The Star-Spangled Banner" is not our national anthem.*
10. SELECT IF NOT (LOCATION = 2) AND NOT (LOCATION = 3)
11. *If a person can be admitted to an R-rated movie, then the person is at least 17 years old.*

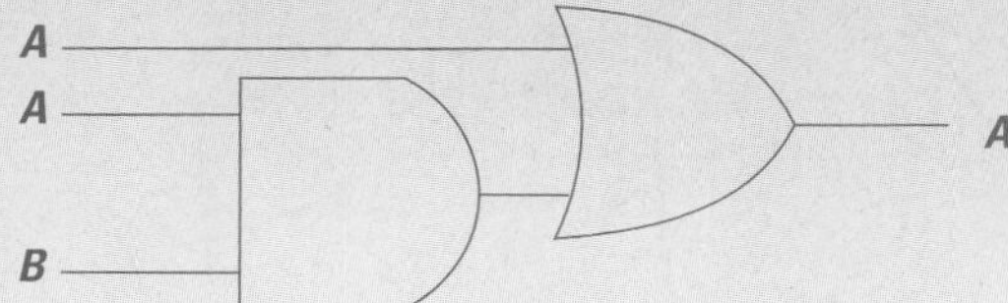

4. Sample:

BASIC

logical variables: integers
logical operators: NOT, AND, OR
logical statements: IF-THEN
IF-THEN-ELSE

Pascal

logical constants: TRUE, FALSE
logical variables: Boolean
logical operators: NOT, AND, OR
logical statements: IF-THEN
IF-THEN-ELSE
CASE

FORTRAN

logical constants: .TRUE., .FALSE.
logical variables: logical
logical operators:. AND., .OR., .NOT.
logical statements: IF (logical or arithmetic) statement

Note that in some versions of programming languages syntax and semantics may vary. Here is a sample of possible syntax and semantic descriptions of the conditional statement for three programming languages:

(Responses continue on page 70.)

CHAPTER ONE

Additional Answers

15. *If two lines are parallel, then when cut by a transversal, corresponding angles have the same measure. If two lines cut by a transversal have corresponding angles with the same measure, then the lines are parallel.*

19. -1; 11;
Proof: It is given that
$2(x + 5)^2 = 40x + 72$.
Expanding the left side, yields
$2x^2 + 20x + 50 = 40x + 72$.
Adding $-40x - 72$ to both sides results in
$2x^2 - 20x + 22 = 0$.
Factoring the left side yields
$2(x + 1)(x - 11) = 0$.
By the Zero Product Theorem,
$x + 1 = 0$ or $x - 11 = 0$.
Therefore, $x = -1$ or $x = 11$.

22.

p	*q*	*p OR q*	*NOT q*	*output*
1	1	1	0	0
1	0	1	1	1
0	1	1	0	0
0	0	0	1	0

23.

p	*q*	*p or q*	*not (p or q)*
T	T	T	F
T	F	T	F
F	T	T	F
F	F	F	T

13. *Multiple choice.* A conditional is logically equivalent to which of the following? c
(a) its converse
(b) its inverse
(c) its contrapositive

14. *Multiple choice.* Identify the sentence which is the contrapositive of

If you travel to Africa, then you need to have a malaria shot. b

(a) *If you need to have a malaria shot, then you are traveling to Africa.*
(b) *If you do not need to have a malaria shot, then you are not traveling to Africa.*
(c) *If you are not traveling to Africa, then you do not need to have a malaria shot.*

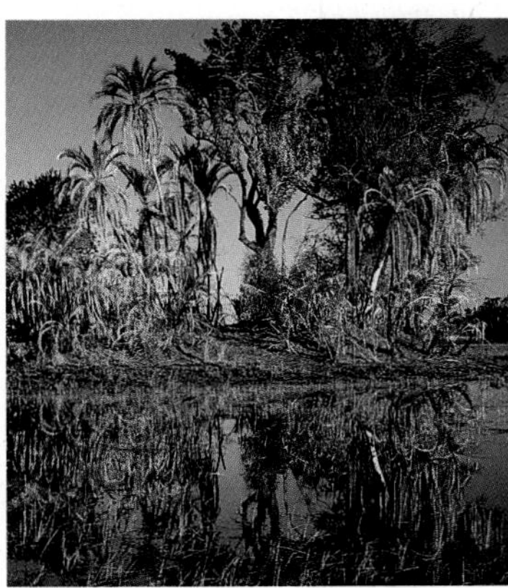

Okavango Delta, Botswana, Africa

15. Write the following theorem in an equivalent way using two *if-then* statements:

Two lines are parallel if and only if, when cut by a transversal, corresponding angles have the same measure. See margin.

In 16 and 17, match the argument with the appropriate argument form and indicate whether the argument is valid or invalid.
(a) Law of Detachment (*modus ponens*)
(b) Law of Indirect Reasoning (*modus tollens*)
(c) Law of Transitivity
(d) Converse Error
(e) Inverse Error
(f) Improper Induction

19, 22, 23) See margin.

16. *For all numbers x,* $x^3 \geq 27 \Rightarrow x \geq 3$.
$\sqrt{8} < 3$
$\therefore \quad (\sqrt{8})^3 < 27$ b, valid

17. *If* $\triangle ABC \cong \triangle DEF$*, then* $\angle ABC \cong \angle DEF$.
$\triangle ABC$ *is not congruent to* $\triangle DEF$.
$\therefore \quad \angle ABC$ *is not congruent to* $\angle DEF$. e, invalid

18. Determine whether the argument is valid or invalid. Justify your reasoning. See below.

If Pete hit three home runs in the game, then his team won. If Pete was not named most valuable player, then his team did not win. Pete hit three home runs in the game. Therefore, Pete was named most valuable player.

19. Finish this statement and supply a proof.
If $2(x + 5)^2 = 40x + 72$,
then $x = \underline{\ ?\ }$ *or* $x = \underline{\ ?\ }$.

20. In a direct proof of $\forall\ x,\ p(x) \Rightarrow q(x)$, what statement is called the "given"? *p(x)*

In 21 and 22, consider the network below.

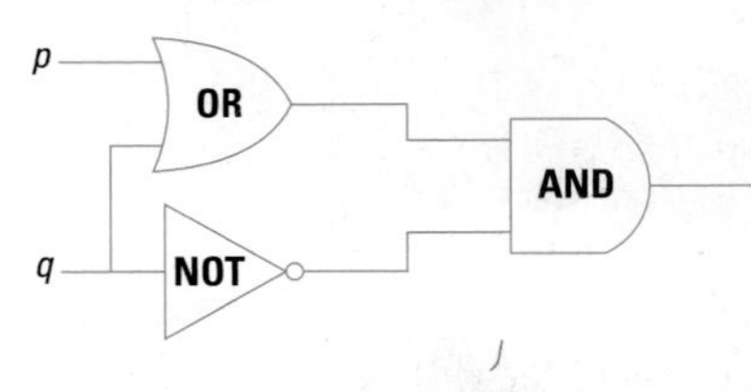

21. Write the logical expression that corresponds to the network. *(p or q) and (not q)*

22. Write an input-output table for the network.

23. Write the truth table for *not (p or q)*.

24. Consider the universal statement
$\forall$ *real numbers x and y,* $\sqrt{\mathbf{x} + \mathbf{y}} = \sqrt{\mathbf{x}} + \sqrt{\mathbf{y}}$.
Is the statement true or false? If true, explain why. If false, give a counterexample.
False; counter example: Let $x = 1$ and $y = 1$. $\sqrt{1 + 1} = \sqrt{2}$, $\sqrt{1} + \sqrt{1} = 2$. But $\sqrt{2} \neq 2$. So $\sqrt{1 + 1} \neq \sqrt{1} + \sqrt{1}$.

18) Valid; using the Law of Detachment followed by the Law of Indirect Reasoning.

Additional Responses, page 67

4. (Project 4, continued)
In BASIC, the syntax is
IF/condition/THEN/statement/.
The condition may be constructed from variables, logical operators, relational operators (i.e., <, >, etc.), and equality operators (i.e., = or <>). The statement is any valid BASIC statement and is often a GOTO statement to change the flow of the program. To execute an IF-THEN statement, the condition is evaluated and if it is true the statement following THEN is executed. Otherwise, the condition is false, and the program advances to the next line in the program without executing the statement following THEN. Some BASIC languages have been enhanced with the IF-THEN-ELSE construct. Its syntax is
IF/condition/THEN/statement/ELSE/statement/.
The semantics are the same as described for the IF-THEN statement with the exception that when the condition is false, the program executes the statement following the ELSE before advancing.

In Pascal, the syntax is
IF/condition/THEN/then-statement/ELSE/else-statement/.
In Pascal, the /then-statement/ is executed if the condition is true and

CHAPTER REVIEW

Questions on SPUR Objectives

SPUR stands for **S**kills, **P**roperties, **U**ses, and **R**epresentations. The Chapter Review questions are grouped according to the SPUR Objectives for this chapter.

SKILLS DEAL WITH THE PROCEDURES USED TO GET ANSWERS.

5–8, 11) See margin.

Objective A: *Identify forms of logical statements.* *(Lessons 1-1, 1-5)*

In 1–3, identify the sentence as an existential statement, a universal statement, or neither.

1. *For all baseball seasons s, s runs from April through October.* universal
2. *–5 is an integer.* neither
3. *∃ a positive integer n such that n is smaller than 1.* existential
4. Consider the statement

   If the ballet is The Nutcracker, *then it is performed during the holiday season.*

   Identify each statement below as its contrapositive, converse, or inverse.

   a. *If the ballet is not* The Nutcracker, *then it is not performed during the holiday season.*

   b. *If the ballet is not performed during the holiday season, then it is not* The Nutcracker.

   c. *If the ballet is performed during the holiday season, then it is* The Nutcracker. converse

   a) inverse b) contrapositive

Objective B: *Write equivalent forms of logical statements.* *(Lessons 1-1, 1-3, 1-5)*

In 5–7, rewrite each sentence as the appropriate universal or existential statement, using *for all* or *there exists*, respectively.

5. *No country has landed people on Mars.*

6. *Every intelligence memo is read by at least one government official.*
7. *Every composite number has a factor other than 1 and the number itself.*
8. Rewrite the given statement in *if-then* form.

   Never practicing after piano lessons is a sufficient condition for not learning to play piano.

9. Determine which of the following is (are) equivalent to

   tan θ < 0 is a necessary condition for θ to be in quadrant II or IV. b, c

   (a) *If tan θ < 0, then θ is in quadrant II or IV.*

   (b) *If θ is in quadrant II or IV, then tan θ < 0.*

   (c) *If tan θ ≮ 0, then θ is not in quadrant II and not in quadrant IV.*

   (d) *If θ is not in quadrant II and not in quadrant IV, then tan θ ≮ 0.*

   (e) None of the above is equivalent to the given conditional.

10. *True or false.* The statement *A student is allowed to take calculus only if the student has taken two years of algebra.* is logically equivalent to the statement *If a student has taken two years of algebra, then the student is allowed to take calculus.* False
11. Write two *if-then* statements which together are equivalent to the statement below.

    Passing a state's bar exam is a necessary and sufficient condition for practicing law in that state.

Pathfinder, the 7th Mars lander, arrived with the Sojourner rover in July, 1997. The USSR's Mars 2 was first, arriving in November, 1971.

Chapter 1 Review

Resources

From the ***Teacher's Resource File***

- Answer Master for Chapter 1 Review
- Assessment Sourcebook: Chapter 1 Test, Forms A–D

Additional Resources

- TestWorks CD-ROM

The main objectives for the chapter are organized in the Chapter Review under the four types of understanding this book promotes—Skills, Properties, Uses, and Representations.

Additional Answers

5. *∀ countries c, c has not landed people on Mars.*
6. *∀ intelligence memos m, ∃ a government official g, such that g reads m.*
7. *∀ composite numbers n, ∃ a positive integer y, such that y ≠ n, y ≠ 1, and y is a factor of n.*
8. *If you never practice your piano lessons, you will not learn to play piano.*
11. *If one passes a state's bar exam, then one can practice law in the state. If one can practice law in a state, then one has passed the state's bar exam.*

the /else-statement/ is executed if the condition is false. One notable feature of Pascal that makes it powerful is that each statement is a series of statements surrounded by the key words "BEGIN" and "END."

In FORTRAN, the syntax is

IF (/logical expression/) /statement/ or
IF (/arithmetic expression/), label1, label2, label3.

In the first case, the logical expression is evaluated and if it is .TRUE. the statement is executed, otherwise the program continues to the next line in the sequence. The arithmetic IF evaluates an expression, and the program jumps to label1 if the result is less than 0, label2 if the result equals 0, and label3 if the result is greater than 0.

5. In UCSMP *Geometry* by Usiskin, Coxford, and Hirschhorn, the proof for the Pythagorean Theorem uses areas of squares and triangles and algebraic manipulation. It assumes the student knows these basic area formulas and can square a quantity. The proof itself is clear and concise but the explanations for the shaded figure being a square is only included in the teacher's edition for discussion with students.

(Responses continue on page 73.)

Skills include simple and complicated procedures for getting answers as well as the study of algorithms.

Properties cover the mathematical justifications for procedures and results, including the writing of proofs and informal arguments.

Uses include real-world applications of the mathematics along with the modeling of real situations.

Representations include graphs and diagrams along with the invention of other metaphors to describe the mathematics.

To the *lay person* basic understanding of mathematics is usually found in Skills. The *mathematician* prefers to think of understanding in terms of Properties. The *engineer* often tests understanding by the ability to Use mathematics. The *psychologist* often views "true" understanding as being achieved through Representations or metaphors. The SPUR framework conveys the authors' views that all of these views have validity, and that together they contribute to the deep understanding of mathematics which we want students to have.

Additional Answers

12. b. ($x = -3$ or $x > -3$) and ($x = 3$ or $x < 3$)
13. *If $x > 1$, then $\log x > 0$.*
14. a. *Sue is not wearing a blue sweater.*
    b. *Sue is wearing a blue sweater and she doesn't have brown eyes.*
15. *Some British bobby carries a gun.*
16. *Some President is not guarded by any Secret Service agent.*
17. A person wants to travel from the U.S. to Europe and doesn't travel by plane or by ship.
19. Excessive bail shall be required, or excessive fines shall be imposed, or cruel and unusual punishments shall be inflicted.

CHAPTER ONE

12b, 13–17, 19, 24, 26a, 33, 34a) See margin.

12. **a.** Rewrite the inequality $|x| \le 3$ using a double inequality. $-3 \le x \le 3$
b. Express the double inequality in part **a** by writing out the implied *and* and *or*.

13. Write a conditional statement that is logically equivalent to
In order for $\log x > 0$, it is sufficient that $x > 1$.

14. Given the statements
p: Sue is wearing a blue sweater.
q: Sue has brown eyes.
Write the statement whose logical expression is given.
a. *not p* **b.** *p and (not q)*

Objective C: *Write the negation of a logical statement.* (Lessons 1-2, 1-3, 1-5)

In 15–19, write the negation of the statement. If the statement is written using informal language, then write the negation using informal language.

15. *No British bobby (police officer) carries a gun.*

16. *Every President is guarded by at least one Secret Service agent.*

17. *If a person wants to travel from the U.S. to Europe, then the person must fly or must travel by ship.*

18. *If $m\angle A = 40°$, then $\angle A$ is not obtuse.*
$m\angle A = 40°$ and $\angle A$ is obtuse.

19. *Excessive bail shall not be required, nor excessive fines imposed, nor cruel and unusual punishments inflicted.* (Amendment VIII of the Bill of Rights)

20. *True or false.* The negation of
$\forall$ *real numbers z, if $z^2 > 1$ then $z > 1$.* is
$\exists$ *a real number z such that $z^2 > 1$ and $z \not> 1$.* True

21. Use De Morgan's Laws to write the negation of the logical expression *(not p) or q*.
p and (not q)

Objective D: *Determine the truth value of a logical statement.* (Lessons 1-1, 1-2, 1-3, 1-5)

In 22 and 23, determine the truth value of each statement, given the following.
$p(x)$: $x < -4$ $q(x)$: $x > 15$ $r(x)$: $x \le 6$

22. $q(7)$ *or* $(\sim r(7))$ True

23. $\sim(p(7)$ *or* $q(7))$ *and* $r(7)$ False

In 24 and 25, determine the truth value of the given statement. If false, provide a counterexample.

24. *Every quadrilateral whose diagonals bisect each other is a rectangle.*

25. $\exists$ *a real number x such that $x^2 < x$.* True

26. Consider the statement
$\forall$ *real numbers x, $\sin^2 x + \cos^2 x = 1$.*
a. Write the negation of this statement.
b. Which is true: the statement or its negation? the statement

PROPERTIES DEAL WITH THE PRINCIPLES BEHIND THE MATHEMATICS.

Objective E: *Identify properties of logical statements.* (Lessons 1-1, 1-2, 1-3, 1-5)

In 27 and 28, determine whether the given sentence is a statement.

27. $7 + 3 = 12$ yes **28.** $2x - 5 \ge 8$ no

29. *True or false.* A conditional and its converse are logically equivalent. False

30. Suppose that z is a real number and consider the following statement:
If $z^2 > 1$ then $z > 1$.
Under what circumstances is this statement false? When z is negative.

31. *True or false.* The negation of an *if-then* statement is another *if-then* statement. False

32. *True or false.* *p or q* is false only when both *p* and *q* are false. True

Objective F: *Use the Law of Substitution to verify specific statements.* (Lesson 1-1)

33. The following statement is true:
$\forall$ *real numbers a and b,*
$(a + b)^3 = a^3 + 3a^2b + 3ab^2 + b^3$.
Use the Law of Substitution to expand $(3x + 4)^3$.

34. **a.** What universal statement can you use to evaluate $(\sqrt{45} + \sqrt{20})^2$?
b. Use your answer to part **a** to evaluate the given expression. 125

24. False, every parallelogram has diagonals bisecting each other. A parallelogram need not be a rectangle.
26. a. *$\exists$ a real number x such that $\sin^2 x + \cos^2 x \ne 1$.*
33. $(3x + 4)^3 = 27x^3 + 108x^2 + 144x + 64$
34. a. $(a + b)^2 = a^2 + 2ab + b^2$
44. Multiplication by $\frac{1}{x^2}$ is meaningless when $x = 0$.
45. $\frac{-b + \sqrt{b^2 - 4ac}}{2a} \cdot \frac{-b - \sqrt{b^2 - 4ac}}{2a} = \frac{b^2 - (b^2 - 4ac)}{4a^2} = \frac{4ac}{4a^2} = \frac{c}{a}$
46.

Conclusions	Justifications
$46 + 9m < 11m - 4$	given
$-2m < -50$	Addition Prop. of Inequality
$m > 25$	Multiplication Prop. of Inequality

Objective G: *Determine whether arguments are valid or invalid.* (Lessons 1-6, 1-7)

In 35–38, tell whether the argument is valid or invalid. Support your answer with a reference to one or more of the following.

I. Law of Detachment (*modus ponens*)
II. Law of Indirect Reasoning (*modus tollens*)
III. Law of Transitivity
IV. Converse Error
V. Inverse Error
VI. Improper Induction

35. *If a polygon is a regular pentagon, then it has five sides.* invalid by IV
Polygon PENTA has five sides.
∴ *Polygon PENTA is a regular pentagon.*

36. $\forall$ *real numbers x*, $x > 10 \Rightarrow x^2 > 100$.
$x^2 \leq 100$
∴ $x \leq 10$ valid by II

37. *If a quadrilateral is a rhombus, then it is a parallelogram.*
If a quadrilateral is a square, then it is a rhombus.
∴ *If a quadrilateral is a square, then it is a parallelogram.* valid by III

38. θ *is not in quadrant I.*
If θ *is in quadrant I, then* $\sin\theta > 0$.
∴ $\sin\theta \leq 0$. invalid by V

39. Consider the argument
$$2^2 \cdot 2^3 = (2 \cdot 2)(2 \cdot 2 \cdot 2) = 2^5 = 2^{2+3}$$
$$2^3 \cdot 2^4 = (2 \cdot 2 \cdot 2)(2 \cdot 2 \cdot 2 \cdot 2) = 2^7 = 2^{3+4}$$
∴ $2^n 2^m = 2^{n+m}$ *for all integers n, m.*

a. Is the conclusion true? yes
b. Is the argument valid? no

45, 46) See margin.

Objective H: *Use logic to prove or disprove statements.* (Lessons 1-1, 1-3, 1-6, 1-8)

40. Consider the conditional True
For all positive real numbers, y, a, and b,
$y = ab \Rightarrow \log y = \log a + \log b$.
Is it true or false? If false, give a counterexample.

41. *Multiple choice.* Which is a valid conclusion using all of the following premises? c
If triangles ADC and ADB are congruent, then triangle ABC is isosceles.
If $\overline{AD} \perp \overline{BC}$, *then triangles ADC and ADB are congruent.*
$\overline{AD} \perp \overline{BC}$.

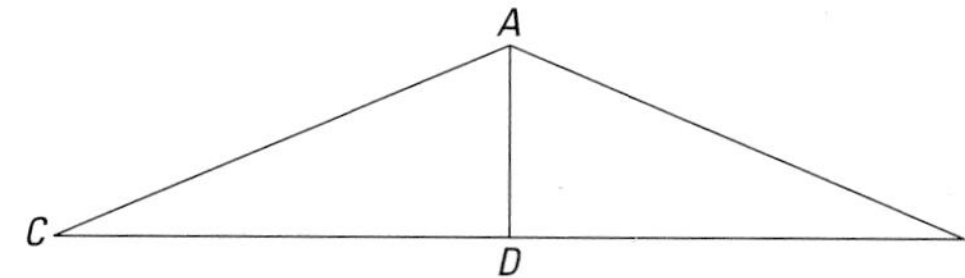

(a) *Triangles ADC and ADB are congruent.*
(b) *If* $\overline{AD} \perp \overline{BC}$, *then triangle ABC is isosceles.*
(c) *Triangle ABC is isosceles.*

In 42 and 43, form a valid conclusion from the given statements and justify your reasoning.

42. *All even numbers are integers.*
All integers are real numbers. See below.

43. $\forall$ *real numbers a and b,*
$|a + b| \leq |a| + |b|$.
π *and -13 are real numbers.* See below.

44. Find the error in this "proof" of:
If $x^3 = x^2$, then $x = 1$. See margin.

Conclusions	Justifications
$x^3 = x^2$	Given
$\frac{1}{x^2} \cdot x^3 = \frac{1}{x^2} \cdot x^2$	Multiplication Property of Equality
$x = 1$	Quotient of Powers Property

45. Prove: *The product of the solutions to the equation* $ax^2 + bx + c = 0$ *is* $\frac{c}{a}$.

46. Prove: *If* $46 + 9m < 11m - 4$, *then* $m > 25$.

42) ***All even numbers are real numbers*** **by Law of Transitivity**

43) $|\pi + -13| \leq |\pi| + |-13| = \pi + 13$ **by Law of Substitution**

Whereas end-of-chapter material may be considered optional in some texts, in UCSMP *Precalculus and Discrete Mathematics* we have selected these objectives and questions with the expectation that they will be covered. Students should be able to answer these questions with about 85% accuracy after studying the chapter.

You may assign these questions over a single night to help students prepare for a test the next day, or you may assign the questions over a two-day period. If you work the questions over two days, then we recommend assigning the *evens* for homework the first night so that students get feedback in class the next day, then assigning the *odds* the night before the test, because answers are provided to the odd-numbered questions.

It is effective to ask students which questions they still do not understand and use the day or days as a total class discussion of the material which the class finds most difficult.

Assessment

Evaluation The Assessment Sourcebook provides four forms of the Chapter 1 Test. Forms A and B present parallel versions in a short-answer format. Forms C and D offer performance assessment.

For information on grading, see *General Teaching Suggestions: Grading* in the *Professional Sourcebook*, which begins on page T20 in Part 1 of the Teacher's Edition.

Feedback After students have taken the test for Chapter 1 and you have scored the results, return the tests to students for discussion. Class discussion of the questions that caused trouble for the most students can be very effective in identifying and clarifying misunderstandings. You might want to have them write down the items they missed and work, either in groups or at home, to correct them. It is important for students to receive feedback on every chapter test, and we recommend that students see and correct their mistakes before proceeding too far into the next chapter.

Additional Responses, page 67
5. (Project 5, continued)

The UCSMP Proof (condensed):

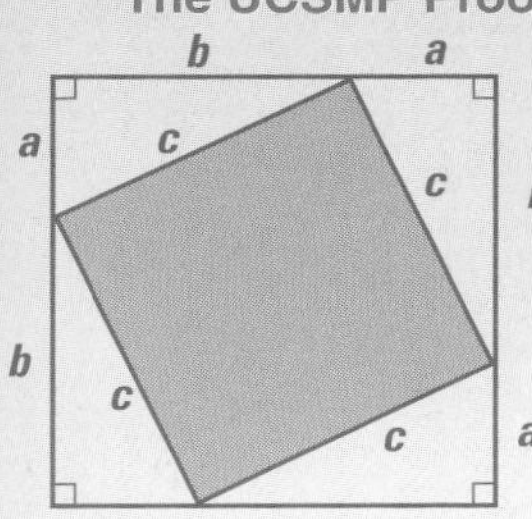

Shaded Area: $(a + b)^2 - 4 \cdot \frac{1}{2}ab = a^2 + 2ab + b^2 - 2ab$. **But the area of the shaded square is** c^2, **so** $c^2 = a^2 + b^2$.

In *Geometry* by Harold Jacobs, the proof is very similar although a bit more complicated. It uses two diagrams and must convince the reader that they are equivalent. It does include an explanation for the construction of each diagram and an explanation that the center figure is a square. Jacob's Proof (condensed) is shown on page 74.

(Responses continue on page 74.)

Additional Answers

47. True; all campers participate in a sports activity.
48. False; no camper participates in all arts and crafts activities.
49. False; no camper participates in all sports activities.
50. False; Oscar does not participate in arts & crafts.
51. False; Oscar participates in nature identification, but he does not participate in arts & crafts.
52. True; Devin participates in entomology, Jennifer, Ruby participate in hiking.
53. False; no camper participates in both jewelry design and in swimming.

Additional Responses, page 67

5. (Project 5 continued) Jacob's proof (condensed):

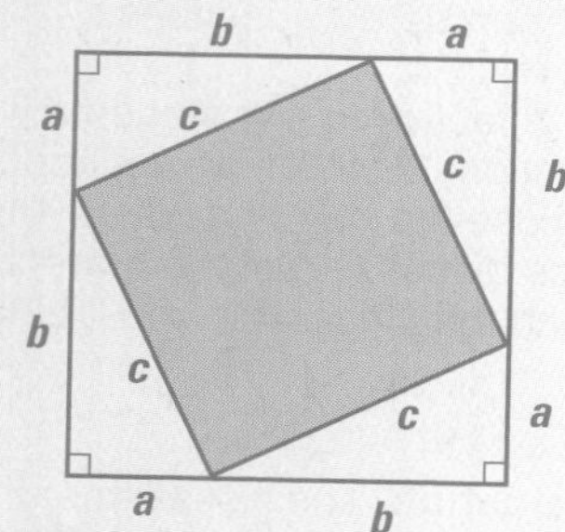

$(a + b)^2 = 4\left(\frac{1}{2}ab\right) + c^2$

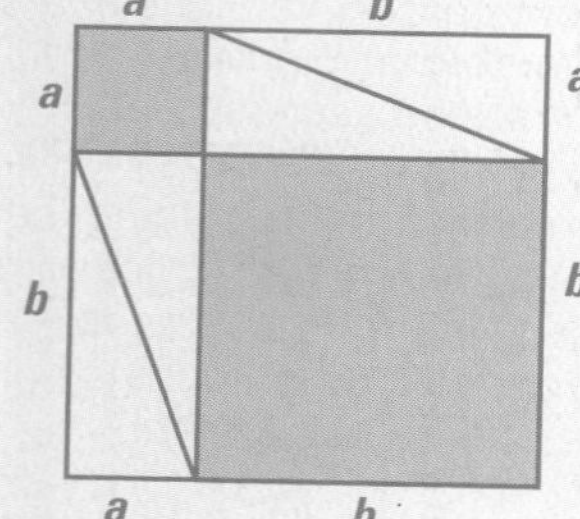

$(a + b)^2 = 4\left(\frac{1}{2}ab\right) + a^2 + b^2$

Hence,

$4\left(\frac{1}{2}ab\right) + c^2 = 4\left(\frac{1}{2}ab\right) + a^2 + b^2$

and $c^2 = a^2 + b^2$.

USES DEAL WITH APPLICATIONS OF MATHEMATICS IN REAL SITUATIONS.

Objective I: *Determine the truth of quantified statements outside of mathematics.* *(Lessons 1-1, 1-2, 1-3, 1-5)*

In 47–53, refer to the table below. See margin.

At a summer camp, students participate in three types of activities: sports, arts and crafts, and nature identification. The activities of four campers are summarized below.

	sports				arts and crafts			nature identification		
camper	swimming	volleyball	canoeing	hiking	pottery	wood-working	jewelry design	bird watching	botany	entomology
Kevin	✓		✓			✓				✓
Jennifer		✓		✓	✓		✓	✓	✓	
Ruby				✓		✓		✓	✓	
Oscar	✓	✓	✓					✓		✓

Use the table to determine if each statement is true or false. Justify your answers.

47. *∀ campers c in the sample, c participates in a sports activity.*

48. *∃ a camper c in the sample such that ∀ arts and crafts activities y, c participates in y.*

49. *Some camper participates in every sports activity.*

50. *No camper fails to participate in arts and crafts.*

51. *For every camper c in the sample, if c participates in nature identification, then c participates in arts and crafts.*

52. *∃ a camper c in the sample such that c participates in entomology or c participates in hiking.*

53. *Some camper participates in jewelry design and in swimming.*

Objective J: *Determine whether or not a logical argument outside of mathematics is valid.* *(Lessons 1-6, 1-7, 1-8)*

In 54–57, tell whether the argument is valid or invalid. Support your answer with a reference to one or more of the following.

I. Law of Detachment (*modus ponens*)
II. Law of Indirect Reasoning (*modus tollens*)
III. Law of Transitivity
IV. Converse Error
V. Inverse Error
VI. Improper Induction

54. *If you dial a number which is busy or has no answer, you may dial the number again by pressing REDIAL. You dialed a number by pressing REDIAL. Therefore, you must have dialed a number which was busy or had no answer.* invalid by IV

Tara Lipinsky, 1997 World Champion

55. *If Tara skates, then she wins the gold medal. Tara is skating. Thus, she will win the gold medal.* valid by I

56. *When it fails to rain within 30 days it is a drought. There was not a drought. Thus there was rain within a 30-day period.* valid by II

57. *The ski lift runs when the ski resort is open. When the ski lift runs, hundreds of skiers try the slopes. Therefore, if there are not hundreds of skiers trying the slopes, then the ski resort is not open.* valid by II and III

In *Geometry* by Rhoad, Milauskas, and Whipple, the proof is done in a very different manner. The format is a two-column proof so that a justification is given for each step. It does include a formula for an altitude to a hypotenuse which may be less familiar to students. This proof is shown at the right:

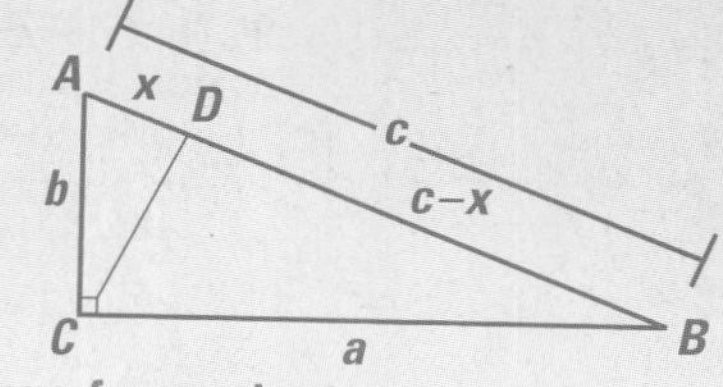

1. $\angle ACB$ is a right $\angle$.	1. Given
2. Draw $\overline{CD} \perp \overline{AB}$.	2 From a point outside a line, only one ⊥ line can be drawn to the line.
3. $\overline{CD}$ is an altitude.	3. A segment drawn from a vertex of a △ ⊥ to the opposite side is an altitude.
4. $a^2 = (c - x)c$	4. In a right △ with an altitude drawn to the hypotenuse, (leg)^2 = (adj. seg.) (hypot.)
5. $a^2 = c^2 - cx$	5. Distributive Property
6. $b^2 = xc$	6. Same as 4
7. $a^2 + b^2 = c^2 - cx + cx$	7. Additive Property
8. $a^2 + b^2 = c^2$	8. Algebra

REPRESENTATIONS DEAL WITH PICTURES, GRAPHS, OR OBJECTS THAT ILLUSTRATE CONCEPTS.

Objective K: *Translate logic networks into logical expressions and determine output signals.* *(Lesson 1-4)*

58. Suppose the logic gate G has the following input-output table. See margin.

p	q	output
1	1	0
1	0	0
0	1	1
0	0	1

Write an input-output table for the following network.

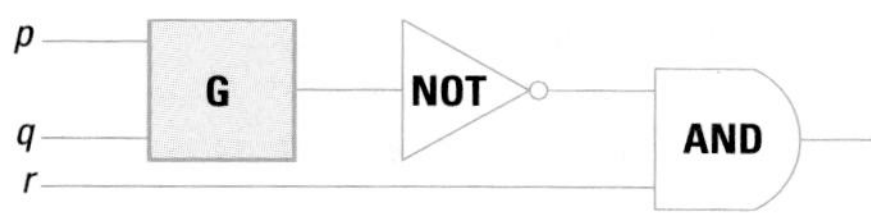

59. a. Write the logical expression that corresponds to the network below.

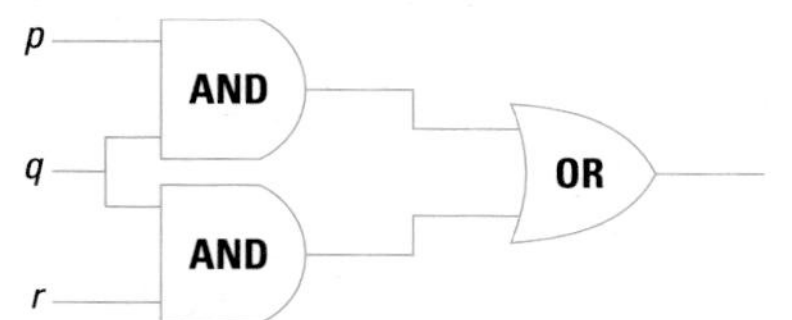

(p and q) or (q and r)

b. Suppose *p* carries a signal of 1, *q* carries a signal of 0, and *r* carries a signal of 1. What output signal will the network produce? 0

60. In **a** and **b**, write the logical expression that corresponds to the network.

a.

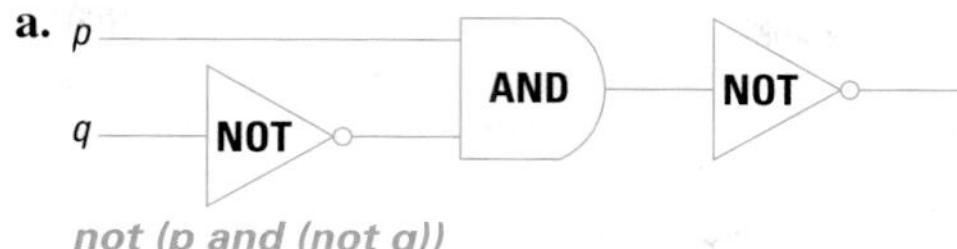

not (p and (not q))

b.

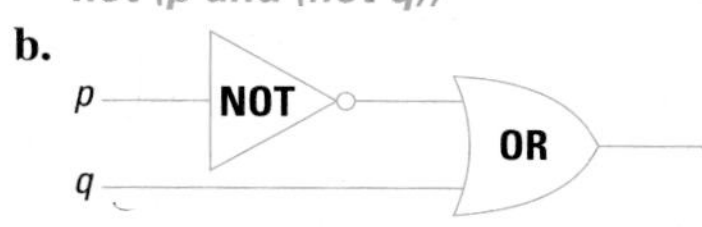

(not p) or q

c. Use input-output tables to show that the networks in parts **a** and **b** are functionally equivalent. See margin.

d. Use De Morgan's Laws to show that the logical expressions obtained in parts **a** and **b** are equivalent. not (p and (not q)) ≡ (not p) or (not (not q)) ≡ (not p) or q

Objective L: *Write truth tables for logical expressions.* *(Lessons 1-3, 1-5)*

In 61–65, write the truth table for the given logical expression. See margin.

61. *p or q*

62. $p \Rightarrow q$

63. $(p \Rightarrow q) \Rightarrow r$

64. *p and (q or r)*

65. Use a truth table to show that

(not p) or (not q) ≡ not (p and q).

Additional Answers

58.

p	q	r	G	NOT G	output (NOT G) AND r
1	1	1	0	1	1
1	1	0	0	1	0
1	0	1	0	1	1
1	0	0	0	1	0
0	1	1	1	0	0
0	1	0	1	0	0
0	0	1	1	0	0
0	0	0	1	0	0

60. c. See below left.

61.

p	q	p or q
T	T	T
T	F	T
F	T	T
F	F	F

62.

p	q	$p \Rightarrow q$
T	T	T
T	F	F
F	T	T
F	F	T

63.

p	q	r	$p \Rightarrow q$	$(p \Rightarrow q) \Rightarrow r$
T	T	T	T	T
T	T	F	T	F
T	F	T	F	T
T	F	F	F	T
F	T	T	T	T
F	T	F	T	F
F	F	T	T	T
F	F	F	T	F

64.

p	q	r	q or r	p and (q or r)
T	T	T	T	T
T	T	F	T	T
T	F	T	T	T
T	F	F	F	F
F	T	T	T	F
F	T	F	T	F
F	F	T	T	F
F	F	F	F	F

65. See below.

60. c.

p	q	NOT q	p AND (NOT q)	NOT (p AND (NOT q))	NOT p	(NOT p) OR q
1	1	0	0	1	0	1
1	0	1	1	0	0	0
0	1	0	0	1	1	1
0	0	1	0	1	1	1

same truth values

d. not (*p* and (~*q*)) ≡ (not *p*) or not (not *q*) ≡ (not *p*) or *q*

65.

p	q	p and q	not (p and q)	not p	not q	(not p) or (not q)
T	T	T	F	F	F	F
T	F	F	T	F	T	T
F	T	F	T	T	F	T
F	F	F	T	T	T	T

same truth values

Chapter 2 Planner

Adapting to Individual Needs

The student text is written for the vast majority of students. The chart at the right suggests two pacing plans to accommodate the needs of your students. Students in the Full Course should complete the entire text by the end of the year. Students in the Minimal Course will spend more time when there are quizzes and more time on the Chapter Review. Therefore, these students may not complete all of the chapters in the text.

Options are also presented to meet the needs of a variety of teaching and learning styles. For each lesson, the Teacher's Edition provides a section entitled *Adapting to Individual Needs.* This section regularly includes **Optional Activities, Challenge** problems, **English Language Development** suggestions, and suggestions for providing **Extra Help.** The Teacher's Edition also frequently includes an **Error Alert,** an **Extension,** and an **Assessment** alternative. The options available in Chapter 2 are summarized in the chart below.

Chapter 2 Pacing Chart

Day	Full Course	Minimal Course
1	2-1	2-1
2	2-2	2-2
3	2-3	2-3
4	2-4	2-4
5	Quiz*; 2-5.	Quiz*; begin 2-5.
6	2-6	Finish 2-5.
7	2-7	2-6
8	Quiz*; 2-8.	2-7
9	2-9	Quiz*; begin 2-8.
10	Self-Test	Finish 2-8.
11	Test*	2-9
12		Self-Test
13		Review
14		Review
15		Test*

*in the Teacher's Resource File

In the Teacher's Edition...

Lesson	Optional Activities	Extra Help	Challenge	English Language Development	Error Alert	Extension	Cooperative Learning	Ongoing Assessment
2-1	●	●	●		●	●		Written
2-2	●	●	●		●	●		Written
2-3	●	●	●		●	●		Oral
2-4	●	●				●	●	Quiz
2-5	●	●	●		●	●		Written
2-6	●	●	●	●	●	●	●	Oral
2-7	●	●	●		●	●		Quiz
2-8	●	●	●		●	●		Written
2-9	●	●	●		●	●	●	Written

In the Additional Resources...

	In the Teacher's Resource File							
Lesson	Lesson Masters	Teaching Aids*	Answer Masters	Technology Sourcebook	Assessment Sourcebook	Visual Aids**	Technology	Explorations Software
2-1	2-1	12, 15	2-1			12, 15, AM		
In-class Activity			2-2					2-2
2-2	2-2	12, 16	2-2	Calc 1		12, 16, AM		
2-3	2-3	12, 17, 18, 19	2-3			12, 17, 18, 19, AM		
2-4	2-4	13, 20	2-4	Calc 2	Quiz	13, 20, AM		
2-5	2-5	13, 21	2-5	Calc 3		13, 21, AM		2-5
2-6	2-6	14, 22	2-6			14, 22, AM		2-6
2-7	2-7	14, 23	2-7		Quiz	14, 23, AM		2-7
2-8	2-8	14, 24	2-8			14, 24, AM		
2-9	2-9	14, 25	2-9			14, 25, AM		2-9
End of chapter					Tests			

*Teaching Aids are pictured on pages 76C and 76D.

**Visual Aids provide transparencies for all Teaching Aids and all Answer Masters.

Also available is the Study Skills Handbook which includes study-skill tips related to reading, note-taking, and comprehension.

Integrating Strands and Applications

	2-1	2-2	2-3	2-4	2-5	2-6	2-7	2-8	2-9
Mathematical Connections									
Number Sense	●	●	●	●		●	●	●	●
Algebra	●	●	●	●	●	●	●	●	●
Geometry	●	●		●		●			
Measurement						●			
Logic and Reasoning		●	●	●	●		●		●
Probability				●					
Statistics/Data Analysis	●		●	●	●		●	●	
Patterns and Functions	●	●	●	●	●	●	●	●	●
Discrete Mathematics	●		●					●	
Interdisciplinary and Other Connections									
Science	●		●					●	●
Social Studies									●
Multicultural	●					●	●		
Technology	●	●		●	●	●	●		●
Consumer	●	●	●	●			●		
Sports	●	●		●	●				

Teaching and Assessing the Chapter Objectives

Chapter 2 Objectives (Organized into the SPUR catetgories—Skills, Properties, Uses, and Representations)	Lessons	Progress Self-Test Questions	Chapter Review Questions	In the Teacher's Resource File: Chapter Test, Forms A and B	Chapter Test, Forms C	Chapter Test, Forms D
Skills						
A: Determine relative minima and maxima of a function and intervals on which it is increasing or decreasing.	2-2, 2-3	4, 5	1–8	3	5	X
B: Rewrite exponential and logarithmic expressions and equations.	2-7, 2-9	7	9–16	2	1	
Properties						
C: Identify the domain, range, and minimum and maximum values of functions.	2-1, 2-2	1, 2	17–27	1	5	X
D: Determine the end behavior of a function.	2-4, 2-6, 2-7, 2-8, 2-9	5	28–37	6, 7	5	X
Uses						
E: Use sequences and exponential and logarithmic functions as models.	2-7, 2-8, 2-9	10, 11	38–43	8, 11	4	
F: Solve max-min problems.	2-2	6	44–45	5	3	
Representations						
G: Analyze a function from its graph.	2-2, 2-3, 2-4, 2-6, 2-7, 2-8, 2-9	3, 9	46–56	4, 10	5	X
H: Find and graph parametric equations.	2-5	8	57–59	9	2	

Assessment Sourcebook
Quiz for Lessons 2-1 through 2-4
Quiz for Lessons 2-5 through 2-7
Chapter 2 Test, Forms A–D
Chapter 2 Test, Cumulative Form

TestWorks CD-ROM

Teaching Aids

TEACHING AID 12

Warm-up
Lesson 2-1

Write the solutions to each inequality using interval notation.

1. $1 \le x \le 8$ **2.** $2 < y \le 9$ **3.** $3 \le z$

4. $w < 4$ **5.** $v > 5$

Warm-up
Lesson 2-2

Graph the function f with $f(r) = 2\pi r^2 + \frac{116}{r}$. Trace along the graph. How close can you get to the values for $f(1)$, $f(2)$, $f(3)$, and $f\left(\frac{1}{2}\right)$ given at the bottom of page 87 of the Student Edition?

Warm-up
Lesson 2-3

In 1–4, a real function f is described by an equation. Tell whether f is increasing, decreasing, or neither increasing nor decreasing on the interval [-1,1].

1. $f(x) = x^2$

2. $f(x) = x^3$

3. $f(x) = \sqrt{x}$

4. $f(x) = |x|$

5. $f(x) = \sin x$

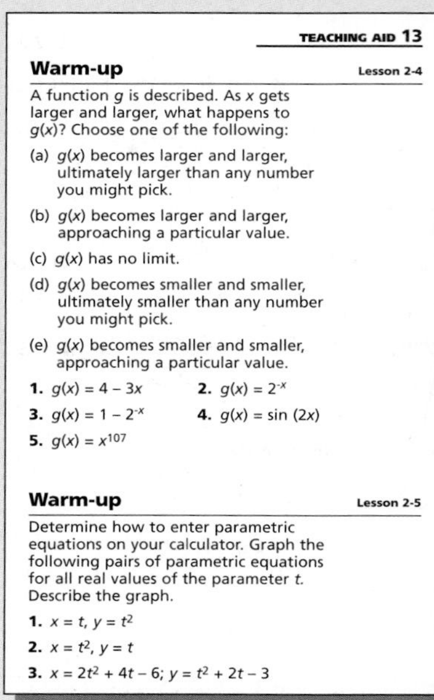

TEACHING AID 13

Warm-up
Lesson 2-4

A function g is described. As x gets larger and larger, what happens to $g(x)$? Choose one of the following:

(a) $g(x)$ becomes larger and larger, ultimately larger than any number you might pick.

(b) $g(x)$ becomes larger and larger, approaching a particular value.

(c) $g(x)$ has no limit.

(d) $g(x)$ becomes smaller and smaller, ultimately smaller than any number you might pick.

(e) $g(x)$ becomes smaller and smaller, approaching a particular value.

1. $g(x) = 4 - 3x$ **2.** $g(x) = 2^{-x}$

3. $g(x) = 1 - 2^{-x}$ **4.** $g(x) = \sin(2x)$

5. $g(x) = x^{107}$

Warm-up
Lesson 2-5

Determine how to enter parametric equations on your calculator. Graph the following pairs of parametric equations for all real values of the parameter t. Describe the graph.

1. $x = t$, $y = t^2$

2. $x = t^2$, $y = t$

3. $x = 2t^2 + 4t - 6$; $y = t^2 + 2t - 3$

TEACHING AID 14

Warm-up
Lesson 2-6

Give the value of each expression.

1. $\cos \frac{5\pi}{6}$ **2.** $\sin \frac{5\pi}{6}$

3. $\cos^2\left(\frac{5\pi}{6}\right) + \sin^2\left(\frac{5\pi}{6}\right)$ **4.** $\tan \frac{5\pi}{6}$

Warm-up
Lesson 2-7

In 1–4, let x be any real number. Give the limit of the expression as $x \to \infty$ and as $x \to -\infty$.

1. 2^x **2.** 0.9^x **3.** $5 \cdot 6^x$ **4.** $-2 \cdot 3^x$

Warm-up
Lesson 2-8

Give an explicit formula and a recursive formula for each sequence.

1. The arithmetic sequence 2000, 2001, 2002, 2003, . . .

2. The geometric sequence 5, 4.5, 4.05, . . .

Warm-up
Lesson 2-9

In 1–4, evaluate each of the following expressions without using a calculator.

1. $\log_2 8$ **2.** $\log_8 2$

3. $\log 2 + \log 50$ **4.** $\ln \sqrt{e}$

5. Explain, without using a calculator, why log 5,000,000 is between 6 and 7.

TEACHING AID 15
Lesson 2-1

Intervals

Intervals whose graphs are segments:

	Interval notation	Set notation
Closed intervals from *a* to *b* (endpoint included)	**[a, b]**	$\{x: a \le x \le b\}$
Open interval from *a* to *b* (endpoints not included)	**(a, b)**	$\{x: a < x < b\}$
Half-open interval from *a* to *b*, including *a* (one endpoint included)	**[a, b)**	$\{x: a \le x < b\}$

Intervals whose graphs are rays:

	Interval notation	Set notation
Closed infinite intervals	**[b, ∞)**	$\{x: b \le x\}$
Open infinite interval	**(-∞, a)**	$\{x: x < a\}$

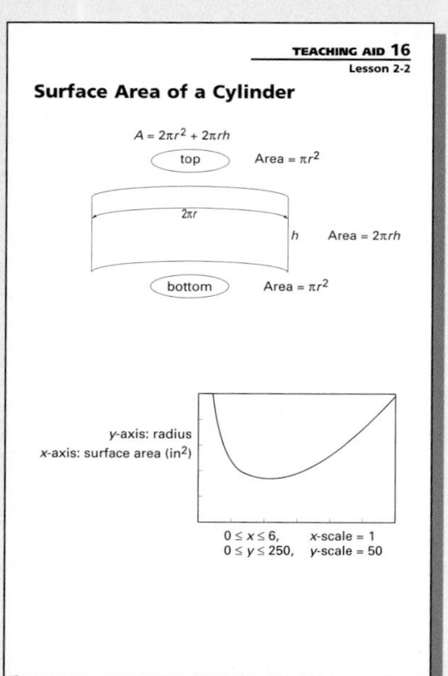

TEACHING AID 16
Lesson 2-2

Surface Area of a Cylinder

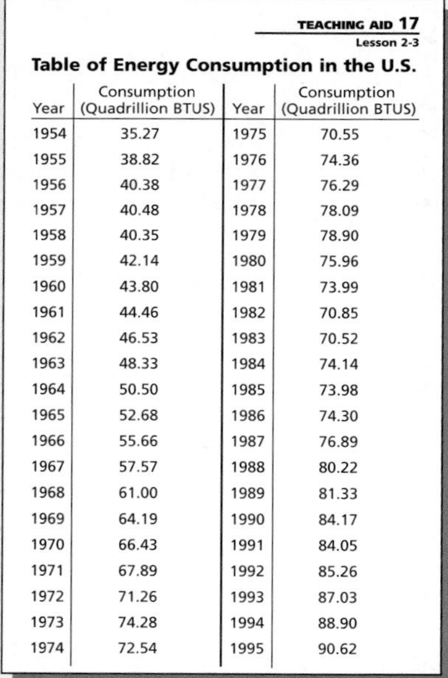

TEACHING AID 17
Lesson 2-3

Table of Energy Consumption in the U.S.

Year	Consumption (Quadrillion BTUS)	Year	Consumption (Quadrillion BTUS)
1954	35.27	1975	70.55
1955	38.82	1976	74.36
1956	40.38	1977	76.29
1957	40.48	1978	78.09
1958	40.35	1979	78.90
1959	42.14	1980	75.96
1960	43.80	1981	73.99
1961	44.46	1982	70.85
1962	46.53	1983	70.52
1963	48.33	1984	74.14
1964	50.50	1985	73.98
1965	52.68	1986	74.30
1966	55.66	1987	76.89
1967	57.57	1988	80.22
1968	61.00	1989	81.33
1969	64.19	1990	84.17
1970	66.43	1991	84.05
1971	67.89	1992	85.26
1972	71.26	1993	87.03
1973	74.28	1994	88.90
1974	72.54	1995	90.62

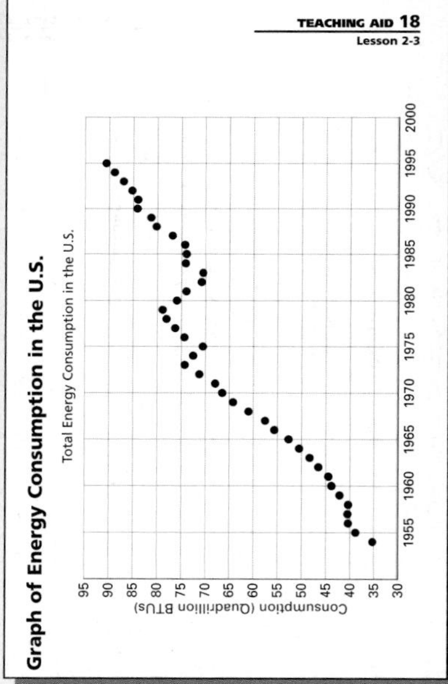

TEACHING AID 18
Lesson 2-3

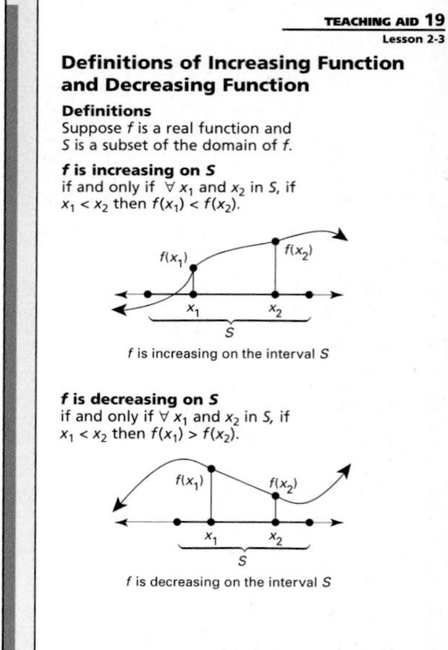

TEACHING AID 19
Lesson 2-3

Definitions of Increasing Function and Decreasing Function

Definitions

Suppose f is a real function and S is a subset of the domain of f.

f* is increasing on *S if and only if $\forall\, x_1$ and x_2 in S, if $x_1 < x_2$ then $f(x_1) < f(x_2)$.

f is increasing on the interval S

f* is decreasing on *S if and only if $\forall\, x_1$ and x_2 in S, if $x_1 < x_2$ then $f(x_1) > f(x_2)$.

f is decreasing on the interval S

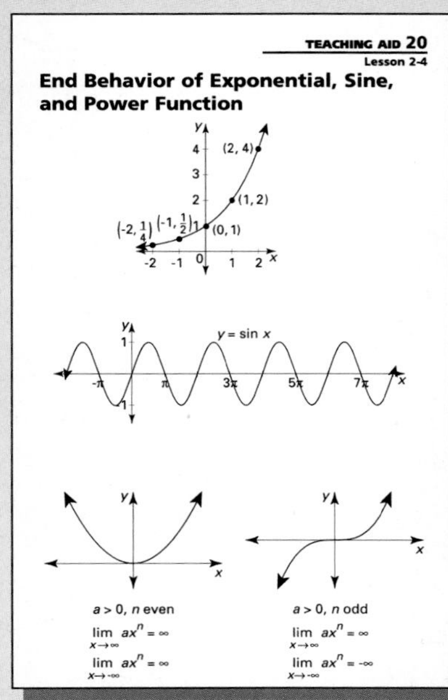

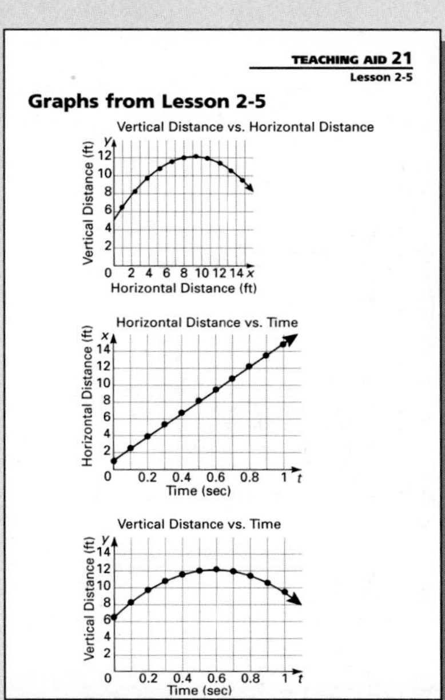

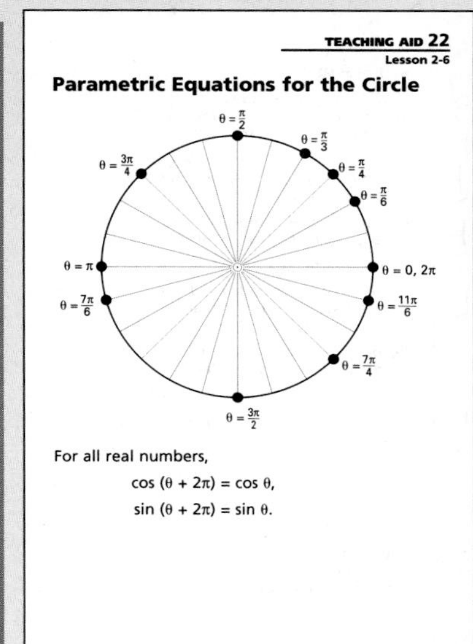

What is meant by "Analyzing a Function"?

1. *Domain.* Identify the values for which *f* is defined.
2. *Range.* Describe the set of all possible values of *f*.
3. *Increasing or Decreasing.* As *x* increases, identify the intervals on which *f* increases and the intervals on which *f* decreases.
4. *End of Behavior.* Describe what happens to *f* as $x \to \infty$ or as $x \to -\infty$.
5. *Maxima or Minima.* Find the greatest or least value of *f*.
6. *Models.* Identify situations which can be modeled by a function like *f*. Know how *f* is normally used in those situations.
7. *Properties.* Be aware of special properties of *f*, and their implications.

Tables from the Lesson

n	U_n
0	2000
1	2400
2	2880
3	3456
4	4147
5	4977
6	5972
7	7166
8	8600
9	10,320
10	12,383
11	14,860
12	17,832
13	21,399
14	25,678
15	30,814
16	36,977
17	44,372
18	53,247
19	63,896
20	76,675

n	U_n
0	2000
1	2373
2	2810
3	3320
4	3910
5	4591
6	5368
7	6250
8	7239
9	8338
10	9542
11	10,843
12	12,228
13	13,677
14	15,165
15	16,665
16	18,146
17	19,580
18	20,941
19	22,205
20	23,359
21	24,393
22	25,305
23	26,097
24	26,776
25	27,352
26	27,835
27	28,236

n	U_n
50	29,989
51	29,991
52	29,993
53	29,994
54	29,995
55	29,996
56	29,997

Definition and Properties of Logarithms

Definition

Let $b \neq 1$ be a positive real number. The ∀ real numbers *x* and *y*, *y* is the **logarithm of *x* to the base *b*,** written $y = \log_b x$, if and only if $x = b^y$.

Theorems

∀ real numbers *r* and *s* and ∀ positive real numbers *b*, *u*, and *v* with $b \neq 1$,

Law of Exponents	Law of Logarithms	
$b^r \cdot b^s = b^{r+s}$	$\log_b(u \cdot v) = \log_b u + \log_b v$	**Logarithm of a Product**
$\frac{b^r}{b^s} = b^{r-s}$	$\log_b\left(\frac{u}{v}\right) = \log_b u - \log_b v$	**Logarithm of a Quotient**
$(b^r)^s = b^{rs}$	$\log_b(u^s) = s \log_b u$	**Logarithm of Power**

Change of Base Theorem

Let *a* and *b* be positive real numbers both unequal to 1, then for all $x > 0$,

$$\log_b x = \log_b a \cdot \log_a x.$$

Chapter Opener

Pacing

All lessons in this chapter are designed to be covered in one day. At the end of the chapter, you should plan to spend 1 day to review the Progress Self-Test, 1–2 days for the Chapter Review, and 1 day for a test. You may wish to spend a day on projects, and possibly a day is needed for quizzes and the In-class Activity. This chapter should therefore take 12–15 days. Spending more than 15 days on this chapter is not recommended; there is ample opportunity to review ideas in later chapters.

Using Pages 76–77

This chapter applies many ideas about functions. Although the chapter contains much that is review, many students need the review. You can use page 77 to determine how much your students know about functions. Can they give equations for each type of elementary function named on the page? Can they give general forms for each type of elementary function? Guide them to recall the following forms:

Linear, $y = mx + b$
Quadratic, $y = ax^2 + bx + c$
Power, $y = ax^n$
Polynomial,
$y = a_n x^n + a_{n-1}x^{n-1} + \ldots + a_1 x + a_0$
Trigonometric (sample), $y = a \sin bx$
Exponential; $y = ab^x$
Logarithmic (sample), $y = a \log bx$.

Ask students how many different ways they know for representing or defining functions. (Samples: equation, graph, arrow diagram, mapping notation.)

CHAPTER 2

Chapter 2 Overview

This chapter has two parts. In the first part, some broad ideas about functions are reviewed. In the second part, these ideas are applied to analyze exponential, logarithmic, and trigonometric functions. Between the two parts parametric equations are introduced as a way to represent some curves. It is assumed that much of this material is review.

This chapter is not about how to obtain values of a particular function. It is assumed that students know how to obtain function values, either by using the definition or with the aid of a calculator. Instead, the focus of this chapter is on properties of the function itself: its usual domain and the corresponding range; its maximum or minimum values (if any); the intervals over which it is increasing or decreasing; its end behavior; the general shape of its graph; the kind of situations it models; and its special properties.

Other differences between the treatment of functions in this chapter and what students might have seen in previous courses is that the discussions are more formal, and, as befits a review, more material is covered in each lesson.

It is assumed that students have access to function graphing technology throughout this chapter and for the remainder of this book, both for classwork and assignments.

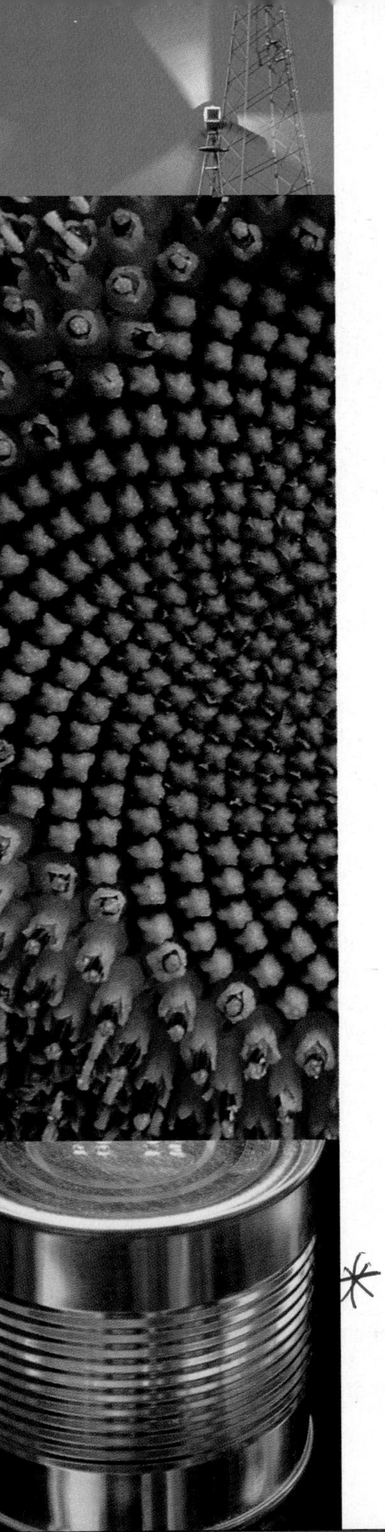

Analyzing Functions

People sometimes identify functions by their equations. We think of $f(x) = x^2$ as defining the *squaring function*. But this formula can define many different functions. Here are three different squaring functions.

(1) The sequence of products of positive integers n with themselves

$$n^2 = 1, 4, 9, 16, \ldots.$$

(2) The formula for the area A of a square in terms of the length s of a side

$$A = s^2.$$

(3) The parabola that is the graph of the equation

$$y = x^2.$$

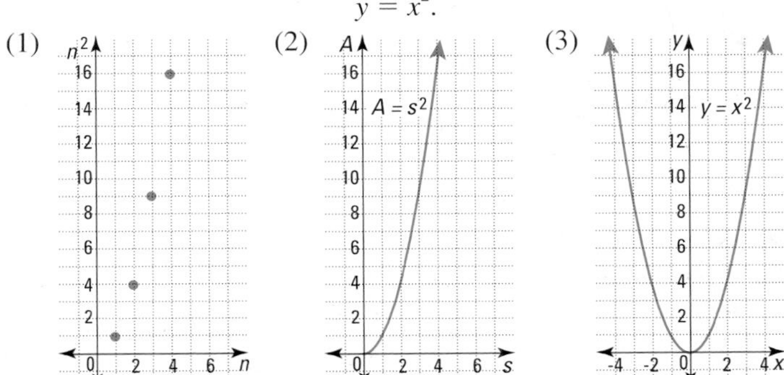

The above graphs show how different these functions are, even though there is a basic similarity among them. The function (1) is a discrete function whose domain is the set of positive integers. The function (2) has the set of positive real numbers as its domain, while the domain of function (3) is the set of all real numbers. In the first part of this chapter, we discuss properties which help to describe and distinguish functions.

The squaring function (3) is an example of one of the *elementary functions*. The **elementary functions** include linear, quadratic, power, polynomial, trigonometric, exponential, and logarithmic functions. They are the basic functions from which more complicated functions may be constructed. Properties of some important types of elementary functions are reviewed in the second half of this chapter.

The specific examples (1), (2), and (3) show that an equation is not enough to completely define a function. Although each of these functions has an equation of the form $y = x^2$, they are different because they have different domains.

Photo Connections

The photo collage makes real-world connections to the content of the chapter: analyzing functions.

Windmills: In 1996, the United States produced over 72.6 quadrillion BTU's of energy. The source of about 40 trillion BTU's of this energy was the wind. In Lesson 2-3 energy consumption is used as an example of a discrete function. In Lesson 2-6 students measure arcs and rotations such as those produced by a windmill.

Planets: Johannes Kepler used logarithms in his study of the motion of planets. In Lesson 2-9 students analyze logarithm functions.

Sunflower: The number of clockwise and counterclockwise spirals formed by the seeds of a sunflower are consecutive terms in the Fibonacci sequence. Students study sequences in Lesson 2-8.

Cows: Students find maximum and minimum points in Lesson 2-2. They apply this concept in **Question 9** where they are asked to find the least amount of fencing needed to enclose a rectangular field with a specific area.

Can: A typical problem in manufacturing involves determining the least amount of material needed to make a container that meets specific requirements. This situation, involving designing a paint can, is considered in Lesson 2-2.

Chapter 2 Projects

At this time, you might want to have students look over the projects on pages 137–138.

Either function graphing calculators or computers with a function graphing program will suffice. We call either an *automatic grapher.*

Pacing More than any other chapter in this book, the ease or difficulty of this chapter and the time it takes to cover it, will depend on the background and ability of your students. Students who have covered UCSMP *Advanced Algebra* and *Functions, Statistics, and Trigonometry* will have seen many of the ideas here twice before; for them the lesson-a-day pace is quite reasonable.

Lesson 2-1

Objectives

C Identify the domain and range of functions.

Resources

From the ***Teacher's Resource File***

- Lesson Master 2-1
- Answer Master 2-1
- Teaching Aids
  12 Warm-up
  15 Intervals

Additional Resources

- Visuals for Teaching Aids 12, 15

Teaching Lesson 2-1

Warm-up

Write the solutions to each inequality using interval notation.

1. $1 \le x \le 8$ $[1, 8]$
2. $2 < y \le 9$ $(2, 9]$
3. $3 \le z$ $[3, \infty)$
4. $w < 4$ $(-\infty, 4)$
5. $v > 5$ $(5, \infty)$

LESSON 2-1 Identifying Functions

Oblate Spheroid. *Earth is not exactly a sphere. Earth bulges at the equator, where its radius is 6380 km, and is flatter at the poles, where its radius is about 6360 km. See Example 2.*

Functions are very important in all branches of mathematics and are studied throughout this book. The term *function* was first used in mathematics by the great German mathematician Gottfried Leibniz (1646–1716). His curiosity about the ways variables relate to each other led him to become one of the two inventors of calculus. In this lesson, we review some basic ideas about functions, and we introduce some language that will help you identify and analyze functions.

Basic Terms Relating to Functions

The idea of a function is rather simple. In every function, there is a first variable (call it x) that takes values from a set (call the set A). To each value of x, there corresponds a value of a second variable (call it y) from a set B. Sometimes we say that the values of x are *mapped* onto the values of y by the function. The function is the *correspondence*, or *mapping*.

❶ **Definition**

A **function** is a correspondence, or mapping, between a set A and a set B in which each element x of A corresponds, or is mapped, to exactly one value y of B.

We call x the **independent variable** and the set A the **domain** of the function, because we think of the values of x as being able to be picked at will from A. The variable y is called the **dependent variable** because each value of y depends on the value of x chosen. The set of values in B that y attains is the **range** of the function. It is important to note, however, that the range is not necessarily the entire set B.

Lesson 2-1 Overview

Broad Goals Lesson 2-1 covers the basic vocabulary of functions and vocabulary and notations for intervals.

Perspective Although the definition of a function as a set of ordered pairs and the definition of a function as a correspondence (or mapping) between two sets are equivalent definitions, the mapping definition used in this lesson is more common in higher mathematics.

The vocabulary and notation that is provided in this lesson for intervals is standard. Because open intervals are described with the same symbols that are used for ordered pairs, we usually precede the notation with the words "the interval" (i.e. "the interval (a, b)") to distinguish it from the point or ordered pair (a, b). The same is true for the closed interval $[a, b]$, because that bracket notation is used in Chapter 8 for polar coordinates.

In this book the terms *open, half-open, closed,* and *infinite* are seldom used as they apply to intervals, but many people like to use them and we know of no difficulty this causes unless it is overdone. On the other hand, we often use the phrases *between a and b* (for an open interval) and *from a to b* (for a closed interval).

Example 1

You are planning to study for a test tomorrow. You know that the amount you study will affect your score. If you study too little, you will do poorly. If you study all night, you will not get enough sleep, and you also will not do your best. You wonder what is the optimum amount to study. For this situation, identify each.

a. a function
b. the independent variable of this function
c. a possible domain
d. the dependent variable of this function
e. a possible range

Solution

a. A natural function arising from this situation is the correspondence between the time a person studies and the person's score on the test. For this function:
b. The independent variable is the time studied (so call the variable t).
c. A possible domain for t is the set of times from 0 hours to 6 hours.
d. The dependent variable is the score on the test (call it s).
e. If the set of possible scores on the test is from 0 to 100 (the set *B*), and you feel you cannot score below a 50, then a possible range for s is the set of scores from 50 to 100.

In Example 1, we say that the score on the test is a function of the amount of time you study, written $s = f(t)$. (The score may also be a function of other variables, such as how much you knew about the topic before you started studying.) For instance, if you studied 3 hours and earned a score of 90, you could write $90 = f(3)$. The $f(x)$ notation for functions was first used by Leonhard Euler (1707–1783).

Defining a Function

There is no formula in Example 1 relating the variables. But functions are often described by rules or formulas that show how to find the value of the dependent variable from the value of the independent variable. If the domain of the function is also known, then the rule or formula *defines* the function.

Example 2

The volume *V* of a sphere is a function of its radius *r*. Suppose $V = f(r)$.

a. Find a formula that defines *f*.
b. Use the formula to estimate the volume of Earth, which is approximately a sphere with radius 6380 km.

Solution

a. In your study of geometry, you should have seen a proof that $V = \frac{4}{3}\pi r^3$. So a formula for the function f is $f(r) = \frac{4}{3}\pi r^3$.
b. The volume of Earth is approximately given by $f(6380) = \frac{4}{3}\pi(6380)^3 \approx 1{,}088{,}000{,}000{,}000$ cubic kilometers.

Notes on Reading

Spend some time discussing the definition of function and the determination of the largest possible domain for a real function. Spend the rest of the time dealing with the notation and vocabulary of intervals. If your class is well-prepared from earlier courses, there will be time to do the In-class Activity on page 85, and you will not have to review the logistics of using an automatic grapher with students. For more information on the use of technology in the classroom, see *General Teaching Suggestions: Using Technology* in the *Professional Sourcebook* which begins on page T20 in Part 1 of the Teacher's Edition.

❶ First, make certain that students interpret correctly the definition of function. Note that not every element of *B* needs to be used. We say that every function *f* maps *A into B*. If every element of *B* is used, then we say that *f* maps *A onto B*.

Students of previous UCSMP courses are familiar with the notation $f: x \to y$, when $f(x) = y$. For instance, if $f(x) = 2x$ for all *x*, then we write $f: x \to 2x$. You may wish to introduce the notation $f: A \to B$, where *A* is the domain and *B* contains the range of *f*. Then, when *A* and *B* are sets of real numbers, *f* is a real function. Emphasize that in $f: A \to B$, *B* is not necessarily the range of the function.

Technically, because an interval is a set of points, when the interval is described with an inequality, there should always be the set builder {*x*: ... } notation. But we will often describe an interval simply with the inequality. That is, we often write $3 < x < 4$ for the interval (3, 4), rather than the technically more accurate $\{x: 3 < x < 4\}$. For instance, in this book we consistently write inequalities when describing the windows of automatic graphers.

Optional Activities

Activity 1 Writing
You might use this activity after students complete the lesson. Gottfried Leibniz (1646–1716) was the first person to use the term *function,* and Leonhard Euler (1707–1783) was the first to use the *f(x)* notation. Have interested students write a report on one of these mathematicians.

You can assess student knowledge of the ideas of domain and range with the questions that follow.

Consider a function f: $A \rightarrow B$. Answer *true* or *false*.

a. Every element of A must correspond to an element of B. [True]

b. Every element of B must correspond to an element of A. [False]

c. An element of A can correspond to different elements of B. [False]

d. An element of B can correspond to more than one element of A. [True]

e. An element of B can correspond to no element of A. [True]

❷ **Sports Connection** In 1994, when 7 foot 7 inch Gheorge Muresan of Romania joined the Washington Bullets, he was the tallest player in NBA history.

❸ These five intervals are on **Teaching Aid 15.**

In Example 2, you can say, "The function f with equation $f(r) = \frac{4}{3}\pi r^3$ maps the radius of a sphere onto the volume of the sphere." For functions defined by formulas, the domain set A and the set B often are not identified explicitly but rather are understood from the context or the values of the variable allowed by the formula. For the sphere-volume function $f(r)$, A and B are understood to be the set of nonnegative real numbers, because the volume and radius of a sphere may have any nonnegative real values,
❷ and only these values.

Player	Height (inches)
Anderson	71.5
Chavez	69
Cramer	78
Heinz	74.5
Holmes	76
Jones	69
Kimura	74.5
Layton	71.5
Robinson	73
Santori	72

Functions may also be defined by tables or lists of values. The basketball team roster at the left lists the height as a function of the player.

The domain of this function is the set of 10 players on the team and the range is the set of the 7 real numbers representing their heights.

Real Functions

Functions can be classified by their domains, ranges, or rules. For instance, the sphere-volume function has a rule that is of the form $f(x) = ax^3$, so it is a *cubic function* and it is also a *polynomial function*. In the last three lessons of this chapter, you will review trigonometric, exponential, and logarithmic functions. All of these classes of functions receive their names from their formulas.

In this lesson and the next, we consider functions classified by their domains and ranges. When the range of a function is a set of real numbers, then the function is called a **real-valued function**. The functions of Examples 1 and 2 and the basketball roster function are all real-valued functions. When both the domain and range of the function are sets of real numbers, then the function is called a **real function**. The functions of Examples 1 and 2 are real functions, but the basketball roster function is not.

Real functions can be graphed on the coordinate plane. For instance, below is a graph of the real function with rule $y = \frac{4}{3}\pi x^3$ as shown on an automatic grapher. (The subset of this function in the first quadrant is the sphere-volume function.)

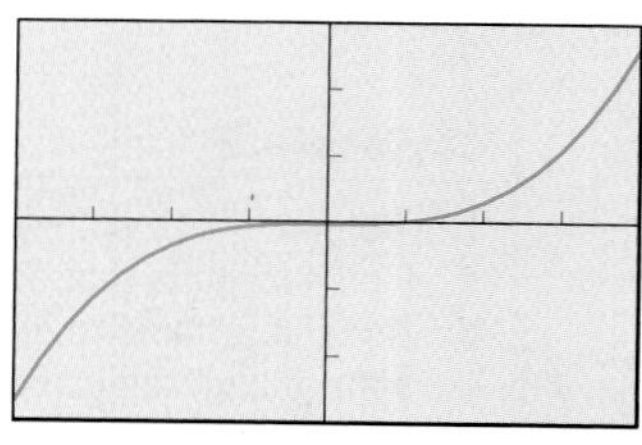

$-4 \le x \le 4$, x-scale = 1
$-300 \le y \le 300$, y-scale = 100

Optional Activities

Activity 2 You might use this activity after students complete the lesson. Have students make up a situation similar to the ones in **Question 4** and in **Example 1.** Then have students identify the function, the independent variable, a possible domain, the dependent variable, and a possible range for their situation. [Sample: You are planning to train for a 5-kilometer cross-country race, and you know that the number of kilometers you run each week during your training will affect the time it takes you to complete the race. The function arising from this situation is the correspondence between the number of kilometers you run weekly to prepare for the race and the time it takes you to complete the race. The independent variable is weekly distance in kilometers, with a possible domain of 50 kilometers to 100 kilometers. The dependent variable is time in minutes with a possible range of 17 minutes to 22 minutes.]

It is impossible to show the entire graph of this function, for its domain is the set of real numbers. So we are forced to show only the graph of this function over an *interval* in the domain of the function. An **interval** is a set of numbers whose graph is a line segment or ray, with or without its endpoints. Intervals are so important that a special *interval notation* is used. The domain interval shown above is the set of real numbers from -4 to 4, or $\{x: -4 \le x \le 4\}$, or in interval notation, [-4, 4]. Shown here are the possible types of intervals and their descriptions in set and interval notation.

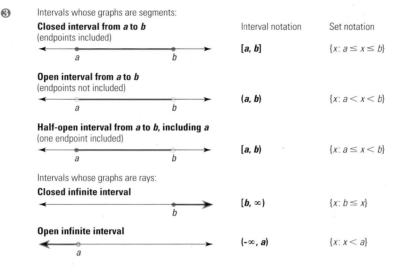

❸ Intervals whose graphs are segments:

	Interval notation	Set notation
Closed interval from *a* to *b* (endpoints included)	**[*a*, *b*]**	$\{x: a \le x \le b\}$
Open interval from *a* to *b* (endpoints not included)	**(*a*, *b*)**	$\{x: a < x < b\}$
Half-open interval from *a* to *b*, including *a* (one endpoint included)	**[*a*, *b*)**	$\{x: a \le x < b\}$

Intervals whose graphs are rays:

	Interval notation	Set notation
Closed infinite interval	**[*b*, ∞)**	$\{x: b \le x\}$
Open infinite interval	**(-∞, *a*)**	$\{x: x < a\}$

In all cases above, the numbers a and b are called **endpoints** of the interval. Notice that if an endpoint is included in the interval, it is next to a square bracket] or [in the interval notation. If the endpoint is not included, it is next to a parenthesis) or (.

Example 3

Use interval notation to describe the domain of the real function *f* with rule $f(x) = \frac{1}{\sqrt{x + 3}}$.

Solution

Because no restriction is indicated for *x*, we assume that this function is defined for all real numbers that give real values. Consequently, $x + 3 > 0$. Solving this inequality, $x > -3$. Thus, **the domain of this function is the interval (-3, ∞).**

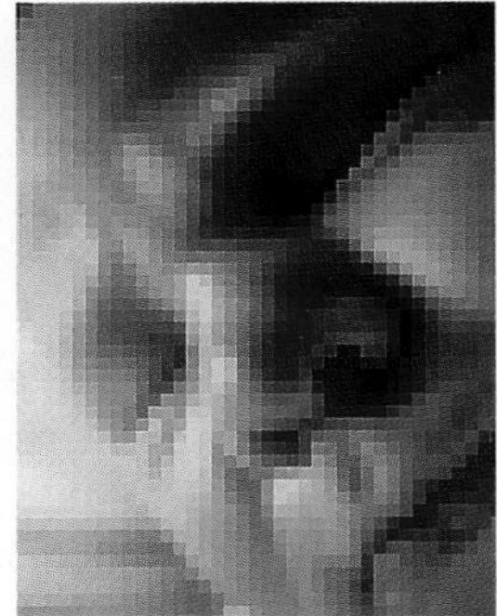

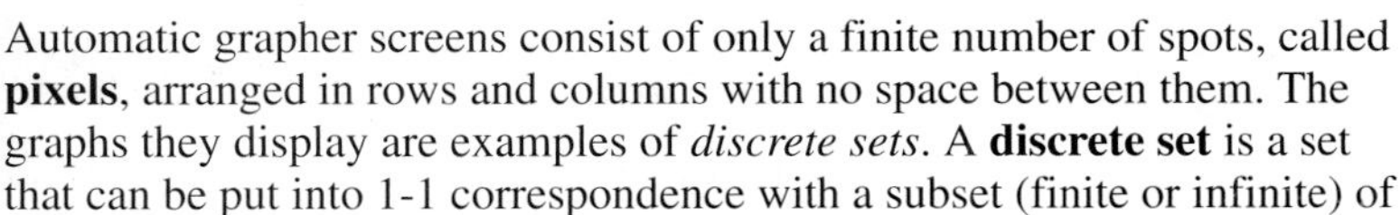

Automatic grapher screens consist of only a finite number of spots, called **pixels**, arranged in rows and columns with no space between them. The graphs they display are examples of *discrete sets*. A **discrete set** is a set that can be put into 1-1 correspondence with a subset (finite or infinite) of

Additional Examples

1. You are writing a report using a word processor. You know that the larger the font you use, the more pages the report will require. For this situation, describe each of the following.
   a. A function **The correspondence between the size of the font and the number of pages the report will require**
   b. The independent variable of this function **The size of the font**
   c. A possible domain **Sample: the interval [6, 14] of integers**
   d. The dependent variable of this function **The number of pages the report will require**
   e. A possible range **Sample: the set of positive integers from 3 to 20**
2. The surface area *S* of a sphere is a function of its radius *r*. Suppose $S = f(r)$.
   a. Find a formula that defines *f*. $S = 4\pi r^2$
   b. Use the formula to estimate the surface area of Earth in square kilometers. Assume $r = 6380$ km. $S \approx 512{,}000{,}000 \text{ km}^2$

(Additional Examples continue on page 82.)

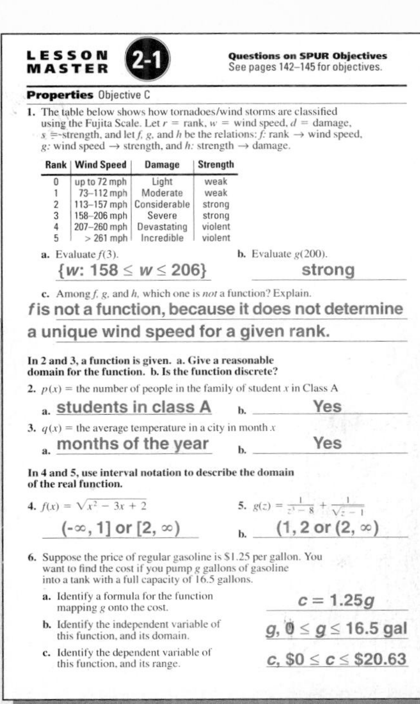

LESSON MASTER 2-1 **Questions on SPUR Objectives** See pages 142–145 for objectives.

Properties Objective C

1. The table below shows how tornadoes/wind storms are classified using the Fujita Scale. Let *r* = rank, *w* = wind speed, *d* = damage, *s* = strength, and let *f*, *g*, and *h* be the relations: *f*: rank → wind speed, *g*: wind speed → strength, and *h*: strength → damage.

Rank	Wind Speed	Damage	Strength
0	up to 72 mph	Light	weak
1	73–112 mph	Moderate	weak
2	113–157 mph	Considerable	strong
3	158–206 mph	Severe	strong
4	207–260 mph	Devastating	violent
5	> 261 mph	Incredible	violent

a. Evaluate *f*(3). $\{w: 158 \le w \le 206\}$
b. Evaluate *g*(200). strong
c. Among *f*, *g*, and *h*, which one is *not* a function? Explain. *f* is not a function, because it does not determine a unique wind speed for a given rank.

In 2 and 3, a function is given. a. Give a reasonable domain for the function. b. Is the function discrete?

2. $p(x)$ = the number of people in the family of student *x* in Class A
   a. students in class A b. Yes
3. $q(x)$ = the average temperature in a city in month *x*
   a. months of the year b. Yes

In 4 and 5, use interval notation to describe the domain of the real function.

4. $f(x) = \sqrt{x^2 - 3x + 2}$ (-∞, 1] or [2, ∞)
5. $g(z) = \frac{1}{z^3 - 8} + \frac{1}{\sqrt{z - 1}}$ b. (1, 2 or (2, ∞)

6. Suppose the price of regular gasoline is $1.25 per gallon. You want to find the cost if you pump *g* gallons of gasoline into a tank with a full capacity of 16.5 gallons.
   a. Identify a formula for the function mapping *g* onto the cost. $c = 1.25g$
   b. Identify the independent variable of this function, and its domain. $g, 0 \le g \le 16.5$ gal
   c. Identify the dependent variable of this function, and its range. $c, \$0 \le c \le \$20.63$

Adapting to Individual Needs

Extra Help

Use this activity with students who are not familiar with automatic graphers.

1. Graph $f(x) = (x - a)^2$ when a = -1, 0, 1, and 2, using the window $-4 \le x \le 5$ and $-1 \le y \le 10$. [The graph is at the right. The four functions are $f_{-1}(x) = (x + 1)^2$; $f_0(x) = x^2$; $f_1(x) = (x - 1)^2$; $f_2(x) = (x - 2)^2$]
2. What happens to the graph as *a* gets larger? [As *a* gets larger, the graph is translated to the right.]

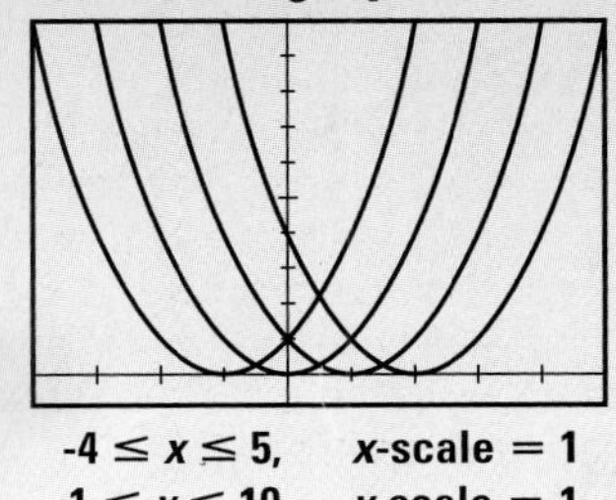

$-4 \le x \le 5$, *x*-scale = 1
$-1 \le y \le 10$, *y*-scale = 1

3. a. Describe the domain for the real function $g: x \rightarrow \sqrt{9 - x^2}$ in interval notation. [-3, 3] (Implicitly we are asking for the largest domain.)

b. Give the domain for the real function $f: x \rightarrow \frac{5}{\sqrt{9 - x^2}}$. (-3, 3)

c. Compare the domains of $h: x \rightarrow \frac{1}{\sqrt{x+3}}$, $f: x \rightarrow \sqrt{x + 3}$, and $g: x \rightarrow \frac{\sqrt{x+1}}{\sqrt{x+3}}$. The domain of f is determined by solving $x + 3 \geq 0$. The domain of h is the same as the domain of f except that x cannot be -3. The domain of g is the intersection of the solution sets to $x + 1 \geq 0$ and $x + 3 > 0$, or $[-1, \infty)$.

d. What is the domain of $d: x \rightarrow \frac{\sqrt{x-1}}{\sqrt{x+3}}$? $(-3, \infty)$; The numerator plays no restrictive role in determining the domain.

4. If a function is discrete, must its range also be a discrete set? Justify your answer. Yes; since each point in the domain corresponds to at most one point in the range, the number of points in the range is at most equal to the number of points in the domain.

Additional Answers

8. a. $r = \sqrt[3]{\frac{3V}{4\pi}}$

b. dependent variable: r
independent variable: V

c. domain: $(0, \infty)$
range: $(0, \infty)$

9.

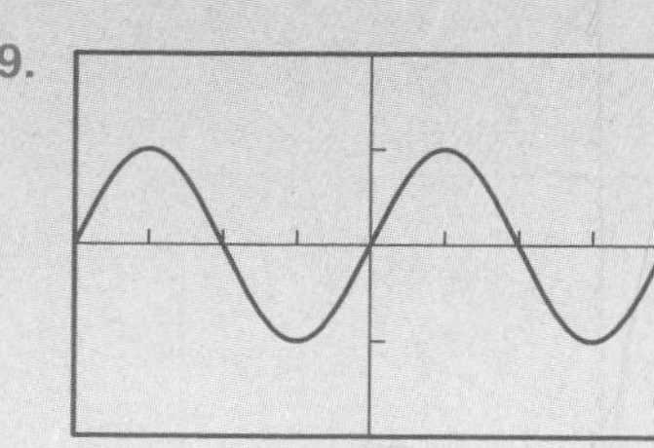

$-2\pi \leq x \leq 2\pi$, x-scale $= \frac{\pi}{2}$
$-2 \leq y \leq 2$, y-scale = 1

1) The range of a function is the set of all possible values of the dependent variable of the function. Example: The range of the function $f(x) = x^3$ is the set of real numbers.

2) A real function is a function whose domain and range are sets of real numbers. Example: $f(x) = 2x + 1$ is a real function.

3) A real-valued function is a function whose range is a set of real numbers. Example:

$$f(x) = \begin{cases} 1, \text{ if } x \text{ is a male} \\ 0, \text{ if } x \text{ is a female} \end{cases}$$

4a) the correspondence between the number of hours spent driving and the number of miles traveled

the set of integers. For example, the basketball roster function is a discrete function whose domain, a set of players, can be put in 1-1 correspondence with the set of positive integers from 1 to 10.

When the domain of a function is a discrete set, then the function is called a **discrete function**. One type of graphing calculator has a screen that is 96 pixels wide. The x-coordinates of the graph can be put into 1-1 correspondence with the set of integers from 1 to 96. So the domain of the function as graphed is discrete, and any graph made by the calculator is actually the graph of a discrete function. Computer screens have more pixels, which enables their graphs to have greater resolution, but still the graphs are discrete sets. Thus, a given function may not be a discrete function but what you see on the screen is the graph of a discrete function that approximates the given function. As another example, a city uses energy continually but it may take a check of energy use only every minute. As still another example, for all practical purposes the population of the United States changes continually, but a census is taken only every 10 years. In each case, the data points form a discrete function.

QUESTIONS

Covering the Reading

In 1–3, define and give an example. See left.

1. range of a function **2.** real function **3.** real-valued function

4. You begin a car trip at 8 A.M. with the odometer reading 23,640 miles. You travel within the speed limit all day, occasionally stopping, and finish driving at 4:30 P.M. For this situation, identify each.

a. a function See left.
b. the independent variable of this function number of hours spent driving
c. a possible domain the set of times between 0 and 8.5 hours
d. the dependent variable of this function number of miles traveled
e. a possible range set of distances between 0 and 276 miles

5. A real function H is defined by the formula $H(z) = \frac{1}{z^2 - 4} + \frac{1}{z}$. Identify the domain of H. $(-\infty, -2), (-2, 0), (0, 2), (2, \infty)$

In 6 and 7, describe the set in interval notation.

6. the set of real numbers greater than $-\pi$ and less than or equal to π $(-\pi, \pi]$

7. the set of points on the number line that are at least 2 units away from the point 3 $(-\infty, 1]$ and $[5, \infty)$

8. a. Find a formula expressing the radius r of a sphere as a function of its volume V.
b. Identify the dependent and independent variables.
c. Give the domain and range for this function.
See margin.

9. Use an automatic grapher to graph the function with equation $y = \sin x$ in the window $-2\pi \leq x \leq 2\pi$, $-2 \leq y \leq 2$. What is the domain interval over which the function is graphed? $[-2\pi, 2\pi]$
See margin for graph.

√ radian mode

10a) The alphabet can be put in a 1–1 correspondence with the set of positive integers from 1 to 26, which is a subset of the set of integers.
b) Any finite set can be put into 1–1 correspondence with a subset of the set of integers.
c) Because a finite set is a discrete set as explained in part b.

10. Explain why the following statements are true. See left.
 a. The alphabet is a discrete set.
 b. Any finite set is a discrete set.
 c. Any function f whose domain is a finite set is a function with a discrete domain.

Applying the Mathematics

11. Suppose that M is the set of 17 equally spaced numbers on the interval $0 \le x \le 1$.

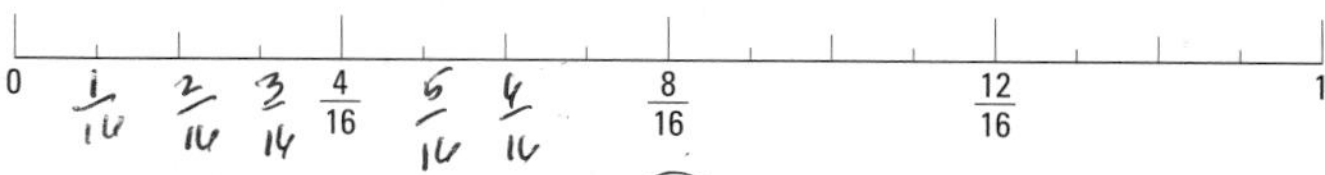

Define a function f on M by $f(x) = p$ for all x in M, where $x = \frac{p}{q}$ in lowest terms. For example, $f\left(\frac{3}{8}\right) = 3$.
 a. What is $f\left(\frac{6}{16}\right)$? 3
 b. Describe the range of f. {0, 1, 3, 5, 7, 9, 11, 13, 15}
 c. Explain why f is a discrete function.
 Its domain is a finite set which is discrete.

In 12–15, the function is a real function. Describe its domain using interval notation, if possible.

12. $f(z) = 3z^2 - z + 1$ $(-\infty, \infty)$

13. $g(t) = \sqrt{4 - t^2}$ $[-2, 2]$

14. $f(x) = \frac{1}{\sqrt{x^2 - 9}}$ $(-\infty, -3), (3, \infty)$

15. $h(x) = \frac{1}{x^2 + x - 2}$ $(-\infty, -2), (-2, 1), (1, \infty)$

16. The table below gives the cost for parking at a downtown garage. Let C be the set of costs and T be the set of times. Define a relation f from C to T and a relation g from T to C as follows:

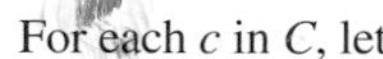

For each c in C, let
 $f(c)$ = the exact length of time a person's car was in the garage if the person's cost was c.

For each t in T, let
 $g(t)$ = the fee paid by a person whose car was in the garage for a length of time t.

PARKING

Cost	Time
\$1.50	$0 < t < \frac{1}{2}$
\$2.25	$\frac{1}{2} \le t < 1$
\$3.75	$1 \le t < 2$
\$5.25	$2 \le t < 3$
\$6.75	$3 \le t < 4$
\$8.25	$4 \le t < 5$
\$9.75	$5 \le t < 6$
\$11.25	$6 \le t \le 24$

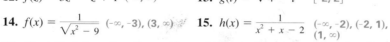

 a. Evaluate $g\left(4\frac{1}{2}\right)$. \$8.25
 b. Evaluate $f(3.75)$.
 c. Evaluate $g(23)$. \$11.25
 d. Evaluate $g\left(\frac{1}{4}\right)$. \$1.50
 e. Is f a function? Explain why or why not.
 f. Is g a function? Explain why or why not.
 g. For g, identify each.
  i. the independent variable t
  ii. the dependent variable c
  iii. the domain $\{t: 0 < t \le 24\}$

b) The exact length of time cannot be determined, but is at least 1 hour and less than 2 hours.
e) No. There are elements c in C for which $f(c)$ has more than one value.
f) Yes. It assigns to each element of T exactly one element of C.

Notes on Questions

Question 9 Error Alert Be sure that students have set their automatic grapher to the radian mode. On some calculators (e.g., the TI-83 and TI-92), the arguments of trigonometric functions must be in parentheses. So to graph $y = \sin x$, one must enter $y = \sin(x)$.

Questions 12–15 You may also wish to discuss the range for these functions. Identifying the range will not only help in getting an informative graph for the functions, but also will provide a preview for the next lesson.

Adapting to Individual Needs

Challenge

For each equation, have students answer the following questions: If this equation defines a relation between m and n, where m and n are real numbers, is m a function of n? Is n a function of m? If not, why not? (These questions can be answered by solving for m and then solving for n.)

1. $3m - 2n + 6 = 0$ [m is a function of n, and n is a function of m.]
2. $m - 2n^2 + 8 = 0$ [m is a function of n, but n is not a function of m, because for some values of m, there are 2 values of n.]
3. $2m^2 + 6n^2 - 9 = 0$ [Neither is a function of the other, because for some values of either variable, there are 2 values of the other.]
4. $m^2n + 8m - 2 = 0$ [n is a function of m, but m is not a function of n, because for some values of n, there are 2 values of m.]

Notes on Questions

Question 17 Questions of this type help review the algebra students need to deal with composite functions (Lesson 3-2) and derivatives (Chapter 9). Be sure to discuss this question.

Follow-up for Lesson 2-1

Practice

For more questions on SPUR Objectives, use **Lesson Master 2-1** (shown on page 81).

Assessment

Written Communication Ask students to write a paragraph explaining the terms *discrete set* and *discrete function.* Then have them give an example of each different from the examples in the text. [Students show understanding of the terms discussed in the lesson.]

Extension

Have students create functions with the given domain or range. Sample responses are given.

1. Domain = $\{x: x \geq 4\}$
   Range = $\{y: y \geq 0\}$
   $[f(x) = \sqrt{x - 4}]$
2. Domain = the set of all reals except $x \neq 0$
   Range = the set of all reals except $y \neq 0$ $[f(x) = \frac{1}{x}]$
3. Domain = the set of all reals except $x \neq 1$
   Range = the set of all reals except $y \neq 0$ $[f(x) = \frac{1}{x-1})]$
4. Domain = the set of all reals
   Range = the set of all reals
   $[f(x) = \lfloor x \rfloor]$
5. Domain = the set of all reals
   Range = $\{y: y \geq -3\}$
   $[f(x) = x^2 - 3]$

Review

17. If $\forall$ a, $h(a) = 3 + 4a$, find $h(2a + 5)$. *(Previous course, Lesson 1-1)* **$8a + 23$**

18. Find the coordinates of the vertex of the parabola $y = 2x^2 - 3x + 1$. *(Previous course)* **$\left(\frac{3}{4}, \frac{-1}{8}\right)$**

19. The height of a cylinder varies directly as its volume and inversely as the square of the radius of its base.

a. Give a formula relating height, volume, and radius. **$h = \frac{V}{\pi r^2}$**

b. If the radius is doubled but the volume is kept constant, what happens to the height? *(Previous course)* **The height will be $\frac{1}{4}$ of its original value.**

20. A single unbiased (fair) die is rolled. Give the probability that the number obtained is greater than 2. *(Previous course)* **$\frac{2}{3}$**

21. Find the coordinates of the vertices of the image of *FIRE* when it is reflected over the line $y = x$. *(Previous course)*

$F' = (2, -1)$
$I' = (1, 0)$
$R' = (1, 1)$
$E' = (2, 0)$

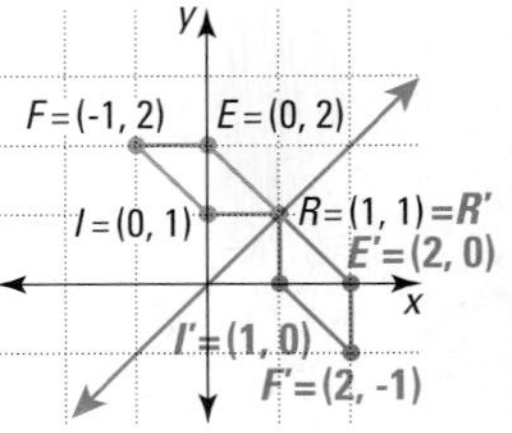

Exploration

22. Find rules for three different functions defined on [-10, 10] whose range is [0, 100].

Answers may vary. Sample: $y = x^2$; $y = |10x|$; $y = |-10x|$

Setting Up Lesson 2-2

Be certain to discuss those questions in Lesson 2-1 that deal with the range of a function.

The In-class Activity on page 85 should be completed before Lesson 2-2 is covered.

Introducing Lesson 2-2

Finding the Range of a Function

ACTIVITY

You may find it useful to work on this activity with a partner. You will need an automatic grapher.

1 Sketch a graph of the function with equation $y = 4x^2 - 3x + 5$. See margin.

2 **a.** From the graph, estimate the minimum value of this function. 4
b. The range is the set of possible values of y. Use the minimum value to determine the range. Describe the range as a closed infinite interval. $[4, \infty)$

3 By using the trace function, find a better approximation to the range. $[4.4, \infty)$

4 By zooming in on the function, find an even more accurate approximation of the range. $[4.4375, \infty)$

5 The graph of the function with equation $y = ax^2 + bx + c$ has its vertex at the point where $x = \frac{-b}{2a}$. a) $\left(\frac{3}{8}, \frac{71}{16}\right)$
a. Use this information to find the exact coordinates of the vertex of the graph.
b. Describe the range exactly. $\left[\frac{71}{16}, \infty\right)$

In-class Activity

Resources

From the ***Teacher's Resource File***
- Answer Master 2-2

Additional Resources
- Exploration 2-2

This activity reviews working with automatic graphers in the context of finding the range of a function. Students are expected to know how to specify a window for a graph, enter a rule for a function, and obtain approximate coordinates of any point on the graph they obtain.

If your students have used automatic graphers in previous courses, you may wish to skip this activity.

While most mathematics textbooks (this one included) distinguish carefully between the domain and the range of a function, many automatic graphers show only *range* as a key or menu selection even for the domain variable. Point this out to students.

Some automatic graphers, if given a new function but not a new range, will use as the default whatever range was used last. This can be quite annoying, for example, if the last user had zoomed in on a particular point on some graph and so has a very small window.

Remind students that although the graphs of some functions on (calculator or computer) screens may look continuous, the graphs consist only of finitely many dots. This means that when the function defined for all real values is plotted with an automatic grapher, the display shows only the graph of a discrete function that approximates the given function in the selected window.

Technology Connection
Materials: Explorations software

Students may use *Exploration 2-2, Analyzing Functions,* to do this In-class Activity. Students can choose from a list of pre-selected functions or enter their own function, generate a table of values, and graph the function. The program shows the minimum and maximum points of the function and allows students to identify the coordinates of any point on the graph.

Additional Answers

1.

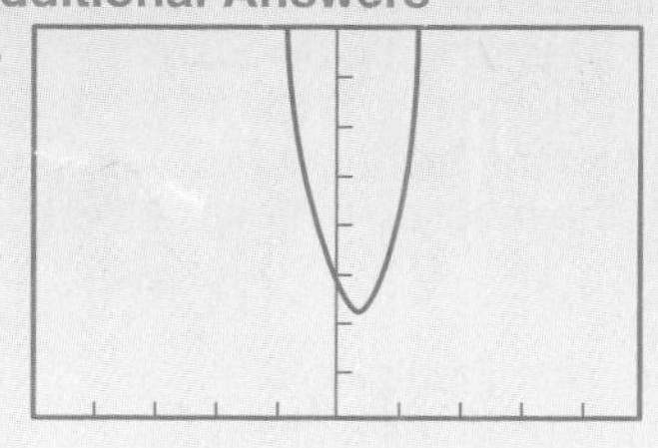

$-5 \le x \le 5$, x-scale = 1
$2 \le y \le 10$, y-scale = 1

Lesson 2-2

Objectives

A Determine relative minima and relative maxima of a function and intervals on which it is increasing or decreasing.

C Identify the domain, range, minimum and maximum values of functions.

F Solve max-min problems.

G Analyze a function from its graph.

Resources

From the ***Teacher's Resource File***

- Lesson Master 2-2
- Answer Master 2-2
- Teaching Aids
  12 Warm-up
  16 Surface Area of a Cylinder
- Technology Sourcebook
  Calculator Master 1

Additional Resources

- Visuals for Teaching Aids 12, 16

Teaching Lesson 2-2

Warm-up

Graph the function f with $f(r) = 2\pi r^2 + \frac{116}{r}$. Trace along the graph. How close can you get to the values for $f(1)$, $f(2)$, $f(3)$, and $f\left(\frac{1}{2}\right)$ given at the bottom of page 87?

Notes on Reading

You may find it convenient to use the word *extremum* (plural: *extrema*) to refer either to a maximum or minimum value. Whereas the range of a function is the set of all possible values of the function, extrema of a function may be associated with the entire domain, or they may be *relative extrema* associated with a particular interval. (Relative extrema are discussed in the next lesson.) Obviously, the extrema of a function restricted to a particular interval might not be the extrema for the function over its entire domain.

❶ The problem of minimizing a cylinder's surface area for a given volume is important and should be examined in detail. **Teaching Aid 16** is provided for this discussion.

LESSON

2-2 Finding Maxima and Minima

Jave-Lynda? *Lynda Lipson throwing the javelin during the 1997 World Championships at Olympic Stadium in Athens, Greece*

A person on a track team wishes to know the angle at which to throw a javelin so that the javelin travels the farthest. A store wants to price shoes so that it makes the most money from their sale. A traveling salesperson has to visit several cities and wants the shortest route that contains all of them. These problems are called **max-min problems** because they ask either for the greatest or the least value of a function. The solution of max-min problems is one of the most important applications of functions.

Solving a max-min problem requires three steps:

(1) a careful statement of the problem;

(2) writing the expression to be maximized or minimized as a function of a single variable;

(3) finding the maximum or minimum value of that function.

Here is a design problem that is rather complicated but leads to a typical kind of function whose maximum or minimum value is of interest.

Statement of the Problem

A container manufacturer wants a cylindrical metal can that will hold one quart of paint with a little extra room for air space. One liquid quart occupies a volume of 57.749 in^3, so the manufacturer decides to design a can with a volume of 58 in^3. Of course, the manufacturer wants to keep the cost of material at a minimum. The amount of sheet metal required to construct the can is equal to the total surface area A of the can. Let r be the radius and h the height of the can. The problem, then, is to find a pair of values r and h which give a volume of 58 in^3 and a minimum value for A.

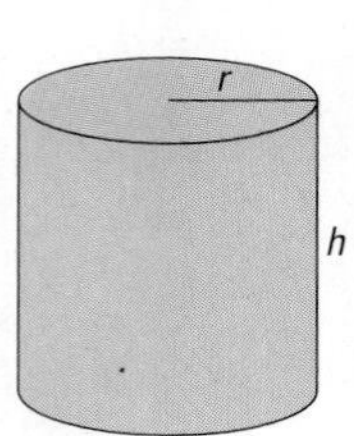

Lesson 2-2 Overview

Broad Goals To graph a function over a given domain, its range must be known. In many cases, the range may be determined from knowing the maximum and/or minimum values. This terminology is reviewed in this lesson and applied to the classic problem of determining the cylinder of minimum surface area for a given volume. The solution to this problem is approximated by graphing.

Perspective The function f defined by $f(r) = 2\pi r^2 + \frac{116}{r}$ is a rational function, of the type to be discussed in Chapter 5.

For calculus students, framing maximum/minimum problems in terms of functions is often the most difficult step in solving such problems.

Finding the Expression to Be Minimized

❶ In order to solve the problem, we develop a formula for A as a function of a single variable. The total surface area A of the can is the sum of the areas of two circles (the top and bottom of the can), and the area of the rectangle that is formed when the side of the can is slit and unrolled. That is, as shown below,

$$A = 2\pi r^2 + 2\pi rh.$$

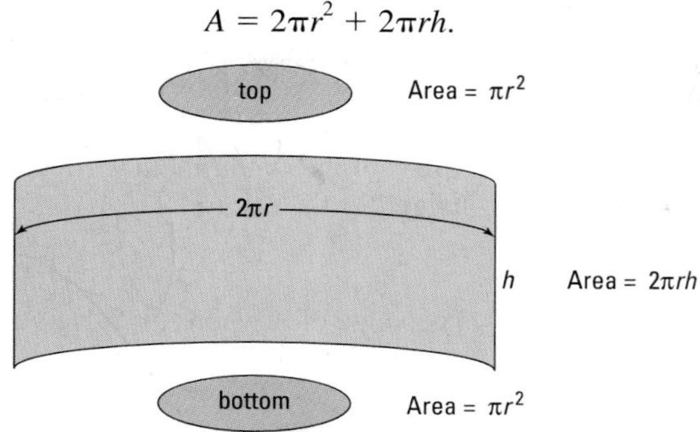

Now, we will write A as a function of one variable only, the radius. To do this, we must find a formula for h in terms of r. The volume V of this cylinder is given by $V = \pi r^2 h$. Because $V = 58$ in^3, it follows that $58 = \pi r^2 h$, and so $h = \frac{58}{\pi r^2}$ expresses h in terms of r. Substitute for h in the area formula.

$$\begin{aligned} A &= 2\pi r^2 + 2\pi r\left(\frac{58}{\pi r^2}\right) \\ &= 2\pi r^2 + \frac{116}{r} \end{aligned}$$

The area is now stated as a function of the radius, so we can write

$$A = f(r) = 2\pi r^2 + \frac{116}{r}.$$

Finding the Minimum Value

Because f is a real function, a graph can be used to determine the value of r which would make the area $f(r)$ of sheet metal as small as possible. However, simply entering the formula

$$f(r) = 2\pi r^2 + \frac{116}{r}$$

into an automatic grapher, and asking for the graph for some interval of positive values of r, may result in a blank screen. The values for the graphing window must be set so that the window contains the part of the graph which contains the minimum. To determine appropriate window values, it is helpful to compute some sample values of $f(r)$.

$$f(1) = 2\pi + 116 \approx 122 \qquad f(2) = 8\pi + 58 \approx 83$$
$$f(3) = 18\pi + \frac{116}{3} \approx 95 \qquad f\left(\frac{1}{2}\right) = \frac{\pi}{2} + 232 \approx 234$$

Ask students to describe the appearance of a can with $r = 0.1$ or less. As r gets close to zero, the term $\frac{116}{r}$ dominates $f(r)$, so $r = 0$ is a vertical asymptote. Now the radius of the can is small but the height is large and a great amount of material needed. (This idea is discussed in Lesson 5-3.)

As r becomes larger and larger, the term $2\pi r^2$ dominates, and the graph of f is indistinguishable from the graph of $y = 2\pi r^2$. When the radius is quite large, since the can has a fixed volume, its height is very small; thus the amount of material needed is just about the same as that needed for the top and bottom circles of the can. (This idea is discussed in Lesson 5-5.)

You might point out that because the formula $A = 2\pi r^2 + 2\pi rh$ has 2 independent variables (r and h), its graph is 3-dimensional and cannot be analyzed fully with a 2-dimensional coordinate system. Thus we must use our knowledge of the actual volume needed to write $\pi r^2 h = 58$, solve for h in terms of r, and use this in the formula for area to get a formula with only one independent variable.

Error Alert Students may have difficulty knowing how to determine accuracy when tracing and zooming in. When tracing a function, have students pay attention to what decimal place is changing in the y-coordinate. From this, the accuracy of the approximation can be determined.

Additional Examples

A box with a square base and no lid is to have a volume of 3000 in^3. Find the dimensions of the box with the given volume that has the least surface area. **Let x be an edge of the base, y be the height of the box, and A be its surface area. Then $3000 = x^2 y$, so $y = \frac{3000}{x^2}$. Then $A = x^2 + 4xy = x^2 + \frac{12000}{x}$. With an automatic grapher, the minimum area occurs when $x \approx 18.2$ in. Substituting into the second equation yields $y \approx 9.1$ in.]**

Other examples of this type of problem which you may want to discuss include minimizing the surface of containers other than cylinders, minimizing cost functions, or maximizing profit functions. Any calculus text will contain an abundance of typical problems, but it does not solve them the way we do.

One advantage of using calculus to solve maximum-minimum problems such as these is that the calculus approach produces exact solutions, while the graphical approach yields only approximations to those solutions. More important, however, is that calculus provides a formal logical framework into which the solutions to these and whole classes of similar problems can be described and analyzed accurately.

Notes on Questions

Question 10 Some students may think that if the area of the rectangle is fixed, then the perimeter is also a constant for all lengths and widths. A spreadsheet or calculator generated table of values will help dispel this misconception.

(Notes on Questions continue on page 90.)

Follow-up for Lesson 2-2

Practice

For more questions on SPUR Objectives, use **Lesson Master 2-2** (shown on page 89).

Assessment

Written Communication Have students repeat **Questions 7–8** using these functions and domains:

$f(x) = -x^3 + 4x$, domain [0, 3]

$g(x) = \frac{x^4}{4} - 2x^3 + 8x$, domain [-2, 2]

[Students determine the range of a function over a given interval.]

Extension

Pose this problem. Suppose that a can manufacturer wants to know the dimensions of the cylindrical can of maximum volume that can be constructed from 82.9 square inches of sheet metal.

1. How does this problem differ from the minimization problem solved in this lesson? [The surface area is given and the volume must be maximized.]
2. Express the volume of the can as a function of the radius. [$V \approx 41.5r - \pi r^3$]

These values indicate that the scale on the y-axis should reach at least 250. With a suitable choice of values on the horizontal axis, the graph of f looks like the one at the right. By using the trace key and zooming in, you can find the coordinates of the minimum point on the curve to be about (2.1, 82.9); that is, the minimum value of A is approximately 82.9, and it occurs when $r = 2.1$. So, the best choice for the radius of the can is about 2.1 inches and, since $h = \frac{58}{\pi r^2}$, the corresponding height for the can is

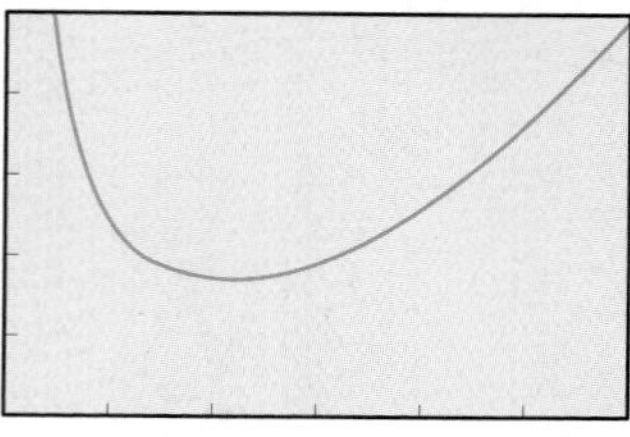

$0 \le x \le 6$, x-scale = 1
$0 \le y \le 250$, y-scale = 50

$$h = \frac{58}{\pi(2.1)^2} \approx 4.2 \text{ inches.}$$

The value of A when $r \approx 2.1$ gives some additional information: approximately 82.9 square inches of sheet metal is required to construct this can.

The Symbolic Definitions of Maximum and Minimum

In the function $f(r) = 2\pi r^2 + \frac{116}{r}$, r could be any real number but zero. When we consider negative values of r, the graph looks quite different than what is shown above. At the right is a graph of f on the domain [-5, 5].

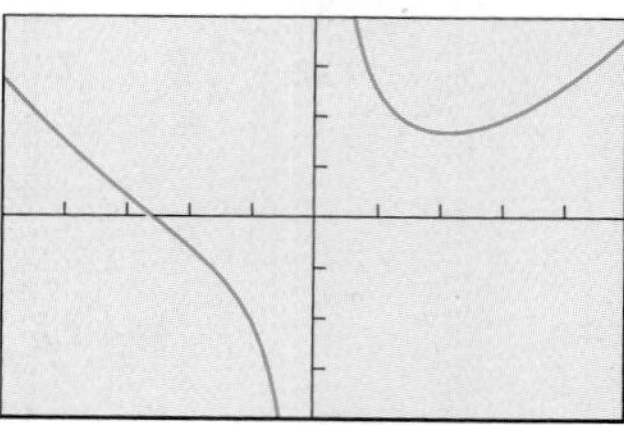

$-5 \le x \le 5$, x-scale = 1
$-200 \le y \le 200$, y-scale = 50

Notice that $f(r)$ decreases sharply when r is negative and approaching 0. In fact, on the domain [-5, 5] there is no minimum value of f. Thus, to know whether a function has a minimum, you must know its domain.

To write a symbolic definition of minimum, we first state the idea in words. The number m is the minimum value of a real function on a domain S if and only if m is a value of the function and every other value is no smaller.

Definition
m is the **minimum value** of a real function f with domain S if and only if $\exists\, x$ in S such that $f(x) = m$ and $\forall\, x$ in S, $m \le f(x)$.

The symbolic definition of maximum value is quite similar.

Definition
m is the **maximum value** of a function f with domain S if and only if $\exists\, x$ in S such that $f(x) = m$ and $\forall\, x$ in S, $m \ge f(x)$.

Optional Activities

Activity 1 Technology Connection You might wish to assign *Technology Sourcebook, Calculator Master 1.* In this activity, students use a graphics calculator to graph a series of polynomial functions in order to determine the relationship between the number of "bends" in the graph of a polynomial and its degree.

Activity 2 You might use this activity after students complete the lesson. Ask students to determine what the function in the lesson would be if the volume of the cylinder were doubled to 116 in^3. Would the value of the radius to achieve a minimum also be doubled? [The function would be $f: r \rightarrow 2\pi r^2 + \frac{232}{r}$. The minimum value occurs when $r \approx 2.6$ in., so it is not doubled.]

Adapting to Individual Needs

Extra Help

You might be surprised to discover that even at this level of their mathematics study, some students feel that if the perimeter of a figure is fixed, so too is its area, and vice versa. (See the notes on **Question 10.**) Take the time to demonstrate with concrete materials, grid paper, or formulas that this is not the case. Extend the discussion, also, to surface area and volume.

QUESTIONS

Covering the Reading

1. Find the exact range of the function $y = -x^2 + x + 1$. $\left(-\infty, \frac{5}{4}\right]$

2. m is a maximum value of a function g with domain D if and only if __?__ in D such that $g(z) = M$ and $\forall$ z in D, __?__. $\exists$ z; $M \geq g(z)$

3. Consider the function with equation $y = \frac{3x}{1 + x^2}$. Estimate its range and its maximum and minimum values.
range: [-1.5, 1.5], maximum: 1.5, minimum: -1.5

4. Let f be the function in this lesson, with $f(r) = 2\pi r^2 + \frac{116}{r}$.
   a. Calculate $f(2.05)$ and $f(2.15)$. $f(2.05) \approx 82.990$; $f(2.15) \approx 82.998$
   b. Explain how you know before calculating that $f(2.05) > 82.5$ and $f(2.15) > 82.5$. Because the minimum value of f is approximately 82.9 which exceeds 82.5.

5. Consider a cylindrical can with height 4.2 inches and radius 2.1 inches.
   a. What is its volume? 58.2 in^3 **b.** What is its surface area? 83.1 in^2
   c. What property does a can with these dimensions possess? The surface area of a can with these dimensions is only slightly greater than the minimum.

6. Suppose that a cylindrical can is to hold a liter of oil. Recall that 1 liter = 1000 cm^3. a) $S(r) = 2\pi r^2 + \frac{2000}{r}$
   a. Give a formula for the surface area of this can in terms of its radius.
   b. Approximate the radius and height (cm) that would use the least amount of material to make the can.
   $r \approx 5.4$ cm; $h \approx 10.8$ cm

Applying the Mathematics

In 7 and 8, graph the function defined by the given rule over the indicated domain. Use the graph to estimate (to the nearest tenth) the range of the function over this domain. See left.

7. $f(x) = x^3 - x^2$, domain [0, 2]
8. $g(x) = 2^x - x^2$, domain [-1, 4]

7)
$0 \leq x \leq 2$, x-scale = $\frac{1}{2}$
$-2 \leq y \leq 5$, y-scale = 1
range: [-0.1, 4]

8)
$-1 \leq x \leq 4$, x-scale = 1
$-2 \leq y \leq 2$, y-scale = 1
range: [-1.1, 1.2]

9. A rancher is planning to fence in a rectangular area of 20,000 m^2 for his cattle to graze. He is interested in determining the least amount of fencing needed. Perform the following steps to obtain an approximate answer to this question. See margin.
   a. Determine a formula which expresses the length ℓ of a 20,000 m^2 piece of land in terms of its width w.
   b. Use part **a** to express the perimeter P of a 20,000 m^2 rectangular piece of land in terms of its width.
   c. Evaluate the expression $P(w)$ in part **b** at $w = 130$, $w = 140$, and $w = 150$.
   d. Use an automatic grapher to approximate the coordinates of the lowest point on the graph of $P(w)$ in the first quadrant.
   e. What is the least amount of fencing that the rancher needs?

10. The manufacturer discussed in the text is also commissioned to make 58 in^3 cylindrical cans with no tops because these will be closed with plastic lids. Once again, the manufacturer is interested in finding the dimensions which require the least amount of metal for each can. Determine approximate values for the optimum dimensions.
radius $\approx$ 2.6 in.; height $\approx$ 2.6 in.

3. Use an automatic grapher to approximate the dimensions of the can of maximum volume. [$r \approx 2.1$ in., $h \approx 4.2$ in^2, maximum volume ≈ 58 in^3]

The exact solutions for the minimization problem and the maximization problem in this extension can be shown to be identical. Such pairs of maximum and minimum problems are called *dual problems.* A class of mathematical results called *duality theorems* provide conditions under which there will be dual problems whose solutions are identical.

Additional Answers

9. a. $l = \frac{20000}{w}$
   b. $P = \frac{40000}{w} + 2w$
   c. $P(130) \approx 567.7$
   $P(140) \approx 565.7$
   $P(150) \approx 566.7$
   d.
   $0 \leq x \leq 250$, x-scale = 50
   $0 \leq y \leq 4000$, y-scale = 1000
   (141.4, 565.7)
   e. 565.7 m

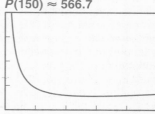

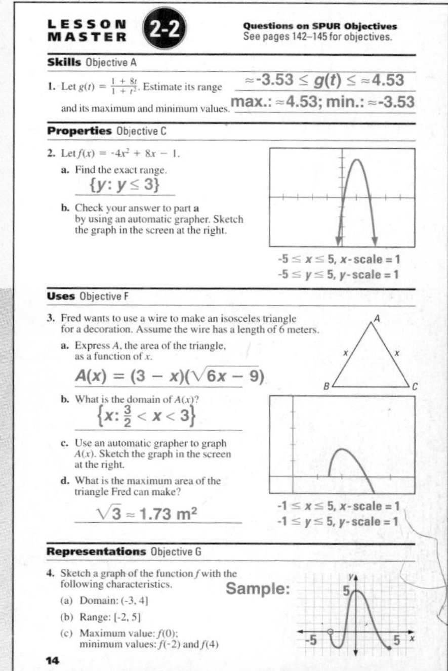
LESSON MASTER 2-2 — Questions on SPUR Objectives. See pages 142–145 for objectives.

Skills Objective A

1. Let $g(t) = \frac{1 + 8t}{1 + t^2}$. Estimate its range and its maximum and minimum values. $\approx -3.53 \leq g(t) \leq \approx 4.53$; max.: ≈ 4.53; min.: ≈ -3.53

Properties Objective C

2. Let $f(x) = -4x^2 + 8x - 1$.
   a. Find the exact range. $\{y: y \leq 3\}$
   b. Check your answer to part a by using an automatic grapher. Sketch the graph in the screen at the right.
   $-5 \leq x \leq 5$, x-scale = 1
   $-5 \leq y \leq 5$, y-scale = 1

Uses Objective F

3. Fred wants to use a wire to make an isosceles triangle for a decoration. Assume the wire has a length of 6 meters.
   a. Express A, the area of the triangle, as a function of x. $A(x) = (3 - x)(\sqrt{6x - 9})$
   b. What is the domain of $A(x)$? $\{x: \frac{3}{2} < x < 3\}$
   c. Use an automatic grapher to graph $A(x)$. Sketch the graph in the screen at the right.
   d. What is the maximum area of the triangle Fred can make? $\sqrt{3} \approx 1.73$ m^2
   $-1 \leq x \leq 5$, x-scale = 1
   $-1 \leq y \leq 5$, y-scale = 1

Representations Objective G

4. Sketch a graph of the function f with the following characteristics. Sample:
   (a) Domain: [-3, 4]
   (b) Range: [-2, 5]
   (c) Maximum value: $f(0)$; minimum values: $f(-2)$ and $f(4)$

14

Adapting to Individual Needs

Challenge

Have students write a function and use a graphics calculator to answer the following questions.

1. A rancher has 300 yards of fencing material and wants to use it to enclose a rectangular region. What dimensions would give a region of maximum area? [Let x be the width and $150 - x$ the length; maximize $A = x(150 - x)$; 75 yd by 75 yd]

2. Suppose the region above is bordered by a river so that fencing is only needed on three sides. Now, what dimensions would give a region of maximum area? [Let x be the width and $300 - 2x$ the length; maximize $A = x(300 - 2x)$; 75 yd by 150 yd]

Notes on Questions

Question 14c Here we have defined h as a quotient of *real* functions, so it cannot be defined where either function is not defined. If we had defined h by

$$h(y) = \frac{\sqrt{y+1}}{\sqrt{y-1}},$$

then we could obtain real values of h when $y \le -1$, so these values would be part of the function. Some calculators do not make this distinction, and show values of h for $x \le -1$ even when h is defined implicitly using f and g.

Question 17 Consumer Connection Discuss with students what factors other than economy of material are considered in designing a container. Appearance, ease of handling, ease of appropriate use, and stackability on store shelves are additional considerations. A sphere is the most economical shape for a container with a given volume (the Isoperimetric Inequality in three dimensions), but a gallon of milk packed in a sphere would roll off the breakfast table. However, the milkman could roll it from his truck to your doorstep, thereby reducing delivery costs!

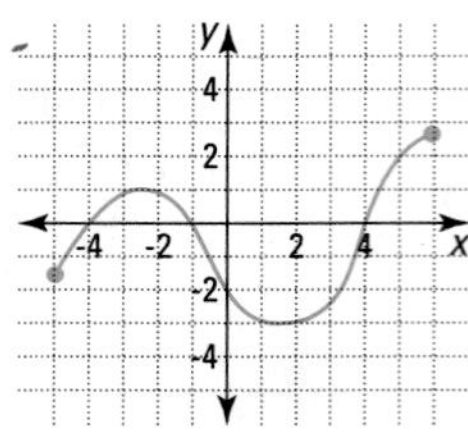

Number of Rolls of Film Purchased	Percent Discount
0–2	0
3–6	5
7–12	8
13–20	10
21 and over	15

13a) Yes, because each element in R corresponds to exactly one element in P.
b) No, because each element in P corresponds to more than one element in R.

11. Let h be the function whose entire graph is shown at the left.
- **a.** Estimate the minimum and maximum values of h.
- **b.** Estimate the domain and range of h.
- **c.** Find all x such $h(x) = -2$. $x = 0$ and $x = 3$
- **d.** Describe the intervals on which $h(x) < 0$. $[-5, -4)$ and $(-1, 4)$

a) minimum: -3; maximum: 3 b) domain: $[-5, 6]$; range $[-3, 3]$

Review

12. Use interval notation to describe the set of solutions to the inequality $x^3 \le 2$. *(Previous course, Lesson 2-1)* $(-\infty, \sqrt[3]{2}]$

13. A camera store uses the chart below to determine the discount earned for quantity purchases. Let R be the set of numbers of rolls of film purchased and let P be the set of percent discounts.
- **a.** For all r in R, let $f(r)$ = percent discount on r rolls. Is f a function? Why or why not? See left.
- **b.** For all p in P, let $g(p)$ = number of rolls receiving discount p. Is g a function? Why or why not? See left.
- **c.** If possible, evaluate.
  i. $f(7)$ 8 **ii.** $g(10)$ not possible **iii.** $f(23)$ 15 *(Lesson 2-1)*

14. Consider the function $h = \frac{f}{g}$, where f and g are real functions with $f(y) = \sqrt{y+1}$ and $g(y) = \sqrt{y-1}$.
- **a.** For what real values of y is f defined? $y \ge -1$
- **b.** For what real values of y is g defined? $y \ge 1$
- **c.** Use the results of parts **a** and **b** to find the domain of h. *(Lesson 2-1)* $(1, \infty)$

15. A stairway light is controlled by two switches—one at each end of the stairs. If the switches are both up or both down, then the light is on. Otherwise, it is off. See margin.
- **a.** Make a table showing whether the light is on or off for every possible combination of switch positions. (Let "on" = 1 and "off" = 0.)
- **b.** Explain how this situation is a physical representation of the logical expression $p \Leftrightarrow q$. *(Lesson 1-5)*

16. Write the negation of the following statement about the range of the function $f: A \rightarrow B$. *(Lesson 1-2)*

$\forall$ *y in B*, $\exists$ *x in A with* $f(x) = y$.

$\exists$ *y in B such that* $\forall$ *x in A*, $f(x) \ne y$.

Exploration

17. Find a soda can and determine its radius, height, volume, and surface area. Using the idea of this lesson, determine whether its dimensions are economical in the sense that the surface area is the smallest possible for the given volume. See margin.

90

Additional Answers

15. a.

Switch 1	Switch 2	Switch 3
1	1	1
1	0	0
0	1	0
0	0	1

A "1" in the first or second column means that the indicated switch is up, and a "0" means that it is down.

b.

p	q	$p \Leftrightarrow q$
T	T	T
T	F	F
F	T	F
F	F	T

If 1 corresponds to T and 0 to F, it is apparent that the two truth tables are equivalent. Hence, the stairway light situation is a physical representation of $p \Leftrightarrow q$.

17. Sample:
Radius: 1.25 inches;
Height: 5.75 inches;
Volume: $\approx$ 28.23 cubic inches;
Surface area: $\approx$ 54.98 square inches;
Optimal height: $\approx$ 3.30 inches;
Optimal radius: $\approx$ 1.65 inches
Economical dimensions are not used to obtain this volume.

LESSON

2-3

Increasing and Decreasing Functions

Year	Consumption	Year	Consumption
1954	35.27	1975	70.55
1955	38.82	1976	74.36
1956	40.38	1977	76.29
1957	40.48	1978	78.09
1958	40.35	1979	78.90
1959	42.14	1980	75.96
1960	43.80	1981	73.99
1961	44.46	1982	70.85
1962	46.53	1983	70.52
1963	48.33	1984	74.14
1964	50.50	1985	73.98
1965	52.68	1986	74.30
1966	55.66	1987	76.89
1967	57.57	1988	80.22
1968	61.00	1989	81.33
1969	64.19	1990	84.17
1970	66.43	1991	84.05
1971	67.89	1992	85.26
1972	71.26	1993	87.03
1973	74.28	1994	88.90
1974	72.54	1995	90.62

An Example with a Discrete Function

Here are a table and a graph of total annual energy consumption (coal, natural gas, petroleum, hydroelectric power, nuclear electric power, geothermal, solar, and wind energy) in the United States from 1954 to 1995. The data are from the 1995 Energy Information Administration Annual Energy Review. Consumption is given in quadrillions of BTUs.

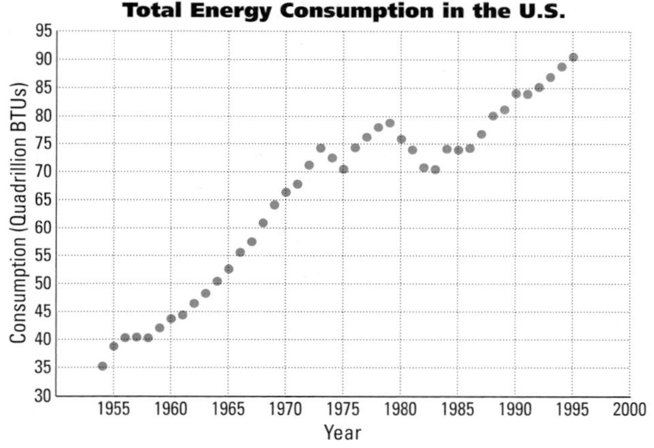

Think of these ordered pairs as determining a function E that maps years onto quadrillions of BTUs. For instance, $E(1985) = 73.98$. E is a discrete function that is defined by the table. The domain of E is the interval [1954, 1995] of integers from 1954 to 1995.

Knowing when energy consumption increases or decreases tells you whether conservation measures are working or not, how much energy might be needed in the future, what it might cost, and so on.

Lesson 2-3

Objectives

A Determine relative minima and maxima of a function and intervals on which it is increasing or decreasing.

G Analyze a function from its graph.

Resources

From the ***Teacher's Resource File***

- Lesson Master 2-3
- Answer Master 2-3
- Teaching Aids
  - 12 Warm-up
  - 17 Table of Energy Consumption in the U.S.
  - 18 Graph of Energy Consumption in the U.S.
  - 19 Definitions of Increasing Function and Decreasing Function

Additional Resources

- Visuals for Teaching Aids 12, 17–19

Teaching Lesson 2-3

Warm-up

In 1–4, a real function f is described by an equation. Tell whether f is increasing, decreasing, or neither increasing nor decreasing on the interval [-1,1].

1. $f(x) = x^2$ **Neither**
2. $f(x) = x^3$ **Increasing**
3. $f(x) = \sqrt{x}$ **Neither; the function is not defined over the entire interval**
4. $f(x) = |x|$ **Neither**
5. $f(x) = \sin x$ **Increasing**

Lesson 2-3 Overview

Broad Goals The emphasis in this lesson is on translating the visual picture of a function increasing (or decreasing) on an interval into its algebraic counterpart and then working with that counterpart.

Perspective What we call *increasing* is sometimes called *strictly increasing.* Some textbooks also provide the following definitions:

1. f is nondecreasing or monotonic increasing on S if and only if $\forall\ x_1, x_2 \in S$, if $x_1 < x_2$, then $f(x_1) \le f(x_2)$.
2. f is nonincreasing or monotonic decreasing on S if and only if $\forall\ x_1, x_2 \in S$, if $x_1 < x_2$, then $f(x_1) \ge f(x_2)$.

Every constant function is both nonincreasing and nondecreasing.

Optional Activities

You might use this activity after discussing the lesson. Given information about where a function is increasing and decreasing, ask students to produce a reasonable graph. [Sample graphs are shown at the right on page 92.]

1. A function is decreasing on (-∞, 2) and increasing on (2, ∞).

(Optional Activities continue on page 92.)

Notes on Reading

❶ **Science Connection** Lignite is a brownish-black coal, which, in the coalification process, comes between peat and bituminous coal. Although an estimated 45% of the world's coal supply is lignite, it is not extensively mined because of its low quality.

Teaching Aids 17–18 contain the table and graph of energy consumption shown on page 91.

❷ **Teaching Aid 19** is provided to make it easier to discuss the definitions of *increasing function* and *decreasing function.* Notice the use of the universal quantifier to express with precision the fact that a function is increasing or decreasing on a set *S*. This makes it evident that increasing on an interval means increasing *everywhere* on that interval.

Error Alert If it is not obvious to students that, for a continuous function, a relative maximum occurs when the function stops increasing and begins decreasing, refer to the discrete example on page 91. Then ask what corresponding statement can be made about the place where a relative minimum occurs.

The **Example** shows how an automatic grapher can be used to find approximate endpoints of intervals where a function is increasing or decreasing. All students should be able to make use of the trace function on an automatic grapher.

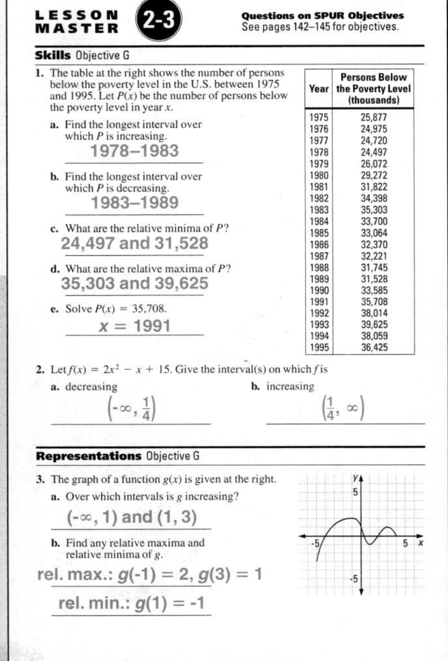

LESSON MASTER 2-3 **Questions on SPUR Objectives**
See pages 142–145 for objectives.

Skills Objective G

1. The table at the right shows the number of persons below the poverty level in the U.S. between 1975 and 1995. Let $P(x)$ be the number of persons below the poverty level in year x.
   a. Find the longest interval over which P is increasing. 1978–1983
   b. Find the longest interval over which P is decreasing. 1983–1989
   c. What are the relative minima of P? 24,497 and 31,528
   d. What are the relative maxima of P? 35,303 and 39,625
   e. Solve $P(x) = 35{,}708$. $x = 1991$

Year	Persons Below the Poverty Level (thousands)
1975	25,877
1976	24,975
1977	24,720
1978	24,497
1979	26,072
1980	29,272
1981	31,822
1982	34,398
1983	35,303
1984	33,700
1985	33,064
1986	32,370
1987	32,221
1988	31,745
1989	31,528
1990	33,585
1991	35,708
1992	38,014
1993	39,625
1994	38,059
1995	36,425

2. Let $f(x) = 2x^2 - x + 15$. Give the interval(s) on which f is
   a. decreasing $\left(-\infty, \frac{1}{4}\right)$
   b. increasing $\left(\frac{1}{4}, \infty\right)$

Representations Objective G

3. The graph of a function $g(x)$ is given at the right.
   a. Over which intervals is g increasing? $(-\infty, 1)$ and $(1, 3)$
   b. Find any relative maxima and relative minima of g.
   rel. max.: $g(-1) = 2$, $g(3) = 1$
   rel. min.: $g(1) = -1$

Lignite coal miners in the early 1900s, Rockdale, Texas

By examining either the table or the graph of E, you can tell when the total energy consumption in the U.S. increased from one year to the next. For instance, since $E(1985) < E(1986)$, energy consumption increased from 1985 to 1986. We also say that annual energy consumption increased during the *time intervals* 1954–1957, 1958–1973, 1975–1979, 1983–1984, 1985–1990, and 1991–1995. Also note that although $E(1984) = 74.14$ and $E(1987) = 76.89$, the function E is not increasing on the interval from 1984 to 1987 because the values of E went down from 1984 to 1985. In order for a function to be *increasing* on an interval, whenever *any* two domain values are chosen from that interval, the greater of the two domain values must yield a greater range value. Graphically, this means that the function always goes up as you trace the graph from left to right.

An Example with a Non-Discrete Function

❶ The function E is discrete, so you can easily determine when it increases and decreases. In contrast, the surface area function f with

$$f(r) = 2\pi r^2 + \frac{116}{r},$$

considered in the can design problem that we solved in the last lesson, is not discrete. Without knowing its exact minimum points, we cannot tell when f changes from decreasing to increasing. From the graph, it appears that the function f is increasing on the interval $(2.1, \infty)$ (approximately) and that f is decreasing on the interval $(0, 2.1)$ (approximately) in its domain. Although $f(1) \approx 122.28$ and $f(3) \approx 95.22$, the function f is not decreasing on the interval $(1, 3)$, because, for example, $f(2) \approx 83.13 < f(3)$. These ideas are embodied in the following definitions.

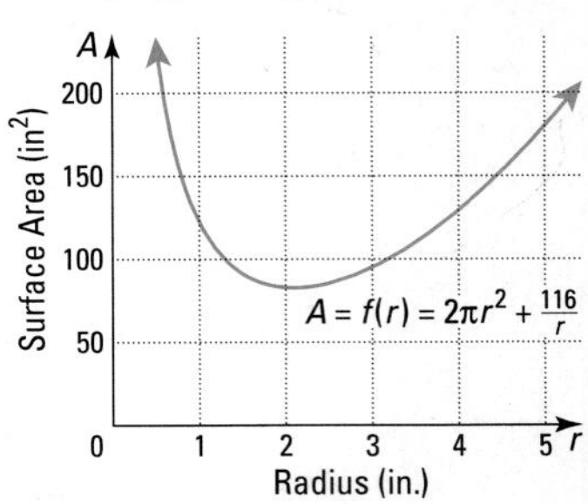

❷ **Definitions**

Suppose f is a real function and S is a subset of the domain of f.

f* is increasing on *S
if and only if $\forall$ x_1 and x_2 in S, if $x_1 < x_2$ then $f(x_1) < f(x_2)$.

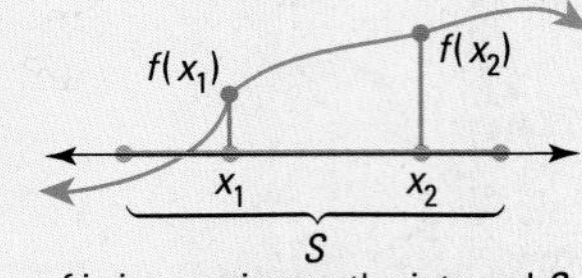

f is increasing on the interval *S*

f* is decreasing on *S
if and only if $\forall$ x_1 and x_2 in S, if $x_1 < x_2$ then $f(x_1) > f(x_2)$.

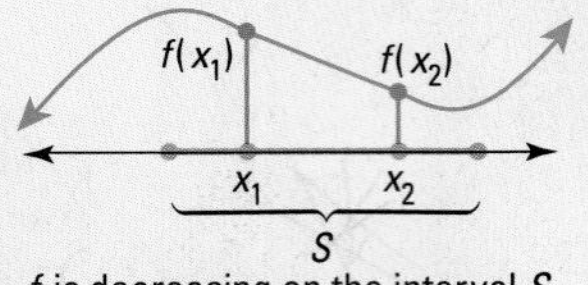

f is decreasing on the interval *S*

2. A function is increasing on $(-\infty, -1)$, decreasing on $(-1, 1)$, and increasing on $(1, \infty)$.
3. A function is increasing on $(-\infty, \infty)$ and has no asymptotes.
4. A function is increasing on $[0, \infty)$ and undefined elsewhere.

1.
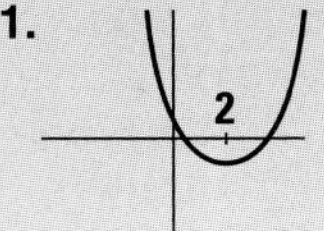

2.
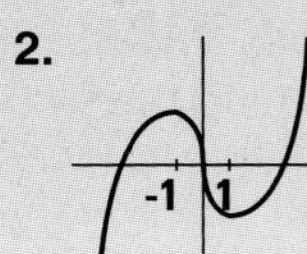

3.
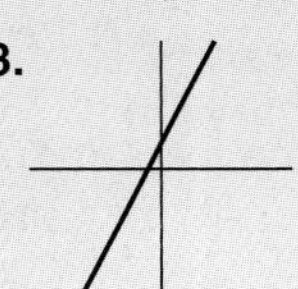

4.
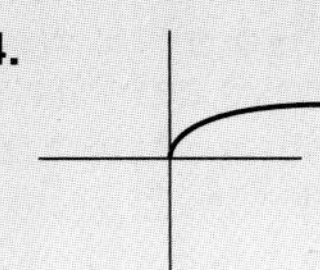

Example

Let f be the function defined by the rule $f(x) = x^3 + x^2 - x - 1$ on the domain $\{x: -2 \le x \le 2\}$. Estimate the intervals in the domain on which f is increasing and on which f is decreasing.

Solution

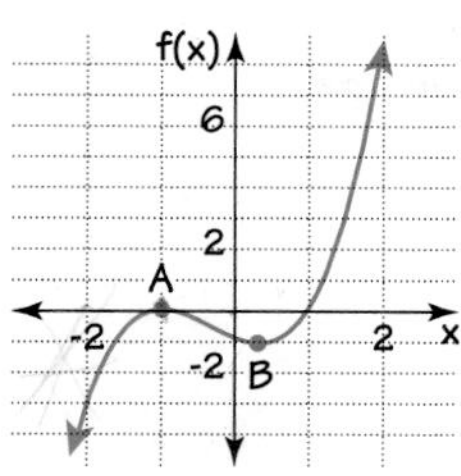

Graph the function on [-2, 2], as shown at the right. Trace along the curve from left to right. When x is -2, y is -3. As you move from $x = -2$ to point A where $x \approx -1$, the y-values increase, and so the graph goes up. Therefore, **f is increasing on the interval [-2, -1].** As you move left to right from point A (at $x \approx -1$) to point B (at $x \approx 0.3$), the values of f decrease, and so the graph goes down. Therefore, **f is decreasing on the interval [-1, 0.3].** As you move to the right of B, the y-values again get larger and the graph goes up, so **f is also increasing on the interval [0.3, 2].**

Points like A and B in the graph of the Example are important for describing the graph precisely, because they identify points at which the function changes from increasing to decreasing, or vice versa. When a function has a maximum or minimum value, then these values occur either at points such as A and B or at endpoints of the domain of the function.

Relative Maxima and Minima

In the Example, $f(-1)$ (which is exactly 0) is greater than or equal to the value of f at any other point near $x = -1$. For instance, for all x in the interval $-2 \le x \le 0, f(-1) \ge f(x)$. Therefore, we say that f has a *relative maximum* at $x = -1$, and that the relative maximum value is 0. The word *relative* is important because obviously there are values of the function, such as $f(2)$, that are larger than $f(-1)$.

Wind turbine farm in the Mojave Desert, California

Similarly, a *relative minimum* occurs at B, where $x \approx .3$. The relative minimum value is approximately $f(.3) \approx -1.2$.

If a function f is constant over an interval, then f is considered to have a relative maximum and a relative minimum at every point in the interval except possibly for the endpoints.

Activity

Examine the energy consumption function E in this lesson. Identify the two places between 1965 and 1990 where there are relative maxima. What are the two relative maximum values?

Sample: $x_1 = 1973$, the relative maximum: 74.28
$x_2 = 1979$, the relative maximum: 78.90

Adapting to Individual Needs

Extra Help

Students can easily identify the minima and maxima on a graph. However, they may have difficulty with using the trace feature of an automatic grapher when finding the value of the minimum and maximum of a function. Some work with tables corresponding to graphs of functions may help students understand the relationship of extrema with the values of y on the grapher. Also, if the automatic grapher has the feature of setting the increment on x for the trace feature, work with different values of this increment might improve understanding of how to find the extrema.

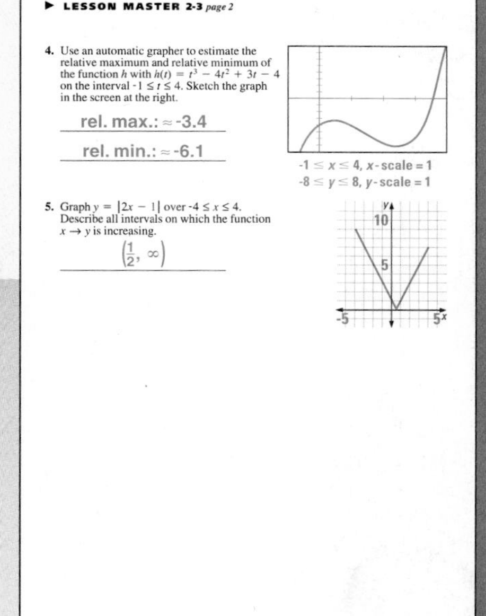

▸ **LESSON MASTER 2-3** *page 2*

4. Use an automatic grapher to estimate the relative maximum and relative minimum of the function h with $h(t) = t^3 - 4t^2 + 3t - 4$ on the interval $-1 \le t \le 4$. Sketch the graph in the screen at the right.

rel. max.: ≈ -3.4

rel. min.: ≈ -6.1

$-1 \le x \le 4$, x-scale = 1
$-8 \le y \le 8$, y-scale = 1

5. Graph $y = |2x - 1|$ over $-4 \le x \le 4$. Describe all intervals on which the function $x \to y$ is increasing.

$\left(\frac{1}{2}, \infty\right)$

❸ For this proof, mastery is not expected, but it is instructive in its use of the definition of *increasing* and in its logic. In the proof, we must let x_1 and x_2 be *any* real numbers in order for the sufficient condition of an increasing function to be satisfied. **Question 9** is similar.

Additional Examples

Let g be the function defined by $g(x) = x^3 - 4x^2 + 2x + 3$ for all real numbers x. Use an automatic grapher to estimate where within the interval $\{x: -1 \le x \le 4\}$ the function g is increasing and where g is decreasing. **Graphing the function for $-1 \le x \le 4$ yields the following:**

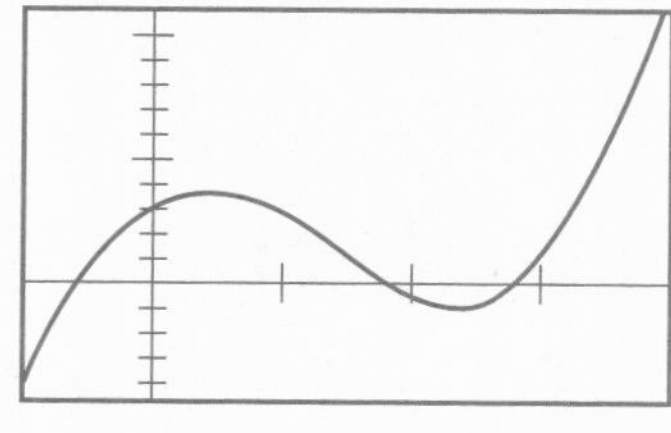

$-1 \le x \le 4$, x-scale = 1
$-5 \le y \le 11$, y-scale = 1

Using the trace key and moving from left to right, we estimate that g is increasing when $-1 \le x \le .3$ or $2.4 \le x \le 4$ and decreasing when $.3 \le x \le 2.4$.

A graph may *suggest* when a function is increasing, but it does not prove that it is increasing. Yet, it is possible to *prove* that certain functions are increasing or decreasing. Methods of calculus beyond the scope of this course are required in many of these proofs, but here is a proof that the logarithm function is increasing.

The proof uses only the following two facts about logarithms that you should recall:

(1) $\log\left(\frac{b}{c}\right) = \log b - \log c$ for all positive numbers b, c.
(2) The logarithm of any number greater than 1 is positive.

❸ **Theorem**
The logarithm function $\log x$ is increasing on its domain $(0, \infty)$.

Proof
We need to show that for any positive real numbers x_1, x_2, if $x_1 < x_2$, then $\log x_1 < \log x_2$.

$0 < x_1 < x_2$	Given
$1 < \frac{x_2}{x_1}$	Multiplication Property of Inequality
$0 < \log\left(\frac{x_2}{x_1}\right)$	Property (2) above
$0 < \log x_2 - \log x_1$	Property (1) above
$\log x_1 < \log x_2$	Addition Property of Inequality

This shows that $\log x_1 < \log x_2$ whenever $0 < x_1 < x_2$, so $\log x$ is increasing on its domain $(0, \infty)$.

QUESTIONS

Covering the Reading

1b) $1979 \le x \le 1983$
c) Sample: $x_1 = 1973$, the relative maximum: 74.28; $x_2 = 1979$, the relative maximum: 78.90

2a)

$-2 \le x \le 12$, x-scale = 1
$-3 \le y \le 3$, y-scale = 1

1. Consider the energy consumption function E in this lesson.
  a. Solve the equation: $E(x) = 70.55$. $x = 1975$
  b. Identify the longest interval over which E is decreasing.
  c. What did you find for the Activity in this lesson?
  d. Name the relative minimum value for E in the time interval [1975, 1985]. 70.52
  b, c) See left.

2. **a.** Draw a graph of the log function (base 10). See left.
  b. If $x_1 < x_2$, what can you say about $\log x_1$ and $\log x_2$? $\log x_1 < \log x_2$

In 3–5, estimate the largest intervals within the given interval on which the function appears to be increasing and those on which it appears to be decreasing. See margin.

3. $f(x) = x^2 - x^3$ $-1 \le x \le 1$

4. $y = x \sin x$ $0 \le x \le 10$

5. $y = x^2e^{-x}$ $-3 \le x \le 6$

Additional Answers
3. increasing region: [0, 0.7]; decreasing region: [-1, 0]; [0.7, 1].
4. increasing regions: [0, 2.0], [5.0, 8.0]; decreasing regions: [2.0, 5.0], [8.0, 10].
5. increasing region: [0, 2.0]; decreasing regions: [-3, 0]; [2.0, 6].

6a) [0, 3]
b) $(-\infty, 0]$
c) $[3, \infty)$
d) relative minimum values: 0, 3; relative maximum value: 3

7a) [-2, 1], $[3, \infty)$
b) $(-\infty, -2]$, [1, 3]
c) None
d) relative minimum value: 1; relative maximum value: 3

8a) [-3, -2]; [-1, 1]
b) [1, 6]
c) [-2, -1]
d) relative minimum value: -1; relative maximum values: -1, 2

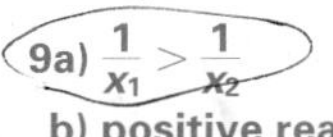

9a) $\frac{1}{x_1} > \frac{1}{x_2}$
b) positive real numbers; $x_1 \cdot \frac{1}{x_1x_2} < x_2 \cdot \frac{1}{x_1x_2}$; >

10a) [1954, 1957], [1958, 1970], [1975, 1980], [1986, 1990], [1993, 1995]
b) [1972, 1975], [1980, 1983], [1984, 1986], [1990, 1993]
c) 41.65, 62.07, 62.42, 64.76, 65.96, 70.75, 71.16
d) 35.13, 38.81, 61.29, 59.86, 61.28, 64.35, 68.32

In 6–8, a function is graphed. See left.

a. Estimate the endpoints of the intervals over which the function is increasing.

b. Estimate the endpoints of the intervals over which the function is decreasing.

c. Estimate the endpoints of the intervals over which the function is constant.

d. Find any relative maximum or relative minimum values for the function.

6.

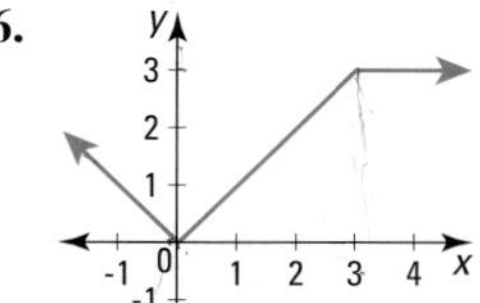

7.

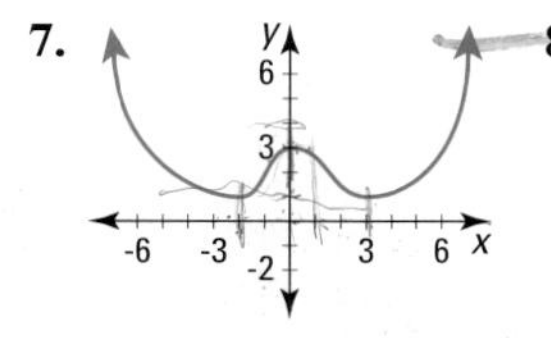

8.

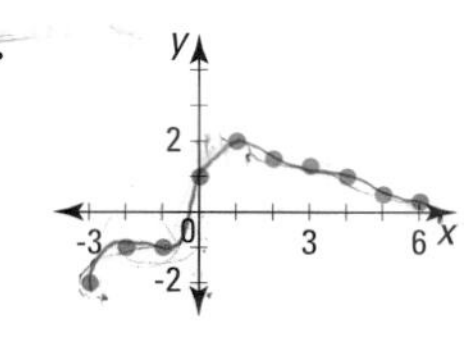

Applying the Mathematics

9. Use the facts that the product and reciprocals of positive numbers are positive to prove that the function $f: x \rightarrow \frac{1}{x}$ is decreasing on the set of all positive real numbers. See left.

a. For this, you must show that if x_1 and x_2 are positive real numbers and $x_1 < x_2$, then __?__.

b. Complete the steps in the proof. Given x_1 and x_2 are __?__ and $x_1 < x_2$. Multiplying both sides of the inequality by $\frac{1}{x_1x_2}$ yields __?__. Consequently, $\frac{1}{x_1}$ __?__ $\frac{1}{x_2}$ whenever $0 < x_1 < x_2$, so f is decreasing on $(0, \infty)$.

10. In the lesson, data are given for total U.S. energy consumption. The total U.S. energy *production* (in quadrillions of BTUs) for the years 1954–1995 is given below. Let P be the function mapping years to production. See left.

1954	35.13	1963	45.85	1972	62.42	1981	64.42	1990	70.75
1955	38.73	1964	47.72	1973	62.06	1982	63.96	1991	70.41
1956	41.21	1965	49.34	1974	60.84	1983	61.28	1992	69.96
1957	41.65	1966	52.17	1975	59.86	1984	65.96	1993	68.32
1958	38.81	1967	55.04	1976	59.89	1985	64.87	1994	70.62
1959	40.60	1968	56.81	1977	60.22	1986	64.35	1995	71.16
1960	41.49	1969	59.10	1978	61.10	1987	64.95		
1961	41.99	1970	62.07	1979	63.80	1988	66.11		
1962	43.58	1971	61.29	1980	64.76	1989	66.13		

a. Identify all intervals of length at least 2 years over which P is increasing.

b. Identify all intervals of length at least 2 years over which P is decreasing.

c. Identify all relative maxima in the interval $1954 \leq x \leq 1995$.

d. Identify all relative minima in the interval $1954 \leq x \leq 1995$.

Notes on Questions

Question 9 Students should use the proof of the theorem of this lesson as a model.

Question 9b Ask why multiplying by x_1x_2 does not switch the sense of the inequalities. [Since x_1 and x_2 are positive, so is their product.]

Adapting to Individual Needs

Challenge

Have students answer the following questions.

1. Give an example of a real function, other than a linear function or an exponential function, with each characteristic:
   a. Increasing on its entire domain [Sample: $y = x^3$]
   b. Decreasing on its entire domain [Sample: $y = -x^3$]
   c. Increasing on the set of positive numbers and decreasing on the set of negative numbers. [Sample: $y = x^2$]
2. Consider the function:
   $$f(x) = \begin{cases} 1 \text{ if } x \text{ is rational} \\ -1 \text{ if } x \text{ is irrational} \end{cases}$$
   a. What is the domain of $f(x)$? [The set of all real numbers]
   b. What is the range? [{-1, 1}]
   c. Is $f(x)$ increasing or decreasing? [Neither]
   d. Describe its graph. [An infinite number of dots with y-values of 1 and -1, but not connected with a line]

Notes on Questions

Questions 15–18 Power and exponential functions are reviewed in Lessons 2-4 and 2-7, respectively.

Follow-up for Lesson 2-3

Practice

For more questions on SPUR Objectives, use **Lesson Master 2-3** (shown on pages 92–93).

Assessment

Oral Communication Give students the function $f(x) = x^3 - 2x^2$. Have them select an appropriate interval and graph the function. Then have the students estimate and state the intervals on which the function appears to be increasing, the intervals on which the function appears to be decreasing, and any relative maxima or minima. [Students determine the maxima and minima of a graph and the intervals.]

Extension

Here is an arithmetic exercise involving large numbers. One kilowatt-hour, the amount of electricity needed to keep a 100-watt bulb lit for 10 hours, is 3,412 BTUs.

1. Using the data in the lesson, convert the amount of energy used in the U.S. in 1995 into kilowatt-hours. [≈ 26.56 trillion kilowatt-hours]
2. How much is this per person? [≈ 100,000 kilowatt-hours per person]
3. How much is this per person per hour? [About 11.7 kilowatt-hours per person per hour]

11. Suppose the height (in meters) t seconds after an object is thrown is given by the formula $h(t) = 1 + 25t - 9.8t^2$.

a. For what values of t is the function h decreasing? $t \geq 1.2755$ sec

b. What is the physical meaning of the answer to part **a**? At $t = 1.2755$ seconds, the object reaches maximum height and starts to descend.

Review

12a) $h = \frac{10}{s^2}$

b) $A(s) = \frac{40}{s} + s^2$

12. A box is to be constructed with a square base and no top. It must hold a volume of 10 cubic meters but be made with a minimum of materials. Let s be the length of a side of the base and let h be the height of the box.

a. Find a formula for h in terms of s. See left.

b. Find a formula for the surface area of the box as a function of s. See left.

c. Estimate the value of s which minimizes the surface area. $S \approx 2.7$m

d. What are the approximate dimensions and surface area of the optimal box? *(Lesson 2-2)* 2.7 m × 2.7 m × 1.4 m; SA ≈ 22.1 m^2

h s s

13. Explain why the function E of this lesson is a discrete function. *(Lesson 2-1)* Its domain is a discrete set, {integers x: $1954 \leq x \leq 1995$}.

14. Consider the following line of a computer program.

```
100    IF (X < Y) AND (Y < Z) THEN PRINT "IN ORDER"
          ELSE PRINT "OUT OF ORDER"
```

Fill in the blank below so that a computer that does not allow ELSE would run the program correctly:

```
100    IF (X < Y) AND (Y < Z) THEN PRINT "IN ORDER"
101    IF _?_ THEN PRINT "OUT OF ORDER"
```

(Lessons 1-3, 1-5) (X ≥ Y) OR (Y ≥ Z)

In 15–18, use the laws of exponents to simplify. *(Previous course)*

15. $8^{30} \cdot 2^{15}$ 2^{105}

16. $(ab)^2(ab)^3$ a^5b^5

17. $\frac{3m^4 \cdot 4m^3}{2m^5 \cdot 5m^2}$ $\frac{6}{5} = 1.2$

18. $\frac{p^2(1 - p^2)}{p(1 - p)^2}$ $\frac{p(1 + p)}{1 - p}$

Exploration

19) Answers may vary. Sample: increased effort at conservation in both decades; increased cost of fuel in the middle 1970s

19. According to the table in this lesson, energy consumption in the U.S. decreased in the middle 1970s and then again in the early 1980s. What were the reasons for these decreases? See left.

Roof-top panels for collecting solar energy are common in many areas today.

LESSON

2-4 End Behavior

Suppose $f: x \to y$ is a real function whose domain includes real intervals of the form (a, ∞), $(-\infty, b)$, or $(-\infty, \infty)$. Informally, we say that x can be made as large as you wish or as small as you wish. The **end behavior** of f is a description of what happens to the values $f(x)$ as $|x|$ grows larger and larger in magnitude. We write $x \to \infty$ to mean that x takes larger and larger values without bound. Informally, many people read "$x \to \infty$" as "x approaches infinity." We write $x \to -\infty$ to mean that x takes values further and further in the negative direction on the x-axis without bound. Informally, many people read "$x \to -\infty$" as "x approaches negative infinity." CAUTION: ∞ and $-\infty$ do not denote real numbers, so x cannot take these values.

The behavior of a real function as $x \to \infty$ (or as $x \to -\infty$) falls into one of three categories. (1) The values of $f(x)$ can approach some real number L; (2) the values of $f(x)$ can increase or decrease without bound, that is, $f(x) \to \infty$ or $f(x) \to -\infty$; or (3) the values of $f(x)$ can follow neither of these patterns.

Exponential functions illustrate the first two types of end behavior. The graph at the right is a graph of the function with equation $f(x) = 2^x$. The first type of end behavior is clearly seen from the graph.

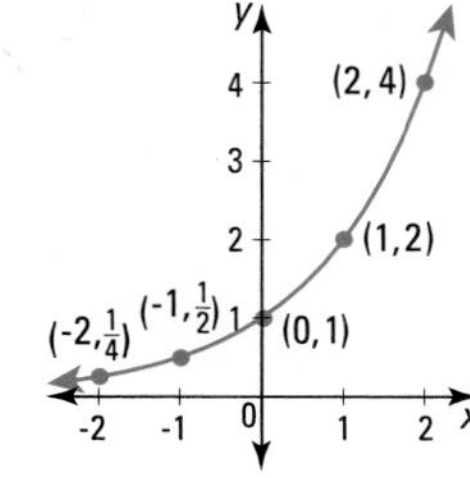

When x gets smaller and smaller (that is, x is farther and farther to the left of the origin), the values of 2^x get closer and closer to zero. For instance, when $x = -30$, $2^x \approx 9.31 \cdot 10^{-10} = 0.000000000931$.

The value of 2^x can be made as close to zero as desired by making x small enough. We write

$$\lim_{x \to -\infty} 2^x = 0,$$

and say, "the limit of 2^x as x approaches negative infinity is 0."

The x-axis is a **horizontal asymptote** for the function $f(x) = 2^x$ because the graph of f gets closer and closer to this horizontal line as $x \to -\infty$.

In general, $\lim_{x \to -\infty} f(x) = L$ means that for any positive number p (no matter how small), $f(x)$ eventually remains within p of L when x is small enough. If $\lim_{x \to -\infty} f(x) = L$, the line $y = L$ is a horizontal asymptote of the function $y = f(x)$.

The graph of $f(x) = 2^x$ also demonstrates the second type of end behavior discussed. As x gets larger and larger, 2^x does also. On a typical graph, when $x = 100$, the values of $f(x)$ are so large that they cannot be shown. (Written in base 10, 2^{100} has over 30 digits.) Since the values of 2^x increase without bound as x increases without bound, we write

$$\lim_{x \to \infty} 2^x = \infty.$$

Objectives

D Determine the end behavior of a function.

G Analyze a function from its graph.

Resources

From the ***Teacher's Resource File***

- Lesson Master 2-4
- Answer Master 2-4
- Assessment Sourcebook: Quiz for Lessons 2-1 through 2-4
- Teaching Aids
  13 Warm-up
  20 End Behavior of Functions
- Technology Sourcebook
  Calculator Master 2

Additional Resources

- Visuals for Teaching Aids 13, 20

Warm-up

A function g is described. As x gets larger and larger, what happens to $g(x)$? Choose one of the following:

(a) $g(x)$ becomes larger and larger, ultimately larger than any number you might pick.

(b) $g(x)$ becomes larger and larger, approaching a particular value.

(c) $g(x)$ has no limit.

(d) $g(x)$ becomes smaller and smaller, ultimately smaller than any number you might pick.

(e) $g(x)$ becomes smaller and smaller, approaching a particular value.

1. $g(x) = 4 - 3x$ (d)
2. $g(x) = 2^{-x}$ (e)
3. $g(x) = 1 - 2^{-x}$ (b)
4. $g(x) = \sin(2x)$ (c)
5. $g(x) = x^{107}$ (a)

Lesson 2-4 Overview

Broad Goals This lesson discusses the end behavior of various functions; that is, what happens to the values of the function as $x \to \infty$ and as $x \to -\infty$.

Perspective The choices for the end behavior of a function are given in the second paragraph of the lesson, and also in the Warm-up on this page. In the case that the function approaches a limit L, that is, if $\lim_{x \to \infty} f(x) = L$ or if $\lim_{x \to -\infty} f(x) = L$, then $y = L$ is a horizontal asymptote to the graph of the function. For some functions, the values of $f(x)$ increase (or decrease) without bound and we call the limit ∞ (or $-\infty$). For still other functions, no such limit exists.

In discussions of end behavior, the power functions (those functions f with equations of the form $f(x) = ax^n$, where n is an integer) are important. Their end behavior forms the basis for the end behavior of rational functions.

The power functions also provide the simplest examples of even and odd functions; they are the functions from which the terms "even function" and "odd function" were derived.

Students who have studied from previous UCSMP courses have seen the definitions of *even* function and *odd* function. This is

(Overview continues on page 98.)

Notes on Reading

In discussing this lesson with students, you might ask them to summarize the content. They should give the possible end behaviors of a real function, and an example of each.

Another way to summarize this lesson is to mention each function in the lesson and ask for the end behaviors of that function. Students should mention the exponential function with equation $y = 2^x$, the sine function, the relative frequency function, the cylinder-volume function of the **Example,** and the various power functions (with positive or negative even or odd exponents). **Teaching Aid 20** summarizes the end behavior of the exponential, sine, and power functions.

Some students might also benefit from the Extra Help suggestion in *Adapting to Individual Needs* on page 99.

Error Alert A few students may think that every function is either even or odd. To dispel this false view, use examples such as this:

Let $f(x) = x^2 + x$
Then $f(3) = 12$.
$f(-3) = 6$.

So $f(-3) \neq f(3)$ and $f(-3) \neq -f(3)$. Thus f is neither even nor odd.

We say, "as x approaches infinity, 2^x increases without bound."

In general, $\lim_{x \to \infty} f(x) = \infty$ means that for any particular y there exists an x in the domain of f such that $f(x) > y$.

The sine function exemplifies the third type of end behavior, the absence of a limit. As x takes values that are further and further either to the right or to the left, without bound, the values of the sine function continue to oscillate between 1 and -1.

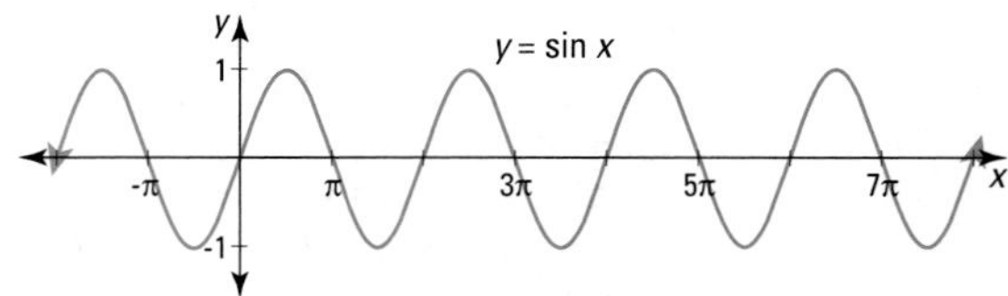

We write

$$\lim_{x \to \infty} \sin x \text{ does not exist}$$

and

$$\lim_{x \to -\infty} \sin x \text{ does not exist.}$$

There can be oscillating behavior and still be a limit. There can also be limits of discrete functions. As an example, think of testing whether a coin is fair or not. The first few tosses may not tell you much, for even an unfair coin could give you a head and then a tail, or a fair coin could give you a few heads in a row. More important is what happens in the long run. After thousands of tosses, will the percentage of heads be near .5 or not? Put symbolically, if $P(n)$ is the relative frequency of heads after n tosses, then P is a discrete function, and what you are testing is whether $\lim_{n \to \infty} P(n) = .5$. You are asking about the end behavior of the function P.

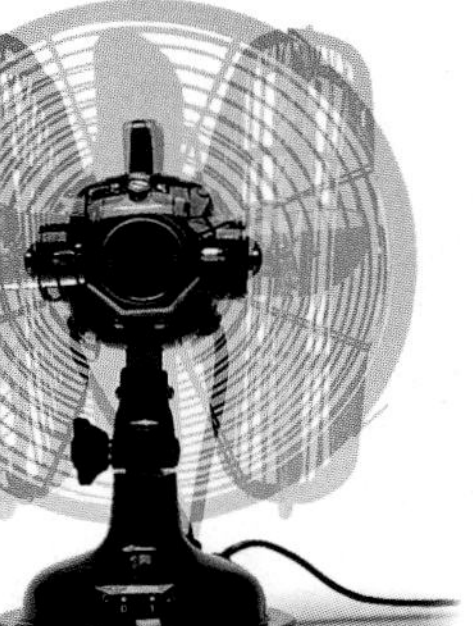

The graph of the position of an oscillating fan over time resembles a sine curve.

We simulated the tossing of a coin 100 times. Below is a graph of P for $1 \leq n \leq 100$. It appears that the conjecture $\lim_{n \to \infty} P(n) = .5$ is reasonable.

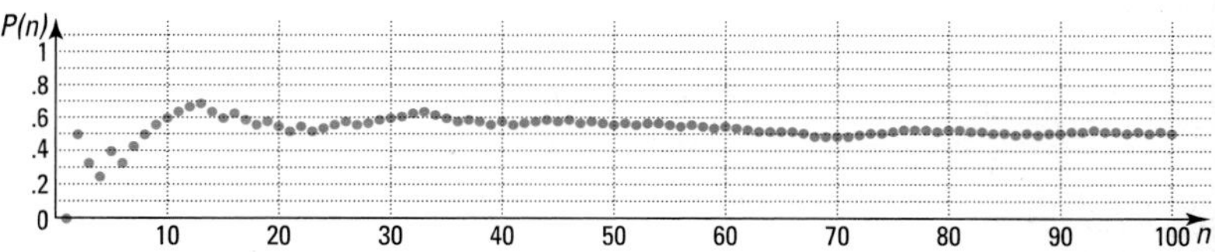

Often the end behavior of one function is best described as being similar to the end behavior of a simpler function.

Example

Describe the behavior as r increases without bound of the surface area function $f(r) = 2\pi r^2 + \frac{116}{r}$, used in the can design problem in Lesson 2-2.

Lesson 2-4 Overview, continued

why we place them in **Questions 12–13** rather than in the body of the lesson.

Symmetries of graphs provide a powerful means of recognizing whether a function might be even or odd. Graphs of even functions are reflection-symmetric with respect to the y-axis. Graphs of odd functions are rotation-symmetric with respect to the origin (point-symmetric).

Optional Activities

Activity 1 Technology Connection
You might wish to assign *Technology Sourcebook, Calculator Master 2.* In this activity, students use graphs and tables on a graphics calculator to determine the end behavior of some polynomial functions, discovering both the efficiency and possible limitations of these technological aids.

Activity 2 Using Physical Models
Materials: bags, pieces of paper in two different colors

After completing the lesson you might have students **work in groups** to do this activity. Give each group a bag with pieces of paper of two different colors. Have each group:

1. Draw 5 pieces and calculate the percent of times one of the colors is drawn.

Solution

A graph of this function was given in Lesson 2-2, but it covers only the interval $0 \le r \le 6$, which does not give a wide enough domain of r values to get an idea of the end behavior. However, the end behavior as $r \to \infty$ is easy to determine by algebraic analysis. Examine the formula for $f(r)$. As r gets larger and larger, $\frac{116}{r}$ gets closer and closer to 0, because the denominator gets larger and larger while the numerator remains 116. Consequently, the term $\frac{116}{r}$ contributes nothing to the end behavior. Thus you can write $\lim_{r\to\infty} f(r) = \lim_{r\to\infty}\left(2\pi r^2 + \frac{116}{r}\right) = \lim_{r\to\infty} 2\pi r^2$. You might also write:
The end behavior of the function f as r increases without bound is the same as the end behavior of the function $y = 2\pi x^2$, whose value increases without bound as x increases without bound.
Therefore, $\lim_{r\to\infty} f(r) = \infty$.

Check

Recall that the function f gives the surface area of a cylinder with constant volume 58 in^3. Increasing the radius r while keeping the volume of the cylinder constant means that the cylinder is getting wider and shorter. Its surface area becomes closer and closer to the sum of the areas of its bases, or $2\pi r^2$, as r becomes larger and larger without bound.

End Behavior of Positive Integer Power Functions

The solution in the Example relies on knowing the end behavior of a quadratic function of the form $y = ax^2$. More generally, it helps to know the end behavior of the **power functions,** those real functions with equations of the form $y = ax^n$, where n is a positive integer. Specifically, when x is positive, the larger x is, the larger its powers. For instance, $\lim_{x\to\infty} x^3 = \lim_{x\to\infty} x^4 = \infty$. However, when x is negative, its odd powers are negative, but its even powers are positive. So $\lim_{x\to-\infty} x^4 = \infty$, but $\lim_{x\to-\infty} x^3 = -\infty$.

The figures below summarize the end behavior of the power functions

$$f(x) = ax^n,$$

where n is a positive integer and a is a positive real number.

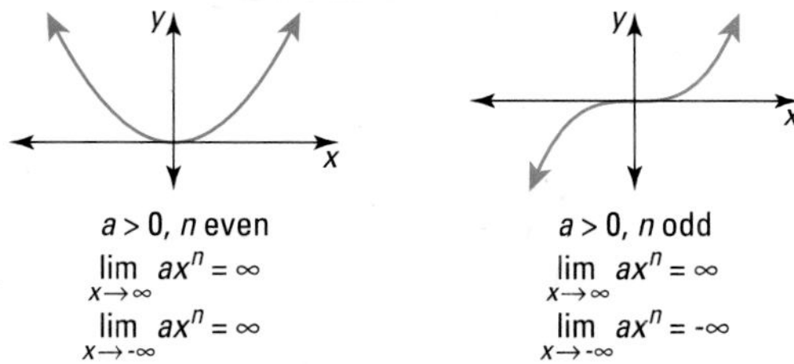

$a > 0$, n even
$\lim_{x\to\infty} ax^n = \infty$
$\lim_{x\to-\infty} ax^n = \infty$

$a > 0$, n odd
$\lim_{x\to\infty} ax^n = \infty$
$\lim_{x\to-\infty} ax^n = -\infty$

If $a < 0$, then the graphs are reflected over the x-axis and the end behavior changes accordingly.

Additional Examples

1. In **Question 12** of Lesson 2-3, the total surface area A of the box in terms of one of its sides, s, is given by $A(s) = s^2 + \frac{40}{s}$. Describe the end behavior of A as s increases without bound. **As s gets larger and larger, $\frac{40}{s}$ approaches 0. $\lim_{s\to\infty} \frac{1}{s} = 0$ and $\lim_{s\to\infty} \frac{40}{s} = 40(\lim_{s\to\infty} \frac{1}{s}) = 40(0) = 0$. Thus $\lim_{s\to\infty} A(s) = \lim_{s\to\infty} (s^2 + \frac{40}{s}) = \lim_{s\to\infty} s^2 + \lim_{s\to\infty} \frac{40}{s} = \lim_{s\to\infty} s^2 = \infty$.**
2. Because $\sin x$ oscillates between -1 and 1 as x increases without bound, $\lim_{x\to\infty} \sin x$ does not exist. What is the end behavior for f, when $f(x) = \frac{1}{x} \sin x$, as $x \to \infty$? **$\lim_{x\to\infty} \frac{1}{x} \sin x = 0$.**
3. Prove that $\forall x$, $g(x) = 5x^4 - 8x^2$ is an even function. **We need to show that $\forall x$, $g(-x) = g(x)$. $\forall x$, $g(-x) = 5(-x)^4 - 8(-x)^2 = 5x^4 - 8x^2 = g(x)$. Therefore $\forall x$, $g(-x) = g(x)$ and so g is an even function.**

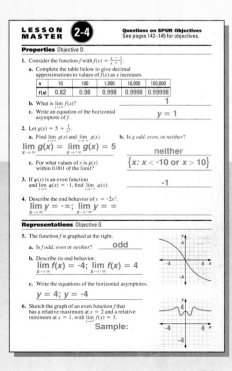

LESSON MASTER 2-4

Questions on SPUR Objectives
See pages 142–145 for objectives.

Properties Objective D

1. Consider the function f with $f(x) = \frac{x-1}{x+1}$.
   a. Complete the table below to give decimal approximations to values of $f(x)$ as x increases.

x	10	100	1,000	10,000	100,000
$f(x)$	0.82	0.98	0.998	0.9998	0.99998

   b. What is $\lim_{x\to\infty} f(x)$? **1**
   c. Write an equation of the horizontal asymptote of f. **$y = 1$**
2. Let $g(x) = 5 + \frac{1}{x^3}$.
   a. Find $\lim_{x\to\infty} g(x)$ and $\lim_{x\to-\infty} g(x)$. **$\lim_{x\to\infty} g(x) = \lim_{x\to-\infty} g(x) = 5$**
   b. Is g *odd, even,* or *neither*? **neither**
   c. For what values of x is $g(x)$ within 0.001 of the limit? **$\{x: x < -10 \text{ or } x > 10\}$**
3. If $\varphi(x)$ is an even function and $\lim_{x\to\infty} \varphi(x) = -1$, find $\lim_{x\to-\infty} \varphi(x)$. **-1**
4. Describe the end behavior of $y = -2x^3$. **$\lim_{x\to\infty} y = -\infty$; $\lim_{x\to-\infty} y = \infty$**

Representations Objective G

5. The function f is graphed at the right.
   a. Is f *odd, even* or *neither*? **odd**
   b. Describe its end behavior. **$\lim_{x\to\infty} f(x) = -4$; $\lim_{x\to-\infty} f(x) = 4$**
   c. Write the equations of the horizontal asymptotes. **$y = 4$; $y = -4$**
6. Sketch the graph of an even function f that has a relative maximum at $x = 2$ and a relative minimum at $x = 1$, with $\lim_{x\to\infty} f(x) = 3$. **Sample:**

Adapting to Individual Needs

Extra Help

When discussing the **Example,** you might have students use an automatic grapher to show that $\lim_{r\to\infty} (2\pi r^2 + \frac{116}{r}) = \lim_{r\to\infty} 2\pi r^2$ by graphing both $y = 2\pi x^2 + \frac{116}{x}$ and $y = 2\pi x^2$ using the domains given below and comparing the graphs.

1. Domain: $0 \le x \le 10$; range: $0 \le y \le 500$
2. Domain: $0 \le x \le 100$; range: $0 \le y \le 50000$

2. Replace the pieces and repeat the process calculating the cumulative percent.
3. Repeat this until 50 or more draws have been made.
4. Draw a graph showing the cumulative percent p after x draws of 5 pieces.

Notes on Questions

Questions 1–4 Reading Mathematics Be certain to go over these questions. It is far more difficult for a student to decipher symbols if they have no words for those symbols.

Question 5a It may be helpful to rewrite the function as $g: x \to \frac{1}{3^x}$.

Question 5b You might have students use an automatic grapher and graph $y = 3^{-x}$, first with window $3 \le x \le 7$, $0 \le y \le .05$, and then with window $7 \le x \le 17$, $0 \le y \le .0001$. This should help them see how rapidly $y = 3^{-x}$ approaches 0 as x gets larger. Remind students that if $x < 0$, then $-x > 0$. Even at this level, some students may still think that "$-x$" always represents a negative number.

Question 7 You might suggest that students sketch a graph of $y = \cos x$ to verify the answers.

Question 8 Sports Connection In the coin toss to determine who starts a football game, the visiting team calls "heads" or "tails." Then the team that wins the toss decides if they want to kick off or receive the kickoff. According to one study, the sides of the coin are not equally likely, with $P(\text{heads}) = .495$.

Question 14 Students who assume that, since $\lim\limits_{x\to\infty}(1 + \frac{1}{x}) = 1$, $\lim\limits_{x\to\infty}(1 + \frac{1}{x})^x = 1$ are surprised by what they see. It is counterintuitive. This question should be discussed, as it helps prepare students for the discussion of e in Lesson 2-7.

2) x approaches negative infinity.

3) The limit of $f(x)$ as x approaches negative infinity is 4.

9a) Sample:

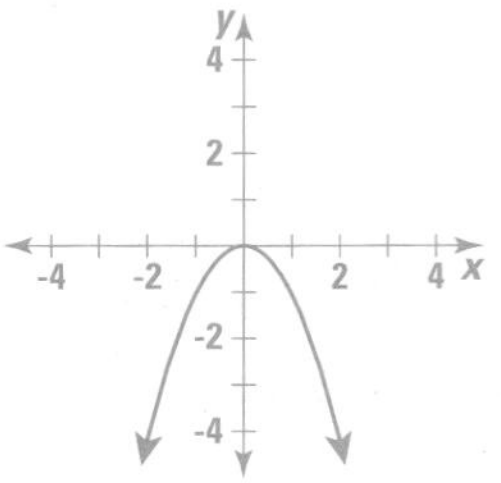

Call it in the Air. *Football games begin with a coin toss to determine who kicks off and who defends which goal.*

11a)

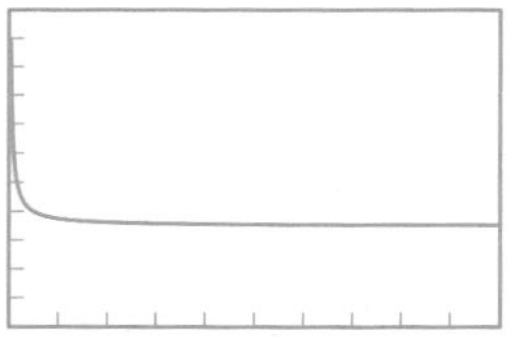

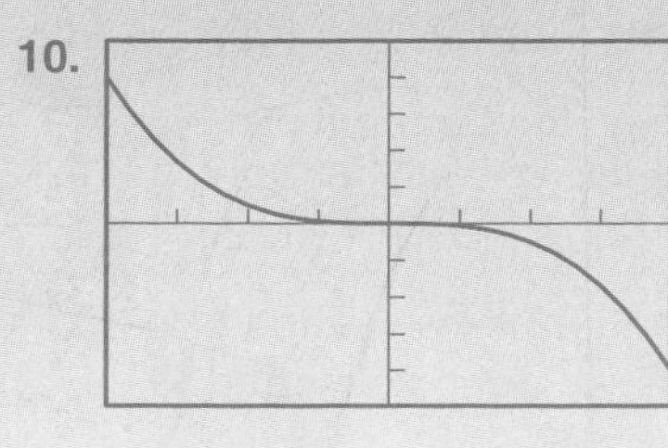

$0 \le x \le 20$, x-scale = 2
$-2 \le y \le 20$, y-scale = 2

The graphs of these power functions possess symmetry. The even integer power functions are reflection-symmetric with respect to the y-axis. This is due to the fact that when n is even, $(-x)^n = x^n\ \forall$ real numbers x. Thus, if f is an even power function, $f(-x) = f(x)\ \forall$ real numbers x.

The odd integer power functions are rotation-symmetric with respect to the origin. That is, the graph of an odd power function coincides with its image under a 180° rotation about the origin. This is because when n is odd, $(-x)^n = -x^n\ \forall$ real numbers x. As a result, if f is an odd power function, then $f(-x) = -f(x)$, $\forall$ real numbers x.

QUESTIONS

Covering the Reading

In 1–4, state in words. 2, 3) See left.

1. $x \to \infty$ *x approaches infinity.*
2. $x \to -\infty$
3. $\lim\limits_{x\to-\infty} f(x) = 4$
4. $\lim\limits_{n\to\infty} g(n) = \infty$ As n approaches infinity, $g(n)$ increases without bound.

5. Consider the function $g: x \to 3^{-x}$.
   a. Explain why $\lim\limits_{x\to\infty} 3^{-x} = 0$. See margin.
   b. What is $\lim\limits_{x\to-\infty} 3^{-x}$? ∞
   c. Does g have a horizontal asymptote? If so, give an equation for it. Yes, the equation is $y = 0$.
6. a. Explain why $\lim\limits_{z\to\infty} \frac{4000}{z^2} = 0$. See margin.
   b. Find a power function whose end behavior is similar to that of the function $g(z) = \frac{4000}{z^2} - 12z^2$. Sample: $f(z) = -12z^2$
7. What is $\lim\limits_{x\to\infty} \cos x$? The limit does not exist.
8. Consider the coin-tossing function P in the lesson. If the coin is fair, give an equation for an asymptote to the graph of P. $y = 0.5$
9. Suppose f is an even integer power function and $\lim\limits_{x\to-\infty} f(x) = -\infty$.
   a. Draw a possible graph of f. See left.
   b. What is $\lim\limits_{x\to\infty} f(x)$? $-\infty$

Applying the Mathematics

10. Sketch a graph of $y = -\frac{1}{1000}x^3$ and describe its end behavior. See margin.
11. Let $f(x) = 5 + \frac{1}{x}$.
    a. Sketch a graph of f over the interval $0 < x \le 20$. See left.
    b. Find $\lim\limits_{x\to\infty} f(x)$. 5
    c. Give an equation of the horizontal asymptote. $y = 5$
    d. Find a value of x so that $f(x)$ is within 0.1 of the limit you found in part **b**. Sample: $x > 10$

5. a. As $x \to \infty$, $3x \to \infty$. So $3^{-x} = \frac{1}{3^x}$ decreases through smaller and smaller values as the denominator 3^x increases. $\therefore$ as $x \to \infty$, $3^{-x} \to 0$.
6. a. As z increases without bound, so does z^2. So $\frac{4000}{z^2}$ comes closer and closer to 0.

10. as $x \to \infty$, $y \to -\infty$
as $x \to -\infty$, $y \to \infty$

$-20 \le x \le 20$, x-scale = 5
$-10 \le y \le 10$, y-scale = 2

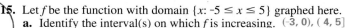

12a) The even integer power functions
b) The odd integer power functions

In 12 and 13, use these definitions.

A real function is an **even function** if and only if $\forall$ x, $f(-x) = f(x)$.

A real function is an **odd function** if and only if $\forall$ x, $f(-x) = -f(x)$.

12. a. Which functions from this lesson are even functions?

b. Which functions are odd functions?

See left.

13. a. If h is an odd function and $\lim_{x \to -\infty} h(x) = 3$, find $\lim_{x \to \infty} h(x)$. $\lim_{x \to \infty} h(x) = -3$

b. Sketch a graph of such a function. See below left.

x	$\left(1 + \frac{1}{x}\right)^x$
100	2.70481
1000	2.71692
10,000	2.71815
100,000	2.71827
1,000,000	2.71828

14. Consider the function f defined on the interval $(0, \infty)$ by $f(x) = \left(1 + \frac{1}{x}\right)^x$.

a. Complete the table at the left to examine the behavior of f as x gets larger and larger. See left.

b. Use the results from part **a** to approximate an equation for a horizontal asymptote to the graph of f. $y = 2.71828$ or $y = e$

c. Use an automatic grapher to check your results from parts **a** and **b**. See left.

Review

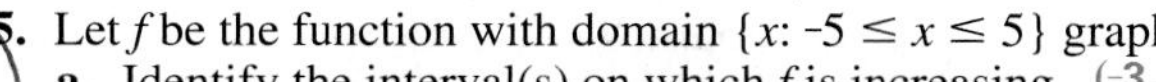

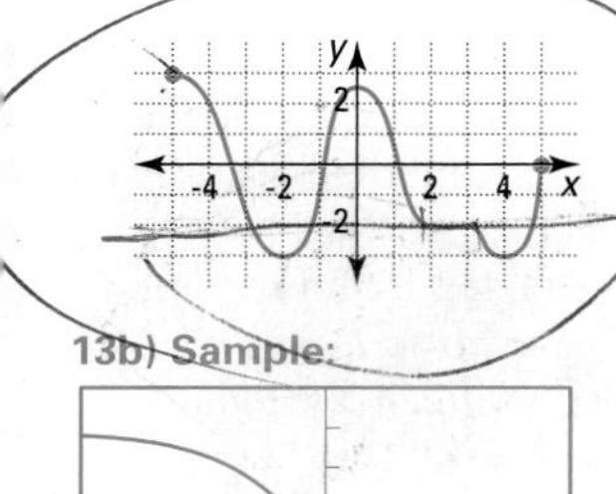

15. Let f be the function with domain $\{x: -5 \le x \le 5\}$ graphed here.

a. Identify the interval(s) on which f is increasing. $(-3, 0)$, $(4, 5]$

b. Estimate the relative maximum and minimum values and tell where they occur. See below left.

c. Give the range of f. $[-3, 3]$

d. Estimate the value(s) of x for which $f(x) = -1$. -3.1; -1; 1.5; 4.8

e. Estimate the value(s) of x for which $f(x) \le -2$. *(Lessons 2-1, 2-3)* $-3 < x < -1$; $3.2 \le x \le 4.8$

16. Find the exact range of the function given by $g(x) = -3x^2 + 4x - 2$. *(Lesson 2-2)* $\left(-\infty, -\frac{2}{3}\right]$

17. Let T be a real function defined by the formula

$$T(p) = \frac{7}{p^2 + p - 6}.$$

Using interval notation, identify the domain and range of T. *(Lessons 2-1, 2-2)* domain: $(-\infty, -3)$, $(-3, 2)$, $(2, \infty)$; range: $(-\infty, -1.12]$, $(0, \infty)$

In 18 and 19, use the laws of exponents to simplify. *(Previous course)*

18. $4^{1/5} \cdot 8^{1/5}$ 2

19. $\frac{x^{1/2}y^{-3/4}}{x^{-2/3}y^{1/4}}$ $\frac{x^{7/6}}{y}$

20. Which is larger, $81^{-1/4}$ or $81^{-1/2}$? *(Previous course)* $81^{-\frac{1}{4}}$

21. Deduce a valid conclusion from the following premises, and identify the argument form. *(Lesson 1-6)*

$\forall$ *real numbers x and y*, $x < y \Rightarrow e^x < e^y$.
$e^n \ge e^5$

$n \ge 5$; Law of Indirect Reasoning

13b) Sample:

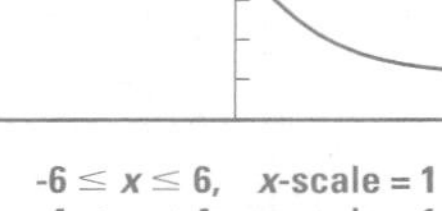

$-6 \le x \le 6$, x-scale = 1
$-4 \le y \le 4$, y-scale = 1

14c)

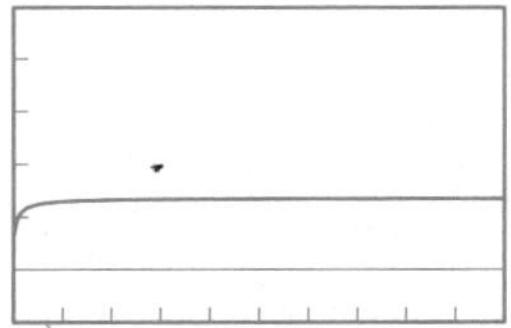

$0 \le x \le 100$, x-scale = 10
$-2 \le y \le 10$, y-scale = 2

15b) relative maximum: 3, occurs at $x = -5$; 2.5, occurs at $x = 0$; 0, occurs at $x = 5$
relative minimum: -3 occurs at $x = -2$; -2, occurs in the interval $(2, 3)$; -3 occurs at $x = 4$

Exploration

22. Suppose f and g are functions so that $g(x) = \frac{1}{f(x)}$ for all x with $f(x) \neq 0$. What is the relationship between the end behavior of f and that of g? See margin.

Follow-up for Lesson 2-4

Practice

For more questions on SPUR Objectives, use **Lesson Master 2-4** (shown on page 99).

Assessment

Quiz A quiz covering Lessons 2-1 through 2-4 is provided in the *Assessment Sourcebook.*

Extension

1. Have students determine the end behavior of any parabola, $f(x) = ax^2 + bx + c$.
[If $a > 0$, then $\lim_{x \to \infty} f(x) = \infty$ and $\lim_{x \to -\infty} f(x) = \infty$; if $a < 0$, then $\lim_{x \to \infty} f(x) = -\infty$ and $\lim_{x \to -\infty} f(x) = -\infty$.]
2. Now have students extend their ideas to any cubic function $g(x) = ax^3 + bx^2 + cx + d$. [Cubic polynomial functions have the same end behavior as odd power functions.]
3. Ask students to conjecture whether any polynomial function will have the same end behavior as the power function of degree equal to the degree of the highest term in the polynomial. [Yes]

Project Update Project 1, *Savings Plans,* on page 137, relates to the content of this lesson.

22. If as $x \to \infty$, $g(x) \to \infty$ or $-\infty$, then as $x \to \infty$, $f(x) \to 0$.

If as $x \to \infty$, $g(x) \to L \neq 0$, then as $x \to \infty$, $f(x) \to \frac{1}{L}$.

If as $x \to \infty$, $g(x) \to 0$, then as $x \to \infty$, $f(x) \to \infty$ or $-\infty$ depending on the function g.

If $\lim_{x \to \infty} g(x) \neq \infty$, $\lim_{x \to \infty} g(x) \neq -\infty$, and $\lim_{x \to \infty} g(x) \neq L$, for any real number L, then $\lim_{x \to \infty} f(x)$ does not exist.

Similar relationships occur when $x \to -\infty$.

Lesson 2-5

Objectives

H Find and graph parametric equations.

Resources

From the ***Teacher's Resource File***

- Lesson Master 2-5
- Answer Master 2-5
- Teaching Aids
  13 Warm-up
  21 Graphs from Lesson 2-5
- Technology Sourcebook
  Calculator Master 3

Additional Resources

- Visuals for Teaching Aids 13, 21
- Exploration 2-5

Teaching Lesson 2-5

Warm-up

Determine how to enter parametric equations on your calculator. Graph the following pairs of parametric equations for all real values of the parameter t. Describe the graph.

1. $x = t$, $y = t^2$ **Parabola with vertex (0, 0), opening up**
2. $x = t^2$, $y = t$ **Parabola with vertex (0, 0), opening to the right**
3. $x = 2t^2 + 4t - 6$; $y = t^2 + 2t - 3$ **Ray with endpoint (-8, -4) along line $y = 0.5x$ in positive direction**

LESSON

2-5 *Parametric Equations*

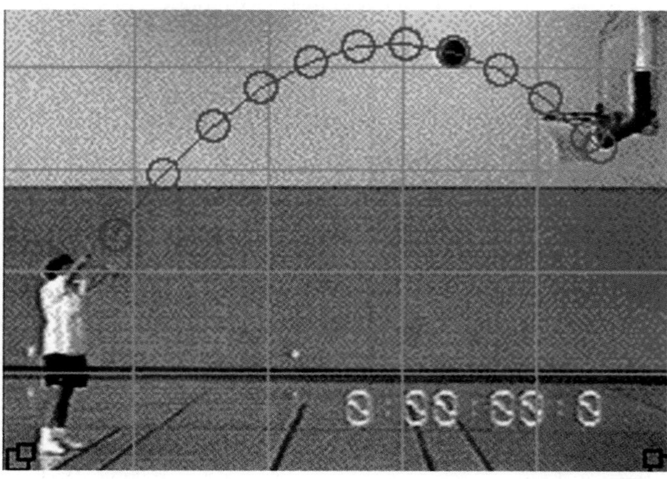

You have learned in previous courses that the path of a projectile affected only by the force of gravity is a parabola. The picture above shows the path of a basketball free throw. This path is very close to a parabola because air resistance is negligible in comparison with the force of gravity. The superimposed circles show where the ball travels each tenth of a second after it is released by the basketball player. Distance measurements (in feet) are taken, using the player's toes as the origin of a coordinate system.

Time (sec)	0.0	0.1	0.2	0.3	0.4	0.5	0.6	0.7	0.8	0.9	1.0
Horizontal Distance (ft)	0.92	2.44	3.82	5.27	6.64	8.02	9.39	10.69	12.14	13.43	14.73
Vertical Distance (ft)	6.49	8.24	9.69	10.76	11.53	11.98	12.14	11.91	11.37	10.53	9.47

A scatterplot showing the eleven data points and a well-fitting parabola is at the right. Using a statistics utility, an equation of the parabola can be found. It is

$$y = -0.0834x^2 + 1.5287x + 5.0761.$$

The coefficients in this equation do not have much meaning, which makes the equation less than satisfactory. It would be nice to have equations that can be developed from information about the ball's release. This can be done by considering x and y as functions of t, the time (in seconds) after the player releases the basketball.

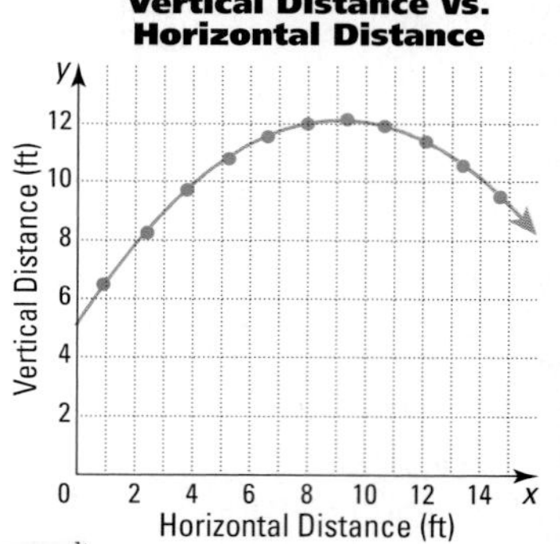

Lesson 2-5 Overview

Broad Goals This lesson introduces parametric equations and shows examples to functions of the type that have already been studied and to the description of curves.

Perspective Students are often wrongly led to believe that a graph on a coordinate system represents a function if and only if it passes the vertical-line test; that is, if and only if its graph does not intersect a vertical line in more than one point. This is true if the graph is of ordered pairs (x, y) on a rectangular x–y coordinate system. But in this book, there are two kinds of graphs of functions which violate the vertical-line test. The first kind comes from functions defined parametrically and is found in this lesson. The second is from functions defined using polar coordinates.

The idea of parametric equations is to define two or more variables as a function of a single variable, the *parameter,* usually identified by the letter t. Although several variables often may depend on the same variable (for instance, the number of items sold by a company may determine the cost of those items, the profit of the company, the number that are sold per day, and so on), parametric equations appear when we are interested in how two of the *dependent* variables are related.

The relation between time t and horizontal distance x is linear, not quadratic. An equation fitted to the data is

$$x = 13.78t + 1.06.$$

The horizontal speed of the ball is $13.78 \frac{\text{ft}}{\text{sec}}$. The constant 1.06 means that the basketball player released the ball about 1.06 ft in front of the free-throw line.

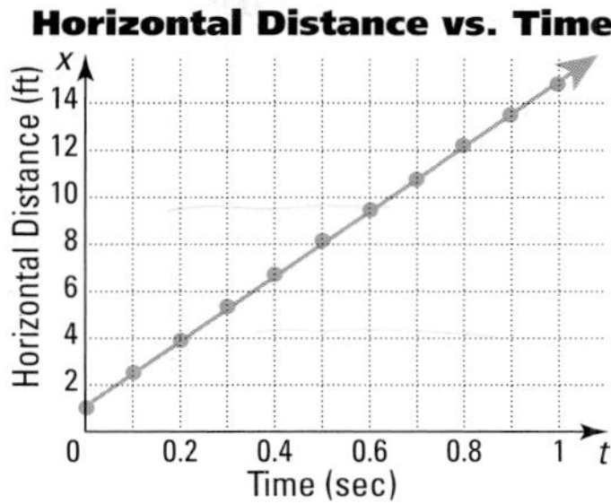

The relation between time t and vertical distance y is quadratic, and its graph is a parabola. The equation

$$y = -16.07t^2 + 18.98t + 6.51$$

fits the (t, y) data points. Each number has meaning. According to the equation, the ball was 6.51 feet above the floor when the player released it. The ball was initially traveling vertically at 18.98 feet per second. The -16.07 is approximately half the acceleration due to gravity, about $-32 \frac{\text{ft}}{\text{sec}^2}$.

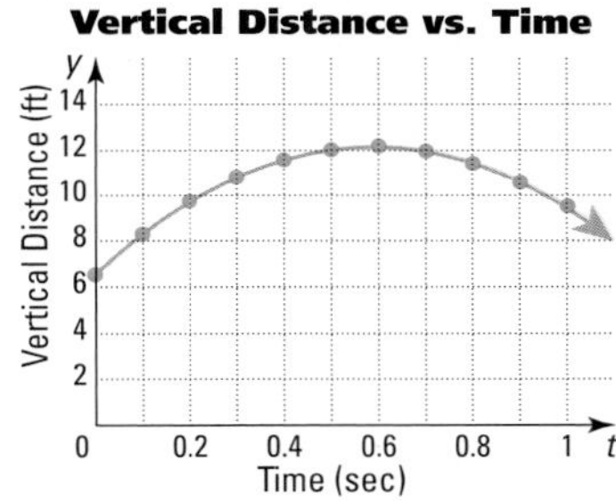

The equations

$$x = 13.78t + 1.06$$
$$y = -16.07t^2 + 18.98t + 6.51$$

describe the path of the basketball in terms of time. The variable t is called a **parameter** because it determines the other variables. The equations for x and y in terms of t are called **parametric equations** for the graph of the basketball path.

These equations apply for all values of t from the time $t = 0$, when the ball is released, until the time when the ball's motion is altered by striking the backboard or basket at $t = 1$.

Notes on Reading

The four graphs from this lesson are on **Teaching Aid 21.**

A traditional application of quadratic equations is to the height of a projectile over time, as shown in the third graph relating to the projectile situation that opens the lesson. Students who have not studied from UCSMP courses may never have seen a quadratic equation for the path of a projectile, as shown in the first graph. And it is likely that students have never seen the graph relating horizontal distance and time. You might remind students that these equations assume constant gravity and no air friction, quite reasonable assumptions for a basketball toss.

The letter t in parametric equations is from the word "time," because many parametric equations arise from situations in which the independent variable is time. Such is the obvious case with the projectile situation that opens the lesson and with **Example 1.** But even in **Example 2,** where time is not mentioned, one can think of t as representing the time of a point that moves along the curve.

Throughout all UCSMP courses we are careful to distinguish between a function f and its values $f(x)$. In **Example 1,** the distinction is necessarily blurred. Both x and $x(t)$ stand for the dependent variable. If students are confused, you might remind them that they have seen this notation before in geometric contexts, for instance, when the area of a triangle DEF might be represented either by the single letter A or by the symbol $A(\triangle DEF)$.

Optional Activities

Activity 1 Technology Connection
Materials: Explorations software

Students may use *Exploration 2-5, Parametric Equations,* as an alternative to **Example 2** on page 105. Students can define two parametric equations as functions of a parameter and see the graph of both equations on the coordinate plane. By changing the value for the parameter, t, students can observe the effect on the location of point P on the graph.

Activity 2 Have students refer back to **Example 1.** On some graphing calculators, there is a Draw menu that allows segments (and other objects) to be drawn on a graph. Have students simulate the basket on a graph of the parametric equations in **Example 1** using this feature. [On some graphing calculators, under Draw, there is a Line command. Line(13,10,15,10) will produce a segment on screen whose endpoints are (13, 10) and (15, 10).] Once students have drawn the basket on their screen, have them experiment to find another different pair of horizontal and vertical velocities that seem to guarantee a basket. *Note:* students will have to replay the Line command every time they graph a new set of equations; on some calculators, the command can be reactivated simply by pressing 2nd, ENTER, and ENTER. [Sample: a horizontal velocity of 17 ft/sec with a vertical velocity of 17.5 ft/sec seems to work.]

In discussing **Example 2,** you might ask students these questions.

1. How could you could tell in advance that all the points of the curve are in the first quadrant? [When $|t| \leq 1$, $1 + t$ and $1 - t$ are positive, so when they are multiplied by the positive number $1 - t^2$, the products $x(t)$ and $y(t)$ are also positive.]
2. What part of the curve is determined by negative values of t? [the part between the line $y = x$ and the y-axis, because when t is negative, $y(t) > x(t)$.]

These questions can help students with the kind of thinking needed for answering **Question 22.**

Activity

Use the parametric equations to determine the location of the basketball $\frac{1}{2}$ second after release. (7.95, 1.98)

In general, assuming that a projectile is unhindered by forces such as wind, its horizontal and vertical distances x and y from the origin are given by

$$\begin{aligned} x &= v_x t + d_0 \\ y &= -\tfrac{1}{2}gt^2 + v_y t + h_0 \quad 0 \leq t \leq T \end{aligned}$$

where v_x is the horizontal velocity at release, v_y is the vertical velocity at release, g is the gravitational constant $\left(32\frac{\text{ft}}{\text{sec}^2} \text{ or } 9.8\frac{\text{m}}{\text{sec}^2}\right)$, and (d_0, h_0) is the point of release. The time of release is $t = 0$, and $t = T$ is the time when the projectile strikes an object in its path.

Example 1

The center of a basket in basketball is 10 ft high and about 14 ft from the point of release of a free throw. Will a basketball player shoot a free throw directly into the basket if it is released from the same point as earlier but with a vertical velocity of $22\frac{\text{ft}}{\text{sec}}$?

Solution

An automatic grapher can be used to plot the parametric equations as an (x, y) coordinate graph. The symbols $x(t)$ and $y(t)$ emphasize that x and y are functions of t. All coefficients are the same as above except $v_y = 22\frac{\text{ft}}{\text{sec}}$.

$$x(t) = 13.78t + 1.06$$
$$y(t) = -\frac{1}{2} \cdot 32t^2 + 22t + 6.51$$

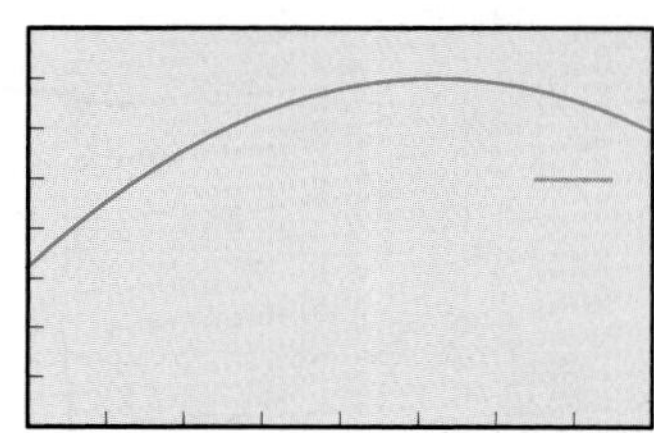

$0 \leq t \leq 1.05$, t-step = 0.05
$0 \leq x \leq 16$, x-scale = 2
$0 \leq y \leq 16$, y-scale = 2

The graph shows that the ball is too high to go directly through the basket. In fact, it seems so high when it hits the backboard that it will probably bounce back over the basket.

Karl Malone has a career free-throw shooting percentage of over 72%.

Optional Activities

Activity 3 Technology Connection
You might wish to assign *Technology Sourcebook, Calculator Master 3.* In this activity, students use the parametric capability of a graphics calculator to explore projectile motion. Students use graphs of parametric equations to analyze a situation where a golfer is trying to sink a hole-in-one.

Adapting to Individual Needs

Extra Help
Some students might have difficulty producing a smooth curve on their automatic drawers. Point out that they should use a small enough step for the t-values to ensure that at least 10 points are plotted. Stress this idea when you cover **Example 2.** Students who use $-1 \leq t \leq 1$, step .5 will produce a quadrilateral. Have them try step .2, and then step .1 so they can notice how smaller steps produce smoother graphs.

Describing Curves by Parametric Equations

The graph of a function $f: x \rightarrow y$ cannot intersect a vertical line more than once. Consequently, closed curves and many other curves cannot be graphs of such functions. But by representing x and y each as functions of a parameter t, it is possible to find equations for some of these curves.

Example 2

Consider the parametric equations

$$x(t) = (1 + t)(1 - t^2)$$
$$y(t) = (1 - t)(1 - t^2)$$

on the interval $-1 \le t \le 1$.

a. Graph the set of ordered pairs $(x(t), y(t))$.

b. Identify the location of the five points A, B, C, D, E on this graph corresponding to $t = -1, -0.5, 0, 0.5,$ and 1.

Solution

a. A graph is shown at the left.

b. When $t = -1$, $x(t) = 0$ and $y(t) = 0$, so $A = (0, 0)$. When $t = -0.5$, $x(t) = \frac{3}{8}$ and $y(t) = \frac{9}{8}$, yielding $B = \left(\frac{3}{8}, \frac{9}{8}\right)$. When $t = 0$, $x(t) = 1$ and $y(t) = 1$, giving $C = (1, 1)$. Similarly, $t = 0.5$ yields $D = \left(\frac{9}{8}, \frac{3}{8}\right)$ and $t = 1$ yields $E = (0, 0)$.

Check

Use an automatic grapher to plot these parametric equations on the window $-.25 \le x \le 1.5$, $-.25 \le y \le 1.5$ with equal-sized units on both axes. You obtain a figure similar to the one at the left.

In Example 2, if values of t are chosen between the five values that are listed, then the points between the five named points will be generated. As the value of t increases, the point moves along the curve. Because objects change direction, parametric equations are useful for describing their paths. In the Questions, you are asked to explore values of t that are not between -1 and 1. You are also asked to examine other parametric equations.

QUESTIONS

Covering the Reading

In 1 and 2, consider the free throw pictured at the start of the lesson. Remember that the axis of symmetry of the parabola $y = ax^2 + bx + c$ has equation $x = \frac{-b}{2a}$. 1a) 12.08 ft

1. a. Use the fitted parabola $y = -0.0834x^2 + 1.5287x + 5.0761$ to determine its maximum height (to the nearest hundredth of a foot).

b. How close is this to the data? very close (differs by 0.06 ft from the maximum height shown in the data)

2. a. Use the equation $y = -16.07t^2 + 18.98t + 6.51$ to compute the maximum height. 12.11 ft

b. Does this agree with the data? very closely (differs by 0.03 ft from the maximum height shown in the data)

Additional Examples

1. A free throw is released from a point 5 feet above the ground and 1 foot in front of the free throw line, with a vertical velocity of 17 feet per second and a horizontal velocity of 15 feet per second.
   a. Give equations for the ball's horizontal distance x and vertical distance y at time t. $x = 15t + 1$; $y = -16t^2 + 17t + 5$
   b. Will the ball go directly into the basket? No, the toss is too low.
2. Graph the parametric equations $x = 6s^2$, $y = s^3$, for $0 < s \le 20$, to show how the surface area x of a cube and its volume y are related.

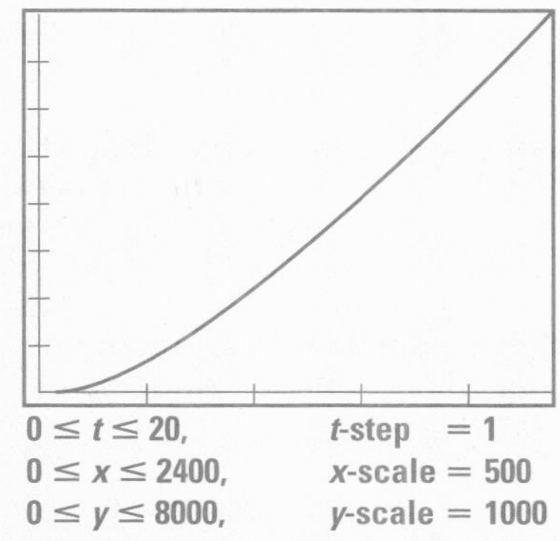

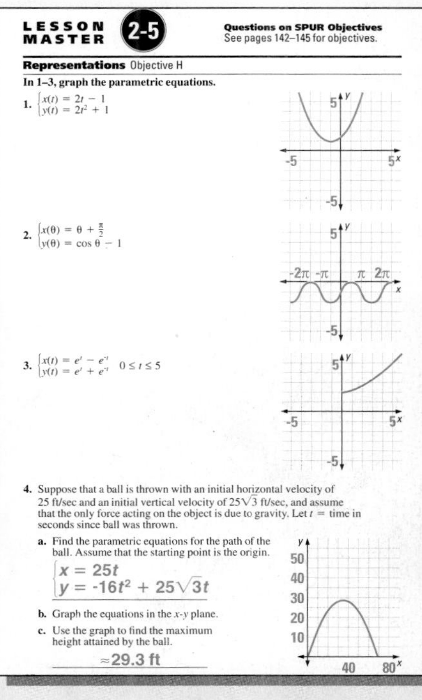

LESSON MASTER 2-5 Questions on SPUR Objectives See pages 142–145 for objectives.

Representations Objective H

In 1–3, graph the parametric equations.

1. $x(t) = 2t - 1$, $y(t) = 2t^2 + 1$
2. $x(\theta) = \theta + \frac{\pi}{2}$, $y(\theta) = \cos\theta - 1$
3. $x(t) = e^t - e^{-t}$, $y(t) = e^t + e^{-t}$, $0 \le t \le 5$
4. Suppose that a ball is thrown with an initial horizontal velocity of 25 ft/sec and an initial vertical velocity of $25\sqrt{3}$ ft/sec, and assume that the only force acting on the object is due to gravity. Let t = time in seconds since ball was thrown.
   a. Find the parametric equations for the path of the ball. Assume that the starting point is the origin. $x = 25t$; $y = -16t^2 + 25\sqrt{3}t$
   b. Graph the equations in the x-y plane.
   c. Use the graph to find the maximum height attained by the ball. ≈29.3 ft

Adapting to Individual Needs

Challenge

Have students find a single equation in x and y for each set of parametric equations and give the possible range of values of t, x, and y.

1. $x = \sqrt{3 - t}$; $y = \sqrt{1 + t}$ [$x^2 + y^2 = 4$; $-1 \le t \le 3$; $0 \le x \le 2$; $0 \le y \le 2$]
2. $x = \sqrt{-\frac{1}{4}t}$; $y = -\sqrt{4 + \frac{1}{9}t}$ [$4x^2 + 9y^2 = 36$; $-36 \le t \le 0$; $0 \le x \le 3$; $-2 \le y \le 0$]
3. $x = \sqrt{t - 4}$; $y = t$ [$y = x^2 + 4$; $t \ge 4$; $x \ge 0$; $y \ge 4$]
4. $x = \sqrt{t + 9}$; $y = \sqrt{t + 5}$ [$x^2 - y^2 = 4$; $t \ge -5$; $x \ge 2$; $y \ge 0$]

Notes on Questions

Question 5 A more difficult question: What is the interval of velocities for which the ball will go through the hoop without hitting the backboard? You might ask interested students to simulate this with a computer—this task could develop into a project.

Question 9 Error Alert The difficult part for most students is knowing what constitutes a proof. Here two things are needed. First one needs to show that if $x(t) = 3t - 7$ and $y(t) = 6t + 5$, then $y = 2x + 19$. That shows that all points on the graph of the parametric equation lie on the line $y = 2x + 19$. But that does not show that the entire line is graphed. To show that no point on the line is missed, one must show that for every value of x, there is a value of t such that $x = 3t - 7$. This can be done by solving that equation for t.

Question 12 This question points out the importance of both parts of the proof in **Question 9.** The graphs of each of the parametric equations lie on the parabola $y = x^2 - 2$, but only the second pair of parametric equations has the full parabola as its graph.

(Notes on questions continue on page 108.)

Additional Answers

5. No. It takes about 0.995 sec for the ball to travel 12.94 ft horizontally to a point 14 ft from the free throw line. At that time it will be 9.5 ft high and too low to go through the hoop.

3d) T is the time when the ball's motion is altered by striking the backboard, basket, or floor.

6a)

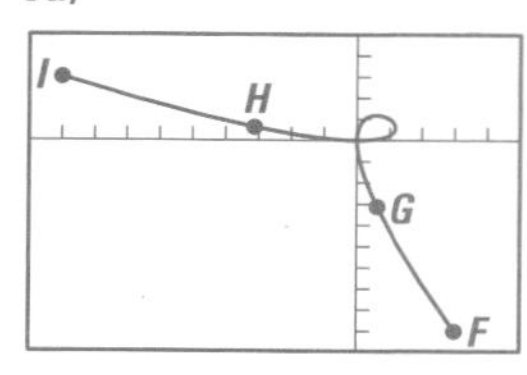

$-2 \le t \le 2$, t-step $= 0.5$
$-10 \le x \le 5$, x-scale $= 1$
$-10 \le y \le 5$, y-scale $= 1$

b) $F = (3, -9)$, $G = (.625, -3.125)$, $H = (-3.125, .625)$, $I = (-9, 3)$

7a)

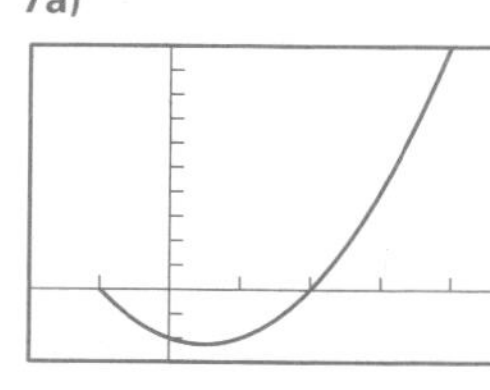

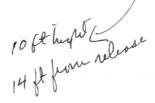

$0 \le t \le 5$, t-step $= 1$
$-2 \le x \le 5$, x-scale $= 1$
$-3 \le y \le 10$, y-scale $= 1$

9) From $x = 3t - 7$, $t = \frac{x + 7}{3}$; therefore, $y = 6 \cdot \frac{x + 7}{3} + 5 = 2x + 19$. This means that the parametric equations are equivalent to the equation $y = 2x + 19$.

3. Here are parametric equations for a free throw different from that in the lesson.

$$\begin{cases} x = 15t + 1.50 \\ y = -16t^2 + 13t + 7.0 \end{cases} \quad 0 \le t \le T$$

a. Give the vertical velocity at release. 13 $\frac{\text{ft}}{\text{sec}}$
b. Give coordinates for the point of release. (1.50, 7.0)
c. Where is the ball after one second? (16.50, 4.0)
d. Describe the meaning of the right endpoint T of the time interval $[0, T]$. See left.

4. In parametric equations for a ball toss, x and y are measured in meters.

$$\begin{cases} x(t) = 5.9t + 0.3 \\ y(t) = -\frac{1}{2}gt^2 + 6.5t + 2.0 \end{cases}$$

a. What does the 5.9 represent? The horizontal velocity is 5.9 $\frac{\text{m}}{\text{sec}}$
b. Give the value and units for v_y. 6.5 $\frac{\text{m}}{\text{sec}}$
c. Give the value and units for the coefficient of t^2. -4.9 $\frac{\text{m}}{\text{sec}^2}$
d. Determine when the ball hits the ground. $t \approx 1.58$ sec

5. In Example 1, the ball missed the basket. If the player uses the same vertical velocity, the same release point, but a lower horizontal velocity of 13 ft/sec, will the ball go through the hoop? Explain your answer. See margin.

6. a. Graph the parametric equations of Example 2 when $-2 \le t \le 2$.
b. On your graph, identify the location of the points F, G, H, and I corresponding to $t = -2, -1.5, 1.5$, and 2.
See left.

7. a. Suppose $0 \le t \le 5$. Plot the set of ordered pairs $(x(t), y(t))$ with See left.

$$\begin{cases} x(t) = t - 1 \\ y(t) = t^2 - 3t. \end{cases}$$

b. Is the graph a graph of a function? yes
c. Explain how the parametric equations enable you to determine the x- and y-intercepts of the xy-graph. Let $x(t) = 0$, then $t = 1$; so y-intercept is $y(1) = 1^2 - 3(1) = -2$. Similarly, let $y(t) = 0$, then $t = 0$ or 3; so x-intercepts are $x(0) = 0 - 1 = -1$, and $x(3) = 3 - 1 = 2$.

Applying the Mathematics

8. Graph the parametric equations. See margin.

a. $\begin{cases} x(t) = t + 1 \\ y(t) = t^2 - 5t + 1 \end{cases}$

b. $\begin{cases} x(t) = t^2 - 5t + 1 \\ y(t) = t + 1 \end{cases}$

c. Compare and contrast the two graphs.

9. Prove that the parametric equations

$$\begin{cases} x(t) = 3t - 7 \\ y(t) = 6t + 5 \end{cases}$$

give the graph of $y = 2x + 19$. See left.

8. a.

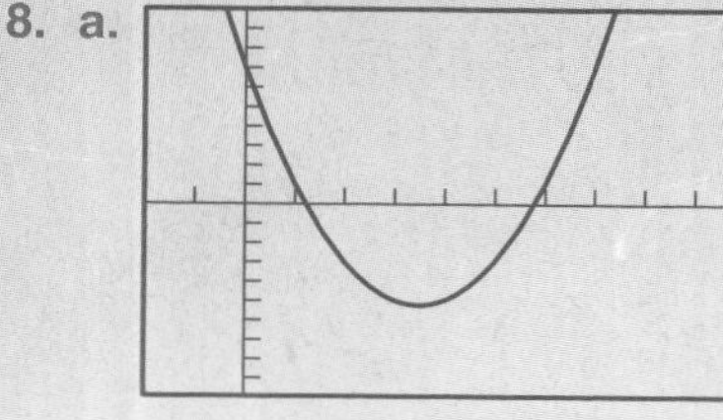

$-2 \le t \le 10$, t-step $= 1$
$-2 \le x \le 10$, x-scale $= 1$
$-10 \le y \le 10$, y-scale $= 1$

b.

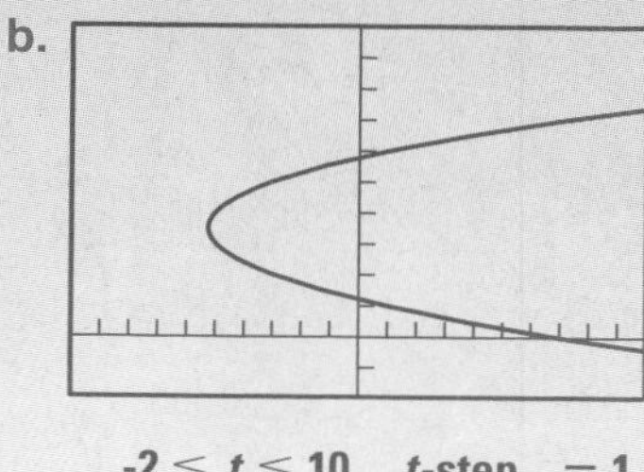

$-2 \le t \le 10$, t-step $= 1$
$-10 \le x \le 10$, x-scale $= 1$
$-2 \le y \le 10$, y-scale $= 1$

c. They are symmetric about the line $y = x$.

In 10 and 11, a golfer hits a ball over a tree 10 m high. The golfer wants to hit the green 55 meters from her position.

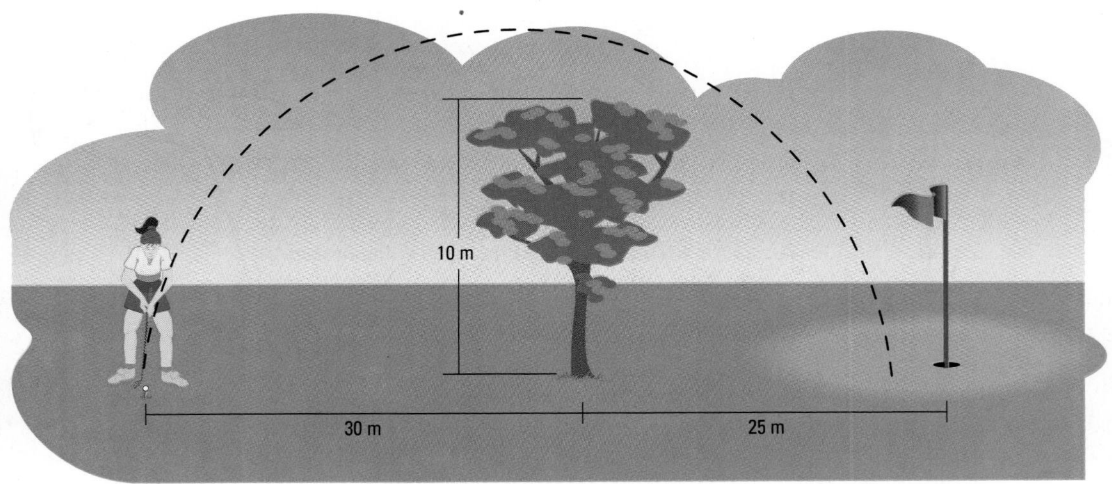

The tree is 30 meters from the golfer and blocks the view of the hole, which is on level ground with respect to the golfer. Assume you can neglect air resistance.

10. Suppose the golfer hits the ball with vertical velocity 20 m/sec and horizontal velocity 15 m/sec. a) See left.

a. Find parametric equations for the path of the ball and graph them in the *xy*-plane. Show the location of the tree and golf hole on the graph.

b. Will the ball go over the tree? yes

c. Will the ball land close to the hole? no

11. Determine a vertical velocity and horizontal velocity that will be good enough for the ball to just miss the tree and come within one meter of the hole. Sample: $V_x = 18.5 \frac{m}{sec}$, $V_y = 14.7 \frac{m}{sec}$

12. a. Graph the parametric equations.

$$\begin{cases} x(t) = \sqrt{t} \\ y(t) = 3t - 2 \end{cases} \quad \text{and} \quad \begin{cases} x(u) = u \\ y(u) = 3u^2 - 2 \end{cases}$$

b. Compare the graphs and explain any differences between them. See margin.

13. Modify the parametric equations in Example 2 to produce a similar but thinner loop graph. Explain why your modification works. See left.

10a) $\begin{cases} x(t) = 15t \\ y(t) = -4.9t^2 + 20t \end{cases}$

Golf hole

13) Sample:

$\begin{cases} x(t) = \frac{1}{2}(1 + t)(1 - t^2) \\ y(t) = \frac{1}{2}(1 - t)(1 - t^2) \end{cases}$

$-1 \le t \le 1$

The graph of these parametric equations is the image of the graph in Example 2 under the size change with center (0, 0) and magnitude $\frac{1}{2}$ (a contraction).

Review

14. Let $f(x) = ax^n$, where $a < 0$ and n is an odd integer.

a. Is the function f even, odd, or neither? Justify your answer.

b. Find $\lim_{x \to -\infty} f(x)$. *(Lesson 2-4)* ∞

a) odd; Because n is odd, $f(-x) = a(-x)^2 = -f(x)$

Follow-up for Lesson 2-5

Practice

For more questions on SPUR Objectives, use **Lesson Master 2-5** (shown on page 105).

Assessment

Written Communication Have students refer to **Question 4.** Ask students to plot the parametric equations on an automatic grapher and give the location of the ball after a certain period of time (providing the ball is still in the area at the selected time). [Students use and graph parametric equations.]

Extension

Have students make up their own situation involving a projectile and create parametric equations to be model the path of the object. The situation can be most easily taken from sports, but does not have to be limited to sports. [Sample topics: students could simulate a home run hit on a baseball diamond, the path of a shot-put throw, or the tossing of a ball between gymnasts in team rhythmic gymnastics.]

Project Update Project 2, *Parametric Equations for Curves,* and Project 3, *Famous Mathematical Curves,* on pages 137–138 relate to the content of this lesson.

Additional Answers

12. a.

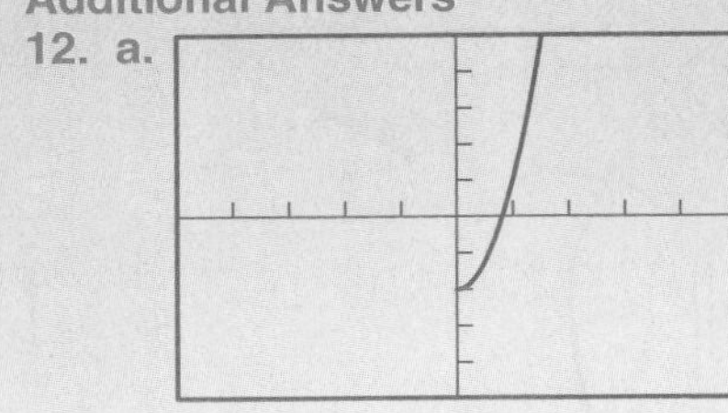

$\begin{cases} x(t) = \sqrt{t} \\ y(t) = 3t - 2 \end{cases}$

$-2 \le t \le 2$, t-step $= 1$
$-5 \le x \le 5$, x-scale $= 1$
$-5 \le y \le 5$, y-scale $= 1$

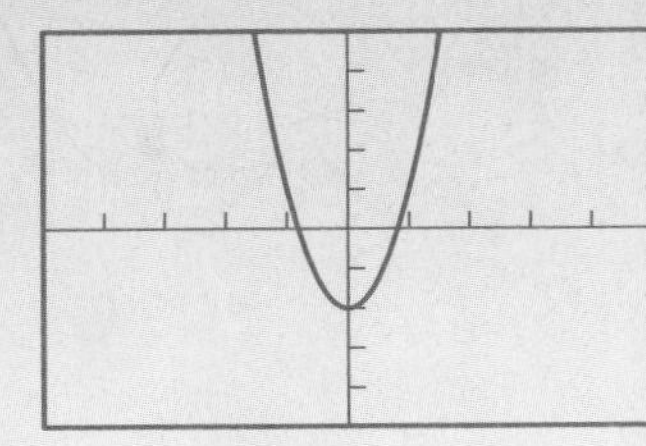

$\begin{cases} x(u) = u \\ y(u) = 3u^2 - 2 \end{cases}$

$-2 \le t \le 2$, t-step $= 1$
$-5 \le x \le 5$, x-scale $= 1$
$-5 \le y \le 5$, y-scale $= 1$

12. b. They both correspond to the equation $y = 3x^2 - 2$, but the first graph limits the domain of x to $[0, \infty]$, while the second has the domain $(-\infty, \infty)$.

Notes on Questions

Questions 17–19 These are review for exponential functions to appear in Lesson 2-7.

Questions 20–21 These are review for the trigonometric functions in Lesson 2-6.

Additional Answers

22. b. Consider any point (c, d) that corresponds to $t = t_0$, where t_0 is in the interval $[-a, a]$. Then $c = (1 + t_0)(1 - t_0^2)$, and $d = (1 - t_0)(1 - t_0^2)$. The image of (c, d) under a reflection over the line $y = x$ is the point (d, c) and is on the graph, since it corresponds to $t = -t_0$, which is also in the interval $[-a, a]$. That is, $d = [1 + (-t_0)][1 - (-t_0)^2]$, and $c = [1 - (-t_0)][1 - (-t_0)^2]$.

15a)

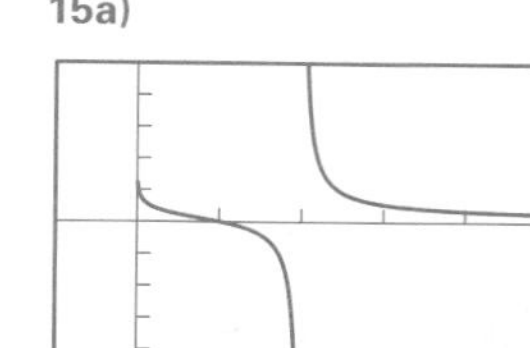

$-1 \le x \le 5$, x-scale = 1
$-5 \le y \le 5$, y-scale = 1

15. a. Graph the real function f with $f(x) = \frac{\log x}{x - 2}$. See left.
 b. Describe the domain of f in terms of intervals. $(0, 2), (2, \infty)$
 c. Determine the largest intervals in the domain of f on which $f(x)$ is a decreasing function. *(Lessons 2-1, 2-3)* $(2, \infty)$

16. Determine when the function $f: x \to 2x^2 + 8x - 9$ is increasing. *(Lesson 2-3)* $x \ge -2$

In 17–19, use the laws of exponents to simplify. *(Previous course)*

17. $\frac{x^5y^3}{x^2y^6} \cdot \frac{(xy)^2}{x^2y}$ $\frac{x^3}{y^2}$

18. $\frac{6(n+1)^3}{4(n+1)^4}$ $\frac{3}{2n+2}$

19. $x^0 + \frac{3}{x^{-2}} + x^2$ $4x^2 + 1$

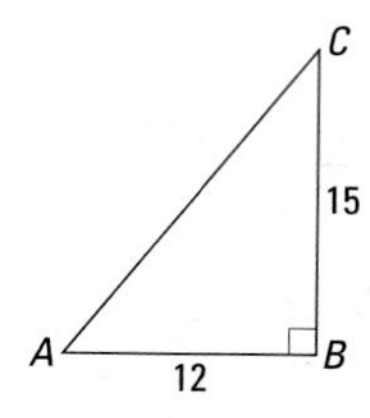

20. In the triangle at the left, give the value of each.
 a. $\sin A$ $\frac{4}{\sqrt{41}} \approx .6247$
 b. $\cos A$ a) $\frac{5}{\sqrt{41}} \approx .7809$
 c. $\tan A$ *(Previous course)* $\frac{5}{4} = 1.25$

21. Give the exact value.
 a. $\sin 30°$ $\frac{1}{2}$ *(Previous course)*
 b. $\cos \frac{\pi}{6}$ $\frac{\sqrt{3}}{2}$
 c. $\sin \frac{\pi}{4}$ $\frac{\sqrt{2}}{2}$

Exploration

22. The graph in Example 2 is symmetric to the line $y = x$.
 a. If the domain of t is taken to be $[-a, a]$ with $a > 1$, is the graph still symmetric? yes
 b. Explain why or why not. See margin.

Setting Up Lesson 2-6

Review the trigonometry required to do **Questions 20** and **21** of this lesson.

LESSON

2-6

The Sine, Cosine, and Tangent Functions

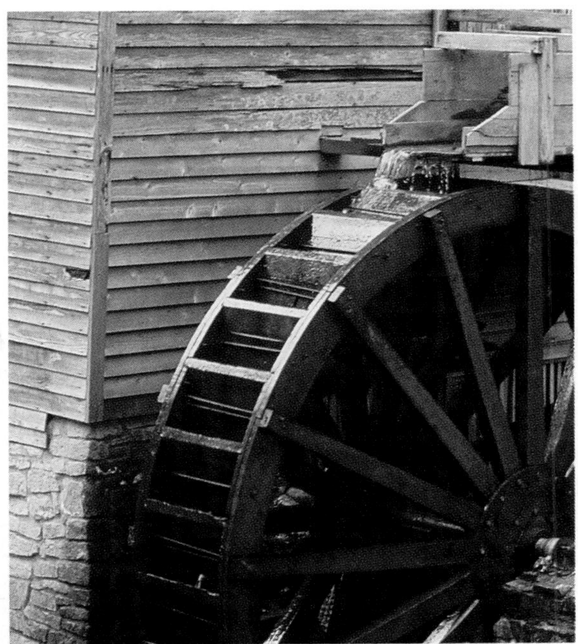

Grain Grinder. *Water rotates the wheel that powers the grindstones of this grist mill at Stone Mountain, GA. A sine curve can represent the distance, over time, of a fixed point on the wheel with respect to the level of the water.*

The sine, cosine, and tangent functions are the basic functions of trigonometry. We assume that you have seen these functions before in two different settings. The first setting in which these functions were studied was as ratios of sides in right triangles. This setting enables trigonometry to be applied to find unknown distances and angle measures and to describe forces in geometry and physics. The second setting is in conjunction with the *unit circle.* It enables trigonometry to be used to describe motion and periodic events. This lesson covers the basics of the second setting, some (but not all) of which you should have seen before.

The **unit circle** is the circle with center (0, 0) and radius 1. It can be described algebraically as the graph of the equation $x^2 + y^2 = 1$. It can also be described geometrically as the set of images (x, y) of the point (1, 0) under a rotation with magnitude θ about the origin.

Measuring Arcs and Rotations

As you know, arcs of circles can be measured by their arc measure or their length. The unit circle's full arc measure is 360°. Because the circumference of a circle with radius r is $2\pi r$, the unit circle's full length is 2π. Related to these two ways of measuring arcs, the magnitude θ of a rotation is customarily measured either in degrees or in radians. A rotation of **1 degree** is $\frac{1}{360}$ of one complete revolution. A rotation of **1 radian** means that the arc connecting preimage and image has length 1 unit.

Lesson 2-6

Objectives

D Determine the end behavior of a function.

G Analyze a function from its graph.

Resources

From the ***Teacher's Resource File***

- Lesson Master 2-6
- Answer Master 2-6
- Teaching Aids
  14 Warm-up
  22 Parametric Equations for the Circle Graph

Additional Resources

- Visuals for Teaching Aids 14, 22
- Exploration 2-6

Teaching Lesson 2-6

Warm-up

Give the value of each expression.

1. $\cos \frac{5\pi}{6}$ — $-\frac{\sqrt{3}}{2}$
2. $\sin \frac{5\pi}{6}$ — 0.5
3. $\cos^2 \frac{5\pi}{6} + \sin^2 (\frac{5\pi}{6})$ — 1
4. $\tan \frac{5\pi}{6}$ — $-\frac{\sqrt{3}}{3}$

Lesson 2-6 Overview

Broad Goals A definition for the sine and cosine in terms of the unit circle is given. These definitions are related to the definition of the tangent, the Pythagorean Identity, and parametric equations for the circle.

Perspective Lesson 2-6 assumes that students bring with them a strong knowledge of trigonometry. The cotangent, secant, and cosecant functions are not mentioned here; they are the subject of Lesson 5-7, where the tangent function is graphed.

We place this lesson after parametric equations because parametric equations offer a different insight into the unit circle definitions of the sine and cosine. Students should have seen the unit circle definition before, but now they should notice that since $x = \cos \theta$ and $y = \sin \theta$, we can think of θ as a parameter. When the parametric equations are graphed, a circle results. Students should see that we have taken the curve first and derived parametric equations for it.

One nice feature of the parametric equations for the circle is that they lead to simple parametric equations for ellipses with horizontal and vertical axes. These are previewed in **Question 18** and discussed in detail in Lesson 3-8.

Notes on Reading

We assume that students are quite familiar with the right triangle properties of the sine, cosine, and tangent. They are discussed in the *three* previous UCSMP courses and some of your students may have also seen them in their physics course. Students should be able to use either the right triangle characterization or the unit circle definition to find values of trigonometric functions at special angles. They also should be able to analyze the sine and cosine functions.

The formula π radians = 180 degrees is the springboard for conversion between radians and degrees. Some students, however, prefer to use a proportion: $\frac{\text{degree measure}}{\text{radian measure}} = \frac{180}{\pi}$. This will help in **Questions 1–2**.

In the unit circle definition of the trigonometric functions, we assume that the magnitude θ is measured in radians unless degrees are explicitly specified. Because radian measure is more common than degree measure in advanced mathematics, try to wean students away from converting radians to degrees.

Because a rotation of 2π radians is a rotation of 360°,

$$\pi \text{ radians} = 180°.$$

You will often (but not always) see radian measures as multiples or fractions of π. Most people work from the above conversion equation to convert from one unit to the other. For instance, dividing both sides by 2, 3, 4, and 6, we obtain the following conversions to the most common angle measures encountered in geometry.

$$\frac{\pi}{2} \text{ radians} = 90° \quad \frac{\pi}{3} \text{ radians} = 60° \quad \frac{\pi}{4} \text{ radians} = 45° \quad \frac{\pi}{6} \text{ radians} = 30°$$

As another example, $\frac{5\pi}{12}$ radians $= \frac{5}{12} \cdot \pi$ radians $= \frac{5}{12} \cdot 180° = 75°$.

It is slightly more difficult to convert with radians not given as multiples of π. Dividing both sides of the conversion equation by π,

$$1 \text{ radian} = \left(\frac{180}{\pi}\right)° = 57.29577951\ldots° \approx 57.3°.$$

Consequently, 2 radians $\approx 2 \cdot 57.3° = 114.6°$. Converting the other way, a magnitude of

$$-130° = -130° \cdot \frac{\pi \text{ radians}}{180°} = -\frac{13}{18}\pi \text{ radians} \approx -2.27 \text{ radians}.$$

It is customary not to write the name "radian" as a unit. Consequently, we always use the degree symbol ° when referring to a magnitude of a rotation in degrees. But when the magnitude of the rotation is in radians, we avoid writing radians. For example, a rotation of π is a rotation of π radians. A rotation of magnitude 2 is a rotation of 2 radians, not 2°.

Definitions of the Cosine, Sine, and Tangent

Cosines and sines of real numbers can be defined in terms of the unit circle and rotations.

Definition
For all θ, $(\cos\theta, \sin\theta)$ is the image of $(1, 0)$ under a rotation of θ about the origin.

For example, if (1, 0) is rotated $\frac{3\pi}{2}$ about the origin, its image is (0, -1). The first coordinate of the image, 0, is $\cos\frac{3\pi}{2}$. The second coordinate, -1, is $\sin\frac{3\pi}{2}$. In this way, cosines and sines of all multiples of $\frac{\pi}{2}$ can be found.

Using properties of special right triangles, cosines and sines of multiples of $\frac{\pi}{6}$ and $\frac{\pi}{4}$ (that is, multiples of 30° or 45°) can be calculated.

Optional Activities

Activity 1 Technology Connection
Materials: Explorations software

You may use *Exploration 2-6, Sine, Cosine, and Tangent Functions,* to introduce Lesson 2-6. Enter an angle in radian measure and observe the angle drawn on the unit circle. Values for sine, cosine, and tangent of the angle are also given. An animation shows the values of these functions as a point rotates around the unit circle.

Activity 2 Cooperative Learning After discussing the lesson, you might have students **work in groups** and brainstorm ways to remember the radian measures of common angles without constantly having to translate into degrees. (You can make an analogy with foreign language—someone who is constantly translating Spanish words into English before responding in Spanish will never become fluent in the language.)

Example 1

Describe how to obtain the exact values of $\cos \frac{\pi}{3}$ and $\sin \frac{\pi}{3}$.

Solution

By the definition of cosine, $\cos \frac{\pi}{3}$ is the first coordinate of the image of (1, 0) under a rotation of $\frac{\pi}{3}$. It takes no longer to find both coordinates.

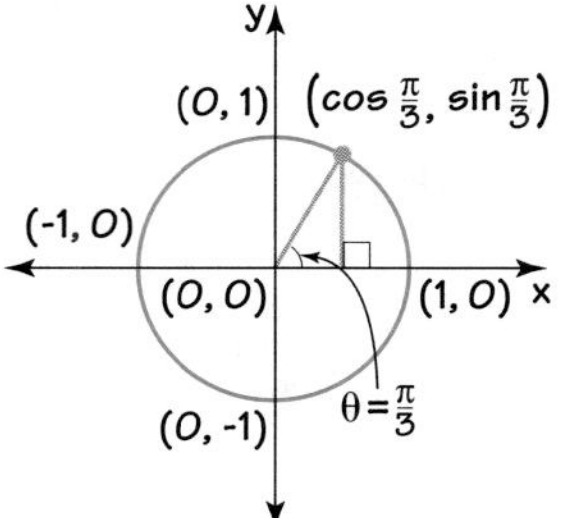

I draw a figure as at the right. A 30-60-90 right triangle with hypotenuse of length 1 is formed. The side opposite the 30° angle is half the length of the hypotenuse. The other side can be found by the Pythagorean Theorem to be $\frac{\sqrt{3}}{2}$. Consequently, the image is $\left(\frac{1}{2}, \frac{\sqrt{3}}{2}\right)$. Now apply the definitions of cosine and sine.

$$\cos \frac{\pi}{3} = \frac{1}{2} = 0.5 \qquad \sin \frac{\pi}{3} = \frac{\sqrt{3}}{2} \approx 0.866\ldots$$

Check

A calculator in radian mode can verify the answer.

The *tangent* of a real number is defined to be the quotient of its sine and cosine.

Definition
For all θ, $\tan \theta = \frac{\sin \theta}{\cos \theta}$.

For instance, using Example 1, $\tan \frac{\pi}{3} = \frac{\sin \frac{\pi}{3}}{\cos \frac{\pi}{3}} = \frac{\frac{\sqrt{3}}{2}}{\frac{1}{2}} = \sqrt{3} \approx 1.732\ldots.$

Notice that from its definition, $\tan \theta$ is the slope of the line containing (0, 0) and $(\cos \theta, \sin \theta)$.

Angles that are multiples of $\frac{\pi}{6}$ and $\frac{\pi}{4}$ appear in isosceles right triangles and regular polygons of 3, 4, 6, or 8 sides. Their sines, cosines, and tangents can be used to give enough points on the graphs of the functions $y = \sin x$, $y = \cos x$, and $y = \tan x$ to enable a rough graph to be drawn. You should know or be able to derive quickly the exact values of these functions that are listed in the following table.

θ	$0° = 0$	$30° = \frac{\pi}{6}$	$45° = \frac{\pi}{4}$	$60° = \frac{\pi}{3}$	$90° = \frac{\pi}{2}$
$\sin \theta$	0	$\frac{1}{2}$	$\frac{\sqrt{2}}{2}$	$\frac{\sqrt{3}}{2}$	1
$\cos \theta$	1	$\frac{\sqrt{3}}{2}$	$\frac{\sqrt{2}}{2}$	$\frac{1}{2}$	0
$\tan \theta$	0	$\frac{\sqrt{3}}{3}$	1	$\sqrt{3}$	undefined

Error Alert Warn students that pressing the "clear" or "all clear" key on some calculators will also set them into degree mode. When problems require radians, this will produce errors.

You may want to ask: What is the image of the point (*r*, 0) under the rotation with magnitude θ about the origin? The image is $(r \cdot \cos \theta, r \cdot \sin \theta)$; this fact will be used in Chapter 8 in the introduction of polar coordinates $[r, \theta]$.)

At this point you might have the urge to review the graphs of functions of the form $f(x) = A\cos(B(x - C)) + D$. Please suppress the urge. There is enough to do in this lesson and the transformations of graphs are studied in Lesson 3-8. However, you may want to use an automatic grapher to graph some of these functions and have students determine the period from the graph. Also, emphasize that the period is usually the *smallest p* such that $f(x + p) = f(x)$ for all *x* in the domain of *f*.

You might ask students to describe common phenomena that are periodic. Examples are day of the week, phases of the moon, hours on an analog watch, etc. Have students give the period for each.

Teaching Aid 22 contains the parametric equations for the circle.

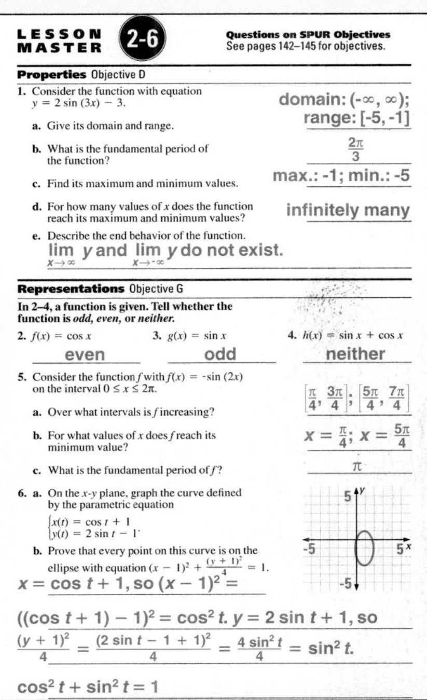

LESSON MASTER 2-6 **Questions on SPUR Objectives** See pages 142–145 for objectives.

Properties Objective D

1. Consider the function with equation $y = 2\sin(3x) - 3$.
   a. Give its domain and range. domain: $(-\infty, \infty)$; range: $[-5, -1]$
   b. What is the fundamental period of the function? $\frac{2\pi}{3}$
   c. Find its maximum and minimum values. max.: -1; min.: -5
   d. For how many values of *x* does the function reach its maximum and minimum values? infinitely many
   e. Describe the end behavior of the function. $\lim_{x \to \infty} y$ and $\lim_{x \to -\infty} y$ do not exist.

Representations Objective G

In 2–4, a function is given. Tell whether the function is *odd, even,* or *neither.*

2. $f(x) = \cos x$ even
3. $g(x) = \sin x$ odd
4. $h(x) = \sin x + \cos x$ neither

5. Consider the function *f* with $f(x) = -\sin(2x)$ on the interval $0 \le x \le 2\pi$.
   a. Over what intervals is *f* increasing? $\left[\frac{\pi}{4}, \frac{3\pi}{4}\right]; \left[\frac{5\pi}{4}, \frac{7\pi}{4}\right]$
   b. For what values of *x* does *f* reach its minimum value? $x = \frac{\pi}{4}; x = \frac{5\pi}{4}$
   c. What is the fundamental period of *f*? π

6. a. On the *x-y* plane, graph the curve defined by the parametric equation $\begin{cases} x(t) = \cos t + 1 \\ y(t) = 2\sin t - 1 \end{cases}$.
   b. Prove that every point on this curve is on the ellipse with equation $(x - 1)^2 + \frac{(y + 1)^2}{4} = 1$.

$x = \cos t + 1$, so $(x - 1)^2 = ((\cos t + 1) - 1)^2 = \cos^2 t$. $y = 2\sin t + 1$, so $\frac{(y + 1)^2}{4} = \frac{(2\sin t - 1 + 1)^2}{4} = \frac{4\sin^2 t}{4} = \sin^2 t$. $\cos^2 t + \sin^2 t = 1$

Activity 3 Technology Graphing calculators can produce a quick and effective simulation to remind students why the sine and cosine graphs appear as they do. In parametric mode, have students enter the equations for producing the unit circle and either the sine or cosine graph: $x_1 = \cos t$; $y_1 = \sin t$; $x_2 = t$; $y_2 = \sin t$ (or $\cos t$). Have them put the calculator into simultaneous graphing mode. On some calculators, a feature in the zoom menu will produce an appropriate window; if not, tell students to set their graphing window as follows: $0 \le t \le 2\pi$ with a *t*-step of $\frac{\pi}{16}$; $-2\pi \le x \le 2\pi$ and $-4 \le y \le 4$. The equations will graph simultaneously, so students can see that the sine graph comes from "unwrapping" the sine values from the unit circle. Use of the trace feature can further emphasize the connection between the unit circle values and the corresponding sine wave.

Additional Examples

1. Give the exact values.
   a. $\cos \frac{3\pi}{2}$ 0
   b. $\sin \frac{2\pi}{3}$ $\frac{\sqrt{3}}{2}$
   c. $\tan \pi$ 0
2. On the interval $[\frac{-\pi}{2}, 0]$, is the function increasing, decreasing, or neither increasing nor decreasing?
   a. sine Increasing
   b. cosine Increasing
   c. tangent Increasing

If the rotation image of (1, 0) about the origin is in any quadrant other than the first, its coordinates can be found by reflecting or rotating a corresponding point in the first quadrant.

Example 2

Find the exact values of $\sin \frac{7\pi}{6}$, $\cos \frac{7\pi}{6}$, and $\tan \frac{5\pi}{6}$.

Solution

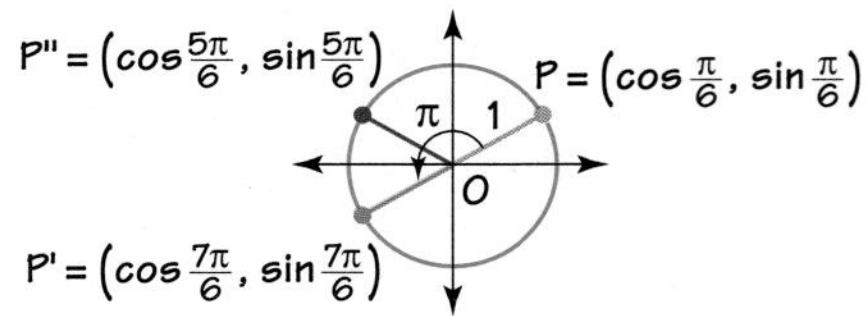

First of all, note that $\frac{7\pi}{6} = \pi + \frac{\pi}{6}$ while $\frac{5\pi}{6} = \pi - \frac{\pi}{6}$. Because a rotation by π radians on the unit circle is a point reflection through the origin, it carries a point $P' = (x, y)$ on the unit circle to a point P with coordinates $P' = (-x, -y)$. In particular, it carries the point $P = \left(\cos \frac{\pi}{6}, \sin \frac{\pi}{6}\right)$ onto the point $P' = \left(\cos \frac{7\pi}{6}, \sin \frac{7\pi}{6}\right)$, because $\frac{7\pi}{6} = \pi + \frac{\pi}{6}$. Consequently, $\sin \frac{7\pi}{6} = -\sin \frac{\pi}{6} \approx -\frac{1}{2}$ and $\cos \frac{7\pi}{6} = -\cos \frac{\pi}{6} = -\frac{\sqrt{3}}{2}$. To compute $\tan \frac{5\pi}{6}$, note that the point $P'' = \left(\cos \frac{5\pi}{6}, \sin \frac{5\pi}{6}\right)$ on the unit circle is the reflection of the point $P' = \left(\cos \frac{7\pi}{6}, \sin \frac{7\pi}{6}\right)$ over the *x*-axis, because $\frac{5\pi}{6} = \pi - \frac{\pi}{6}$ and $\frac{7\pi}{6} = \pi + \frac{\pi}{6}$. Thus, the point $P'' = \left(\cos \frac{5\pi}{6}, \sin \frac{5\pi}{6}\right)$ is obtained from the point $P = \left(\cos \frac{\pi}{6}, \sin \frac{\pi}{6}\right)$, by a point reflection through the origin to obtain P' (slope $\overline{OP}$ = slope $\overline{OP'}$), followed by a reflection of P' across the x-axis to obtain P'' (slope $\overline{OP''}$ = -slope $\overline{OP'}$). Therefore, $\tan \frac{5\pi}{6} = -\tan \frac{\pi}{6} = -\frac{\sqrt{3}}{3}$.

The Pythagorean Identity

The results of Examples 1 and 2 can be checked in a simple way. Since for all θ, the point (cos θ, sin θ) is on the circle with equation $x^2 + y^2 = 1$, the following theorem holds: For all θ, $(\cos\theta)^2 + (\sin\theta)^2 = 1$. It is called a *Pythagorean Identity,* because the equation of the circle comes from the Pythagorean Theorem and because it is true for all values of the variable.

It is customary to write $\cos^2\theta$ for $(\cos\theta)^2$, and $\sin^2\theta$ for $(\sin\theta)^2$. Most people think of sines before cosines (even though the cosine is the first coordinate), so you will usually see this Pythagorean Identity written this way.

Adapting to Individual Needs

Extra Help

Students should be able to reproduce the analysis in **Example 2** when they are determining the sign of the sine, cosine, or tangent in Quadrants II, III, or IV. Some students might benefit from summarizing the results in a table, such as the one shown at the right.

Quadrant	I	II	III	IV
sin θ	+	+	−	−
cos θ	+	−	−	+
tan θ	+	−	+	−

Theorem (Pythagorean Identity)
For all θ, $\sin^2\theta + \cos^2\theta = 1$.

To check Example 2, notice that we should have $\left(\sin \frac{7\pi}{6}\right)^2 + \left(\cos \frac{7\pi}{6}\right)^2 = 1$. Substitution shows this is so. $\left(-\frac{1}{2}\right)^2 + \left(-\frac{\sqrt{3}}{2}\right)^2 = \frac{1}{4} + \frac{3}{4} = 1$

Parametric Equations for the Circle

Notice that for each point on the circle,

$$x = \cos\theta$$

and

$$y = \sin\theta.$$

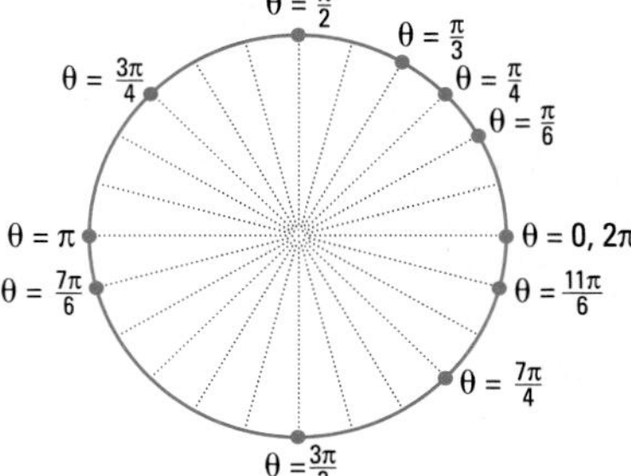

Does this look familiar? These are *parametric equations* of the circle, with θ as the parameter. In the figure at the right, we have associated points of the circle with some values of θ from 0 to 2π.

As the parameter θ increases from 0 to 2π, the point (x, y) travels a complete revolution around the circle counterclockwise. For this reason, the values that the cosine and sine functions assume over the interval $[0, 2\pi]$ comprise all the possible values of these functions. A further increase (or decrease) of any value of θ by 2π means one more (or less) complete revolution, and so leads to the same image. That is, for all real numbers θ,

$$\cos(\theta + 2\pi) = \cos\theta,$$
$$\sin(\theta + 2\pi) = \sin\theta.$$

These properties imply that the cosine and sine functions are *periodic functions* with *fundamental period* 2π.

Definitions
A function f is **periodic** if and only if there is a positive number p such that $f(x + p) = f(x)\ \forall\ x$ in the domain of f. Any such p is called a **period** of f. The smallest such p is called the **fundamental period** of f.

The values of a periodic function repeat. Since the fundamental period of the sine and cosine functions is 2π, their graphs are mapped onto themselves by a horizontal translation of 2π. These graphs, displayed at the top of page 114 on the interval $[-7, 7]$, should be familiar to you.

Adapting to Individual Needs

English Language Development
The words sine, cosine, and tangent are universally used, so students who have studied this material in other countries should have no need for translation.

Notes on Questions

Question 3–7 Students should be encouraged to draw a unit circle to assist them in answering these questions.

Question 17 In graphing trigonometric functions, encourage students to set tick marks on the x-axis as multiples of $\frac{\pi}{4}$ or $\frac{\pi}{2}$. Doing so makes it easier to determine the period of the function.

Question 18 This question previews material to be discussed in Lesson 3-8.

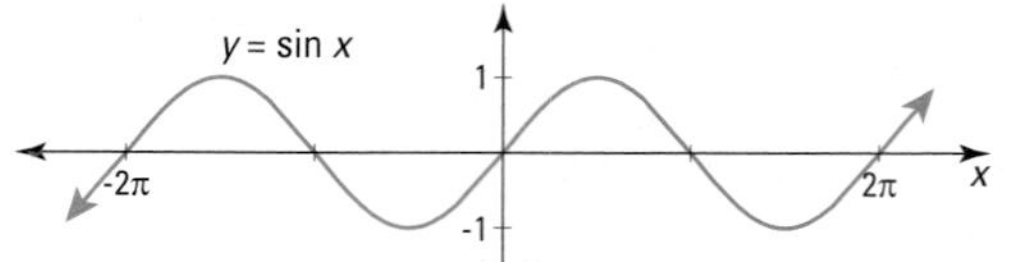

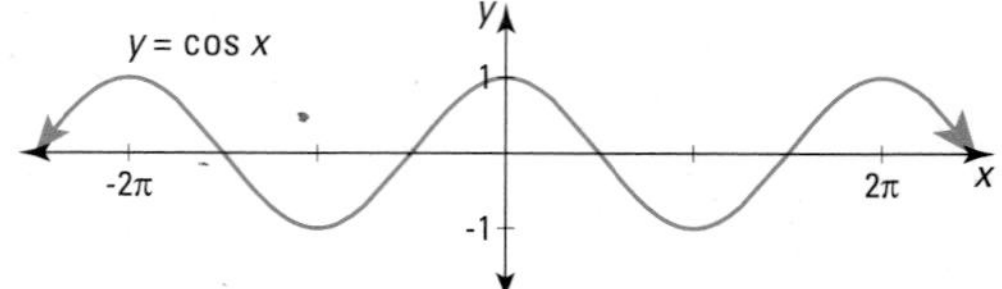

Bobbing Buoy. *The graph of the up and down motion of this buoy as it floats is sinusoidal.*

The graphs verify many aspects of the sine and cosine functions that can be proved from the definitions of the sine and cosine and that are verified by the table and examples in this lesson.

1. The *domain* of the sine function is the set of real numbers.
2. The *range* of the sine function is the interval [-1, 1].
3. The sine function is *increasing* on the interval $\left[0, \frac{\pi}{2}\right]$, *decreasing* on $\left[\frac{\pi}{2}, \frac{3\pi}{2}\right]$, *increasing* on $\left[\frac{3\pi}{2}, \frac{5\pi}{2}\right]$, etc.
4. The *maximum* value of the sine function is 1; the *minimum* value is -1. Each maximum and minimum is reached infinitely many times.
5. *End behavior.* Because sin x oscillates through its entire range of values on any interval larger than 2π, $\lim_{x\to\infty} \sin x$ and $\lim_{x\to-\infty} \sin x$ do not exist.

In the Questions, you are asked for a similar analysis of the cosine and tangent functions.

QUESTIONS

Covering the Reading

1. Convert 100° to radian measure. $\frac{5\pi}{9} \approx 1.75$

2. Convert $-\frac{7\pi}{12}$ to degree measure. -105°

3. Use $\cos \frac{\pi}{3} = \frac{1}{2}$ to find the value of each expression.
a. $\cos\left(-\frac{\pi}{3}\right)$ $\frac{1}{2}$ **b.** $\cos \frac{2\pi}{3}$ $-\frac{1}{2}$ **c.** $\sin \frac{2\pi}{3}$ $\frac{\sqrt{3}}{2}$
d. $\cos \frac{5\pi}{3}$ $\frac{1}{2}$ **e.** $\tan \frac{\pi}{3}$ $\sqrt{3}$ **f.** $\tan \frac{5\pi}{3}$ $-\sqrt{3}$

4. Find the value of each.
a. $\cos \frac{3\pi}{4}$ $-\frac{\sqrt{2}}{2}$ **b.** $\sin \frac{3\pi}{4}$ $\frac{\sqrt{2}}{2}$ **c.** $\tan \frac{3\pi}{4}$ -1

5. For a particular value of θ, you calculate that $\sin \theta = .1$ and $\cos \theta = .9$.
a. Is this possible? no
b. If so, estimate a value of θ for which this is true. If not, tell why not. Because $\sin^2 \theta + \cos^2 \theta = 1$, but $.1^2 + .9^2 = .82 \neq 1$.

6. If $\sin x = \frac{7}{24}$, give all possible values of $\cos x$. $\pm\frac{\sqrt{527}}{24} \approx \pm 1.75$

7. If $\cos x = \frac{2}{3}$, give the value of each expression.
a. $\cos(x + 2\pi)$ $\frac{2}{3}$ **b.** $\cos(x - 2\pi)$ $\frac{2}{3}$ **c.** $\cos(x + 6\pi)$ $\frac{2}{3}$

Adapting to Individual Needs

Challenge

Have students find a single equation for each set of parametric equations and give the possible range of values of t, x, and y. Have them compare these results with those of the Challenge in *Adapting to Individual Needs* on page 105 in Lesson 2-5. Note that these trigonometric parametric equations give the same x-y equations as those in the Lesson 2-5 Challenge.

1. $x = 2 \sin t$; $y = 2 \cos t$ [$x^2 + y^2 = 4$; $-\infty < t < \infty$; $-2 \le x \le 2$; $-2 \le y \le 2$]
2. $x = 3 \sin t$; $y = 2 \cos t$ [$4x^2 + 9y^2 = 36$; $-\infty \le t \le \infty$; $-3 \le x \le 3$; $-2 \le y \le 2$]
3. $x = 2 \tan t$; $y = \frac{4}{\cos^2 t}$ [$y = x^2 + 4$; $t \neq \pi n$; $-\infty < x < \infty$; $y \ge 4$]
4. $x = \frac{2}{\cos t}$; $y = 2 \tan t$ [$x^2 - y^2 = 4$; $t \neq \pi n$; $x \ge 2$ or $x \le -2$; $-\infty \le y \le \infty$]

8) $\begin{cases} x(t) = \cos t \\ y(t) = \sin t \end{cases}$

14a)

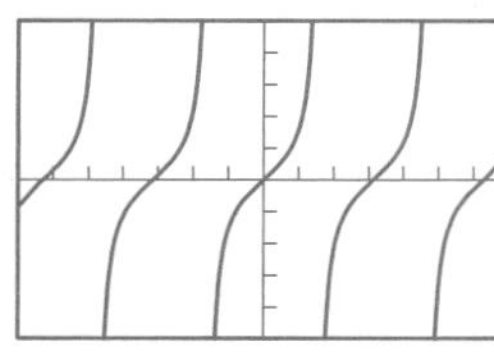

$-7 \le x \le 7$, x-scale = 1
$-5 \le y \le 5$, y-scale = 1

b) Sample: $(0, 0)$, $\left(\frac{\pi}{4}, 1\right)$, $\left(\frac{3\pi}{4}, -1\right)$, $\left(-\frac{\pi}{4}, -1\right)$, $\left(-\frac{3\pi}{4}, 1\right)$

17a) Sample:
$0 \le x \le \pi$;
$-7 \le y \le 23$

8. Give parametric equations for the unit circle, with t as the parameter. See left.

In 9–13, consider the cosine function $\{(x, y): y = \cos x\}$.

9. Name five points of this function. Sample: $(0, 1)$, $\left(\frac{\pi}{3}, \frac{1}{2}\right)$, $\left(\frac{\pi}{2}, 0\right)$, $(\pi, -1)$ $(3\pi/2, 0)$

10. Give its domain and range. domain: $(-\infty, \infty)$; range: $[-1, 1]$

11. For the given interval, state whether the function is increasing, decreasing, or neither increasing nor decreasing.

a. $\left[0, \frac{\pi}{2}\right]$ decreasing **b.** $\left[\frac{\pi}{2}, \pi\right]$ decreasing **c.** $[\pi, 2\pi]$ increasing

12. Give its maximum and minimum values.
maximum: 1; minimum: -1

13. Describe its end behavior. $\cos x$ oscillates as $x \to \infty$ and as $x \to -\infty$. Therefore $\lim_{x\to\infty} \cos x$ and $\lim_{x\to-\infty} \cos x$ do not exist.

14. Consider the tangent function.

a. Draw a graph of this function on the interval [-7, 7]. See left.

b. Name five points of this function. See left.

c. Give its fundamental period. π

d. Give the largest interval containing 0 on which this function is increasing. (Hint: This is an open interval.) $-\frac{\pi}{2}, \frac{\pi}{2}$

e. Name a value for which this function is undefined.
Sample: $x = \frac{\pi}{2}$ d) $\left(-\frac{\pi}{2}, \frac{\pi}{2}\right)$

Applying the Mathematics

15. Use the unit circle to prove that

$$\cos(-\theta) = \cos\theta,$$
$$\sin(-\theta) = -\sin\theta.$$

See margin.

16. Suppose $\cos\theta = \frac{5}{13}$ and $\frac{3\pi}{2} \le \theta \le 2\pi$.

a. Find the value of $\sin\theta$. $-\frac{12}{13}$ **b.** Find the value of $\tan\theta$. $-\frac{12}{5}$

17. Consider the function with equation $y = 15\cos(4x) + 8$.

a. What is a suitable window for graphing this function so that you can see at least 2 full cycles of it (that is, 2 full periods)? See left.

b. What is the fundamental period of the function? $\frac{\pi}{2}$

c. Give its maximum and minimum values.
maximum: 23; minimum: -7

18. a. Graph the curve defined by the parametric equations

$$\begin{cases} x(t) = 2\sin t + 1 \\ y(t) = 3\cos t - 4. \end{cases}$$

b. Prove algebraically that every point on this curve is on the ellipse with equation

$$\frac{(x-1)^2}{4} + \frac{(y+4)^2}{9} = 1.$$

c. What characteristic of the ellipse is determined by each of the coefficients in the parametric equation: 2, 1, 3, and -4?
See margin.

Additional Answers

15.

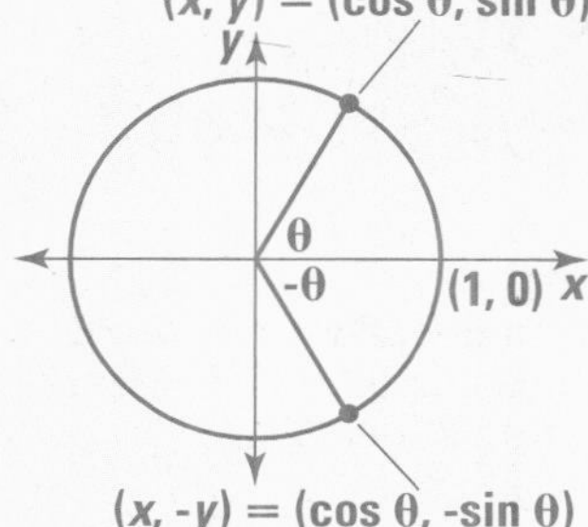

Because $(\cos\theta, \sin\theta)$ is the image of (1, 0) under a counterclockwise rotation of θ about the origin and $[\cos(-\theta), \sin(-\theta)]$ can be considered as the image of (1, 0) under a clockwise rotation of θ about the origin.
$\cos(-\theta) = \cos\theta$
$\sin(-\theta) = -\sin\theta$

18. a.

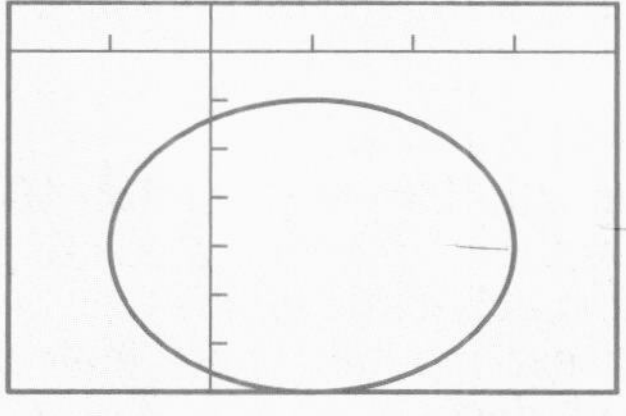

$0 \le t \le 7$, t-step = 1
$-2 \le x \le 4$, x-scale = 1
$-7 \le y \le 1$, y-scale = 1

b. From
$\begin{cases} x(t) = 2\sin t + 1 \\ y(t) = 3\cos t - 4 \end{cases}$
we have
$\begin{cases} \frac{x(t) - 1}{2} = \sin t \\ \frac{y(t) + 4}{2} = \cos t \end{cases}$
therefore
$\left(\frac{x-1}{2}\right)^2 + \left(\frac{y+4}{3}\right)^2 = \sin^2 t + \cos^2 t = 1.$
Namely, $\frac{(x-1)^2}{4} + \frac{(y+4)^2}{9} = 1$

c. 2 is the half length of the minor axis; 3 is the half length of the major axis; and (1, -4) is the center of the ellipse.

Follow-up for Lesson 2-6

Practice

For more questions on SPUR Objectives, use **Lesson Master 2-6** (shown on page 111).

Assessment

Oral Communication Have students graph the sine, cosine, or tangent function on the coordinate plane and state the domain, range, and period. Then have them describe intervals on which the function is increasing and intervals on which the function is decreasing (if such exist). [Students describe the graphs of the sine, cosine, and tangent functions.]

Extension

Refer students to **Question 18.** Have them try to find a pair of parametric equations for the following ellipses, and then check their work by graphing.

1. The ellipse has center (2, -3) and has a longer horizontal axis than vertical axis. [$x = 5 \sin t + 2$; $y = 3 \cos t - 3$]
2. The ellipse has center (-3, -5) and has a longer vertical axis than horizontal axis. [$x = 2 \sin t - 3$; $y = 4 \cos t - 5$]
3. The ellipse has center on the y-axis and has a vertical axis of 6 units. [$x = \sin t$; $y = 3 \cos t + 1$]
4. The ellipse has center on the x-axis and has a horizontal axis of 8 units. [$x = 4 \sin t - 2$; $y = 5 \cos t$]

Review

19. *Multiple choice.* On which interval is the function graphed at the right increasing?

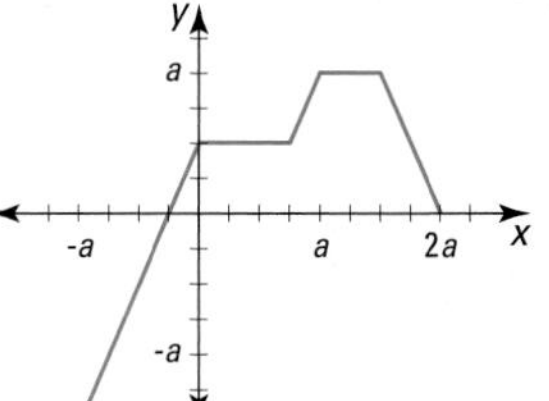

(a) $-a \le x \le a$
(b) $\frac{a}{2} \le x \le a$
(c) $-\frac{a}{4} \le x \le 2a$
(d) $-\frac{a}{4} \le x \le 0$ *(Lesson 2-3)* d

20. Determine whether the following argument is valid or invalid, and identify the form of argument or error. invalid; inverse error

If each element of a set S can be matched with a positive integer, then S is a discrete set.
The real numbers cannot be matched with the positive integers.
$\therefore$ *The set of real numbers is not discrete.*

(Lesson 3-10 will tell you whether or not the conclusion is true.) *(Lessons 1-6, 1-7)*

In 21–23, simplify by using the laws of exponents. *(Previous course)*

21. $\frac{(x + y)^{-3}}{(x + y)^{-5}}$ $(x + y)^2$

22. $\left(\frac{p}{q}\right)^2 \left(\frac{q}{p}\right)^3$ $\frac{q}{p}$

23. $\frac{m^3 + n^3}{m^2 + n^2}$ Cannot be Simplified.

Exploration

24. Below is a graph of $y = \sin 2x + \cos x$. Explore other combinations of sine and cosine functions and sketch the three most interesting combinations you find. For each one, estimate the period p, and count the number of relative maxima and minima that occur in an interval of length p. Answers may vary.

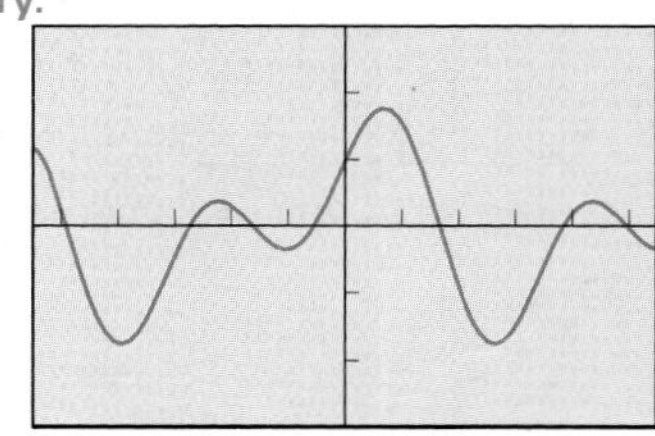

$-5.25 \le x \le 5.25$, x-scale = 1
$-3 \le y \le 3$, y-scale = 1

Setting Up Lesson 2-7

Questions 21–23 provide more review for Lesson 2-7.

LESSON

2-7

Analyzing Exponential Functions

As in the case of the trigonometric functions sine, cosine, and tangent, we expect that you have studied exponential and logarithmic functions before, so that much of the material in this lesson and the next is familiar to you.

What Is Meant by "Analyzing a Function"?

By "analyzing" a particular real function f we mean describing *in mathematical language* the following characteristics of the function:

1. *Domain.* Identify the values for which f is defined.
2. *Range.* Describe the set of all possible values of f.
3. *Increasing or Decreasing.* As x increases, identify the intervals on which f increases and the intervals on which f decreases.
4. *End Behavior.* Describe what happens to f as $x \to \infty$ or as $x \to -\infty$.
5. *Maxima or Minima.* Find the greatest or least value of f.

A good graph can help you accomplish all five of these tasks. Consequently, it is important to be able to graph f with an automatic grapher and to sketch a graph of f by hand.

However, these tasks mean very little unless you know what makes the function important.

6. *Models.* Identify situations which can be modeled by a function like f. Know how f is normally used in those situations.
7. *Properties.* Be aware of special properties of f, and their implications.

Now we consider these seven characteristics as they apply to exponential functions. Recall that if b is a positive real number and $b \neq 1$, then an **exponential function with base *b*** is any function defined by a formula

$$f(x) = ab^x$$

where a is a given nonzero real number. The number a is often called the **initial value** of f because $f(0) = ab^0 = a$.

Domain

The first domain of an exponential function that you studied was the set of positive integers. This was done by defining

$$b^n = \underbrace{b \cdot b \cdot \cdots \cdot b}_{n \text{ factors}}, \ \forall\, n \geq 1.$$

Then the domain was extended to all nonnegative integers by using

$$b^0 = 1.$$

Lesson 2-7

Objectives

B Rewrite exponential expressions and equations.
D Determine the end behavior of an exponential function.
E Use exponential functions as models.
G Analyze an exponential function from its graph.

Resources

From the ***Teacher's Resource File***
- Lesson Master 2-7
- Answer Master 2-7
- Assessment Sourcebook: Quiz for Lessons 2-5 through 2-7
- Teaching Aids
  14 Warm-up
  23 What Is Meant by Analyzing a Function?

Additional Resources
- Visuals for Teaching Aids 14, 23
- Exploration 2-7

Teaching Lesson 2-7

Warm-up

In 1–4, let x be any real number. Give the limit of the expression as $x \to \infty$ and as $x \to -\infty$.

1. 2^x $\infty, 0$ **2.** 0.9^x $0, \infty$
3. $5 \cdot 6^x$ $\infty, 0$ **4.** $-2 \cdot 3^x$ $\infty, 0$

Notes on Reading

❶ The seven tasks listed here can be applied to any real-valued function whose domain is the set of the real numbers. Exponential functions are taken first because their behavior is not trivial, yet it is still reasonably easy to describe. These tasks are also shown on **Teaching Aid 23.**

Lesson 2-7 Overview

Broad Goals This lesson uses the exponential functions, defined by $f\colon x \to ab^x$ for all real numbers x, as a vehicle for discussing what it means to *analyze* a function.

Perspective Exponential functions should be quite familiar to students with previous UCSMP experience; their properties, including the applications to growth and compound interest, are discussed in three previous courses.

The information about functions conveyed in the titles of Lessons 2-1, 2-2, 2-3, and 2-4 constitutes a significant part of what it means to analyze a real function. Also important in the analysis are the maximum or minimum values of the function, the situations in which the function is employed as a model, and the function's special properties.

In this lesson, the familiar laws of exponents are thought of as properties of exponential functions. Of course, they are properties of the *values* of these functions, but we use the function language just as we do when we think of relationships between sines and cosines as properties of the trigonometric functions. In Lesson 2-9, the corresponding properties of logarithms are viewed as properties of logarithm functions.

With this domain for $f(x) = ab^x$, f is the geometric sequence

$$f = \{a, ab, ab^2, ab^3, \ldots\}$$

with first term a and constant ratio b.

The domain can be enlarged to all integers by using

$$b^{-n} = \frac{1}{b^n}.$$

For any *positive* base b, the nth root $\sqrt[n]{b}$ is a positive real number. This enables us to extend the domain of $f(x) = ab^x$ to the set of all rational numbers $q = \frac{m}{n}$ where m and n are integers, $n > 0$, and

$$b^q = \left(\sqrt[n]{b}\right)^m.$$

Finally, we can extend the domain of f to all real numbers r by using sequences of rational numbers whose limit is r. For example, the sequence $q = 3, 3.1, 3.14, 3.141, 3.1415, \ldots$ with $\lim_{k\to\infty} q_k = \pi$ enables us to define 2^π as $\lim_{k\to\infty} 2^{q_k}$.

In general, if $\lim_{k\to\infty} q_k = r$, then

$$b^r = \lim_{k\to\infty} b^{q_k}.$$

This is how, when $b > 0$, $f(x) = ab^x$ is defined for all real numbers x.

Range

In these successive extensions of the domain of f, the values of b^x remain positive, for any *positive* base $b \neq 1$. If we consider only positive values of x, then $b^x > 1$ or $b^x < 1$ according as $b > 1$ or $b < 1$. That is,

1. $b^x > 0\ \forall$ real numbers x.
2. For all b with $b > 1$, $b^x > 1$ if and only if x is positive.
3. For all b with $0 < b < 1$, $b^x < 1$ if and only if x is positive.

Increasing or Decreasing?

In Lesson 2-4 it was noted from a graph of $y = 2^x$ that this exponential function is an increasing function throughout its domain. This property is true of all exponential functions whose bases are greater than 1, and is verified below. That is, if $b > 1$ and $x_1 < x_2$, then $b^{x_1} < b^{x_2}$.

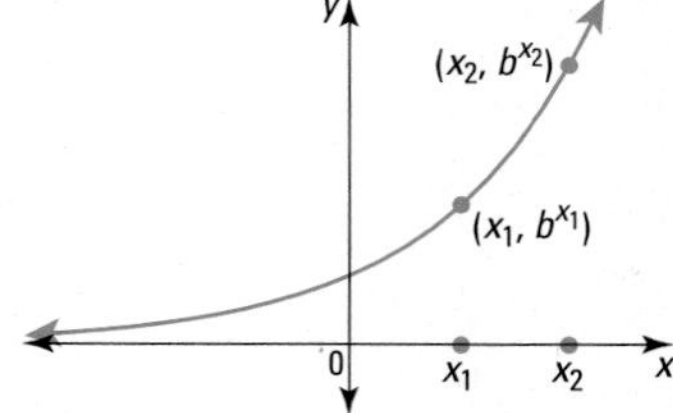

Theorem
For any real numbers a and b with $a > 0$ and $b > 1$, the exponential function f with $f(x) = ab^x$ is increasing on the set $(-\infty, \infty)$ of all real numbers.

118

LESSON MASTER 2-7

Questions on SPUR Objectives
See pages 142–145 for objectives.

Skills Objective B

In 1 and 2, rewrite the expression without using "+" or "−".

1. 5^{1-x} $\frac{5}{5^x}$ 2. e^{x+y} $e^x \cdot e^y$

Properties Objective D

3. Contrast the end behavior of $f: x \to 2^x$ with that of $g: x \to 2^{-x}$.
$\lim_{x\to\infty} f(x) = \infty$ but $\lim_{x\to\infty} g(x) = 0$; $\lim_{x\to-\infty} f(x) = 0$ but $\lim_{x\to\infty} g(x) = \infty$

Uses Objective E

In 4–6, use the following table, which shows the GDP (gross domestic product) of the U.S. from 1992 to 1996 in billions of dollars.

Year	1992	1993	1994	1995	1996
GDP	6,038.5	6,343.3	6,736.1	7,265.4	7,636.0

4. Find the formula predicting the GDP of the United States x years after 1992, assuming a discrete model and an annual growth rate of 5.1%.
$y = 6038.5(1 + 0.051)^x$

5. Calculate the GDP predicted by the formula in Question 4 for
a. 1993. 6346.5 b. 1994. 6670.1 c. 1995. 7010.3 d. 1996. 7367.8
e. Compare the predicted GDP and the actual GDP between 1993 and 1996. How accurate is the formula for the prediction?
The predicted GDP for each year is several hundred billions less than the actual GDP

6. Use the formula in Question 4 to predict the GDP of the United States in the year 2000. $8989.8 billions

Optional Activities

Activity 1 Technology Connection
Materials: Explorations software

Exploration 2-7, Exponential Functions, may be used as an alternative to Example 2 on page 121. An exponential function, $f(x) = ab^x$, is defined by choosing values for a and b. The graphs of $f(x)$ and its reflection image over the y-axis are shown. By changing the x-coordinate of a point P, changes to P and its image are observed.

Activity 2 After completing the lesson, you might ask students to compare the value of $\frac{1}{0!} + \frac{1}{1!} + \frac{1}{2!} + \frac{1}{3!} + \ldots + \frac{1}{n!}$ with the value of $\left(1 + \frac{1}{n}\right)^n$ for various values of n. Then ask, for a given value of n, which formula provides a better approximation for e. $\left[\frac{1}{0!} + \frac{1}{1!} + \frac{1}{2!} + \frac{1}{3!} + \ldots + \frac{1}{n!}\right]$

Proof

We are given f with $f(x) = ab^x$, $a > 0$, and $b > 1$. We need to prove that if $x_1 < x_2$, then $f(x_1) < f(x_2)$. Notice how the three properties on page 118 and the given information are used in the proof argument.

1. $x_1 < x_2$ is given. Thus $x_2 - x_1 > 0$ by the Addition Property of Inequality.
2. $b > 1$ is given. Thus $b^{x_2 - x_1} > 1$ by property (2).
3. From a law of exponents you learned years ago, $b^{x_2 - x_1} = \frac{b^{x_2}}{b^{x_1}}$. Substituting in Step 2,
$$\frac{b^{x_2}}{b^{x_1}} > 1.$$
4. Now b^{x_1} is positive by property (1). Multiplying both sides by b^{x_1},
$$b^{x_2} > b^{x_1}.$$
5. Finally, $a > 0$ is given. Thus,
$$ab^{x_2} > ab^{x_1},$$
which means $f(x_1) < f(x_2)$. This was to be proved.

In the Questions for this lesson, you are asked to modify the proof of the preceding theorem to show that if the base b is between 0 and 1 and if a is a positive real number, then the exponential function f with $f(x) = ab^x$ is a decreasing function on the set $(-\infty, \infty)$ of real numbers.

End Behavior

In Lesson 2-4 we noted the end behavior of $y = 2^x$. The end behavior of all exponential functions with base $b > 1$ and $a > 0$ is similar.

$$\lim_{x \to \infty} b^x = \infty \quad \text{and} \quad \lim_{x \to -\infty} b^x = 0 \quad \text{for } b > 1.$$

In the Questions, you are asked to consider the end behavior of $y = b^x$ when $b < 1$.

Maxima or Minima

The values of $f(x) = ab^x$ with positive bases b are positive if $a > 0$ and negative if $a < 0$. This fact, combined with their end behavior, shows that the range of exponential functions $f(x) = ab^x$ is the set of positive real numbers if $a > 0$, and the set of negative real numbers if $a < 0$. Since exponential functions are either increasing or decreasing, their minimum value on a finite closed interval will always be at one end of the interval, their maximum value at the other end. However, they have no maxima or minima over the set of *all* real numbers.

Three bases are more commonly used than any others. Base 2 is found in computer science applications. Base 10 is the foundation of our decimal system and scientific notation. The irrational base $e = \lim_{x \to \infty} \left(1 + \frac{1}{x}\right)^x = 2.718281828459045\ldots$ is the most commonly used base in calculus and its applications. The reason that e is so important is that, as x increases, the values of $y = e^x$ increase at a rate exactly equal to the value of the function. You will study this feature in more detail in Chapter 9.

Activity 3 You might use this activity after discussing the lesson. Explain that $\lim_{n \to \infty} \left(1 + \frac{1}{n}\right)^n$ and $\lim_{n \to -\infty} \left(1 + \frac{1}{n}\right)^n$ can be explored using a calculator, as the table at the right shows. Ask students how large n must be before $\left(1 + \frac{1}{n}\right)^n$ is within .0001 of e. [$n \geq 13591$ or $n \leq -13593$]

n	$\left(1 + \frac{1}{n}\right)^n$	$\approx e$
10	1.1^{10}	≈ 2.5937
-10	0.9^{-10}	≈ 2.8680
100	1.01^{100}	≈ 2.7048
-100	0.99^{-100}	≈ 2.7320
1000	1.001^{1000}	≈ 2.7169
-1000	0.999^{-1000}	≈ 2.7196

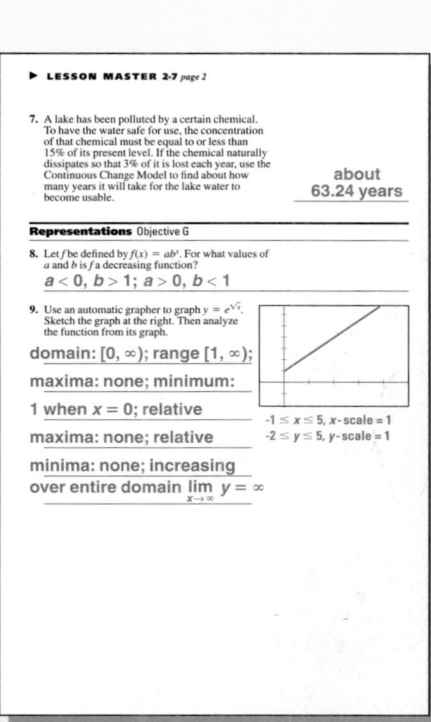

▶ **LESSON MASTER 2-7** *page 2*

7. A lake has been polluted by a certain chemical. To have the water safe for use, the concentration of that chemical must be equal to or less than 15% of its present level. If the chemical naturally dissipates so that 3% of it is lost each year, use the Continuous Change Model to find about how many years it will take for the lake water to become usable. about 63.24 years

Representations Objective G

8. Let f be defined by $f(x) = ab^x$. For what values of a and b is f a decreasing function?
$a < 0, b > 1; a > 0, b < 1$

9. Use an automatic grapher to graph $y = e^{\sqrt{x}}$. Sketch the graph at the right. Then analyze the function from its graph.
domain: $[0, \infty)$; range $[1, \infty)$; maxima: none; minimum: 1 when $x = 0$; relative maxima: none; relative minima: none; increasing over entire domain $\lim_{x \to \infty} y = \infty$

$-1 \leq x \leq 5$, x-scale = 1
$-2 \leq y \leq 5$, y-scale = 1

❷ Students who have studied from UCSMP *Advanced Algebra* or *Functions, Statistics, and Trigonometry* should be familiar with the Continuous Change Model. Remind students that in the Continuous Change Model, a value for r that is greater than 1 is synonymous with growth. A value for r that is less than 1 is synonymous with decay.

You can use the fact that $\lim_{x \to 0} (1 + h)^{\frac{1}{h}} = e$ to show that the Continuous Change Model is the limit of what you get if you invested something at compound interest as the number n of compounding periods goes to infinity. If a principle B is invested at an annual rate r, then the amount $A(t)$ after t years is given by the formula $A(t) = B(1 + \frac{r}{n})^{nt} = B\left((1 + \frac{r}{n})^{\frac{n}{r}}\right)^{rt}$ which approaches Be^{rt} as $n \to \infty$.

Additional Examples

1. In this lesson it is asserted that if $b > 0$, then $b^x > 0$ ∀ real numbers x. The general proof is beyond the scope of this course, but the following case can be proved. Prove: If $b > 0$, then $b^2 > 0$.
   Multiply all sides by b. This does not change the sense of the inequality because b is positive.

Models

One of the most important applications of the number e occurs in the *Continuous Change Model.* You may have seen this use before in models of the growth of bacteria cultures, the decay of radioactive substances, and continuously compounded interest.

Continuous Change Model
If a quantity grows or decays continuously at a periodic rate r, the amount $A(t)$ after t periods is given by
$$A(t) = Be^{rt},$$
where $B = A(0)$.

In the case of continuous growth, r is positive. In the case of continuous decay, r is negative.

The requirement that the quantity increases or decreases *continuously* is important. When this is not satisfied, the model becomes only an approximation; the shorter the time between increments (or decrements) the better the approximation.

University of California, Los Angeles

Example 1

When Rhonda started high school, her parents gave her a certificate of deposit for \$5,000 to help pay her college expenses four years later. If the bank pays an annual rate of 5.9% compounded continuously, about how much will Rhonda have when starting college?

Solution

Because the investment is growing continuously, we can apply the Continuous Change Model. $A(t) = Be^{rt}$. In this case, $B = 5000$, $r = .059$, and $t = 4$. So the amount Rhonda will have four years later is

$$A(4) = 5000 \cdot e^{(.059)(4)}$$
$$\approx 6330.87.$$

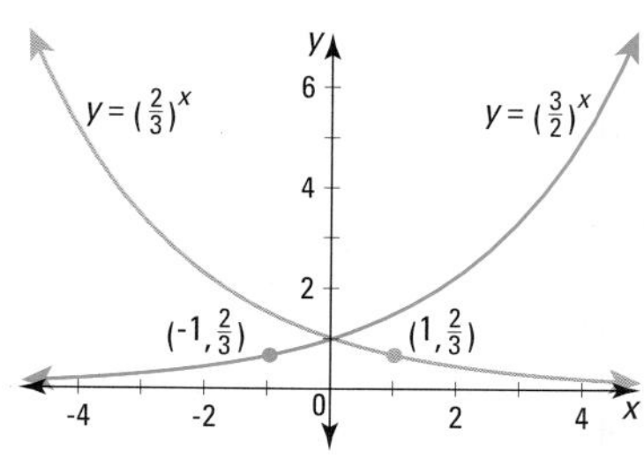

Properties

Many properties of exponential functions have been given in this lesson. Here is one related to the models. For every exponential growth function, there is an exponential decay function with a congruent graph. Specifically, the graphs of $f(x) = ab^x$ and $g(x) = a\left(\frac{1}{b}\right)^x$ are reflection images of each other over the y-axis. This relationship follows from the laws of exponents:

$$g(x) = \left(\tfrac{1}{b}\right)^x = (b^{-1})^x = b^{-x} = f(-x).$$

An example is pictured at the left with the graph of $y = \left(\frac{2}{3}\right)^x$. It is the reflection image of the graph of $y = \left(\frac{3}{2}\right)^x$ over the y-axis.

Adapting to Individual Needs

Extra Help

Be sure students are aware that rational exponents are not defined with negative bases. You might want to provide an example of some of the difficulties that would ensue should negative bases be allowed. Consider $(-2)^5$ and $(-2)^{\frac{10}{2}}$. It appears that these expressions should be equal since $5 = \frac{10}{2}$. But $(-2)^5 = -32$, while if $(-2)^{\frac{m}{n}}$ were to equal $\sqrt[n]{(-2)^m}$, then $(-2)^{\frac{10}{2}} = \sqrt{(-2)^{10}} = \sqrt{1024} = 32$.

Challenge

Have students prove the following. If $1 < b$, then $b^4 < b^6$. [Proof: $b < b^2$, $b^2 < b^3$, $b^3 < b^4$, $b^4 < b^5$, $b^5 < b^6$ by repeated multiplications of both sides by the positive number b. Thus, by transitivity of inequality, $b^4 < b^6$.]

Here is how you might summarize the analysis of exponential functions.

Example 2

Analyze the exponential function $f: x \rightarrow ab^x$ where $b > 1$ and $a > 0$.

Solution

Usual domain: set of real numbers.
Range: set of positive real numbers.
Maxima or minima: none.
Increasing or decreasing: increasing over its entire domain.
End behavior: $\lim_{x \to \infty} f(x) = \infty$; $\lim_{x \to -\infty} f(x) = 0$.
Model: growth and decay, compound interest. When b = e, the function models continuous growth.
Special properties: The graph of $g: x \rightarrow a\left(\frac{1}{b}\right)^x$ is the reflection image over the y-axis of the graph of f.

QUESTIONS

Covering the Reading

1. *Multiple choice.* Which of the following could be the graph of $y = .6^x$? b

(a)

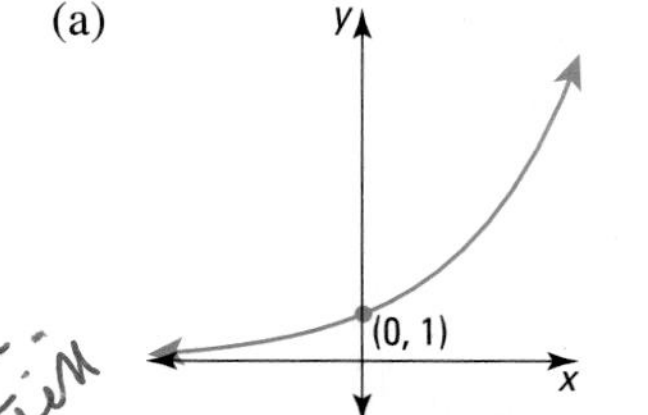

(b)

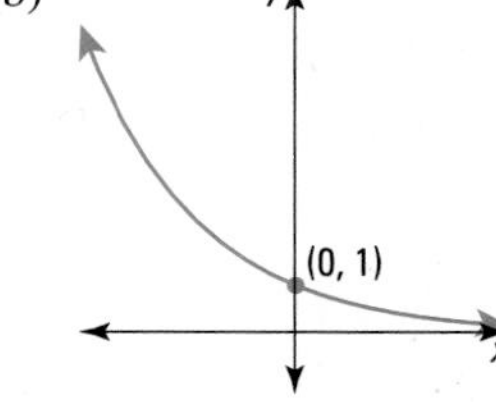

2. Consider the function f with equation $f(x) = 8(2.7)^x$.
   a. Give the domain of this function. the set of all real numbers
   b. What is its range? the set of positive real numbers
   c. Describe its end behavior. $\lim_{x \to \infty} f(x) = \infty$; $\lim_{x \to -\infty} f(x) = 0$

3. Give a formula for the exponential function determined by the geometric sequence 3, 9, 27, 81, 243, ... $f(x) = 3^x$ where x is a positive integer

4. Prove: For any real numbers a and b with $a > 0$ and $0 < b < 1$, the exponential function g with $g(x) = ab^x$ is decreasing on the set $(-\infty, \infty)$ of real numbers. See margin.

5. If a person puts \$5000 in a retirement account at age 30, paying an annual rate of 7% compounded continuously, how much will it grow to by retirement at age 62 if no additional deposits or withdrawals are made? \$46,966.66

6. a. *True or false.* $\exists$ real numbers x and y such that $x < y$ and $\left(\frac{3}{4}\right)^x < \left(\frac{3}{4}\right)^y$.
   b. Justify your answer to part **a.** See left.
   a) False

6b) Sample: It was proved in Question 4 that ab^x is decreasing on the set $(-\infty, \infty)$, if $0 < b < 1$ and $a > 0$, $\left(\frac{3}{4}\right)^x$ has this form, where $a = 1$ and $b = \frac{3}{4}$.

2. Suppose that shortly after Rhonda's birth, her parents decided to open a savings account for her with an initial principle that would ensure having \$50,000 for her college education 18 years later. Assuming that the account pays an annual interest rate of 6.5% compounded continuously, what must that initial deposit of principle be? Use the continuous rate of change model with $t = 18$, $r = .065$, and $A(t) = 50{,}000$. Thus $50{,}000 = Be^{(.065)(18)}$ or $50{,}000 = Be^{1.17}$. From this, $B = \frac{50000}{e^{1.17}} \approx 15{,}518.35$. Notice that to find B only a linear equation needs to be solved; the variable is not in the exponent.

Notes on Questions

Question 5 Consumer Connection You might ask students to set up equations whose solutions would answer the following questions. This will help motivate the need to solve exponential equations, discussed in Lesson 2-9.

1. If the annual rate is only 5%, what initial deposit is needed to provide the same balance at age 62? $[Be^{(.05 \cdot 32)} = 5000e^{(.07 \cdot 32)}]$
2. If the initial deposit is \$4000, what annual rate is needed to provide the same balance at age 62? $[4000e^{32r} = 5000e^{(.07 \cdot 32)}]$
3. If the initial deposit is \$6000, at what age will this person be able to retire with the same amount as the \$5000 deposit would have provided at age 62? $[6000e^{.07t} = 5000e^{(.07 \cdot 32)}]$

Additional Answers

4. Sample: $x_1 < x_2$ is given. Thus,

$x_2 - x_1 > 0$ by Addition Property of Inequality.

$b^{x_2 - x_1} < 1$ by property (3) on page 117.

$b^{x_2 - x_1} = \frac{b^{x_2}}{b^{x_1}}$ by basic laws of exponents.

So $\frac{b^{x_2}}{b^{x_1}} < 1$ by substitution.

Since $b^{x_1} > 0$ by property (1) on page 117, multiplication by b^{x_1} yields $b^{x_2} < b^{x_1}$. Since $a > 0$, $ab^{x_2} < ab^{x_1}$.

Notes on Questions

Question 9 Students may be interested in improving this model. One way is to create a table that shows the predicted value given by the model for each year, discuss why some of the discrepancies occur, and then work to come up with a better model.

Error Alert Be sure students understand how *t* is defined: In year *y*, $t = y - 1790$. The most common error is using the value of *y* itself, which results in function values that are far too large.

Questions 9–10 Multicultural Connection Governments have taken censuses for various reasons since ancient times. In China records dating back to 3000 B.C. show lists of households paying taxes. The Bible tells us that lists of military men among the Israelites were made as early as 1500 B.C. Registrations of people and property were also conducted in ancient Egypt, Persia, and Greece. However, the most complete of the ancient censuses were taken by the Romans for the purpose of taxation and military service. (The word *census* comes from the Latin meaning *to tax*.) The first census in the United States took place in 1790, as required by the constitution that had been ratified in 1787.

Question 12 Students who have studied *Functions, Statistics, and Trigonometry* should be familiar with this function.

Question 17 Another name for arithmetic sequence is *linear sequence.*

7a)

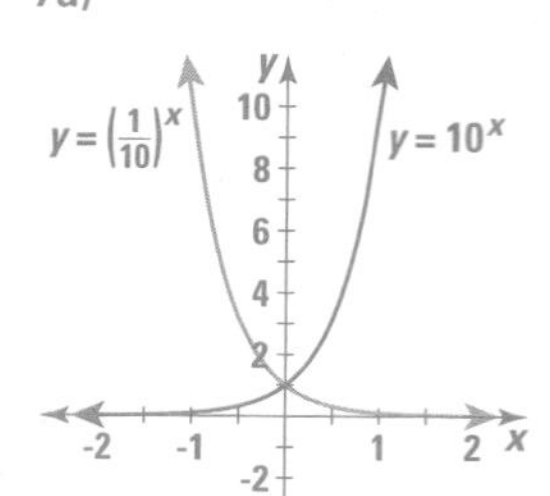

9c) The formula is a reasonably accurate predictor of the population for the period from 1790 to 1850.

10b) The values increase less rapidly than the data up to about 1860, but grow much more rapidly after about 1890. The values produced by the continuous model always exceed those produced by the discrete model.

7. a. Sketch the graphs of $f: x \to 10^x$ and $g: x \to \left(\frac{1}{10}\right)^x$ on the same axes. a) See left.

b. How are the graphs related? The graphs are reflection images of each other over the *y*-axis.

8. Analyze the exponential function $g: x \to ab^x$ with $0 < b < 1$, and $a > 0$, following the form of Example 2. See margin.

Applying the Mathematics

In Questions 9 and 10, use the following table, which lists the population of the United States at each 10-year census between 1790 and 1990 (in millions).

Year	Pop.	Year	Pop.	Year	Pop.
1790	3.93	1860	31.44	1930	122.78
1800	5.31	1870	39.82	1940	131.67
1810	7.24	1880	50.16	1950	150.70
1820	9.64	1890	62.95	1960	179.32
1830	12.87	1900	76.00	1970	203.30
1840	17.07	1910	91.97	1980	226.54
1850	23.19	1920	105.71	1990	248.72

9. a. Use the Continuous Change Model to obtain a formula for the population $P(t)$ of the United States t years after 1790, based on an annual growth rate of 2.9655%. $P(t) = (3.93)(e^{.029655t})$

b. Compute the predicted population of the United States for the year 2000 based on the formula for $P(t)$ obtained in part **a.** 1990.6 million

c. Calculate the population predicted by the formula $P(t)$ in part **a** for the given years. i) 23.29 million ii) 102.59 million

i. 1850 **ii.** 1900 **iii.** 1950 451.89 million

For which period is the formula obtained in part **a** a reasonably accurate predictor of the actual population of the United States? See left.

10. a. Write a formula for the United States population P_n n years after 1790 based on an annual growth rate of 2.9655%. $P_n = 3.93\,(1.029655)^n$

b. Use a calculator to compare the predictions of this discrete model with the continuous model in Question 9 and with the data in the table. See left.

11. One of the best examples of continuous decrease in nature is radioactive decay. The radioactive isotope Cesium 137, sometimes used to treat tumors, disintegrates at the annual rate of .0227. If an amount of Cesium 137 were used to treat a child's tumor, how much of it would be present 50 years later? ≈ 32% of the original amount

12. The **standard normal distribution** in statistics is described by a bell-shaped curve whose equation is

$$y = \frac{1}{\sqrt{2\pi}} e^{-x^2/2}$$

a. On what interval(s) is the function increasing? decreasing? See below.

b. Find any maxima or minima. See below.

c. Describe the apparent end behavior. $\lim_{x \to \pm\infty} f(x) = 0$

d. Estimate the range.

$0 < y \le \frac{1}{\sqrt{2\pi}}$

a) increasing: $(-\infty, 0]$; decreasing: $[0, \infty)$

b) relative maximum: $\frac{1}{\sqrt{2\pi}}$

122

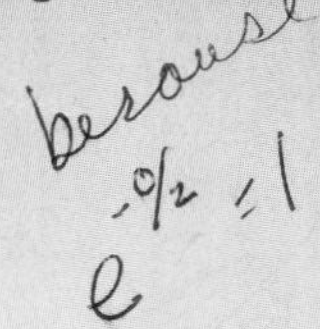

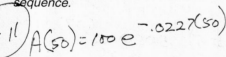

Additional Answers

8. Domain: set of real numbers
Range: set of positive real numbers
Maxima and minima: none
Increasing or decreasing: decreasing over its entire domain
End behavior: $\lim_{x \to \infty} g(x) = 0$
$\lim_{x \to -\infty} g(x) = \infty$
Model: decay
Special properties: Values of the function are related by the laws of exponents.

Review

13. Give the exact value.
a. $\sin 30°$ $\frac{1}{2}$
b. $\cos \frac{7\pi}{6}$ $-\frac{\sqrt{3}}{2}$
c. $\sin -\frac{5\pi}{4}$ $\frac{\sqrt{2}}{2}$
d. $\tan -\frac{5\pi}{4}$ -1
(Lesson 2-6)

14. Consider the function f with $f(x) = \sin^2 x$.
a. What is its domain? **the set of real numbers**
b. What is its range? $0 \le y \le 1$
c. In the interval $[0, 2\pi]$, at what point(s) does f reach its maximum value? **See left.**
d. What is its end behavior? *(Lessons 2-2, 2-4, 2-6)* **no limit**

14c) $\frac{\pi}{2}, \frac{3\pi}{2}$

15. Use a calculator to conjecture a value for $\lim_{x \to 0} \frac{\sin x}{x}$ where x is in radians. *(Lessons 2-4, 2-6)* **1**

Step Right Up. *The heights of equally spaced steps form an arithmetic sequence.*

16. Determine when the function f with $f(x) = x^3 + 3x^2 - 2x - 4$ is increasing. *(Lesson 2-3)* $x \le -2.29, x \ge 0.29$

17. Recall that an **arithmetic sequence** is a sequence in which the difference between consecutive terms is constant. If the first two terms of an arithmetic sequence are 4 and 8, what are the next five terms of this sequence? *(Previous course)* **12, 16, 20, 24, 28**

18. Recall that a **geometric** or **exponential sequence** is a sequence in which the ratio of consecutive terms is constant. Write the first five terms of the geometric sequence defined by $g_n = 4(.8)^{n-1}$ for $n \ge 1$. *(Previous course)*

4, 3.2, 2.56, 2.048, 1.6384

Exploration

19. Suppose g and h are exponential functions with different bases. For all x, let

$$f_1(x) = g(x) + h(x)$$
$$f_2(x) = g(x) - h(x)$$

$$f_3(x) = g(x) \cdot h(x)$$
$$f_4(x) = \frac{g(x)}{h(x)}.$$

Which of the functions $f_1, f_2, f_3,$ and f_4 (if any) are exponential functions? Explain why or why not.

Sample:
$f_1(x)$ is not necessarily exponential (if $f_1(x) = b^x + c^x$, where $b = 2$ and $c = .5$, then $f_1(-x) = f(x)$, which is not possible for an exponential function).
$f_2(x)$ is not necessarily exponential (if $f_2(x) = b^x - c^x$, where $b = 2$ and $c = .5$, then $f_2(-x) = -f_2(x)$, which is not possible for an exponential function).
$f_3(x)$ is not necessarily exponential ($f_3(x) = b^x \cdot c^x$ where $c = \frac{1}{b} \to f_3(x) = 1\ \forall x$).
$f_4(x)$ is always exponential, since there is no function $f_4(x) = \frac{b^x}{c^x}$ with $b \ne c$ such that $\left(\frac{b}{c}\right)^x = 1$.

Follow-up for Lesson 2-7

Practice

For more questions on SPUR Objectives, use **Lesson Master 2-7** (shown on pages 118–119).

Assessment

Quiz A quiz covering Lesson 2-5 through 2-7 is provided in the *Assessment Sourcebook.*

Extension

Refer students to **Question 5.** Ask them to determine graphically how long it will take the money in the account to:
1. Double [≈ 9.9 years]
2. Triple [≈ 15.7 years]
3. Quadruple. [≈ 19.8 years]

Then ask students if they think it's true that the length of time it will take the money to double will always be exactly twice the amount of time it will take the money to quadruple. [It is true and can be proven with log properties.
Suppose $Be^{rt_1} = 2B$ and $Be^{rt_2} = 4B$. Then $e^{rt_1} = 2$ and $e^{rt_2} = 4$, so $e^{rt_2} = (e^{rt_1})^2 = e^{2rt_1}$. Taking the natural logarithm of each side, $rt_2 = 2rt_1$, from which $t_2 = 2t_1$.]

Project Update Project 1, *Savings Plans,* on page 137, relates to the content of this lesson.

Setting Up Lesson 2-8

Discuss **Questions 17–18** to review some of the language and symbolism of sequences.

Lesson 2-8

Objectives

D Determine the end behavior of a sequence.
E Use sequences and exponential functions as models.
G Analyze a sequence from its graph.

Resources

From the ***Teacher's Resource File***
- Lesson Master 2-8
- Answer Master 2-8
- Teaching Aids
  14: Warm-up
  24: Tables from the Lesson

Additional Resources
- Visuals for Teaching Aid 14, 24

Teaching Lesson 2-8

Warm-up

Give an explicit formula and a recursive formula for each sequence.

1. The arithmetic sequence 2000, 2001, 2002, 2003, ...
   Explicit formula: $a_n = n + 1999$; **recursive formula:** $a_1 = 2000$, $a_{n+1} = a_n + 1$ for all $n \geq 2$
2. The geometric sequence 5, 4.5, 4.05, ...
   Explicit formula: $g_n = 5(.9)^{n-1}$; **recursive formula:** $g_1 = 5$, $g_{n+1} = .9g_n$ for all $n \geq 2$

LESSON

2-8 Sequences and Logistic Functions

Fishing Logistics. *These baby black bullheads, a variety of catfish, may weigh over two pounds as adults. Their population will grow exponentially for a period of time. See Example 2.*

Among the most common discrete functions are *sequences.* A **sequence** is a function whose domain is the interval of integers $[a, \infty)$, in which case the sequence is an **infinite sequence,** or the interval of integers $[a, b]$, in which case the sequence is a **finite sequence.**

You may wonder why a sequence can be thought of as a function. Remember that a function is a correspondence from one set A to another. For sequences, the domain set A is very often the set of positive integers $\{1, 2, 3, 4, \ldots\}$. We identify that set as the domain of the sequence when we say "1st term, 2nd term, 3rd term, 4th term, . . . " or when we write $a_1, a_2, a_3, a_4, \ldots$. That is, the ***n*th term** a_n of a sequence is the term that corresponds to the number n.

For example, consider the sequence 5, 8, 11, 14, . . . , in which each term is 3 more than the previous. In this sequence, $a_1 = 5$, $a_2 = 8$, $a_3 = 11$, $a_4 = 14$, and so on. We can define this sequence algebraically either by the *explicit formula*

$$a_n = 3n + 2,$$

❶ or by the *recursive formula*

$$\begin{cases} a_1 = 5 & \text{(initial condition)} \\ a_{n+1} = a_n + 3. & \text{(difference equation or recurrence relation)} \end{cases}$$

Notice that a recursive formula has two parts: the **initial conditions,** which give the first or first few terms of the sequence, and a **difference equation** or **recurrence relation,** which tells how the next ("n plus first") term of the sequence can be determined from preceding terms. The term "difference equation" arises from the ability to write $a_{n+1} = a_n + 3$ as the difference $a_{n+1} - a_n = 3$, but in more complicated sequences you may not see the

124

Lesson 2-8 Overview

Broad Goals This lesson reviews explicit and recursive formulas for sequences from previous UCSMP courses. The new content is the notion of a difference equation and the example of a logistic model.

Perspective We assume that students have studied arithmetic (linear) and geometric (exponential) sequences before, and have seen both explicit and recursive definitions. So the first three paragraphs of this lesson is expected to be review. We also assume students have seen the Fibonacci sequence.

A logistic curve is one that has a shape roughly like a severely distorted *S*, with its left part nearly exponential and its right part approaching a limit. Such curves occur when there are limits to growth, as in the population example of the lesson. Another example of a logistic curve is in the expected score on a test after studying a certain amount of time: the first hours of study would be expected to give greater growth than later hours, and there is a limit to the top test score that can be attained.

Arithmetic and geometric sequences can be defined in terms of difference equations: An arithmetic sequence a is one in which $\exists$ a real number k such that $\forall n$, $a_{n+1} - a_n = k$. A geometric sequence g is one in which $\exists$ a real number k such that $\forall n$, $\frac{g_{n+1}}{g_n} = k$.

see the subtraction. For example, the **Fibonacci sequence** (named after Leonardo of Pisa, also known as Fibonacci, a great mathematician of the early 13th century) is the infinite sequence 1, 1, 2, 3, 5, 8, 13, 21, . . . , in which each term is the sum of the two previous terms, and in which the first two terms both equal 1:

$$\begin{cases} a_1 &= 1 \\ a_2 &= 1 \\ a_{n+1} &= a_n + a_{n-1} \quad \forall \text{ integers } n \geq 2. \end{cases}$$

If a sequence is defined by a difference equation and the first few terms of the sequence, then additional terms of the sequence can be calculated in succession up to any desired term. For example, the difference equation for the Fibonacci sequence generates additional terms from the initial conditions $a_1 = 1$, $a_2 = 1$ as follows:

$$\begin{aligned} a_3 &= a_2 + a_1 = 1 + 1 = 2, \\ a_4 &= a_3 + a_2 = 2 + 1 = 3, \\ a_5 &= a_4 + a_3 = 3 + 2 = 5, \\ a_6 &= a_5 + a_4 = 5 + 3 = 8, \end{aligned}$$

and so on. However, to calculate the 50th term a_{50} of the Fibonacci sequence by using its difference equation, it would be necessary to continue the series of calculations above to obtain

$$a_7, a_8, a_9, \ldots, a_{48}, a_{49}, \text{ and finally, } a_{50}.$$

On the other hand, if we had an explicit formula for the Fibonacci sequence, we could use it to calculate a_{50} directly, without first computing $a_3, a_4, \ldots, a_{49}$. An explicit formula for the Fibonacci sequence is not obvious from its definition; however, we will find an explicit formula for this sequence later in this course by using limits.

Example 1

Find an explicit formula and a difference equation for the general geometric or exponential sequence

$$g = \{b, br, br^2, br^3, \ldots\}$$

with first term *b* and constant ratio *r*.

Solution

If the domain of *g* is the interval of integers $[0, \infty)$, then an explicit formula for *g* is

$$g_n = br^n, \quad \forall \text{ integers } n \geq 0$$

because

$$g_0 = br^0 = b,\ g_1 = br^1,\ g_2 = br^2,\ g_3 = br^3, \text{ and so on.}$$

Each term of *g* after the first is *r* times the preceding term. Consequently, a difference equation for *g* is:

$$g_{n+1} = rg_n \quad \forall \text{ integers } n \geq 0.$$

The following example shows how sequences defined by difference equations can be used to analyze population growth.

Notes on Reading

Students who have studied from UCSMP *Advanced Algebra* or *Functions, Statistics, and Trigonometry* will have seen recursive definitions for sequences and will be familiar with the language and notation used here. They even will have seen programs for generating sequences using either kind of definition. In Chapter 7, we use mathematical induction to establish that certain sequences have certain recursive formulas.

For other students, recursion may be a new idea. You may wish to define a few arithmetic and geometric sequences both explicitly and recursively. Discuss commonalties and differences in these definitions. Point out that the explicit definition is preferable if one needs the thousandth term of a sequence. Also mention that some sequences are much more easily defined recursively than explicitly. The Fibonacci sequence is an example.

❶ In this recursive formula for the sequence, the sentence $a_{n+1} = a_n + 3$ is a *recurrence relation.* It defines the next term of the sequence using previous terms. The equivalent sentence $a_{n+1} - a_n = 3$ is a *difference equation.* It shows the difference between two consecutive terms.

Why do we say that a sequence is a function? The sequence 5, 8, 11, 14, ... can be thought of as an ordered set. To describe the order, we say the first term is 5; the second term is 8; the third term is 11; ... ; the *n*th term is $3n + 2$. From this there is a natural correspondence $1 \to 5$, $2 \to 8$, $3 \to 11$, with the general rule $n \to 3n + 2$. That correspondence, whose domain is the set of positive integers, is a function, and the original ordered set of numbers is seen to contain the range elements of the function. Another example of the sequence of Fibonacci numbers 1, 1, 2, 3, 5, 8, 13, ... is the ordered set of *y*-coordinates of the function (1, 1), (2, 1), (3, 2), (4, 3), (5, 5), (6, 8), (7, 13), ...

Optional Activities

As you discuss **Questions 3–5,** you may wish to ask students to give a recursive definition for each sequence.

[3. $a_2 = 2$; $a_{n+1} = \left(\frac{n^2-1}{n^2}\right)a_n$ for all $n > 2$
4. $a_1 = 3$; $a_{n+1} = 3a_n$ for all $n > 1$
5. $a_0 = 3$, $a_{n+1} = -2a_n$ for all $n > 0$]

Adapting to Individual Needs

Extra Help

Be sure students note whether the first of the list of terms of a sequence is indicated with a subscript of 0 or 1. Point out, for example, that in the discussion of the Fibonacci sequence, a_1 refers to the first term. However, in **Example 2,** P_0 is used to indicate the first term so that P_n denotes the *n*th year population. Thus, P_n is actually the $n + 1$st term of the sequence.

Tiger Shovelnose catfish

Example 2

An artificial lake is to be stocked with catfish to provide recreational fishing. With ample food and without fishing or disease, the catfish population will grow about 20% each year. On the basis of the size and the condition of this lake, a representative for the Fish and Game Commission estimates that the lake can support a maximum of about 30,000 catfish. If the lake is initially stocked with 2000 fish, analyze the growth of the catfish population in the lake.

Solution

Suppose that P_n is the number of catfish in the lake at the end of the nth year. We are given that $P_0 = 2000$. Under ideal growth conditions, with a 20% growth rate, the population is given by the difference equation

P_{n+1}	$=$	P_n	$+$	$.20P_n$	$= (1.2)P_n, \quad \forall$ integers $n \geq 0$.
$(n+1)$st year population		nth year population		population growth in $(n+1)$st year	

This difference equation, together with the information that $P_0 = 2000$, indicates that the sequence P of successive annual catfish populations in the lake is a geometric sequence with first term $P_0 = 2000$ and common ratio 1.2. Therefore, using the explicit formula for a geometric sequence,

$$P_n = 2000\,(1.2)^n, \quad \forall \text{ integers } n \geq 0.$$

These tables were produced by a calculator with the sequence $U_n = 2000\,(1.2)^n$.

n	U_n	n	U_n	n	U_n
0	2000	7	7166	14	25678
1	2400	8	8600	15	30814
2	2880	9	10320	16	36977
3	3456	10	12383	17	44372
4	4147	11	14860	18	53247
5	4977	12	17832	19	63896
6	5972	13	21399	20	76675

The model in Example 2 is clearly unrealistic in the long term because it predicts that, during the 15th year, the fish population will exceed the 30,000 fish support limit of the lake and yet will continue to grow each following year by ever increasing amounts.

One way to incorporate the fish support limit of the lake into the model is to modify the difference equation,

$$P_{n+1} = P_n + .2P_n,$$

by multiplying the growth term, $.2P_n$, by a factor that is nearly 1 for small values of P_n, and that decreases to 0 as P_n gets close to the 30,000 fish support limit of the lake. Such a factor is $\left(\frac{30{,}000 - P_n}{30{,}000}\right)$, so the modified difference equation is:

$$\begin{aligned} P_{n+1} &= P_n + .2P_n\left(\frac{30{,}000 - P_n}{30{,}000}\right) \\ &= (1.2)P_n - \frac{.2}{30{,}000}P_n^{\,2}. \end{aligned}$$

In some books, the sequence with rule $s_n = \ldots$ is called $\{s_n\}$. We prefer the single letter s because it is a simple extension of function notation. While the geometric sequence g with first term 2 and constant factor 0.9 could be written as $g(n) = 2(0.9)^{n-1}$, writing $g_n = 2(0.9)^{n-1}$ is more customary. Were we to write it as $g(n)$ ..., then we would call the sequence g, so why not do so even though we use g_n?

In many books, the domain of a sequence is restricted to the set of positive integers or the set of integers from 1 to n. In this book we allow any set of integers from a to b to be the domain of a sequence. In Chapter 7 we apply mathematical induction to statements whose domain is any set of integers greater than or equal to a given number, and our definition of sequences does not have to be changed for that broader use.

Teaching Aid 24 contains the tables on pages 126–128.

Example 2 Error Alert Students often use the incorrect common ratio in growth situations. As you discuss this example, be sure students understand that the 20% growth rate leads to the explicit formula $P_n = 2000(1.2)^n$, not $P_n = 2000(.2)^n$.

❷ Remind students that in $\lim\limits_{n\to\infty} 2^n = \infty$, the symbol ∞ does not represent a number, but the idea that 2^n can take on values larger than any number we might think of.

LESSON MASTER 2-8

Questions on SPUR Objectives
See pages 142–145 for objectives.

Properties Objective D

1. Find $\lim\limits_{n\to\infty} a_n$ if $\begin{cases} a_1 = -5 \\ a_{k+1} = \frac{a_k}{4} \;\forall\, k \geq 1 \end{cases}$. **0**

2. Let $\begin{cases} c_1 = 3 \\ c_{k+1} = \frac{1}{3}c_k \;\forall\, k \geq 1 \end{cases}$.
   a. What is the limit of c_n as $n \to \infty$? **0**
   b. For what values of n is c_n within 0.001 of the limit? **$n \geq 9$**

3. Use limit notation to describe and then find the limit of $S_n = \left(-\frac{4}{5}\right)^{2n+1}$ as n increases without bound.
   $\lim\limits_{n\to\infty} S_n = \lim\limits_{n\to\infty}\left(-\frac{4}{5}\right)^{2n+1} = 0$

Uses Objective E

4. Square $ABCD$ has sides of length a. A_1, B_1, C_1, and D_1 are the midpoints of $\overline{AB}$, $\overline{BC}$, $\overline{CD}$, and $\overline{DA}$, respectively. Also, from $n \geq 2$, A_n, B_n, C_n, and D_n, are the midpoints of $\overline{A_{n-1}B_{n-1}}$, $\overline{B_{n-1}C_{n-1}}$, $\overline{C_{n-1}D_{n-1}}$, and $\overline{D_{n-1}A_{n-1}}$, respectively. Let S_n be the area of square $A_nB_nC_nD_n$.

   a. Find S_1. **$S_1 = \frac{1}{2}a^2$**
   b. Give an equation relating S_n and S_{n-1}. **$S_n = \frac{1}{2}S_{n-1}$**
   c. Find $\lim\limits_{x\to\infty} S_n$ and explain what it means.
   $\lim\limits_{n\to\infty} S_n = 0$; this means that the squares approach the point at the center of $ABCD$.

Adapting to Individual Needs

Challenge

Give these problems to students.

Suppose $p_1 = 1$, $q_1 = 2$, $p_{n+1} = q_n + 3$ and $q_{n+1} = p_n + 4$ for all $n \geq 2$.

1. Give the first six values of each of the sequences p and q. [The sequence p begins 1, 5, 8, 12, 15, 19, ... The sequence q begins 2, 5, 9, 12, 16, 19, ...]
2. An explicit formula for each sequence can be found with the help of the expression $0.25(-1)^n$. Find such a formula. [$p_n = 3.5n - 2.25 + 0.25(-1)^n$; $q_n = 3.5n - 1.75 - 0.25(-1)^n$]
3. Use the explicit formulas to prove that $p_n = q_n$ for all even positive integers n. [Work backwards from $p_n = q_n$ to see where the proof should start. When n is even, $(-1)^n = 1$. So $2 \cdot (-1)^n = 2$. Consequently, $(-1)^n = 2 - (-1)^n$. Add -9

If this sequence is entered in a calculator as

$$U_n = 1.2 \cdot U_{n-1} - \left(\frac{.2}{30{,}000}\right)U_{n-1}^{\ 2}$$

and $U_0 = 2000$, the following table of fish populations is produced.

n	U_n	n	U_n	n	U_n	n	U_n
0	2000	7	6250	14	15,165	21	24,393
1	2373	8	7239	15	16,665	22	25,305
2	2810	9	8338	16	18,146	23	26,097
3	3320	10	9542	17	19,580	24	26,776
4	3910	11	10,843	18	20,941	25	27,352
5	4591	12	12,228	19	22,205	26	27,835
6	5368	13	13,677	20	23,359	27	28,236

Notice that this model predicts that the lake's fish population grows with increasing rapidity for the first 15 years. The population continues to grow after that but the rate of growth decreases.

The first crude model of the growth of the fish population,

$$P_{n+1} = (1.2)P_n \qquad P_0 = 2000,$$

is an example of an exponential growth model, while the second model,

$$P_{n+1} = (1.2)P_n - \frac{.2}{30{,}000}P_n^{\ 2} \qquad P_0 = 2000,$$

is an example of a *logistic* or *limited growth model*.

Notice that the statement of the lake stocking situation led quite naturally to the difference equations for the two models that we developed. For the exponential model, it was easy to proceed to an explicit formula

$$P_n = 2000(1.2)^n \qquad \forall\ n \geq 0$$

for the fish population sequence P because P is a geometric sequence. However, an explicit formula for the logistic model is not as easily obtained from the difference equation. The process of developing an explicit formula for a sequence from a difference equation for that sequence is often referred to as **solving the difference equation.**

❷ Limits of Sequences

An infinite sequence s is a discrete function with an interval $[a, \infty)$ of integers as its domain. Thus, it makes sense to talk about only one type of end behavior for a sequence s, the behavior of s_n as $n \to \infty$. We use the symbol

$$\lim_{n\to\infty} s_n,$$

read "the limit of s-sub-n as n approaches infinity," to describe this end behavior. For example, when $s_n = \frac{1}{n}$, $\lim_{n\to\infty} s_n = \lim_{n\to\infty} \frac{1}{n} = 0$, because the value of $\frac{1}{n}$ approaches 0 as the positive integer n increases without bound. On the other hand, when $s_n = 2^n$, $\lim_{n\to\infty} s_n = \lim_{n\to\infty} 2^n = \infty$ because the value of 2^n increases without bound as n gets larger and larger.

Additional Examples

1. Give a table and sketch the graph of the sequence b defined by the rule $b_n = \frac{n+1}{n}$ $\forall$ positive integers n. What is the limit of this sequence as $n \to \infty$?

n	$b_n = \frac{n+1}{n}$
1	2
2	$\frac{3}{2} = 1.5$
3	$\frac{4}{3} = 1.33$
4	$\frac{5}{4} = 1.25$
5	$\frac{6}{5} = 1.2$
6	$\frac{7}{6} \approx 1.17$
7	$\frac{8}{7} \approx 1.14$

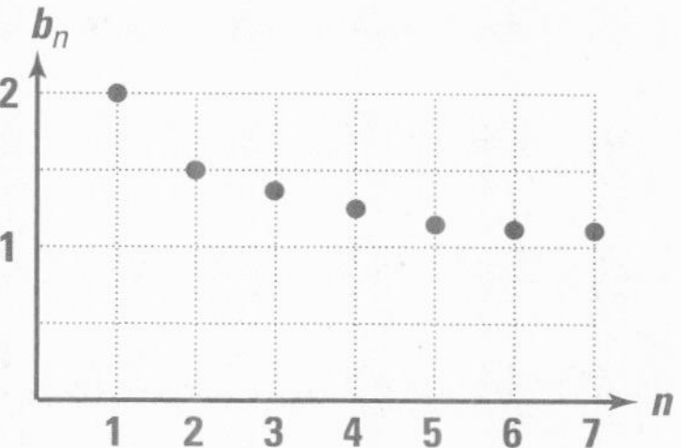

The limit seems to be 1.

(Additional Examples continue on page 128.)

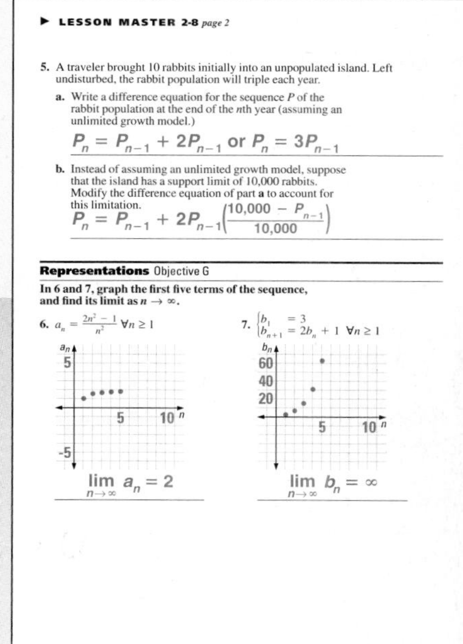

▶ **LESSON MASTER 2-8** *page 2*

5. A traveler brought 10 rabbits initially into an unpopulated island. Left undisturbed, the rabbit population will triple each year.
   a. Write a difference equation for the sequence P of the rabbit population at the end of the nth year (assuming an unlimited growth model.)
   $P_n = P_{n-1} + 2P_{n-1}$ or $P_n = 3P_{n-1}$
   b. Instead of assuming an unlimited growth model, suppose that the island has a support limit of 10,000 rabbits. Modify the difference equation of part **a** to account for this limitation.
   $P_n = P_{n-1} + 2P_{n-1}\left(\frac{10{,}000 - P_{n-1}}{10{,}000}\right)$

Representations Objective G

In 6 and 7, graph the first five terms of the sequence, and find its limit as $n \to \infty$.

6. $a_n = \frac{2n^2 - 1}{n^2}$ $\forall n \geq 1$

$\lim_{n\to\infty} a_n = 2$

7. $\begin{cases} b_1 = 3 \\ b_{n+1} = 2b_n + 1 \ \forall n \geq 1 \end{cases}$

$\lim_{n\to\infty} b_n = \infty$

to each side to get $-9 + (-1)^n = -7 - (-1)^n$. Divide both sides by 4 to obtain $-2.25 + 0.25(-1)^n = -1.75 - 0.25(-1)^n$. Add $3.5n$ to each side and $p_n = q_n$.]

2. The deer population in a certain reserve grows about 12% a year under normal conditions and no hunting. Let D_n be the deer population n years from now.
   a. Under this assumption, if there are 900 deer now, give a formula for D_n.
   $D_n = 900(1.12)^n$
   b. About how many deer will there be 10 years from now?
   $900(1.12)^{10} \approx 2795 \approx 2800$
   c. Consider the situation of **parts a and b** above, but create a logistic model using the additional assumption that there is a limit to the population of 4000 deer. How many deer will there be 10 years from now?
   The logistic model has $D_0 = 900$ and
   $D_{n+1} = 1.12D_n - \frac{.12}{4000} D_n^2$
   for all $n \geq 1$. From this, $D_{10} \approx 1941$.
   d. Find $\lim\limits_{n\to\infty} D_n$. 4000
3. Consider the situation of Additional Example 2c, but add a third assumption, that hunters be allowed to kill 75 deer a year after the growth for that year takes place.
   a. Under these assumptions, how many deer will there be 10 years from now?
   $D_{10} \approx 1941$
   b. Under these assumptions, find $\lim\limits_{n\to\infty} D_n$. 3225

Notes on Questions

Questions 3–5 These questions are extended in the *Optional Activity* on page 125.

Question 6 You may wish to ask students to give an explicit formula for this sequence. $[a_n = 6 \cdot 4^{n-1}]$

Question 12 For students who have had previous UCSMP courses, this may be the first question that covers new content. **Question 18** is related.

Question 15 Students are expected to graph the parametric equations, not to determine the answer by analysis. The analysis is done in Chapter 3.

Question 17 This question reviews simple ideas about logarithms in preparation for the next lesson.

Example 3

For the growth model for the fish population discussed in Example 2, find some evidence to suggest that

$$\lim_{n\to\infty} P_n = 30{,}000$$

where P_n is the catfish population of the lake n years after it is initially stocked with 2000 fish.

Solution

The growth model defines P_n by the recursive relation

$$P_{n+1} = (1.2)P_n - \frac{.2}{30{,}000} P_n^{\,2} \quad \forall \text{ integers } n \geq 0$$

and the initial value $P_0 = 2000$. The table of values of P_n listed here for $n = 50$ through $n = 56$ was produced by a calculator in SEQUENCE mode by entering

$$U_n = 1.2 \cdot U_{n-1} - \left(\frac{.2}{30{,}000}\right) U_{n-1}^{\,2}$$

n	U_n
50	29989
51	29991
52	29993
53	29994
54	29995
55	29996
56	29997

and $U_0 = 2000$. By scrolling through larger values of n, the displayed value of U_n remains constant at 30,000 for $n \geq 64$, which is strong evidence that $\lim\limits_{n\to\infty} P_n = 30{,}000$, the fish support limit of the lake.

QUESTIONS

Covering the Reading

1. A sequence is a function with domain __?__. See margin.
2. Write the first five terms of the sequence f whose initial conditions are $f_1 = 3, f_2 = 4$ and that has the same recursive formula as the Fibonacci sequence. $f_1 = 3, f_2 = 4, f_3 = 7, f_4 = 11, f_5 = 18$

In 3–6, a formula for the nth term of a sequence is given. **a.** Identify the sequence as arithmetic, geometric, or neither. **b.** Give the first five terms of the sequence. See left.

3. $a_n = \frac{n}{n-1} \quad \forall n \geq 2$
4. $a_n = 3^n \quad \forall n \geq 1$
5. $a_n = 3(-1)^n 2^n \quad \forall n \geq 0$
6. $\begin{cases} a_1 = 6 \\ a_{n+1} = 4a_n \quad \forall n \geq 1 \end{cases}$

In 7 and 8, find an explicit formula for the sequence defined. That is, solve the difference equation.

7. $S_{n+1} = \frac{1}{2} S_n \quad \forall n \geq 1, \quad S_1 = 7$ $\quad S_n = 7\left(\frac{1}{2}\right)^{n-1}$
8. $S_{n+1} = S_n - 2 \quad \forall n \geq 1, \quad S_1 = 3$ $\quad S_n = 3 - 2(n-1)$
9. A ball is dropped from a height of 10 feet and each time bounces back 80% of its previous height. See left.
   a. Give a recursive formula for the sequence of successive heights.
   b. Give an explicit formula for the sequence of successive heights.

3a) neither
b) $2, \frac{3}{2}, \frac{4}{3}, \frac{5}{4}, \frac{6}{5}$

4a) geometric
b) 3, 9, 27, 81, 243

5a) geometric
b) 3, -6, 12, -24, 48

6a) geometric
b) 6, 24, 96, 384, 1536

9a) $H_{n+1} = 0.8(H_n)$, $H_1 = 10$
b) $H_n = 10(0.8)^{n-1}$

Additional Answers
1. The set of all integers greater than or equal to a fixed integer a, if the sequence is infinite, or the set of all integers greater than or equal to a but not greater than another fixed integer b, where $b \geq a$, if the sequence is finite.

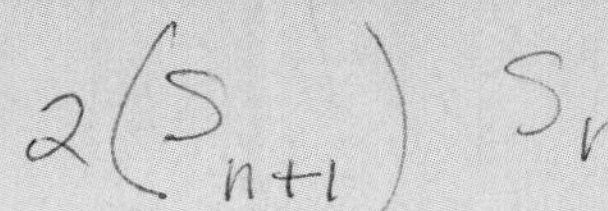

10b)

A — P_4 P_3 — P_2 — P_1 — B

11) difference equation: $a_{n+1} = a_n + d$, explicit formula: $a_n = b + (n - 1)d$

14) $\lim_{x\to\infty}\left(\frac{2}{3}\right)^x = 0$; $\lim_{x\to-\infty}\left(\frac{12}{3}\right)^x = \infty$

15) An ellipse with center (5, -4), minor axis with vertices (3, -4) and (7, -4), and major axis with vertices (5, -1) and (5, -7)

Applying the Mathematics

10. A sequence is defined as follows. P_1 is the midpoint of $\overline{AB}$. P_n is the midpoint of $\overline{AP_{n-1}}$ $\forall\, n > 1$.

a. Is this a recursive or an explicit definition? recursive

b. Graph the first four terms of the sequence. See left.

c. As n gets larger, P_n gets nearer and nearer to __?__. A

11. Find a difference equation and an explicit formula for the arithmetic sequence a with $a_1 = b$ and constant difference d. (See Example 1.) See left.

12. Modify the logistic growth difference equation for the fish population problem which follows Example 2 to account for each of the following new pieces of information. At an annual ice fishing derby, fisherman

a. catch and keep 500 fish.

b. catch and keep 3% of the fish in the lake at the time.

See margin.

13. Give the first five terms of the sequence and find $\lim_{n\to\infty} s_n$.

a. $s_n = \frac{\sin(n\pi)}{n}$ $\forall\, n \geq 1$ — 0, 0, 0, 0, 0; lim = 0

b. $s_n = \frac{\sin\left(\frac{n\pi}{2}\right)}{n}$ $\forall\, n \geq 1$ — $1, 0, -\frac{1}{3}, 0, \frac{1}{5}$; lim = 0

Review

14. Suppose $f: x \to \left(\frac{2}{3}\right)^x$. Describe the end behavior of f. *(Lessons 2-4, 2-7)* See left.

15. Describe the curve generated by the parametric equations See left.

$$\begin{cases} x = 2\cos t + 5 \\ y = 3\sin t - 4. \end{cases}$$ *(Lesson 2-5)*

16. *True or false.* Refer to the graph at right. *(Lesson 2-3)*

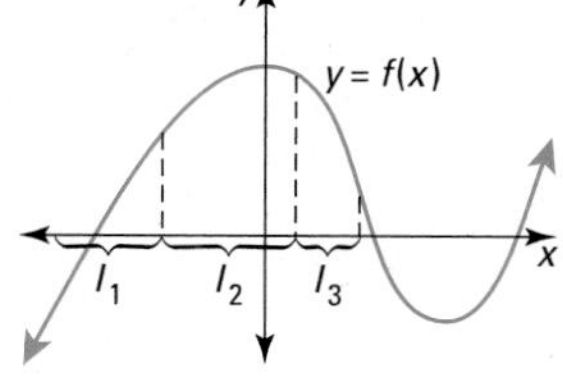

a. $\forall\, x_1$ and x_2 in I_1, if $x_1 < x_2$ then $f(x_1) < f(x_2)$. True

b. f is increasing on I_2. False

c. $\exists\, x_1$ and x_2 in I_2 such that $x_1 < x_2$ and $f(x_1) < f(x_2)$. True

d. $\forall\, x_1$ and x_2 in I_3, if $x_1 < x_2$ then $f(x_1) < f(x_2)$. False

17. Use the definition of logarithm to evaluate each expression.

a. $\log_3 81$ 4

b. $\log 100$ *(Previous course)* 2

Exploration

18. In Example 2, suppose that the lake had been stocked initially with 50,000 catfish instead of 2000. Use the limited growth model and a calculator with sequence tabulating capabilities to explore the sequence P of annual fish populations when the lake is initially overstocked as it is in this case. Do your results increase or decrease your faith in the model? See margin.

Question 18 Science Connection Catfish range in size from the flathead and channel variety, which can weigh over 70 pounds, to bullheads that weigh less than a pound. In the U.S., catfish used for food are raised on fish farms, most of which are located in Alabama, Arkansas, and Mississippi.

Follow-up for Lesson 2-8

Practice

For more questions on SPUR Objectives, use **Lesson Master 2-8** (shown on pages 126–127).

Assessment

Written Communication Have students **work with a partner.** Ask each student to define an arithmetic and a geometric sequence by giving a difference equation and first term for each sequence, as in **Questions 7–8.** Then have students find the explicit formulas for their partner's sequences. [Students write explicit formulas for sequences defined by a difference equation and first term.]

Extension

Have students enter the following program and observe how 1 – TERMN approaches 0 as N increases.

```
10  LET N = 1
20  LET TERMN = N/(N + 1)
30  PRINT N, TERMN, 1 – TERMN
40  GOTO 20
```

Then ask:

1. What is the smallest value of N for which the computer prints TERMN = 1 and 1 – TERMN = 0? [Answers will vary.]

2. Given the *n*th term should never equal 1, why does the computer print 1? [The computer can only use finite decimals, so it rounds.]

Project Update Project 5, *Sequences for Fractals,* on page 138, relates to the content of this lesson.

Additional Answers

12. a. $P_{n+1} = 1.2P_n - \frac{0.2}{30000}P_n^2 - 500$

b. $P_{n+1} = 1.2P_n - \frac{0.2}{30000}P_n^2 - 0.03P_n$

18. Sample: The results decrease to about 30,000 and then level off. This increases faith in the model, because the population decreases when the lake is overstocked.

Lesson 2-9

Objectives

B Rewrite exponential and logarithmic expressions and equations.
D Determine the end behavior of a logarithmic function.
E Use logarithmic functions as models.
G Analyze a logarithmic function from its graph.

Resources

From the ***Teacher's Resource File***
- Lesson Master 2-9
- Answer Master 2-9
- Teaching Aids
  14 Warm-up
  25 Definition and Properties of Logarithms

Additional Resources
- Visuals for Teaching Aids 14, 25
- Exploration 2-9

Teaching Lesson 2-9

Warm-up

In 1–4, evaluate each of the following expressions without using a calculator.

1. $\log_2 8$ 3
2. $\log_8 2$ $\frac{1}{3}$
3. $\log 2 + \log 50$ 2
4. $\ln \sqrt{e}$ 1
5. Explain, without using a calculator, why log 5,000,000 is between 6 and 7.
   log 1,000,000 = 6 and log 10,000,000 = 7. Since log is an increasing function, $6 < \log 5{,}000{,}000 < 7$.

LESSON

2-9 Analyzing Logarithmic Functions

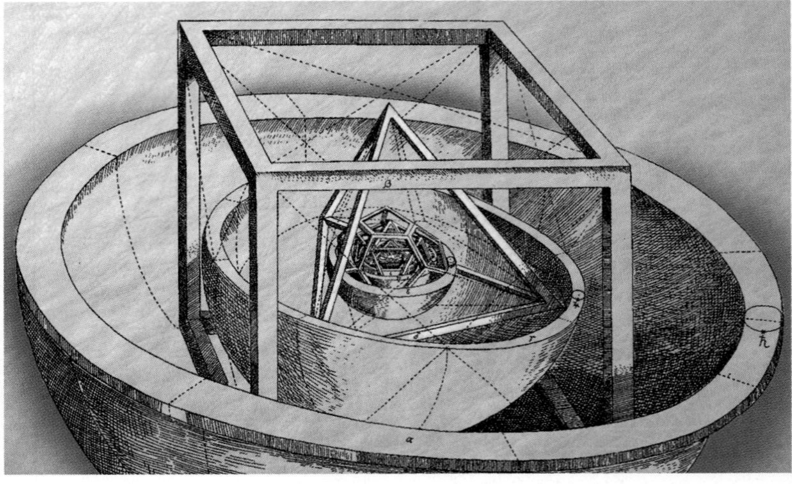

Kepler initially modeled the planetary system under the false assumption that planets had circular orbits with radii based on the five regular polyhedra as shown. Later calculations showed this model to be false.

A Brief History

Logarithms were introduced in 1614 by the Scottish mathematician John Napier (1550–1617) as an aid for calculation. By using logarithms, multiplication and division problems were "transformed" into addition and subtraction problems, making them easier to solve by hand calculation. Henry Briggs (1561–1630) first realized that base 10 would be a useful base for logarithms. Within just a few years, Johannes Kepler (1571–1630) found logarithms to be so useful in his studies of motions of the planets that he included a dedicatory letter to Napier in his treatise on the planets, called *Ephemeris,* which was published in 1620.

Logarithms remained important as a computational tool until the advent of modern calculators and computers. Today, logarithmic functions are still very important because they arise frequently in mathematics and its applications, and because of their relationship to the exponential functions. This relationship was discovered by Euler in the 1740s while looking for a solution to the equation $a^x = b$. He realized that the logarithms of Napier and Briggs would work, and gave what is today the standard definition of logarithms.

Definition
Let $b \neq 1$ be a positive real number. Then $\forall$ real numbers x and y, y is the **logarithm of x to the base b,** written $y = \log_b x$, if and only if $x = b^y$.

Lesson 2-9 Overview

Broad Goals This lesson reviews logarithms and logarithm functions. Students should be able to use the definition and properties of logarithms to evaluate expressions and solve equations involving logarithms.

Perspective The logarithm functions to the base b, defined by $y = \log_b x$, are analyzed in this lesson. The special cases $b = 10$ (common logarithm function) and $b = e$ (natural logarithm function) are emphasized. The Change of Base Theorem is deduced and applied in the solving of exponential equations of the form $a^x = b$. (The inverse relationship between the exponential function $f: x \rightarrow b^x$ and the logarithmic function $g: x \rightarrow \log_b x$ is discussed in Chapter 3.)

This material should be review for all students. Most teachers have found the review to be necessary.

Finding Logarithms Directly from the Definition

For example, to find $\log_2 32$, notice that if $n = \log_2 32$, then $2^n = 32$. It is easy to see that $n = 5$, so $\log_2 32 = 5$. In general, *$\log_b x$ is the power to which the base b must be raised in order to equal x.*

Example 1

Use the definition of logarithms to evaluate the following.

a. $\log_{10} 1000$ **b.** $\log_{1000} 10$

c. $\log_b 1$ **d.** $\log_b b$

Solution

a. $\log_{10} 1000 = 3$, because $10^3 = 1000$.

b. $\log_{1000} 10 = \frac{1}{3}$, because $(1000)^{1/3} = \sqrt[3]{1000} = 10$.

c. $\log_b 1 = 0$, because $b > 0$ and $b^0 = 1$.

d. $\log_b b = 1$, because $b > 0$ and $b^1 = b$.

Relating Logarithm and Exponential Functions

The **logarithm function with base $b > 0$, $b \neq 1$,** is the function $\log_b$ (read "log to the base b") defined by the rule

$$x \to \log_b x, \text{ for all positive real numbers } x.$$

The graphs of the exponential function $f(x) = b^x$ and the logarithmic function $g(x) = \log_b x$ are closely related.

$\forall$ x and y, (x, y) is on the graph of the exponential function f

$\Leftrightarrow y = b^x = f(x)$ definition of graph

$\Leftrightarrow x = \log_b y$ definition of logarithm to base b

$\Leftrightarrow (y, x)$ is on the graph of the logarithm function g.

Domain and Range

The switching of x and y in these functions has many implications. First, it means that the domain of $y = b^x$ (the set of real numbers) is the range of $y = \log_b x$, and the domain of $y = \log_b x$ is the range of $y = b^x$ (the set of positive real numbers).

Second, the graph of $y = \log_b x$ is the reflection image of the graph of $y = b^x$ over the line $y = x$ because (y, x) is the reflection image of (x, y) over the line $y = x$.

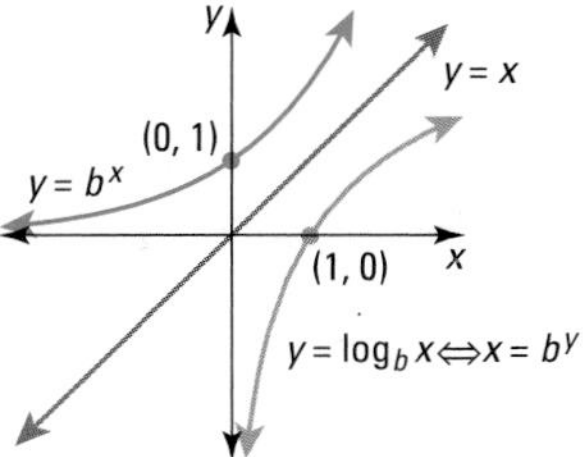

Notes on Reading

In the solutions to parts **c** and **d** of **Example 1,** the stipulation that $b > 0$ is required by the definition of logarithm.

Some students may need to think of solving equations to obtain the values of logarithms like those in **Example 1.** For instance, to evaluate the expression $\log_{10} 1000$, first set it equal to a variable:

$$q = \log_{10} 1000.$$

Now use the definition to convert the equation to an exponential equation:

$$10^q = 1000.$$

Since $10^q = 10^3$, it follows that $q = 3$. But why does it follow? This is a question that is considered in some detail in Lesson 3-3, where we ask what functions can be applied to both sides of an equation without losing or gaining solutions. The answer given there is that any 1-1 function can be applied. In going from $10^q = 10^3$ to $q = 3$, we are essentially applying the log function, which is 1-1 because it is an increasing function.

The Change of Base Theorem is a powerful result that enables calculators to be used to compute logarithms to any base. Some students may have trouble remembering the formula. An easy way to remember the Change of Base Theorem is to "cancel" a in the formula $\log_b x = (\log_b a)(\log_a x)$. Emphasize, of course, that thinking of canceling is simply a mnemonic device. The proof involves no canceling.

Optional Activities

Activity 1 Technology Connection
Materials: Explorations software

You may use *Exploration 2-9, Logarithmic Functions,* to introduce Lesson 2-9. By defining an exponential function of the form $f(x) = b^x$, students can observe the graph of the exponential function and its reflection image over the line $y = x$. You can also locate a point on the graph of either function by choosing a value for the x-coordinate.

Activity 2 Cooperative Learning You might use this lesson to allow students to gain facility at evaluating some logarithms without using a calculator. Make a chart with the class of the powers of 2, 3, 4, 5, ..., 10 that you expect students to know (without the aid of a calculator.) For example, you might want students to know up through the sixth power of 2, the fourth power of 3, the third powers of 4 and 5, the squares of 6 through 9, and all powers of 10.

Ask students to write logarithm questions similar to **Questions 1–4** and **9** using the chart. Have them exchange papers and, without looking at the chart or using a calculator, evaluate each others' questions.

An equivalent formulation of the Change of Base Theorem is as follows: If a and b are positive numbers both unequal to 1, then for all $x > 0$, $\log_a x = \frac{\log_b x}{\log_b a}$. This method is illustrated in the solution of **Example 2** with $b = e$.

An alternative method of solution for **Example 2** avoids the Change of Base Theorem by essentially going through the steps of the proof of that theorem.

$$\begin{aligned} \log_2 61 &= x \\ \Rightarrow \quad 2^x &= 61 \\ \Rightarrow \quad \ln 2^x &= \ln 61 \\ \Rightarrow \quad x \ln 2 &= \ln 61 \\ \Rightarrow \quad x &= \frac{\ln 61}{\ln 2}. \end{aligned}$$

The application of the natural log function to obtain the third line of this equation does not change the solutions to the equation because (as mentioned above) every logarithm function is an increasing function, and so is 1-1.

In the introduction to Chapter 6, students will learn that logarithms were not the first tool used to "transform" multiplication into addition. Trigonometric identities were used to do this before logarithms were invented.

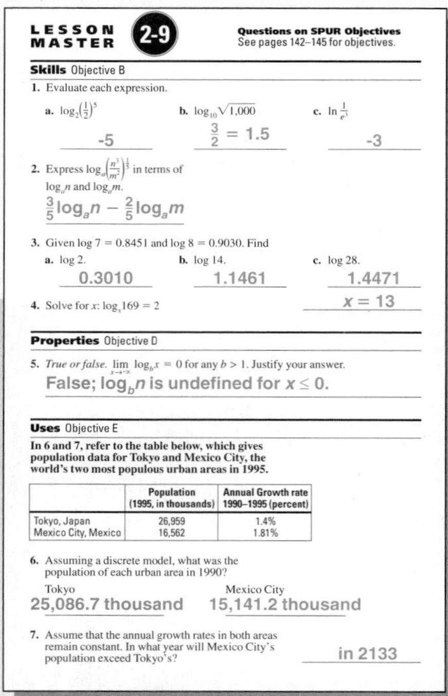
LESSON MASTER 2-9
Questions on SPUR Objectives
See pages 142–145 for objectives.

Skills Objective B

1. Evaluate each expression.
   a. $\log_2\left(\frac{1}{2}\right)^5$ — -5
   b. $\log_{10}\sqrt{1{,}000}$ — $\frac{3}{2} = 1.5$
   c. $\ln \frac{1}{e^3}$ — -3
2. Express $\log_a\left(\frac{n^3}{m^2}\right)^{\frac{1}{5}}$ in terms of $\log_a n$ and $\log_a m$.
   $\frac{3}{5}\log_a n - \frac{2}{5}\log_a m$
3. Given $\log 7 = 0.8451$ and $\log 8 = 0.9030$. Find
   a. log 2. — 0.3010
   b. log 14. — 1.1461
   c. log 28. — 1.4471
4. Solve for x: $\log_x 169 = 2$ — $x = 13$

Properties Objective D

5. *True or false.* $\lim_{x \to -\infty} \log_b x = 0$ for any $b > 1$. Justify your answer.
   False; $\log_b n$ is undefined for $x \leq 0$.

Uses Objective E

In 6 and 7, refer to the table below, which gives population data for Tokyo and Mexico City, the world's two most populous urban areas in 1995.

	Population (1995, in thousands)	Annual Growth rate 1990–1995 (percent)
Tokyo, Japan	26,959	1.4%
Mexico City, Mexico	16,562	1.81%

6. Assuming a discrete model, what was the population of each urban area in 1990?
   Tokyo: 25,086.7 thousand
   Mexico City: 15,141.2 thousand
7. Assume that the annual growth rates in both areas remain constant. In what year will Mexico City's population exceed Tokyo's? — in 2133

The height of this water slide decreases for its entire length.

Increasing or Decreasing?

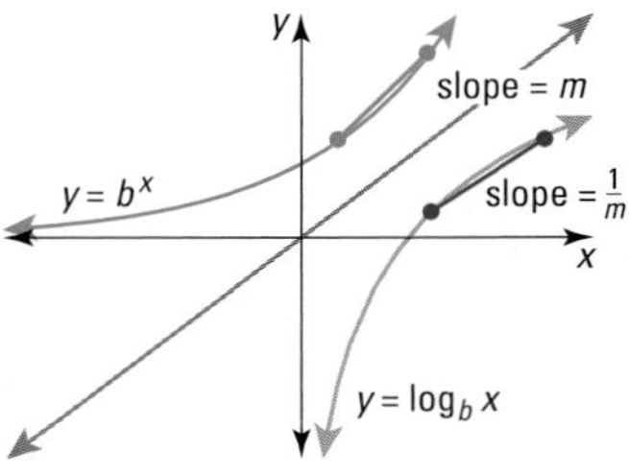

The exponential function with base $b > 1$ is increasing throughout its domain. The corresponding logarithm function $\log_b x$ also increases throughout its domain $(0, \infty)$. This can also be proved geometrically as follows: Note that the segment connecting any two points of the exponential function has a positive slope (because the function is increasing), and if the slope of a segment is positive, so is the slope of its reflection image over the line $y = x$. (More precisely, the slopes of the segments are reciprocals.) You are asked to verify this in the Questions. Note also that since the exponential function is increasing and $\lim_{x \to \infty} b^x = \infty$, so also $\lim_{x \to \infty} \log_b x = \infty$.

Fundamental Properties of Logarithms

The definition of logarithm sets up a correspondence between the laws of exponents and the laws of logarithms. In the table below, $r = \log_b u$ and $s = \log_b v$. That is, $b^r = u$ and $b^s = v$.

Theorems
$\forall$ real numbers r and s and $\forall$ positive real numbers b, u, and v with $b \neq 1$,

Law of Exponents	Law of Logarithms	
$b^r \cdot b^s = b^{r+s}$	$\log_b (u \cdot v) = \log_b u + \log_b v$	**Logarithm of a Product**
$\frac{b^r}{b^s} = b^{r-s}$	$\log_b \left(\frac{u}{v}\right) = \log_b u - \log_b v$	**Logarithm of a Quotient**
$(b^r)^s = b^{rs}$	$\log_b (u^s) = s \log_b u$	**Logarithm of a Power**

The correspondence between exponents and logarithms is used in proving the properties of logarithms. We prove the Logarithm of a Product Theorem and leave the other proofs to the Questions.

Proof

1. Begin with $\quad b^r \cdot b^s = b^{r+s}$.
2. Let $\quad u = b^r$
   and $\quad v = b^s$.
3. Substituting in Step 1, $\quad uv = b^{r+s}$.
4. Now translate the equations of Steps 2 and 3 into their logarithmic equivalents, using the definition of logarithm.
   $\log_b u = r$
   and $\quad \log_b v = s$
   and most importantly,
   $\log_b (uv) = r + s$.
5. Substitute back, using Step 4. $\quad \log_b (uv) = \log_b u + \log_b v$

Optional Activities

Activity 3 After discussing the lesson, you might refer students to the Extension for Lesson 2-7. Ask them to prove that the amount of time it takes for the money in an account to quadruple under continuous compounding is exactly twice the amount of time it takes for the money in the account to double.

Adapting to Individual Needs

Extra Help
Some students might have difficulty understanding the formula in **Example 4a.** It might seem more reasonable to them if you verify that after 40 days (the substance's half-life), half of the initial 9 grams of the substance remains:

$P(40) = 9\left(\frac{1}{2}\right)^{40/40} = 9\left(\frac{1}{2}\right)^1 = \frac{9}{2}$.

The theorems on page 132 can be used to manipulate expressions involving logarithms. For instance,

$$\log 6 = \log (2 \cdot 3) = \log 2 + \log 3$$
$$\log \left(\tfrac{1}{4}\right) = \log 1 - \log 4 = 0 - \log 4 = -\log 4$$
$$\log 8^{17} = 17 \log 8.$$

Relating Logarithms with Different Bases

The two numbers used most often as bases of logarithms are 10 and e. When 10 is the base it is customary to write "**log**" instead of "$\log_{10}$," and $\log x$ is called the **common logarithm** of x. When the base is e, "**ln**" is written in place of "$\log_e$," and **ln x** is called the **natural logarithm** of x. Scientific calculators have keys for each of these functions.

There is a surprisingly simple relationship between the logarithms of the same number to two different bases a and b. One is $\log_b a$ times the other. To prove this, let x be any positive real number and let $y = \log_a x$. Then $\forall$ x,

$x = a^y$	Definition of logarithm
$\Rightarrow \log_b x = \log_b a^y$	Take $\log_b$ of both sides.
$\Rightarrow \log_b x = y (\log_b a)$	Logarithm of a Power Theorem
$\Rightarrow \log_b x = (\log_b a) \log_a x$	Substitution for y, Commutative Property of Multiplication

Change of Base Theorem
Let a and b be positive real numbers both unequal to 1, then for all $x > 0$,
$$\log_b x = \log_b a \cdot \log_a x.$$

Because the conversion factor from $\log_a x$ to $\log_b x$ is $\log_b a$, which is a constant, you can calculate logarithms to any positive base. This is an important result because calculators have keys for only log and ln. Base 2 is often used in computer applications.

Example 2

Estimate $\log_2 61$.

Solution

First choose the base of the logarithm to be one you can compute with your calculator. We choose e and use the ln key and the Change of Base Theorem to get

$$\ln 61 = \ln 2 \cdot \log_2 61, \text{ from which}$$
$$\log_2 61 = \frac{\ln 61}{\ln 2}$$
$$\approx 5.9307.$$

Check

If $\log_2 61 \approx 5.9307$, then $2^{5.9307} \approx 61$. Using a calculator, we find $2^{5.9307} \approx 60.9984$.

The inverse relationship between the logarithmic function $x \to \log_b x$ and the corresponding exponential function $x \to b^x$ is discussed in Lesson 3-2.

Error Alert Knowing and reviewing the *names* of each of these theorems (Logarithm of a Product, Logarithm of a Quotient, Logarithm of a Power) should help students avoid common errors such as "$\log (x + y) = \log x + \log y$."

Teaching Aid 25 summarizes the definition and properties of logarithms.

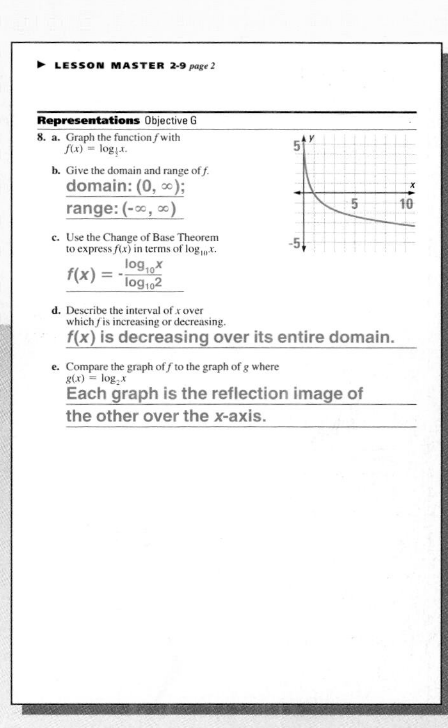

► LESSON MASTER 2-9 *page 2*

Representations Objective G

8. a. Graph the function f with $f(x) = \log_{\frac{1}{2}} x$.

b. Give the domain and range of f.
domain: $(0, \infty)$;
range: $(-\infty, \infty)$

c. Use the Change of Base Theorem to express $f(x)$ in terms of $\log_{10} x$.
$f(x) = -\frac{\log_{10} x}{\log_{10} 2}$

d. Describe the interval of x over which f is increasing or decreasing.
$f(x)$ is decreasing over its entire domain.

e. Compare the graph of f to the graph of g where $g(x) = \log_2 x$
Each graph is the reflection image of the other over the x-axis.

Adapting to Individual Needs

Challenge

Have students answer the following questions.

1. Let $A(t) = Be^{rt}$ be any continuous growth model. Let t_2 be the doubling time. How are r and t_2 related? $[t_2 = \frac{\ln 2}{r}]$
2. Let $A(t) = Be^{rt}$ be any continuous decay model. Let $t_{1/2}$ be the half-life. How are r and $t_{1/2}$ related? $[t_{1/2} = \frac{\ln .5}{r}]$
3. Give a Change of Base Theorem for Exponents; i.e. let $a^x = b^y$ and solve for y in terms of x. $[y = \frac{x \ln a}{\ln b}$, thus, $a^x = b^{(\ln a/\ln b)x}]$

Additional Examples

1. Use the definition of logarithms to evaluate the following.
   a. $\log_8 64$ **$\log_8 64 = 2$ because $8^2 = 64$.**
   b. $\log_{64} 8$ **$\log_{64} 8 = \frac{1}{2}$ because $64^{1/2} = \sqrt{64} = 8$.**
   c. $\log_b b^2$ **$\log_b b^2 = 2$ because $b^2 = b^2$.**
   d. $\log_b b^n$, where n is a real number. **$\log_b b^n = n$ because $b^n = b^n$.**
2. Estimate $\log_5 101$. **2.8675**
3. Solve $5^x = 101$. **By the definition of logarithm, $x = \log_5 101$. From the Additional Example 2 above, $x \approx 2.8675$.**
4. Suppose that the half-life of a radioactive substance is 15,000 years.
   a. Given an initial sample of 1 gram of the radioactive substance, write a formula for a function that expresses the mass of radioactive material left after t years. **$P(t) = \left(\frac{1}{2}\right)^{t/15000} = 2^{-t/15000}$**
   b. Convert the equation so that its base is e, and use that equation to determine the percentage of the substance that decays each year. **$P(t) \approx e^{-.00004621t}$, so about .0046% of the substance is decaying each year.**
   c. How long does it take for the mass of the radioactive substance to be reduced to 0.8 gram? **Solve $0.8 = e^{-.00004621t}$ to find $t \approx 4830$ years.**

The Change of Base Theorem can help solve exponential equations.

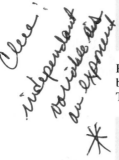

Example 3

Solve $2^t = 61$.

Solution

By the definition of logarithm, $t = \log_2 61$. From the result of Example 2, $t \approx 5.9307$.

Problems involving population growth or half-life use base 2. However, base e is easier to use when working in calculus. The Change of Base Theorem and definition of logarithm allow you to work with either base.

Example 4

a. The half-life of a radioactive substance is 40 days. Write a formula for a function that expresses number of grams of radioactive material left t days after an initial sample of 9 grams is taken.

b. Convert the equation to base e, and determine the percentage of the substance that decays each day.

c. How long will it take for the sample to decay to 1 gram?

Solution

a. Let $P(t)$ be the number of grams of the substance remaining in the sample t days after the sample is taken. Then, because the half-life of the substance is 40 days, and the initial sample (at $t = 0$) contained 9 grams,

$$P(t) = 9\left(\frac{1}{2}\right)^{\frac{t}{40}} = 9 \cdot 2^{\frac{-t}{40}}.$$

b. The number 2 is related to e by $e^{\ln 2} = 2$, so

$$P(t) = 9\left(e^{\ln 2}\right)^{\frac{-t}{40}} = 9 \cdot e^{\frac{-t \ln 2}{40}}$$

Because $\frac{\ln 2}{40}$ is approximately .01733,

$$P(t) = 9e^{-.01733t}$$

approximately, and the Continuous Change Model asserts that the substance is decaying by 1.733% per day.

c. If t is the number of days required for the substance to decay to 1 gram, then

$$1 = 9e^{\frac{-t \ln 2}{40}}.$$

This equation can be solved for t by using logarithms as follows.

$$\frac{1}{9} = e^{\frac{-t \ln 2}{40}}$$

$$\ln\left(\frac{1}{9}\right) = -t\,\frac{\ln 2}{40}$$

$$\therefore \quad t = -40 \cdot \frac{\ln\left(\frac{1}{9}\right)}{\ln 2} = 40\,\frac{\ln 9}{\ln 2} \approx 127 \text{ days}$$

134

QUESTIONS

Covering the Reading

In 1–4, simplify the expression. 5) $\frac{4}{9}$; $\frac{2}{3}$; 2

1. $\log_{10} 10{,}000$ 4 **2.** $\log_3 \sqrt{27}$ $\frac{3}{2}$ **3.** $\log_b \left(\frac{1}{b}\right)$ -1 **4.** $\ln e^5$ 5

5. Since $\left(\frac{2}{3}\right)^2 = \frac{4}{9}$, the logarithm of __?__ to the base __?__ is __?__.

6. Evaluate $\log_2 n$ for n = 1, 2, 3, 4, 5, 6, 7, 8, and 9.
0, 1, ≈ 1.585, 2, ≈ 2.322, ≈ 2.585, ≈ 2.807, 3, ≈ 3.170

7. Analyze the logarithm function with base $b > 1$. (Use the form of Example 2 of Lesson 2-7.) See margin.

8. By beginning with $\frac{b^r}{b^s} = b^{r-s}$, prove the Logarithm of a Quotient Theorem. See left.

8) $\frac{b^r}{b^s} = b^{r-s}$
Let $u = b^r$ and $v = b^s$; therefore, $\log_b u = r$ and $\log_b v = s$; $\frac{u}{v} = b^{r-s}$;
$\log_b \left(\frac{u}{v}\right) = r - s$;
$\log_b \left(\frac{u}{v}\right) = \log_b u - \log_b v$

9. Solve for x: $\log_x 625 = 2$. $x = 25$

In 10 and 11, express the logarithm in terms of log 2, log 3, or log 5.

10. $\log \frac{2^5}{3}$ $5 \log 2 - \log 3$ **11.** log 30 $\log 2 + \log 3 + \log 5$ **12.** Solve $15^t = 30$. $t \approx 1.256$

Applying the Mathematics

In 13 and 14, express the logarithm in terms of $\log_b n$ and $\log_b w$. See left.

13. $\log_b \frac{5n^2}{w}$ **14.** $\log_b \sqrt[4]{nw^3}$

13) $\log_b 5 + 2 \log_b n - \log_b w$
14) $\frac{1}{4} \log_b n + \frac{3}{4} \log_b w$

15. Africa's population during the decade 1980–1990 grew at the average annual rate of 2.9%, the highest of any continent. Determine the number of years (to the nearest tenth) the population will take to double at this growth rate. about 23.9 years

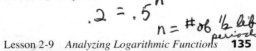

16. a. Compute $\log_{12} 98$. ≈ 1.845
b. Compute $\log_{98} 12$. ≈ .542
c. Generalize the result you found in parts **a** and **b**, and prove your generalization. See margin.

17. Use the definition and properties of logarithms to solve the equation $\log (x - 15) + \log x = 2$. $x = 20$

18. Carbon 14 has a half-life of 5715 years. Using the Continuous Change Model, this means that if B is the initial amount, then the amount after 5715 years is $\frac{B}{2}$, where

$$\frac{B}{2} = Be^{5715r}.$$

a. Solve the equation above for r to determine the annual rate at which Carbon 14 decays. $r \approx 0.000121$
b. Suppose the skull of a prehistoric relative of the rhinoceros is discovered and analyses show that it contains only 20% of the Carbon 14 that bones of living animals do. Use the result in part **a** to estimate the age of the skull. about 13,000 years

white rhinoceros

Notes on Questions

Questions 1–5 and 9–11 These questions should be done *without* a calculator.

Question 6 Note from the answers that the logarithm function base 2 is an increasing function. How many of these could be done without a calculator? [n = 1, 2, 4, and 8, but also n = 6 and n = 9 could be found from the others if n = 3 were found; thus a calculator is needed only for n = 3, n = 5, and n = 7.]

Question 8 This question should not be skipped, as it provides a way to use the logic of Chapter 1 to reinforce students' learning of the properties of logarithms. Point out the parallels between the laws of exponents and the laws of logarithms.

Question 12 A solution to this equation can be approximated using an automatic grapher. Find the x-coordinate of the point where the graphs of $y = 15^x$ and $y = 30$ intersect.

Question 15 Social Studies Connection According to the United Nations Department of International Economic and Social Affairs, the population of Africa was 642 million in 1990, which was 12.1% of the world's population. It is estimated that the population of Africa will be over 2 billion by 2050, or about 22.6% of the world's population.

Question 16 The generalization sought here is sometimes called the *Interchange Theorem.*

Question 17 As in **Question 12,** a solution can be approximated using an automatic grapher. Graph $f(x) = \log(x - 15) + \log x$ and look for the x-coordinate when the value of $f(x)$ is 2.

Additional Answers

7. $\log_b x$ has domain: $x > 0$
range: set of reals
maxima or minima: none
$\lim_{x\to\infty} = \infty$; $\lim_{x\to 0} = -\infty$
model: sound intensity, logarithmic scales increasing over entire domain
special properties: relation to exponential functions, Change of Base Theorem

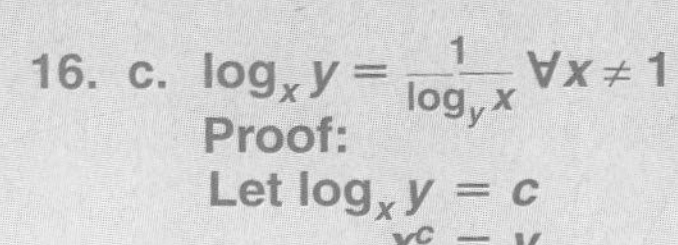

16. c. $\log_x y = \frac{1}{\log_y x}$ $\forall x \neq 1$
Proof:
Let $\log_x y = c$
$x^c = y$
$\log_y x^c = \log_y y$
$c \log_y x = 1$
$c = \frac{1}{\log_y x}$
$\log_x y = \frac{1}{\log_y x}$

Notes on Questions

Question 24 This result is related to the fact that for an integer N, $\lfloor \log N \rfloor + 1$ is the number of decimal digits in N. Students may be interested to know that $\lfloor \log_2 N \rfloor + 1$ is the number of *binary* digits in the binary expansion of N. Binary expressions are considered in Lesson 4-6.

Follow-up for Lesson 2-9

Practice

For more questions on SPUR Objectives, use **Lesson Master 2-9** (shown on pages 132–133).

Assessment

Written Communication Have students write examples of each of the laws of exponents and the related laws of logarithms (six examples in all). [Students show understanding of the laws of exponents and the laws of logarithms.]

Extension

Have students use an automatic grapher to investigate the rate of growth of different types of functions. For example, the graphs of $y = 2^x$, $y = x^2$, $y = x$, $y = \sqrt{x}$, and $y = \log_2 x$ on a common set of axes would show the differences between exponential, quadratic, linear, square root, and logarithmic rates of growth.

Project Update Project 4, *Logarithmic Scales*, on page 138, relates to the content of this lesson.

19) recursive: $a_{n+1} = a_n - 4$, $a_1 = 100$; explicit: $a_n = 104 - 4n$

20b) 2, 10.5, 7.060, 6.221, 6.165

22b) $x^2 = 4$, but $x \neq 2$

23) slope: $\ell = \left(\frac{b-d}{a-c}\right)$, $\ell^1 = \frac{a-c}{b-d} = \left(\frac{b-d}{a-c}\right)^{1}$ $= \ell^{-1}$

Review

19. Give an explicit and a recursive definition for the sequence 100, 96, 92, . . . , in which each term is 4 less than the preceding. *(Lesson 2-8)* See left.

20. a. Compute the first five terms of the sequence defined by

$$S_{n+1} = \frac{1}{2}\left(S_n + \frac{2}{S_n}\right) \quad \forall\, n \geq 1,$$

given that $S_1 = 2$. 2, 1.5, 1.417, 1.414, 1.411

b. Repeat part **a** with $S_{n+1} = \frac{1}{2}\left(S_n + \frac{38}{S_n}\right) \forall\, n \geq 1$. See left.

c. Compare the values obtained in parts **a** and **b** with the values of $\sqrt{2}$ and $\sqrt{38}$. *(Lesson 2-8)* $\sqrt{2} \approx 1.414$, which is the limit of part **a**; $\sqrt{38} \approx 6.164$, which is the limit of part **b**.

21. Refer to the sequence h below.

$h_n = \frac{n+1}{2n}$ $\qquad \frac{2}{2}, \frac{3}{4}, \frac{4}{6}, \frac{5}{8}, \frac{6}{10}, \frac{7}{12}, \ldots$

upto 21 inclusive.

a. Assuming that the suggested pattern persists, find an explicit formula for h_n. See above.

b. Write the decimal forms of h_{10}, h_{100}, and h_{1000}. .55, .505, .5005

c. What does $\lim_{n \to \infty} h_n$ appear to be? *(Lessons 2-5, 2-8)* 0.5

22. In logic, the word *but* means *and*. Consider the sentence

$$x^2 \neq 4 \text{ or } x = 2.$$

a. If the sentence is false, what is x? $x = -2$

b. Write the negation of the sentence using the word *but*. *(Lesson 1-3)* See left.

23. Let ℓ be the line containing the points (a, b) and (c, d), and let ℓ' be its image under a reflection over the line $y = x$. Thus, ℓ' contains the points (b, a) and (d, c). Prove that the slope of ℓ' is the reciprocal of the slope of ℓ. *(Previous course)* See left.

Exploration

24. a. Find the common logarithms of the following numbers.

2385 ≈ 3.377
238.5 ≈ 2.377
23.85 ≈ 1.377
2.385 ≈ 0.377
0.2385 $\approx -.623$

b. Generalize the results of what you found in part **a**.

c. Relate the generalization to scientific notation.

$\log(a + 10^n) = \log a + n$

b) $\log\left(\frac{1}{10}a\right)$ $\log a - \log 10 = \log a - 1$

Possible Responses, page 137

1. a. From the continuous change model, the amount $A(t)$ in the account t years after the student begins college would be $A(t) = Be^{rt}$, if there were no withdrawals. Let n be the number of the student's college year, b be the amount withdrawn from the account at the beginning of each year, and $A(n)$ be the amount in the account immediately after the withdrawal of b dollars has been made at the beginning of the nth year. Find the amount $A(n)$ for $n = 1, 2, 3, 4$:

$A(1) = B - b$
$A(2) = (B - b)e^{r \cdot 1} - b = Be^r - b(1 + e^r)$
$A(3) = [Be^r - b(1 + e^r)]\, e^{r \cdot 1} - b = Be^{2r} - b(1 + e^r + e^{2r})$
$A(4) = [Be^{2r} - b(1 + e^r + e^{2r})]e^{r \cdot 1} - b = Be^{3r} - b(1 + e^r + e^{2r} + e^{3r})$

Since the amount after the beginning of the fourth year is to be zero, $A(4) = 0 \Rightarrow b = \frac{Be^{3r}}{1 + e^r + e^{2r} + e^{3r}}$.

Sample: $B = \$\,5{,}000$, $r = 0.059$, $b \approx \frac{5{,}000(1.1936)}{4.3798} \approx \$1{,}362.70$

A project presents an opportunity for you to extend your knowledge of a topic related to the material of this chapter. You should allow more time for a project than you do for typical homework questions.

1 Savings Plans

a. Let B be the amount of money you expect to have when you begin college. It is in an account paying 5.9% annual interest compounded continuously. Suppose also that you use the money to help pay your tuition at the beginning of each of 4 years of college, taking out an equal amount each year and leaving the remainder in the account. If you use all the money, how much should you withdraw each year?

b. The situation in part **a** is similar to that of a person planning for retirement. Suppose a person retires with d dollars in an account earning r% annual interest compounded continuously. The money is to be withdrawn in equal amounts each month for y years, at which time it will be gone. How much should each monthly withdrawal be? Write a computer program to answer this question. Have tables printed showing monthly balances for two different situations.

2 Parametric Equations for Curves

In Example 2 of Lesson 2-5, we showed the graph of the parametric equations

$$\begin{cases} x(t) = (1 + t)(1 - t^2) \\ y(t) = (1 - t)(1 - t^2) \end{cases} \quad -1 \le t \le 1.$$

This project will show you how the parametric equations for this loop were created and how you can find parametric equations for other curves.

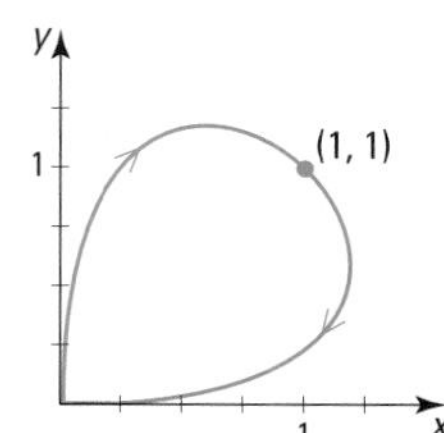

a. Sketch the graphs of the functions f and g with $f(t) = 1 - t^2$ and $g(t) = t(1 - t^2)$ on the interval $-1 \le t \le 1$.

b. Find the values of $f(t)$ and $g(t)$ at $t = -1$, $t = 0$, and $t = 1$. Then find the largest subintervals of $(-1, 1)$ on which $f(t)$ is positive. Do the same for $g(t)$.

c. Use the information gathered in part **b** to explain why the parametric equations

$$\begin{cases} x(t) = f(t) + g(t) \\ y(t) = f(t) - g(t) \end{cases} \quad -1 \le t \le 1$$

have a graph that is a clockwise oriented loop.

d. Show that the equations in part **c** are equivalent to those in Example 2 of Lesson 2-5.

e. The parametric equations

$$\begin{cases} x(t) = \cos t \\ y(t) = \sin t \end{cases} \quad 0 \le t \le 2\pi$$

describe a circle of radius 1 centered at the origin, generated counterclockwise starting at (1, 0). Modify these equations with an exponential term to obtain a curve that spirals inward gradually from (1, 0) toward the origin and completes 4 full loops of the spiral.

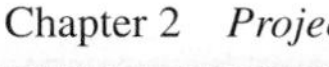

Chapter 2 Projects

The projects relate chiefly to the content of the lessons of this chapter as follows:

Project	Lesson(s)
1	2-4, 2-7
2	2-5
3	2-5
4	2-9
5	2-8

1 Savings Plans This is a straightforward project, and may be quite easy for students who have had all previous UCSMP courses.

2 Parametric Equations for Curves Most students have little, if any, intuition about the graphs of parametric equations. This project attempts to give some insight into one of the pairs of parametric equations used in Lesson 2-5, and extends the ideas from that lesson.

3 Famous Mathematical Curves A dictionary of mathematics, or an old book discussing analytic geometry, or an encyclopedia may be used as a reference. Students should describe the curve in detail and indicate the significance of any parameters in the equations.

4 Logarithmic Scales A source for this project is *The Mathematical Tourist*, by Ivars Peterson (New York: W. H. Freeman and Company, 1988).

5 Sequences for Fractals Logarithmic scales are the subject of a lesson in UCSMP *Advanced Algebra*, so some students may be quite familiar with this content.

1. b. PROGRAM: RETIRE (BASIC language)

```
10 CLS
20 INPUT "INITIAL AMOUNT OF
   RETIREMENT FUND? $";D
30 INPUT "ANNUAL INTEREST
   RATE (EXPRESSED AS A
   PERCENT)?";R
40 INPUT "NUMBER OF YEARS
   MONTHLY WITHDRAWALS ARE
   TO OCCUR?";Y
50 REM CALCULATE NUMBER OF
   MONTHS M
60 LET M = 12*Y
70 REM CALCULATE MONTHLY
   INTEREST RATE AS A
   DECIMAL Q
80 LET Q = R/1200
90 LET A = D*EXP((M-1)*Q)
100 FOR J = 0 TO M-1
110 LET B = EXP(J*Q)+B
120 NEXT J
130 LET W = A/B
140 PRINT "AMOUNT OF MONTHLY
    WITHDRAWAL = S";W
150 LET BAL = D
160 PRINT
170 PRINT "MONTH", "BALANCE"
180 FOR J = 0 TO M
190 PRINT J,"$";BAL
200 LET BAL = (BAL-W)*   EXP(Q)
210 NEXT J
220 END
```

(Responses continue on page 138.)

Additional Responses, page 137

2. a.

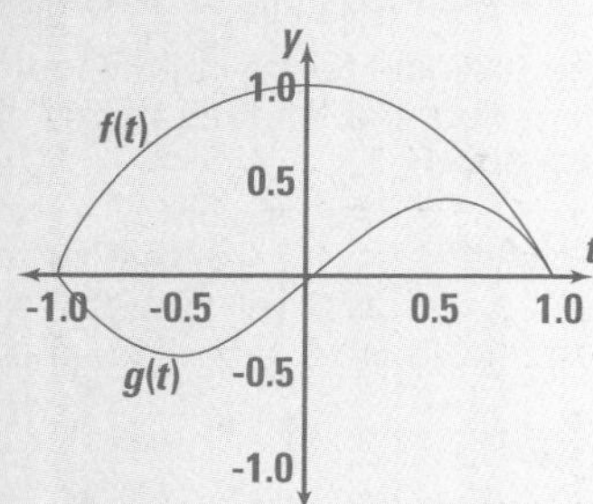

b. $f(-1) = 0$, $f(0) = 1$, $f(1) = 0$; $g(-1) = 0$, $g(0) = 0$, $g(1) = 0$; $f(t)$ is positive on the interval (-1,1); $g(t)$ is positive on the interval (0,1).

c. Since $x(t) = f(t) + g(t)$ and $y(t) = f(t) - g(t)$, the point $(x(t), y(t))$ is (0, 0) when $t = -1$. As t increases from -1 to 0, $f(t) + g(t)$ and $f(t) - g(t)$ both increase and attain the value 1 when $t = 0$. As t increases from 0 to 1, $f(t) + g(t)$ and $f(t) - g(t)$ both decrease and attain the value 0 when $t = 1$. So as t increases from -1 to 1, the point $(x(t), y(t))$ moves from the origin (0, 0) into the first quadrant, with both $x(t)$ and $y(t)$ increasing until $(x(t), y(t)) = (1, 1)$ when $t = 0$. Then both $x(t)$ and $y(t)$ decrease until $(x(t), y(t))$ returns to the origin when $t = 1$. Since $g(t) < 0$ when $-1 < t < 0$, and $g(t) > 0$ when $0 < t < 1$, $f(t) - g(t)$ increases faster than $f(t) + g(t)$ for $-1 < t < 0$ and vice-versa for $0 < t < 1$. This causes the clockwise motion with the y-coordinate increasing faster than the x-coordinate forming the upper part of the loop. Then the x-coordinate decreases faster than the y-coordinate forming the bottom part of the loop.

(continued)

3 Famous Mathematical Curves

a. Investigate parametric equations for two of the following famous curves.

i. Folium of Descartes **ii.** Hypocycloid
iii. Involute of a circle **iv.** Nephroid

b. Use an automatic grapher to plot these in the *xy*-plane.

4 Logarithmic Scales

Logarithmic functions with base $b > 1$ increase quite slowly when x is large. This makes **logarithmic scales** appropriate to use when the range of measurements is very large. For example, human perception of certain sensory stimuli (such as loudness of sound) is approximately logarithmically related to the physical quantity that produces it (sound intensity).

a. Investigate how a logarithmic scale is used to measure some quantity such as star brightness, earthquake magnitude, or acidity. Find out what physical characteristics underlie the quantity, how the quantity is measured, how it is "transformed" to a logarithmic scale, and why or how the logarithmic scale is more useful than the original scale.

b. What is the Weber-Fechner law in physiology, and how does it relate to these issues?

5 Sequences for Fractals

The fractal called a Sierpinski Carpet results from a sequence of figures formed in the following manner. Draw a square with area 1. Then, divide the square into 9 squares and shade the middle square. Then, divide each of the unshaded squares into 9 units and shade the middle square. Repeat this indefinitely. Let $A(n)$ be the total shaded area after the nth step of this procedure.

a. Write a computer program to calculate $A(n)$ for $n = 1, 2, 3, \ldots, 100$.

b. Graph A for $n \leq 10$.

c. Describe the behavior of A as $n \to \infty$. What does this mean in terms of the Sierpinski Carpet?

d. Find a formula for $A(n)$ and use it to explain the behavior you noticed in part **c.**

e. Construct a similar sequence using a geometric figure of your own choice, and repeat parts **a–d** for your sequence.

$A(0) = 0$

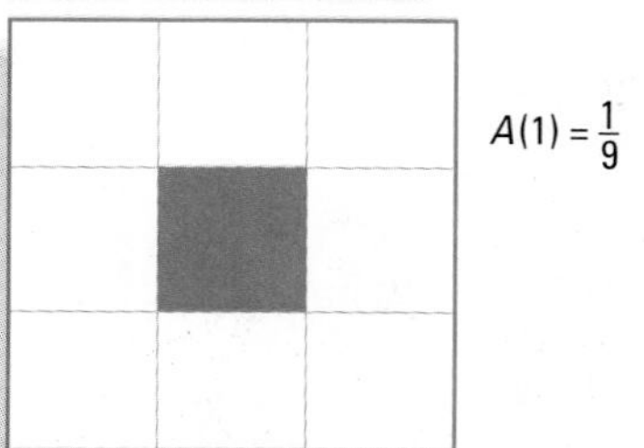

$A(1) = \frac{1}{9}$

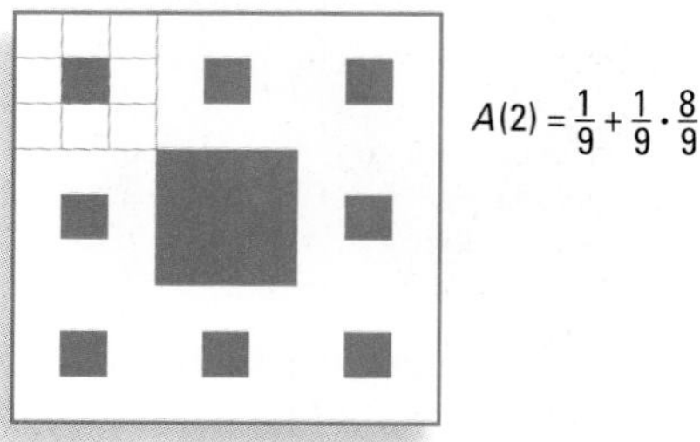

$A(2) = \frac{1}{9} + \frac{1}{9} \cdot \frac{8}{9}$

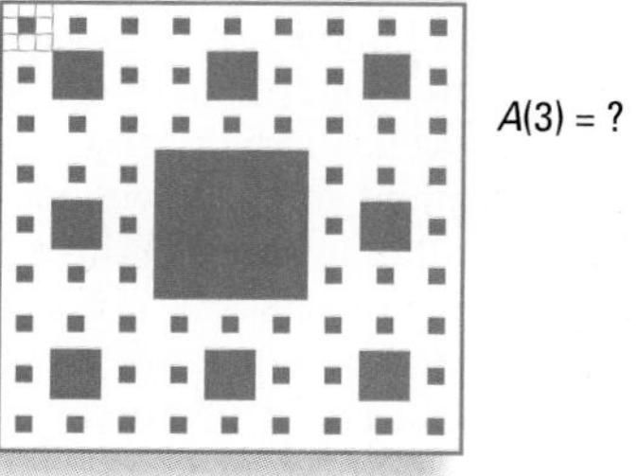

$A(3) = ?$

2. d. $x(t) = f(t) + g(t)$
$= (1 - t^2) + t(1 - t^2)$
$= (1 - t^2)(1 + t)$
$y(t) = f(t) - g(t)$
$= (1 - t^2) - t(1 - t^2)$
$= (1 - t^2)(1 - t)$

e. Sample: $\begin{cases} x(t) = e^{(-0.1t)} \cdot \cos t \\ y(t) = e^{(-0.1t)} \cdot \sin t, \end{cases}$

$0 \leq t \leq 8\pi$

3. a.

i. The Folium of Descartes is a plane cubic curve consisting of a single loop, a node, and two branches asymptotic to the same line. Its rectangular Cartesian equation is $x^3 + y^3 = 3axy$. It passes through the origin and is asymptotic to the line $x + y + a = 0$. The parametric equations are

$x(t) = \frac{3at}{t^3 + 1}$, $\quad y(t) = \frac{3at^2}{t^3 + 1}$.

ii. The hypocycloid is the curve traced by a point fixed on the circumference of a circle of radius b when this circle rolls along the inside of a circle of radius a, with $a > b$. The parametric equations are

$x = (a - b) \cos\theta + b \cos\left(\frac{a-b}{b}\right) \cdot \theta)$

$y = (a - b) \sin\theta - b \sin\left(\frac{a-b}{b}\right) \cdot \theta)$.

SUMMARY

A function f is a correspondence from one set A (the domain) to another set B which assigns to every element of A exactly one element of B. If the domain and range of f both consist of real numbers, then f is a real function. If the domain of f can be put into a 1-1 correspondence with a subset of the set of integers, then f is a function with a discrete domain.

A sequence is a function whose domain is the set of integers in the interval $[a, b]$ or $[a, \infty)$, where $a \geq 0$. A sequence may be defined by an explicit formula that gives the value of any term of the sequence directly, or it may be defined by a recursive formula (difference equation) that gives the value of any term of the sequence indirectly in terms of the values of preceding terms. Sequence models of real-world problems usually lead to sequences defined by difference equations. The process of finding an explicit formula for a sequence from a difference equation for that sequence is called "solving" the difference equation.

Many properties of a function f can be inferred from its graph and proven algebraically. Analyzing the function includes studying the following:

1. the domain of f.
2. the range of f.
3. the intervals on which f is increasing and decreasing.
4. the end behavior of f; that is, the limit of f as x becomes larger or smaller without bound. Since an infinite sequence is a function defined on the interval $[a, \infty)$, its end behavior is defined in the same way.
5. maximum and minimum values of f. If a value of f is a maximum or minimum only over a particular interval, it is called a relative maximum or minimum.
6. situations which are modeled by f.
7. special properties unique to f or functions of the same type.

Exponential functions and geometric sequences arise from situations of continuous growth or decay. Limited growth or decay is modeled by logistic sequences and functions.

Logarithmic functions are inverses of exponential functions. When the base of a logarithmic function g is greater than 1, g is increasing and $\lim\limits_{x\to\infty} g(x) = \infty$.

The trigonometric functions sine and cosine can be defined in terms of the unit circle. The sine and cosine functions are periodic of period 2π, and their range is $[-1, 1]$. They are alternately increasing and decreasing on intervals of length π, and have relative maxima and minima at regular intervals. The tangent function has period π and its range is the set of all real numbers. It is increasing on all intervals in its domain. Limits of the sine, cosine, and tangent of x as $x \to \infty$ and as $x \to -\infty$ do not exist.

When two or more variables are defined in terms of a particular variable, then they are said to be defined parametrically. Parametric equations for x and y in terms of a parameter enable a wide variety of curves to be defined, including many that are not graphs of functions mapping x onto y. In particular, the unit circle can be defined by the parametric equations $x = \cos\theta$, $y = \sin\theta$.

Summary

The Summary gives an overview of the entire chapter and provides an opportunity for students to consider the material as a whole. Thus, the Summary can be used to help students relate and unify the concepts presented in the chapter.

3. b.

i. Folium of Descartes ($a = 1$)

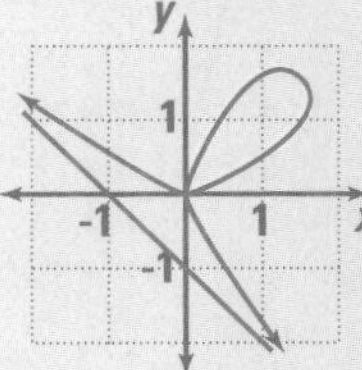

ii. Hypocycloid ($a = 3$, $b = 1$)

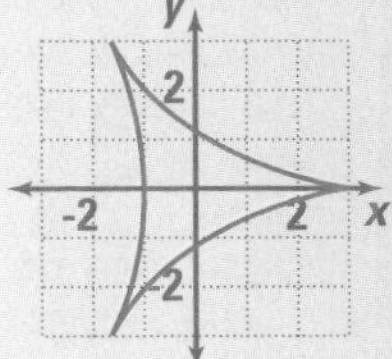

iii. Involute of a Circle ($a = 1$)

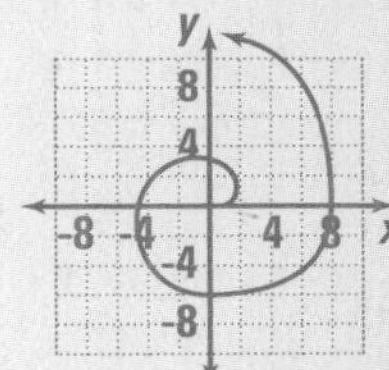

iv. Nephroid ($a = 1$)

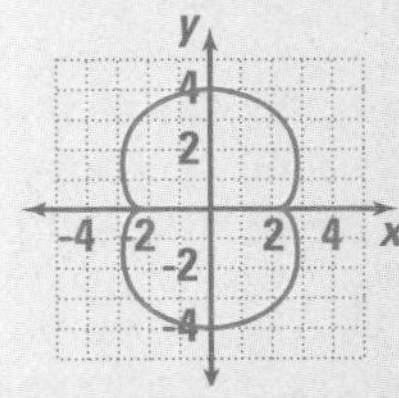

4. a. Earthquakes vary greatly in their magnitude, from quakes that people cannot feel to those that cause massive destruction. The amplitudes of the vibrations caused by earthquakes that are recorded by seismographs cover an extremely wide range. The Richter scale, developed by Charles Richter of the California Institute of Technology in 1935, is used to provide a more convenient measurement scale, in which the magnitude of an earthquake is represented by the

(Responses continue on page 140.)

iii. The involute of a circle is the curve described by the end of a thread as it is tautly unwound from a stationary spool. Parametric equations are
$x = a(\cos q + q\sin q)$
$y = a(\sin q - q\cos q)$,
where q is the angle from the x-axis to the radial line from the axis of the spool to the point of tangency of the unwound thread with the spool.

iv. The nephroid is the epicycloid formed by a circle of radius a rolling externally on a fixed circle of radius $2a$. Parametric equations are
$x = a(3\cos q - \cos 3q)$
$y = a(3\sin q - \sin 3q)$.
The curve can be observed as the pattern formed on the bottom of an empty flat-bottomed coffee mug when parallel light rays come in and bounce off the circular sides.

Vocabulary

Terms, symbols, and properties are listed by lesson to provide a checklist of concepts a student must know. Emphasize to students that they should read the vocabulary list carefully before starting the Progress Self-Test. If students do not understand the meaning of a term, they should refer back to the indicated lesson.

Additional Responses, page 138
Project 4. a. continued

common logarithm of the amplitude of the vibrations recorded by seismographs. Magnitudes of recorded earthquakes have varied on the Richter scale from 0 to about 8.9. An earthquake with a magnitude of 5.0 is generally considered moderate, those with magnitudes above 6.0 might be considered strong. Note that an increase of 1 in the Richter scale corresponds to a ten-fold increase in the amplitude of the recorded vibrations. Thus, an earthquake of magnitude 7.5 is 31 times more severe than one with magnitude 6.

4. b. The physiologists Ernest Weber and Gustav Fechner conducted research during the 19th century, in which they observed that the differences in the intensities of stimuli, like sound, light, and pressure, that people can detect are approximately proportional to the magnitude of the stimuli. For example, if a person can feel that an 11-pound weight is heavier than a 10-pound weight, he can feel that a 22-pound weight is heavier than a 20-pound weight. This research led to formulation of the "Weber-Fechner" law that the intensity of a stimulus perceived by a person is proportional to the actual intensity of the stimulus; i.e., $P = k \log(S/S_0)$, where S is the intensity of the stimulus, S_0 is a standard or baseline intensity level, and P is the perceived intensity. For example, for the decibel scale used to measure the perceived intensity of sound, $k = 10$ and S_0 is some reference level of sound intensity. e.g., $S_0 = 10^{-6}$ micro-watts/mm^2. Although the Weber-Fechner law works well for some intensity ranges of various stimuli, it has been found to be too inflexible to match a wider range of experimental results. For this reason, more flexible logarithmic equations that are modifications of the Weber-Fechner law have been adopted.

5. See Additional Answers at the back of this book.

CHAPTER TWO

VOCABULARY

Below are the most important terms and phrases for this chapter. You should be able to give a general description and a specific example of each and a precise definition for those marked with an asterisk (*).

Lesson 2-1
elementary functions
* function
independent variable
* domain
dependent variable
* range
real-valued function
* real function
interval
interval notation
* closed interval, $[a, b]$
* open interval, (a, b)
half-open interval, $[a, b)$
closed infinite interval, $[b, \infty)$
open infinite interval, $(-\infty, a)$
* discrete set
discrete function

Lesson 2-2
max-min problems
minimum value of a function
maximum value of a function

Lesson 2-3
increasing function
decreasing function
relative maximum value
relative minimum value

Lesson 2-4
end behavior
$\lim_{x\to\infty} f(x)$, $\lim_{x\to-\infty} f(x)$
horizontal asymptote
* power function
even, odd functions

Lesson 2-5
parameter
parametric equations

Lesson 2-6
unit circle
1 radian, 1 degree
sine, sin
cosine, cos
tangent, tan
Pythagorean Identity
periodic function
period of a function
fundamental period

Lesson 2-7
exponential function with base b
initial value
Continuous Change Model
standard normal distribution
arithmetic sequence
geometric sequence, exponential sequence

Lesson 2-8
* sequence
infinite sequence
finite sequence
nth term
explicit formula
recursive formula
initial conditions
difference equation, recurrence relation
Fibonacci sequence
logistic model, limited growth model
solving the difference equation

Lesson 2-9
* logarithm of x to the base b, $\log_b x$
logarithm function
* common logarithm, log
* natural logarithm, ln
Change of Base Theorem

CHAPTER TWO

PROGRESS SELF-TEST

2) See below right.

Give yourself 40 minutes to take this test. Check the test yourself, using the answers at the end of this book. 3a, b, 5a, 6, 8b, 9) See margin.

1. Consider the real function defined by $w = g(z) = \frac{z-2}{\sqrt{z+5}}$.
- **a.** Identify the dependent variable. w
- **b.** Identify the independent variable. z
- **c.** What is the domain of the function? $\{z: z > -5\}$

2. Suppose $f(x) = 2x^2 + 4x + 3$. Find the minimum value of f and give its range.

3. Consider the function g graphed here.
- **a.** Identify the interval(s) over which g is increasing and over which g is decreasing.
- **b.** Find any relative maximum and minimum values.
- **c.** Find $\lim_{x \to \infty} g(x)$. ∞
- **d.** Describe the values of x such that $g(x) \le 0$ and write the answer in interval notation. $(-\infty, -2] \cup [0, 2]$

4. Give one interval of length π where the cosine function is increasing. $[\pi, 2\pi]$

5. a. Graph the sequence $d_n = \frac{-8}{2^n}$ for $n = 1, 2, 3, 4, 5, 6$. b) increasing
- **b.** Is d increasing, decreasing, or neither?
- **c.** Find $\lim_{n \to \infty} d_n$. 0

6. A farmer is going to fence off a rectangular pen along one wall of the chicken coop. The area of the pen is to be 300 square feet, and a minimum of fencing is to be used. Note that fencing is needed on only three sides of the pen.
- **a.** Express the length of the pen in terms of the width w.
- **b.** Express the amount of fencing $f(w)$ in terms of the width.
- **c.** Using an automatic grapher, sketch a graph of f.
- **d.** Find the dimensions of the pen that use the least amount of fencing.

7) $\frac{1}{\log_{10} a}(2 \log_{10} N - \log_{10} P)$

7. Rewrite the expression $\log_a \frac{N^2}{P}$ in terms of $\log_{10} N$, $\log_{10} P$, and $\log_{10} a$.

8. Consider this problem. A baseball is hit with a horizontal velocity of 70 ft/sec and a vertical velocity of 30 ft/sec. If home plate is the origin of a coordinate system for the path of the ball, will the ball go over the right field wall, which is 365 feet from home plate and 15 feet high?
- **a.** Write parametric equations for the path of the ball. $x(t) = 70t$, $y(t) = -16t^2 + 30t$
- **b.** Graph the equations in the xy-plane and use it to answer the question.

9. Analyze the function f, where $f(x) = -2\sin x$.

10. The radioactive isotope Carbon 14 used to date fossils decays continuously with a half-life of 5715 years. If a fossil is found which originally had 2 mg of Carbon 14, and it now has 0.18 mg, how old is it? $t \approx 19{,}854$ years

11. Gamma Tool Company had sales of 14.7 million dollars in 1990, and annual sales have grown by 2.5 million each year since 1990. Assuming this trend continues, find a difference equation and an explicit formula for the sequence G, where G_n = annual sales for the Gamma Tool Company n years after 1990.
Let $G_0 = 14.7$, then $G_{n+1} = G_n + 2.5$ (in millions of dollars); $G_n = 14.7 + 2.5n$ (in millions of dollars)

2) minimum value: 1; range: $\{y: y \le 1\}$

Progress Self-Test

For the development of mathematical competence, feedback and correction, along with the opportunity to practice, are necessary. The Progress Self-Test provides the opportunity for feedback and correction; the Chapter Review provides additional opportunities and practice. We cannot overemphasize the importance of these end-of-chapter materials. It is at this point that the material "gels" for many students, allowing them to solidify skills and understanding. In general, student performance should be markedly improved after these pages.

Assign the Progress Self-Test as a one-night assignment. Worked-out *solutions* for all questions are in the Selected Answers section of the student book. Encourage students to take the Progress Self-Test honestly, grade themselves, and then be prepared to discuss the test in class.

Advise students to pay special attention to those Chapter Review questions (pages 142–145) that correspond to questions missed on the Progress Self-Test.

8. b.

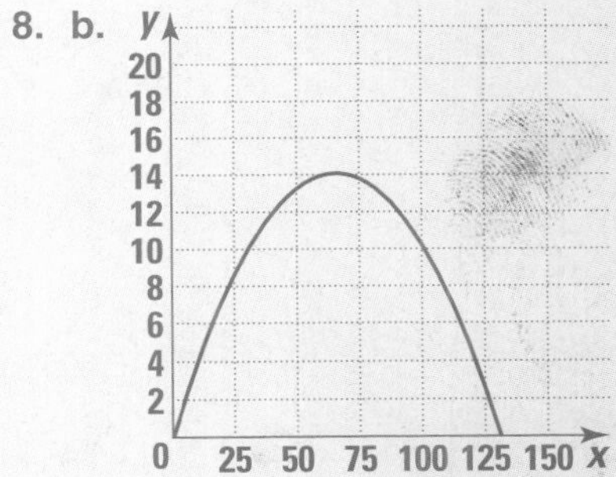

The ball lands about 131 ft from home plate; it will not clear the right field wall.

9. domain: real numbers
range $-2 \le y \le 2$
relative max = 2;
relative min = -2
increasing: $[\frac{\pi}{2} + 2n\pi, \frac{3\pi}{2} + 2n\pi]$, $\forall$ integers n;
decreasing: $[-\frac{\pi}{2} + 2n\pi, \frac{\pi}{2} + 2n\pi]$, $\forall$ integers n limits undefined
model: phenomena based on rotations, sound waves
special properties: period = 2π, odd function

Additional Answers

3. a. increasing over $(-\infty, -1)$, $(1, \infty)$
decreasing over $(-1, 1)$
b. relative max. = 1;
relative min. = -1

5. a.

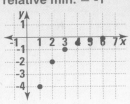

6. a. $l = \frac{300}{w}$
b. $f(w) = \frac{300}{w} + 2w$
c. See graph at the right.
d. $w \approx 12.25$ ft; $l \approx 24.49$ ft

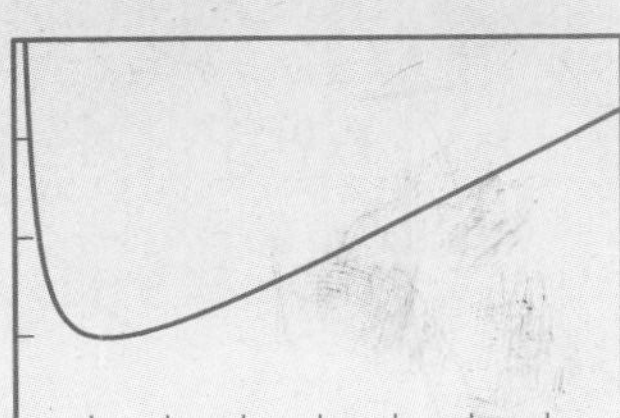

$0 \le x \le 80$, x-scale = 10
$0 \le y \le 200$, y-scale = 50

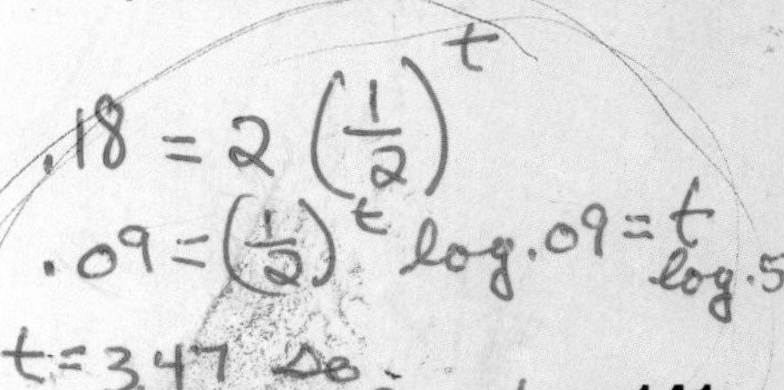

Chapter 2 Review

Resources

From the ***Teacher's Resource File***

- Answer Master for Chapter 2 Review
- Assessment Sourcebook:
  Chapter 2 Test, Forms A–D
  Chapter 2 Test, Cumulative Form

Additional Resources

- TestWorks CD-ROM

The main objectives for the chapter are organized in the Chapter Review under the four types of understanding this book promotes—Skills, Properties, Uses, and Representations.

Whereas end-of chapter material may be considered optional in some texts, in UCSMP *Precalculus and Discrete Mathematics* we have selected these objectives and questions with the expectation that they will be covered. Students should be able to answer these questions with about 85% accuracy after studying the chapter.

Additional Answers

1. a. increasing on [1900, 1930] and [1950, 1970]
   decreasing on [1930, 1950] and [1970, 1990]
   b. No; 1930 , 1940 but 25,678 . 25,111
2. a. max: (1930, 25,678); (1970, 45,619)
   min: (1950, 25,111)
   b. Sample: (1930, 1990)
5. a. arithmetic
   b. decreasing
6. a. neither
   b. neither
7. a. neither
   b. decreasing
9. $2^x = 8$; $x = 3$
10. $2^8 = x$; $x = 256$
11. $b^2 = 9$; $b = 3$
12. $t = \log_6 42 = \frac{\log 42}{\log 6} = 2.086$
13. $3^{-2} = \frac{2z}{5}$; $z = \frac{5}{18}$
14. $x = \log_7 12 = \frac{\log 12}{\log 7} = 1.277$
15. $2 \log N + 3 \log M - \log P$
16. $\frac{1}{2} \log N + \log M - \frac{3}{2} \log P$
17. No, each element in S corresponds to more than one element in R.

CHAPTER REVIEW

Questions on SPUR Objectives

SPUR stands for **S**kills, **P**roperties, **U**ses, and **R**epresentations. The Chapter Review questions are grouped according to the SPUR Objectives for this chapter.

SKILLS DEAL WITH THE PROCEDURES USED TO GET ANSWERS.

1, 2, 5, 6, 7, 9 – 16) See margin.

Objective A: *Determine relative minima and maxima of a function and intervals on which it is increasing or decreasing.* *(Lessons 2-2, 2-3)*

In 1 and 2, refer to the table below, which gives total enrollment (in thousands) in U.S. public elementary and secondary schools. Let E be the function that maps year to enrollment.

Year	Enrollment	Year	Enrollment
1900	15,503	1950	25,111
1910	17,814	1960	36,087
1920	21,578	1970	45,619
1930	25,678	1980	41,645
1940	25,434	1990	41,217

(Source: *The World Almanac and Book of Facts* 1996)

1. a. Find the intervals on which E is increasing and on which E is decreasing.

b. Note that $E(1900) < E(1940)$. Is E increasing on the interval $1900 \le x \le 1940$? Justify your answer.

2. a. Find all relative minimum and maximum values of E and give the years at which they occur.

b. Choose one of the relative minima from part **a,** and find an interval (containing the year in which the relative minimum occurs) on which E is greater than or equal to that minimum value.

3. Consider the function $f(t) = -3t^2 + 4t + 1$.

a. Find the intervals on which f is increasing and on which f is decreasing. See below.

b. Find any relative minimum and maximum values of f. relative minimum: $\frac{2}{3}$

a) increasing on $\left(-\infty, \frac{2}{3}\right]$; decreasing on $\left[\frac{2}{3}, \infty\right)$

4. Consider the sequence $s_n = \sin \frac{n\pi}{2}$.

a. Find s_n for all integers n in the interval $0 \le n \le 8$. 0, 1, 0, -1, 0, 1, 0, -1, 0

b. Find an interval of longest possible length on which s is increasing. $3 \le n \le 5$

c. Find an interval of longest possible length on which s is decreasing. $1 \le n \le 3$

d. Find the first three values of n at which s has a relative maximum. 1, 5, 9

e. Find the first three values of n at which s has a relative minimum. 3, 7, 11

In 5–7, a sequence is defined. **a.** Identify the sequence as geometric, arithmetic, or neither. **b.** Determine whether it is increasing, decreasing, or neither.

5. $a_n = 5 - 2n \quad \forall$ integers $n > 0$

6. $c_n = \cos n\pi \quad \forall$ integers $n > 0$

7. $\begin{cases} b_1 = 1 \\ b_k = \frac{k}{k+1} b_{k-1} \quad \forall k > 1 \end{cases}$

8. If a function g is decreasing on an interval $a \le x \le b$ and increasing on an interval $b \le x \le c$, then g has a _?_ at b. relative minimum

Objective B: *Rewrite exponential and logarithmic expressions and equations.* *(Lessons 2-7, 2-9)*

In 9–14, use the definition or properties of logarithms to rewrite the equation and solve.

9. $\log_2 8 = x$

10. $\log_2 x = 8$

11. $\log_b 9 = 2$

12. $6^t = 42$

13. $\log_3 2z - \log_3 5 = -2$

14. $\log_7 12 = x$

In 15 and 16, rewrite the expression in terms of $\log N$, $\log M$, and $\log P$.

15. $\log \frac{N^2 \cdot M^3}{P}$

16. $\log \left(\frac{N \cdot M^2}{P^3}\right)^{1/2}$

18. Yes, each element in R corresponds to exactly one element in S. Yes, it is discrete.
    domain: $\{x: x \text{ an integer}, 1 \le x \le 25\}$
    range: {18, 56.25, 45}
    minimum: 18
    maximum: 56.25
19. a. Yes, it is a function. It is not discrete since L can take any real values between 0 and 320.
    b. L, length of skid marks
    c. speed of the car, S
    d. $\{L: 0 \le L \le 320\}$
    e. $\{s: 0 \le s \le 80\}$
20. the set of real numbers
21. the set of real numbers except $r \ne 5$, $r \ne -4$

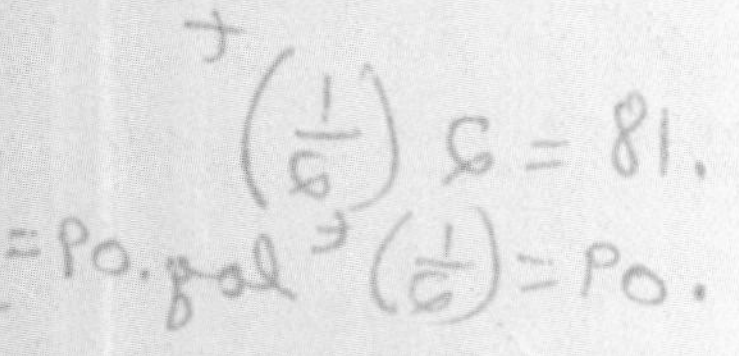

PROPERTIES DEAL WITH THE PRINCIPLES BEHIND THE MATHEMATICS.

17–21, 23–25, 28–30b, 34–37) See margin.

Objective C: *Identify the domain, range, and minimum and maximum values of functions.* *(Lessons 2-1, 2-2)*

In 17 and 18, refer to the table below which gives student prices for a series of symphony orchestra concerts based on the row assignment. Let R be the set of row numbers and S be the set of series prices.

Row Number	Series Price
1–2	\$18.00
3–13	\$56.25
14–25	\$45.00

17. For each s in S, let $f(s)$ = a particular row number associated with series price s. Is $f: S \to R$ a function? Why or why not? If it is a function, tell whether it is a discrete function and identify its domain, range, minimum value, and maximum value.

18. For each r in R, let $g(r)$ = the series price associated with row r. Is $g: R \to S$ a function? Why or why not? If it is a function, tell whether it is a discrete function and identify its domain, range, minimum value, and maximum value.

19. For $0 \le s \le 80$, the equation $f(L) = s = 2\sqrt{5L}$ relates the speed s of a car in miles per hour to the length L of the skid marks in feet once brakes are applied.

a. Does this equation define a function? If so, is it a discrete function? If not, why not?

b. Identify the independent variable.

c. Identify the dependent variable.

d. Identify the domain.

e. Identify the range.

In 20–22, a real function f is defined according to the indicated rule. Identify the domain.

20. $f(p) = 4p^3 - 2p^2 + 3p + 1$

21. $f(r) = \dfrac{r^2 - 7r + 10}{r^2 - r - 20}$

22. $f(z) = 3\sqrt{z - 7}$ $\{z: z \ge 7\}$

In 23–25, suppose g is defined by $g(x) = 2x - 1$ and has the indicated domain. Find the minimum and maximum values of g (if they exist) and give the range of g.

23. {-1, -5, 0, 5, 10}

24. the set of positive integers

25. the set of real numbers

26. Find the range of $h: t \to -4t^2 + 6t - 7$ if the domain is as indicated.

a. the interval $-1 \le t \le 2$ $[-17, -4.75]$

b. the set of real numbers $(-\infty, -4.75]$

27. A function k is defined by $k(x) = x^3 + 1$ on the domain $5 \le x \le 10$. What is the range? $[126, 1001]$

Objective D: *Determine the end behavior of a function.* *(Lessons 2-4, 2-6, 2-7, 2-8, 2-9)*

28. Describe the end behavior of $f: x \to 2e^x$.

29. Describe the end behavior of the cosine function.

30. Consider the sequence given in Question 5.

a. Find the values of n for which $a_n < -100$.

b. Find the values of n for which $a_n < -1000$.

c. Find $\lim_{x\to-\infty} a_n$. $-\infty$

31. Find the limit of the sequence given in Question 6. no limit exists

32. Find the limit of the sequence given in Question 7. 0

33. Let $h(x) = x \sin\left(\frac{1}{x}\right)$.

a. Use a calculator to estimate $\lim_{x\to-\infty} h(x)$. 1

b. For what values of x is $h(x)$ within .001 of that limit? $|x| \ge 13$

c. Estimate $\lim_{x\to-\infty} h(x)$. 1

d. Find the equations of all horizontal asymptotes. $y = 1$

In 34 and 35, a function is defined. **a.** Describe its end behavior. **b.** Give the equations of any horizontal asymptotes.

34. $f(y) = -4 - \frac{1}{y^3}$

35. $g(y) = -4y^4 - \frac{1}{y^3}$

36. Suppose the function h is odd and $\lim_{z\to\infty} h(z) = 10$. Find $\lim_{z\to-\infty} h(z)$.

37. Describe the end behavior of the function $f(x) = b^x$ for each of the following.

a. $b = .99$ **b.** $b = 1.00$ **c.** $b = 1.01$

You may assign these questions over a single night, or you may assign the questions over a two-day period. If you work the questions over two days, we recommend assigning the *evens* first so that students get feedback the next day, then assigning the *odds* the night before the test, because answers are provided to the odd-numbered questions.

It is effective to ask students which questions they still do not understand and use the day or days as a total class discussion of the material which the class finds most difficult.

Assessment

Evaluation The Assessment Sourcebook provides five forms of the Chapter 2 Test. Forms A and B present parallel versions in a short-answer format. Forms C and D offer performance assessment. The fifth test is Chapter 2 Test, Cumulative Form. About 50% of this test covers Chapter 2, 50% of it covers Chapter 1.

For information on grading, see *General Teaching Suggestions: Grading* in the *Professional Sourcebook,* which begins on page T20 in the Teacher's Edition.

23. minimum: -11
maximum: 19
y: {-11, -3, -1, 9, 19}

24. minimum: 1
no maximum
range: the set of positive odd integers

25. range: (∞, ∞)
no maximum or minimum

28. $\lim_{x\to\infty} 2e^x = \infty$, $\lim_{x\to-\infty} 2e^x = 0$

29. $\lim_{x\to-\infty} \cos x$ = undefined,
$\lim_{x\to\infty} \cos x$ = undefined

30. a. $n \ge 53$
b. $n \ge 503$

34. a. $\lim_{y\to\infty} f(y) = -4$, $\lim_{y\to-\infty} f(y) = -4$
b. $y = -4$

35. a. $\lim_{y\to\infty} g(y) = -\infty$, $\lim_{y\to-\infty} g(y) = -\infty$
b. none

36. -10

37. a. $\lim_{x\to\infty} b^x = 0$, $\lim_{x\to-\infty} b^x = \infty$
b. $\lim_{x\to\infty} b^x = \lim_{x\to-\infty} b^x = 1$
c. $\lim_{x\to\infty} b^x = \infty$, $\lim_{x\to-\infty} b^x = 0$

Feedback After students have taken the test for Chapter 2 and you have scored the results, return the tests to students for discussion. Class discussion of the questions that caused trouble for the most students can be very effective in identifying and clarifying misunderstandings. You might want to have them write down the items they missed and work, either in groups or at home, to correct them. It is important for students to receive feedback on every chapter test, and we recommend that students see and correct their mistakes before proceeding too far into the next chapter.

Additional Answers

43. a. $P_{n+1} = (1.25)P_n$
b. $P_{n+1} = (1.25)P_n + 500$
c. $P_{n+1} = (1.25)P_n - \frac{.25P_n^2}{15000}$

44. a. $h = \frac{25}{b}$
b. $A = (b + 1)\left(\frac{25}{b} + 2\right)$
c. About 4.54 in. by 9[illegible].7 in.

46. a. Increasing over: [-4, -2], [0, 3]
Decreasing over: (-∞, -4], [-2, 0], [3, ∞)
b. relative minima: (-4, -3), (0, -4.5)
relative maxima: (-2, 4), (3, 0.5)
c. neither

47. a. increasing over: [-4, 0]
decreasing over: [0, 4]
b. relative maxima at (0, 4)
c. even

48. a. increasing over: (-∞, -4], [-3, -2], [2, 3], [4, ∞)
decreasing over: [-4, -3], [-1, 1], [3, 4]
b. relative maxima at (-4, 3), (3, -1.5), $-1 \le x \le 2$, $y = -2$, and $-2 \le x \le -1$, $y = 2$
relative minima at (-3, 1.5), (4, -3), $-2 \le x \le -1$, $y = 2$, and $1 \le x \le 2$, $y = -2$
c. odd

49. a. $x = \{-6, -3, -1, 2, 4\}$
b. in the intervals (-6, -3), (-1, 2), (4, ∞)
c. in the intervals (∞, -6), (-3, -1), (2, 4)
d. $x = -1.5$, $x = -2.5$, $x = -7$
e. x in the intervals (-∞, -7), (-2.5, -1.5)

CHAPTER TWO

USES DEAL WITH APPLICATIONS OF MATHEMATICS IN REAL SITUATIONS.

43, 44) See margin.

Objective E: *Use sequences and exponential and logarithmic functions as models.* *(Lessons 2-7, 2-8, 2-9)*

38. A sheet of paper is 0.1 mm thick. When it is folded in half once, the folded sheet is 0.2 mm thick. Folding it in half again produces a stack 0.4 mm thick. Define the function g so that $g(n)$ is the thickness when folded n times.

a. Is g discrete? yes

b. Find a formula for $g(n)$. 12.8 mm

c. How thick is the stack after 7 folds? $g(n) = 2^n(.1)$

d. How many folds are required to obtain a stack that at least reaches the moon, which is 380,000 km from the earth? 42 folds

39. a. At what interest rate, compounded continuously, will \$1500 grow to \$2500 in 5 years? ≈ 10.22%

b. At what rate of simple interest would \$1500 grow to \$2500 in 5 years? (Simple interest adds the same amount, a percent of the original investment, each year.) ≈ 13.33%

40. The pH of a chemical solution is given by

$$\text{pH} = -\log x$$

where x is the H_3O^+ ion concentration in moles per liter. a) ≈ 11.6 b) 1×10^{-7} moles/liter

a. What is the pH of a solution whose H_3O^+ concentration is $2.7 \cdot 10^{-12}$ moles per liter?

b. What H_3O^+ concentration corresponds to a pH of 7?

41. Suppose each time a liquid is passed through a filter, 73% of the impurities are removed. If a liquid starts out 60% pure, how many times must it be filtered to obtain a liquid that is at least 99.9% pure? (Hint: Study the percentage of impurity instead of the percentage of purity.) 20

42. The loudness L of a sound, measured in decibels (dB), is given by the formula $L = 10 \log_{10}(I \cdot 10^{12})$, where I is the intensity of the sound, measured in watts/m^2. Near an airport, suppose that an overhead airplane creates a noise level of 60 dB. Assuming that the intensity of the sound is directly proportional to the number of such planes, how many planes could be overhead simultaneously without surpassing the "annoyance level" of 65 dB? 3 planes

43. A lake is initially stocked with 2000 fish of a new species. Left undisturbed, the fish population will grow about 25% each year.

a. Write a difference equation for the sequence P of fish populations at the end of n years (assuming an unlimited growth model).

b. Suppose that an additional 500 fish are stocked each year after the initial stocking. Modify the difference equation in part **a** to account for this.

c. Instead of assuming an unlimited growth model, suppose the lake has a support limit of 15,000 fish of this species. Modify the difference equation of part **a** to account for this.

Objective F: *Solve max-min problems.* *(Lesson 2-2)*

44. A rectangular flyer contains 25 in^2 of printed material with a 1 in. margin at the top and bottom and a $\frac{1}{2}$ in. margin on either side. Let b and h represent the dimensions of the printed material.

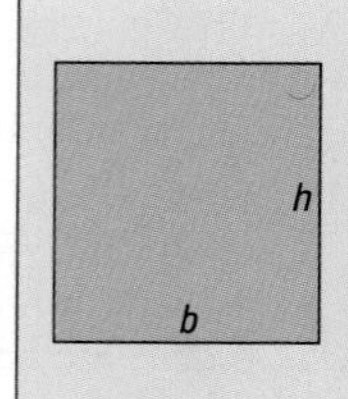

a. Write an equation for h in terms of b.

b. Write an equation giving the area, A, of the entire flyer as a function of b.

c. Find the dimensions of the flyer that uses the least amount of paper.

45. A restaurant determines that it costs \$5 to make a small cheese pizza, and that the number of these pizzas it can sell in a day is approximately $100 - 10p$, where p is the price it charges per pizza.

a. Write an expression for the profit the restaurant makes on each cheese pizza in terms of p. $p - 5$ b) $-10p^2 + 150p - 500$

b. Write the profit it makes in a day from all small cheese pizzas sold as a function of p.

c. Find the price the restaurant should charge to maximize its total profit from these pizzas. What is that profit? price = \$7.50; profit = \$62.50

52. Sample:

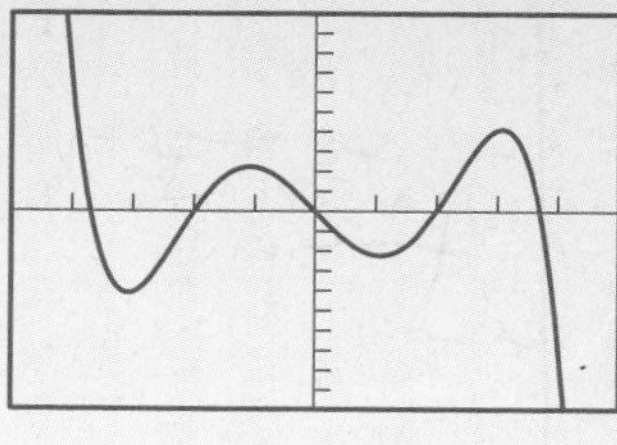

$-5 \le x \le 5$, x-scale = 1
$-10 \le y \le 10$, y-scale = 1

53. a. decreasing over: (-∞, 2.1]
increasing over: [2.1, ∞)
b. relative minimum: $y = -4$
c. $\lim_{x\to-\infty} f(x) = \infty$, $\lim_{x\to\infty} f(x) = \infty$
d. $\{y: y \ge -4\}$
e. neither

54. a. increasing on the reals; decreasing nowhere
b. none
c. $\lim_{x\to\infty} f(x) = 1$, $\lim_{x\to-\infty} f(x) = -1$
d. $\{y: -1 < y < 1\}$
e. odd

REPRESENTATIONS DEAL WITH PICTURES, GRAPHS, OR OBJECTS THAT ILLUSTRATE CONCEPTS.

46–49, 52–59) See margin.

Objective G: *Analyze a function from its graph.* *(Lessons 2-2, 2-3, 2-4, 2-6, 2-7, 2-8, 2-9)*

In 46–48, the graph of a function is given.

a. Estimate the interval(s) over which the function is increasing and over which it is decreasing.

b. Estimate the locations and values of any relative minima and maxima.

c. Is the function even, odd, or neither?

46. **47.**

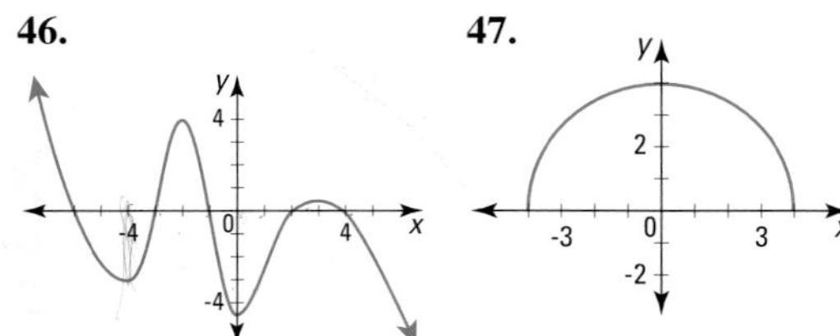

48.

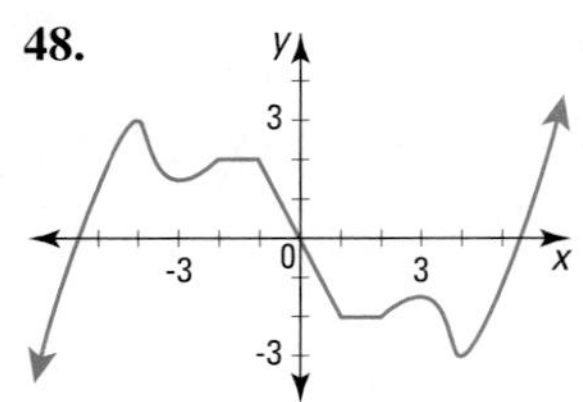

49. Refer to the function f graphed in Question 46. Approximately, for which values of x is

a. $f(x) = 0$? **b.** $f(x) < 0$? **c.** $f(x) > 0$?

d. $f(x) = 3$? **e.** $f(x) > 3$?

50. What is the range of the function graphed in Question 47? **$\{y: 0 \le y \le 4\}$**

51. Refer to function g, graphed at the right.

a. Identify the domain of g.

b. Identify the range of g.

c. *True or false.* g is decreasing on the interval $-5 \le x \le 0$. **False**

d. *True or false.* g has a relative minimum at $x = 0$. **True**

a) $\{x: -6 \le x \le 6\}$ b) $\{0, 1, 2, 3, 4, 5\}$

52. Sketch the graph of an odd function h such that $\lim_{t \to -\infty} h(t) = \infty$, h is increasing on the interval $-3 \le t \le -1$, h has a relative maximum at $t = -1$, and $h(-1) = 2$.

In 53 and 54, use an automatic grapher.

a. Estimate the interval(s) over which the function is increasing and over which it is decreasing.

b. Estimate any relative minima and maxima to the nearest tenth.

c. Determine the end behavior of the function.

d. Estimate the range of the function.

e. Determine if the function is even, odd, or neither.

53. $f(x) = x^4 - 3x^3 + 2x^2 - 5x + 6$

54. $f: x \to \frac{e^x - 1}{e^x + 1}$

55. Analyze the function $f(x) = ax^2$ for

a. $a > 0$. **b.** $a < 0$.

56. Analyze the function $h(z) = 3 - 2 \cos z$.

Objective H: *Find and graph parametric equations.* *(Lesson 2-5)*

In 57 and 58, graph the given parametric equations.

57. $\begin{cases} x(t) = t^2 \\ y(t) = t \end{cases}$ $-10 \le t \le 10$

58. $\begin{cases} x(t) = 2 \cos t + 1 \\ y(t) = \sin t - 2 \end{cases}$ $0 \le t \le 2\pi$

59. Consider this situation. A ball is thrown off the roof of a building 15 m high in the direction of a neighboring building 30 m away with a roof which is 20 m high. If the ball is thrown with a horizontal velocity of 20 m/sec and a vertical velocity of 25 m/sec, and assuming negligible air resistance, is it possible for the ball to hit the roof of the neighboring building?

a. Write parametric equations for the path of the ball.

b. Graph the equations in the xy-plane and use the graphs to answer the question.

56. i. Domain: the set of real numbers
ii. range: $\{y: 1 \le y \le 5\}$
iii. increasing over $2n\pi, \pi + 2n\pi]$, $\forall$ integers n; decreasing over $2(n-1)\pi \le y \le 2n\pi$
iv. maximum = 5; minimum = 1
v. no limits
vi. models: sound waves, periodic phenomena
vii. properties: even function, period = 2π

57.

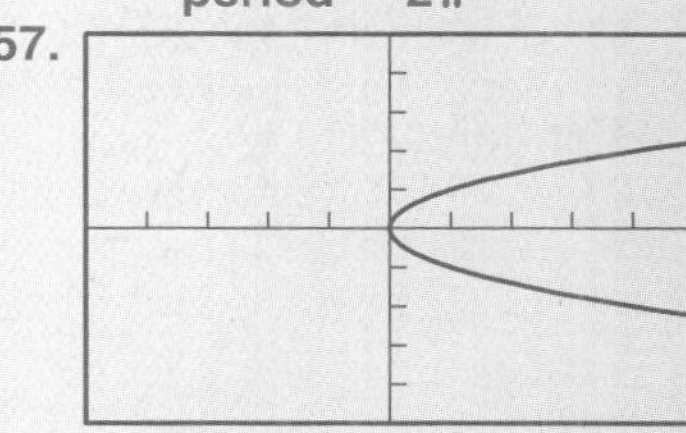

$-10 \le t \le 10$, t-step = 1
$-5 \le x \le 5$, x-scale = 1
$-5 \le y \le 5$, y-scale = 1

58.

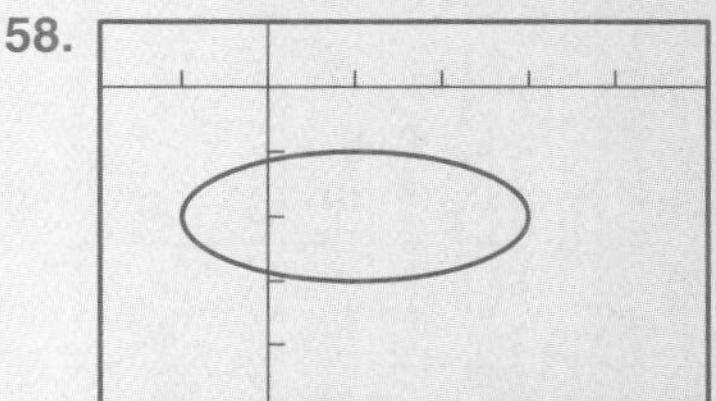

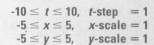

$0 \le t \le 2\pi$, t-step = $\frac{\pi}{2}$
$-2 \le x \le 5$, x-scale = 1
$-5 \le y \le 1$, y-scale = 1

59. a. $x = 20t$, $y = -4.9t^2 + 25t + 15$

b.

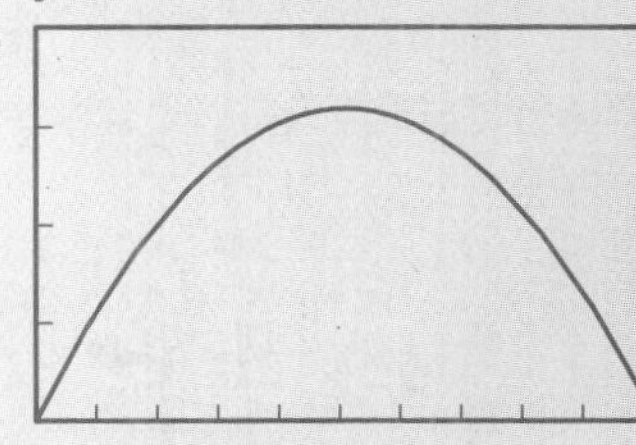

$0 \le t \le 10$, t-step = 1
$0 \le x \le 100$, x-scale = 10
$0 \le y \le 40$, y-scale = 10

Answers will vary. It will depend on the width of the neighboring building.

55. a. i. Domain: the set of real numbers
ii. range: $\{y: y \ge 0\}$
iii. increasing over: $[0, \infty)$ decreasing over: $(-\infty, 0]$
iv. no maximum value minimum = 0
v. $\lim_{x \to \pm\infty} f(x) = \infty$
vi. models: optics, acoustics (subject to restrictions on domain)
vii. properties: even

b. i. Domain: set of real numbers
ii. range: $\{y: y \le 0\}$
iii. increasing over: $(-\infty, 0]$ decreasing over: $[0, \infty)$
iv. maximum = 0; no minimum
v. $\lim_{x \to \pm\infty} f(x) = -\infty$
vi. model: projectile motion (subject to restrictions on domain)
vii. properties: even, a reflection image of $y = |a| x^2$ over the x-axis

Chapter 3 Planner

Adapting to Individual Needs

The student text is written for the vast majority of students. The chart at the right suggests two pacing plans to accommodate the needs of your students. Students in the Full Course should complete the entire text by the end of the year. Students in the Minimal Course will spend more time when there are quizzes and more time on the Chapter Review. Therefore, these students may not complete all of the chapters in the text.

Options are also presented to meet the needs of a variety of teaching and learning styles. For each lesson, the Teacher's Edition provides a section entitled *Adapting to Individual Needs.* This section regularly includes **Optional Activities, Challenge** problems, **English Language Development** suggestions, and suggestions for providing **Extra Help.** The Teacher's Edition also frequently includes an **Error Alert,** an **Extension,** and an **Assessment** alternative. The options available in Chapter 3 are summarized in the chart below.

Chapter 3 Pacing Chart

Day	Full Course	Minimal Course
1	3-1	3-1
2	3-2	3-2
3	3-3	3-3
4	3-4	3-4
5	Quiz*; 3-5.	Quiz*; begin 3-5.
6	3-6	Finish 3-5.
7	3-7	3-6
8	3-8	3-7
9	Quiz*; 3-9.	3-8
10	3-10	Quiz*; begin 3-9.
11	Self-Test	Finish 3-9.
12	Test*	3-10
13	Comprehensive Test*	Self-Test
14		Review
15		Review
16		Test*
17		Comprehensive Test*

*in the Teacher's Resource File

In the Teacher's Edition...

Lesson	Optional Activities	Extra Help	Challenge	English Language Development	Error Alert	Extension	Cooperative Learning	Ongoing Assessment
3-1	●	●	●		●	●	●	Group
3-2	●	●	●		●	●	●	Written
3-3	●	●	●		●	●		Oral
3-4	●	●	●		●	●	●	Quiz
3-5	●	●	●		●	●	●	Written
3-6	●	●	●		●	●	●	Oral
3-7	●	●	●		●	●		Oral
3-8	●	●	●		●	●		Quiz
3-9	●	●	●		●	●	●	Written
3-10	●	●	●		●	●	●	Written

In the Additional Resources...

	In the Teacher's Resource File							
Lesson	Lesson Masters	Teaching Aids*	Answer Masters	Technology Sourcebook	Assessment Sourcebook	Visual Aids**	Technology	Explorations Software
3-1	3-1	26, 28	3-1			26, 28, AM		3-1
3-2	3-2	26	3-2			26, AM		3-2
3-3	3-3	26	3-3			26, AM		
3-4	3-4	26	3-4		Quiz	26, AM		3-4
3-5	3-5	26, 29, 30	3-5			26, 29, 30, AM		
3-6	3-6	27	3-6			27, AM		
3-7	3-7	27	3-7	Calc 4		27, AM		
3-8	3-8	27, 31	3-8		Quiz	27, 31, AM		3-8
3-9	3-9	27	3-9			27, AM		
3-10		27	3-10			27, AM		
End of chapter					Tests			

*Teaching Aids are pictured on pages 146C.

**Visual Aids provide transparencies for all Teaching Aids and all Answer Masters.

Also available is the Study Skills Handbook which includes study-skill tips related to reading, note-taking, and comprehension.

Integrating Strands and Applications

	3-1	3-2	3-3	3-4	3-5	3-6	3-7	3-8	3-9	3-10
Mathematical Connections										
Number Sense						●	●	●	●	●
Algebra	●	●	●	●	●	●	●	●	●	
Logic and Reasoning	●		●	●	●	●			●	●
Patterns and Functions	●	●	●	●	●	●	●	●	●	
Discrete Mathematics	●								●	
Interdisciplinary and Other Connections										
Art						●				
Music				●						
Literature										●
Science	●		●	●		●				●
Social Studies	●		●							
Multicultural										●
Technology	●	●	●	●	●		●	●		
Career	●		●	●					●	
Consumer	●	●	●	●	●	●	●			
Sports		●				●				

Teaching and Assessing the Chapter Objectives

				In the Teacher's Resource File		
Chapter 3 Objectives (Organized into the SPUR catetgories—Skills, Properties, Uses, and Representations)	**Lessons**	**Progress Self-Test Questions**	**Chapter Review Questions**	**Chapter Test, Forms A and B**	**Chapter Test, Forms C**	**D**
Skills						
A: Solve equations by applying a function to each side, taking into account nonreversible steps.	3-3, 3-9	1, 2	1–14	11	2	
B: Describe the sum, difference, product, quotient, and composite of two given functions.	3-1, 3-2	6, 7	15–19	1, 2	1	
C: Find zeros of functions using factoring or chunking.	3-6	10, 13	20–25	4	4	
D: Solve inequalities algebraically.	3-5, 3-7, 3-8, 3-9	3, 12	26–31	7	3	
Properties						
E: Analyze the reversibility of steps used in solving equations and inequalities.	3-3, 3-5	4	32–36	12	2	
F: Identify and prove properties of inverse functions.	3-2, 3-5	11	37–39	5		
G: Identify continuous functions and their properties, such as the Intermediate Value Theorem.	3-4	9, 14	40–44	8, 9, 10	5	
Uses						
H: Apply equation-solving techniques to real-world problems.	3-3, 3-4, 3-6	15	45–48	15		X
I: Use arithmetic operations on functions to find formulas which model realistic situations.	3-1, 3-2	8	49–50	16		
J: Use inequalities to solve real-world problems.	3-5, 3-9	18	51–52	14	3	
Representations						
K: Graph functions obtained from other functions by function operations or inverses.	3-1, 3-2, 3-5	5	53–58	3		
L: Find an equation of a graph after a transformation.	3-8	16	59–61	6	6	X
M: Use graphs to approximate zeros of functions and solve equations and inequalities.	3-4, 3-8	17	61–64	13		

Assessment Sourcebook
Quiz for Lessons 3-1 through 3-4
Quiz for Lessons 3-5 through 3-8
Chapter 3 Test, Forms A–D
Chapter 3 Test, Cumulative Form
Comprehensive Test, Chapters 1–3

TestWorks CD-ROM

Teaching Aids

TEACHING AID 26

Warm-up
Lesson 3-1

Suppose that for all x, $f(x) = \sin x$ and $g(x) = \cos x$.

1. Describe the graph of h, where $h(x) = \sin x + \cos x$.
2. Describe the graph of p, where $p(x) = \frac{\sin x}{\cos x}$.

Warm-up
Lesson 3-2

Let $f(z) = 2z^3 + 4$ and $g(z) = 5z^6 + 7$.

1. Calculate $f(0)$, $g(0)$, $f \circ g(0)$, and $g \circ f(0)$.
2. Give a formula for $f \circ g(z)$, and a formula for $g \circ f(z)$.

Warm-up
Lesson 3-3

The equation $ax + b = cx + d$ is solved for x and there is exactly one solution.

1. What is the solution?
2. What must be true of a and c?

Warm-up
Lesson 3-4

Does the graph of $y = \frac{(x-2)^2}{x-2}$ ever intersect the x-axis? Explain.

Warm-up
Lesson 3-5

The sum of a positive number and its reciprocal is less than 2. What is the number?

TEACHING AID 27

Warm-up
Lesson 3-6

Find the zeros of the function h defined by $h(x) = (x + 3)^4 + (x + 3)^2 - 5 = 7$.

Warm-up
Lesson 3-7

Find all solutions to $(4x + 5)(\sin x - 0.5) = 0$ on the interval $[-2\pi, 2\pi]$.

Warm-up
Lesson 3-8

If the scale change S is defined as $S:(x, y) \to (4x, 5y)$ and the translation T is defined as $T:(x, y) \to (x + 1, y - 6)$, what is the image of the equation $y = x^2$ under the composite $T \circ S$?

Warm-up
Lesson 3-9

1. Graph $y = |3x - 22|$.
2. Graph $y = 2x$ on the graph from Question 1. Use this graph to solve the equation $|3x - 2| = 2x$.
3. Solve $|3x - 2| = 2x$ algebraically.

Warm-up
Lesson 3-10

Consider two segments, one with unit length and the other with length 6. Explain how to set up a 1-1 correspondence between the points of these two segments.

TEACHING AID 28
Lesson 3-1

Graphs

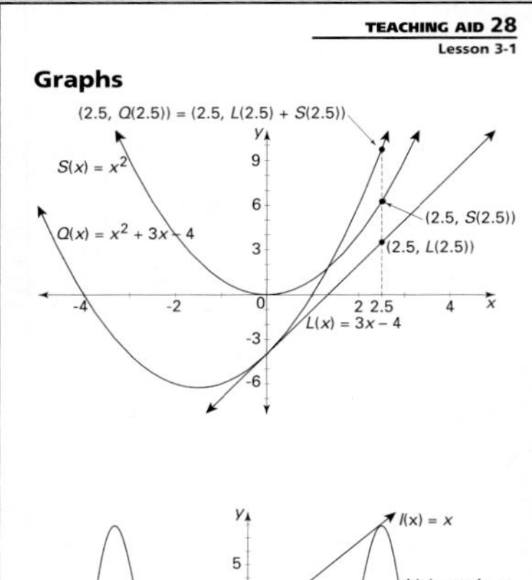

f(x) = x

h(x) = x sin x

f(x) = sin x

TEACHING AID 29
Lesson 3-5

Properties of Theorems I

Properties of Inequality and Operations

For any real expressions $f(x)$ and $g(x)$: if $f(x) < g(x)$, then

$f(x) + c < g(x) + c$ — **Addition Property of Inequality**

$f(x) \cdot c < g(x) \cdot c$, if $c > 0$
$f(x) \cdot c > g(x) \cdot c$, if $c < 0$ — **Multiplication Properties of Inequality**

Theorem

Suppose that f is a real function. If f is increasing throughout its domain, or if f is decreasing throughout its domain, then f is a 1-1 function.

Corollary

If f is an increasing function throughout its domain, or if f is a decreasing function throughout its domain, then the inverse of f is a function.

Theorem

Let f be a real function.

(1) If f is increasing on its entire domain, then f^{-1} is increasing on its entire domain.

(2) If f is decreasing on its entire domain, then f^{-1} is decreasing on its entire domain.

TEACHING AID 30
Lesson 3-5

Properties of Theorems II

Function Composition and Inequality Property (1)

For any real expressions $f(x)$, $g(x)$, and an increasing real function h: $f(x) < g(x) \Leftrightarrow h(f(x)) < h(g(x))$.

Function Composition and Inequality Property (2)

For any real expressions $f(x)$, $g(x)$, and a decreasing real function h: $f(x) < g(x) \Leftrightarrow h(f(x)) > h(g(x))$.

Reversible Steps Theorems for Inequalities

Let $f(x)$ and $g(x)$ be any real expressions. Then for all real expressions c and real function h:

(1) $f(x) < g(x) \Leftrightarrow f(x) + c < g(x) + c$.

(2) $f(x) < g(x) \Leftrightarrow f(x) \cdot c < g(x) \cdot c$, if $c > 0$.
$f(x) < g(x) \Leftrightarrow f(x) \cdot c > g(x) \cdot c$, if $c < 0$.

(3) $f(x) < g(x) \Leftrightarrow h(f(x)) < h(g(x))$, if h is increasing.
$f(x) < g(x) \Leftrightarrow h(f(x)) > h(g(x))$, if h is decreasing.

TEACHING AID 31
Lesson 3-8

Circles and Ellipse

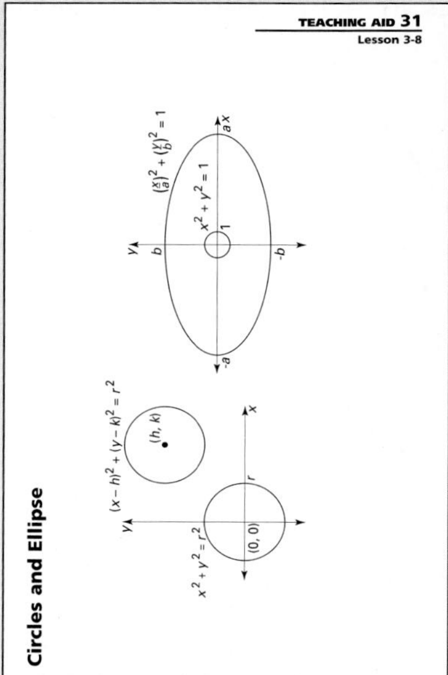

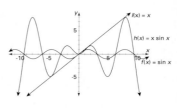

Chapter Opener 3

Pacing

All lessons in this chapter are designed to be covered in one day. At the end of the chapter, you should plan to spend 1 day to review the Progress Self-Test, 1–2 days for the Chapter Review, and 1 day for a test. You may wish to spend a day on projects, and possibly a day is needed for quizzes and the In-class Activities. This chapter should therefore take 13–16 days. Spending more than 18 days on this chapter is not recommended; there is ample opportunity to review ideas in later chapters.

Using Pages 146–147

The equation on this page is solved in Lesson 3-6. At this time, you may ask students if they can find any solutions to it (0, 1, and -1 are three of them), and if so, can they find them all. The inequality on this page is solved at the beginning of Lesson 3-4. For the inequality, note the situation from which it is derived, and ask if anyone has a gut feeling regarding the answer (no pencils or calculators allowed). [The answer is that after 9 years, teachers in the second school will earn more.]

Point out to students that in this chapter they will review the solving of equations and inequalities studied in previous years, and they also will learn some more general methods. The sentences to be solved may be more complicated, but they will have more powerful methods.

Chapter 3 Overview

When students first learn to solve equations and inequalities, they do not have the background to understand the general principles involved. Although students learn that they can add the same number to both sides of an equation or multiply both sides of an equation by the same number without affecting the solution, it is still too early to ask questions such as: What else can you do to both sides? Are there times when these methods do not work?

In this chapter, the logic from Chapter 1 and the work with functions in Chapter 2 are applied to solving equations and inequalities, and to developing some tools for solving all open sentences.

Throughout the chapter it is useful to think of an equation to be solved for x as a sentence of the form $f(x) = g(x)$ and an inequality as a sentence of the form $f(x)$ __ $g(x)$, where the blank is filled with $<$, $\le$, $>$, or $\ge$.

The goal of solving a sentence is to find all values of x that make the sentence true. The algebraic process of solving usually involves transforming the original sentence into equivalent sentences that are simpler than the original sentence. The process is continued until $x = k$ or $x \le k$ results.

Lessons 3-1 and 3-2 provide the special function preparation needed for the chapter. Function addition, subtraction,

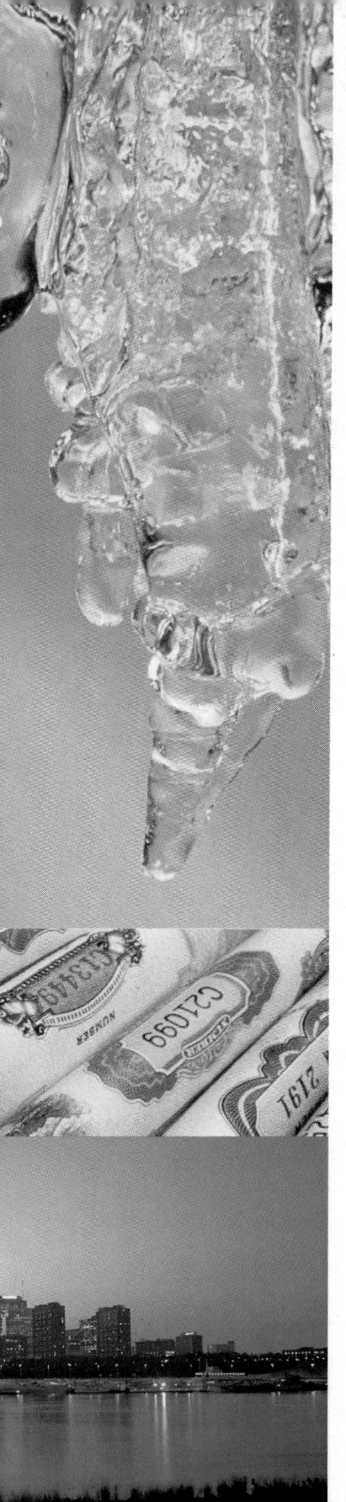

FUNCTIONS, EQUATIONS, AND INEQUALITIES

For many years you have solved equations and inequalities. You know methods for getting exact solutions to linear equations, quadratic equations, equations of the form $a^x = b$, and some others. These methods can be combined to find exact solutions to equations like

$$y^{10} - 5y^6 + 4y^2 = 0,$$

for which you might think no method exists.

Yet for some equations, there are no theorems or formulas that give exact solutions. For example, consider the following situation.

> The teachers in one school earn \$29,000 per year + \$1,000 for each year of teaching experience. The salaries in another school start at \$27,000 per year and increase 4% for each year of teaching experience. After how many years (if ever) do teachers in the second school earn more than teachers in the first?

The question leads to solving an inequality relating arithmetic and geometric sequences.

$$27{,}000(1.04)^x > 29{,}000 + 1000x$$

Although there is no formula for solving such an equation, there are algebraic and graphical ways to estimate the solutions to any desired accuracy.

In this chapter, the logic you encountered in Chapter 1 and the function ideas of Chapter 2 are combined to derive powerful methods for solving equations and inequalities like these, to examine why these methods work, and to explain why some other methods work some of the time but not always.

Photo Connections

The photo collage makes real-world connections to the content of the chapter: functions, equations, and inequalities.

Graduate: A function is used in Lesson 3-8 to estimate how much the average cost of an undergraduate education might increase based on the annual inflation rate.

Ice: Water is transformed into ice over a period of time. At 32°F, water molecules move apart and form crystals; the water freezes and expands.

Stock: In Lesson 3-4, stock prices are shown not to be continuous functions of time.

Hiker: Conditions change as you climb a mountain. The temperature usually drops 3° or 4°F for each 1,000-foot increase in altitude. Boiling points and flammability of liquids change too. In Lesson 3-6, students find the boiling point of water at a high altitude.

Arch: In Lesson 3-6, a function whose graph is a catenary—the curve used in the design of the St. Louis Gateway Arch—is graphed and discussed.

Chapter 3 Projects

At this time, you might want to have students look over the projects on pages 213–214.

multiplication, and division are discussed in Lesson 3-1. The properties of these operations can be used when one adds, subtracts, multiplies, or divides both sides of the equation by the same number or expression. Applying the same operation to both sides of the equation can be interpreted as composing both f and g with a function h to give $h(f(x)) = h(g(x))$; thus, function composition and equation-solving are linked naturally in Lesson 3-2.

Three lessons apply this approach to solving equations. The logic of checking solutions and of reversible steps is given in Lesson 3-3. Techniques for solving equations are reviewed in Lessons 3-4 and 3-6. Chunking is discussed as a means to solve difficult-looking problems.

Properties of increasing and decreasing functions are applied in Lesson 3-5 to the solving of inequalities. Certain inequalities can be solved by the technique of using test points, as discussed in Lesson 3-7.

Solving and graphing techniques for inequalities and equations are discussed in both Lessons 3-8 and 3-9. Lesson 3-8 deals with the effects of certain transformations on solutions to sentences and on their graphs. In Lesson 3-9, the sentences involve absolute value. Lesson 3-10 deals with limits and infinity.

Lesson 3-1

Objectives

B Describe the sum, difference, product, and quotient of two given functions.

I Use arithmetic operations on functions to find formulas which model realistic situations.

K Graph functions obtained from other functions by function operations.

Resources

From the ***Teacher's Resource File***

- Lesson Master 3-1
- Answer Master 3-1
- Teaching Aids
  26 Warm-up
  28 Graphs

Additional Resources

- Visuals for Teaching Aids 26, 28
- Exploration 3-1

Teaching Lesson 3-1

Warm-up

Suppose that for all x, $f(x) = \sin x$ and $g(x) = \cos x$.

1. Describe the graph of h, where $h(x) = f(x) + g(x)$. **The graph of h is a rubberband transformation image of the graph of the sine function, the composite of a translation to the left $\frac{\pi}{4}$ units and a vertical stretch of magnitude $\sqrt{2}$.**
2. Describe p, where $p(x) = \frac{f(x)}{g(x)}$. **p is the tangent function.**

LESSON

3-1 Arithmetic Operations on Functions

Moo-ving on. *In 1994, more than 90 percent of farm businesses were organized as family operations. Saving money after a profitable year can offset potential hardship in a year when there is no profit.*

The following situation naturally leads to combining simple functions with arithmetic operations.

Addition and Subtraction of Functions

The amount that a family saves is the difference of its income and its expenses. If we let $S(x)$, $I(x)$, and $E(x)$ be the savings, income, and expenses in year x, then for all x,

$$S(x) = I(x) - E(x).$$

We say that the function S is the *difference of the functions I and E*. That is, $S = I - E$, and we have an example of *subtraction of functions*. This subtraction has clear meaning. If for a particular value of x, $I(x)$ is greater than $E(x)$, then $S(x)$ is positive and the family has saved money during the year. But if for a particular value of x, $E(x)$ is greater than $I(x)$, then $S(x)$ is negative and the family has had to dip into its savings.

If the family has two wage earners, the husband and wife, then the income for the family is the sum of the income of the husband $H(x)$ and the income of the wife $W(x)$. That is, for all x,

$$I(x) = H(x) + W(x).$$

Here the function I is the *sum of the functions H and W*, and we write $I = H + W$. This is an example of *addition of functions*. We could also split the expenses into taxes $T(x)$ and after-tax expenses $A(x)$. Then for all x,

$$E(x) = T(x) + A(x),$$

and so $E = T + A$.

Lesson 3-1 Overview

Broad Goals The operations of addition, subtraction, multiplication, and division of functions are motivated through the use of an application, displayed graphically, and then applied to explain a function's behavior.

Perspective As the Warm-up shows, performing operations on functions can result in some surprises, occasionally leading to familiar functions or their variants.

Still, it is appropriate to wonder why the arithmetic operations are so important. Sums are applied in examples like the one in this lesson, in the breaking up of sound waves into their pure tones, and in the general analysis of functions. Subtraction is employed in Lesson 3-3 in the theory of solving equations. Applications of products of functions are found in many places, including this lesson and Lesson 3-6. Division is basic to the construction and analysis of rational functions from polynomial functions.

This situation does not lend itself to multiplication of these functions, but division does have some meaning. Then the portion of income that is devoted to taxes is $\frac{T(x)}{I(x)}$. We could call this portion $P(x)$. Then the function P is the result of dividing the function T by the function I, so $P = \frac{T}{I}$. Notice that P is not defined when $I(x) = 0$.

This discussion shows that it is often useful to combine functions to obtain new functions. Here are the definitions of the basic arithmetic operations on functions, shown by telling what the new function does with each element of its domain.

❶ **Definitions**

Suppose f and g are real-valued functions defined on a set S of real numbers. Then $f + g$, $f - g$, $f \cdot g$, and $\frac{f}{g}$ are the functions defined such that $\forall$ x in S:

$$(f + g)(x) = f(x) + g(x)$$
$$(f - g)(x) = f(x) - g(x)$$
$$(f \cdot g)(x) = f(x) \cdot g(x)$$
$$\left(\frac{f}{g}\right)(x) = \frac{f(x)}{g(x)}, \text{ provided } g(x) \neq 0.$$

Arithmetic Operations on Sequences

These definitions also apply to sequences because we can take the set S to be an interval $[a, \infty)$ of integers for some fixed integer a. For sequences u and v, the notation used for defining these operations is: $\forall$ integers $n \geq a$,

$$(u + v)_n = u_n + v_n$$
$$(u - v)_n = u_n - v_n$$
$$(u \cdot v)_n = u_n \cdot v_n$$
$$\left(\frac{u}{v}\right) = \frac{u_n}{v_n}, \text{ provided } v_n \neq 0.$$

Example 1

Let u and v be sequences defined on the interval $[2, \infty)$ of integers by

$$u_n = \frac{n}{n - 1} \text{ and } v_n = \frac{2n^2}{n^2 - 1}.$$

a. Find and simplify an explicit formula for $u + v$.

b. Find and simplify an explicit formula for $\frac{u}{v}$.

Solution

a.
$$(u + v)_n = \frac{n}{n - 1} + \frac{2n^2}{n^2 - 1}$$
$$= \frac{n}{n - 1} + \frac{2n^2}{(n + 1)(n - 1)}$$
$$= \frac{n(n + 1) + 2n^2}{n^2 - 1}$$
$$= \frac{3n^2 + n}{n^2 - 1}$$

b.
$$\left(\frac{u}{v}\right)_n = \frac{\frac{n}{n - 1}}{\frac{2n^2}{n^2 - 1}}$$
$$= \left(\frac{n}{n - 1}\right)\left(\frac{n^2 - 1}{2n^2}\right)$$
$$= \frac{n}{n - 1} \cdot \frac{(n - 1)(n + 1)}{2n^2}$$
$$= \frac{n + 1}{2n}$$

Notes on Reading

When graphing two functions and their sum, product, difference, or quotient, use different colors if possible. Ask students to do the same. **Teaching Aid 28** shows the two graphs on pages 150–151.

Technology If you discuss the family savings situation of this lesson, it will be obvious that each of the functions S, I, and E is itself a sum of many functions. For instance, $E(x)$ is the sum of expenses for housing, food, clothing, entertainment, education, etc. In software like *Quicken®*, that enables families to keep track of expenses, each of these categories is pre-programmed, and then sums and differences are calculated automatically as needed.

❶ In the definitions of the function operations, emphasize that it is a necessary condition that both functions be defined for a value of x in order for the result of the operation to be defined. This is not a sufficient condition, however. When $x = 0$, the sine and cosine functions are defined, but their quotients, the tangent and cotangent functions, are not defined. That is why there is the additional restriction for division of functions, requiring that the denominator not be zero. It is for this reason that, in **Example 1,** the sequences u and v are not defined when $n = 1$.

Optional Activities

Activity 1 Technology Connection
Materials: Explorations software

You may use *Exploration 3-1, Arithmetic Operations on Functions,* to introduce function operations. You can define two functions $f(x)$ and $g(x)$, and choose one of four arithmetic operations. Each function appears on an individual graph and the graphical result of the operation appears on a separate graph.

Activity 2 Cooperative Learning
Materials: Colored pencils

You may wish to have students **work in groups.** After discussing the diagram on page 150, refer students to **Question 9** on page 152. Ask them to determine what points $f + g$ and $f - g$ have in common and to generalize their response. [$f + g$ and $f - g$ will have points in common where $g = 0$.]

Error Alert Students may find the various operations with functions confusing and make errors in interpreting the notation. Stress the following:

Notation	Definition
$f \cdot g$	a function: the product of f and g
$f \cdot g(x)$	a number: the value of $f \cdot g$ at x
$f(x) \cdot g(x)$	a formula for calculating the value

In the next lesson, students will see a new function, $f \circ g$, the composite of f with g.

❷ The first coordinate of an ordered pair also has a technical name: *abscissa*. We do not use that term in this book.

The graph in **Example 2** on page 151 merits some discussion with students, so that they see that the graph of h makes sense. (They may think that the graph continues down forever.) **Teaching Aid 28** contains this graph. Write the equation $h(x) = x \cdot \sin x$ on the chalkboard or overhead. Note that both x and $\sin x$ contribute to the value of $h(x)$. Point out that as x gets larger, $\sin x$ continues to oscillate between 1 and -1, and so the relative maxima and minima of $h(x)$ oscillates between x and $-x$. It may help to graph $y = -x$ to show that this line contains the other relative maxima and minima of the function h.

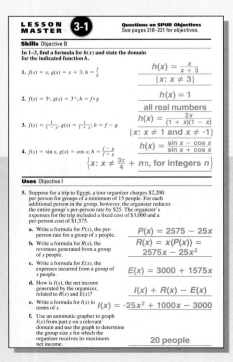

LESSON MASTER 3-1

Questions on SPUR Objectives
See pages 218–221 for objectives.

Skills Objective B

In 1–3, find a formula for $h(x)$ and state the domain for the indicated function h.

1. $f(x) = x$, $g(x) = x + 3$; $h = \frac{f}{g}$ — $h(x) = \frac{x}{x+3}$; $\{x: x \neq 3\}$
2. $f(x) = 3^x$, $g(x) = 3^{-x}$; $h = f \cdot g$ — $h(x) = 1$; all real numbers
3. $f(x) = \frac{1}{1-x}$, $g(x) = \frac{1}{1+x}$; $h = f - g$ — $h(x) = \frac{2x}{(1+x)(1-x)}$; $\{x: x \neq 1 \text{ and } x \neq -1\}$
4. $f(x) = \sin x$, $g(x) = \cos x$; $h = \frac{f-g}{f+g}$ — $h(x) = \frac{\sin x - \cos x}{\sin x + \cos x}$; $\left\{x: x \neq \frac{3\pi}{4} + n\pi, \text{ for integers } n\right\}$

Uses Objective I

5. Suppose for a trip to Egypt, a tour organizer charges \$2,200 per person for groups of a minimum of 15 people. For each additional person in the group, however, the organizer reduces the entire group's per-person rate by \$25. The organizer's expenses for the trip included a fixed cost of \$3,000 and a per-person cost of \$1,575.
   a. Write a formula for $P(x)$, the per-person rate for a group of x people. — $P(x) = 2575 - 25x$
   b. Write a formula for $R(x)$, the revenues generated from a group of x people. — $R(x) = x(P(x)) = 2575x - 25x^2$
   c. Write a formula for $E(x)$, the expenses incurred from a group of x people. — $E(x) = 3000 + 1575x$
   d. How is $I(x)$, the net income generated by the organizer, related to $R(x)$ and $E(x)$? — $I(x) + R(x) - E(x)$
   e. Write a formula for $I(x)$ in terms of x. — $I(x) = -25x^2 + 1000x - 3000$
   f. Use an automatic grapher to graph $I(x)$ from part e on a relevant domain and use the graph to determine the group size x for which the organizer receives its maximum net income. — 20 people

Graphical Interpretation of Function Operations

Arithmetic operations on functions can be interpreted geometrically. Consider the quadratic function defined for all x by $Q(x) = x^2 + 3x - 4$. Q is the sum of the linear function L, with $L(x) = 3x - 4$, and the squaring function S, with $S(x) = x^2$. A graph of Q, L, and S shows how the values are related.

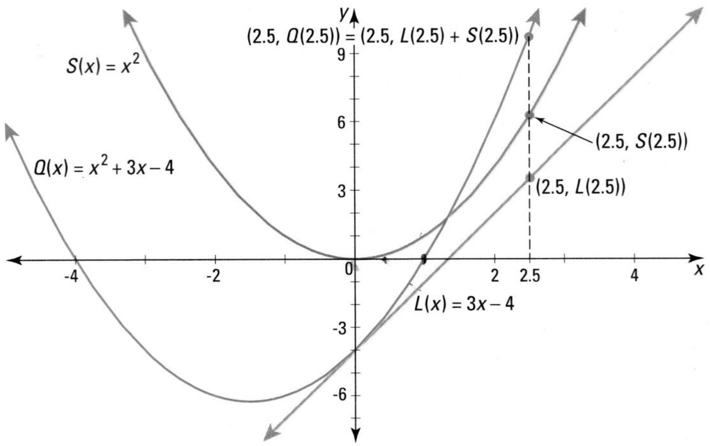

Since $Q = L + S$, for every x,

$$Q(x) = L(x) + S(x).$$

Thus, when $L(x) = 0$, as it does when $x = \frac{4}{3}$, the graphs of Q and S intersect. When $L(x)$ is negative, as it is whenever $x < \frac{4}{3}$, the graph of Q is below the graph of S. The graphs also show that the difference between the functions Q and S increases as x increases.

❷ The second coordinate of an ordered pair is called its **ordinate**. The sum, difference, product, or quotient of two functions can be found by adding, subtracting, multiplying, or dividing ordinates, respectively. You will see in Question 15 that graphical interpretation of the sequences in Example 1 can also lead to some interesting conclusions about these sequences. Sometimes the result is quite unusual.

An Example of Multiplication of Functions

In Example 2 on page 151, the sine function is multiplied by the identity function $I(x) = x$.

Adapting to Individual Needs

Extra Help

Refer students to **Question 7** on page 152. To sketch $g + f$, students may either wish to add ordinates or start with points on the graph of f and add the corresponding values on the graph of g. To sketch $f - g$, you may suggest that students sketch $-g$ by reflecting g over the x-axis and then add $f + (-g)$. This reinforces the notion that subtraction is "adding the opposite."

Challenge

Have students answer the following questions.

1. Give the domain of the following in terms of the domain of f and the domain of g.
   a. $f + g$ $[D_f \cap D_g]$
   b. $f - g$ $[D_f \cap D_g]$
   c. $f \cdot g$ $[D_f \cap D_g]$
   d. f / g $[D_f \cap D_g$ for all x such that $g(x) \neq 0]$

Example 2

$\forall x$, let h be the function defined by $h(x) = x \sin x$. Give some properties of h.

Solution

We show the three functions $I(x) = x$, $f(x) = \sin x$, and $h(x) = x \sin x$.

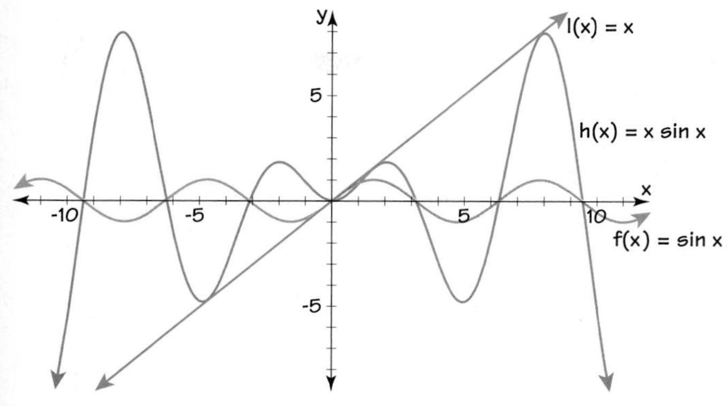

The domain of h is the set of real numbers. Since h = I • f, whenever f(x) = sin x = 1, h(x) = I(x) = x, so its range is the set of all real numbers. h crosses the x-axis whenever I(x) = 0 or f(x) = sin x = 0. h seems to be an even function with relative maxima and minima that get farther from the x-axis as |x| becomes larger.

Additional Example

Let F be the Fibonacci sequence 1, 1, 2, 3, 5, 8, ... , defined by $F_1 = 1$, $F_2 = 1$, and $F_{n+1} = F_n + F_{n-1}$. Let L be the Lucas sequence 1, 3, 4, 7, 11, ... defined by $L_1 = 1$, $L_2 = 3$, and $L_{n+1} = L_n + L_{n-1}$. Let P and Q be the sequences defined by $P_n = F_n \cdot L_n$ and let $Q_n = \frac{F_n}{L_n}$.

a. Calculate P_n and Q_n for $1 \le n \le 8$.
P: 1, 3, 8, 21, 55, 144, 377, 987, ...; Q: 1, $\frac{1}{3}$, 0.5, 0.428571 ..., 0.454545 ..., 0.444444 ..., 0.448275 ..., 0.446808 ..., ...

b. Conjecture a property of P and a property of Q.
Samples: The terms of P are the even-numbered terms of the Fibonacci sequence. That is, for all n, $P_n = F_{2n}$. (This can be proved by mathematical induction.) The terms of Q seem to approach a limit near 0.447. (The limit is $\frac{1}{\sqrt{5}}$.)

QUESTIONS

Covering the Reading

In 1–4, consider functions defined in the analysis of family savings in this lesson.

1. If $E(1999) = \$80{,}000$ and $I(1999) = \$70{,}000$, what is the value of $S(1999)$ and what does the value signify? **See margin.**

2. Suppose that, in a particular year, a family's income is \$65,000, of which \$11,000 goes to taxes and the rest is spent. Determine as many of the values of I, H, W, E, T, and A as you can from this information. **See margin.**

3. Explain why $A = E - T$ by using the definitions of these functions. **See margin.**

4. A function f is defined for all x by $f(x) = \frac{T(x)}{E(x)}$. What is the meaning of this function? **The annual fraction of expenses due to taxes.**

In Question 2, which variable includes the amount of money that a family spends on vacation?

5. Suppose f, g, and h are functions with the same domain, $x \neq 0$, and $f(x) = 3x^2$, $g(x) = 3x^3$, and $h(x) = x$. *True or false.*

a. $\frac{f}{g} = h$ **False**
b. $\frac{g}{f} = h$ **True**
c. $h \cdot f = g$ **True**
d. $g - f = h$ **False**

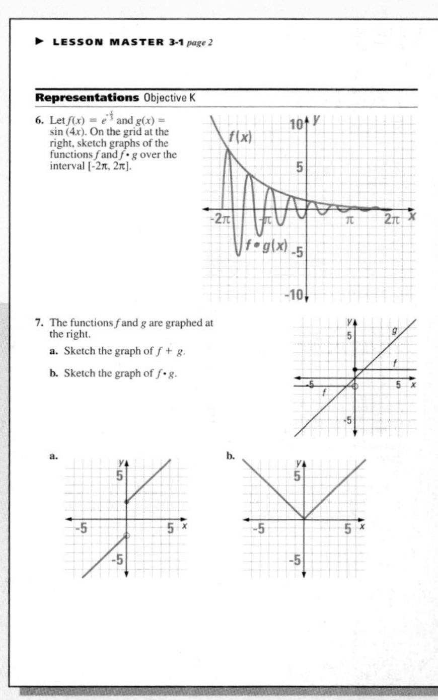
► LESSON MASTER 3-1 *page 2*

Representations Objective K

6. Let $f(x) = e^{-\frac{x}{2}}$ and $g(x) = \sin(4x)$. On the grid at the right, sketch graphs of the functions f and $f \cdot g$ over the interval $[-2\pi, 2\pi]$.

7. The functions f and g are graphed at the right.
a. Sketch the graph of $f + g$.
b. Sketch the graph of $f \cdot g$.

2. Let $g(x) = c$, where c is any positive constant. Compare the graph of each function with the graph of f.
a. $f + g$ [Translation of graph of f c units upwards]
b. $f - g$ [Translation of graph of f c units downwards]
c. $f \cdot g$ [Vertical stretch of graph of f by magnitude c (or shrinking if $c < 1$)]
d. f / g [Vertical stretch of graph of f by a magnitude of $\frac{1}{c}$]

Additional Answers

1. $S(1999) = -\$10{,}000$; This value is the amount the family had to take out of savings or borrow for the year 1999.
2. For the given year Y, $I(Y) = \$65{,}000$, $E(Y) = \$65{,}000$, $T(Y) = \$11{,}000$, $A(Y) = \$54{,}000$.
3. The annual expenses less the annual taxes is equal to the annual after-tax expenses.

Notes on Questions

Question 8c This question reinforces the fact that the zero power of a number equals 1.

Question 16 Use this question to determine whether students remember what they have learned about inverse functions.

Question 17 Notice here that the notation for sequences is applied to sequences of points and lines.

Question 18b History Connection One such person *p* is pictured in the photo at the left.

Question 19 This question requires the computation needed for function composition.

Question 20 Responses to this question can indicate how much of Lesson 3-9 will be review.

Additional Answers

6. The domain of *f* is the set of real numbers. Let $h(x) = \cos x$, then, since $f = I \cdot h$, whenever $h(x) = \cos x = 1$, $f(x) = I(x) = x$, so the range of *f* is the set of real numbers. The graph of *f* crosses the *x*-axis whenever $I(x) = 0$ or $h(x) = \cos x = 0$. *f* is an odd function with relative maxima and minima that get larger in absolute value as *x* is farther from the origin.

9.

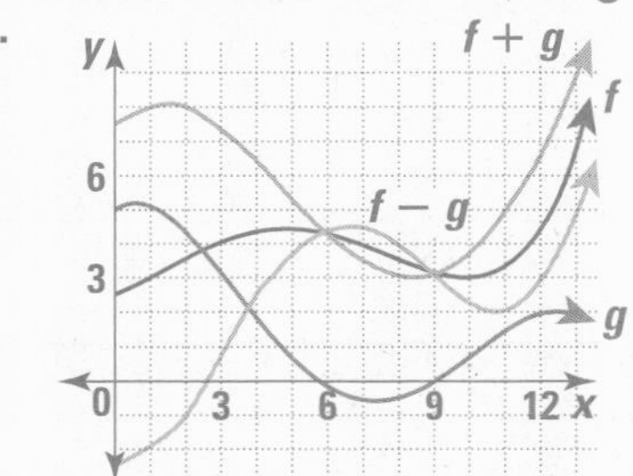

11. a.

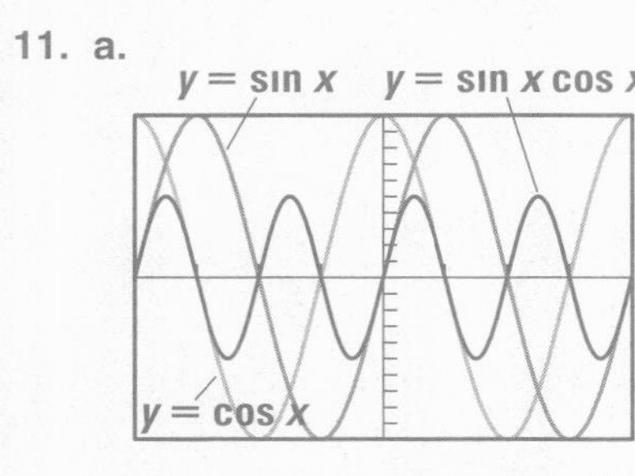

$-2\pi \le x \le 2\pi$, x-scale $= \frac{\pi}{2}$
$-1 \le y \le 1$, y-scale $= 0.1$

7a) $2x^2$; $\{x: x \ne 0\}$
b) $\frac{-2}{x}$; $\{x: x \ne 0\}$
c) $\frac{x^4 - 1}{x^2}$; $\{x: x \ne 0\}$
d) $\frac{x^3 - 1}{x^3 + 1}$; $\{x: x \ne 0, x \ne -1\}$

8a)

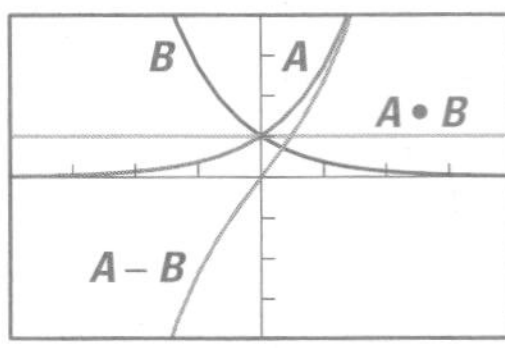

$-4 \le x \le 4$, x-scale = 1
$-4 \le y \le 4$, y-scale = 1

b) *B* is positive over its entire domain, so *A* − *B* must always be less than *A*.

12) Counterexample: consider $f = x$, $g = 2x$. Then $f \cdot g = 2x^2$, which is increasing only for $x \ge 0$.

6. Let $f: x \rightarrow x \cos x$. Give some properties of *f*. See margin.

7. Let $f(x) = x^2 - \frac{1}{x}$ and $g(x) = x^2 + \frac{1}{x}$. Compute and simplify formulas for each of the following. See left.

a. $(g + f)(x)$ **b.** $(f - g)(x)$ **c.** $(g \cdot f)(x)$ **d.** $\left(\frac{f}{g}\right)(x)$

8. Suppose *A* and *B* are functions with $A(x) = e^x$ and $B(x) = e^{-x}$.

a. Use an automatic grapher to sketch *A*, *B*, $A - B$, and $A \cdot B$ on the interval $-5 \le x \le 5$. See left.

b. Explain why the graph of $A - B$ is always below the graph of *A*.

c. Give a formula for $A \cdot B(x)$. $A \cdot B(x) = 1$

b) See left.

9. Trace the graphs of *f* and *g* shown below. Then sketch the graphs of $f + g$ and $f - g$. See margin.

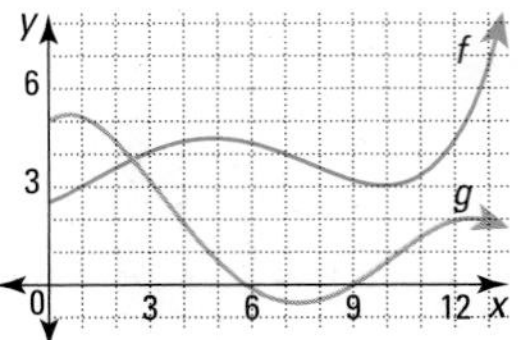

Applying the Mathematics

10. The population $P(Y)$ of a particular country in the year *Y* changes as a result of number of births $B(Y)$, number of deaths $D(Y)$, number of people who emigrate $E(Y)$, and number of people who immigrate $I(Y)$. How is the function *P* related to the functions *B*, *D*, *E*, and *I*?
$P(Y) = P(Y - 1) + B(Y) + I(Y) - D(Y) - E(Y)$

11. a. Sketch the graphs of $y = \sin x$ and $y = \cos x$. Then use multiplication of ordinates at key points (points where either function is -1, 0, or 1) to sketch the graph of $f(x) = \sin x \cos x$. Check your graph with an automatic grapher.

b. What do the range, amplitude, and period of *f* appear to be?
See margin.

12. Disprove the following statement. See left.

For all real functions f and g, if f and g are increasing functions, then $f \cdot g$ is an increasing function.

13. For the sequences *a* and *b* defined for all nonnegative integers *n* by $a_n = n^2$ and $b_n = 2^n$, find the first 8 terms of the sequence $\frac{a}{b}$. Discuss the end behavior of this sequence. See margin.

14. At time $t = 0$ a cargo boat is in a harbor with its deck level with the pier. It is being loaded with grain, which causes the boat to sink 0.1 meter every minute. At the same time, the wave action raises and lowers the boat according to the formula $h = \sin(.5t)$, where h = height in meters after *t* seconds.

a. Write a formula for the function *s*, where $s(t)$ is the height above or below the pier after *t* seconds. See below.

b. *s* is the sum of a sine wave and what other kind of function?

a linear function a) $s(t) = \sin(0.5t) - \frac{1}{600}t$

11. b. range: $\{y: -0.5 \le y \le 0.5\}$; amplitude: 0.5; period: *p*

13. $\{\frac{1}{2}, 1, \frac{9}{8}, 1, \frac{25}{32}, \frac{9}{16}, \frac{49}{128}, \frac{16}{63}\}$.
As $n \rightarrow \infty$, $\frac{a_n}{b_n} \rightarrow 0$.

15. a.

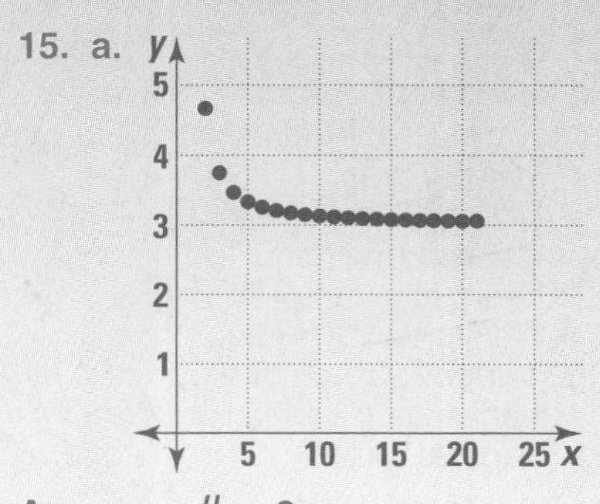

As $x \rightarrow \infty$, $\frac{u}{v} \rightarrow 3$.

15. Consider the sequence $u + v$ in Example 1. See margin.
   a. Graph the first twenty terms of the sequence and make a conjecture about its end behavior.
   b. Prove algebraically that
$$(u + v)_n = \frac{3 + \frac{1}{n}}{1 - \frac{1}{n^2}}$$
   for all $n \geq 2$.
   c. Use part **b** to verify or adjust the conjecture that you made in part **a**.

Review

16) $f(g(x)) = x$ for any real number x; $g(f(x)) = x$ $\{x: x > 0\}$

16. Suppose $f(x) = \log x$ for all positive real numbers x, and $g(x) = 10^x$ for all real numbers x. Compute and simplify $f(g(x))$ and $g(f(x))$. *(Previous course, Lessons 2-8, 2-9)* See left.

17. Consider a circle with points P and Q. Let ℓ be a sequence of lines defined by
$$\begin{cases} \ell_1 = \overleftrightarrow{PQ_1} \\ \ell_{n+1} = \overleftrightarrow{PQ_{n+1}} \end{cases}$$
where Q_{n+1} is the midpoint of $\overparen{PQ_n}$ for all $n \geq 1$.
What is $\lim_{n\to\infty} \ell_n$? *(Lesson 2-8)* the line through P tangent to the circle

Peaceful March. *Lech Walesa was awarded the Nobel Peace Prize in 1983 for his leadership of the Solidarity movement in Poland.*

18. Write the negation of each statement. See margin.
   a. *∀ satellites s, s is a military spy satellite.*
   b. *∃ a person p such that p was a leader of a trade union and p has received the Nobel Peace Prize.* *(Lessons 1-2, 1-3)*

19. Let f and g be functions defined by $f(x) = 4x + 2$ and $g(x) = x^2 + 1$. Find each.
   a. $f(g(2))$ 22
   b. $g(f(5))$ *(Previous course)* 485

20. Sketch the graph of $y = |x^2 - 2|$. *(Previous course)* See margin.

21. If $x^2 - 3x + c$ is a perfect square trinomial, what is c? *(Previous course)*

22. If $x^2 + kx + 100$ is a perfect square trinomial, what is k? *(Previous course)*

21) $c = \frac{9}{4}$ $k = 20$

Exploration

23. Graph the identity function $I(x) = x$ and the reciprocal function $R(x) = \frac{1}{x}$ for $x > 0$. Use the graphs to explain why $x + \frac{1}{x} \geq 2$ for all x. See margin.

Follow-up for Lesson 3-1

Practice

For more questions on SPUR Objectives, use **Lesson Master 3-1** (shown on pages 150–151).

Assessment

Group Assessment Define two functions, $f(x)$ and $g(x)$. Then divide the students into four groups. Have each group sketch these two functions on the same coordinate grid. Then assign each group one of the following: $(f + g)(x)$, $(f - g)(x)$, $(f \cdot g)(x)$, or $(\frac{f}{g})(x)$. Ask the group to write an appropriate formula and sketch the graph. Groups should share their results with the class. [Students describe and graph the sum, difference, product, or quotient of two functions.]

Extension

Project Update Project 1, *Creating Fonts,* on page 213, relates to the content of this lesson.

Additional Answers

20.
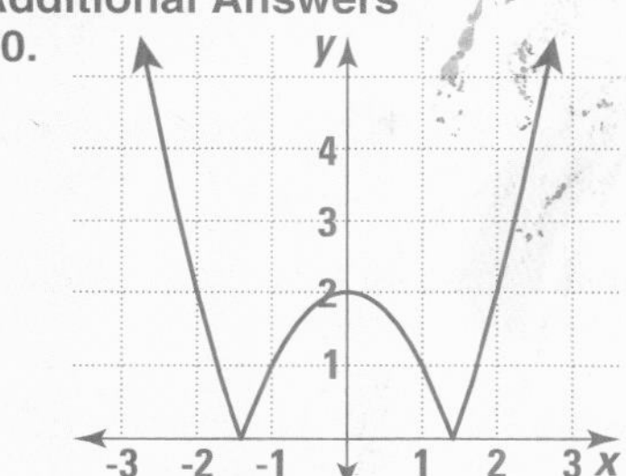

23.
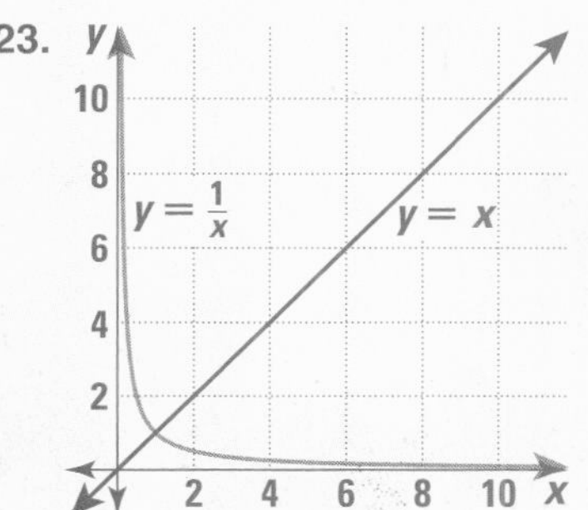

For $x = 1$, $I(x) = R(x) = 1$; so $I(x) + R(x) = 2$. As x increases in the interval $\{x: x \geq 1\}$, $I(x)$ increases faster than $R(x)$. As x decreases in the interval $\{x: 0 < x \leq 1\}$, $R(x)$ increases faster than $I(x)$ decreases.

b. $(u + v)_n = \dfrac{3n^2 + n}{n^2 - 1} \cdot \dfrac{\frac{1}{n^2}}{\frac{1}{n^2}} = \dfrac{\frac{3n^2}{n^2} + \frac{n}{n^2}}{\frac{n^2}{n^2} - \frac{1}{n^2}} = \dfrac{3 + \frac{1}{n}}{1 - \frac{1}{n^2}}$

c. $\lim_{n \to \infty} \dfrac{3 + \frac{1}{n}}{1 - \frac{1}{n^2}} = 3$

18. a. ∃ some satellite such that s is not a military spy satellite.
   b. ∀ persons p, p is not the leader of a trade union or p has not received the Nobel Peace Prize.

Lesson 3-2

Objectives

B Describe the composite of two given functions.
F Identify and prove properties of inverse functions.
I Use arithmetic operations on functions to find formulas which model realistic situations.
K Graph functions obtained from other functions by function operations or inverses.

Resources

From the ***Teacher's Resource File***
- Lesson Master 3-2
- Answer Master 3-2
- Teaching Aid 26: Warm-up

Additional Resources
- Visual for Teaching Aid 26
- Exploration 3-2

Teaching Lesson 3-2

Warm-up

Let $f(z) = 2z^3 + 4$ and $g(z) = 5z^6 + 7$.
1. Calculate $f(0)$, $g(0)$, $f \circ g(0)$, and $g \circ f(0)$. 4, 7, 690, 20487
2. Give a formula for $f \circ g(z)$, and a formula for $g \circ f(z)$. $f \circ g(z) = 2(5z^6 + 7)^3 + 4$; $g \circ f(z) = 5(2z^3 + 4)^6 + 7$

LESSON

3-2 Composition and Inverses of Functions

What Is Function Composition?

Think of an equation in the variable x as being of the form

$$f(x) = h(x).$$

Then, for the equation

$$\sqrt{x-2} = 4 - x,$$

$f(x) = \sqrt{x-2}$ and $h(x) = 4 - x$. To solve the equation, we can begin by squaring both sides. The resulting equation

$$x - 2 = (4 - x)^2$$

is of the form

$$g(f(x)) = g(h(x)),$$

where g is the squaring function $g(x) = x^2$. The function g can be applied to both sides since its domain, the set of real numbers, contains the ranges of f and h. Each side of the resulting equation now defines the *composite* of two functions. The left side is the composite of g with f; the right side is the composite of g with h.

Recall from earlier courses that the operation of combining functions in this way is called **function composition** and is denoted by a small circle, $\circ$.

Definition
Suppose that f and g are functions. The **composite of *g* with *f***, written $g \circ f$, is the function with rule

$$g \circ f(x) = g(f(x))$$

whose domain is all x in the domain of f for which $f(x)$ is in the domain of g.

The composite function value $g \circ f(x)$ is obtained by first performing the operation f on x to obtain $f(x)$ and then performing the operation g on $f(x)$ to obtain $g(f(x))$.

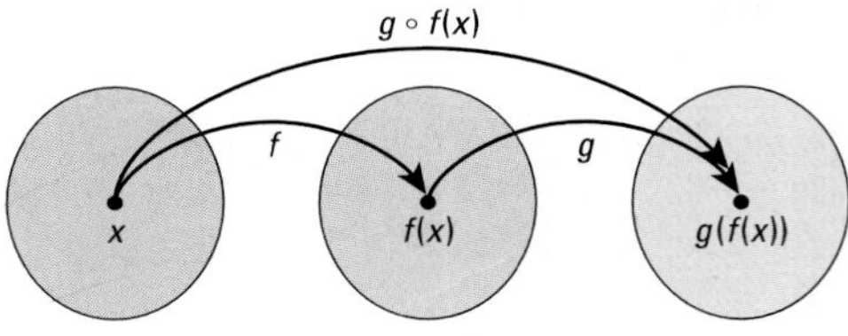

The domain of the composite function $g \circ f$ can also be thought of as the largest set of values of x for which $g(f(x))$ makes sense. First, x must be in the domain of f for $f(x)$ to be defined, and also $f(x)$ must be in the domain of g for $g(f(x))$ to be defined.

Lesson 3-2 Overview

Broad Goals Composition of functions and inverses of functions are reviewed in a discussion motivated by equation-solving.

Perspective If you have not done so, you should read Lesson 3-3 to see how the ideas of function composition are applied in the next lesson to produce general theorems that relate to equation solving. In Lesson 2-9, students saw a specific instance of the generalizations to come.

Consider an equation $f(x) = g(x)$. If the log base b of both sides of the equation is taken, then the result is $\log_b(f(x)) = \log_b(g(x))$. This equation is of the form $h(f(x)) = h(g(x))$, where $h = \log_b$. Given $f(x) = k$, if f has an inverse function f^{-1}, then it could be applied to both sides to yield $x = f^{-1}(k)$.

For the equation $\sqrt{x-2} = 4 - x$ that opens the lesson, the function h is the squaring function. On the domain of real numbers, this function's inverse is not a function. That spawns the possibility of trouble, as seen in **Example 3** of Lesson 3-3. In contrast, in **Example 2,** the function applied to both sides is the function g defined by $g(x) = x^{3/2}$ for $x \geq 0$. This function's inverse is a function and the solution follows easily.

For instance, let f and g be the real functions on page 154 defined by $f(x) = \sqrt{x - 2}$ and $g(x) = x^2$. The domain of $g \circ f$ is the intersection of the domain of f and the set of x for which $f(x)$ is in the domain of g.

The domain of f is $\{x: x \geq 2\}$ and the domain of g is the set of all real numbers. Hence, the domain of $g \circ f$ is $\{x: x \geq 2\}$.

Example 1

Suppose f and g are defined by $g(x) = 2x + 1$ and $f(x) = x^5 - 4$ for all real numbers x. Find a formula for $g \circ f$.

Solution

We want $g \circ f(x)$, which is the same as $g(f(x))$. Since the domain of both f and g is the set of all real numbers, the domain of $g \circ f$ is also that set. Thus, for all real numbers x,

$$g \circ f(x) = g(f(x)) = 2(f(x)) + 1.$$
$$= 2(x^5 - 4) + 1 \quad \text{Substitute } x^5 - 4 \text{ for } f(x).$$
$$= 2x^5 - 7.$$

Is Function Composition a Commutative Operation?

Function composition is *not* commutative. For instance, the squaring function f and the sine function g can be composed in two different possible orders. $r = g \circ f$ is the "sine of the square" while $s = f \circ g$ is the "square of the sine." You can see from the graphs below that r and s are not the same function. For instance, the sine of the square can be negative, but the square of the sine is never negative.

The distinction can be verified by considering a specific value of x, say $x = \frac{\pi}{4}$. Then

$$r(x) = \sin(x^2) = \sin\left(\frac{\pi^2}{16}\right) \approx 0.5784\ldots, \text{ whereas}$$
$$s(x) = (\sin x)^2 = \left(\sin \frac{\pi}{4}\right)^2 = \left(\frac{\sqrt{2}}{2}\right)^2 = 0.5 \text{ exactly.}$$

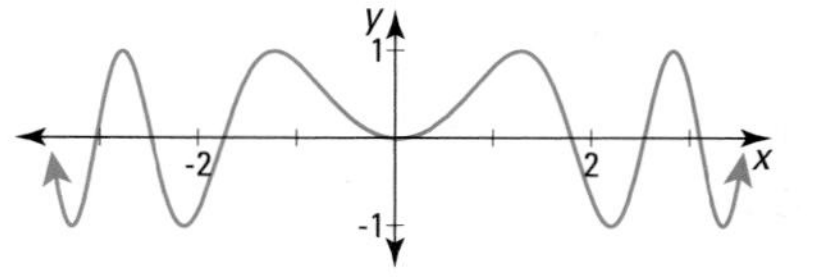

$r(x) = g(f(x)) = g(x^2) = \sin(x^2)$

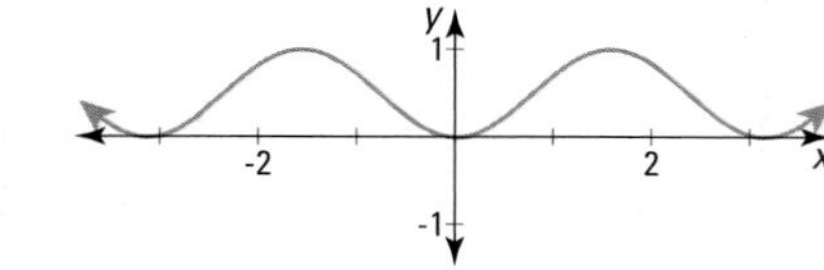

$s(x) = f(g(x)) = f(\sin x) = (\sin x)^2$

Caution: Function composition and multiplication are both written with parentheses, but do not confuse them.

$$f \circ g(x) = f(g(x))$$
$$f \cdot g(x) = f(x) \cdot g(x)$$

For example, when $f(x) = \sin x$ and $g(x) = x^2$, $f \circ g(x) = \sin(x^2)$ but $f \cdot g(x) = x^2 \sin x$.

Notes on Reading

Error Alert Students often can determine a formula for the composite of two functions but frequently have difficulty determining the domain of the composite. The key to finding the domain of $f \circ g$ is to find the set of values in the domain of g such that the result is in the domain of f. Just finding a formula for $f \circ g$ and then finding the domain is not sufficient. To illustrate this, consider the functions f and g defined as follows: $f(x) = x^2$ and $g(x) = \sqrt{x - 4}$. Then $f \circ g(x) = x - 4$, so you might think x can be any real number. But the domain of g is $\{x: x \geq 4\}$ and thus the domain of $f \circ g$ is also $\{x: x \geq 4\}$. In this case, if students consider only the rule for $f \circ g$, they will obtain the wrong domain.

Reading Mathematics Because function composition is not commutative, you should read $f \circ g$ with language that is more descriptive of the roles the functions play. Rather than saying "the composite of f with g," you might say "f following g," or "g followed by f."

Alternate Approach For **Example 1**, some students may prefer to work from right to left.

$g \circ f(x) = g(f(x))$
replacing $f(x)$ by $x^5 - 4$
$= g(x^5 - 4)$
replacing the x in $g(x)$ by $x^5 - 4$
$= 2(x^5 - 4) + 1$
$= 2x^5 - 7$

Notice that we allow any function to have an inverse. Only some inverses are themselves functions.

Error Alert The notation f^{-1} could mean $\frac{1}{f}$, that is, the function whose formula is the reciprocal of the formula of f, but by convention, it does not. Since it is convention and not logic or a pattern that has decided what the symbol f^{-1} represents, this symbol can be quite confusing to students. Remind students that f^{-1} is not "f to the negative one power" and is not $\frac{1}{f}$. It is the "inverse of f."

Solving Equations Using Function Composition

By selecting an appropriate function g, composition of functions can be employed to solve equations. Every equation with a variable x on only one side can be considered to be of the form

$$f(x) = k,$$

where k is a fixed number. Applying a function g to both sides results in the equation

$$g(f(x)) = g(k),$$

where $g(k)$ is also a fixed number. Should g also have the property that $\forall x$ in the domain of f, $g(f(x)) = x$, then g has "undone" f, with the result that

$$x = g(k),$$

and the sentence has been rather easily solved. You may have already used this procedure to solve equations, although you may not have thought of it in terms of function composition.

Example 2

Solve: $x^{2/3} = 64$.

Solution

It is understood that $x \geq 0$ because a noninteger power of x is being taken. This equation is of the form $f(x) = k$, where $f(x) = x^{2/3}$ and $k = 64$. Apply $g(x) = x^{3/2}$ to each side.

$$g(x^{2/3}) = g(64)$$
$$(x^{2/3})^{3/2} = 64^{3/2}$$
$$x = 512$$

Check

Does $512^{2/3} = 64$? $512^{2/3} = (2^9)^{2/3} = 2^{9 \cdot 2/3} = 2^6 = 64$. Yes.

Inverse of a Function

In Example 2, the function g is the *inverse* of the function f. The **inverse** of a function f: $x \to y$ is the relation formed by reversing the ordered pairs. If g is itself a function, then we write $g = f^{-1}$.

Definition

f and g are **inverse functions**, written $f = g^{-1}$ or $g = f^{-1}$, if and only if $f \circ g(x) = x$ for all x in the domain of g and $g \circ f(x) = x$ for all x in the domain of f.

Optional Activities

Activity 1 To introduce the lesson, describe a series of related actions and ask students for the sequence of steps that would "undo" these actions. Which inverse actions make sense?

1. Unload the dishwasher, put away the clean dishes, shut the cabinet doors [Open the cabinet doors, take out the clean dishes, put the clean dishes into the dishwasher; does not make sense]
2. Climb up the ladder to a diving board, walk to the edge of the board, dive off the board [Dive up onto the diving board, walk along the board to the ladder, climb down the ladder; does not make sense]
3. Pour a cup of coffee from the thermos, heat it in the microwave, add a spoonful of sugar [Remove a spoonful of sugar from a cup of coffee, cool off the coffee in the microwave, pour the coffee back into the thermos; does not make sense]
4. Step into the elevator, ride down five floors, step off the elevator [Step into the elevator, ride up five floors, step off the elevator; does make sense]

In general, if f has an inverse f^{-1} and if

$$f(a) = b,$$

then $$f^{-1} \circ f(a) = f^{-1}(b).$$

So $$a = f^{-1}(b).$$

This is why inverse functions are so useful in solving equations.

Thus if f is a real function and (a, b) is on the graph of f, then (b, a) is on the graph of f^{-1}. Therefore, when a real function f has an inverse f^{-1}, the graphs of f and f^{-1} are reflection images of one another over the line $y = x$. Consequently, the domain of f^{-1} is the range of f, and vice versa.

The composite of two inverse functions f and f^{-1} is the function that maps each element onto itself. As a result, this function is called the **identity function** and denoted by the symbol $\boldsymbol{I}$. If f is a real function, the graph of $\boldsymbol{I}$ is the line $y = x$.

One-to-one Functions

Every function has an inverse. There is a simple way to tell if the inverse is a function. Suppose $f(a) = c$ and $f(b) = c$. Then (c, a) and (c, b) are on the inverse. Only if $a = b$ for all c will the inverse be a function. So in order for the inverse of f to be a function, we need for all a and b, $f(a) = f(b) \Rightarrow a = b$. Such a function is called a *1-1 function* because it is a 1-1 correspondence between domain and range.

Definition
A function g is a **one-to-one** or **1-1 function** if and only if for all u and v in the domain of g,

$$g(u) = g(v) \Rightarrow u = v.$$

Theorem
A function has an inverse function if and only if it is a 1-1 function.

Proof
If f has an inverse f^{-1} and if $f(x) = f(y)$, then $f^{-1} \circ f(x) = f^{-1} \circ f(y)$, so $x = y$, and so f is a 1-1 function. If f is a 1-1 function, then switching the components of its ordered pairs yields a function, its inverse function.

❶ Here are some examples of inverse functions.

Adding and Subtracting k

Let $f: x \to x + k \quad \forall$ real numbers x
$\quad g: x \to x - k \quad \forall$ real numbers x.

Then $\forall$ real numbers x, $f(g(x)) = f(x - k) = (x - k) + k = x$. (You should verify that $g(f(x)) = x$.) Hence, f and g are inverses.

❶ Students have seen many examples of inverse functions. Given here are the inverses of some important parent functions. The relationship between the graph of a function and the graph of its inverse function also is one that students should have seen before. This type of visual display reinforces the fact that if (a, b) is on the graph of f, then (b, a) must be on the graph of f^{-1}.

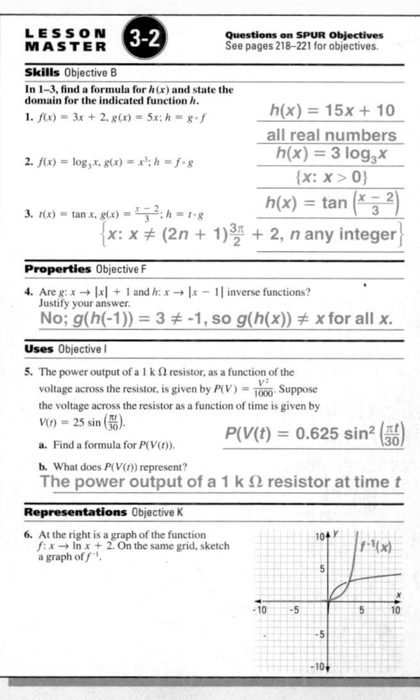
LESSON MASTER 3-2

Questions on SPUR Objectives
See pages 218–221 for objectives.

Skills Objective B

In 1–3, find a formula for $h(x)$ and state the domain for the indicated function h.

1. $f(x) = 3x + 2$, $g(x) = 5x$; $h = g \circ f$ — $h(x) = 15x + 10$; all real numbers
2. $f(x) = \log_3 x$, $g(x) = x^3$; $h = f \circ g$ — $h(x) = 3 \log_3 x$; $\{x: x > 0\}$
3. $t(x) = \tan x$, $g(x) = \frac{x-2}{3}$; $h = t \circ g$ — $h(x) = \tan\left(\frac{x-2}{3}\right)$; $\left\{x: x \neq (2n+1)\frac{3\pi}{2} + 2, n \text{ any integer}\right\}$

Properties Objective F

4. Are $g: x \to |x| + 1$ and $h: x \to |x - 1|$ inverse functions? Justify your answer.
No; $g(h(-1)) = 3 \neq -1$, so $g(h(x)) \neq x$ for all x.

Uses Objective I

5. The power output of a 1 kΩ resistor, as a function of the voltage across the resistor, is given by $P(V) = \frac{V^2}{1000}$. Suppose the voltage across the resistor as a function of time is given by $V(t) = 25 \sin\left(\frac{\pi t}{30}\right)$.
a. Find a formula for $P(V(t))$. $P(V(t)) = 0.625 \sin^2\left(\frac{\pi t}{30}\right)$
b. What does $P(V(t))$ represent?
The power output of a 1 kΩ resistor at time t

Representations Objective K

6. At the right is a graph of the function $f: x \to \ln x + 2$. On the same grid, sketch a graph of f^{-1}.

Activity 2 Technology Connection
Materials: Explorations software

Students may use *Exploration 3-2, Composite Functions,* as an alternative to Example 1 in Lesson 3-2. Students can define two functions and see the graphs of those functions on separate coordinate grids. The two possible compositions of those functions are shown on a third coordinate grid.

Adapting to Individual Needs

Extra Help
Some students may be confused about sketching the inverse of a function. They may want to sketch the 90° rotation image about the origin rather than the reflection image over the line $y = x$. A good strategy is to graph $y = x$, locate two or more points on the graph of f, and plot the corresponding points of the inverse before sketching the entire graph.

Have students record the results of the **Activity** for **Question 6** on page 159.

❷ Be certain to emphasize the point made in the last section of this lesson: When $f: x \rightarrow x^2$, then f is not a 1-1 function on the set of all real numbers. Consequently, using the theorem on page 157, the inverse of f is not a function.

Additional Examples

1. Suppose $f(x) = 3x - 2$ and $g(x) = x^3 + 1$ for all real numbers x.
   a. Determine a formula for $f \circ g(x)$. $f \circ g(x) = 3x^3 + 1$
   b. Determine a formula for $g \circ f(x)$. $g \circ f(x) = 27x^3 - 54x^2 + 36x - 7$
   c. Compare the results in **parts a and b.** What does this tell you about commutativity of composition? $f \circ g \neq g \circ f$ This one counterexample proves that composition of functions is not a commutative operation.
2. Solve $x^{5/7} = 243$. 2187

Multiplying and Dividing by $k \neq 0$

Let $f: x \rightarrow kx$ $\quad\forall$ real numbers x
$g: x \rightarrow \frac{x}{k}$ $\quad\forall$ real numbers x.

Activity

Verify that $\forall$ real numbers x, $f(g(x)) = g(f(x)) = x$ and so f and g are inverse functions. See Question 6 on page 159.

Exponential and Logarithmic Functions

Let b be a positive number, $b \neq 1$, and

let $f: x \rightarrow b^x$ $\quad\forall$ real numbers x
$g: x \rightarrow \log_b x$ $\quad\forall$ positive real numbers x.

Then $f(g(x)) = f(\log_b x) = b^{\log_b x} = x$, from the definition of log, and $g(f(x)) = g(b^x) = \log_b (b^x) = x$, from the definition of log. So f and g are inverse functions.

❷ Restricting Functions so that Their Inverses Are Functions

A function may have no inverse function over its entire domain, but may have an inverse function over a restricted domain. For instance,

let $f: x \rightarrow x^2$ and $g: x \rightarrow \sqrt{x}$.

f and g are not inverse functions if their domains are the set of real numbers. They are inverse functions if their domains are the set of nonnegative real numbers, because $\sqrt{x^2} = x$ and $(\sqrt{x})^2 = x$ for all nonnegative x but not for all real x.

The sine and cosine functions defined over the set of real numbers are not 1-1 so they do not have inverse functions. Yet, if their domains are restricted so that the functions are 1-1, then they do. These inverses are discussed in Chapter 6.

QUESTIONS

Covering the Reading

1a) $-x^4 + 3$
c) $\frac{1}{2}(-2x + 3)^4$

1. Let $h(x) = -2x + 3$ and $k(x) = \frac{1}{2}x^4$ for all real numbers x.
   a. Give a formula for $h \circ k(x)$. See left.
   b. Compute $h \circ k(7)$. -2398
   c. Give a formula for $k \circ h(x)$. See left.
   d. Compute $k \circ h(7)$. 7320.5
   e. Is it true that $h \circ k = k \circ h$? No
2. Let $f: x \rightarrow \cos x$ and $g: x \rightarrow x^3$ $\forall$ real numbers x. Show that $\exists$ a real number x such that $f \circ g(x) \neq g \circ f(x)$. See margin.

Adapting to Individual Needs

Challenge

Have students answer the following.

1. Let g be any real function. Compare the graphs of $g \circ f$ and $f \circ g$ to the graph of g in the given situation.
   a. $f(x) = x + c$, where c is any constant [The graph of $g \circ f$ is a horizontal translation of the graph of g; the graph of $f \circ g$ is a vertical translation of the graph of g.]
   b. $f(x) = x$ [$g \circ f = f \circ g = g$]
2. **a.** Show that if $g: x \rightarrow \frac{x}{x-1}$, then g is its own inverse. [$g(g(\frac{x}{x-1})) = \frac{\frac{x}{x-1}}{\frac{x}{x-1} - 1} = \frac{\frac{x}{x-1}}{\frac{1}{x-1}} = x$]
   b. Repeat **part a** given $g: x \rightarrow \frac{1}{x}$. [$g(g(\frac{1}{x})) = \frac{1}{\frac{1}{x}} = x$]
3. When a function is its own inverse, what can be said about its graph? [The graph of such a function is symmetric to the line $y = x$.]

4) $\dfrac{1}{x^2 + \frac{1}{x^2} - 2}$;
domain: $\{x: x \neq -1, 0, 1\}$

5)
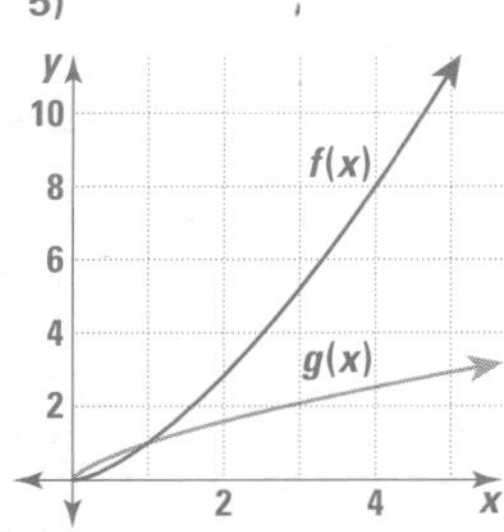

6) $f \circ g(x) = f(g(x)) = k\left(\frac{x}{k}\right) = x$, $g \circ f(x) = g(f(x)) = \left(\frac{kx}{k}\right) = x$, therefore, $f \circ g = g \circ f = I$.

17a) Yes, 5^x is a 1-1 for all real numbers. Therefore its inverse, $\log_5 x$, is 1-1 over the positive real numbers.

In 3 and 4, two real functions, f and g, are defined by formulas. Find a formula for the composite function $f \circ g$ and give its domain.

3. $f(x) = 3x + 1$ $\quad g(x) = 2x^3$ $\quad 6x^3 + 1$; domain: all reals

4. $f(x) = \frac{1}{x^2 - 4}$ $\quad g(x) = x + \frac{1}{x}$ See left.

5. Graph the inverse functions $f(x) = x^{3/2}$ and $g(x) = x^{2/3}$ for all nonnegative x. See left.

6. Give the results that you found for the Activity in this lesson. See left.

7. a. For what domain are these functions inverses? all reals ≥ 0

$$f(x) = x^4 \qquad g(x) = \sqrt[4]{x}$$

b. Graph these functions over a part of that domain containing the origin. See margin.

In 8–11, solve using inverse functions.

8. $x^{3/4} = 4096$ $\quad x = 65{,}536$

9. $\sqrt{x^2 + 2} = 3$ $\quad x = \pm\sqrt{7}$

10. $e^y = 7000$ $\quad y \approx 8.854$

11. $3 \log_2 x = 1.5$ $\quad x = \sqrt{2}$

Applying the Mathematics

12. Explain why the function h graphed below does not have an inverse function.

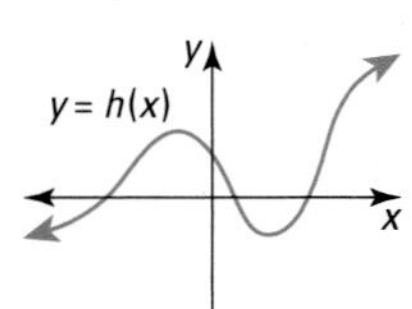

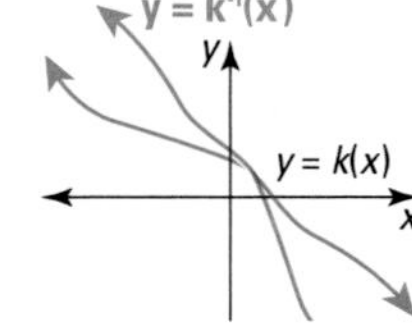

h is not a 1-1 function.

13. Explain why the function k graphed above has an inverse function and sketch the graph of k^{-1}. k is a 1-1 function. See above.

14. Give a formula for the inverse of $f: x \rightarrow \frac{2}{3}x + 6$. $\quad f^{-1}: x \rightarrow \frac{3}{2}x - 9$

In 15 and 16, use inverse functions to help simplify the expression.

15. $e^{3 \ln x}$ $\quad x^3$

16. $\log_{10} 1000^x$ $\quad 3x$

17. a. Is $f: x \rightarrow \log_5 x$ a 1-1 function? Explain your answer.

b. Solve: $\log_5 (x + 3) = 2 \log_5 (x + 1)$. $\quad x = 1$

a) See left.

Notes on Questions

Question 13 The graph of the inverse will appear to be congruent to the reflection image of the graph of the function if and only if the scales on the axes are the same.

Question 14 Alternative Approach The following is an alternative way of determining a formula for the inverse of f when $f(x) = \frac{2}{3}x + 6$.
To get $f(x)$ from x, we have multiplied x by $\frac{2}{3}$ and then added 6. Thus, to get f^{-1}, perform the inverse operations in reverse order: subtract 6, then divide by $\frac{2}{3}$.
That is, $f^{-1}(x) = \frac{x - 6}{\frac{2}{3}} = \frac{3}{2}(x - 6)$.

(Notes on Questions continue on page 160.)

Follow-up for Lesson 3-2

Practice

For more questions on SPUR Objectives, use **Lesson Master 3-2** (shown on page 157).

Assessment

Written Communication Have students give a formula for a linear function f of their choice. Ask them to give a formula for the inverse of f, graph f and its inverse, and explain why the inverse is a function. Then have students show that $f^{-1} \circ f(x) = x$ and $f \circ f^{-1}(x) = x$ for several values of x. [Check students' understanding of linear function and its inverse.]

(Follow-up continues on page 160.)

Additional Answers

2. Sample: $x = \frac{\pi}{2}$; $f \circ g(x) = \cos(x^3) = \cos \frac{\pi^3}{8} \approx -.7424$; $g \circ f(x) = (\cos x)^3 = (\cos \frac{\pi}{2})^3 = 0$

7. b.

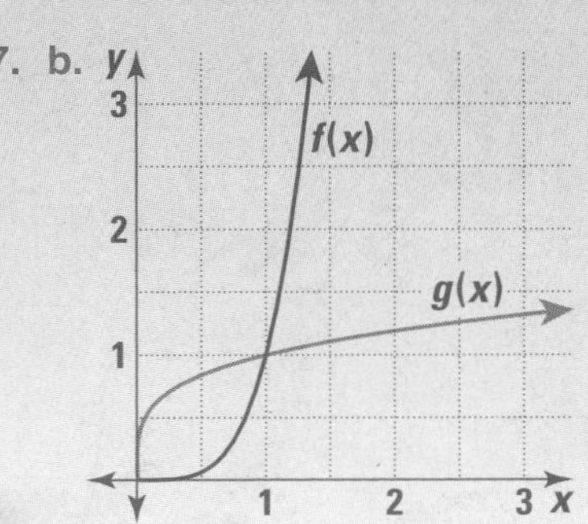

Extension

Cooperative Learning Having students write a complicated function as a composite of two or more functions (as in **Question 22**) is a useful exercise and one that often gives many calculus students difficulty. You might have students **work in groups** to answer the following questions.

1. Let f be the function defined by $f(x) = \sin x^2$. If $f = g \circ h$, what could g and h be? [We could have $g(x) = \sin x$ and $h(x) = x^2$.]
2. Let p be the function defined by $p(x) = \log(x - 5)^{1/3}$. Suppose p is the composite of three functions. What could those functions be? [It could be that $p = \log \circ h \circ r$ where $r: x \rightarrow x - 5$, $h: x \rightarrow x^{1/3}$, and $\log: x \rightarrow \log x$.]

Notes on Questions

Question 18 This question should be easy for students. Part of it is in the Warm-up to Lesson 3-1.

Question 20 Consumer Connection An investment is the use of money to earn income or profit. All investments involve some risk. Normally, the larger the projected profit of the investment, the greater the risk. Major types of investments include savings accounts, life insurance, business investments, real estate, bonds, stocks, and mutual funds.

Question 22 See the Extension.

Review

18. Let $f: x \rightarrow \sin x$ and $g: x \rightarrow \cos x$ for $-2\pi \le x \le 2\pi$.

a. For what values of x is $\frac{f}{g}$ not defined? $-\frac{3\pi}{2}, -\frac{\pi}{2}, \frac{\pi}{2}, \frac{3\pi}{2}$

b. Graph $\frac{f}{g}$ and describe the result. See left.

c. What is the period of $\frac{f}{g}$? *(Lessons 2-6, 3-1)* π

18b)

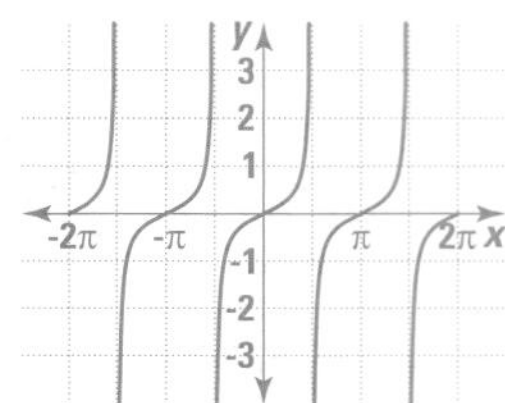

This is the graph of tan x.

19. Use the graph of $f: x \rightarrow \frac{2x - 7}{x - 4}$ shown at the right.

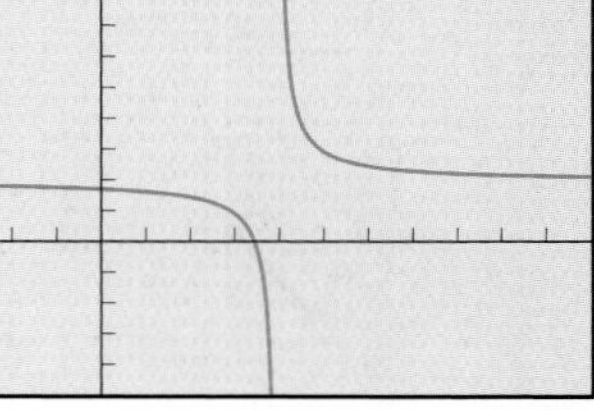

$-3 \le x \le 11$, x-scale = 1
$-5 \le y \le 8$, y-scale = 1

a. What is the domain of f?

b. Identify the x- and y-intercepts.

c. Use limit notation to describe the end behavior of f. *(Lessons 2-1, 2-4)*

a. $\{x : x \text{ is real and } x \neq 4\}$

b. x-intercept $= \left(\frac{7}{2}, 0\right)$, y-intercept $= \left(\frac{7}{4}, 0\right)$

c. See left.

19c) $\lim_{x \to \infty} f(x) = 2$, $\lim_{x \to -\infty} f(x) = 2$

20. Consider the following argument. See below left.

If the interest rate drops, investment drops.
Investment has dropped.
$\therefore$ *The interest rate has dropped.*

a. Write the form of this argument.

b. Is the argument valid or invalid? *(Lessons 1-6, 1-7)*

Stock Response. *Stocks are a common investment.*

20a) $p \Rightarrow q$
q
$\therefore p$
b) invalid

21. Prove that if n is odd, then $n^2 + 1$ is even. *(Lesson 1-8)* See margin.

Exploration

22. Suppose $f(x) = \frac{1}{e^{(x^2)}}$ for all real numbers x.

a. Express f as the composite of three simpler functions.

b. Graph f over a reasonable domain. See margin.

c. Explain how each of the three simpler functions contributes something to the graph. See margin.

a) $g = x^2$, $h = e^x$, $k = \frac{1}{x}$, $f = k \circ h \circ g$

Additional Answers

21. Let n be odd. Then for some integer m, $n = 2m + 1$. Therefore $n^2 + 1 = (2m + 1)^2 + 1 = 4m^2 + 4m + 2 = 2 \cdot (2m^2 + 2m + 1)$. Because the integers are closed under addition and multiplication, $(2m^2 + 2m + 1)$ is an integer. Therefore, $n^2 + 1 = 2 \cdot p$, where p is an integer. Therefore $n^2 + 1$ is even.

22. b.

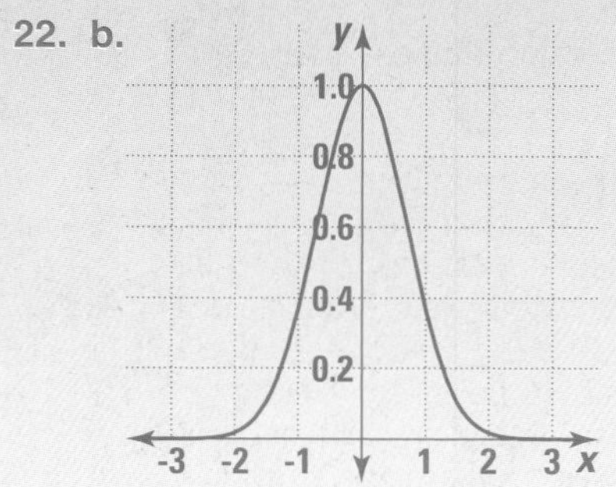

c. k insures $\lim_{x \to \infty} f(x) = 0$, h makes the graph quickly approach the limit, g makes the function symmetric about the y-axis.

LESSON

3-3 The Logic of Equation-Solving

An equation is like a balance scale in that what is done to one side must be done to the other in order to keep it balanced.

When you solve an equation, you can always apply properties that hold for all real numbers, such as the Distributive Property in any of its forms (adding fractions, expanding polynomials, factoring, adding or subtracting like terms) or the Zero-Product Property ($ab = 0 \Leftrightarrow a = 0$ or $b = 0$).

But the most significant steps often involve what is usually called "doing the same thing to both sides." For example, you might add $3x$ to both sides or multiply both sides by $\frac{2}{7}$. You are then applying special cases of the following two properties, which we state here in function language for reasons that will soon be obvious.

Properties of Equality and Operations
For any real expressions $f(x)$ and $g(x)$: if $f(x) = g(x)$, then

$f(x) + c = g(x) + c$	**Addition Property of Equality**
$f(x) \cdot c = g(x) \cdot c$	**Multiplication Property of Equality**

These properties are another way of stating that addition and multiplication are binary operations; equal numbers always yield equal results. In Example 1, we abbreviate the first property as A_c and the second as M_c.

Lesson 3-3

Objectives

A Solve equations by applying a function to each side, taking into account nonreversible steps.
E Analyze the reversibility of steps used in solving equations and inequalities.
H Apply equation-solving techniques to real-world problems.

Resources

From the ***Teacher's Resource File***
- Lesson Master 3-3
- Answer Master 3-3
- Teaching Aids 26: Warm-up

Additional Resources
- Visual for Teaching Aid 26

Teaching Lesson 3-3

Warm-up

The equation $ax + b = cx + d$ is solved for x and there is exactly one solution.

1. What is the solution? $\frac{d-b}{a-c}$
2. What must be true of a and c? $a - c \neq 0$

Lesson 3-3 Overview

Broad Goals This lesson uses the logic that students have studied in Chapter 1 and the function operations of Lessons 3-1 and 3-2 to explain the process of solving equations.

Perspective It is very important that students learn to distinguish between steps that are reversible and steps that are not; the distinction is the difference between *if-then* statements and *if and only if* statements. Reversible steps are linked with 1-1 functions, and equations related by reversible steps have the same solutions.

When the same number is added to both sides of an equation, you can think of this as adding a constant function to both sides. When both sides are multiplied by the same number, you can think of this as multiplying both sides by a constant function. If expressions replace numbers, the same properties apply. The only difference is that we would rarely think of multiplying both sides by 0, but in an expression this might be disguised, leading to a result like that found in **Example 2.** When we take the logarithm of both sides of an equation, or take both sides to some power, we are now composing functions, and the Function Composition and Equality Property applies. The only problem is that we cannot be certain the

(Overview continues on page 162.)

Notes on Reading

After the students have read the text, you may want to synthesize the key vocabulary and points of the lesson. There is only one new idea—*reversibility*.

Example 1 illustrates that the solving of a typical linear equation has only reversible steps. This is why, if we have made no error, the check always works.

Example 2 shows that multiplying by 0 is not a reversible step. That is, the expression in the denominator of each rational expression has a value of 0 when $x = 3$, so when both sides of the equation were multiplied by the product of these denominators, the number 3 suddenly appears as a solution to the equation that arises.

Example 3 shows that squaring both sides is also a nonreversible step.

You may have to connect the informal treatment students have seen of equation-solving to the more formal treatment given in this lesson. For instance, in **Example 3** most students do not equate the colloquial "squaring of both sides" with the formalism of "applying the squaring function."

Error Alert Emphasize the *reversibility of steps* idea. Point out that just one nonreversible step among many reversible steps makes possible the loss of zeros or the introduction of extraneous zeros.

Example 1

Identify the properties used in solving $100x + 13 = 98x - 6$.

Solution

Here is a solution in two-column form.

Conclusions	Justifications
0. $100x + 13 = 98x - 6$	Given
1. $2x + 13 = -6$	A_{-98x}
2. $2x = -19$	A_{-13}
3. $x = \frac{-19}{2}$	$M_{0.5}$

Check

Substitute $\frac{-19}{2}$ for x in the given equation, and it is true.

Why do we check the solution found in step 3? The answer seems obvious: to show that we did not make a mistake. But there is another reason: The steps written in the solution only show *If* $100x + 13 = 98x - 6$, *then* $x = \frac{-19}{2}$. They show that $\frac{-19}{2}$ is the only possible solution to the equation, but they do not show that it is a solution. The check shows the converse: *If* $x = \frac{-19}{2}$, *then* $100x + 13 = 98x - 6$. The check guarantees the solution, and technically, without the check, the equation is not solved!

That a check is necessary is shown by the next example, which again uses only properties of real numbers and the Addition and Multiplication Properties of Equality.

Example 2

Find all solutions to $\frac{1}{15 - 5x} = \frac{1}{x^2 - 4x + 3}$.

Solution

We solve it as we did in Example 1.

Conclusions	Justifications
0. $\frac{1}{15 - 5x} = \frac{1}{x^2 - 4x + 3}$	Given
1. $x^2 - 4x + 3 = 15 - 5x$	$M_{(15-5x)(x^2-4x+3)}$
2. $x^2 + x - 12 = 0$	A_{5x-15}
3. $(x + 4)(x - 3) = 0$	Factor the left side.
4. $x = -4$ or $x = 3$	Zero-Product Property

Check

At this point we do not know that -4 and 3 are solutions of the given equation. We know only that *If a real number satisfies the equation* $\frac{1}{15 - 5x} = \frac{1}{x^2 - 4x + 3}$, *then it must be either* -4 *or* 3. In fact, the following check shows that -4 is a solution, but 3 is not.

Does $\frac{1}{15 - 5 \cdot -4} = \frac{1}{(-4)^2 - 4 \cdot -4 + 3}$? Yes, so -4 is a solution.

Does $\frac{1}{15 - 5 \cdot 3} = \frac{1}{3^2 - 4 \cdot 3 + 3}$? No, so 3 is not a solution.

Lesson 3-3 Overview, continued

new equation that results is equivalent to the old unless the function applied to both sides has an inverse that is a function.

A Logical Analysis of Example 2

What went wrong in Example 2? Could we have known there was trouble in advance? The answers to these questions can be found by a logical analysis of the steps in the solution. Conclusions 0–4 in Example 2 are shorthand for a sequence of four if-then statements.

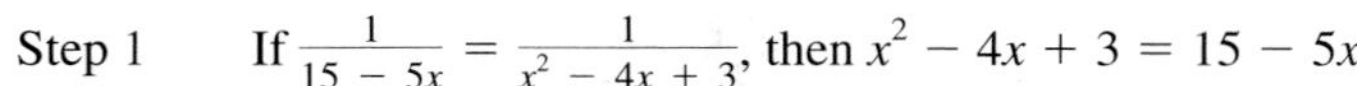

Step 1 If $\frac{1}{15 - 5x} = \frac{1}{x^2 - 4x + 3}$, then $x^2 - 4x + 3 = 15 - 5x$.

Step 2 If $x^2 - 4x + 3 = 15 - 5x$, then $x^2 + x - 12 = 0$.

Step 3 If $x^2 + x - 12 = 0$, then $(x + 4)(x - 3) = 0$.

Step 4 If $(x + 4)(x - 3) = 0$, then $x = -4$ or $x = 3$.

By the Law of Transitivity, the following conclusion can be drawn.

$$\text{If } \frac{1}{15 - 5x} = \frac{1}{x^2 - 4x + 3}, \text{ then } x = -4 \text{ or } x = 3.$$

But in order for -4 and 3 both to be solutions, the converse of this conclusion must be true. That is, we must know *If* $x = -4$ *or* $x = 3$*, then* $\frac{1}{15 - 5x} = \frac{1}{x^2 - 4x + 3}$. This converse will be true if the converse of each if-then statement in Steps 1–4 above is true for any real number x. The converses of the if-then statements in Steps 2–4 are true for any real number x. Consequently, for any such number the following if-and-only-if statements are true.

Step 2 $x^2 - 4x + 3 = 15 - 5x$ if and only if $x^2 + x - 12 = 0$.

Step 3 $x^2 + x - 12 = 0$ if and only if $(x + 4)(x - 3) = 0$.

Step 4 $(x + 4)(x - 3) = 0$ if and only if $x = -4$ or $x = 3$.

Therefore, by the Law of Transitivity:

x satisfies the equation $x^2 - 4x + 3 = 15 - 5x$ if and only if $x = -4$ or $x = 3$.

On the other hand, the converse of the if-then statement in Step 1 is false for $x = 3$, because 3 satisfies the second equation but not the first.

These observations are often summarized by saying that Steps 2–4 are *reversible*, while Step 1 is *nonreversible*. In general, **reversible** steps in solving an equation or inequality correspond to justifications that are if-and-only-if statements. Equations related by reversible steps have the same solutions and are called **equivalent equations**. **Nonreversible** steps correspond to true if-then statements for which the converse is false. In the example above, multiplying both sides of $\frac{1}{15 - 5x} = \frac{1}{x^2 - 4x + 3}$ by $(15 - 5x)(x^2 - 4x + 3)$ is not a reversible step.

Reversibility and Inverse Functions

The reversibility of a step in solving an equation is related to the existence of inverse functions. Consider the two equation-solving properties one at a time.

Addition Property of Equality: In Step 2 of Example 2, $5x - 15$ was added to each side. To perform the converse of this step, *If* $x^2 + x - 12 = 0$*, then* $x^2 - 4x + 3 = 15 - 5x$, you can subtract $5x - 15$. In general, the "adding c" function $g: x \rightarrow x + c$ always has an inverse, the "subtracting c"

You may want to introduce the term *extraneous solution.* Extraneous solutions satisfy an equation in one of the intermediate steps but fail to satisfy the original equation because some nonreversible process was used to find a solution. However, if you use this term, stress that an extraneous solution is not a solution!

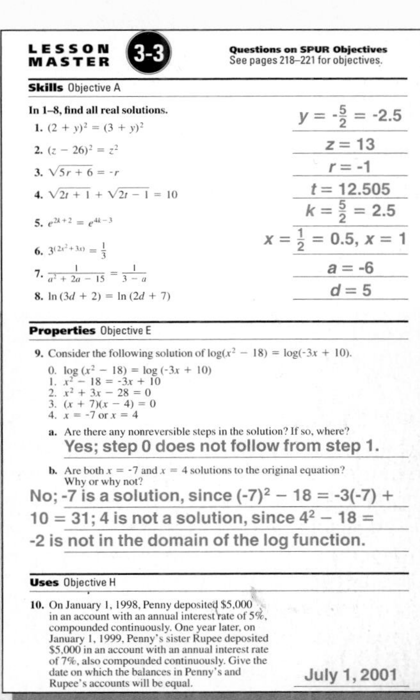

LESSON MASTER 3-3 **Questions on SPUR Objectives** See pages 218–221 for objectives.

Skills Objective A

In 1–8, find all real solutions.

1. $(2 + y)^2 = (3 + y)^2$ — $y = -\frac{5}{2} = -2.5$
2. $(z - 26)^2 = z^2$ — $z = 13$
3. $\sqrt{5r + 6} = -r$ — $r = -1$
4. $\sqrt{2t + 1} + \sqrt{2t - 1} = 10$ — $t = 12.505$
5. $e^{2k+2} = e^{4k-3}$ — $k = \frac{5}{2} = 2.5$
6. $3^{(2x^2 + 3x)} = \frac{1}{3}$ — $x = \frac{1}{2} = 0.5, x = 1$
7. $\frac{1}{a^2 + 2a - 15} = \frac{1}{3 - a}$ — $a = -6$
8. $\ln(3d + 2) = \ln(2d + 7)$ — $d = 5$

Properties Objective E

9. Consider the following solution of $\log(x^2 - 18) = \log(-3x + 10)$.

0. $\log(x^2 - 18) = \log(-3x + 10)$
1. $x^2 - 18 = -3x + 10$
2. $x^2 + 3x - 28 = 0$
3. $(x + 7)(x - 4) = 0$
4. $x = -7$ or $x = 4$

a. Are there any nonreversible steps in the solution? If so, where? Yes; step 0 does not follow from step 1.

b. Are both $x = -7$ and $x = 4$ solutions to the original equation? Why or why not? No; -7 is a solution, since $(-7)^2 - 18 = -3(-7) + 10 = 31$; 4 is not a solution, since $4^2 - 18 = -2$ is not in the domain of the log function.

Uses Objective H

10. On January 1, 1998, Penny deposited \$5,000 in an account with an annual interest rate of 5%, compounded continuously. One year later, on January 1, 1999, Penny's sister Rupee deposited \$5,000 in an account with an annual interest rate of 7%, also compounded continuously. Give the date on which the balances in Penny's and Rupee's accounts will be equal. — July 1, 2001

Optional Activities

Writing To summarize the lesson, have students write a paragraph explaining *reversibility.* Ask them to include an example of a step that is reversible and an example of a step that is not reversible. Students should explain their choices.

function: $g^{-1}: x \to x - c$, and it is the justification for the converse. So you never have to worry about adding the same number or expression to both sides of an equation.

Multiplication Property of Equality: Step 1 is troublesome in Example 2. In this step, both sides were multiplied by $(15 - 5x)(x^2 - 4x + 3)$. The converse step requires that both sides be divided by $(15 - 5x)(x^2 - 4x + 3)$. This cannot be done when the expression equals 0. And, as it happens, the expression does equal zero when $x = 3$, which explains why 3 is not a solution.

In general, the "multiplying by c" function $g: x \to cx$ has an inverse except when $c = 0$, the "dividing by c" function: $g^{-1}: x \to \frac{x}{c}$. So you only have to worry about multiplying both sides of an equation by the same number or expression when that number or expression equals zero.

Applying a Function to Both Sides of an Equation

When you square both sides of an equation, or take both sides to a power, or take the log of both sides, you are applying the fact that function composition is a well-defined operation.

Function Composition and Equality Property
For any real functions f, g, and h and values of x for which f, g, $h \circ f$, and $h \circ g$ are defined: if $f(x) = g(x)$, then

$$h(f(x)) = h(g(x)).$$

In the next example, h is the squaring function. You can see that applying h to both sides causes a problem.

Example 3

Find all real numbers x satisfying $4 - x = \sqrt{x - 2}$.

Solution

Conclusions	Justifications
0. $4 - x = \sqrt{x - 2}$	Given
1. $(4 - x)^2 = x - 2$	Square both sides.
2. $x^2 - 8x + 16 = x - 2$	Expand the left side.
3. $x^2 - 9x + 18 = 0$	A_{-x+2}
4. $(x - 6)(x - 3) = 0$	Factor the left side.
5. $x = 6$ or $x = 3$	Zero-Product Property

By the Law of Transitivity, we can conclude:

If $4 - x = \sqrt{x - 2}$, then $x = 6$ or $x = 3$.

This conclusion does not imply that 6 and 3 are solutions of the given equation. It only restricts the possible solutions to those two numbers. In fact, a check shows that 3 is a solution but 6 is not.

Additional Examples

1. Find all values of x satisfying $\frac{1}{2x^2 + 7x - 3} = \frac{1}{x^2 + 12x + 11}$.
   For all values of x for which neither denominator is zero, we can multiply both sides by the product of the denominators, resulting in
   $x^2 + 12x + 11 = 2x^2 + 7x - 3$
   $x^2 - 5x - 14 = 0$
   $(x - 7)(x + 2) = 0$
   $x = 7$ or $x = -2$
   Thus, 7 and -2 are candidates for solutions. When $x = -2$, does
   $\frac{1}{2(-2)^2 + 7(-2) - 3} = \frac{1}{(-2)^2 + 12(-2) + 11}$?
   $-\frac{1}{9} = -\frac{1}{9}$? Yes.
   When $x = 7$, does
   $\frac{1}{2(7)^2 + 7(7) - 3} = \frac{1}{(7)^2 + 12(7) + 11}$?
   $\frac{1}{144} = \frac{1}{144}$? Yes.
2. Solve $\sqrt{x + 14} = x + 2$.
   $\sqrt{x + 14} = x + 2$
   $\Rightarrow x + 14 = (x + 2)^2$
   $\Leftrightarrow x + 14 = x^2 + 4x + 4$
   $\Leftrightarrow x^2 + 3x - 10 = 0$
   $\Leftrightarrow (x + 5)(x - 2) = 0$
   $\Leftrightarrow x = -5$ or $x = 2$
   Thus, -5 and 2 are possible solutions. The only solution is 2.
3. Solve $\sqrt[5]{4n} = 3$.
   $\sqrt[5]{4n} = 3 \Leftrightarrow 4n = 3^5$
   $\Leftrightarrow 4n = 243$
   $\Leftrightarrow n = \frac{243}{4}$

Adapting to Individual Needs

Extra Help

Remind students that whenever they use an irreversible step, they must check all solutions to the final equation. Stress that an irreversible step presents the *possibility* of the loss of zeros or the introduction of extraneous roots. Caution students not to infer from **Examples 2–3** that this *always* happens. For example, suppose the equation in **Example 2** were $\frac{1}{x} = \frac{1}{4x - 30}$. Then in Step 1 we would multiply both sides by $(x)(4x - 30)$. This is not a reversible step because the converse step requires that both sides be divided by $(x)(4x - 30)$, which is not allowed when the expression equals 0. However, in this case, if we continue solving the equation, we get $x = 10$ and a check shows that $x = 10$ is, in fact, a solution.

Check

Does $4 - 3 = \sqrt{3 - 2}$? Yes, so 3 is a solution.
Does $4 - 6 = \sqrt{6 - 2}$? No, so 6 is not a solution.

Therefore, if $4 - x = \sqrt{x - 2}$, then $x = 3$.

What has happened in Example 3 is similar to what happened in Example 2. Steps 2–5 are reversible, but Step 1 is not. In order for Step 1 to be reversible, the inverse of the squaring function needs to be a function, but it is not. Although in some situations squaring may be reversible, whenever you use squaring, you must check all solutions to your final equation to determine whether they are solutions to the given equation.

Here is a summary of the discussion of this lesson:

Reversible Steps Theorem
Let $f(x)$ and $g(x)$ be any real expressions. Then for all real expressions c and real functions h:

(1) $f(x) = g(x) \Leftrightarrow f(x) + c = g(x) + c$.
(2) $f(x) = g(x) \Leftrightarrow f(x) \cdot c = g(x) \cdot c$, provided $c \neq 0$.
(3) $f(x) = g(x) \Leftrightarrow h(f(x)) = h(g(x))$, provided h^{-1} exists.

QUESTIONS

Covering the Reading

1. Show that for any real number x, $2x + 5 = 3x - 2 \Leftrightarrow x = 7$. See margin
2. When is a reasoning step *reversible*? See left.

2) When the justification is an if-and-only-if (biconditional) statement.

3. *True or false.* Nonreversible steps in the solution process of an equation may lead to values of the variable that fail to satisfy the equation. True

In 4–7, in an equation involving real numbers, tell whether the reasoning step is always reversible.

4. adding the same number to both sides Yes
5. squaring both sides No
6. multiplying both sides by 3 Yes
7. multiplying both sides by 0 No

8. Consider solving the equation $\sqrt{y - 3} = 3 - y$ below. Replace the ___?___ with a $\Leftrightarrow$ for a reversible step or with a $\Rightarrow$ for a nonreversible step.

a. i. $\sqrt{y - 3} = 3 - y$ ___?___ $y - 3 = (3 - y)^2$ $\Rightarrow$
ii. ___?___ $y - 3 = 9 - 6y + y^2$ $\Leftrightarrow$
iii. ___?___ $y^2 - 7y + 12 = 0$ $\Leftrightarrow$
iv. ___?___ $(y - 3)(y - 4) = 0$ $\Leftrightarrow$
v. ___?___ $y - 3 = 0$ or $y - 4 = 0$ $\Leftrightarrow$
vi. ___?___ $y = 3$ or $y = 4$ $\Leftrightarrow$

b. Write all solutions to $\sqrt{y - 3} = 3 - y$.
$y = 3$

4. Solve $\log(t^3 + 3t^2 + 5t - 7) = 3\log(t + 1)$.
$\log(t^3 + 3t^2 + 5t - 7) = 3\log(t + 1)$
$\Leftrightarrow \log(t^3 + 3t^2 + 5t - 7) = \log(t + 1)^3$
$\Leftrightarrow t^3 + 3t^2 + 5t - 7 = (t + 1)^3$
$\Leftrightarrow t^3 + 3t^2 + 5t - 7 = t^3 + 3t^2 + 3t + 1$
$\Leftrightarrow 5t - 7 = 3t + 1$
$\Leftrightarrow t = 4$

Notes on Questions

Questions 4–7 You might ask students to give the result in function language if the given equation is $f(x) = g(x)$.
[4. $f(x) + a = g(x) + a$;
5. $h(f(x)) = h(g(x))$, where $h(x) = x^2$;
6. $h(f(x)) = h(g(x))$, where $h(x) = 3x$;
7. $0 = 0$]

Question 8 Ask students in which equation the solution $y = 4$ first does not work. [step i] Notice that this is the equation resulting from the only nonreversible operation.

Additional Answers

1. $2x + 5 = 3x - 2$ Given
$5 = x - 2$ A_{-2x}
$7 = x$ A_2
Therefore, $2x + 5 = 3x - 2 \Leftrightarrow x = 7$ by the Transitive Property.

Adapting to Individual Needs

Challenge

Have students answer the following questions.

1. Explain why it is true that if $\ln A = \ln B$, then $A = B$. [$\ln x$ is 1-to-1]
2. Then why does the following produce a possible solution that does not work in the given equation?

$\ln(x^2 - 3) = \ln(2x)$	Given
$x^2 - 3 = 2x$	$\ln A = \ln B \Rightarrow A = B$
$x^2 - 2x - 3 = 0$	Subtract $2x$ from both sides.
$(x - 3)(x + 1) = 0$	Factor
$x = 3$ or $x = -1$	Zero Factor Thm.

-1 does not check. [-1 is not in the domain of the ln function.]

Notes on Questions

Questions 11 and 13–15 You might begin by asking what function is applied to both sides to solve the equation.

Question 16 Error Alert Some students might forget that irreversible steps may not only introduce extraneous solutions, but might also cause the loss of solutions. This equation is an example of such a case. The student could correct the solution by indicating on the second line that the division can be done only if $4x - 1 \neq 0$, so there is still a possibility that $4x - 1 \neq 0$.

Question 17 See the Extension on page 167 for an analysis of the ratio of d to h.

Question 17 Science Connection A satellite is an object that orbits a planet. There are some scientists who believe that natural satellites were formed at about the same time as the planets, and in the same way. Some students may be interested in exploring this topic.

Question 18 The algorithm described is simply two applications of the strategy used in solving **Example 3.**

9) $f: x \to x^3$ is a 1–1 function over its entire domain.

16) When $x = \frac{1}{4}$, $\frac{1}{4x-1} = \frac{1}{0}$, which is undefined. The second step should be qualified to exclude $4x - 1 = 0$.

9. Explain why cubing both sides of an equation is a reversible step. See left.

10. *True or false.* Taking the 6th power of both sides of an equation is a reversible operation. Justify your answer. False. Sample: $(2)^6 = 64$ and $(-2)^6 = 64$

Applying the Mathematics

In 11–13, solve for x.

11. $\log x = \log (x^2 - 30)$ $x = 6$

12. $\frac{1}{x^2 - 9} = \frac{1}{x - 3}$ $x = -2$

13. $\sqrt[3]{x} = \sqrt[3]{2x - 2}$ $x = 2$

SAT II

In 14 and 15, solve.

14. $e^{t^2} = e^{2t}$ $t = 0, t = 2$

15. $\log_{10}(3x + 5) = \log_{10}(4x + 9)$ No real solution

16. A student attempted to solve the equation $4x^3 - x^2 = 4x - 1$ as follows. See left.

$$x^2(4x - 1) = 4x - 1$$
$$\frac{1}{4x-1} \cdot x^2(4x - 1) = (4x - 1) \cdot \frac{1}{4x-1}$$
$$x^2 = 1$$
$$x = 1 \quad \text{or} \quad x = -1.$$

The solution $\frac{1}{4}$ to the original equation has been lost. What happened?

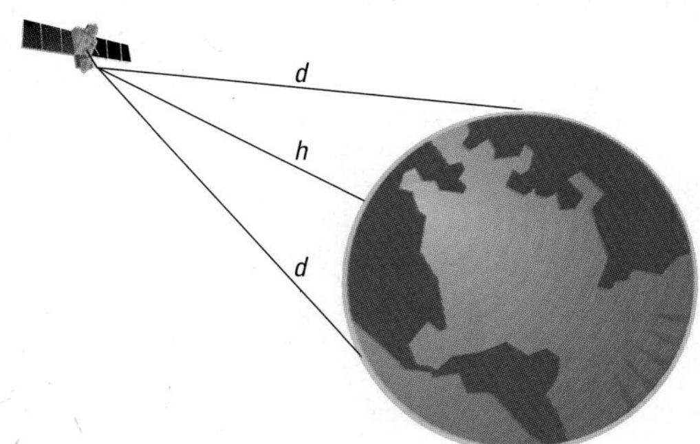

17. A satellite is in a circular orbit above the surface of Earth. Let h and d be the distances in miles from the satellite to the nearest and farthest points on Earth's surface that are visible from the satellite. If we assume that Earth is a sphere of radius 3960 miles, d and h are related by the equation

$$d = \sqrt{7920h + h^2}.$$

Determine the height h of the satellite for which the farthest observable distance is $2h$ by solving:

$$2h = \sqrt{7920h + h^2}.$$ $h = 2640$ miles

18. The equation $\sqrt{x - 3} = 3 - \sqrt{x}$ contains two square roots. Use the following procedure to find all real numbers that satisfy this equation.

a. Square both sides. $x - 3 = 9 - 6\sqrt{x} + x$

b. Simplify to obtain an equation in which there is a radical on one side of the equation, and all other terms are on the other side. $6\sqrt{x} = 12$

c. Square both sides of the equation obtained in part **b**. $36x = 144$

d. Solve the resulting equation. $x = 4$

e. The solutions of the given equation (if any) are found among the solutions of the equation in part **d**. Determine if any of the solutions in part **d** are solutions to the given equation. $x = 4$ is a solution.

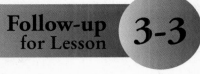

Review

19. Let $h(x) = 5x - 4$ and $k(x) = -2x^3$.

a. Give a formula for $h \circ k(x)$. $-10x^3 - 4$

b. Compute $h \circ k(-8)$. 5116

c. Give a formula for $k \circ h(x)$. $-2(5x - 4)^3$

d. Compute $k \circ h(-8)$. 170,368

e. Is it true that $h \circ k = k \circ h$? *(Lesson 3-2)* No

20. Suppose f and g are the real-valued functions defined by

$$f(x) = -x^2 \qquad g(x) = \log_{10} x.$$

a. Find the formula and the domain for the function $f \circ g$.

b. Explain why the composite function $g \circ f$ is undefined. *(Lesson 3-2)*

See left.

21. Let $f(x) = 10^x$ and $g(x) = \log_{10} x$.

a. Find $f(-2)$. $\frac{1}{100}$

b. Find $g\left(\frac{1}{100}\right)$. -2

c. Graph $f(x)$ and $g(x)$ on the same axes. How are the graphs related? *(Lesson 3-2)* They are mutual inverses. See left for graph.

22. Let $f(x) = \frac{1}{2 - 4x}$ and $g(x) = 2x - 1$.

a. Find and simplify the formula for $f \cdot g(x)$. $f \circ g(x) = -\frac{1}{2}$

b. What is the domain of $f \cdot g$? *(Lesson 3-1)* $\left\{x\text{: } x \text{ is real and } x \neq \frac{1}{2}\right\}$

23. Let $f(x) = x$ and $g(x) = x^2 - 8x + 16$ and $h = f \cdot g$. a) See left.

a. Graph h on an automatic grapher. Describe some properties of h.

b. Describe how special values of functions f and g determine the graph of h. *(Lesson 3-1)* $x = 0$ and $x = 4$ are zeros. Zeros of $f(x)$ and $g(x)$ are zeros of $h(x)$.

24. Write a logical expression that describes the network below. *(Lesson 1-4)*

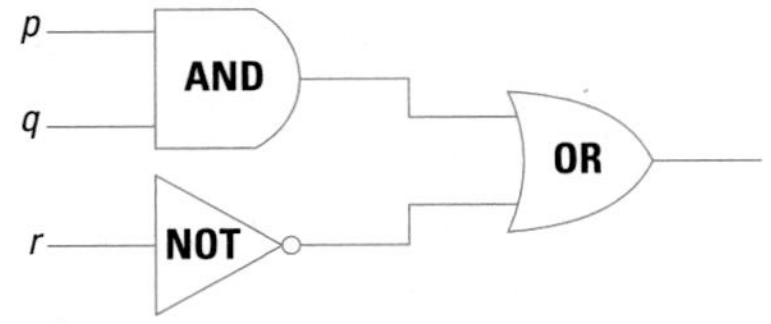

(p and q) or (not r)

25. Find all solutions between 0 and 2π.

a. $\sin x = \frac{1}{2}$ $\quad \frac{\pi}{6}, \frac{5\pi}{6}$

b. $\sin^2 x = \frac{1}{4}$ *(Previous course)* $\quad \frac{\pi}{6}, \frac{5\pi}{6}, \frac{7\pi}{6}, \frac{11\pi}{6}$

Exploration

26. Make up an equation different from any in this lesson in which the use of nonreversible steps leads to potential solutions that do not satisfy the original equation.

Sample: $\frac{1}{\sqrt{4x + 2}} = \frac{1}{2x - 3} \Leftrightarrow 2x - 3 = \sqrt{4x + 2}$

20a) $-(\log_{10} x)^2$; all reals > 0

b) $f(x) \leq 0$ for all real numbers. $g(x)$ is undefined for $x \leq 0$. Hence, $g \circ f$ is undefined.

21c)

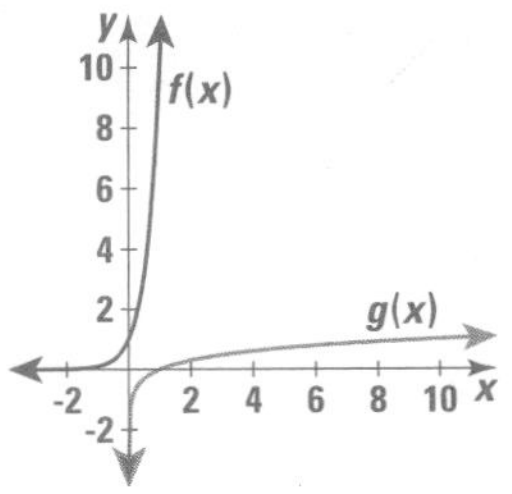

23a)

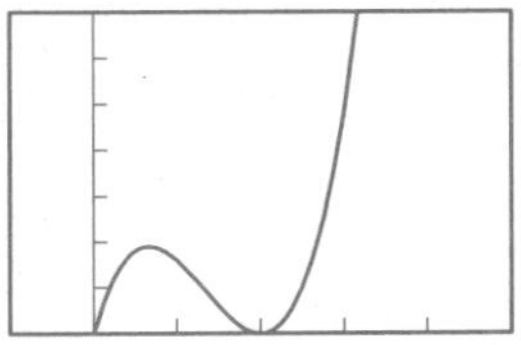

$-2 \leq x \leq 10$, x-scale = 2
$0 \leq y \leq 35$, y-scale = 5

Follow-up for Lesson 3-3

Practice

For more questions on SPUR Objectives, use **Lesson Master 3-3** (shown on page 163).

Assessment

Oral Communication Have students explain why each step in **Question 8** is either reversible or irreversible. Then have them explain why their answer to **part b** does not match the last line of **part a.** [Students solve equations and analyze the reversibility of steps used in solving equations.]

Extension

Refer students to **Question 17.** Ask them how d compares to h, as the values of h increase. In other words, what is $\lim_{h \to \infty} \frac{\sqrt{7920h + h^2}}{h}$?

[$\lim_{h \to \infty} \frac{\sqrt{7920h + h^2}}{h} = \lim_{h \to \infty} \frac{\sqrt{h^2}}{h} = \frac{h}{h} = 1$; h becomes closer and closer to d.]

Lesson 3-4

Objectives

G Identify continuous functions and their properties, such as the Intermediate Value Theorem.
H Apply equation-solving techniques to real-world problems.
M Use graphs to approximate zeros of functions and solve equations and inequalities.

Resources

From the ***Teacher's Resource File***

- Lesson Master 3-4
- Answer Master 3-4
- Assessment Sourcebook: Quiz for Lessons 3-1 through 3-4
- Teaching Aid 26: Warm-up

Additional Resources

- Visual for Teaching Aid 26
- Exploration 3-4

Teaching Lesson 3-4

Warm-up

Does the graph of $y = \frac{(x-2)^2}{x-2}$ ever intersect the x-axis? Explain. **No. The graph is the line $y = x - 2$ except when $x = 2$, so it contains all points on the line except (2, 0). (The function f with $f(x) = \frac{(x-2)^2}{x-2}$ is not continuous on the set of real numbers.)**

LESSON

3-4 *The Intermediate Value Theorem*

Chalk It Up to Experience. *In many schools, teachers receive more pay for each year they have taught. The average annual salary of public school teachers in the United States in 1995 was \$37,436. The average beginning salary was \$24,463.*

❶ On the first page of the chapter, a situation was described.

> The teachers in one school earn \$29,000 per year + \$1,000 for each year of teaching experience. The salaries in another school start at \$27,000 per year and increase 4% for each year of teaching experience. After how many years (if ever) do teachers in the second school earn more than teachers in the first?

To answer the question, let x be the number of years of teaching experience. Then teachers in the first school earn $29{,}000 + 1000x$, and teachers in the second school earn $27{,}000(1.04)^x$. We want to know when

$$27{,}000(1.04)^x > 29{,}000 + 1000x.$$

If we let

$$f(x) = 27{,}000(1.04)^x$$

and

$$g(x) = 29{,}000 + 1000x,$$

we wish to know when

$$f(x) > g(x).$$

Because f is an exponential function and g a linear function, there is no simple algebraic method for solving this inequality. However, graphing and successive approximation can be used. You can graph f and g and look for those values of x for which the graph of f is above the graph of g. Or you can define the function $h = f - g$ and look for those places where h is greater than zero. In this situation,

$$h(x) = 27{,}000(1.04)^x - (29{,}000 + 1000x).$$

Lesson 3-4 Overview

Broad Goals Continuity and the Intermediate Value Theorem are applied to justify certain trial-and-error methods for obtaining more accurate solutions.

Perspective Automatic graphers have made it much easier to approximate real solutions to equations. The two ideas in this lesson provide the underlying theory behind what is done when using calculators and many other trial-and-error techniques.

A formal treatment of these ideas, continuity and the Intermediate Value Theorem, requires calculus.

Optional Activities

Activity 1 Technology Connection
Materials: Explorations software

Students may use *Exploration 3-4, The Intermediate Value Theorem* to do Activity 2 on page 171. Students choose from a list of pre-selected functions or enter their own function. By defining an interval on the x-axis, $[a,b]$, and then choosing a point on the y-axis between $f(a)$ and $f(b)$, students can observe algebraically and graphically

The graphs of f, g, and h as drawn by an automatic grapher are shown here.

A trace on the graph by our automatic grapher gave $h(8.0084034) = -44.85833$ and $h(8.1428571) = 16.125273$. It appears that h is an increasing function, so the values of f are greater than the values of g at 9 years or later.

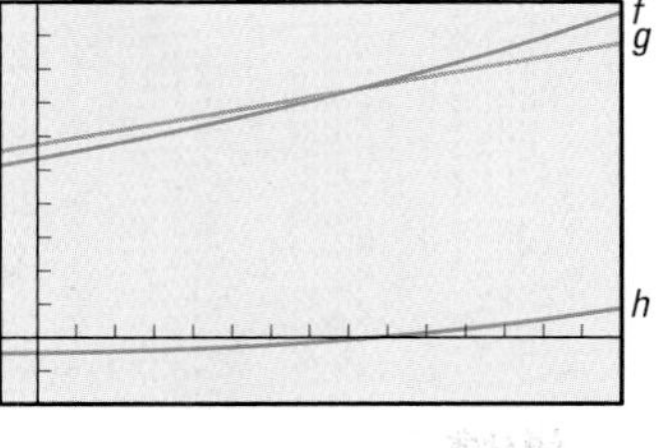

$-1 \le x \le 15$, x-scale = 1
$-10000 \le y \le 50000$, y-scale = 5000

Activity 1

Make a table of values of $f(x)$, $g(x)$, and $h(x)$, for $x = 6, 7, 8, 9$, and 10, to verify the solution shown by the graph. See Question 1 on page 172.

Continuous Functions

In the teacher-pay situation, the salary is set only once each year. So the domain of f and the domain of g is the set of positive integers, and no value of the domain is a zero of h. The domain of the graph of h drawn by our automatic grapher also did not contain the zero of h. This is often the case with automatic graphers, because their graphs are made from pixels. One brand of grapher has a screen that is 96 pixels wide, so the x-interval is split as closely as possible into 95 sub-intervals and the values of the function at their 96 endpoints are graphed.

But suppose the domain of h is the set of all numbers. Is there any real number c such that $h(c) = 0$ exactly? The answer is yes, and the reason has to do with the fact that h is then a continuous function.

Informally, a function f is **continuous on an interval** of real numbers $[a, b]$ if the graph of $y = f(x)$ is an unbroken curve for values of x between a and b. Although this description of the term *continuous* is not a precise definition (because the term *unbroken curve* has not been defined), it does serve as a useful test for the idea in relatively simple situations. All polynomial, exponential, logarithmic, and trigonometric functions are continuous on any interval in their domains.

❷ If f and g are continuous functions on an interval $[a, b]$, then $f + g$, $f - g$, and $f \cdot g$ are also continuous on $[a, b]$. If g has no zeros in $[a, b]$, then $\frac{f}{g}$ is continuous on $[a, b]$. The function h above is the sum of a polynomial function and an exponential function, so it is continuous.

Some familiar functions are not continuous. The tangent function is not continuous on any interval $[a, b]$ that includes an odd multiple of $\frac{\pi}{2}$. More generally, if an interval $[a, b]$ contains a point c that is not in the domain of a function f, then f is not continuous on $[a, b]$. However, a function may be defined at all points of an interval and still fail to be continuous on that interval.

Notes on Reading

Career Connection In 1997, the average public school teacher in the United States earned $39,580. (Source: *Statistical Abstract of the United States,* 1997)

❶ The lesson opener shows how graphing suggests solutions to equations or inequalities that cannot be solved exactly. We graph the continuous functions f, g, and h even though the situation is discrete (values are only meaningful when x is a nonnegative integer). If the continuous functions were not graphed, it would be difficult to determine at what points the graph of f was above the graph of g. Even in this discrete situation, we look for the point of intersection of the graphs of f and g between integers (between $x = 8$ and $x = 9$), and so we think of the Intermediate Value Theorem even in a situation to which it does not apply in theory.

❷ We do not provide a formal definition of *continuous*. The intuitive notion of an unbroken curve on some interval provides students with a sufficient understanding of the term for this course. In particular, students need to understand the Intermediate Value Theorem so they can determine appropriate intervals where zeros can be expected. Ask students to determine whether the Intermediate Value Theorem applies to these functions.

a. $f(x) = x^3 + x^2 + 4$, on the interval [-3, 3] [yes]

b. $g(x) = \log x$, on the interval [-1, 10] [no]

c. $h(x) = e^x - 2$, on the set of real numbers [yes]

whether the point x_0 exists such that x_0 is between a and b.

Activity 2 Cooperative Learning You may wish to have students **work in groups.** After discussing the Intermediate Value Theorem, refer students to **Question 13** on page 174. Ask them what the initial temperature of the bottle was. [150°] Ask students what happens to the temperature of the bottle if it is left on the counter indefinitely. [The temperature "levels off" to 70°; that is, $\lim_{x \to \infty} f(x) = 70°$.] Have them use a table or graph to determine how long it takes for the bottle's temperature to come close to this "leveling off" value. [approximately 22 minutes] Encourage groups to discuss their results.

Problems such as those above also serve to review ideas from earlier lessons of this chapter and give students an opportunity to discuss the domains of these functions.

Social Studies Connection Until 1997, stock prices on the New York Stock Exchange were normally in increments of $\frac{1}{8}$ dollar. Now they can be to the penny. Still, the price can jump.

For **Example 2,** project the screen of an automatic grapher to show the graphs of $y = 2^x$, $y = 3x^2$, and $y = 2^x - 3x^2$ on one screen. Point out that at the points where $y = 2^x$ and $y = 3x^2$ intersect, $y = 2^x - 3x^2$ has its zeros. Many students prefer to find zeros of $h(x) = f(x) - g(x)$ rather than the x-value of the intersection of $f(x)$ and $g(x)$.

Technology A spreadsheet can generate a table similar to that for **Example 3** very easily. Only columns for x and $2^x - 3x^2$ are needed. For intervals with sign changes, students may use the spreadsheet to "zoom in" on zeros. For example, to zoom in on zero(s) in the interval [7, 8], have the spreadsheet calculate $f(x)$ when $7 \le x \le 8$ for x values incremented by .1. Then repeat on an appropriate interval with x increments of .01, and so on.

Example 1

Sketch a graph to decide if the floor function F, defined by $F(x) = \lfloor x \rfloor =$ the greatest integer less than or equal to x, is continuous on the interval $-2 \le x \le 2$.

Solution

Using the definition of $\lfloor x \rfloor$, if $-2 \le x < -1$, then $F(x) = -2$; if $-1 \le x < 0$, then $F(x) = -1$; if $0 \le x < 1$, then $F(x) = 0$; if $1 \le x < 2$, then $F(x) = 1$; and finally, $F(2) = 2$. A graph of F is given at the right. The graph of F is broken at x = -1, 0, 1, and 2 in the interval $-2 \le x \le 2$. Therefore, F is not continuous on this interval.

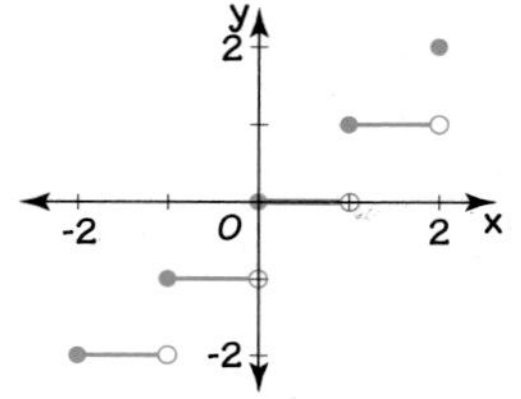

The Intermediate Value Theorem

Notice that $F(-2) = -2$ and $F(2) = 2$ but that there are many real numbers between -2 and 2 which are not attained as values of the function. For instance, there is no real number c in the interval [-2, 2] such that $F(c) = \frac{1}{2}$. Thus, the function F "skips" over some y-values between $F(-2)$ and $F(2)$. The *Intermediate Value Theorem*, whose proof is beyond the scope of this course, states that such "skipping" is not possible for a continuous function. It says that if a continuous function takes two distinct values on some interval, then it must take all values between these two.

The Intermediate Value Theorem
Suppose that f is a continuous function on the interval $[a, b]$. Then for every real number y_0 between $f(a)$ and $f(b)$, there is at least one real number x_0 between a and b such that $f(x_0) = y_0$.

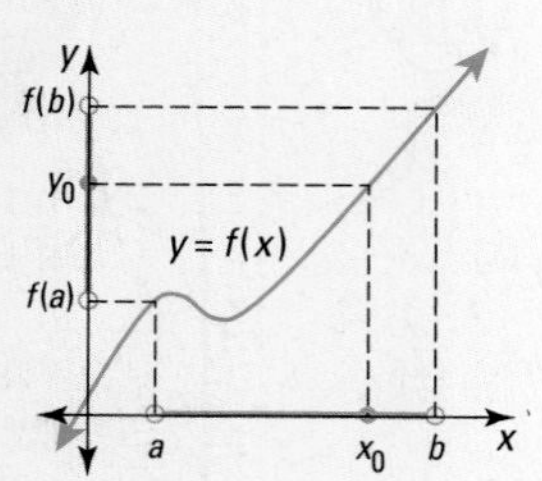

Many real-world functions are continuous and are thus consistent with the Intermediate Value Theorem. For instance, if the temperature is 27° at 9 a.m. and 35° at noon, then in theory every temperature between 27° and 35° occurred during that time. Other real-life functions are not continuous functions and therefore are not described by the Intermediate Value Theorem. For example, if a stock on the stock market sells for \$27 at 9 a.m. and \$35 at noon, it did not have to sell for \$34 at some point during that time. Stock prices are not continuous functions of time.

A stock trader often must make deals quickly before the market closes.

Adapting to Individual Needs

Extra Help
When searching for zeros, it is usually easiest to work with functions that are continuous over all the reals because you need not be concerned about any points of discontinuity. For functions that are not continuous over all real numbers, suggest to students that they carefully determine intervals on which the functions are continuous before applying the Intermediate Value Theorem. You may wish to discuss **Questions 3–4** and the corresponding comments in Notes on Questions.

Example 2

Consider the equation $2^x = 3x^2$. Use the Intermediate Value Theorem to explain why there must be a solution between 0 and 1.

Solution

Let h be the function obtained by subtracting $3x^2$ from 2^x.

$$h(x) = 2^x - 3x^2.$$

Compute $h(0)$ and $h(1)$:

$h(0) = 2^0 - 3(0)^2 = 1$ h(0) is positive.

$h(1) = 2^1 - 3(1)^2 = -1$ h(1) is negative.

The function h is continuous on any interval because it is the difference of an exponential function and a polynomial function, both of which are continuous on any interval. Because h(0) and h(1) have opposite signs, the Intermediate Value Theorem guarantees that there is some number c between 0 and 1 such that $h(c) = 0$. This value of c is a zero of the function h and a solution to the equation.

Example 3

Find another pair of consecutive integers between which there is a zero of the function h in Example 2.

Solution

A table or a graph of the function h can show that h has two other zeros. You can see from the table below or the graph on the right that there is a real solution in the interval (7, 8) because $2^x - 3x^2$ has different signs at the endpoints of this interval.

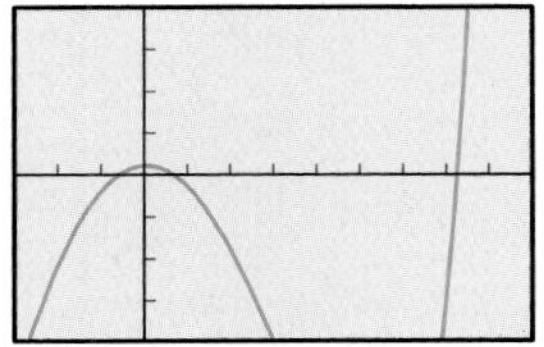

$-3 \le x \le 9$, x-scale = 1
$-20 \le y \le 20$, y-scale = 5

x	-2	-1	0	1	2	3	4	5	6	7	8	9	10
2^x	$\frac{1}{4}$	$\frac{1}{2}$	1	2	4	8	16	32	64	128	256	512	1024
$3x^2$	12	3	0	3	12	27	48	75	108	147	192	243	300
$h(x) = 2^x - 3x^2$	-11.75	-2.5	1	-1	-8	-19	-32	-43	-44	-19	64	269	724
sign of $h(x) = 2^x - 3x^2$	–	–	+	–	–	–	–	–	–	–	+	+	+

Activity 2

Find a third pair of consecutive integers between which there is a zero of the function h in Example 2. (-1, 0)

Have students record the results of **Activity 1** for **Question 1** on page 172.

Error Alert Some students assume that the inverse of the following statement is true: If $f(a)$ and $f(b)$ have opposite signs, then there would be at least one zero c between a and b. That is, they think that if $f(a)$ and $f(b)$ have the same signs, there is not a zero between a and b. You can dispel this misconception with a table and graph of $f(x) = 9x^2 - 45x + 56$. $f(2) = 2$ and $f(3) = 2$, but the zeros of f are $x = \frac{7}{3}$ and $x = \frac{8}{3}$, both between 2 and 3.

Additional Examples

1. In 1998, the postal service charged 32 cents for up to a one-ounce first class letter and 23 cents for each additional ounce or fraction thereof:
   a. Write a formula for the cost of sending a first class letter as a function of its weight (in ounces).
   $f(x) = 32 + 23\lceil x - 1 \rceil$

(Additional Examples continue on page 172.)

LESSON MASTER 3-4 **Questions on SPUR Objectives** See pages 218–221 for objectives.

Properties Objective G

1. a. Tell whether the function $f: x \to \frac{1}{\cos x}$ is continuous on the given interval.
   i. $\left[0, \frac{\pi}{4}\right]$ Yes
   ii. $\left[\frac{\pi}{4}, \frac{3\pi}{4}\right]$ No
   iii. $\left[-\frac{\pi}{4}, 0\right]$ Yes

   b. For the function of part a, $f\left(\frac{\pi}{4}\right) > 0$ and $f\left(\frac{3\pi}{4}\right) < 0$, yet there is no x in the interval $\left[\frac{\pi}{4}, \frac{3\pi}{4}\right]$ such that $f(x) = 0$. Does this contradict the Intermediate Value Theorem? Why or why not?
   No; $f(x)$ is not continuous on the interval $\left[\frac{\pi}{4}, \frac{3\pi}{4}\right]$.

2. *True or false.* If a function g is continuous on the interval [3, 6], $g(3) = 12$, and $g(6) = 19$, then, according to the Intermediate Value Theorem, $12 \le g(4) \le 19$. False

Uses Objective H

3. On January 1, 1998, Frank deposited $5,000 in an account with an annual interest rate of 5%, compounded continuously. One year later, on January 1, 1999, Frank's brother Mark deposited $5,000 in an account with an annual interest rate of 7%, also compounded continuously. Give the date on which Mark's account will have $10 more than Frank's account. Aug. 1, 2001

Representations Objective M

4. Consider the equation $e^{-x} \sin x = 1$.
   a. *Multiple choice.* In which one of the following intervals must there be a solution to the equation? a
   (a) $\left[\frac{3\pi}{2}, -\pi\right]$ (b) $\left[-\pi, \frac{\pi}{2}\right]$ (c) $\left[\frac{\pi}{2}, 0\right]$ (d) $\left[0, \frac{\pi}{2}\right]$
   b. Use an automatic grapher to find an interval of length 0.05 that contains a solution to the equation. Sample: [-3.20, -3.15]

b. Sketch the graph to decide if the function mapping weight to cost is continuous on the interval of weights x, where $0 < x \le 6$.

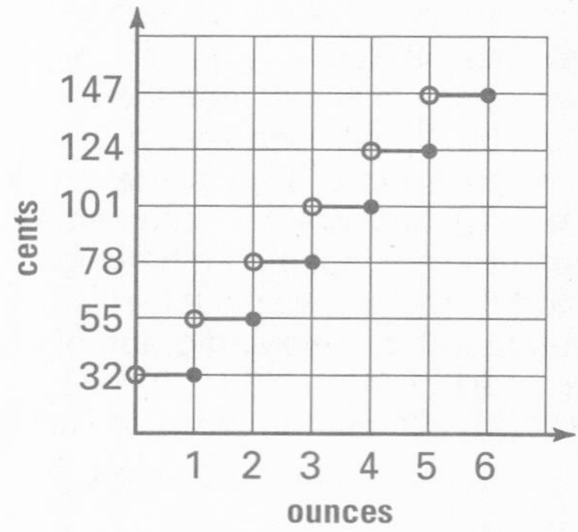

The function is not continuous on the interval (0, 6].

2. a. Use the Intermediate Value Theorem to show that there must be a solution to the equation $\sin x = .4 \ln x$, between 2 and 3. Remind students to have their calculators in radian mode.

Let $f(x) = \sin x - .4 \ln x$.
$f(2) = \sin 2 - .4 \ln 2 \approx .6320$
$f(3) = \sin 3 - .4 \ln 3 \approx -.2983$
Thus $f(2) > 0$ and $f(3) < 0$. Since both $\sin x$ and $\ln x$ are continuous on $2 < x < 3$, we may apply the Intermediate Value Theorem. Since $f(2)$ and $f(3)$ have opposite signs, $\exists$ c such that $2 < c < 3$ and $f(c) = 0$.

b. How many solutions does the equation have? **Graphing suggests there are three solutions. (Use $0 \le x \le 20$ and $-2 \le y \le 2$.)**

The Intermediate Value Theorem is behind the following general technique for approximating solutions to $f(x) = g(x)$. Suppose f and g are real functions and you want to find the approximate locations of real solutions of the equation

$$f(x) = g(x).$$

Let h be the function defined by $h(x) = f(x) - g(x)$. You are looking for values of x for which $h(x) = 0$. Find intervals $[a, b]$ of real numbers that lie entirely in the domains of both f and g and are such that $h(a)$ and $h(b)$ have different signs. That is, at one endpoint the value of h is positive and at the other endpoint the value of h is negative. If h is a continuous function on $[a, b]$, the Intermediate Value Theorem guarantees that, since 0 is between $h(a)$ and $h(b)$, there must be at least one number c in the interval $[a, b]$ such that $h(c) = 0$. Thus, the Intermediate Value Theorem allows you to find intervals containing zeros of continuous functions. By taking smaller and smaller intervals containing a given zero of h, the zero can be approximated to any desired level of accuracy.

$h(b) < 0 < h(a) \Rightarrow$
$\exists$ c between a and b such that $h(c) = 0$

Most calculators and mathematical software packages have built-in programs for computing approximate zeros for a function $h(x)$. To use these programs it is usually necessary to enter an "initial guess" that is reasonably close to the desired solution or zero. Such initial guesses can be determined from the Intermediate Value Theorem or graphically as in Example 3, where one might use -1, 1, and 8 as initial guesses for the three solutions.

Once an initial guess for a solution of an equation $f(x) = g(x)$ or for a zero of a function $h(x)$ is entered, these built-in programs are designed to compute a sequence of better and better approximations to the desired solution or zero and to terminate these calculations when a predetermined level of accuracy is achieved. Normally, the only output that you see is the final "answer." However, your computer or calculator actually calculates, stores, and reutilizes a succession of values between the initial guess and the displayed value of the approximation.

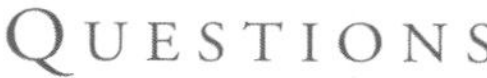

QUESTIONS

Covering the Reading

1. Give the table requested in Activity 1. **See margin.**
2. Teachers in school A earn \$25,000 per year and an increase of 5% for every year of teaching experience, up to 20 years. Teachers in school B earn \$28,000 per year and an increase of \$1000 per year.
   a. With 5 years experience, in which school do teachers earn more?
   b. After how many years do teachers in school A begin to earn more than teachers in school B? **7 years**
   a) School *B* (\$33,000 vs. \$31,907)
3. **a.** Is the floor function continuous on the interval [1, 1.5]? **Yes**
   b. Is the floor function continuous on the interval [1.5, 2.5]? **No**

Adapting to Individual Needs

Challenge

Writing Have students answer *True* or *False* to each of the following. If true, explain why. If false, give a counterexample and change the statement so that it is true.

1. If f is a continuous function on $[a, b]$ that is never negative, then $f(x)$ has no zeros in $[a, b]$. [False, $f(x) = x^2$ is continuous and never negative on [-1, 1] but has a zero. Sample: change *never negative* to *always positive* in the hypothesis.]
2. Suppose f is not continuous on $[a, b]$. Then there is a real number y_0 between $f(a)$ and $f(b)$, such that no x_0 between a and b has $f(x_0) = y_0$. [False, $f(x) = \tan x$ is not continuous on $[-\pi, \pi]$ but the conclusion does not hold. Sample: change the conclusion to: there is no guarantee that for every real number y_0 between $f(a)$ and $f(b)$, there is at least one real number x_0 between a and b such that $f(x_0) = y_0$.]
3. Suppose f is defined by $f(x) = \frac{3}{x+1}$. Even though $f(-2)$ is negative and $f(2)$ is positive, there is no x_0 between -2 and 2 such that $f(x_0) = 0$. [True; $f(x)$ is not continuous on [-2, 2]]

4. A function is graphed at the right. Tell whether the function is continuous on the given interval.
   a. $(p, 0)$ Yes
   b. $(0, q]$ No
   c. (q, r) Yes
   d. (r, s) No

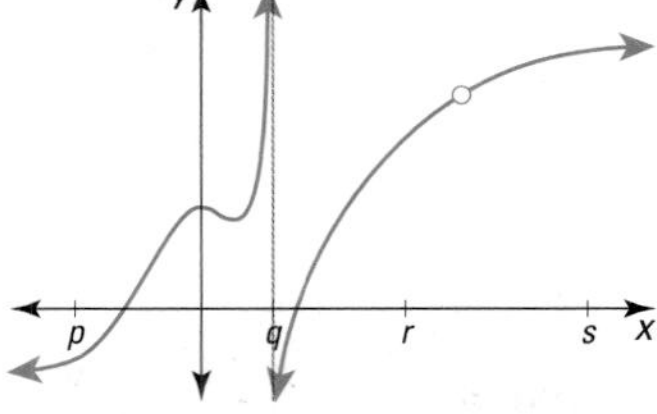

5. Assume f is a continuous function on the interval [-2, 3] of real numbers. Some values of f are given in the table below.

x	-2	-1	0	1	2	3
$f(x)$	-4	2	10	1	3	-5

   a. Find two consecutive integers such that $\exists$ some number x_0 between them with $f(x_0) = 7.5$. [-1, 0] or [0, 1]
   b. The function f has at least how many zeros? 2
   c. One zero of f occurs between what two consecutive integers? [-2, -1] or [2, 3]

6. Rewrite the conclusion of the Intermediate Value Theorem using the $\forall$ and $\exists$ symbols. See left.

6) $\forall$ real numbers y_0 between $f(a)$ and $f(b)$, $\exists$ at least one real number x_0 between a and b such that $f(x_0) = y_0$.

7. Explain why the function $f(x) = \frac{\sin x + e^{-x}}{x^2 + 1}$ is a continuous function on any interval $[a, b]$ of real numbers. See margin.

Applying the Mathematics

8. Use the Intermediate Value Theorem to find an interval between two consecutive integers that contains a zero of the function h defined by $h(x) = e^x - 5x^2 + 3$. [-1, 0] or [1, 2], [4, 5]

9. a. Use the Intermediate Value Theorem to find an interval between two integers that contains a solution to the equation $2x^3 - 3x + 2 = 5$.
   b. Use an automatic grapher to find an interval of length 0.1 which contains the zero of the function $f(x) = 2x^3 - 3x - 3$.
   See left.

9a) [1, 2]
b) [1.5, 1.6]

10. a. Determine the number of solutions of the equation $\sin x = .3x$ in the interval $(-\pi, \pi)$. 3
    b. Find a positive value of x so that the difference between $\sin x$ and $.3x$ is less than .01 Values between [2.347, 2.366] are acceptable.

11. Is the given function continuous on the interval [-2, 2]? If not, tell where there is a discontinuity.
    a. $f(x) = |x|$ Yes
    b. $g(x) = \frac{x}{|x|}$ No, g is discontinuous at $x = 0$.

12. Let $f(x) = \frac{x}{x-2}$. Then $f(1) = -1$ and $f(3) = 3$.
    a. Does f have a zero between 1 and 3? No
    b. Explain your answer. $\frac{x}{x-2}$ is not continuous on [1, 3], so the Intermediate Value Theorem does not apply.

Notes on Questions

Question 2 UCSMP students have compared exponential growth with linear growth in previous courses, and know that the percentage growth will overtake the constant-increase growth eventually. The question is whether this will occur soon enough to make a difference.

Questions 3–4 The domain is a critical part of the criterion for continuity. Theorems that specify continuity in their hypotheses must be applied carefully (if applied at all) to functions that are not continuous over all real numbers.

Question 9b Students should realize that f has the same zero as the solution to $2x^3 - 3x + 2 = 5$. Do they?

Question 10b Put this in the language of absolute value, in preparation for Lesson 3-9. The goal is to find a value of x such that $|\sin x - 0.3x| < 0.01$.

(Notes on Questions continue on page 174.)

Follow-up for Lesson 3-4

Practice

For more questions on SPUR Objectives, use **Lesson Master 3-4** (shown on page 171).

Assessment

Quiz A quiz covering Lessons 3-1 through 3-4 is provided in the *Assessment Sourcebook.*

(Follow-up continues on page 174.)

Additional Answers

1.

x	$f(x)$	$g(x)$	$h(x)$
6	34164	35000	-836
7	35530	36000	-470
8	36951	37000	-49
9	38429	38000	429
10	39967	39000	967

7. Sin x and e^{-x} are both continuous over the real numbers. Function addition preserves continuity so $\sin x + e^{-x}$ is continuous over the real numbers. $x^2 + 1$ is continuous over the real numbers and is never equal to zero. Since (nonzero) function division preserves continuity, $\frac{\sin x + e^{-x}}{x^2 + 1}$ is continuous over the real numbers.

Extension

Two algorithms for approximating zeros to functions are given in the Projects: the Bisection Method and the Secant Method. You may wish to explain one of these in class (but you should allow one as a project). If you explain the Bisection Method, then you might point out that students can apply the Bisection Method to identify words. Have students **work in groups** of three. The first student selects a word in a dictionary. The second student chooses a word approximately in the middle of the dictionary and asks if the first student's word is alphabetically before or after it. A third student splits the half into halves and asks again. This continues until the second or third student has identified the first student's word.

Project Update Project 2, *Approximating Zeros Using the Secant Method,* and Project 4, *Approximating Zeros Using the Bisection Method,* on pages 213–214, relate to the content of this lesson.

Notes on Questions

Question 20 Ask students to keep zooming in as they keep track of the count of zeros. Eventually the answer will be clear. Challenge them to explain why. [As x approaches 0, $\frac{1}{x}$ gets larger and larger and so its sine vacillates between 1 and -1 faster and faster.]

13. A hot baby bottle is set on a table to cool. Its temperature (in degrees Fahrenheit) after x minutes is given by

$$f(x) = 80e^{-0.555x} + 70.$$

When will the drink reach body temperature (98.6°F)?
after about 1.9 minutes

Review

14. Refer to Question 17 of Lesson 3-3.
 a. Derive the equation $d = \sqrt{7920h + h^2}$.
 See margin.
 b. At what satellite altitude is the observed distance 1000 miles greater than the height of the satellite? (Assume h must be between 50 and 500 miles.) *(Previous course, Lesson 3-3)* ≈ 169 miles.

In 15 and 16, two real-valued functions, f and g, are defined by formulas. Find a formula for the composite function $f \circ g$ and give its domain. *(Lesson 3-2)*

15. $f(x) = e^x$ $\quad g(x) = \frac{1}{4 + x^2}$ $\quad e^{1/(4+x^2)}$; domain: all reals

16. $f(x) = \frac{1}{x^2 - 4}$ $\quad g(x) = x + \frac{1}{x}$ $\quad \frac{x^2}{x^2 - 2x^2 + 1}$; domain: $\{x: x \neq -2, -1, 0, 1, 2\}$

17. The note n piano keys above the A (call it middle A) above middle C has frequency $f(n) = 440(2^{n/12})$ hertz. (A negative value for n means the key is below middle A.)
 a. Is f a function with a discrete domain? Yes
 b. Determine the location of the note with frequency approximately 329.6 hertz. $n = -5$, 5 keys below middle C
 c. Find the frequency of a note 4 keys above middle A. *(Lessons 2-1, 2-8)*
 ≈ 554.4 hertz

18. Describe the end behavior of the function $f: x \to x^2$. *(Lesson 2-4)*
 See left.

19. *Multiple choice.* Which is the contrapositive of $(p \text{ or } q) \Rightarrow r$? *(Lessons 1-3, 1-5)* b
 (a) *not r* ⇒ *not p or not q* (b) *not r* ⇒ *not p and not q*
 (c) *not p or not q* ⇒ *not r* (d) *not p and not q* ⇒ *not r*

18) $\lim_{x\to\infty} f(x) = \infty$; $\lim_{x\to-\infty} f(x) = \infty$

20) An infinite number: $x = \left\{\frac{1}{\pi}, \frac{1}{2\pi}, \frac{1}{3\pi}, \dots\right\}$

Exploration

20. How many zeros does the function $f(x) = \sin\left(\frac{1}{x}\right)$ have between 0 and 1?
 See left.

21. Consult the owner's manual for your calculator to see if it has built-in programs to solve equations or find zeros of functions.
 a. If it performs either of these tasks, use it to find the approximate solutions of $2^x = 3x^2$. $x \approx \{-0.488, 0.748, 7.33\}$
 b. Determine from the owner's manual if the accuracy of the programs for solving equations or finding zeros can be specified by the user or if it is specified by the program itself.
 Answers will vary.

Additional Answers

14. a. $\overline{AB}$ is tangent to $\odot C$ at B so ABC is a right triangle. So

$$r^2 + d^2 = (r + h)^2$$
$$r^2 + d^2 = r^2 + 2rh + h^2$$
$$d^2 = 2rh + h^2$$
$$d = \sqrt{2rh + h^2}$$
$$d = \sqrt{7920h + h^2}$$

LESSON

3-5 The Logic of Inequality-Solving

Now We're Cooking! *The electromagnetic waves of a microwave oven create heat by vibrating water molecules about 2.5 billion times a second. Doubling the amount of food does not double the cooking time. See Example 3.*

Solving inequalities is a little more complicated than solving equations. Although the major steps are still based on doing the same thing to both sides, the *sense* of the inequality (whether it is < or >) is of critical importance. The basic properties of inequality and operations take this into account.

Properties of Inequality and Operations
For any real expressions $f(x)$ and $g(x)$: if $f(x) < g(x)$, then

$f(x) + c < g(x) + c$	**Addition Property of Inequality**
$f(x) \cdot c < g(x) \cdot c$, if $c > 0$ $f(x) \cdot c > g(x) \cdot c$, if $c < 0$.	**Multiplication Properties of Inequality**

For instance, to solve

$$-5x < 100,$$

if you multiply both sides by $-\frac{1}{5}$, then you must reverse the sense of the inequality. The given inequality implies

$$x > -20.$$

Conversely, if $x > -20$, then multiplying both sides by -5 gives $-5x < 100$. Thus the two inequalities are equivalent.

$$-5x < 100 \Leftrightarrow x > -20$$

This illustrates that multiplication of both sides of an inequality by a negative number is a reversible step that changes the sense of the inequality.

Lesson 3-5

Objectives

D Solve inequalities algebraically.
E Analyze the reversibility of steps used in solving inequalities.
F Identify and prove properties of inverse functions.
J Use inequalities to solve real-world problems.
K Graph functions obtained from other functions by function operations or inverses.

Resources

From the ***Teacher's Resource File***
- Lesson Master 3-5
- Answer Master 3-5
- Teaching Aids
  26 Warm-up
  29 Properties and Theorems I
  30 Properties and Theorems II

Additional Resources
- Visuals for Teaching Aids 26, 29, 30

Teaching Lesson 3-5

Warm-up

The sum of a positive number and its reciprocal is less than 2. What is the number? **Solve $x + \frac{1}{x} < 2$ by multiplying both sides by x. Since $x > 0$, the sense of the inequality remains; equivalent inequalities are $x^2 + 1 < 2x$, $x^2 - 2x + 1 < 0$, $(x - 1)^2 < 0$. Since x is a real number, the left side cannot be negative, so there is no number satisfying the given conditions.**

Lesson 3-5 Overview

Broad Goals This lesson does for inequalities what was done for equations in Lesson 3-3. The fundamental properties of solving inequalities are considered from a function standpoint, and, in turn, the properties of functions are used to develop powerful methods for solving inequalities.

Perspective Given a graph of a continuous real function, it is very easy to determine whether the function is increasing or decreasing on an interval.

One would think there could be no important applications of this simple idea. This lesson shows that view to be incorrect: If g is increasing on an interval containing $f(x)$ and $h(x)$, and if $f(x) < h(x)$, then $g(f(x)) < g(h(x))$. If g is decreasing, the sense of the inequality is reversed. Thus increasing and decreasing functions provide a general framework for discussing how to solve inequalities.

Inverses of Increasing and Decreasing Functions

If the situation is this complicated with an operation as simple as multiplication, you might expect even greater problems trying to find the exact solution set for an inequality like

$$2^x < 3.$$

However, this inequality can be solved by applying a relationship between increasing functions and their inverses. We develop this relationship in three steps. First we show that a function that is always increasing or always decreasing is a 1-1 function.

Theorem
Suppose that f is a real function. If f is increasing throughout its domain, or if f is decreasing throughout its domain, then f is a 1-1 function.

Proof
Think of the theorem as a statement of the form (a *or* b) $\Rightarrow c$. We prove its contrapositive: *not* $c \Rightarrow$ *not* a *and not* b.

Suppose f is not a 1-1 function. Then there exist x and y such that $x \neq y$ and $f(x) = f(y)$. Whether $x > y$ or $x < y$, $f(x) \nless f(y)$ and $f(x) \ngtr f(y)$. So f is neither increasing nor decreasing.

Thus, in all cases when $x \neq y$, $f(x) \neq f(y)$. By the Law of the Contrapositive, the theorem is true.

The proof for decreasing functions is left to you in the Questions.

Recall from Lesson 3-2 that the inverse of a 1-1 function is a function. That single statement proves the corollary below. (Recall that a corollary to a theorem is a statement that follows easily from that theorem.)

Corollary
If f is an increasing function throughout its domain, or if f is a decreasing function throughout its domain, then the inverse of f is a function.

This corollary does not tell us much about the inverse of f. But if you draw a picture of an increasing function and its inverse, it seems that the inverse is also an increasing function.

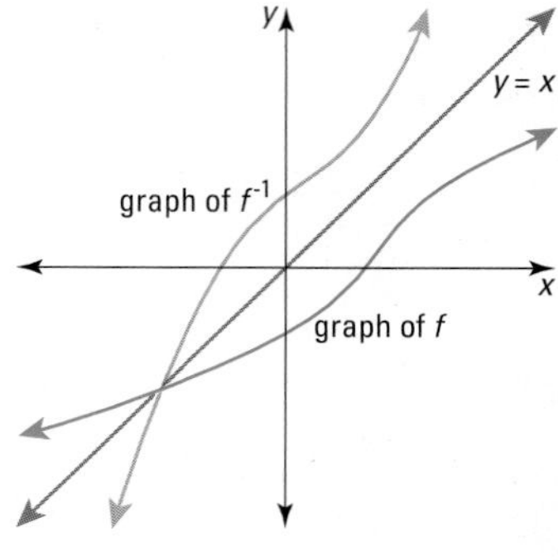

Notes on Reading

You might point out that the familiar procedure of multiplying both sides of an inequality by a positive or a negative number is a special case of the Properties of Inequality and Operations on page 175 in which $g(x) = kx$ and $k \neq 0$. When k is positive, g is increasing; when k is negative, g is decreasing. For example, suppose $f(x) = -3x$ and $h(x) = 12$ and we wish to solve $f(x) > h(x)$, that is, $-3x > 12$. Let $g(x) = -\frac{1}{3}x$, a decreasing function. So $g(f(x)) < g(h(x))$. That is, $-\frac{1}{3}f(x) < -\frac{1}{3}h(x)$. Thus, $x < -4$.

Teaching Aids 29–30 list the theorems and properties discussed in this lesson.

LESSON MASTER 3-5 — **Questions on SPUR Objectives** See pages 218–221 for objectives.

Skills Objective D

In 1–8, solve the inequality for all real-number solutions.

1. $-7n + 3 > 38$ — $n < -5$
2. $\ln z \leq -2$ — $0 < z \leq e^{-2} \approx 0.135$
3. $3^r > 3^{2-r}$ — $r < 1$
4. $\log_7 (2t + 3) \geq \log_7 (5t - 4)$ — $\frac{4}{5} < t \leq \frac{7}{3}$
5. $k^{1.5} \geq 20$ — $k \geq 20^{\frac{2}{3}} \approx 7.37$
6. $\sqrt[3]{x - 5} < -2$ — $x < -3$
7. $(7x - 3.2)^5 \geq (-x + 4.8)^5$ — $x \geq 1$
8. $x^3 + 3x^2 + 3x + 1 < 125$ — $x < 4$

Properties Objective E

9. Consider the following solution of $\frac{1}{x} > \frac{1}{x+1}$.

Conclusion	Justification
0. $\frac{1}{x} > \frac{1}{x+1}$	Given
1. $x < x + 1$	Apply $h(x) = \frac{1}{x}$ to both sides.
2. $0 < 1$	Add $-x$ to both sides.
3. All real values of x are solutions.	

a. The solution is not correct. Give the values of x which are not solutions to the original inequality.
No; $-1 \leq x \leq 0$

b. The function h in the solution is 1 - 1 and is decreasing on the intervals $(-\infty, 0)$ and $(0, \infty)$, so where is the mistake in the solution?
h is not always decreasing, so step 1 is invalid.

Optional Activities

Cooperative Learning After discussing the Reversible Steps Theorem for Inequalities, have students **work in groups** to summarize the similarities and differences between what constitutes reversible steps for equations and inequalities. Ask them to support their responses with examples. [Step (1) in the Reversible Steps Theorems is similar for both equations and inequalities—the same number can be added to both sides without changing the equation or the inequality. Step (2) in the Theorems—multiplying both sides of the equation or inequality by any number—results in reversing the sign of the inequality if the number is negative. Step (3) depends on the existence of h^{-1}. Examples will vary.]

❶ **Theorem**
Let f be a real function.

(1) If f is increasing on its entire domain, then f^{-1} is increasing on its entire domain.
(2) If f is decreasing on its entire domain, then f^{-1} is decreasing on its entire domain.

Proof (1)
We use an indirect proof. We are given that f is increasing on its entire domain. Suppose f^{-1} was decreasing somewhere. This would mean that there are u and v such that $u < v$ and $f^{-1}(u) > f^{-1}(v)$. But let $a = f^{-1}(u)$ and $b = f^{-1}(v)$, which means $f(a) = u$ and $f(b) = v$. By substitution in the previous inequality, $a > b$. But then $f(a) > f(b)$ because f is increasing, and this is the same (by substitution again) as $u > v$. But we began with $u < v$. We cannot have both $u < v$ and $u > v$. This contradiction tells us that we cannot have an increasing function f and a decreasing inverse function f^{-1}.

Proof (2)
This is left to you as a Question.

Notice that the above theorem yields another statement about an increasing function f: if $f(a) < f(b)$, then $a < b$.

Applying a Function to Both Sides of an Inequality

These theorems supply the tools to solve $2^x < 3$.

Example 1

Find the solution set for the inequality $2^x < 3$.

Solution

This is an inequality of the form $f(x) < k$, where f is the function $f(x) = 2^x$. It is natural to apply the inverse of f to each side. The inverse here is the logarithm function to the base 2, which is an increasing function. This means that the sense of the inequality is preserved and the step is reversible.

$$2^x < 3$$
$$\Leftrightarrow \quad \log_2(2^x) < \log_2 3$$
$$\Leftrightarrow \quad x < \log_2 3$$

Transforming Inequalities with Increasing and Decreasing Functions

The argument of Example 1 can be generalized and provides the basis for solving inequalities. Any increasing function can be applied to both sides of an inequality without changing the sense of the inequality. Furthermore, the step is reversible.

❶ **Examples 1–3** apply the theorems on increasing and decreasing functions. In **Example 1,** $h(x) = \log_2 x$, and so h is an increasing function. In **Example 2,** the function g^{-1} being applied to both sides has $g^{-1}(x) = x^{-1/5}$, a decreasing function. In **Example 3,** the function h being applied to both sides is $h(x) = x^{1/0.585}$, an increasing function.

The formula of **Example 3** can be derived as follows: We are looking for a function f: $A \rightarrow t$ such that $\frac{f(2A)}{f(A)} = 1.5$ for all $A > 0$. One function f that has the property that $\frac{f(bx)}{f(x)} = m$ for all $x > 0$ is the function $f(x) = x^p$, where $p = \log_b m$. Here is a proof: With this f, $\frac{f(bx)}{f(x)} = \frac{(bx)^p}{x^p} = b^p$. But since the ratio must be constant, $b^p = m$, from which $p = \log_b m$. In **Example 2,** $b = 2$ and $m = 1.5$, and so $\log_b m = \log_2 1.5 \approx 0.585$.

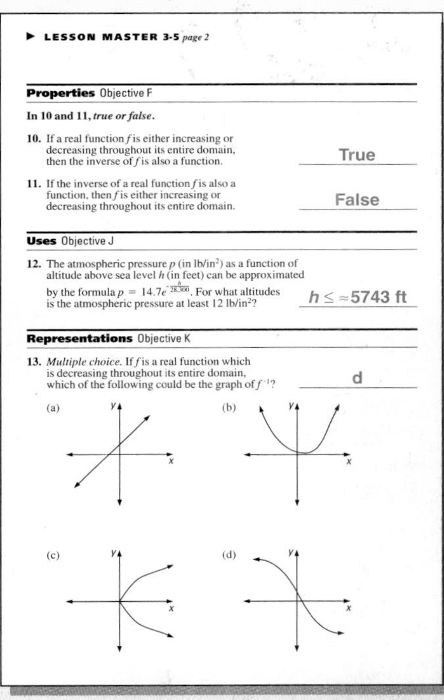
► LESSON MASTER 3-5 *page 2*

Properties Objective F

In 10 and 11, *true or false*.

10. If a real function f is either increasing or decreasing throughout its entire domain, then the inverse of f is also a function. True

11. If the inverse of a real function f is also a function, then f is either increasing or decreasing throughout its entire domain. False

Uses Objective J

12. The atmospheric pressure p (in lb/in²) as a function of altitude above sea level h (in feet) can be approximated by the formula $p = 14.7e^{-\frac{h}{28,300}}$. For what altitudes is the atmospheric pressure at least 12 lb/in²? $h \le \approx 5743$ ft

Representations Objective K

13. *Multiple choice.* If f is a real function which is decreasing throughout its entire domain, which of the following could be the graph of f^{-1}? d

(a) (b) (c) (d)

Adapting to Individual Needs

Extra Help

Some students might incorrectly assume that if a function increases throughout its domain, its inverse should decrease throughout its domain. To help students better understand the theorem at the top of page 177, have them sketch several increasing or decreasing functions on grid paper, then fold the paper in half and trace the function to produce its image over the line $y = x$. (Refer to the diagram at the bottom of page 176.) Encourage students to share their results.

❷ The theorems on applying increasing or decreasing functions to solve inequalities are quite elegant and powerful. Emphasize: applying an increasing function preserves the sense of the inequality, applying a decreasing function reverses the sense.

Additional Examples

1. Solve $5^x < 7$. $5^x < 7 \Leftrightarrow \log_5 5^x < \log_5 7 \Leftrightarrow x < \log_5 7$. So $x < 1.2091$ approximately.
2. Find all solutions to $\sin x > 0.5$ between $-\frac{\pi}{2}$ and $\frac{\pi}{2}$.
Because $\sin x$ is increasing on the interval $-\frac{\pi}{2} < x < \frac{\pi}{2}$, applying $\sin^{-1}$ preserves the sense of the inequality. $\sin x > 0.5 \Leftrightarrow \sin^{-1}(\sin x) > \sin^{-1}(0.5) \Leftrightarrow x > \frac{\pi}{6}$. Since we assumed $-\frac{\pi}{2} < x < \frac{\pi}{2}$, the solution is $\frac{\pi}{6} < x < \frac{\pi}{2}$.
3. In the same microwave oven as in Example 3, one potato cooks in 4 minutes. If you are hosting a dinner party and guests are arriving in one hour, at most, how many potatoes can you cook before they are expected to arrive?
$4w^{0.585} \le 60$
$(w^{0.585})^{1/0.585} \le (15)^{1/0.585}$
$w \le 15^{1/0.585}$
$w \le 102.43$
At most 102 potatoes could be cooked in one hour—but will they fit in the oven?

(Notes on Questions begin on page 180.)

❷ **Function Composition and Inequality Property (1)**
For any real expressions $f(x)$, $g(x)$, and an increasing real function h: $f(x) < g(x) \Leftrightarrow h(f(x)) < h(g(x))$.

Proof
From the definition of an increasing function, $\forall\, a$ and $\forall\, b$, $a < b \Rightarrow h(a) < h(b)$. The $\Rightarrow$ direction of the theorem follows by substituting $f(x)$ for a and $g(x)$ for b. Now because h is an increasing function, it has an inverse h^{-1} which is also increasing. Applying h^{-1} to both sides of $h(f(x)) < h(g(x))$ yields the $\Leftarrow$ direction.

The same ideas apply to decreasing functions. By definition, a function f is decreasing if and only if whenever $x_1 < x_2$, then $f(x_1) > f(x_2)$. Already this tells us: decreasing functions cause the sense of the inequality to be switched.

Function Composition and Inequality Property (2)
For any real expressions $f(x)$, $g(x)$, and a decreasing real function h: $f(x) < g(x) \Leftrightarrow h(f(x)) > h(g(x))$.

Example 2

Find all positive solutions to $x^{-5} > 32$.

Solution

Think of this inequality as being of the form $g(x) > k$, where $g: x \to x^{-5}$. Here $g^{-1}: x \to x^{-1/5}$, and so we take both sides to the $-\frac{1}{5}$ power. In this case, g is a decreasing function, and so is its inverse. When applying g^{-1} to both sides the sense of the inequality is reversed. Thus an inequality equivalent to the given inequality is

$$(x^{-5})^{-1/5} < 32^{-1/5}.$$

That is,

$$x < \frac{1}{2}.$$

Check

Since the inequalities are equivalent, a check is not logically necessary, but it is still wise to check work. Let x be a value satisfying $0 < x < \frac{1}{2}$, say 0.1. Then $x^{-5} = 100{,}000$, which satisfies the original inequality.

Adapting to Individual Needs

Challenge
Cooperative Learning Have students **work in groups** to answer the following. Find the error in this argument.

$(\frac{1}{2})^3 < (\frac{1}{2})^2$	Since $\frac{1}{8} < \frac{1}{4}$.
$\ln(\frac{1}{2})^3 < \ln(\frac{1}{2})^2$	Since ln is increasing.
$3\ln(\frac{1}{2}) < 2\ln(\frac{1}{2})$	Since $\ln A^b = b \ln A$.
$3 < 2$	Divide both sides by $\ln(\frac{1}{2})$.

[$\ln(\frac{1}{2})$ is a negative number, so dividing by it reverses the inequality.]

Here is a summary of the discussion of this lesson:

Reversible Steps Theorem for Inequalities
Let $f(x)$ and $g(x)$ be any real expressions. Then for all real expressions c and real functions h:

(1) $f(x) < g(x) \Leftrightarrow f(x) + c < g(x) + c$.
(2) $f(x) < g(x) \Leftrightarrow f(x) \cdot c < g(x) \cdot c$, if $c > 0$.
$f(x) < g(x) \Leftrightarrow f(x) \cdot c > g(x) \cdot c$, if $c < 0$.
(3) $f(x) < g(x) \Leftrightarrow h(f(x)) < h(g(x))$, if h is increasing.
$f(x) < g(x) \Leftrightarrow h(f(x)) > h(g(x))$, if h is decreasing.

We finish with an application.

Example 3

According to one microwave cookbook, if you double the amount of a particular food to be cooked, you should multiply the cooking time by 1.5. From this, it can be deduced that amount A and cooking time t are related by the formula $t = kA^{0.585}$, where k is a constant determined by the particular food being cooked. If one hot dog can be cooked in 40 seconds, at most how many hot dogs can be cooked in 2 minutes?

Solution

First we need to find k in the formula $t = kA^{0.585}$. *Since $t = 40$ seconds when $A = 1$, $k = 40$.* If the time is less than 2 minutes, which is 120 seconds, the inequality to solve is

$$40A^{0.585} \le 120.$$

Then divide both sides by 40 to isolate the power.

$$A^{0.585} \le 3$$

Now take the $\frac{1}{0.585}$ power of each side. All positive power functions are increasing on the set of positive reals, so this will not change the sense of the inequality.

$$(A^{0.585})^{1/0.585} \le 3^{1/0.585}$$
$$A \le 6.54$$

At most 6 hot dogs could be cooked in 2 minutes.

Check

From the given information, 1 hot dog could be cooked in 40 seconds; 2 in 1.5 times as long, or 60 seconds; 4 in 1.5 times as long or 90 seconds; 8 in 1.5 times as long or 135 seconds. So 6 is reasonable for 2 minutes. Caution: Microwave ovens and foods vary. Do not apply this formula without confirming it for the oven and food being used.

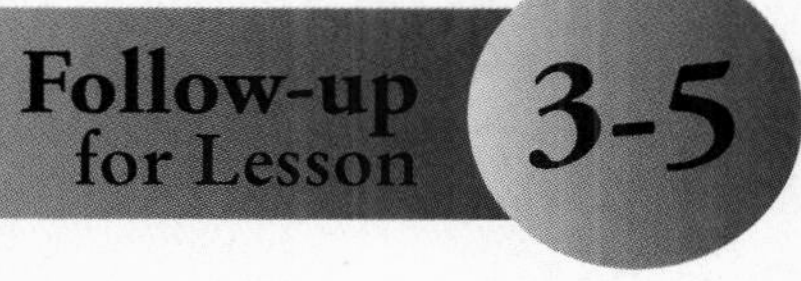

Practice

For more questions on SPUR Objectives, use **Lesson Master 3-5** (shown on pages 176–177).

Assessment

Written Communication Have students write the appropriate step from the Reversible Steps Theorem for Inequalities for **Question 5, 6, 7,** or **8** on page 180 to justify each step they used to solve the inequality. [Students identify the reversible steps used in solving inequalities.]

Extension

Have students compile lists of real functions that are increasing and decreasing. They should be able to express the function generally, and give restrictions where necessary. [Samples: The following equations describe increasing functions:
$y = x^n$, $n \in$ odd positive integers;
$y = x^{1/n}$, $n \in$ odd positive integers;
$y = ab^x$, $a > 0$, $b > 1$;
$y = ab^x$, $a < 0$, $0 < b < 1$;
$y = \log_b x$, $b > 1$.
The following equations describe decreasing functions:
$y = -x^n$, $n \in$ odd positive integers;
$y = -x^{1/n}$, $n \in$ odd positive integers;
$y = ab^x$, $a > 0$, $0 < b < 1$;
$y = ab^x$, $a < 0$, $b > 1$;
$y = \log_b x$, $0 < b < 1$]

Notes on Questions

Questions 2–3 Students are expected to mimic the proofs in the lesson.

Question 5 After obtaining $x < \log_3 6$, some students may be tentative about applying the Change of Base Theorem. Reassure them that simplifying one side of an inequality does not affect the sense of the inequality.

Question 6 Error Alert Many will apply $\log_{0.5}$ to both sides without reversing the sense of the inequality. To show that $f(x) = \log_{0.5}x$ is a decreasing function (defined only $x > 0$), you may use an automatic grapher to graph $y = \frac{\log_{10}x}{\log_{10}0.5}$ or $y = \frac{\ln x}{\ln 0.5}$. Alternatively, rewrite $(0.5)^y$ as $(2^{-1})^y = (2)^{-y}$ and solve $2^{-y} \geq 16$ by taking $\log_2$ of both sides.

Question 11 Error Alert Students may be tempted to "cross multiply" and then solve the resulting linear inequality. Point out that this easily can result in the wrong solution, since it assumes that the quantities t and $8t - 40$ must be positive. A correct solution can be obtained by subtracting one fraction from another and comparing the resulting fraction with 0, using the Sign of the Product Property.

1) $60 - 4y < 12$
Given
$-4y < -48$
Addition Property of Inequality
$y > 12$
Multiplication Property of Inequality

14a) -3 and -2, -1 and 0, 0 and 1

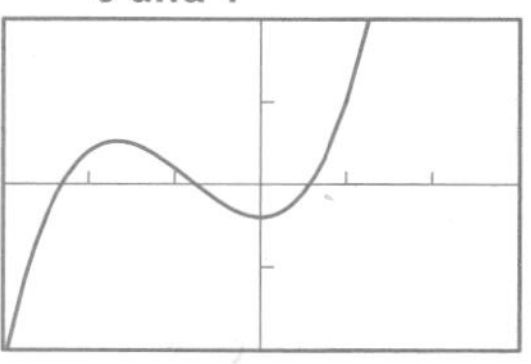

$-3 \leq x \leq 3$, x-scale = 1
$-10 \leq y \leq 10$, y-scale = 5

b) any interval of length 0.25 that includes the interval (0.5706, 0.5707). Sample: $.5 \leq x \leq .75$

QUESTIONS

Covering the Reading

1. Solve $60 - 4y < 12$ for y, justifying each step in your solution. See left.
2. Prove: If f is a decreasing function throughout its domain, then f is a 1-1 function. See margin.
3. Prove: If f is decreasing on its entire domain, then f^{-1} is decreasing on its entire domain. See margin.
4. *Multiple choice.* Suppose a function is applied to both sides of an inequality. What property of the function determines whether the sense of the inequality changes or remains the same? b
   (a) whether the function is 1-1 or not
   (b) whether the function is increasing or decreasing
   (c) whether the function has an inverse or not
   (d) whether the function has a maximum or minimum value

In 5–8, solve.

5. $3^x < 6$ $x < 1.63$
6. $(0.5)^y \geq 16$ $y \leq -4$
7. $9x^{-3} < 18$ $x < 0, x > 0.794$
8. $t^{2.5} < 100$ $0 \leq t < 6.31$
9. Refer to Example 3. If 2 pieces of fried chicken take 4 minutes to cook in the microwave, at most how many pieces could be cooked in 12 minutes? 13 pieces

Applying the Mathematics

10. The common logarithm of an integer is less than 6. What are the possible values of the integer? $0 < x < 1{,}000{,}000$
11. Find all real numbers t such that $\frac{1}{t} > \frac{5}{8t - 40}$. $t > \frac{40}{3}$ or $0 < t < 5$
12. The half-life of carbon-14, used to date ancient artifacts, is about 5730 years. If between 20% and 30% of the carbon-14 originally in an artifact remains, about how old is the artifact? 10,000 to 13,000 years old

Review

13. Use the Intermediate Value Theorem to explain why the function g defined by $g(x) = x^2 - \ln x - 4$ must have a zero between 2 and 3. *(Lesson 3-4)* $g(2) = -\ln 2 < 0$ and $g(3) = 5 - \ln 3 > 0$. Thus, by the Intermediate Value Theorem, g must have a zero between 2 and 3.
14. Let the function h be defined by $h(t) = 2t^3 + 5t^2 - 2$.
   a. Use an automatic grapher to determine three intervals between successive integers in which the zeros of h lie.
   b. Find an interval of length 0.25 that includes the largest zero. *(Lesson 3-4)*
   See left.

Additional Answers

2. Let f be a real function that is decreasing on its entire domain. Let x and y be two values in the domain of f. Because f is decreasing, if $x < y$, then $f(x) > f(y)$ for all x and y in the domain of f. Similarly, if $x > y$, then $f(x) < f(y)$ for all x and y in the domain of f. Thus, whenever $x \neq y$, $f(x) \neq f(y)$. By the Law of the Contrapositive, $f(x) = f(y) \Rightarrow x = y$, that is, f is a 1-1 function.

3. Let f be a real function that is decreasing on its entire domain. Assume that on some portion of its domain f^{-1} is increasing. Then there exist some values u and v such that $u < v$ implies $f^{-1}(u) < f^{-1}(v)$. Since f is everywhere decreasing, it is decreasing on $[f^{-1}(u), f^{-1}(v)]$. Therefore we must have $f(f^{-1}(u)) > f(f^{-1}(v))$ or, equivalently, $u > v$. This contradicts our assumption that $u < v$. Therefore f^{-1} cannot be increasing on any portion of its domain. Hence, f^{-1} must be decreasing on its entire domain.

15. Consider the function $h: x \rightarrow x^4$.
   a. Is h a 1-1 function when its domain is the set of all real numbers? No
   b. Is h a 1-1 function when its domain is $\{x: x \geq 3\}$? Yes
   c. Solve $\sqrt[4]{x-3} = \frac{1}{16}$. *(Lesson 3-2)* $x = 3.00002$

16. Analyze the exponential function $g: x \rightarrow 2^{-x^2}$. Discuss the domain, range, maximum and minimum values, intervals on which the function is increasing or decreasing, and the end behavior. *(Lesson 2-7)*
See left.

16) domain: all real numbers; range: all positive real numbers ≤ 1; maximum: 1; minimum: none; increasing on $x \leq 0$; decreasing on $x \geq 0$; $\lim_{x \to \pm\infty} = 0$

17. *Multiple choice.* Which of the following statements is true? b
   (a) $\forall$ *positive real numbers x, log x < 0.*
   (b) $\exists$ *a positive real number x such that log x < 0.* *(Lessons 1-1, 2-9)*

18. a. Write the contrapositive of the following statement:

   If $x > 0$, then $6x > 1$.

   If $6x \leq 1$, then $x \leq 0$.
   b. Compare the truth values of the contrapositive and of the statement in part **a**. *(Lesson 1-5)*
   They have the same truth value; they are both false.

19. *Multiple choice.* Which is *not* true for real numbers a and b? c
   (a) If $a = 0$ and $b = 0$, then $ab = 0$.
   (b) If $a = 0$ or $b = 0$, then $ab = 0$.
   (c) If $ab = 0$, then $a = 0$ and $b = 0$.
   (d) If $ab = 0$, then $a = 0$ or $b = 0$. *(Previous course)*

Exploration

20. Explore the following conjecture. When x and y are positive numbers whose sum is 10, then the largest value of x^y occurs when $x^y = 1000x$.
This conjecture is false. The maximum value of f occurs when $x \approx 4.134$. At this point, $x^{(10-x)} \approx 4127$, which is not equal to $1000x$.

Question 20 Technology Since $y = 10 - x$, one can explore the conjecture by considering the point of intersection of the graphs of the functions $f(x) = x^{10-x}$ and $g(x) = 1000x$. Does the point of intersection occur at a relative maximum of f? You may want to have students **work in groups.** Even after several zooms with an automatic grapher, it is not easy to see that the answer is no. This question begs for an algebraic solution, but that is inaccessible until calculus. (Analyzing the derivative of the function $f(x) = x^{10-x}$ will answer the question.)

Lesson 3-6

Objectives

C Find zeros of functions using factoring or chunking.

H Apply equation-solving techniques to real-world problems.

Resources

From the ***Teacher's Resource File***

- Lesson Master 3-6
- Answer Master 3-6
- Teaching Aid 27: Warm-up

Additional Resources

- Visual for Teaching Aid 27

Teaching Lesson 3-6

Warm-up

Find the zeros of the function h defined by
$h(x) = (x + 3)^4 + (x + 3)^2 - 5 = 7$.
$\sqrt{3} - 3$ and $-\sqrt{3} - 3$

LESSON

3-6 Solving Equations by Chunking or Factoring

Using Chunking to Solve Equations

Chunking is thinking of an expression as a single variable. It is a very powerful method for solving equations.

Example 1

Find the exact real solutions of the equation $e^{2x} = e^x + 6$.

Solution

Think of e^x as a chunk. The equation in e^x is a quadratic equation which you know how to solve.

$$\begin{aligned} & e^{2x} - e^x - 6 = 0 \\ \Leftrightarrow\ & (e^x)^2 - e^x - 6 = 0 \\ \Leftrightarrow\ & (e^x - 3)(e^x + 2) = 0 \\ \Leftrightarrow\ & e^x - 3 = 0 \quad \text{or} \quad e^x + 2 = 0 \\ \Leftrightarrow\ & x = \ln 3 \end{aligned}$$

(Because x is real, e^x is always positive, so the equation $e^x + 2 = 0$ has no real solutions.)

Check

Graph $y = e^{2x}$ and $y = e^x + 6$. The x-coordinate of the point of intersection is the solution to $e^{2x} = e^x + 6$.

The trace function shows that the x-coordinate of P is approximately 1.10. This is very close to ln 3.

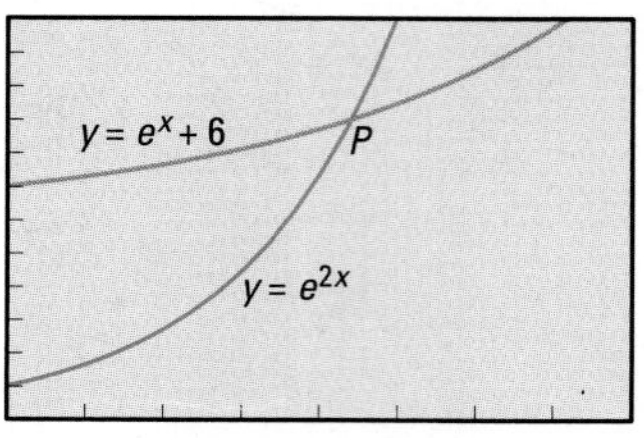

$0 \le x \le 2$, x-scale = .25
$0 \le y \le 12$, y-scale = 1

Using the Zero-Product Property to Solve Equations

The equation in Example 1 is of the form

$$f(x) = g(x).$$

To solve this equation, we again let $h(x) = f(x) - g(x)$ so that

$$h(x) = 0,$$

which has the same solutions.

Lesson 3-6 Overview

Broad Goals This lesson shows the power of combining chunking with factoring to solve certain equations.

Perspective Chunking is a term used in psychology to describe how the brain often puts together individual pieces to form a whole; for instance, as you read these sentences you are reading chunks of letters rather than individual letters. From at least as early as the time students have had to consider a two-digit number as a single number, they have been chunking. In this lesson, chunking is applied to an algebraic expression by thinking of the expression as a single variable, solving for e^x or sin x first in an equation rather than solving directly for x.

Factoring is an overrated process for solving equations. The great majority of the examples and questions in this book in which factoring is used for solving an equation needed to be contrived so that would happen. However, the relationship between factors and zeros is very important, and in Lesson 3-7, factoring is shown to be a powerful tool for finding solutions to inequalities.

One advantage of working with $h(x) = 0$ is that it may be possible to factor $h(x)$ as it was in Example 1. Then the Zero-Product Property can be used. In the language of functions, the Zero-Product Property is:

Let f, g, and h be functions. If there exists c such that $h(c) = 0$ and $h = f \cdot g$, then either $f(c) = 0$ or $g(c) = 0$.

Stated another way: For all functions f, g, and h, if $h = f \cdot g$, then $\forall\, x$,

$$h(x) = 0 \Leftrightarrow f(x) = 0 \text{ or } g(x) = 0.$$

Thus if an expression for a function is factored, the task of finding its zeros is reduced to finding the zeros of the factors.

Example 2

Find the exact zeros of the function p defined by

$$p(x) = (x^2 - 3)(5x + 8)^2.$$

Solution

Here $p = f \cdot g$, where $f(x) = x^2 - 3$ and $g(x) = (5x + 8)^2$. So $\forall\, x$ such that $p(x) = 0$ if and only if

$$\begin{array}{lrcr} & f(x) = 0 & \text{or} & g(x) = 0 \\ \Leftrightarrow & x^2 - 3 = 0 & \text{or} & (5x + 8)^2 = 0 \\ \Leftrightarrow & x^2 = 3 & \text{or} & 5x = -8 \\ \Leftrightarrow & x = \pm\sqrt{3} & \text{or} & x = -\frac{8}{5}. \end{array}$$

Therefore, p has three zeros, $\sqrt{3}$, $-\sqrt{3}$, and $-\frac{8}{5}$.

The function $p(x)$ in Example 2 is a polynomial function of degree 4 which can be written in standard form as

$$p(x) = 25x^4 + 80x^3 - 11x^2 - 240x - 192.$$

If you had been asked to find the exact zeros of $p(x)$, given this way in standard form, you could do this if you could factor $p(x)$. However, factoring a polynomial such as $p(x)$ cannot normally be done by inspection or standard factoring techniques. Methods you will see in Chapters 4 and 5 enable you to factor many polynomials, including the polynomial $p(x)$ given above.

❶ Factoring Using a Symbol Manipulator

Symbol manipulators can also factor such polynomial functions. For example, on one symbol manipulator we entered

```
factor(25x^4 + 80x^3 – 11x^2 – 240x – 192)
```

and received the response

$(5 \cdot x + 8)^2 \cdot (x^2 - 3)$.

Notes on Reading

Chunking is, in theory, simply the use of the Substitution Property from Lesson 1-1. In **Example 1,** you may wish to make the chunking explicit by substituting u for e^x as follows:

$$\begin{array}{ll} & e^{2x} - e^x - 6 = 0 \\ \Leftrightarrow & (e^x)^2 - e^x - 6 = 0 \\ \Leftrightarrow & u^2 - u - 6 = 0 \\ \Leftrightarrow & (u - 3)(u + 2) = 0. \end{array}$$

Now the chunking idea is used again. Both $u - 3$ and $u + 2$ can be thought of as single numbers whose product is zero. Thus, one or the other is zero.

$$\begin{array}{ll} \Leftrightarrow & u - 3 = 0 \text{ or } u + 2 = 0 \\ \Leftrightarrow & u = 3 \text{ or } u = -2 \end{array}$$

Now, let $e^x = u$.

$e^x = 3$ or $e^x = -2$ (impossible)

Thus $x = \ln 3$.

Chunking is made explicit in **Examples 3–4** also.

❶ We should let you in on a secret. All of the authors were educated at a time when symbol manipulators were not available, yet in constructing and solving equations, we often used symbol manipulators. The purpose of revealing such a secret is not to announce guilt, but rather to point out that symbol manipulators make some mathematics so easy that the smart person will put them to use rather than avoid them.

Optional Activities

After discussing **Example 3** on page 184, have students solve each of the following equations by chunking. Have them show what they used for the chunk.

1. $4(y - 1)^{-2} - 9(y - 1)^{-1} + 5 = 0$

$[\{\frac{9}{5}, 2\}; x = (y - 1)^{-1}]$

2. $2(\sqrt{x} + 3)^2 - 15(\sqrt{x} + 3) + 28 = 0$

$[\{\frac{1}{4}, 1\}; y = \sqrt{x} + 3]$

Additional Examples

1. Find all real solutions to the equation $e^{4x} = 13e^{2x} - 36$.
   Think of e^{2x} as a chunk.
   $(e^{2x})^2 = 13e^{2x} - 36$
   $\Leftrightarrow (e^{2x})^2 - 13e^{2x} + 36 = 0$
   $\Leftrightarrow (e^{2x} - 4)(e^{2x} - 9) = 0$
   Now chunk again, thinking of e^{2x} as $(e^x)^2$.
   $((e^x)^2 - 4)((e^x)^2 - 9) = 0$
   $\Leftrightarrow (e^x)^2 - 4 = 0$ or $(e^x)^2 - 9 = 0$
   $\Leftrightarrow (e^x + 2)(e^x - 2) = 0$ or $(e^x + 3)(e^x - 3) = 0$
   $\Leftrightarrow e^x = -2$ or $e^x = 2$ or $e^x = -3$ or $e^x = 3$
   $\Leftrightarrow x = \ln 2 \approx .6931$ or $x = \ln 3 \approx 1.0986$
   ($e^x = -2$ and $e^x = -3$ do not have real solutions.)
2. Find the zeros of the function q defined by $q(x) = (4x^2 - 5)(3x - 7)^2$.
   Here $q = f \cdot g$ where $f(x) = 4x^2 - 5$ and $g(x) = (3x - 7)^2$.
   So $q(x) = 0$ if and only if $f(x) = 0$ or $g(x) = 0$.
   $\Leftrightarrow 4x^2 - 5 = 0$ or $(3x - 7)^2 = 0$
   $\Leftrightarrow x^2 = \frac{5}{4}$ or $3x = 7$
   $\Leftrightarrow x = \pm\frac{\sqrt{5}}{2}$ or $x = \frac{7}{3}$
   Therefore q has three zeros: $\frac{\sqrt{5}}{2}$, $-\frac{\sqrt{5}}{2}$ and $\frac{7}{3}$.
3. Find all real solutions to $(m + 5)^4 - 5 = m$.
   $(m + 5)^4 - 5 = m$
   $\Leftrightarrow (m + 5)^4 = m + 5$
   Let $x = m + 5$
   $\Leftrightarrow x^4 = x$
   $\Leftrightarrow x^4 - x = 0$
   $\Leftrightarrow x(x^3 - 1) = 0$
   $\Leftrightarrow x = 0$ or $x^3 - 1 = 0$
   $\Leftrightarrow x = 0$ or $x = 1$
   (Substitute back $m + 5$ for x.)
   $\Leftrightarrow m = -5$ or $m = -4$.

Some symbol manipulators are even smart enough to do some chunking. For example, for the expression $e^{2x} - e^x - 6$ in Example 1, we entered

```
factor(e^(2x) – e^(x) – 6)
```

and received the output

$(e^x - 3) \cdot (e^x + 2)$.

Because symbol manipulators are so proficient at manipulative tasks such as factoring polynomials, finding exact solutions of equations, and simplifying algebraic expressions, the need for you to perform these tasks by hand is not as great as it was in the past. However, symbol manipulators do not eliminate the need for you to decide which form of an algebraic expression can be most useful for solving a given problem.

Combining Chunking and Factoring

The next example combines chunking and factoring to solve the equation given on the first page of this chapter.

Example 3

Solve $y^{10} - 5y^6 + 4y^2 = 0$.

Solution 1

The left side can be factored.

$$y^2(y^8 - 5y^4 + 4) = 0$$

So either $y^2 = 0$ or $y^8 - 5y^4 + 4 = 0$. The first equation gives 0 as a solution. Concentrate now on the second equation, and think of y^4 as a chunk.

Let $x = y^4$, so $x^2 = (y^4)^2 = y^8$. Substituting,

$\Leftrightarrow x^2 - 5x + 4 = 0$
$\Leftrightarrow (x - 4)(x - 1) = 0$
$\Leftrightarrow x = 4$ or $x = 1$
$\Leftrightarrow y^4 = 4$ or $y^4 = 1$
$\Leftrightarrow y = \sqrt[4]{4}$ or $y = -\sqrt[4]{4}$ or $y = \sqrt[4]{1} = 1$ or $y = -\sqrt[4]{1} = -1$.

There are thus five real solutions: 0, 1, -1, $\sqrt[4]{4}$, and $-\sqrt[4]{4}$.

Solution 2

Use a symbol manipulator. Enter the following key sequence.

```
solve(y^10 – 5y^6 + 4y^2 = 0, y)
```

The display shows this solution.

$y = -\sqrt{2}$ or $y = \sqrt{2}$ or $y = 1$ or $y = 0$ or $y = -1$

Adapting to Individual Needs

Extra Help

Some students may need help determining the final solution of an equation which was solved by chunking. Remind students that if a new variable was introduced through chunking, their work is not finished when they arrive at a solution for that variable. They must equate the value of the new variable to the "chunk," and solve this equation for the value of the original variable.

Challenge

Given each set of zeros for a function, ask students to come up with an equation for a possible function. (Note: Students who have taken previous UCSMP courses have created polynomial functions from a given set of zeros; now that skill can be expanded to include logarithmic, trigonometric, and exponential functions.)

1. 2, 4, -1 [Sample: $f(x) = (x - 2)(x - 4)(x + 1) = x^3 - 5x^2 + 2x + 8$]
2. ln 3, ln 5 [Sample: $f(x) = (e^x - 3)(e^x - 5) = e^{2x} - 8e^x + 15$]

Be sure to point out to students there are multiple functions which have a given set of zeros and ask them for reasons why. [Sample: Any function with zeros a, b, and c can undergo a vertical size change (i.e., can be stretched or shrunk vertically, or reflected over the x-axis) and still maintain the zeros a, b, and c.]

The solutions are identical because: $\sqrt[4]{4} = 4^{\frac{1}{4}} = (2^2)^{\frac{1}{4}} = 2^{\frac{1}{2}} = \sqrt{2}$; $-\sqrt[4]{4} = -4^{\frac{1}{4}} = -(2^2)^{\frac{1}{4}} = -(2^{\frac{1}{2}}) = -\sqrt{2}$

Activity

Explain why the two solutions are identical. See left.

Example 4

Find all real solutions, if any exist, of the equation

$$\sin^2 x - \cos^2 x = 3 \sin x + 1.$$

Solution

Because sin *x* and cos *x* have period 2π, the functions *f* and *g* with $f(x) = \sin^2 x - \cos^2 x$ and $g(x) = 3 \sin x + 1$ have period at most 2π. Therefore, if we can determine the solutions, if any, in the interval $[0, 2\pi)$, then all other solutions can be obtained by adding integer multiples of 2π to the solutions in $[0, 2\pi)$. Here is a graph of *f* and *g* on the interval $[0, 2\pi]$.

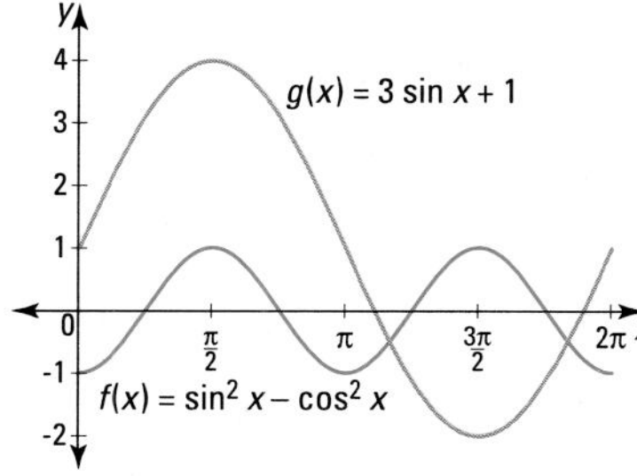

It is clear from this graph that there are two solutions in $[0, 2\pi)$, one between π and $\frac{3\pi}{2}$ and the other between $\frac{3\pi}{2}$ and 2π.

To find the exact values of these two solutions, we consider the function $h = f - g$.

$$h(x) = \sin^2 x - \cos^2 x - 3 \sin x - 1$$

We use the Pythagorean Identity

$$\sin^2 x + \cos^2 x = 1 \quad \forall \text{ real numbers } x$$

to replace $\cos^2 x$ by $1 - \sin^2 x$.

$$h(x) = \sin^2 x - (1 - \sin^2 x) - 3 \sin x - 1$$
$$= 2 \sin^2 x - 3 \sin x - 2$$

This shows $h(x)$ as a quadratic polynomial in sin *x*. Let y = sin x to obtain the quadratic equation

$$2y^2 - 3y - 2 = 0.$$

This equation factors easily to the form

$$(2y + 1)(y - 2) = 0.$$

Thus, $y = -\frac{1}{2}$ or $y = 2$ are the solutions of the quadratic equation in *y*. Therefore, the real zeros of $h(x)$ are the real solutions of the equations

$$\sin x = -\frac{1}{2} \quad \text{or} \quad \sin x = 2.$$

The equation on the left has the real solutions $x = \frac{7\pi}{6}$ and $x = \frac{11\pi}{6}$ in $[0, 2\pi)$. The equation on the right has no real solutions because $|\sin x| \le 1$ for all real x. Therefore,

$$x = \frac{7\pi}{6} + 2k\pi \text{ or } x = \frac{11\pi}{6} + 2k\pi \quad \forall \text{ integers } k.$$

4. Find all real solutions to $y^8 - 8y^5 + 12y^2 = 0$.
Factor out y^2 on the left side.
$\Leftrightarrow \quad y^2(y^6 - 8y^3 + 12) = 0$
$\Leftrightarrow \quad y^2 = 0$ or $y^6 - 8y^3 + 12 = 0$
$\Leftrightarrow \quad y = 0$ or $y^6 - 8y^3 + 12 = 0$
Let $x = y^3$
$\Leftrightarrow \quad y = 0$ or $x^2 - 8x + 12 = 0$
$\Leftrightarrow \quad y = 0$ or $(x - 2)(x - 6) = 0$
$\Leftrightarrow \quad y = 0$ or $x = 2$ or $x = 6$
$\Leftrightarrow \quad y = y^3 = 2$ or $y^3 = 6$
$\Leftrightarrow \quad y = 0$ or $y = \sqrt[3]{2}$ or $y = \sqrt[3]{6}$

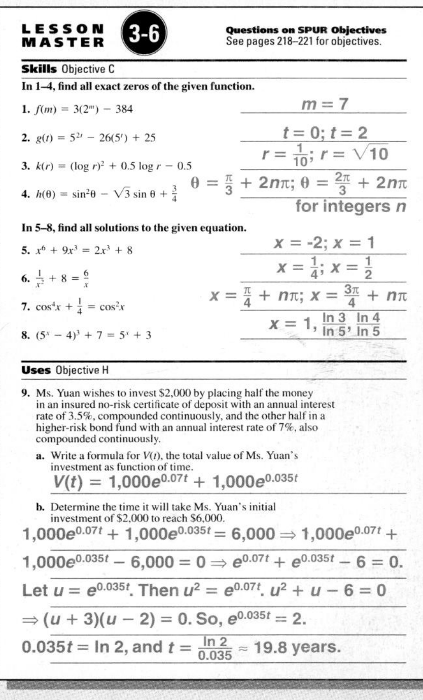

LESSON MASTER 3-6

Questions on SPUR Objectives
See pages 218–221 for objectives.

Skills Objective C

In 1–4, find all exact zeros of the given function.

1. $f(m) = 3(2^m) - 384$ — $m = 7$
2. $g(t) = 5^{2t} - 26(5^t) + 25$ — $t = 0; t = 2$
3. $k(r) = (\log r)^2 + 0.5 \log r - 0.5$ — $r = \frac{1}{10}; r = \sqrt{10}$
4. $h(\theta) = \sin^2\theta - \sqrt{3} \sin \theta + \frac{3}{4}$ — $\theta = \frac{\pi}{3} + 2n\pi; \theta = \frac{2\pi}{3} + 2n\pi$ for integers *n*

In 5–8, find all solutions to the given equation.

5. $x^6 + 9x^3 = 2x^3 + 8$ — $x = -2; x = 1$
6. $\frac{1}{x^2} + 8 = \frac{6}{x}$ — $x = \frac{1}{4}; x = \frac{1}{2}$
7. $\cos^4 x + \frac{1}{4} = \cos^2 x$ — $x = \frac{\pi}{4} + n\pi; x = \frac{3\pi}{4} + n\pi$
8. $(5^x - 4)^3 + 7 = 5^x + 3$ — $x = 1, \frac{\ln 3}{\ln 5}, \frac{\ln 4}{\ln 5}$

Uses Objective H

9. Ms. Yuan wishes to invest \$2,000 by placing half the money in an insured no-risk certificate of deposit with an annual interest rate of 3.5%, compounded continuously, and the other half in a higher-risk bond fund with an annual interest rate of 7%, also compounded continuously.
   a. Write a formula for $V(t)$, the total value of Ms. Yuan's investment as function of time.
   $V(t) = 1{,}000e^{0.07t} + 1{,}000e^{0.035t}$
   b. Determine the time it will take Ms. Yuan's initial investment of \$2,000 to reach \$6,000.
   $1{,}000e^{0.07t} + 1{,}000e^{0.035t} = 6{,}000 \Rightarrow 1{,}000e^{0.07t} + 1{,}000e^{0.035t} - 6{,}000 = 0 \Rightarrow e^{0.07t} + e^{0.035t} - 6 = 0.$ Let $u = e^{0.035t}$. Then $u^2 = e^{0.07t}$. $u^2 + u - 6 = 0 \Rightarrow (u + 3)(u - 2) = 0$. So, $e^{0.035t} = 2$. $0.035t = \ln 2$, and $t = \frac{\ln 2}{0.035} \approx 19.8$ years.

Notes on Questions

Question 11 Error Alert This equation may confuse some students, who will replace T by 1512. Remind them what E and T represent. Then you may have to suggest chunking. What is true if $T = 100$? [$E = 0$; you are at sea level.]

Consumer Connection High altitudes affect the many chemical reactions that happen when you bake a cake. Since most recipes are written for sea-level cooking, cooks must adjust recipes to use them at higher altitiudes. For example, to adjust a cake recipe for Albuquerque, you increase the baking temperature 14°C, decrease the amounts of baking powder and sugar, and increase the amount of liquid.

Question 16 Students may wonder where the equation for c comes from. For the car, the position is given by the product of half the acceleration and the square of the time. Half the acceleration is 20. Because the runner started 2 seconds before the car, the time that the car has traveled is $t - 2$.

Question 22 Some students may wish to estimate the answer to **part a** by using an automatic grapher, but they should be able to obtain the vertex of the parabola exactly.

3) $\forall$ functions f, g, h where $h = f \cdot g$ and $\forall x$, $h(x) = 0$ if and only if $f(x) = 0$ or $g(x) = 0$

8) $x = \left\{2, \left(-\frac{4}{3}\right)^{\frac{1}{3}}\right\}$

12) $x = \{\pi n\}$ where n is any interger

Many camping conditions change with altitude, for example, the boiling point of water and the flammability of fuel.

16c) $t^2 - 5t + 4 = 0$, $t \geq 2$

d) The distance (in feet) that the runner is ahead of the car

QUESTIONS

Covering the Reading

In 1 and 2, an equation is given to be solved.
  a. What expression might be thought of as a chunk?
  b. Solve the equation.

1b) $x = -\frac{1}{3}$ 2b) $d = \left\{2, \frac{5}{2}, 3\right\}$

1. $4 \cdot 8^{2x} = 4 \cdot 8^x - 1$ a) 8^x

2. $(2d - 5)^3 + 5 = 2d$ a) $(2d - 5)$

3. State the Zero-Product Property in function language. See left.

4. Finding the solutions to $3x = 2^x + 1$ is equivalent to finding the zeros of what function? $f: x \rightarrow 2^x + 1 - 3x$

In 5–7, find the zeros of the function.

5. $f(x) = x(x + 1)(x + 2)$ $x = \{-2, -1, 0\}$

6. $g(t) = (t^2 - 1)^3$ $t = \{-1, 1\}$

7. $h(n) = n^3 + 2n^2 - 2n$ $n = \{0, -1 \pm \sqrt{3}\}$

In 8–10, find all real solutions to the equation.

8. $3x^6 - 20x^3 = 32$ See left.

9. $(\log_2 x)^2 - 10(\log_2 x) = -16$ $x = \{4, 256\}$

10. $4 \sin^2 \theta = 4 \sin \theta - 1$

$\theta = \left\{\frac{\pi}{6} + 2\pi n, \frac{5\pi}{6} + 2\pi n\right\}$ where n is any integer

Applying the Mathematics

11. At higher altitudes water boils at lower temperatures. The equation $E \approx 1000(100 - T) + 580(100 - T)^2$ relates the temperature T (in °C) at which water boils to the elevation E meters above sea level. To the nearest degree, find the boiling point of water in Albuquerque, about 1512 meters above sea level. 99°C

In 12–15, use chunking to solve the given equation.

12. $\tan^3 x + 3 \tan x = 0$ See left.

13. $2t^4 + 3t^2 = 2$ $x = \left\{\pm \frac{1}{\sqrt{2}}\right\}$

14. $2^{2x-1} = 10$ $x \approx 2.161$

15. $(8n - 7)^2 = 7 - 8n$ $n = \left\{\frac{3}{4}, \frac{7}{8}\right\}$

16. A runner travels at a speed of 20 ft/sec. Two seconds after the runner begins, a car leaves the same location and heads in the same direction with a constant acceleration of 40 ft/sec^2. As a result, the distance in feet traveled by the car t seconds after the runner starts is given by $c(t) = 20(t - 2)^2$.
  a. Write a formula for the distance $r(t)$ traveled by the runner after t seconds. $r(t) = 20t$
  b. Write the equation which expresses the condition that the car has caught up with the runner. $20t = 20(t - 2)^2$, $t \geq 2$
  c. Write the equation from part **b** in the form $h(t) = 0$. See left.
  d. What is the meaning of $h(t)$? See left.
  e. Solve the equation from part **c.** $t = 4$. The car catches the runner 4 seconds after the runner has started.

17. a. Find all real solutions to $e^{-x} = e^{-2x} - 2$. $-\ln 2 \approx -0.693$
b. Find the coordinates of the point of intersection of the graphs of $g(x) = e^{-x}$ and $f(x) = e^{-2x} - 2$. (-0.693, 2)

Review

18. a. Solve $5^x = 100$. $x \approx 2.861$ b. Solve $5^x < 100$. *(Lessons 3-3, 3-5)* $x < 2.861$

19. Let f be defined by $f(x) = x^4 - 2x^2 + 3x + 1$.
a. Between what consecutive integers do the zeros of f lie?
b. Find the minimum value of f to the nearest tenth. *(Lessons 2-2, 3-4)* ≈ -1.3 a) (-2, -1) and (-1, 0)

20. Suppose f and g are functions defined by

$$f(x) = (\log x) + 5 \text{ and } g(x) = 10^{x-5}.$$

Show that f and g are inverse functions. *(Lesson 3-2)* See left.

21. Let $f(x) = \frac{1}{2 - 4x}$ and $g(x) = 2x - 1$. a) $\frac{2x-1}{-4x+2} = -\frac{1}{2}$
a. Find and simplify the formula for $f \cdot g$.
b. What is the domain of $f \cdot g$? *(Lesson 3-1)* $x \neq \frac{1}{2}$

22. The height h of an object thrown upward from a height of 6 ft with a velocity of 20 ft/sec is given by the equation $h(t) = -16t^2 + 20t + 6$, where t is the time in seconds. a) $0 \le t \le 0.625$
a. Estimate the interval over which the function is increasing.
b. What is the physical meaning of your answer to part **a**? *(Lesson 2-3)* During this interval, the object is rising and reaches its maximum height at $t = .625$.

Exploration

23. The curve in the design of the Gateway Arch in St. Louis, the catenary, was selected not only for its beauty but also because it is the best shape to support its own weight. This is the same type of curve as the graph of the function f defined by

$$f(x) = 8 - (e^x + e^{-x}).$$

a. Show that the graph of f is symmetric with respect to the y-axis.
b. Find its y-intercept. 6 a) $f(-x) = 8 - (e^{-x} + e^x) = f(x)$
c. Sketch a graph of f. See left.
d. Use chunking to find the exact values of the zeros of f. $x = \{-2.06, 2.06\}$

24. In parts **a–c** factor $x^6 - 2x^4 - 71x^2 + 252$ using a symbol manipulator in the indicated mode.
a. approximate mode Answers will vary.
b. exact mode $(x-2)(x+2)(x-\sqrt{7})(x+\sqrt{7})(x^2+9)$
c. complex mode See left.
d. Explain the differences (if any) in the answers to parts **a**, **b**, and **c**. The differences arise because this equation has 2 integer roots, 2 irrational roots, and 2 complex roots.

20) $f \circ g(x) = f(g(x)) = \log 10^{(x-5)} + 5 = x - 5 + 5 = x$, $\forall x$ in the domain of g. $g \circ f(x) = g(f(x)) = 10^{\log x + 5 - 5} = 10^{\log x} = x$, $\forall x$ in the domain of f.

23c)

24c) Answers will vary. It should factor $(x^2 + 9)$ as $(x + 3i)(x - 3i)$.

At 630 feet, the Gateway Arch is America's tallest monument.

Follow-up for Lesson 3-6

Practice

For more questions on SPUR Objectives, use **Lesson Master 3-6** (shown on page 185).

Assessment

Oral Communication Have students show their work for **Question 8, 9,** or **10** on page 186 and explain how they used chunking and factoring to solve the equation. [Students use chunking and factoring to find the zeros of a function.]

Extension

Cooperative Learning Have students **work in groups** to come up with an equation that looks difficult to solve but becomes a reasonably simple equation with an unexpected or complicated chunk. [Sample: $\sqrt[6]{x} + 2 = \sqrt[3]{x}$; here, $x = 64$; solutions are found by letting $y = \sqrt[6]{x}$ and solving $y + 2 = y^2$.]

Additional Answers
18. b. $x < 2.861$

Lesson 3-7

Objectives

D Solve inequalities algebraically.

Resources

From the ***Teacher's Resource File***

- Lesson Master 3-7
- Answer Master 3-7
- Teaching Aid 27: Warm-up
- Technology Sourcebook Calculator Master 4

Additional Resources

- Visual for Teaching Aid 27

Teaching Lesson 3-7

Warm-up

Find all solutions to $(4x + 5)(\sin x - 0.5) = 0$ on the interval $[-2\pi, 2\pi]$.

$-1.25, -\frac{11\pi}{6}, -\frac{7\pi}{6}, -\frac{\pi}{6}, -\frac{5\pi}{6}$

(See Additional Example 1 for the corresponding inequality.)

Notes on Reading

In the solution to **Example 1,** stress the importance of concise tracking of possible solutions. Due to the commentary, we have written $(x - 2)(x + 1) > 0$ twice, but once would be enough.

LESSON

3-7 *Solving Inequalities by Factoring*

Positive and negative numbers have a fundamental relationship to inequalities because

$$x \text{ is positive} \Leftrightarrow x > 0,$$
$$\text{and } x \text{ is negative} \Leftrightarrow x < 0.$$

If x is multiplied by a negative number in either of these circumstances, then the Multiplication Property of Inequality applies, and the sense of the inequality changes. Each time, multiplication by a negative number changes the sense of the inequality. For this reason, the product of an odd number of negative numbers is negative, and the product of an even number of negative numbers is positive. In this lesson, this property of numbers is used to solve some inequalities which at first look complicated.

Function Composition and Factoring

Example 1

Find all real numbers x such that

$$10^{x^2} > 10^{x+2}.$$

Solution

The functions on both sides of the given inequality have positive values for all real x. The inverse of the exponential function $f: x \to 10^x$ is the log function, which is increasing on its entire domain $(0, \infty)$. So if we apply log to both sides of the given inequality, the sense of the inequality is unchanged, and we are left only with the exponents.

	$\log(10^{x^2}) > \log(10^{x+2})$	Apply log to both sides.
$\Leftrightarrow$	$x^2 > x + 2$	$\log_{10}10^x = x$
$\Leftrightarrow$	$x^2 - x - 2 > 0$	A_{-x-2}
$\Leftrightarrow$	$(x - 2)(x + 1) > 0$	Factor.

Because the product of two numbers is positive if and only if either both numbers are positive or both numbers are negative, it follows that

$$(x-2)(x+1) > 0 \Leftrightarrow \begin{Bmatrix} x - 2 > 0 \\ \text{and} \\ x + 1 > 0 \end{Bmatrix} \text{ or } \begin{Bmatrix} x - 2 < 0 \\ \text{and} \\ x + 1 < 0 \end{Bmatrix}$$
$$\Leftrightarrow \quad x > 2 \quad \text{or} \quad x < -1$$

Thus, the solution set of the inequality $10^{x^2} > 10^{x+2}$ consists of the intervals of real numbers $(2, \infty)$ and $(-\infty, -1)$.

Lesson 3-7 Overview

Broad Goals This lesson applies factoring to the solution of inequalities, making use of the fact that the product of n negative numbers is negative if n is odd, positive if n is even.

Perspective The lesson begins by applying a function to both sides of an inequality, and then finding that the resulting inequality can be written in the form $mn > 0$, that is, as asserting that the product of two numbers is positive.

Example 2 is less complicated, but becomes equivalent to the statement that the product of two numbers is negative. The first and second examples illustrate the two possibilities with inequalities and positive and negative numbers.

The Test-Point Method relies on the Function Inequality Theorem. Stress in the Function Inequality Theorem (which may give some students FITs!!), that there must be *no zeros* between a and b in order to be certain that the function is positive or negative on the interval. The intuition of this theorem comes from looking at the graph of the function. Its proof involves the Intermediate Value Theorem.

The execution of the Test-Point Method utilizes the logic of *and* and *or*. This lesson brings together many topics that students have studied thus far in this course.

In Example 1, the quadratic inequality $x^2 > x + 2$ was transformed into an inequality with 0 on one side. Then the other side was factored. This is also the case in Example 2, but now the product of the factors is negative.

Example 2

Describe the exact solutions to the inequality $5x + 2 > 15x^2 + 3x - 6$.

Solution

$$\begin{aligned} & 5x + 2 > 15x^2 + 3x - 6 && \text{Given} \\ \Leftrightarrow\ & 0 > 15x^2 - 2x - 8 && A_{-5x-2} \\ \Leftrightarrow\ & 0 > (5x - 4)(3x + 2) && \text{Factor.} \end{aligned}$$

The product on the right side is negative if and only if one of the factors is positive and the other is negative.

$$\begin{aligned} \Leftrightarrow\ & (5x - 4 < 0 \text{ and } 3x + 2 > 0) && \text{or} && (5x - 4 > 0 \text{ and } 3x + 2 < 0) \\ \Leftrightarrow\ & (5x < 4 \text{ and } 3x > -2) && \text{or} && (5x > 4 \text{ and } 3x < -2) \\ \Leftrightarrow\ & \left(x < \tfrac{4}{5} \text{ and } x > -\tfrac{2}{3}\right) && \text{or} && \left(x > \tfrac{4}{5} \text{ and } x < -\tfrac{2}{3}\right) \\ \Leftrightarrow\ & -\tfrac{2}{3} < x < \tfrac{4}{5} && \text{or} && \text{impossible} \end{aligned}$$

Thus, $5x + 2 > 15x^2 + 3x - 6$ if and only if $-\frac{2}{3} < x < \frac{4}{5}$.

Check 1

Substitute the endpoint $-\frac{2}{3}$ for x in the inequality. It should give equal values on both sides.

Does $5 \cdot \left(-\frac{2}{3}\right) + 2 = 15 \cdot \left(-\frac{2}{3}\right)^2 + 3 \cdot \left(-\frac{2}{3}\right) - 6$?

Does $\frac{-10}{3} + \frac{6}{3} = 15 \cdot \frac{4}{9} + (-2) - 6$?

Does $-\frac{4}{3} = \frac{20}{3} - 8$? Yes, it does.

You should check the other endpoint.

Check 2

Graph $f(x) = 5x + 2$ and $g(x) = 15x^2 + 3x - 6$. By zooming in on the two intersection points A and B of these graphs, we determine that their x-coordinates are $x \approx -.66$ and $x \approx .80$. Note from the graphs that $5x + 2 > 15x^2 + 3x - 6$ for values of x where the line is above the parabola. This is when x is between the two points found above. Therefore, an approximate solution of the given inequality is the set of all real numbers x such that $-.66 < x < .80$. This is a very good approximation to $-\frac{2}{3} < x < \frac{4}{5}$.

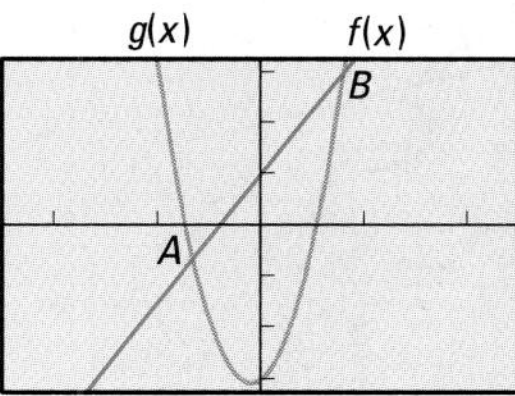

$-2.5 \le x \le 2.5$, x-scale = 1
$-6.5 \le y \le 6.5$, y-scale = 2

Students often have far more difficulty with inequalities than with equations. Display the graph for **Example 2.** Give visual meaning to the inequality by extending vertical segments from points A and B to the x-axis. Ask students for the significance of the intersections of these segments with the x-axis. Also, ask for the solutions to $5x + 2 < 15x^2 + 3x - 6$. Elicit from students that with our graphical interpretation of these as inequalities of function values, ">" means "is above" and "<" means "is below."

Error Alert Then be sure to discuss the algebraic solution of **Example 2** with students, since a common error is to consider only one case to determine the solution. Students need to understand that the solutions from the different cases are connected by the word *or.* Also point out that for very large values of $|x|$, the $15x^2$ of $15x^2 + 3x - 6$ dominates and thus $15x^2 + 3x - 6 > 5x + 2$. For values of $|x|$ near 0, the -6 becomes the dominant value of $15x^2 + 3x - 6$ and thus $5x + 2 > 15x^2 + 3x - 6$ becomes true near zero.

The Function Inequality Theorem is essentially proved by proving its contrapositive. To write the antecedent of the contrapositive involves writing the negation of an *or* statement, which is an *and* statement. And, we must negate the inequalities. Thus we obtain for the contrapositive: If f is continuous $\exists\, x_2$ between a and b such that $f(x_2) < 0$, and $\exists\, x_1$ between a and b such that $f(x_1) > 0$, then f must have a zero between a and b.

Optional Activities

Activity 1 Technology Connection You might wish to assign *Technology Sourcebook, Calculator Master 4.* In this activity, students use a graphics calculator to solve inequalities in one variable by graphing their corresponding functions in two variables. Where factoring is not obvious or possible, this technique can be invaluable.

Activity 2 You may wish to play a game of *Name That Inequality* with students. Graph a solution for an inequality on a number line and ask students to give a corresponding inequality. Ask for more than one inequality. For instance, given

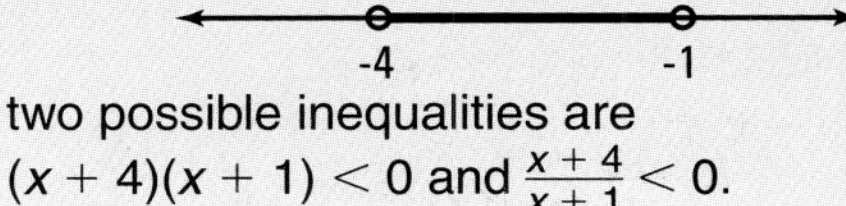

two possible inequalities are $(x + 4)(x + 1) < 0$ and $\frac{x + 4}{x + 1} < 0$.

❶ The Test-Point Method for Solving Inequalities when the function is continuous is a very useful technique. Many students will be more successful with this technique than with the algebraic technique of solving cases. Also, if there are more than two factors to be considered, the Test-Point Method usually is more efficient.

In **Example 3,** point out to students that it is not necessary to evaluate the function in each interval. You simply need to determine whether the function is positive or negative in that interval. If the function can be factored, this is easy. Simply determine whether each factor is positive or negative and then determine the sign of the product.

In **Example 3,** discuss the use of the Test Point Method to make a rough sketch of *h*. When a function keeps the same sign throughout an open interval, you can easily determine whether it lies above or below the axis in that interval. The zeros complete the graph. This type of analysis allows students to check the reasonableness of a result gotten using an automatic grapher.

Example 4 involves a quotient as well as some products, but the same rules apply because dividing by a number gives the same result as multiplying by the reciprocal of the number, and numbers and their reciprocals have the same signs. Consequently, $\frac{x^2 - x - 12}{x^2 - x} > 0$ has the same solutions as $(x^2 - x - 1) \cdot (x^2 - x) > 0$. This will come as a surprise to many students because the corresponding equations do not have the same solutions.

The Test-Point Method of Solving Inequalities

In Example 2, the expression that is factored is $15x^2 - 2x - 8$. Let $h(x) = 15x^2 - 2x - 8$. Notice that the endpoints $-\frac{2}{3}$ and $\frac{4}{5}$ in the solution to Example 2 are the zeros of h.

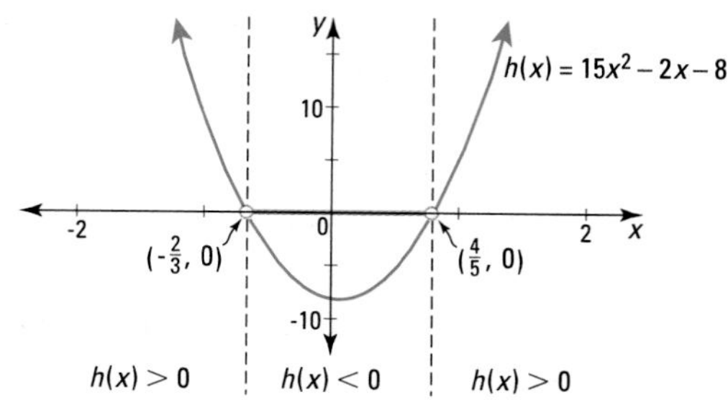

Between these zeros, all values of the function h are negative, illustrating the following general theorem.

Function Inequality Theorem
Suppose that f is a continuous real function. If f has zeros a and b and no zeros between a and b, then either

$$f(x) > 0 \text{ for all } x \text{ between } a \text{ and } b$$

or

$$f(x) < 0 \text{ for all } x \text{ between } a \text{ and } b.$$

Proof
Suppose that x_1 and x_2 are between a and b and $f(x_1) > 0$ and $f(x_2) < 0$. Then due to the Intermediate Value Theorem, there must be a number c between x_1 and x_2 such that $f(c) = 0$. But then c is a zero of the function. This contradicts the given information, and indicates that f must be strictly positive or strictly negative on the interval.

❶ This theorem implies that if you separate the domain of a function by its zeros, you can determine whether $f(x) > 0$ or $f(x) < 0$ by testing a point in each interval determined by the zeros. This procedure for solving inequalities is called the **Test-Point Method**.

Adapting to Individual Needs

Extra Help
Students may have difficulty determining the interval of the solution of an inequality. Suggest that students first check that 0 appears on one side of the inequality before trying to determine a solution. Change the inequality to this form if necessary.

Example 3

Find all real numbers x such that

$$x^2 \log_3 x < 5x \log_3 x.$$

Solution

Notice first that $\log_3 x$ is defined only when $x > 0$. Think of the inequality as $f(x) < g(x)$. Let $h(x) = f(x) - g(x)$ and find the zeros of h.

$$h(x) = x^2 \log_3 x - 5x \log_3 x = 0$$

$$(x - 5) \cdot x \cdot \log_3 x = 0 \quad \text{Factor.}$$

Either $x - 5 = 0$ or $x = 0$ or $\log_3 x = 0$ Zero-Product Property

Either $x = 5$ or $x = 0$ or $x = 3^0 = 1$

The solution $x = 0$ is rejected because $\log_3 x$ is defined only if $x > 0$.

Thus, the zeros are 1 and 5. They determine 3 intervals: (0, 1), (1, 5), and (5, ∞).

Test a point in each interval to determine whether the product, $(x - 5) \cdot x \cdot \log_3 x$, is positive or negative. Since the base is 3, we choose values of x that can be calculated exactly without a calculator.

For the interval (0, 1), let $x = \frac{1}{3}$. Then

$$(x - 5)x \log_3 x = \left(\frac{1}{3} - 5\right) \cdot \frac{1}{3} \cdot \log_3 \frac{1}{3} > 0.$$

For the interval (1, 5), let $x = 3$. Then

$$(x - 5)x \log_3 x = (3 - 5) \cdot 3 \cdot \log_3 3 < 0.$$

For the interval (5, ∞), let $x = 9$. Then

$$(x - 5)x \log_3 x = (9 - 5) \cdot 9 \cdot \log_3 9 > 0.$$

```
   +        −        +
 |----|-----------|------->
 0    1           5      x
```

Thus $h(x)$ is negative only on the interval (1, 5). Consequently,

$$x^2 \log_3 x < 5x \log_3 x \Leftrightarrow 1 < x < 5.$$

Factoring with Quotients

If x is positive, so is its reciprocal $\frac{1}{x}$. (If x were positive and its reciprocal were negative, then their product could not equal 1.) And if x is negative, so is its reciprocal. Consequently, dividing by a negative number also changes the sense of an inequality. As a further consequence, any product *or quotient* of an odd number of negative numbers is negative. And any product or quotient of an even number of negative numbers is positive. This property, which we call the **Sign of Products and Quotients Property,** is applied in Example 4.

Additional Examples

1. Find all solutions to $(4x + 5)(\sin x - 0.5) > 0$ on the interval $[-2\pi, 2\pi]$. (See the Warm-up for the corresponding equality, which should be solved before this example is covered.)
   $-2\pi \le x < -\frac{11\pi}{6}$ or $-\frac{7\pi}{6} < x < -1.25$ or $\frac{\pi}{6} < x < \frac{5\pi}{6}$.
2. Consider the inequality $5x^2 + 6x - 23 < -x^2 + 5x + 12$.
   a. Approximate the solutions of the inequality.

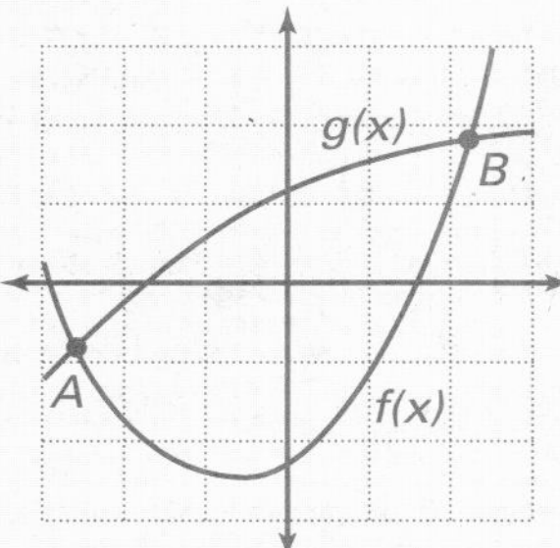

$-3 \le x \le 3$, x-scale = 1
$-30 \le y \le 30$, y-scale = 10

The solution is approximately $-2.50 < x < 2.33$, since in the interval, the graph of $f(x) = 5x^2 + 6x - 23$ is below that of $g(x) = -x^2 + 5x + 12$.

   b. Describe the exact solutions to the inequality.
   $-\frac{5}{2} < x < \frac{7}{3}$

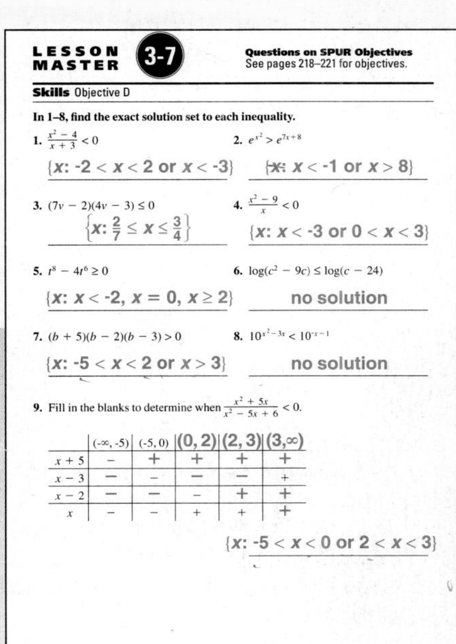

LESSON MASTER 3-7 — **Questions on SPUR Objectives** See pages 218–221 for objectives.

Skills Objective D

In 1–8, find the exact solution set to each inequality.

1. $\frac{x^2 - 4}{x + 3} < 0$ — $\{x: -2 < x < 2 \text{ or } x < -3\}$
2. $e^{x^2} > e^{7x+8}$ — $\{x: x < -1 \text{ or } x > 8\}$
3. $(7v - 2)(4v - 3) \le 0$ — $\left\{x: \frac{2}{7} \le x \le \frac{3}{4}\right\}$
4. $\frac{x^2 - 9}{x} < 0$ — $\{x: x < -3 \text{ or } 0 < x < 3\}$
5. $t^8 - 4t^6 \ge 0$ — $\{x: x < -2, x = 0, x \ge 2\}$
6. $\log(c^2 - 9c) \le \log(c - 24)$ — no solution
7. $(b + 5)(b - 2)(b - 3) > 0$ — $\{x: -5 < x < 2 \text{ or } x > 3\}$
8. $10^{x^2 - 3x} < 10^{-x-1}$ — no solution
9. Fill in the blanks to determine when $\frac{x^2 + 5x}{x^2 - 5x + 6} < 0$.

	(-∞, -5)	(-5, 0)	(0, 2)	(2, 3)	(3, ∞)
$x + 5$	–	+	+	+	+
$x - 3$	–	–	–	–	+
$x - 2$	–	–	–	+	+
x	–	–	+	+	+

$\{x: -5 < x < 0 \text{ or } 2 < x < 3\}$

3. Solve the inequality $8x^4 + 4x^3 - 17x^2 > 2x^4 + 3x^3 + 18x^2$. **An equivalent inequality is $x^2(3x - 7)(2x + 5) > 0$. $x < -\frac{5}{2}$ or $x > \frac{7}{3}$.**
4. Find all real numbers r such that $\frac{r^2 - 1}{r^2 - 4} \leq 0$. **$-2 \leq r \leq -1$ or $1 \leq r < 2$**

Notes on Questions

Question 5 Ask students what the union of the solutions to **parts a and b** represents. [The solution set to $(3x - 2)(x - 5) \geq 0$] What real numbers are not in this union? [The solutions to the inequality $(3x - 2)(x - 5) < 0$]

Question 5b You might ask for the solutions to $\frac{3x - 2}{x - 5} > 0$. [They are the same as for the given inequality.]

Question 9 A graph of $f(x) = x^2(x - 1)(x + 4)$ will clarify the situation.

Question 10 A graph is useful.

Question 14 Error Alert Students may come up with an incorrect solution if they ignore the fact that the domain of the ln function is the set of positive real numbers. Remind students that the solution set must be a subset of the domain of the original function and to check their solution against it.

Question 21 Because we have not defined noninteger powers of negative numbers, the restriction that y be an integer is necessary.

Example 4

Find all real numbers x such that

$$\frac{x^2 - x - 12}{x^2 - x} > 0.$$

Solution

The quadratics factor easily as follows:

$$\frac{(x - 4)(x + 3)}{x(x - 1)} > 0.$$

The endpoints of the intervals to be tested are the values of x for which either the numerator or the denominator is zero, namely, -3, 0, 1, and 4. The following table gives the signs of the factors in each of the intervals determined by these endpoints.

	$(-\infty, -3)$	$(-3, 0)$	$(0, 1)$	$(1, 4)$	$(4, \infty)$
$x - 4$	−	−	−	−	+
$x + 3$	−	+	+	+	+
x	−	−	+	+	+
$x - 1$	−	−	−	+	+

From this table and the Sign of Products and Quotients Property, one can see that **the solution set for the given inequality consists of the intervals $(-\infty, -3)$, $(0, 1)$, and $(4, \infty)$.**

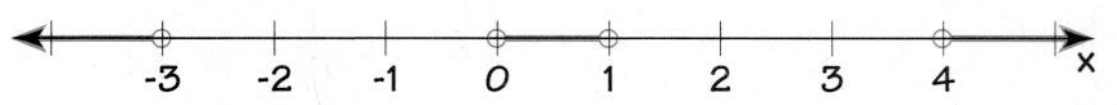

QUESTIONS

Covering the Reading

In 1–3, state in the language of inequalities.

1. x is positive. **$x > 0$**
2. z is negative. **$z < 0$**
3. The graph of the function $f: x \rightarrow e^x + 3$ is always above the line with equation $y = x$. **$e^x + 3 > x$**
4. Find the exact solution set of $7^{x^2} < 7^{3x - 2}$. **$1 < x < 2$**
5. Solve each sentence.
   a. $(3x - 2)(x - 5) = 0$ **$x = \left\{\frac{2}{3}, 5\right\}$**
   b. $(3x - 2)(x - 5) > 0$ **b) $x < \frac{2}{3}$ or $x > 5$**
   c. $(3x - 2)(x - 5) \leq 0$ **$\frac{2}{3} \leq x \leq 5$**
6. Solve each sentence.
   a. $\frac{x^2 - 1}{x + 4} > 0$ **$-4 < x < -1$ or $x > 1$**
   b. $\frac{x^2 - 1}{x + 4} = 0$ **$x = \{-1, 1\}$**
   c. $\frac{x^2 - 1}{x + 4} < 0$ **$x < -4$ or $-1 < x < 1$**

Adapting to Individual Needs

Challenge

Have students answer the following questions.

1. Give the solution and explain how knowing the properties of a function gives the solution without any factoring or chunking.
   a. $\sin 2x - 2 < 0$ [$(-\infty, \infty)$; since $\forall$ x, $\sin 2x$ is less than 2.]
   b. $x^3 \leq x^2$ [$(-\infty, 1)$; since cubes of positive numbers are less than their squares when the numbers are less than 1, $0^3 = 0$, and cubes of negative numbers are negative while squares of negative numbers are positive.]
   c. $7^x < 5^x$ [$(-\infty, 0)$; since the inequality is equivalent to $e^{2x} < 1$, which is equivalent to $2x < 0$ (taking ln of both sides) so $x < 0$.]
   d. $e^x < e^{-x}$ [$(-\infty, 0)$ since this is equivalent to $x \log 7 < x \log 5$, which is equivalent to the true statement $\log 5 < \log 7$ if and only if $x < 0$.]
2. Use the principles of this lesson to:
   a. Show that the sum of any positive number and its reciprocal is at least 2. [$x + \frac{1}{x} \geq 2 \Leftrightarrow x > 0$]
   b. What real numbers can be in the domain of $f(x) = \sqrt{x^2 + 2x - 3}$? [$(-\infty, -3) \cup (1, \infty)$]
   c. If $s(t) = -16t^2 + 80t + 4$ gives the height, in feet, of a projectile in

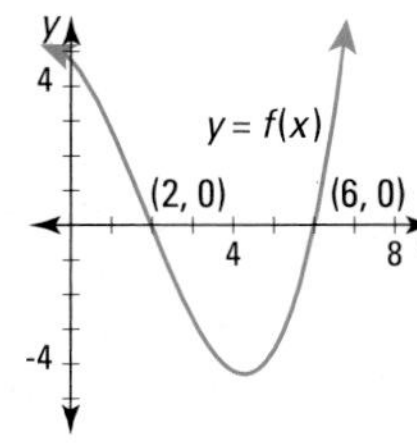

7. Use the graph of the function f at the left to describe the solutions to $f(x) < 0$ when $0 \le x \le 7$. $2 < x < 6$

8. Can the sum of twice a real number and half its square ever be negative? **Yes, this is true for values on the interval (-4, 0).**

In 9 and 10, use the Test-Point Method to solve.

9. $c^2(c - 1)(c + 4) > 0$ $c < -4$ or $c > 1$

10. $b^3 - 6b^2 + 8b > b^2 - 4b$ $0 < b < 3$ or $b > 4$

17) $x = \{-1, \left(\frac{4}{5}\right)^{\frac{1}{3}} \approx .928\}$

18) $\frac{\pi}{3} < \theta \le \frac{\pi}{2}$

20a)

21)

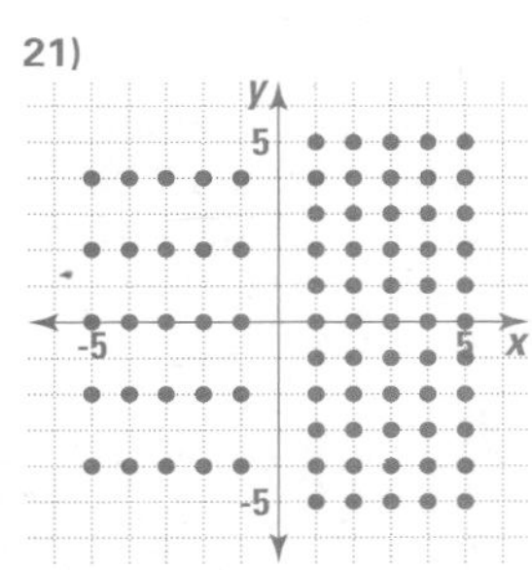

Applying the Mathematics

11. Can the sum of a real number and its fourth power ever be negative? **Yes, this is true for values on the interval (-1, 0).**

12. Find all values of x such that $7x^2 - 11x + 4 < 0$. $\frac{4}{7} < x < 1$

13. Approximate the solutions to $\sin x > \frac{1}{2}x$. $x < -1.9$ or $0 < x < 1.9$ radians

14. Find the exact solution set of the inequality $\ln (x^2) > \ln (x + 2)$. $-2 < x < -1$ and $x > 2$

15. A rocket's height in feet t seconds after take-off is given by $h(t) = -16t^2 + 300t + 20$. At what time is it over 1000 ft in the air? between $\approx$ 4.21 and $\approx$ 14.5 seconds

16. The function $g(x) = \frac{x^2 - 9}{x}$ has zeros -3 and 3. Both -1 and 1 are in the interval $-3 \le x \le 3$ but $g(-1) > 0$ and $g(1) < 0$. Explain why this does not contradict the Function Inequality Theorem. **$g(x)$ is discontinuous at $x = 0$. Therefore, the Function Inequality Theorem does not apply.**

Review

17. Find all real solutions to $5x^6 + x^3 = 4$. *(Lesson 3-6)* See left.

18. Find all values of θ between 0 and $\frac{\pi}{2}$ such that $\cos \theta < \frac{1}{2}$. *(Lesson 3-5)* See left.

19. Let h be the function defined by $h(x) = 2x^3 + 5x^2 - 4$. *(Lesson 3-4)*

a. Use an automatic grapher to determine the number of real zeros of h.

b. Between which successive integers do the zeros of h lie?

c. Find an interval of length 0.1 that includes the largest zero.

(0.7, 0.8) a) 3 b) [-2, -1) and (0, 1)

20. The system of parametric equations

$$\begin{cases} x = 10t \\ y = -16t^2 + 30t \end{cases}$$

gives the distance x along the ground and the height y of a projectile.

a. Graph the path in the xy-plane. See left.

b. When and where does the projectile hit the ground? *(Lesson 2-5)* after 1.875 seconds, 18.75 units from the starting position

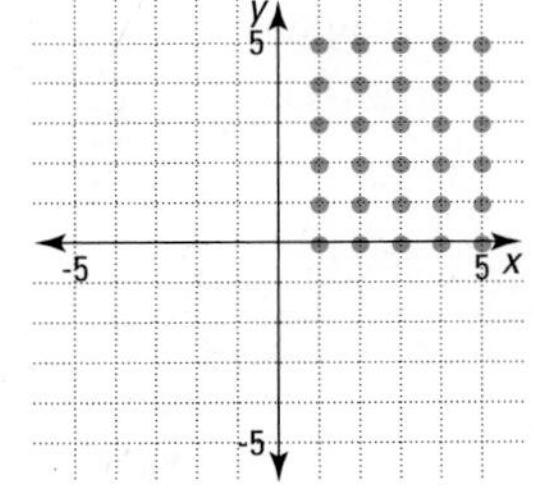

Exploration

21. Let x and y be any integers. Identify a point (x, y) with a dot if $x^y > 0$. What will the other quadrants look like? See left. For all integers x and y, $x^y > 0$ whenever $x > 0$ or ($x < 0$ and y is even).

Follow-up for Lesson 3-7

Practice

For more questions on SPUR Objectives, use **Lesson Master 3-7** (shown on page 191).

Assessment

Oral Communication Ask students to explain how the Test Point Method relies on the Function Inequality Theorem. Then have students explain how they used the Test Point Method to solve the inequality in **Question 9–10.**

Extension

Extend **Question 11** by asking students: Can the sum of a real number and positive even integer power of the number ever be negative? [Yes, for all positive even integer powers n, $x + x^n < 0$ on the interval (-1, 0).] Then ask: Can the sum of a real number and any positive odd integer power ever be negative? [Yes, for all positive odd integer powers n, $x + x^n < 0$ on the interval $(-\infty, 0)$.] Finally, ask students to investigate negative integer powers of n. [For even negative integer powers of n, $x + x^n < 0$ on the interval $(-\infty, -1)$; for odd negative integer powers of n, $x + x^n < 0$ on the interval $(-\infty, 0)$.]

t seconds, find the time interval for which the projectile is at least 100 feet high. [$2 \le t \le 3$]

Lesson 3-8

Objectives

D Solve inequalities algebraically.
L Find an equation of a graph after a transformation.
M Use graphs to approximate zeros of functions and solve equations and inequalities.

Resources

From the ***Teacher's Resource File***
- Lesson Master 3-8
- Answer Master 3-8
- Assessment Sourcebook: Quiz for Lessons 3-5 through 3-8
- Teaching Aids
  27 Warm-up
  31 Circle and Ellipse

Additional Resources
- Visuals for Teaching Aids 27, 31
- Exploration 3-8

Teaching Lesson 3-8

Warm-up

If the scale change S is defined as $S:(x, y) \rightarrow (4x, 5y)$ and the translation T is defined as $T:(x, y) \rightarrow (x + 1, y - 6)$, what is the image of the equation $y = x^2$ under the composite $T \circ S$?
$\frac{y+6}{5} = (\frac{x-1}{4})^2$

LESSON 3-8

Graphs, Transformations, and Solutions

A design studio at Cornell University, Ithaca, NY

Translations

According to *Peterson's Guides Annual Survey of Undergraduate Institutions,* the average cost of tuition, mandatory fees, and room and board at four-year private colleges in the U.S. in 1996–97 was $15,880. Although this was the most recent information when this book was being readied for publication, it will be outdated as you read this paragraph. Still, you can use this value to estimate what the corresponding fees might be in a later year. Assuming a 4% annual increase due to inflation, then the pattern of costs forms a geometric sequence.

1996	starting point	15,880
1997	one year later	15,880(1.04)
1998	two years later	$15{,}880(1.04)^2$
	. . .	
$1996 + n$	n years later	$15{,}880(1.04)^n$

A formula for the function mapping the numbers in the middle column onto the numbers in the right column is evident. Let n be the number of years after 1996 and C be the cost. Then

$$C = 15{,}880(1.04)^n.$$

A second and perhaps more useful formula would be to match the actual year number Y to the cost. This would be a function mapping the left column of the chart onto the right column. Because $Y = 1996 + n$, $n = Y - 1996$. Thus a formula matching year number to cost is

$$C = 15{,}880(1.04)^{Y-1996}.$$

Replacing n and Y by x yields two functions defined by the formulas

$$C = 15{,}880(1.04)^x$$

and

$$C = 15{,}880(1.04)^{x-1996}.$$

Lesson 3-8 Overview

Broad Goals The three Graph-Transformation Theorems in this lesson deal with the effects on the graph of a sentence in x and y by the replacements $x - h$ and $y - k$ (translation) and by the replacements $\frac{x}{a}$ and $\frac{y}{b}$ (scale change), and the composite of these transformations, which we call a *rubberband transformation*. These widely applicable theorems are used in this lesson to graph offspring of parent functions in the coordinate plane defined either directly or parametrically.

Perspective All but the parametric equations in this lesson is review for students who have studied from UCSMP *Functions, Statistics, and Trigonometry*. A summary of the effects of the three types of transformations of this lesson on the solutions to sentences and graphs of equations is given in Extra Help on page 196. This summary chart may help students make the necessary connections.

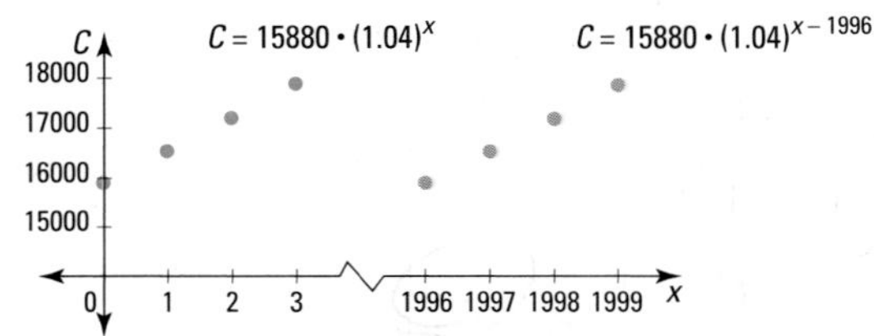

The graph of the second function is 1996 units to the right of the first function, exhibiting the first of the two fundamental theorems relating graphs, transformations, and solutions.

Graph-Translation Theorem
In a relation described by a sentence in x and y, the following two processes yield the same graph:

(1) replacing x by $x - h$, and y by $y - k$;
(2) applying the translation $T_{h,k}: (x, y) \rightarrow (x + h, y + k)$ to the graph of the original relation.

The significance of this theorem for solving equations and inequalities is that replacing x by $x - h$ increases each solution by h. For instance,

$$\text{since 2 is a solution to } x^5 = 32,$$
$$1874 \text{ is a solution to } (x - 1872)^5 = 32.$$

You also could have found this solution to the equation $(x - 1872)^5 = 32$ by chunking, but the Graph-Translation Theorem provides a geometric interpretation. The graph of $y = (x - 1872)^5$ intersects the line $y = 32$ at a point that is 1872 units to the right of the intersection of the graph of $y = x^5$ with this line.

In general, solutions to the equation $f(x - h) = g(x - h)$ are h larger than solutions to the equation $f(x) = g(x)$. Also, solutions to the inequality $f(x - h) < g(x - h)$ are h larger than solutions to the inequality $f(x) < g(x)$.

Example 1

Solve $(x + 3)^2 < 4(x + 3)$ using the idea of the Graph-Translation Theorem.

Solution

Solutions to the given inequality are 3 less than solutions to $x^2 < 4x$. Solve this simpler inequality.

$$x^2 < 4x$$
$$x^2 - 4x < 0$$
$$x(x - 4) < 0$$
$$\text{Either } (x > 0 \text{ and } x - 4 < 0) \quad \text{or} \quad (x < 0 \text{ and } x - 4 > 0).$$

So the solution set to $x^2 < 4x$ is $\{x: 0 < x < 4\}$.
Thus the solution set to the given inequality is $\{x: -3 < x < 1\}$.

Notes on Reading

This is a long lesson, and you may find it helpful to provide an overview of the lesson. There are three parts to the lesson, with the third part being the longest. The first page and **Example 1** deal with the effects of translations on graphs and on solutions to equations. The Graph Scale-Change Theorem and its effects on a circle constitute the second part. Rubberband transformations with parametric equations, and then with equations in x and y, make up the third part.

This material is tricky. The substitutions often use operations that are the inverses of those students would expect. For example, while students understand that the scale change $S_{a,b}$ maps (x, y) to (ax, by), they may fail to understand why the image is described by replacing x with $\frac{x}{a}$ and y with $\frac{y}{b}$. Here is a proof. In a scale change, $x' = ax$ and $y' = by$. Then $\frac{x'}{a} = x$ and $\frac{y'}{b} = y$. Thus we can substitute $\frac{x'}{a}$ for x and $\frac{y'}{b}$ for y. This describes the image. In practice, we drop the primes. A similar discussion can be used to prove the Graph-Translation Theorem. Let $x' = x + h$ and $y' = y + k$. Then $x' - h = x$ and $y' - k = y$. Appropriate substitution now gives the theorem.

Optional Activities

Activity 1 Technology Connection
Materials: Explorations software

Students may use *Exploration 3-8, The Graph Standardization Theorem,* to explore the Graph Standardization Theorem by choosing from pre-selected functions or their own function. By choosing different values for a, b, h, and k, the result of various transformations appears on the same graph with the original function.

Activity 2 Technology Connection You might ask students to "make their graphing calculator smile" by graphing half-circles and half-ellipses in parametric mode. Have them brainstorm the values for t that will produce the lower half of a circle or ellipse. To get them started, you can show them all or part of the sample given below. [Sample: In parametric mode, with $\pi \le t \le 2\pi$, and window set approximately at $-12 \le x \le 12$, $-8 \le y \le 8$, the following equations produce a "smiley face:"

$x = .5 \cos t$, $y = 2 \sin t$
$x = \cos t + 3$, $y = \sin t + 5$
$x = \cos t - 3$, $y = \sin t + 5$
$x = 5 \cos t$, $y = 2 \sin t - 4$]

❶ For students new to UCSMP materials, the notations $S_{a,b}$ and $T_{h,k}$ probably will need to be explained. You can do this by using the graphs following the Graph Scale-Change Theorem. **Teaching Aid 31** contains these graphs. Note that the center (0, 0) of the circle $x^2 + y^2 = r^2$ has been moved to $(0 + h, 0 + k) = (h, k)$. For example, with $x^2 + y^2 = 9$ and $h = 6$ and $k = 5$, the center of the circle after translation is (6, 5).

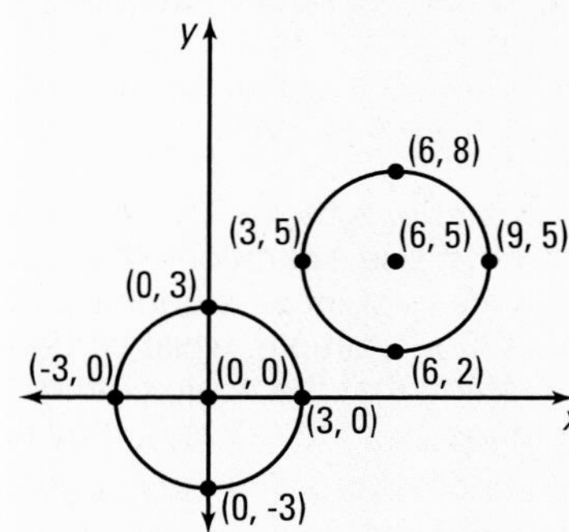

Point out that the coordinates of every point on the circle $(x - 6)^2 + (y - 5)^2 = 9$ are found by adding 6 to the x-coordinate and 5 to the y-coordinate of every point on the original circle.

Scale Changes

The Graph-Translation Theorem involves subtraction and addition. A counterpart, the *Graph Scale-Change Theorem*, involves division and multiplication.

Graph Scale-Change Theorem
In a relation described by a sentence in x and y, the following two processes yield the same graph:
(1) replacing x by $\frac{x}{a}$, and y by $\frac{y}{b}$;
(2) applying the scale change $S_{a,b}: (x, y) \rightarrow (ax, by)$ to the graph of the original relation.

This theorem shows that solutions to the equation $f\left(\frac{x}{a}\right) = g\left(\frac{x}{a}\right)$ are a times the corresponding solutions to the equation $f(x) = g(x)$. Also, solutions to the inequality $f\left(\frac{x}{a}\right) < g\left(\frac{x}{a}\right)$ are a times the corresponding solutions to the inequality $f(x) < g(x)$.

❶ The graph at the left below pictures the circle $x^2 + y^2 = r^2$ and its image under the translation $T_{h,k}$: $(x - h)^2 + (y - k)^2 = r^2$ with center (h, k) and radius r. The graph at the right pictures the circle $x^2 + y^2 = 1$ and its image under the scale change $S_{a,b}$ resulting from the substitutions $\frac{x}{a}$ for x and $\frac{y}{b}$ for y. The image is an ellipse.

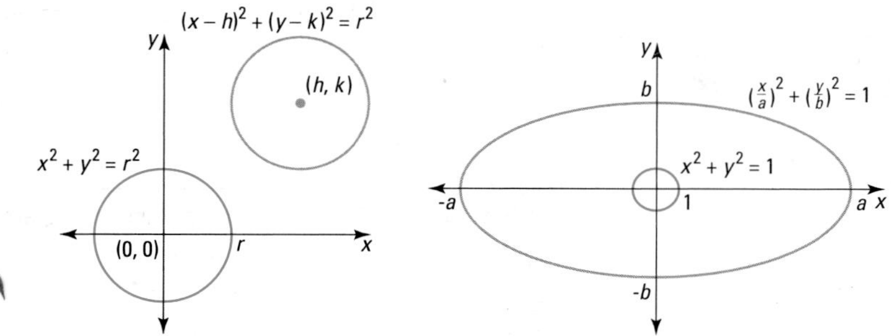

Translations and scale changes can also be done simultaneously. If the ellipse is now translated so that its center is (h, k), then we have applied a *rubberband transformation* to the original unit circle. A general equation for a rubberband transformation can be found by composing the translation with the scale change.

From $\quad T(x, y) = (x + h, y + k)$
and $\quad S(x, y) = (ax, by)$
we have $\quad T \circ S(x, y) = T(ax, by) = (ax + h, by + k)$.

Adapting to Individual Needs

Extra Help

As suggested in the *Perspective* on page 194, students may benefit from the summary given in the chart at the right.

For relations expressed in x- and y-coordinates, or expressed parametrically as $x = f(t)$, $y = g(t)$:

Replacement	Effect on solutions (x, y)	Effect on graph
x by $x - h$, y by $y - k$; $f(t)$ by $f(t) + h$, $g(t)$ by $g(t) + k$	increases x by h, y by k	translates h units to the right, k units up
x by $\frac{x}{a}$, y by $\frac{y}{b}$; $f(t)$ by $af(t)$, $g(t)$ by $bg(t)$	multiplies x by a, y by b	scale changes by factor a horizontally, by factor b vertically
x by $\frac{x}{a}$, y by $\frac{y}{b}$; $f(t)$ by $af(t) + h$, $g(t)$ by $bg(t) + k$	multiplies x by a and adds h to the product, multiplies y by b and adds k to the product	scale change by factor a horizontally then a translation h units to the right, scale change by factor b vertically then a translation k units up

Rubberband Transformations with Parametric Equations

Recall that parametric equations for a circle can be found from the definitions for the sine and cosine:

$$\begin{cases} x = \cos t \\ y = \sin t \end{cases}, \quad 0 \le t < 2\pi.$$

Introducing a multiplier in each equation scales the graph, transforming it into an ellipse. For example, the graph of

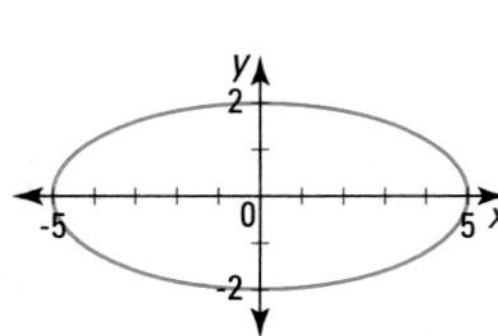

$$\begin{cases} x = 5\cos t \\ y = 2\sin t \end{cases}, \quad 0 \le t < 2\pi$$

is the ellipse shown at the left.

For this ellipse, since $\cos t = \frac{x}{5}$ and $\sin t = \frac{y}{2}$, the Pythagorean Identity can be used to find an equation in x and y.

$$\cos^2 t + \sin^2 t = 1$$
$$\left(\frac{x}{5}\right)^2 + \left(\frac{y}{2}\right)^2 = 1$$

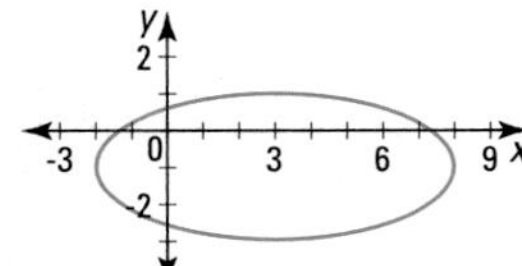

The ellipse is centered at (0, 0). To translate it to a different center, add a constant to either or both of the parametric equations. For example, if you want the center at (3, −1), use

$$\begin{cases} x = 5\cos t + 3 \\ y = 2\sin t - 1 \end{cases}, \quad 0 \le t < 2\pi.$$

The result is the ellipse graphed at the left.

To determine the substitutions which will give an equation for an image under a rubberband transformation, let a point on the image be (x', y'). Then $x' = ax + h$ and $y' = by + k$. Solve these equations for x and y to find $x = \frac{x' - h}{a}$ and $y = \frac{y' - k}{b}$.

Example 2

Find an equation in x and y for the ellipse with parametric equations

$$\begin{cases} x = 5\cos t + 3 \\ y = 2\sin t - 1 \end{cases} \quad 0 < t < 2\pi.$$

Solution

This ellipse is the image of the unit circle $x^2 + y^2 = 1$ under the composite $T \circ S$, where $S(x, y) = (5x, 2y)$ and $T(x, y) = (x + 3, y - 1)$. That is, it has been stretched by a magnitude of 5 in the horizontal direction, stretched by a magnitude of 2 in the vertical direction, and then translated so that its center is (3, -1). So $a = 5$, $b = 2$, $h = 3$, and $k = -1$, from which an equation for the ellipse is $\left(\frac{x - 3}{5}\right)^2 + \left(\frac{y + 1}{2}\right)^2 = 1$.

Activity

Check the solution to Example 2 by solving the parametric equations for $\sin t$ and $\cos t$. Then use the Pythagorean Identity to find an equation for the ellipse.

See left.

$\cos t = \frac{x - 3}{5}$;
$\sin t = \frac{y + 1}{2}$;
$\sin^2 t + \cos^2 t = 1$;
$\frac{(x - 3)^2}{25} + \frac{(y + 1)^2}{4} = 1$

For the graph of the ellipse, do an example with $a = 5$ and $b = 2$. Sketch both the original circle and its image after the scale change.

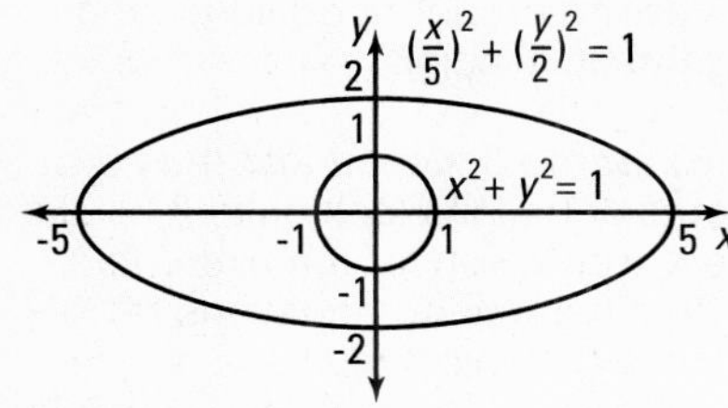

Point out that
(0, 0) → (0, 0)
(1, 0) → (5, 0)
(0, 1) → (0, 2)
(-1, 0) → (-5, 0)
(0, -1) → (0, -2)
That is, $x_{new} = 5x_{old}$, $y_{new} = 2y_{old}$.

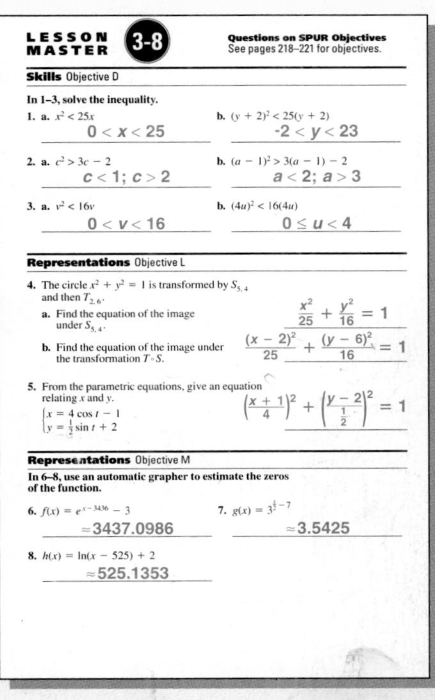

LESSON MASTER 3-8 Questions on SPUR Objectives. See pages 218–221 for objectives.

Skills Objective D

In 1–3, solve the inequality.

1. a. $x^2 < 25x$ — $0 < x < 25$
   b. $(y + 2)^2 < 25(y + 2)$ — $-2 < y < 23$
2. a. $c^2 > 3c - 2$ — $c < 1$; $c > 2$
   b. $(a - 1)^2 > 3(a - 1) - 2$ — $a < 2$; $a > 3$
3. a. $v^2 < 16v$ — $0 < v < 16$
   b. $(4u)^2 < 16(4u)$ — $0 \le u < 4$

Representations Objective L

4. The circle $x^2 + y^2 = 1$ is transformed by $S_{5,4}$ and then $T_{2,6}$.
   a. Find the equation of the image under $S_{5,4}$. — $\frac{x^2}{25} + \frac{y^2}{16} = 1$
   b. Find the equation of the image under the transformation $T \circ S$. — $\frac{(x - 2)^2}{25} + \frac{(y - 6)^2}{16} = 1$
5. From the parametric equations, give an equation relating x and y. $\begin{cases} x = 4\cos t - 1 \\ y = \frac{1}{2}\sin t + 2 \end{cases}$ — $\left(\frac{x + 1}{4}\right)^2 + \left(\frac{y - 2}{\frac{1}{2}}\right)^2 = 1$

Representations Objective M

In 6–8, use an automatic grapher to estimate the zeros of the function.

6. $f(x) = e^{x - 3436} - 3$ — ≈ 3437.0986
7. $g(x) = 3^{\frac{1}{x} - 7}$ — ≈ 3.5425
8. $h(x) = \ln(x - 525) + 2$ — ≈ 525.1353

❷ Notice that the parametric form of the Graph-Standardization Theorem is quite a bit simpler than the x-y form. The substitutions seem to use the proper operations, and the algebra is simpler.

In **Example 3,** notice that the parametric equations look quite a bit like the x-y equation for the hyperbola. To find parametric equations for a curve for which you have an x-y description, it is always possible to let $x = t$, and then y equals the same expression as in the x-y form, but with t replacing x.

Error Alert Students may have difficulty distinguishing the graph of a parent function from the graph of the function under consideration. Encourage students to use colored pencils when sketching the graphs.

The arguments are summarized in the Graph-Standardization Theorem.

❷ **Graph-Standardization Theorem**

Suppose that G is the graph of a relation in x and y. Let h and k be any real numbers and let a and b be nonzero real numbers. Let G' be the image of G under the rubberband transformation $T: (x, y) \rightarrow (ax + h, by + k)$.

x-y form: If G is described by a rule relating x and y, then a rule for G' is found by replacing x by $\frac{x-h}{a}$ and y by $\frac{y-k}{b}$.

parametric form:

If G is described by $\begin{cases} x = f(t) \\ y = g(t) \end{cases}$, then G' is described by $\begin{cases} x = a f(t) + h \\ y = b g(t) + k \end{cases}$.

Example 3

One set of parametric equations for the hyperbola $y = \frac{1}{x}$ is $\begin{cases} x = t \\ y = \frac{1}{t} \end{cases}$, for all $t \neq 0$.

a. Describe the rubberband transformation that maps this hyperbola onto the hyperbola $\begin{cases} x = \frac{1}{2}t - 1 \\ y = \frac{4}{t} + 3 \end{cases}$.

b. Find an equation in x and y for the image hyperbola.

c. Give equations for asymptotes of the image hyperbola.

Solution

a. The scale change $(x, y) \rightarrow (ax, by)$ is first, then the translation.

$$\begin{cases} x = t \\ y = \frac{1}{t} \end{cases} \xrightarrow[\left(\frac{1}{2}x,\ 4y\right)]{\text{scale change}} \begin{cases} x = \frac{1}{2}t \\ y = \frac{4}{t} \end{cases} \xrightarrow[(x - 1,\ y + 3)]{\text{translation}} \begin{cases} x = \frac{1}{2}t - 1 \\ y = \frac{4}{t} + 3 \end{cases}$$

The transformation is the composite of the scale change $S: (x, y) \rightarrow \left(\frac{1}{2}x, 4y\right)$ followed by the translation $T: (x, y) \rightarrow (x - 1, y + 3)$.

b. Solve the first equation for t (in terms of x).

$$x = \frac{1}{2}t - 1 \Rightarrow t = 2x + 2$$

Now substitute $2x + 2$ for t in the second equation.

$$y = \frac{4}{2x + 2} + 3$$

The fraction can be simplified.

$$y = \frac{2}{x + 1} + 3$$

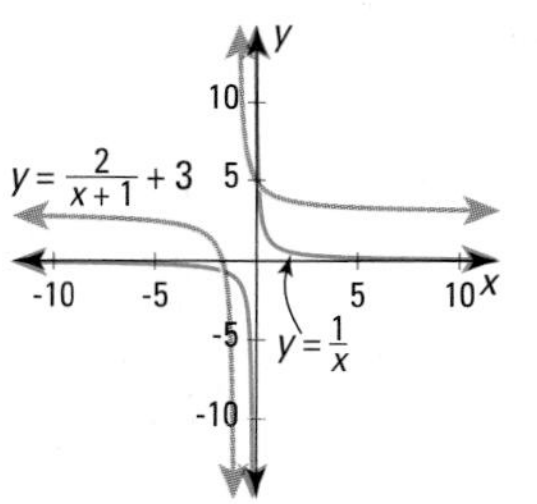

c. The asymptotes of $y = \frac{1}{x}$ are the axes $y = 0$ and $x = 0$. The scale change does not change the axes, but the translation slides them 1 unit to the left and 3 units up. The asymptotes of $y = \frac{2}{x + 1} + 3$ are $x = -1$ and $y = 3$.

Check

Graph $y = \frac{1}{x}$ and $y = \frac{2}{x + 1} + 3$ on the same axes as shown at the left.

Adapting to Individual Needs

Challenge

Have students answer the following questions.

1. The graph of $y = e^x + 1$ is a vertical translation image 1 unit up of the graph of $y = e^x$. The graph of $y = e^{x+1}$ is a horizontal translation image 1 unit to the left of the graph of $y = e^x$. Which one is shown at the right? Explain your answer. [You can't tell.]

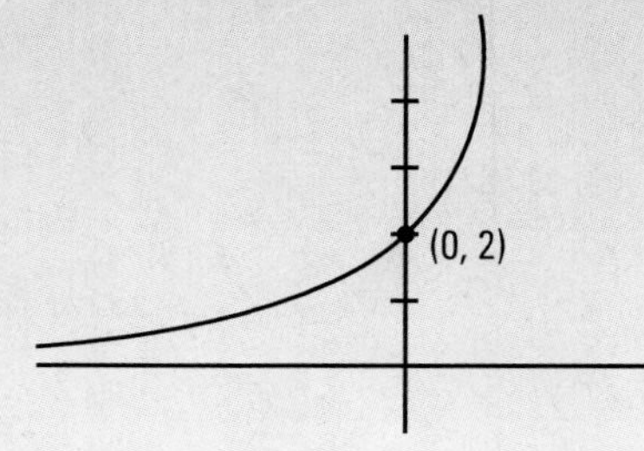

2. Is it possible that $y = e^{x+a}$ yields the same graph as $y = e^x + b$, for some values of a and b? If so, what is the relationship between a and b? [Not possible unless $a = b = 0$.]

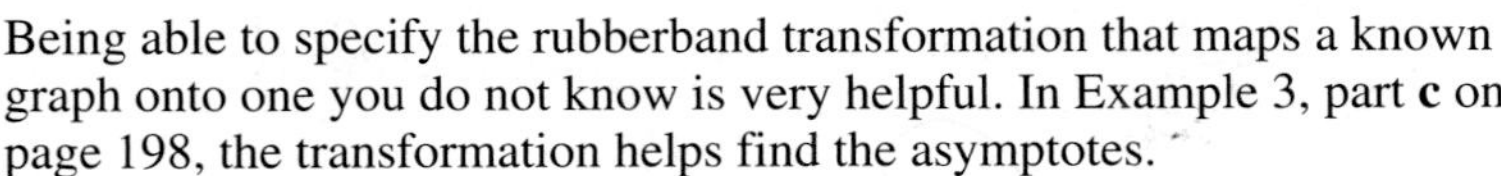

Being able to specify the rubberband transformation that maps a known graph onto one you do not know is very helpful. In Example 3, part **c** on page 198, the transformation helps find the asymptotes.

QUESTIONS

Covering the Reading

1. According to *Peterson's Guides Annual Survey of Undergraduate Institutions*, the average cost of tuition, mandatory fees, and room and board at a state university in 1996–97 was \$7,020 for residents of the state and \$11,799 for nonresidents. Assume a 4% inflation rate.

a. Give a formula for the average cost for residents x years after 1996.

b. Give a formula for the average cost for residents in the year x.

c. Assuming a 4% inflation rate, what would be the average cost for residents in the year 2005? **\$9,992**

d. Assuming a 5% inflation rate, what would be the average cost for nonresidents in the year 2005? **\$18,304**

a) $c = 7020(1.04)^x$ b) $c = 7020(1.04)^{(x - 1996)}$

2. a. Explain how the graph of $g(x) = (x + 77)^3$ is related to the graph of $f(x) = x^3$. **See left.**

b. Find all real solutions to $(x + 77)^3 > 1000$. **$x > -67$**

3. Give an equation for the circle with center (50, 30) and radius 25. **$(x - 50)^2 + (y - 30)^2 = 625$**

4. Explain how the graph of the ellipse $\frac{x^2}{9} + \frac{y^2}{16} = 1$ is related to the graph of the unit circle. **$(x, y) \to (3x, 4y)$**

5. Consider the graph of $y = \frac{1}{x}$. Write an equation for the image of this graph under the given transformation. **See left.**

a. $T_{3,2}$ **b.** $S_{5, 1/3}$

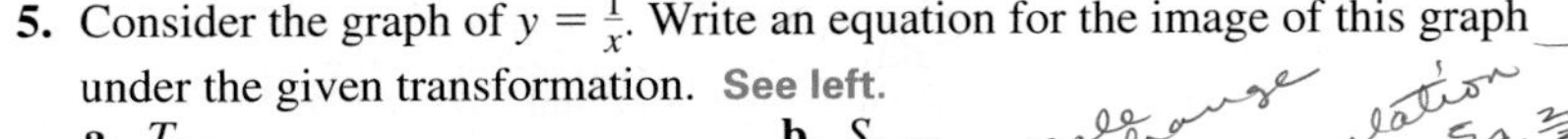

6. Consider the ellipse that is the graph of $\begin{cases} x = 4\cos t - 8 \\ y = \frac{2}{3}\sin t + 5 \end{cases}$, $0 \le t < 2\pi$.

a. Describe the scale change and translation that transforms the unit circle into this ellipse. **a–c) See left.**

b. Use the Pythagorean Identity to find an equation in x and y for the image ellipse.

c. Graph the unit circle and the image ellipse on the same axes.

7. Write the equation of the image of $y = \frac{1}{x}$ under the scale change $S: (x, y) \to \left(\frac{2}{3}x, 4y\right)$ followed by the translation $T: (x, y) \to (x - 5, y - 1)$. **See left.**

8. The hyperbola $x^2 - y^2 = 1$ is transformed by the scale change $S: (x, y) \to \left(2x, \frac{1}{5}y\right)$ followed by the translation $T: (x, y) \to (x - 2, y + 3)$.

a. Use the Graph-Standardization Theorem to determine the equation of the image hyperbola. **a–c) See margin.**

b. Graph $x^2 - y^2 = 1$ and its image on the same axes.

c. An asymptote for $x^2 - y^2 = 1$ is the line $y = x$. Use the Graph-Standardization Theorem to give an equation for the corresponding asymptote.

2a) They are congruent and related by the translation $T_{-77, 0}$.

5a) $y = \frac{1}{x - 3} + 2$

b) $3y = \frac{5}{x}$

6a) $S_{4, 2/3}$, $T_{-8, 5}$

b) $\frac{(x+8)^2}{16} + \frac{9(y-5)^2}{4} = 1$

c)

7) $y = \frac{8}{3(x + 5)} - 1$

Additional Examples

1. Solve each equation.

a. $x^2 - 2x - 8 = 0$
$x = -2$ or $x = 4$

b. $(x - 5)^2 - 2(x - 5) - 8 = 0$
$x = 3$ or $x = 9$

c. $(\frac{x}{5})^2 - 2(\frac{x}{5}) - 8 = 0$
$x = -10$ or $x = 20$

2. Find an equation in x and y for the ellipse with parametric equations
$x = \cos t + 6$
$y = 8\sin t - 5$.
$(x - 6)^2 + (\frac{y+5}{8})^2 = 1$

Additional Answers

8. a. $(\frac{x+2}{2})^2 - (5y - 15)^2 = 1$

b. $\left(\frac{x+2}{2}\right)^2 - \left(\frac{y-3}{\frac{1}{5}}\right)^2 = 1$; $x^2 - y^2 = 1$

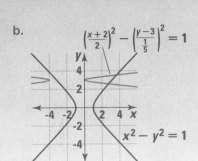

c. $y = \frac{x}{10} + \frac{32}{10}$

Notes on Questions

Question 9 Students are expected to use the answer to **part a** to answer the other parts; that is, **parts b and c** should not be solved independently.

Question 11 These functions are related to the standard normal curve and may be quite familiar to students who have studied from *Functions, Statistics, and Trigonometry.*

Questions 14–15 Symbolically, multiplication and composition of functions may look quite similar, but mathematically, they are quite different.

Question 19 This question is preparation for Lesson 3-9.

Follow-up for Lesson 3-8

Practice

For more questions on SPUR Objectives, use **Lesson Master 3-8** (shown on page 197).

Assessment

Quiz A quiz covering Lessons 3-5 through 3-8 is provided in the *Assessment Sourcebook.*

Extension

Ask students what their answer to **Question 10** would be if the restrictions that a and b are both positive were removed. [$\frac{y}{b} = f(\frac{x}{a})$ would be increasing as long as a and b were both positive or both negative. If a and b have different signs, the function will be decreasing.]

Applying the Mathematics

9. Solve each.
a. $\log_2 x = -3$ $\frac{1}{8}$ **b.** $\log_2 (x + 1) = -3$ $-\frac{7}{8}$ **c.** $\log_2 \left(\frac{x+1}{4}\right) = -3$ $-\frac{1}{2}$

10. A function $y = f(x)$ is increasing. The scale change $S_{a,b}$ where a and b are positive is applied to f, resulting in the new function $\frac{y}{b} = f\left(\frac{x}{a}\right)$. For what values of a and b will this new function be an increasing function? all positive values

11. Tell how the graph of the standard normal curve $y = \frac{1}{\sqrt{2\pi}} e^{-x^2/2}$ can be produced by applying a scale change to the graph of $y = e^{-x^2}$.
Apply the scale change $(x, y) \rightarrow \left(\sqrt{2}x, \frac{1}{\sqrt{2\pi}} y\right)$.

Review

12. **a.** Use the Test-Point Method to find the exact solutions to $x^3 - 25x < 0$. a) $x < -5$, $0 < x < 5$
b. Explain how your solutions to part **a** relate to the graph of $y = x^3 - 25x$. *(Lesson 3-7)* The solutions are the intervals in which the graph lies below the x-axis.

13. Solve $\frac{2}{3} A^{2/3} = 486$. *(Lesson 3-3)* $A = 19{,}683$

In 14 and 15, suppose f and g are functions whose graphs are lines, with $f(x) = mx + b$ and $g(x) = nx + c$ where $m \neq 0$ and $n \neq 0$. *(Lessons 3-1, 3-2)*

14. Prove that the graph of $f \cdot g$ is never a line. See left.

15. Prove that the graph of $f \circ g$ is always a line. See left.

14) Let $f(x) = mx + b$ and $g(x) = nx + c$, where we assume $m \neq 0$ and $n \neq 0$. By definition, $f \cdot g = (mx + b)(nx + c) = mnx^2 + (bn + mc)x + bc$. Since $mn \neq 0$ (because $m \neq 0$ and $n \neq 0$), $f \cdot g$ has a nonzero quadratic term and, hence, cannot be a line.

15) Let $f(x) = mx + b$ and $g(x) = nx + c$. By definition, $f \circ g = (m(nx + c) + b) = mnx + (mc + b)$. This is a line for all values of m and n. Therefore, $f \circ g$ is always a line.

16. Let $p(x) = .1x^2$ and $q(x) = \sin x$. What is $\lim_{x \to \infty} \frac{q(x)}{p(x)}$? *(Lesson 2-4)* 0

17. Give the amplitude, period, and phase shift of the cosine function. *(Previous course, Lesson 2-6)* amplitude = 1; period = 2π; phase shift = 0

18. Write the negation of the statement

$\forall$ *real numbers x, if* $|x - 4| > 3$*, then* $x > 6$ *or* $x < 2$.

(Lessons 1-3, 1-5)
$\exists$ a real number x such that $|x - 4| > 3$ and $x \leq 6$ and $x \geq 2$.

19. Suppose v and w are both negative numbers. *True or false.*
a. $|v + w| = |v| + |w|$ True **b.** $|v - w| = |v| - |w|$ False
c. $|vw| = vw$ True **d.** $\left|\frac{v}{w}\right| = \frac{|v|}{|w|}$ True
(Previous course)

Exploration

20. A curve is described by the equations $\begin{cases} x = 2 + 2\cos t \\ y = 1 - 3\sin^2 t \end{cases}$, $0 \leq t < 2\pi$.
a. What curve is it? a section of a parabola
b. Find an equation in x and y for this curve.
$y = \frac{3}{4}x^2 - 3x + 1$

Additional Answers

18. $\exists$ a real number x such that $|x - 4| > 3$ and $x \leq 6$ and $x \geq 2$.

Setting Up Lesson 3-9

Be sure to discuss **Question 19,** to ensure that all students remember the definition and some properties of absolute value before they get into this lesson.

LESSON

3-9

Absolute Value Equations and Inequalities

In this lesson, the ideas of the preceding lessons are applied to inequalities involving the absolute value function. Algebraically, the **absolute value** of x, written $|x|$, is found from the piecewise definition: if $x \geq 0$, then $|x| = x$; if $x < 0$, then $|x| = -x$.

From the definition, notice that $|x|$ is never negative, for when x is negative then its absolute value is its opposite, and when $x \geq 0$ then $|x| = x$.

This shows that the equation $|x| = a$ has

(i) no solutions if $a < 0$;

(ii) one solution, $x = 0$, if $a = 0$;

(iii) two solutions, $x = a$ and $x = -a$, if $a > 0$.

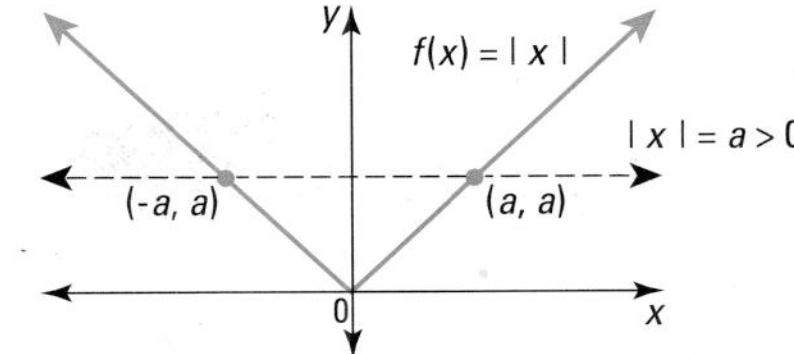

Distance Definition of Absolute Value

Recall the relation between absolute value and distance: $|x|$ is the distance from x to 0 on a number line. More generally, recall that $|x_1 - x_2|$ is the distance between two points on a number line with coordinates x_1 and x_2. In applications, this is called the **absolute error** of x_1 from x_2.

For example, if the true value of a certain quantity is x and if x_m is the measured value obtained from an experiment, then the statement

The absolute error of x_m from x is at most .01.

can be expressed as

$$|x - x_m| \leq .01.$$

The geometric interpretation of this statement is that the distance from x to x_m on a number line is at most .01 unit.

The Inequality $|x| < a$

The following theorem provides the basis for solving an absolute value inequality, by changing it into a compound inequality.

Theorem
For all real numbers x and a with $a > 0$, $|x| < a$ if and only if $-a < x < a$; that is, the solution set of $|x| < a$ is the interval $(-a, a)$ of real numbers.

-a 0 a x

Lesson 3-9

Objectives

A Solve equations by applying a function to each side, taking into account nonreversible steps.
D Solve inequalities algebraically.
J Use inequalities to solve real-world problems.

Resources

From the ***Teacher's Resource File***
- Lesson Master 3-9
- Answer Master 3-9
- Teaching Aid 27: Warm-up

Additional Resources
- Visual for Teaching Aid 27

Warm-up

1. Graph $y = |3x - 2|$.

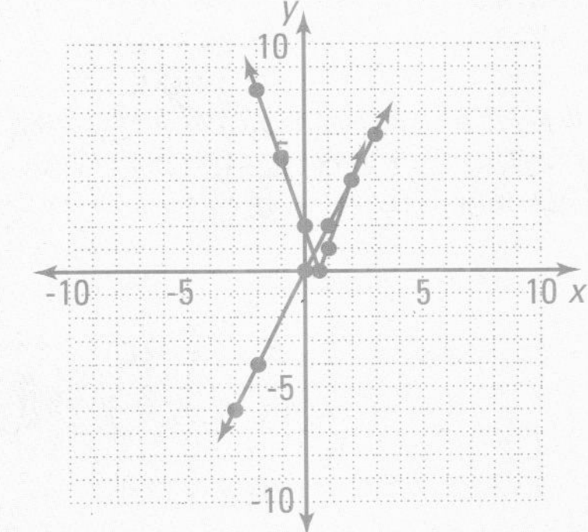

(Warm-up continues on page 202.)

Lesson 3-9 Overview

Broad Goals This lesson covers absolute value equations in one variable, with applications to limits. Its purpose is to introduce students to the types of sentences involving absolute value that they may encounter in a calculus course.

Perspective Another application of *and-or* logic appears in the solving of absolute value sentences. The solutions to $|x| = a$, $|x| > a$, and $|x| < a$ can be applied to the more general situations $|f(x)| = g(x)$, $|f(x)| < g(x)$, $|f(x)| > g(x)$.

2. Graph $y = 2x$ on the graph from Question 1. Use this graph to solve the equation $y = |3x - 2| = 2x$.
The graphs intersect at (2, 4) and (.4, .8).
3. Solve $|3x - 2| = 2x$ algebraically.
Either $3x - 2 = 2x$ or $3x - 2 = -2x$. In the first case, $x = 2$. In the second case, $x = .4$.

Notes on Reading

We assume that students have seen the absolute value function before. The first paragraphs of the lesson are meant to be review.

Example 1 is of a type that should be familiar to students who have studied from UCSMP *Algebra* or *Advanced Algebra*. It is placed here to prepare students for **Example 2.** Just as $|x|$ is the distance between x and 0 on a number line, $|x_1 - x_2|$ is the distance between two points x_1 and x_2 on a number line. In **Example 2,** $x_1 = s_n$ and $x_2 = L$ to get $|s_n - 2|$, which we want to be less than .01 .

Example 3 on page 204 is similar to **Example 1** but with $>$ rather than $\leq$. An alternative method of solution is to solve $|5 - 2x| \leq 4$, and then realize that all real numbers that are not solutions to this sentence must be solutions to $|5 - 2x| > 4$.

Proof

Let x and a be real numbers with $a > 0$. From the definition of $|x|$, either $|x| = x$ (when $x \geq 0$) or $|x| = -x$ (when $x < 0$). Thus

$$\begin{aligned} |x| < a &\Leftrightarrow (x \geq 0 \text{ and } x < a) \text{ or } (x < 0 \text{ and } -x < a) \\ &\Leftrightarrow (x \geq 0 \text{ and } x < a) \text{ or } (x < 0 \text{ and } x > -a) \\ &\Leftrightarrow 0 \leq x < a \quad \text{or} \quad -a < x < 0 \\ &\Leftrightarrow -a < x < a \end{aligned}$$

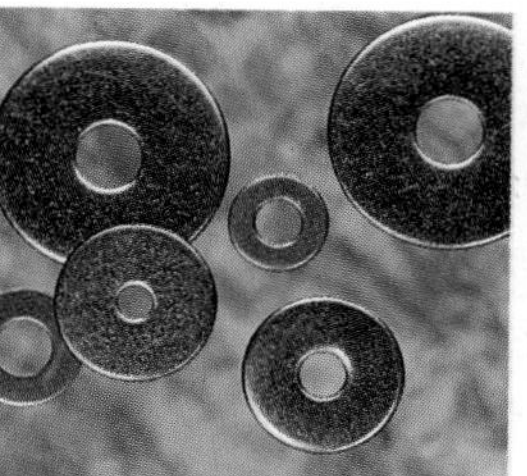

Example 1

A machine stamps out circular washers that are supposed to have a hole with diameter 0.80 cm. The absolute error can be no more than 0.03 cm. Let d be an acceptable diameter.

a. Write an absolute value inequality d must satisfy.
b. Write a double inequality d must satisfy.
c. Solve the inequality from part **b**.

Solution

a. The fact that the absolute error can be no more than 0.03 cm indicates that d must satisfy

$$|d - 0.80| \leq 0.03 \text{ cm}.$$

b. According to the theorem, this inequality can be written as

$$-0.03 \text{ cm} \leq d - 0.80 \leq 0.03 \text{ cm}.$$

c. Convert the double inequality into an *and* statement.

$$-0.03 \leq d - 0.80 \quad \text{and} \quad d - 0.80 \leq 0.03$$

Thus, $\quad 0.77 \leq d \quad$ and $\quad d \leq 0.83.$

Hence, $|d - 0.80| \leq 0.03$ cm is equivalent to $0.77 \text{ cm} \leq d \leq 0.83$ cm.

Absolute Value and Limits of Sequences

Absolute value inequalities arise when a sequence is approaching a limit and you wish to know when it gets as close as possible to a certain value.

Example 2

The sequence $s_n = \frac{2n + 5}{n + 3}$ has terms $\frac{7}{4}, \frac{9}{5}, \frac{11}{6}, \frac{13}{7}, \ldots$, and $\lim_{n \to \infty} s_n = 2$. For what values of n is s_n within .01 of its limit?

Solution

Restated using absolute value, the question is to solve

$$|s_n - 2| < .01.$$

That is, $$\left|\frac{2n + 5}{n + 3} - 2\right| < .01.$$

From the theorem, this inequality can be rewritten as a double inequality without employing absolute value.

$$-.01 < \frac{2n + 5}{n + 3} - 2 < .01$$

Optional Activities

Cooperative Learning Have students **work in groups** to solve **Question 10** using the methods of Lesson 3-8. Suggest that they rewrite the inequality in the form $\left|\frac{(t - h)}{a}\right| > 1$ and transform the solution of $|t| > 1$ accordingly. Have groups share their conclusions and discuss any discrepancies in their solutions. [$\left|\frac{t - \frac{9}{7}}{\frac{1}{7}}\right| > 1$. Since the solution of $|t| > 1$ is $t > 1$ or $t < -1$, the solutions of the original inequality must be $t > \frac{1}{7} \cdot 1 - \frac{9}{7} = -\frac{8}{7}$ or $t < -\frac{1}{7} \cdot 1 - \frac{9}{7} = -\frac{10}{7}$.]

By the meaning of the double inequality,

$$-.01 < \frac{2n+5}{n+3} - 2 \quad \text{and} \quad \frac{2n+5}{n+3} - 2 < .01$$

$$1.99 < \frac{2n+5}{n+3} \quad \text{and} \quad \frac{2n+5}{n+3} < 2.01.$$

Multiply both sides of each inequality by $n + 3$. Since n is a positive integer, $n + 3$ is positive and so the sense of each inequality does not change.

$$\begin{aligned} 1.99(n+3) &< 2n+5 & &\text{and} & 2n+5 &< 2.01(n+3) \\ 1.99n + 5.97 &< 2n+5 & &\text{and} & 2n+5 &< 2.01n + 6.03 \\ .97 &< .01n & &\text{and} & -1.03 &< .01n \\ 97 &< n & &\text{and} & -103 &< n \end{aligned}$$

Any integer greater than 97 is greater than −103. So $n > 97$. Thus all terms of the sequence after the 97th term are within .01 of 2.

Check

The 97th term, $s_{97} = \frac{199}{100} = 1.99$, which is exactly .01 from 2.

The 98th term $s_{98} = \frac{201}{101} = 1.\overline{9900}$, which is less than .01 from 2.

In Lesson 2-4, we gave an informal definition for *limit*. The idea in Example 2 can be generalized to give a precise definition for limit in terms of the distance interpretation of absolute value.

Definition
For any sequence s of real numbers,

$$\lim_{n \to \infty} s_n = L$$

if and only if, for any positive number p, there is an integer N such that $|s_n - L| < p$ for all $n \geq N$.

In words, the definition says that the limit of the sequence is L if and only if for any positive number p you pick (no matter how small), after a certain point (N) every term of the sequence is closer to the limit than p. Example 2 shows that if $p = .01$, then N can be any integer greater than 97.

Here is a graphical interpretation for another sequence.

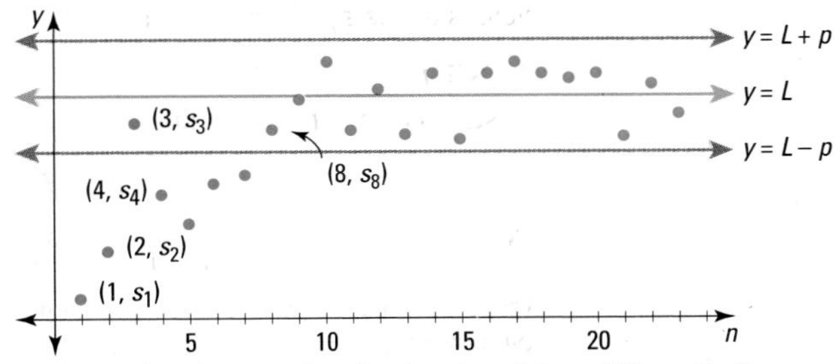

$\lim_{x \to \infty} s_n = L \Leftrightarrow$ for any value of p, there is an integer N (here $N = 8$) so that the point (n, s_n) lies within p of the line $y = L$ for all $n \geq N$.

In reviewing **Example 4,** stress the importance of form. One goal of mathematics is to transform the unfamiliar into the familiar. If a function can be expressed as $\frac{y-k}{a} = f\left(\frac{x-h}{a}\right)$, then the information needed to determine the parent function, scale change, and translation are all neatly packaged and waiting to be used.

Error Alert Students may be confused in **Example 4** as to why the equation was not rewritten as $y - 3.3 = \frac{|1.25x - 5|}{\frac{1}{2}}$, indicating a scale change of $S_{\frac{1}{2},1}$ rather than $S_{1,2}$. Point out that these scale changes yield an identical graph in this case, since they correspond to the same change in the slopes of the graph.

LESSON MASTER 3-9

Questions on SPUR Objectives
See pages 218–221 for objectives.

Skills Objective A

In 1–4, solve the equation.

1. $|a + 5| = 3a$ — $a = \frac{5}{2} = 2.5$
2. $1 = |3x - 2|$ — $x = 1;\ x = \frac{1}{3}$
3. $|c^2 - 9| = 7$ — $c = \pm\sqrt{2};\ c = \pm 4$
4. $|d^3 - 13| = 14$ — $d = -1;\ d = 3$

Skills Objective D

In 5–8, solve the inequality.

5. $|x + 5| \leq 3$ — $8 \leq x \leq -2$
6. $|4t - 5| > t + 1$ — $t < \frac{4}{5};\ t > 2$
7. $4 > |s^2 + 3|$ — $-1 < s < 1$
8. $6 < |x^2 - 5x|$ — $x < -1;\ 2 < x < 3;\ x > 6$

Uses Objective J

9. A poll is conducted to calculate the approval rating of a politician. The poll results vary from the true amount by at most 5% with a confidence of 90%. The poll finds the approval rating to be 60%.
   a. Write the possible values t for the 90% confidence interval using a double inequality. — $55\% \leq t \leq 65\%$
   b. Describe the possible values t for the 90% confidence interval using an absolute value. — $|t - 60\%| \leq 5\%$

Additional Examples

1. Solve $|2x - 10| = 3x$. $x = 2$
2. If the absolute error can be no more than 0.04 cm for oversize circular washers with a hole of diameter 1.4 cm, write inequalities that an acceptable diameter d must satisfy:
   a. using absolute value
   $|d - 1.4| \le .04$
   b. without using absolute value.
   $-.04 \le d - 1.4 \le .04$
3. The sequence $b_n = \frac{5n+2}{2n+3}$ has terms $\frac{7}{5}, \frac{12}{7}, \frac{17}{9}, \frac{22}{11}, \frac{27}{13}, \ldots$ and $\lim_{n \to \infty} b_n = \frac{5}{2}$. For what values of n is b_n within .01 of its limit?
   $n \ge 274$
4. Find all real numbers x such that $|7 - 4x| < 3$. Graph them.
   $1 < x < 2.5$
   -2 0 2
5. Describe the rubberband transformation that maps $y = |x|$ onto $y = 3|x - 2| - 4$.
   The scale change $(x, y) \to (x, 3y)$ followed by the translation $(x, y) \to (x + 2, y - 4)$

Rubberband Transformations with Absolute-Value Functions

Rubberband transformations can help to find key points on graphs of absolute-value functions.

The Inequality $|x| > a$

Suppose that x is a real number. Then the distance of x from the origin is greater than a if and only if x is to the left of $-a$ or to the right of a.

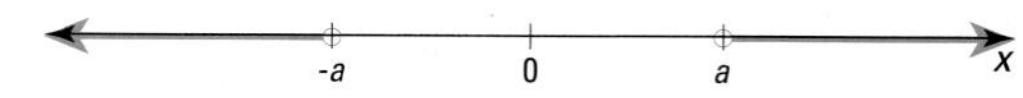

This geometric statement can be expressed algebraically as follows:

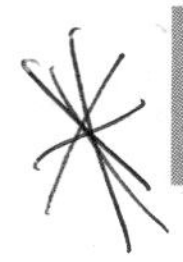

Theorem
For all real numbers x and a, $|x| > a$ if and only if $x < -a$ or $x > a$.

Example 3

Find and graph all real numbers x such that $|5 - 2x| > 4$.

Solution

Let x be a real number. From the theorem,

$$\begin{aligned} |5 - 2x| > 4 &\Leftrightarrow 5 - 2x < -4 \text{ or } 5 - 2x > 4 \\ &\Leftrightarrow -2x < -9 \text{ or } -2x > -1 \\ &\Leftrightarrow x > 4.5 \text{ or } x < 0.5. \end{aligned}$$

0.5 4.5
-2 0 2 4 6 x

Check

When $x = 4.5$ or $x = 0.5$, then $|5 - 2x| = 4$. This checks the endpoints of the intervals. Now check a point within each interval, for example, 0, 3, and 5. You should find that 0 and 5 work, and 3 doesn't.

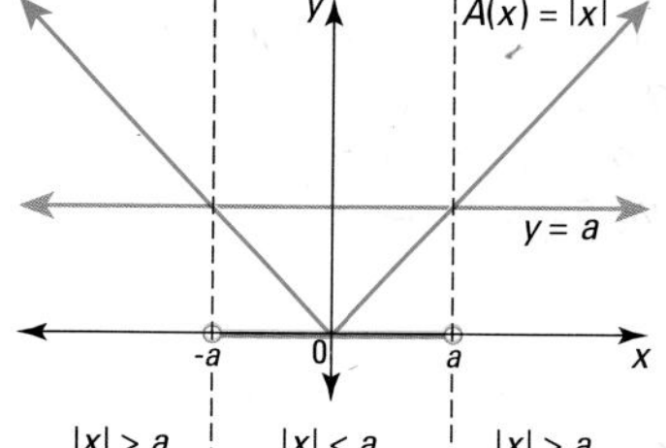

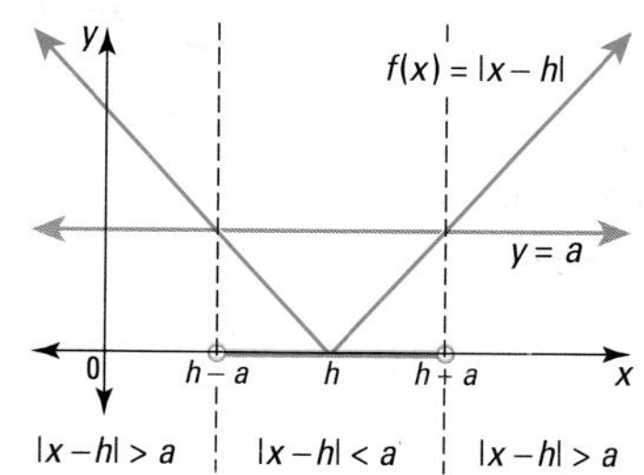

The inequality theorems of this lesson can be interpreted using the graph of the absolute value function, $A(x) = |x|$.

The graph of A is below the line $y = a$ when

$$-a < x < a.$$

These are the solutions to $|x| < a$.

Because of the Graph-Translation Theorem, the solutions to $|x - h| < a$ are h larger than corresponding solutions to $|x| < a$. So they are

$$-a + h < x < a + h.$$

The graph of A is above the line $y = a$ when

$$x > a \text{ or } x < -a.$$

These are the solutions to $|x| > a$. So, because of the Graph-Translation Theorem, the sentence $|x - h| > a$ is equivalent to

$$x > a + h \text{ or } x < -a + h.$$

Adapting to Individual Needs

Extra Help

Stress that for $a > 0$, $|x| < a$ if and only if $-a < x < a$, an *and* statement ($-a < x$ and $x < a$). On the other hand, $|x| > a$ if and only if $x < -a$ or $x > a$, an *or* statement. Show a number-line graph of each case and compare. Students may find it helpful to substitute a value for a.

Challenge

Have students answer the following.

1. Solve: $||x + 2| - x|| = 5$ [-3.5]
2. Use chunking to solve:
   $|x + 2|^2 + 3|x + 2| - 4 = 0$ [{-1, -3}]
3. Prove: If a is a positive number and x is any real number such that $x^2 < a$, then $-\sqrt{a} < x < \sqrt{a}$. [$\sqrt{x^2} = |x|$; $h(x) = \sqrt{x}$ is an increasing function. So if $x^2 < a$, then $\sqrt{x^2} < \sqrt{a}$. So $|x| < \sqrt{a}$, which means that $-\sqrt{a} < x < \sqrt{a}$.]

Example 4

Consider the graph of $y = 2|1.25x - 5| + 3.3$.

a. This graph is congruent to the graph of $y = m|x|$. Find m.

b. Find the vertex of the graph.

Solution

a. Isolate $|1.25x - 5|$ on one side of the equation.

$$y = 2|1.25x - 5| + 3.3$$

$$\frac{y - 3.3}{2} = |1.25x - 5|$$

The left side is in the desired $\frac{y-k}{b}$ form. The right side requires two steps: factor 1.25 from the expression and use the reciprocal of 1.25 as the denominator.

$$1.25x - 5 = 1.25(x - 4)$$

$$= \frac{x - 4}{\frac{1}{1.25}}$$

$$= \frac{x - 4}{.8}$$

So the given equation is equivalent to:

$$\frac{y - 3.3}{2} = \left|\frac{x - 4}{.8}\right|.$$

To change the graph of $y = |x|$ to that of the given equation, first scale x by .8 and y by 2. This gives

$$\frac{y}{2} = \left|\frac{x}{.8}\right|.$$

Thus $$y = \frac{2}{.8}|x|$$

$$= 2.5|x|.$$

Then translate the graph 4 units right and 3.3 units up.

$$y - 3.3 = 2.5|x - 4|$$

But since a translation is a congruence relation, the given equation is congruent to $y = 2.5|x|$ and $m = 2.5$.

b. Since the point (0, 0) is the vertex of the graph of $y = 2.5|x|$, the point (4, 3.3) is the vertex of the graph of $y = 2|1.25x - 5| + 3.3$.

QUESTIONS

Covering the Reading

In 1–4, interpret each absolute value in terms of distance. See margin.

1. $|x| = 7$

2. $|y - 11| = 2$

3. $|a_n - 6| < .01$

4. $|x - 7| > 3$

Additional Answers

1. The distance from x to 0 on a number line is 7 units.
2. The distance from y to 11 on a number line is 2 units.
3. The distance from a_n to 6 on a number line is less than 0.01 units.
4. The distance from x to 7 on a number line is greater than 3 units.

Notes on Questions

Question 15 Students could graph either $y = |x^2 + 10x|$ or $y = |x^2 + 10x| - 4$. It is easier to see the solutions from the latter graph.

Question 19 Error Alert Students might not realize that they can use the Graph-Standardization Theorem even though there is no y-term.

Additional Answers

15. a. $-4 \le x \le 2$, $-12 \le x \le -6$

b.

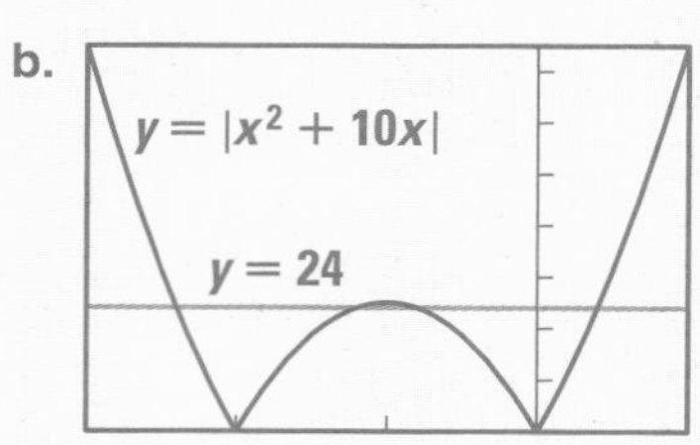

$-15 \le x \le 5$, x-scale = 5
$0 \le y \le 75$, y-scale = 10

17. $|x| < a$ if and only if $-a < x$ and $x < a$
1st theorem of lesson
$\sim(|x| < a)$ if and only if $\sim(-a < x$ and $x < a)$
$|x| \ge a$ if and only if $\sim(-a < x)$ or $\sim(x < a)$
De Morgan's Law
$|x| \ge a$ if and only if $x \le -a$ or $x \ge a$
Considering only the case when $|x| > a$, $|x| > a$ if and only if $x < -a$ or $x > a$

19. b. The solution set of $|x| < 4$ is $-4 < x < 4$. Scaling this by $\frac{1}{2}$ changes the solution set to $-2 < x < 2$. Translating this by $\frac{5}{2}$ gives $\frac{1}{2} < x < \frac{9}{2}$ which is the solution set of $\dfrac{\left|x - \frac{5}{2}\right|}{\frac{1}{2}} < 4$.

5. *Multiple choice.* Which graph below represents the solution set of the inequality $|x - 4| < 3$? a

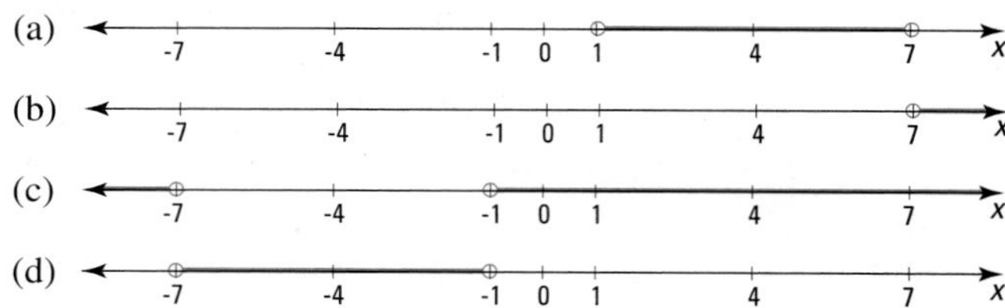

6. *Multiple choice.* Which statement is equivalent to the inequality $|2x + 1| > 2$? b
(a) $-2 > 2x + 1 > 2$
(b) $2x + 1 < -2$ or $2x + 1 > 2$
(c) $2x + 1 > -2$ or $2x + 1 < 2$
(d) $2x + 1 > -2$ and $2x + 1 > 2$

In 7 and 8, write an absolute value inequality to describe the situation.

7. When the thermostat is set for $k°$, the actual room temperature T may vary at most 3° from $k°$. $|T - k| \le 3°$

8) $|L - 15.7| > 0.5$ cm to reject the part

8. A manufacturer makes spindles that are supposed to be 15.7 cm long. A part is rejected if its length is off by more than 0.5 cm. See left.

9. For the sequence s in Example 2, for what values of n is s_n within .001 of the limit? $n = 997$

10. Solve $|7t + 9| > 1$. $t < -\frac{10}{7}$, $t > -\frac{8}{7}$

14a) $-\frac{1}{3}, \frac{1}{2}, 1, \frac{4}{3}, \frac{11}{7}, \frac{7}{4}, \frac{17}{9}, 2, \frac{23}{11}, \frac{13}{6}, \frac{29}{13}, \frac{16}{7}, \frac{7}{3}, \frac{19}{8}, \frac{41}{17}, \frac{22}{9}, \frac{47}{19}, \frac{5}{2}, \frac{53}{21}, \frac{28}{11}$

Applying the Mathematics

11. Consider the graph of $y = \frac{1}{3}|2x + 6| - 4.2$.
a. This graph is congruent to the graph of $y = m|x|$. Find m. $m = \frac{2}{3}$
b. Find the vertex of the graph. $(-3, -4.2)$

12. If a poll percent is within 3% of the true percent p, and the poll shows 31%, describe the possible values of p in the indicated way.
a. using a double inequality $p > 0.28$ and $p < 0.34$
b. using absolute value $|p - .31| < 0.03$

13. Use an absolute value inequality to describe the interval graphed below.

55 59 x

$|x - 57| > 2$

14. Let S be the sequence defined by $S_n = \frac{3n - 4}{n + 2}$.
a. List the first 20 terms of this sequence. See left.
b. Fill in the blanks. After the _?_th term, all terms are within .01 of the limit _?_. 998, 3

15. a. Solve $|x^2 + 10x| \le 24$ algebraically.
b. Verify your solution with an automatic grapher.
a, b) See margin.

Many polls are conducted by phone.

16) False; counterexample: Let $f(x) = -2$, $g(x) = -1$. $\forall x, f(x) < g(x)$, but $\forall x, |f(x)| \geq |g(x)|$.

16. *True or false.*
Suppose f and g are real functions. If $\exists$ a real number x such that $f(x) < g(x)$, then $\exists$ a real number x such that $|f(x)| < |g(x)|$. Justify your answer. See left.

17. Using one of De Morgan's Laws, show how the second theorem of the lesson can be proved from the first theorem of the lesson. See margin.

18. **a.** Is the absolute value function a 1-1 function? No
b. On what interval is the absolute value function increasing? $x \geq 0$

Review

19. **a.** Fill in the blanks. The sentence $|5 - 2x| < 4$ of Example 3 can be rewritten as $\frac{\left|x - \frac{5}{2}\right|}{\frac{1}{2}} < 4$. This means that its solutions are the result of applying a scale change of magnitude ___?___ followed by a translation of ___?___ to the solutions of $|x| < 4$. $\frac{1}{2}, \frac{5}{2}$
b. Verify that the statement in part **a** is true. *(Lesson 3-8)* See margin.

20. **a.** Is $f: x \rightarrow 2^x$ a 1-1 function? Yes
b. Solve and check: $2^{x^2} > 2^{x+6}$.
(Lessons 3-2, 3-5) $x < -2$, $x > 3$

21a) [graph]

21. The ceiling function C is defined as

$$C(x) = \lceil x \rceil = \text{the least integer} \geq x.$$

a. Sketch the graph of C on $-2 \leq x \leq 2$. See left.
b. Is C continuous on this interval? Explain. *(Lesson 3-4)* No. There is a discontinuity at each integral value.

22. Let $h(x) = \sqrt{2x + 3}$ and $g(x) = x$.
a. Find a formula for $(h - g)(x)$. $(h - g)x = \sqrt{2x + 3} - x$
b. What is the domain of $h - g$? all real values $x \geq -\frac{3}{2}$
c. Find the zeros of $h - g$. *(Lessons 2-1, 3-1)* $x = 3$

23. Prove: *If m and n are even integers and p is an odd integer, then mn − p is an odd integer.* *(Lesson 1-8)* See margin.

Exploration

24. **a.** Find real numbers x and y such that $|x| + |y| \neq |x + y|$.
b. Find real numbers x and y such that $|x| + |y| = |x + y|$.
c. Prove: $\forall$ real numbers x and y, $|x| + |y| \geq |x + y|$.
(Hint: Consider the four possible cases: $x \geq 0, y \geq 0$; $x \geq 0, y < 0$; $x < 0, y \geq 0$; $x < 0, y < 0$.)
See margin.

Follow-up for Lesson 3-9

Practice

For more questions on SPUR Objectives, use **Lesson Master 3-9** (shown on page 203).

Assessment

Written Communication Have students **work in pairs.** Ask each student to write an inequality like that in **Example 3,** one student using "<" and the other ">." Then have students solve and graph their partner's inequality. [Students solve inequalities algebraically and graph the solutions.]

Extension

Have students analyze graphs of the form $y = |x^3 - h|$. When $h = 0$, the graph will look quite a bit like the graph of an even-powered function. Have students come up with conjectures for the y-intercept and zero of this family of graphs. [The y-intercept will always be $|h|$; the zero will be the same as the zero for $y = x^3 - h$, that is $x = \sqrt[3]{h}$. Students may find the shapes produced by these graphs quite interesting.]

Project Update Project 1, *Creating Fonts,* and Project 3, *Drawing Graphs Piecewise,* on page 213, relate to the content of this lesson.

23. Let m and n be even integers and p be an odd integer. Then, by definition, $m = 2r$ and $n = 2s$ for some integers r and s. Likewise, by definition, $p = 2q + 1$ for some integer q. Then $mn - p = (2r)(2s) - (2q + 1) = 2(2rs - q - 1) + 1$. Since the integers are closed under both multiplication and subtraction, $2rs - q - 1$ is an integer, making $2(2rs - q - 1) + 1$ an odd integer. Therefore, $mn - p$ is an odd integer.

24. a. Sample: $|-1| + |1| \neq |1 + -1|$
b. Sample: $|0| + |3| = |0 + 3|$
c. Case 1: Let $x \geq 0$ and $y \geq 0$, then $|x| = x$ and $|y| = y$ and $|x| + |y| = x + y = |x + y|$
Case 2: Let $x \geq 0$ and $y < 0$, if $y < 0$ then $|y| > y$ so $|x| + |y| > |x + y|$
Case 3: Let $x < 0$ and $y \geq 0$, if $x < 0$ then $|x| > x$ so $|x| + |y| > |x + y|$.
Case 4: Let $x < 0$ and $y < 0$, if $x < 0$ then $|x| > x$, if $y < 0$ then, $|y| > y$ so $|x| + |y| > |x + y|$.
Thus, $|x| + |y| \geq |x + y|$.

Lesson 3-10

Resources

From the ***Teacher's Resource File***

- Answer Master 3-10
- Teaching Aid 27: Warm-up

Additional Resources

- Visual for Teaching Aid 27

Teaching Lesson 3-10

Warm-up

Consider two segments, one with unit length and the other with length 6. Explain how to set up a 1-1 correspondence between the points of these two segments.

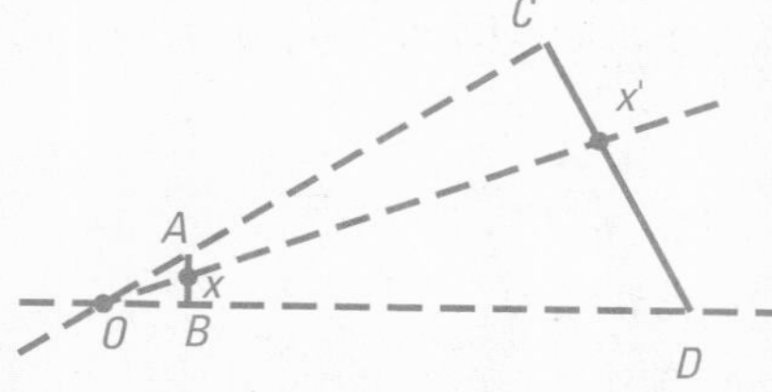

Suppose the given segments are $\overline{AB}$ and $\overline{CD}$. Let $O = \overleftrightarrow{AC} \cap \overleftrightarrow{BD}$ or $O = \overleftrightarrow{AD} \cap \overleftrightarrow{BC}$. Then the point on $\overline{CD}$ corresponding to X on $\overline{AB}$ is $\overrightarrow{OX} \cap \overline{CD}$.

LESSON

3-10 What Is Infinity?

The number of stars in space is often called infinite.

You have seen the expressions $\lim\limits_{x \to -\infty} f(x)$ and $\lim\limits_{n \to \infty} a_n$.

Perhaps these expressions confused you. Can a number approach infinity? Is infinity itself a number? This question has been a subject of discussion since at least as long ago as the time of Zeno, the Greek philosopher of the 6th century B.C. However, the mathematical resolution to this problem has come about only within the past 200 years.

First let us resolve the meaning of infinity as used in the expressions "$\lim\limits_{x \to -\infty} f(x)$" and "$\lim\limits_{n \to \infty} a_n$." In this case, "approaches infinity" is merely a shorthand for "gets larger and larger without bound," and "approaches negative infinity" is short for "gets smaller and smaller without bound." There is no number that is being approached. The sentence $\lim\limits_{x \to \infty} 2^x = \infty$ means that, whatever large number L you might pick, there is a number h such that $\forall$ x greater than h, $2^x > L$.

Graphically, $\lim\limits_{x \to \infty} f(x) = \infty$ means that however high a horizontal line $y = L$ might be, there is a vertical line $x = h$ so that all points on the graph of the function to the right of that line are also above the horizontal line.

A different meaning of the idea of infinity, the meaning "goes on forever," is found in *infinite decimals.* Going on forever means that wherever you are, you are not at the end, because there is always more to follow. This meaning also is related to limits. For instance, an infinite decimal (one that goes on forever) is the limit of a sequence of finite decimals. The number

$$.\overline{32} = .32323232323232323232323232323232\ldots$$

is the limit of the sequence .32, .3232, .323232, .32323232, . . . , which happens to be $\frac{32}{99}$.

Lesson 3-10 Overview

Broad Goals This reading lesson covers various uses of the word *infinity* and the symbol ∞, starting from the meanings as found in the discussion of limits in Lessons 2-4 and 3-9. The work of Georg Cantor regarding the cardinalities of the positive integers, the positive rationals, and the reals is discussed.

Perspective Notice the extraordinary ingenuity of Georg Cantor. First, he realized that the way to approach the cardinality of infinite sets was through the idea of 1-1 correspondence. Second, he developed a nonintuitive way of showing that the sets of integers and rational numbers had the same cardinality. Third, he found a startling way to show that the set of real numbers did not have this cardinality. Finally, he developed an arithmetic of his infinite cardinals.

Cantor used a Hebrew letter to represent the cardinality of infinite sets because virtually all of the Greek letters (the traditional symbols to use) had some interpretation in mathematics or physics. He chose $\aleph_0$ because, being Jewish, he was quite familiar with the Hebrew alphabet. Aleph is the first letter of that alphabet; bet is the second. The Hebrew "Aleph-bet" may have predated the Greek "alpha-beta" from which the English word "alphabet" is derived.

In the uses on page 208, infinity is a figure of speech, describing things without bound or things that continue forever, but infinity is not a number. However, there is a sense in which there is a number called *infinity*. To the question "How many integers are there?" an answer is "There are infinitely many."

The theory of the number of elements in infinite sets was developed by a German mathematician, Georg Cantor, in 1895. The number of elements in a set is called its **cardinality**. The cardinality of {8, 4, 11} is 3; Cantor called the cardinality of the set of positive integers $\aleph_0$ (aleph-null), using the first letter of the Hebrew alphabet.

There are many brilliant ideas in Cantor's theory. Normally we think of deciding whether two sets have the same cardinality by counting their elements. This would not work for infinite sets, because you would never finish counting. Cantor realized that sometimes people use a different strategy. For example, in deciding whether there are enough chairs for students, a teacher may simply ask students to sit in chairs and see if there are any students or chairs left over. This led Cantor to a definition of equal cardinality that could apply either to finite or to infinite sets.

Definition
Two sets A and B have the same cardinality $\Leftrightarrow$ there is a 1-1 correspondence between A and B; that is, there is a 1-1 function from A onto B whose range is B.

For instance, the set {2, 4, 6, 8, 10, 12, 14, . . . } of positive even integers has cardinality $\aleph_0$ because there is a 1-1 correspondence between the set of positive even integers and the set of positive integers.

$$\begin{array}{cccccc} 2 & 4 & 6 & 8 & 10 & 12\ldots \\ \updownarrow & \updownarrow & \updownarrow & \updownarrow & \updownarrow & \updownarrow \\ 1 & 2 & 3 & 4 & 5 & 6\ldots \end{array}$$

This means that infinite sets can have the same cardinality as some of their subsets, a fact noticed also by Galileo. If the elements of a set can be listed in an order, then there is an automatic 1-1 correspondence between the set and the set of positive integers; the number of the element in the list is its corresponding integer. Such sets are called **countably infinite**. A set that is either finite or countably infinite is called **countable**. Notice that a set is a discrete set if and only if it is countable.

Surprises arise from this definition. Some sets we think of as much bigger than the set of integers turn out to be countable. For instance, the positive rational numbers can be listed in order of the sum of their numerator and denominator when they are written in lowest terms. Here is the beginning of such a list:

$$\frac{1}{1}, \frac{1}{2}, \frac{2}{1}, \frac{1}{3}, \frac{3}{1}, \frac{1}{4}, \frac{2}{3}, \frac{3}{2}, \frac{4}{1}, \frac{1}{5}, \frac{5}{1}, \frac{1}{6}, \frac{2}{5}, \frac{3}{4}, \frac{4}{3}, \frac{5}{2}, \frac{6}{1}, \ldots$$

Notes on Reading

Reading Mathematics For some students it is worth saying that "x approaches negative infinity" means both that "x gets smaller and smaller without bound" and "the absolute value of x gets larger and larger without bound." Some people say "gets larger and larger in the negative direction." Choose the phrase with which you are most comfortable.

Mentioning that .99999 ... = 1 is almost guaranteed to lead to some lively discussion. Do not say this unless you are prepared to spend some time explaining why.

Students may enjoy the following limerick. (Trinity is a college of Cambridge University in England.)

There was a young fellow from Trinity
Who took $\sqrt{\infty}$
But the number of digits
Gave him the fidgets;
He dropped Math and took up Divinity.

[Source: Gamow, George, *One, Two, Three ... Infinity,* Bantam Books]

You might ask students to try to give a graphical description of what is meant by such statements as $\lim_{x \to 0} \log_b x = -\infty$ and $\lim_{x \to 0} f(x) = 1$. [Whichever number N you choose, $\exists$ a value h such that $\forall\ x < h$, $\log_b x < -N$. Whichever small positive value L you choose, $\exists$ a value h such that whenever $x > h$, $|f(x) - 1| < L$.]

Another way to show the countability of the set of rational numbers is shown at the right. Every rational number can be written in the form $\frac{a}{b}$, where a and b are integers, and all these numbers can be put in an array, with $\frac{a}{b}$ in the ath column and bth row. For example, $\frac{3}{4}$ is found in the third column and fourth row of the table at the right.

1	2	3	4	5	6	7	...
$\frac{1}{2}$	$\frac{2}{2}$	$\frac{3}{2}$	$\frac{4}{2}$	$\frac{5}{2}$	$\frac{6}{2}$	$\frac{7}{2}$	...
$\frac{1}{3}$	$\frac{2}{3}$	$\frac{3}{3}$	$\frac{4}{3}$	$\frac{5}{3}$	$\frac{6}{3}$	$\frac{7}{3}$	...
$\frac{1}{4}$	$\frac{2}{4}$	$\frac{3}{4}$	$\frac{4}{4}$	$\frac{5}{4}$	$\frac{6}{4}$	$\frac{7}{4}$	...
$\frac{1}{5}$	$\frac{2}{5}$	$\frac{3}{5}$	$\frac{4}{5}$	$\frac{5}{5}$	$\frac{6}{5}$	$\frac{7}{5}$	...
$\frac{1}{6}$	$\frac{2}{6}$	$\frac{3}{6}$	$\frac{4}{6}$	$\frac{5}{6}$	$\frac{6}{6}$	$\frac{7}{6}$	...
...	...	...	...	...	...	...	...

All the positive rational numbers may now be ordered according to the following scheme: in the array just defined, draw a continuous, broken line that goes through all the numbers in the array. Starting at 1, go horizontally to the next place on the right, obtaining 2, then diagonally down to the left to $\frac{1}{2}$, then vertically down one place *(Overview continues on page 210.)*

Error Alert Be sure students do not confuse *uncountable* with *infinitely*. In common language usage, people might say that the set of positive integers is uncountable because one cannot count them. Stress that *mathematically* the set of positive integers is *countable*. More specifically, it is *countably infinite*.

(Notes on Questions begin on page 212.)

The numbers are ordered by the sum of their numerator and denominator; if two numbers have the same sum, the one with the smaller numerator is placed first. Since every positive rational number must appear somewhere on this list, the set of positive rational numbers is countable and its cardinality is $\aleph_0$.

Through an ingenious construction, Cantor proved that not all sets are countable. Specifically, the set of real numbers is **uncountable**. That is, no 1-1 correspondence is possible between the set of reals and the set of positive integers. His proof relies on the fact that every real number can be written as a decimal. It uses indirect reasoning, as follows:

Suppose there were a list of all the real numbers. Perhaps it would start as follows

1st	3.1497852345 . . .
2nd	2.0000000000 . . .
3rd	687.8855885588 . . .
4th	3.1415925635 . . .
5th	18.7500000000 . . .
6th	0.0000000286 . . .

and so on, where each decimal is thought of as an infinite decimal. (If the decimal terminates, write zeros for all of its remaining digits.) Now we show that there is a real number r that is not on the list. Simply choose a number whose 1st decimal place is different from the 1st decimal place in the 1st number, whose 2nd decimal place is different from the 2nd decimal place in the 2nd number, and so on. (The digits that are different from those in r are shown above in blue.) One such number is $r = 0.216611\ldots.$ Since r is a real number which differs from every number on the list, the list does not contain all real numbers. Since this argument can be used with any list, no list can include all the reals.

Consequently, the number of real numbers is infinite, but this is a different infinity from $\aleph_0$. Often the letter c (for continuum) is used to represent the cardinality of the reals. c is larger than $\aleph_0$.

The cardinalities of infinite sets of points can also be compared. Consider the three graphs shown here. Which graph has the most points?

(A) $x^2 + y^2 = 1$ (B) $x^2 + y^2 = 9$ (C) $|x| + |y| = 5$

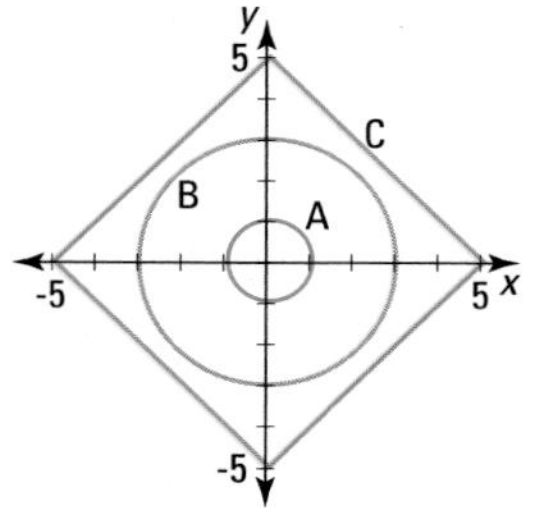

From the picture it appears that the graph of (C), $|x| + |y| = 5$, has the most points because it is the longest, and the graph of (A), $x^2 + y^2 = 1$, has the fewest points because it is shortest. However, all three have the same number of points! A 1-1 correspondence is as follows: any ray with endpoint (0, 0) contains the corresponding points on the three figures.

This argument answers the question about the relative number of points, but doesn't assign a cardinality to the sets. It can be shown that all three sets have the same cardinality as the cardinality c of the real numbers.

Cantor went on to prove that there are cardinalities larger than c, and indeed, that there is an infinite sequence of infinities each larger than the previous!

to $\frac{1}{3}$, diagonally up to $\frac{2}{2}$, and so on as shown below.

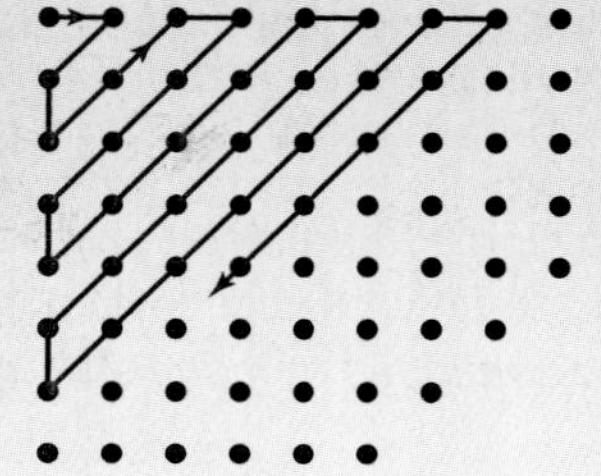

The sequence 1, 2, $\frac{1}{2}$, $\frac{1}{3}$, $\frac{2}{2}$, 3, 4, $\frac{3}{2}$, $\frac{2}{3}$, $\frac{1}{4}$, $\frac{1}{5}$, $\frac{2}{4}$, $\frac{3}{3}$, $\frac{4}{2}$, 5, contains the rational numbers in the order in which they occur along the broken line. Now delete all those numbers $\frac{a}{b}$ in this sequence for which a and b have a common factor, so that each rational number r will appear exactly once and in its simplest form. This results in the following sequence: 1, 2, $\frac{1}{2}$, $\frac{1}{3}$, 3, 4, $\frac{3}{2}$, $\frac{2}{3}$, $\frac{1}{4}$, $\frac{1}{5}$, 5, ... which contains each positive rational number once and only once. This shows that the set of all positive rational numbers is countable.

Cantor also developed an arithmetic of these infinities, called **transfinite arithmetic**. As an example of transfinite arithmetic, consider Cantor's Hotel, a hotel with a countably infinite number of rooms in which all the rooms are filled. There are thus $\aleph_0$ people in the hotel. Now suppose a new person wants to check in. Is there space? Of course there is. Simply move the person currently in room 1 to room 2, the person in room 2 to room 3, and in general move the person in room n to room $n + 1$. Then put the new guest in room 1. This example illustrates the transfinite arithmetic fact

$$\aleph_0 + 1 = \aleph_0.$$

Clearly, transfinite arithmetic does not operate in the same way as typical arithmetic. In general, what holds for finite sets does not necessarily hold for infinite sets, and vice versa.

QUESTIONS

Covering the Reading

5) The function $f(n) = 2n - 1$, where n is a positive integer, is a 1 - 1 correspondence between the positive integers and the positive odd integers. Therefore, the positive odd integers have the same cardinality as the positive integers, which is $\aleph_0$.

6) The union of the set of positive odd integers and the set of positive even integers is the set of all positive integers. All three sets have cardinality $\aleph_0$. Therefore, $\aleph_0 + \aleph_0 = \aleph_0$.

In 1–3, give the cardinality of the set.

1. the set of negative integers $\aleph_0$ **2.** the set of rational numbers $\aleph_0$

3. the set of positive real numbers c

4. Give the next ten numbers in the list of positive rational numbers begun on page 209. $\frac{1}{7}, \frac{3}{5}, \frac{5}{3}, \frac{7}{1}, \frac{1}{8}, \frac{2}{7}, \frac{4}{5}, \frac{5}{4}, \frac{7}{2}, \frac{8}{1}$

5. Show that the set of positive odd integers has cardinality $\aleph_0$. See left.

6. Use the result of Question 5 to aid in demonstrating that $\aleph_0 + \aleph_0 = \aleph_0$. See left.

7. Use Cantor's hotel to show that $\aleph_0 + 100 = \aleph_0$. See margin.

8. Suppose the list of rational numbers in this lesson were used to try to list all the real numbers. Give the first six decimal places of a real number that is not on the list. Sample: 0.211111

9. Draw two line segments of different lengths. Show how to form a 1-1 correspondence between their points. (In so doing, you have proved that any two line segments have the same cardinality.) See margin.

10. Write the formula for a size change that gives a 1-1 correspondence between the graph of $x^2 + y^2 = 9$ and the unit circle. $(x, y) \to (3x, 3y)$

11. How does this diagram help prove that the number of points on an open semicircle is uncountable and has cardinality c?

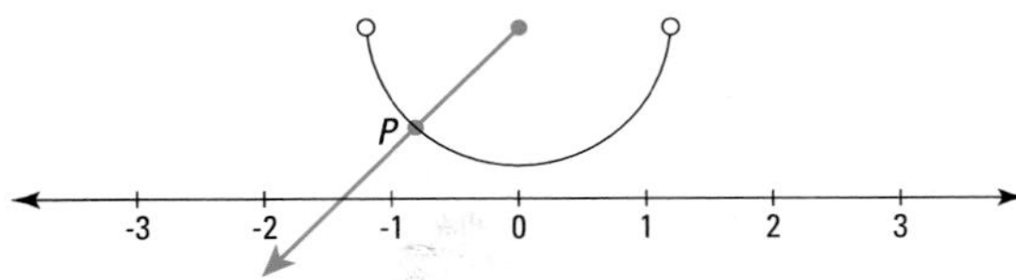

This shows that the unit circle has at least cardinality c. See margin.

Follow-up for Lesson 3-10

Assessment

Written Communication Have students **work with a partner** to generate examples of infinite sets, some countable and some uncountable. Have them compare their results to those of another pair of students. [Students demonstrate understanding of countable and uncountable infinite sets.]

Extension

Students may be interested in these facts about large numbers; you can ask them to find out some more!

- One calculation says that if the entire universe were filled with protons and electrons so that no space was left, the total number would be 10^{110}, still less than a googolplex.
- The number of grains of sand on Coney Island is 10^{20}.
- The number of words printed since the Gutenberg Bible (1456) until the 1940's was about 10^{16}.*

*This information is from *The Joy of Mathematics,* by Theoni Pappas, copyright 1986, 1987, 1989.

Additional Answers

7. Suppose a hotel has a countably infinite number of rooms, all full, and 100 new guests wish to check in. If the guests in Room 1 move to Room 101, the guests in Room 2 to Room 102, and so on, there will be 100 vacant rooms for the new guests. All of the new guests have been accomodated without displacing any of the old guests. Therefore, $\aleph_0 + 100 = \aleph_0$.

9. Label the segments $\overline{AB}$ and $\overline{CD}$. Extend a line through B and D and a line through A and C. SInce $\overline{AB}$ and $\overline{CD}$ have different lengths, these lines intersect at some point P. To establish a 1-1 correspondence, pair each point E on $\overline{AB}$ with the intersection of PE and $\overline{CD}$.

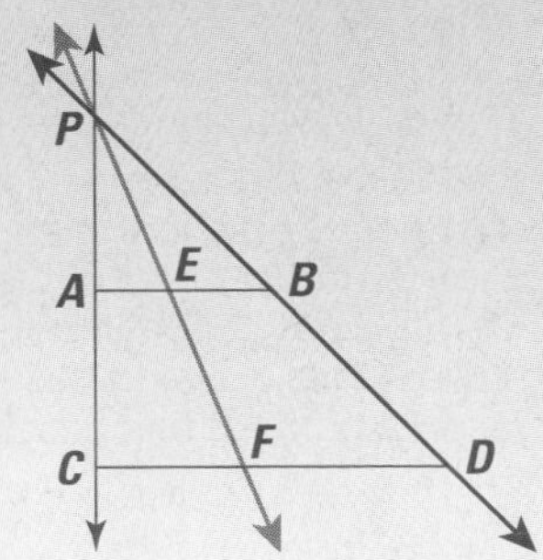

11. The distinct rays originating at the center of the semicircle and passing through each distinct point of the semicircle each intersect the real number line at a distinct point. Therefore, the set of points of the semicircle are in a 1-1 correspondence with the real numbers, and, hence, have cardinality c.

Notes on Questions

Question 13 There is a tacit assumption in this question that time will extend infinitely into the future.

Additional Answers

12. a. For any two values x_1 and x_2 in the interval $(-\frac{\pi}{2}, \frac{\pi}{2})$, if $x_1 \neq x_2$, then $\tan x_1 \neq \tan x_2$. So $f(x) = \tan x$ is one-to-one on the interval $(-\frac{\pi}{2}, \frac{\pi}{2})$. For any real number y, $x = \arctan y$ lies in the interval $(-\frac{\pi}{2}, \frac{\pi}{2})$ and $y = \tan x$. So the range of the function $f(x) = \tan x$ with domain $(-\frac{\pi}{2}, \frac{\pi}{2})$ is the entire real line. Therefore, $f(x) = \tan x$ is a 1-1 correspondence between $(-\frac{\pi}{2}, \frac{\pi}{2})$ and the reals.

21. Sample:

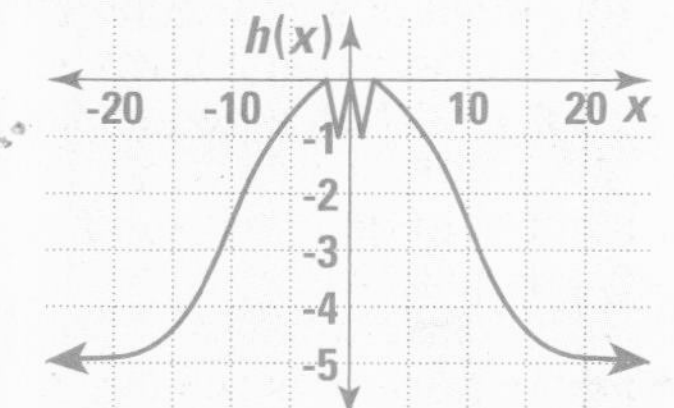

22. The Cantor set is the subset of the real interval [0, 1] consisting of all numbers of the form $\sum_{i=1}^{\infty} \frac{a_i}{3^i}$, where a_i is 0 or 2. Geometrically, it may be described as follows: one removes from [0, 1] its middle third interval $(\frac{1}{3}, \frac{2}{3})$, then the middle thirds of $[0, \frac{1}{3}]$ and $[\frac{2}{3}, 1]$, and so on. Among the properties of this set is that it is nowhere dense in the real line, but does have cardinality c.

12. a. Explain why $y = \tan x$ is a 1-1 correspondence between the interval $\left(-\frac{\pi}{2}, \frac{\pi}{2}\right)$ of real numbers and the set of all real numbers. See margin.
 b. What is the cardinality of the interval $\left(-\frac{\pi}{2}, \frac{\pi}{2}\right)$? c

13. What assumption about time underlies the following words from the hymn "Amazing Grace," written by John Newton? Explain your answer.

When we've been there ten thousand years
Bright shining as the sun,
We've no less days to sing God's praise
Than when we've first begun.

Time has cardinality c, and $c + 10{,}000 = c$.

Review

14a)

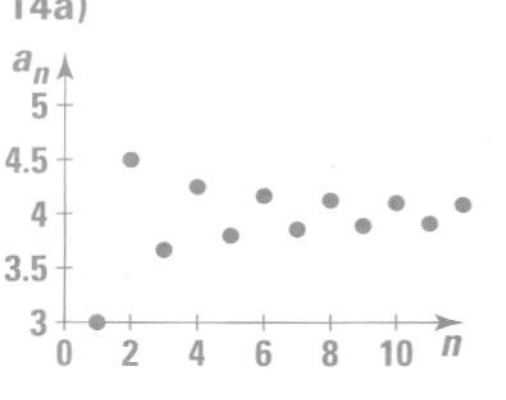

18a)

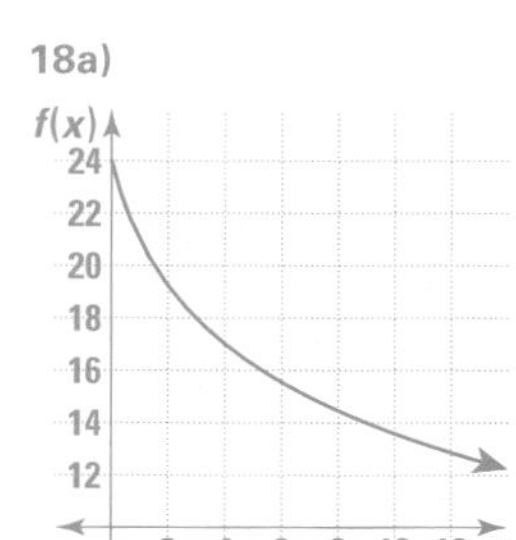

***Rodin's* The Thinker.**
Some people must think long and hard to remember.

14. Consider the sequence given by the explicit formula: See left.
$$a_n = 4 + \frac{(-1)^n}{n}.$$
 a. Graph the first ten terms of the sequence.
 b. If $\lim_{n \to \infty} a_n = L$, find L. 4
 c. How large must n be so that a_n is within .02 units of L? *(Lesson 3-9)* 50

15. Write as an absolute value statement: The measured value M is within .001 of the true value T. *(Lesson 3-9)* $|T - M| \leq 0.001$

16. Solve $|8x - 3| > 5$. *(Lesson 3-9)* $x < -\frac{1}{4}, x > 1$

17. Estimate all real solutions to each equation to the nearest tenth.
 a. $x^3 - 4x - 6 = 0$ 2.5
 b. $(y + 10)^3 - 4(y + 10) - 6 = 0$ -7.5
 c. $(\log z)^3 - 4(\log z) - 6 = 0$ *(Lessons 3-4, 3-6, 3-8)* 316.2

18. In a study of memory, a sample of people studied a topic for 3 hours and were then tested on it monthly. The function defined by
$$f(x) = 24 - 10 \log (x + 1)$$
approximates the group's average score $f(x)$ after x months.
 a. Sketch a graph of the function. See left.
 b. Relate the graph to the graph of $y = \log x$. *(Lessons 2-8, 3-8)* $(x, y) \to (x - 1, 10y + 24)$

19. Find all real numbers x such that $(\log x)(x - 2)(x - 5) < 0$. *(Lesson 3-7)* $0 < x < 1$, $2 < x < 5$

20. Solve $\sqrt{2m} - 20 = 10 - m$. *(Lesson 3-3)* $m = 10$

21. Sketch the graph of an even function h which is decreasing on the interval $2 \leq x \leq 4$, which has a relative minimum at $x = 1$, and for which $\lim_{x \to -\infty} h(x) = -5$. *(Lessons 2-2, 2-3, 2-4)* See margin.

Exploration

22. Georg Cantor has lent his name to a set called the *Cantor set*. Find out what this set is and describe its special properties. See margin.

Optional Activities

Ask students to suppose that an infinite train load of passengers arrived at Cantor's Hotel in search of rooms. Can they be accommodated, and if so, how? [Move the occupant of each room into a room with double their former room number. That is, person in room #1 moves to room #2, person in room #2 moves to room #4, etc. As a result, all the odd numbered rooms are vacated and can be filled by the infinite train load of passengers.]

Adapting to Individual Needs

Extra Help

Some students might be troubled by the fact that the rational numbers are not listed in numerical order. In fact, such a list would be impossible to construct. Stress that the rational numbers are listed in order of the sum of their numerator and denominator when written in lowest terms. Using this method, every rational number has a position on the list.

Challenge

Have students do either or both of the following:

1. Give a report on the life of Georg Cantor.
2. Give the cardinality of each set.
 a. the set of negative integers [$\aleph_0$]
 b. the real numbers between 0 and 1 [c]
 c. the set of irrational numbers [c]

A project presents an opportunity for you to extend your knowledge of a topic related to the material of this chapter. You should allow more time for a project than you do for a typical homework question.

1 Creating Fonts

Using equations for semicircles and lines and restricting domains, give equations for five of the letters of the alphabet. Try to make all your letters the same size, and position them in some consistent fashion on the coordinate plane.

a b c d e

2 Approximating Zeros Using the Secant Method

The secant method for approximating the zeros of a continuous function h begins with two values x_0 and x_1, for which it is known that $h(x_0) < 0$ and $h(x_1) > 0$. The point x_2 at which the secant line joining $(x_0, h(x_0))$ to $(x_1, h(x_1))$ crosses the x-axis is used as a better approximation to a zero of h than x_0 or x_1.

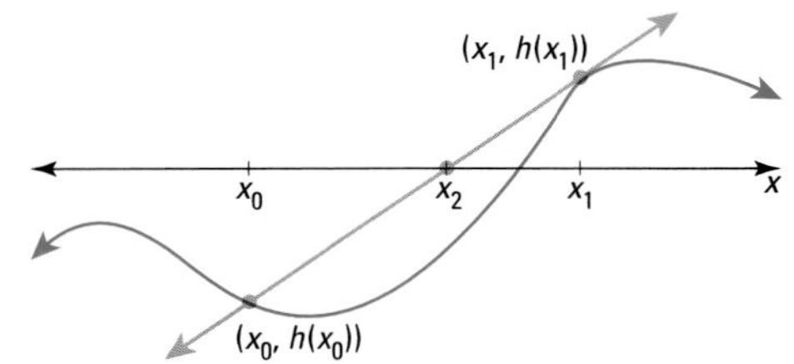

a. Find an equation for the secant line through $(x_0, h(x_0))$ and $(x_1, h(x_1))$ and write it in the form $y = f(x)$.

b. Prove that the point x_2 between x_0 and x_1 where the line $y = f(x)$ crosses the x-axis is given by the formula

$$x_2 = x_1 - \frac{h(x_1)(x_1 - x_0)}{h(x_1) - h(x_0)}.$$

After x_2 has been computed, the secant method proceeds as follows: If the positive number p is the predetermined level of accuracy required and if:

(i) $|h(x_2)| \le p$, then stop and let x_2 be the desired approximation to the zero of h.

(ii) $|h(x_2)| > p$, then choose the interval $[x_0, x_2]$ or $[x_2, x_1]$ so that $h(x)$ has a zero in the selected interval. (In the diagram shown in column one, the choice would be the interval $[x_2, x_1]$.)

The secant method then repeats the secant line approximation for the new interval to obtain a new approximation x_3 to a zero of $h(x)$ and a new interval on which $h(x)$ changes sign until the stopping condition (i) is satisfied.

c. Starting with $x_0 = -1$, $x_1 = 0$, and level of accuracy $.05 = p$, use the secant method to compute the approximate solution of the equation $2^x = 3x^2$ that lies between -1 and 0.

3 Drawing Graphs Piecewise

Many automatic graphers are not designed to graph functions that are defined piecewise. However, such graphs can be defined by manipulating the domain of the function.

a. How does the graph of $f(x) = x^2$ differ from those of $g(x) = x^2 + \frac{0}{|x| + x}$ and $h(x) = x^2 + \frac{0}{|x| - x}$? Why?

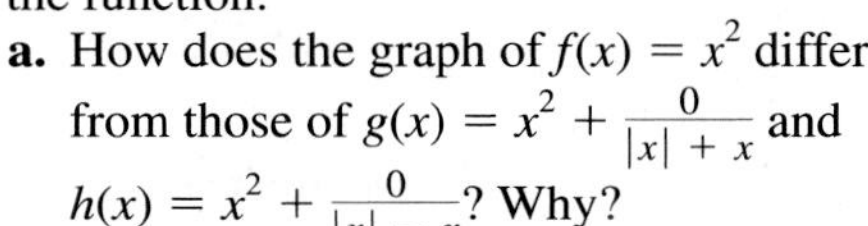

b. Let c be a function defined by $c(x) = \frac{0}{|x - 5| + (x - 5)}$. What is the domain of c? If g is another function, describe the domain of $c + g$.

c. Describe a function f so that $f + g$ is undefined outside the interval $a \le x \le b$.

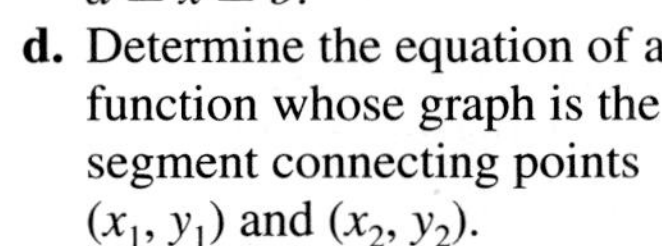

d. Determine the equation of a function whose graph is the segment connecting points (x_1, y_1) and (x_2, y_2).

e. Use restrictions to draw the stick figure shown at the right.

Chapter 3 Projects

The projects relate chiefly to the content of the lessons of this chapter as follows:

Project	Lesson(s)
1	3-1, 3-9
2	3-4
3	3-9
4	3-4

1 Creating Fonts This is an appropriate project for an artist, and may use the idea in Project 2. It can be quite time-consuming, and partial completion of the project is not unusual.

2 Approximating Zeros Using the Secant Method The advantage of the secant method over the bisection method of Project 4 is that it takes the values of the function at the endpoints of the interval into account when making its approximation. A student could modify the program in Project 4 to carry out this method.

3 Drawing Graphs Piecewise The drawing of the stick figure should be done as the union of the graphs of relations. The mouth might be considered as a semicircle, and the eyes as the interiors of two small circles.

4 Approximating Zeros Using the Bisection Method The advantage of the bisection method over the secant method of Project 2 is that it is easier to determine the endpoints of the intervals at each step, and the length of the interval of approximation after every number of steps is known in advance.

Possible responses

1. Samples:

(A) left leg: $x \to 2.5x + \frac{0}{|x| + x} + \frac{0}{|x - 2| - (x - 2)}$,

right leg: $x \to -2.5 + 10 + \frac{0}{|x - 2| + (x - 2)} + \frac{0}{|x - 4| - (x - 4)}$,

cross piece: $x \to 2.5 + \frac{0}{|x - 1| + (x - 1)} + \frac{0}{|x - 3| - (x - 3)}$

(C) c: $x \to \sqrt{2.5^2 - (x - 2.5)^2} + 2.5 + \frac{0}{|x - 4| - (x - 4)}$

2. a. $y = \frac{h(x_1) - h(x_0)}{x_1 - x_0}(x - x_1) + h(x_1)$

b. At $(x_2, 0)$ we have: $0 = \frac{h(x_1) - h(x_0)}{x_1 - x_0}(x_2 - x_1) + h(x_1)$ which can be rearranged to give $x_2 = x_1 - \frac{h(x_1)(x_1 - x_0)}{h(x_1) - h(x_0)}$

c. $x \approx -0.50$

(Responses continue on page 214.)

Additional Responses

3. a. $g(x)$ is not defined for any values of $x \leq 0$. $h(x)$ is not defined for any values $x \geq 0$.

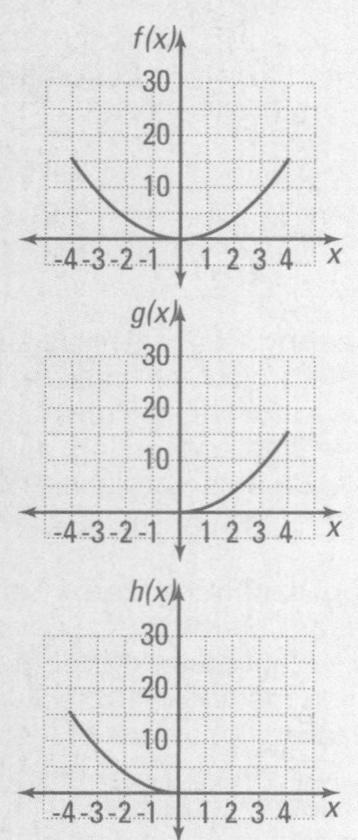

3. b. c is defined on the domain $x > 5$. The domain of $c + g$ will be similarly restricted and may be more restricted if g is not defined for some $x > 5$.

c. $f(x) = \dfrac{0}{|x-a| + (x-a)} + \dfrac{0}{|x-b| - (x-b)}$.
Other answers are possible.

d. Assuming $x_1 < x_2$,
$f(x) = \dfrac{y_2 - y_1}{x_2 - x_1}(x - x_1) + y_1 + \dfrac{0}{|x - x_1| + (x - x_1)} + \dfrac{0}{|x - x_2| - (x - x_2)}$.
Other answers are possible.

e. One possible solution is
body: $x \to 0$,
head: $x \to x^2 + (y - 10)^2$,
arms: $x \to -|x| + 7 + r(x)$,
legs: $x \to |x| + r(x)$,
where $r(x) = \dfrac{0}{|x+2| + (x+2)} + \dfrac{0}{|x-2| - (x-2)}$
Other answers are possible.

4. a. To allow the program user to correct the interval if it has been incorrectly entered.
b. Answers will vary.
c. To the nearest 0.005, this function has zeros at $x = \{-0.275, 0.385, 5.830\}$.
d. Answers will vary.

(continued)

4 Approximating Zeros Using the Bisection Method

The bisection method is another method for approximating the zeros of a function $h(x)$. This method is like the strategy used in this child's game: "I am thinking of a number between 0 and 100. I will tell you if your guess is too large or too small. Guess my number in as few tries as possible." The best strategy is to split the interval in half (bisect it) and first guess 50. Then, depending on the answer to the first guess, you either guess 25 (bisecting the interval between 0 and 50) or 75 (bisecting the interval between 50 and 100), and so on.

For a solution to $2^x - 3x^2 = 0$ between 0 and 1, first test the midpoint 0.5. Since $h(0.5) \approx .6642 > 0$ and $h(1) < 0$, there is a solution between 0.5 and 1. So bisect that interval and calculate $h(0.75)$. Since $h(0.75) \approx -.00571 < 0$ and $h(0.5) > 0$, there is a solution between 0.5 and 0.75. The next number to try would be 0.625. Repeating this method, you can get as close to a zero as you wish.

The bisection method is fairly easy to implement on a computer. The BASIC program below executes the bisection method. Line 20 defines the function whose zero you wish to approximate.

```
10  REM BISECTION METHOD
20  DEF FN F(X) = X^3 – X^2 + X/3 – 1/27
30  INPUT "ENTER ERROR BOUND.",E
40  IF E > 0 THEN 70
50  PRINT "ERROR BOUND MUST BE POSITIVE."
60  GOTO 30
70  INPUT "ENTER INTERVAL A < B
    CONTAINING A ZERO.",A,B
80  IF A < B THEN 110
90  PRINT "A MUST BE LESS THAN B."
100 GOTO 70
110 IF (FN F(A)*FN F(B)) < 0 THEN 150
120 PRINT "THE INTERVAL";A;" < X < ";B;"MAY
    NOT CONTAIN A ZERO."
130 PRINT "F(";A;") AND F(";B;") HAVE THE
    SAME SIGN."
140 GOTO 70
150 LET T = (A + B)/2
160 IF (B – A) < (2 * E) THEN 190
170 IF (FN F(A)*FN F(T)) > 0 THEN LET A = T
    ELSE LET B = T
180 GOTO 150
190 PRINT T, "APPROXIMATES A ZERO."
200 PRINT "F(";T;") ="; FN F(T)
210 END
```

a. What is the purpose of line 110?

b. Run the program with the function

$$f: x \to x^3 - x^2 + \tfrac{x}{3} - \tfrac{1}{27}$$

given in line 20. Find the zero within 0.005. How close is the approximation you found to $\frac{1}{3}$, the true zero?

c. Repeat part **b** for the function $f: x \to e^x - 10x^2$.

d. Repeat part **b** for several functions of your own choosing.

214

SUMMARY

The main purpose of this chapter is to discuss methods for solving algebraic sentences (equations and inequalities) that apply to a wide variety of sentences. An equation to be solved for the one variable x can be thought of as being of the form $f(x) = g(x)$. Analogously, an inequality in the variable x can be thought of as being of the form $f(x) < g(x)$.

One method is to apply the same operation to both sides of the sentence. The main concern in this method is not to gain or lose solutions. Solutions will not be gained or lost if the operation is reversible. Reversible operations correspond to functions whose inverses are functions.

Reversible operation	Function
Adding c to both sides	$x \to x + c$; inverse $x \to x - c$
Multiplying both sides by $a \neq 0$	$x \to ax$, $a \neq 0$; inverse $x \to \frac{x}{a}$, $a \neq 0$
Applying the function h to both sides, provided h^{-1} exists	$x \to h(x)$; inverse $x \to h^{-1}(x)$

With inequalities there is an additional concern, the sense of the inequality. The sense will be kept if the reversible operation corresponds to an increasing function. It will be reversed if the reversible operation corresponds to a decreasing function.

Reversible operation	Function
Adding c to both sides	$x \to x + c$; sense kept
Multiplying both sides by $a > 0$	$x \to ax$, $a > 0$; increasing; sense kept
Multiplying both sides by $a < 0$	$x \to ax$, $a < 0$; decreasing; sense reversed
Applying the function h to both sides, provided h^{-1} exists	$x \to h(x)$; sense kept if h increasing, sense reversed if h decreasing

A second method for solving $f(x) = g(x)$ or $f(x) < g(x)$ is to subtract $g(x)$ from each side, and then let $h(x) = f(x) - g(x)$ so as to consider $h(x) = 0$ or $h(x) < 0$. If h is a continuous function and you know values a and b such that $h(a) > 0$ and $h(b) < 0$, then the Intermediate Value Theorem guarantees a value c between a and b such that $h(c) = 0$. If $h(x)$ can be factored, then $h(x) = 0$ can be solved using the Zero-Product Property, and $h(x) < 0$ can be solved using the Test-Point Method.

If f and g are functions of an expression, then that expression can be treated as a single variable, that is, chunked. Then the equation or inequality is solved for that expression, and a second equation is solved to determine the solutions to the original sentence. For instance, to solve $(\log x)^2 + 2 \log x + 1 = 0$, think of $\log x$ as a chunk, solve for $\log x$, and then finding (in this case) that $\log x = -1$, solve that sentence to determine x. Chunks of the form $x - h$ or $\frac{x}{a}$ or $\frac{x - h}{a}$ can be pictured as the results of translations, scale changes, or rubberband transformations of graphs of functions.

The absolute value function helps in describing error and enables a precise definition of the idea of limit. The expression $|x - h|$ can be thought of as the distance from x to h; when $|x - h| < p$, then x is within p of h. A sequence has a limit L when all of its terms after some term are within p of L, regardless of how small p is taken to be.

Summary

The Summary gives an overview of the entire chapter and provides an opportunity for students to consider the material as a whole. Thus, the Summary can be used to help students relate and unify the concepts presented in the chapter.

Vocabulary

Terms, symbols, and properties are listed by lesson to provide a checklist of concepts a student must know. Emphasize to students that they should read the vocabulary list carefully before starting the Progress Self-Test. If students do not understand the meaning of a term, they should refer back to the indicated lesson.

CHAPTER THREE

VOCABULARY

Below are the most important terms and phrases for this chapter. You should be able to give a general description and a specific example of each and a precise definition for those marked with an asterisk (*).

Lesson 3-1
$f + g, f - g, f \cdot g, \frac{g}{f}$
ordinate

Lesson 3-2
function composition, $\circ$
composite of g with f, $g \circ f$
inverse
* inverse functions, f^{-1}
identity function, $\boldsymbol{I}$
* one-to-one, 1-1 function

Lesson 3-3
Zero-Product Property
Addition Property of Equality
Multiplication Property of Equality
reversible
equivalent equations
nonreversible
Function Composition and Equality Property
Reversible Steps Theorem

Lesson 3-4
continuous on an interval
Intermediate Value Theorem

Lesson 3-5
Addition Property of Inequality
Multiplication Property of Inequality
Function Composition and Inequality Properties
Reversible Steps Theorem for Inequalities

Lesson 3-6
chunking

Lesson 3-7
Function Inequality Theorem
Test-Point Method
Sign of Products and Quotients Property

Lesson 3-8
Graph-Translation Theorem
Graph Scale-Change Theorem
Graph-Standardization Theorem (x-y form, parametric form)

Lesson 3-9
absolute value
absolute error
$\lim_{n \to \infty} s_n$

Additional Answers, page 217

2. $x = 2$ or $x = 4$
3. $-1 \le z \le \frac{5}{2}$
5. $(f + g)(x)$

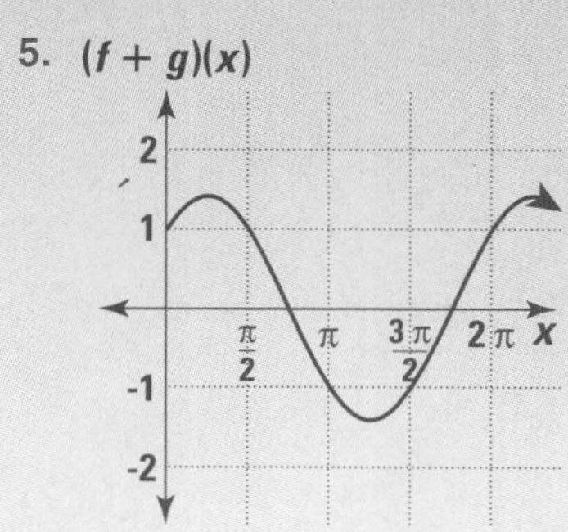

PROGRESS SELF-TEST

Take this test as you would take a test in class. You will need an automatic grapher. Then check the test yourself using the solutions at the back of the book.
2, 3, 5–8, 10, 14) See margin.

In 1–3, solve the equation for all real number solutions.

1. $\sqrt{8x + 12} = x - 1$ $x = 11$
2. $2 \log x = \log (6x - 8)$
3. $|4z - 3| \leq 7$
4. *Multiple choice.* Which of the following procedures results in a nonreversible step?
   (a) subtracting the same number from both sides of an equation
   (b) raising both sides of an equation to the fifth power
   (c) raising both sides of an equation to the sixth power
   (d) dividing both sides of an equation by a nonzero number c
5. Let $f(x) = \sin x$ and $g(x) = \cos x$. Sketch a graph of $f + g$ over the interval $[0, 2\pi]$.
6. Let $a(x) = 5x + 4$ and $b(x) = 3x^2 + 9$. Give a simplified formula for $(a \cdot b)(x)$.
7. Let $f(x) = x^2$ and $g(x) = \sqrt{x}$. Write a simplified formula for $f \circ g$ and $g \circ f$, and give their domains.
8. The function $W(x) = \frac{11(x - 40)}{2}$ gives the weight in pounds W of a person whose height is x inches. The function $Q(x) = .325x$ approximates the number of quarts of water Q in the body of a person who weighs x pounds. For the function $Q \circ W$:
   (a) what does x measure?
   (b) what does $Q \circ W(x)$ measure?
9. *Multiple choice.* Which of the intervals listed below must contain a zero of the function f defined by $f(x) = 2x^3 - 7x^2 + 2x - 7$? c
   (a) [-1, 0] (b) [1, 2] (c) [3, 4] (d) [4, 5]
10. Use chunking to solve $(\sqrt[3]{x})^2 + 2\sqrt[3]{x} = 3$.
11. *True or false.* If a function is 1-1, then it has an inverse function. True
12. Solve $|x^2 - 8| > 1$. $-\sqrt{7} < x < \sqrt{7}$ or $x > 3$ or $x < -3$

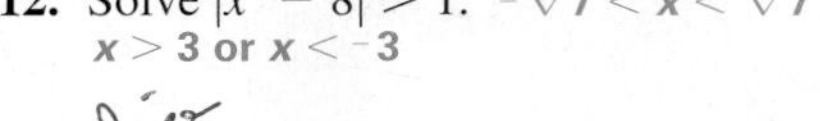

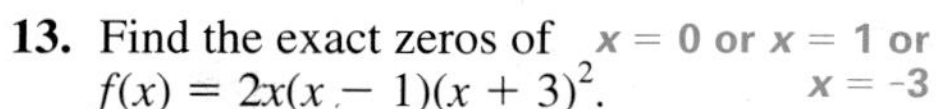

13. Find the exact zeros of $f(x) = 2x(x - 1)(x + 3)^2$. $x = 0$ or $x = 1$ or $x = -3$
14. A function is graphed below. Is f a continuous function? Explain your answer.

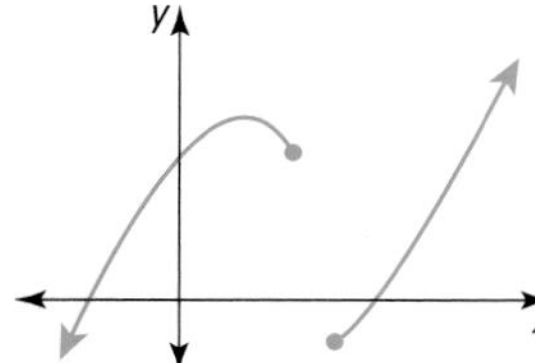

15. The formula
$$L = L_0\sqrt{1 - \left(\frac{v}{c}\right)^2}$$
relates the length of an object at rest, L_0, to its length L when traveling at a velocity of v. (c represents the speed of light.) Determine the velocity, as a function of the speed of light, for which the traveling length is one-third the resting length. $v = c(2\sqrt{2})/3$
16. Consider the sine wave graphed below. Write an equation for this wave. $y = 4 \sin\left(2\left(x - \frac{\pi}{4}\right)\right)$

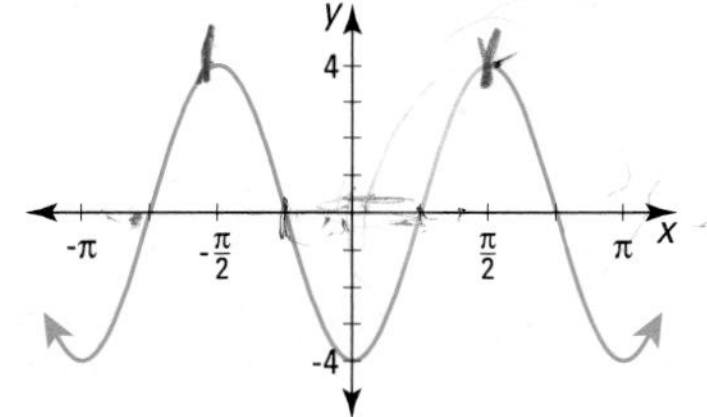

17. Approximate the zero of $f: x \to \sin x + 2x - 1$ to within 0.1 of the true value. ≈ 0.3
18. Radioactive carbon-14 (^{14}C), used to date fossils, has a half-life of 5730 years. If A_0 is the original amount of ^{14}C in the bones, then the amount A left after t years is given by
$$A = A_0e^{-.00012t}.$$
If less than 30% of the original ^{14}C content is found in the fossil, about how old is it?
$t > \frac{\ln 0.3}{-0.00012} \approx 10033$ years old

Progress Self-Test

For the development of mathematical competence, feedback and correction, along with the opportunity to practice, are necessary. The Progress Self-Test provides the opportunity for feedback and correction; the Chapter Review provides additional opportunities and practice. We cannot overemphasize the importance of these end-of-chapter materials. It is at this point that the material "gels" for many students, allowing them to solidify skills and understanding. In general, student performance should be markedly improved after these pages.

Assign the Progress Self-Test as a one-night assignment. Worked-out *solutions* for all questions are in the Selected Answers section of the student book. Encourage students to take the Progress Self-Test honestly, grade themselves, and then be prepared to discuss the test in class.

Advise students to pay special attention to those Chapter Review questions (pages 218–221) that correspond to questions missed on the Progress Self-Test.

6. $(a \cdot b)(x) = (5x + 4)(3x^2 + 9) = 15x^3 + 12x^2 + 45x + 36$
7. $(f \circ g)(x) = f(g(x)) = (\sqrt{x})^2 = x$, domain all real numbers $x \geq 0$, $(g \circ f)(x) = g(f(x)) = \sqrt{x^2} = x$, domain all real numbers
8. a. the height of a person in inches
   b. the quarts of water in the body of a person as a function of their height in inches
10. Let $y = \sqrt[3]{x}$, then $y^2 + 2y = 3 \Leftrightarrow y^2 + 2y - 3 = 0 \Leftrightarrow (y + 3)(y - 1) = 0 \Leftrightarrow y = -3$ or $y = 1$. Then either $\sqrt[3]{x} = -3 \Leftrightarrow x = -27$ or $\sqrt[3]{x} = 1 \Leftrightarrow x = 1$.
14. No. The given graph of the function is not "unbroken."

Chapter 3 Review

Resources

From the ***Teacher's Resource File***

- Answer Master for Chapter 3 Review
- Assessment Sourcebook: Chapter 3 Test, Forms A–D Chapter 3 Test, Cumulative Form Comprehensive Test, Chapters 1–3

Additional Resources

- TestWorks CD-ROM

The main objectives for the chapter are organized in the Chapter Review under the four types of understanding this book promotes—Skills, Properties, Uses, and Representations.

Whereas end-of-chapter material may be considered optional in some texts, in UCSMP *Precalculus and Discrete Mathematics,* we have selected these objectives and questions with the expectation that they will be covered. Students should be able to answer these questions with about 85% accuracy after studying the chapter.

You may assign these questions over a single night to help students prepare for a test the next day, or you may assign the questions over a two-day period. If you work the questions over two days, then we recommend assigning the *evens* for homework the first night so that students get feedback in class the next day, then assigning the *odds* the night before the test, because answers are provided to the odd-numbered questions.

CHAPTER REVIEW

Questions on SPUR Objectives

SPUR stands for **S**kills, **P**roperties, **U**ses, and **R**epresentations. The Chapter Review questions are grouped according to the SPUR Objectives for this chapter.

SKILLS DEAL WITH THE PROCEDURES USED TO GET ANSWERS.

Objective A: *Solve equations by applying a function to each side, taking into account nonreversible steps.* *(Lesson 3-3, 3-9)*

In 1–14, find all real solutions of the given equation or inequality. 14) $t = \frac{5}{7}, t = 1$

1. $\sqrt{3x + 10} = x$ $x = 5$
2. $\sqrt{y + 1} = 5 - y$ $y = 3$
3. $4 \log_5 t = \log_5 (2t^2 - 1)$ $t = 1$
4. $2 \log (x + 1) = \log (x + 13)$ $x = 3$
5. $\frac{1}{x + 5} = \frac{1}{x^2 + 3}$ $x = -1, x = 2$
6. $\frac{1}{3x - 2} = \frac{1}{7x + 4}$ $x = -\frac{3}{2}$
7. $3^v = 9^{-4v + 1}$ $v = \frac{2}{9}$
8. $4^w = 8^{w - 1}$ $w = 3$
9. $\sqrt{z - 1} + 1 = \sqrt{z + 6}$ $z = 10$
10. $\sqrt{2p} - 4 = \sqrt{p - 14}$ $p = 18, p = 50$
11. $(y - 3)^2 = 16$
12. $(4x + 1)^2 = 49$
13. $|s + 2| = 3s$ $s = 1$
14. $|6t - 5| = t$

11) $y = -1, y = 7$ 12) $x = -2, x = 3/2$

Objective B: *Describe the sum, difference, product, quotient, and composite of two given functions.* *(Lessons 3-1, 3-2)*

In 15 and 16, find simplified formulas for the functions $f \cdot g$, $\frac{f}{g}$, $f \circ g$, and $g \circ f$, and identify their domains. 15, 16) See margin.

15. $f(x) = \ln x$ $g(x) = -x^3$
16. $f(x) = \frac{1}{x}$ $g(x) = x - 6$

In 17–19, for all $x \geq 0$ let $f(x) = \sqrt{x}$, $g(x) = x^3$, and $h(x) = x^2 + 6$. Identify the single function that is equal to each.

17. $\frac{h}{f}$ $\frac{x^2 + 6}{\sqrt{x}}$
18. $f \circ g$ $\sqrt{x^3}$
19. $g - h$ $x^3 - x^2 - 6$

Objective C: *Find zeros of functions using factoring or chunking.* *(Lesson 3-6)*

In 20–23, find the exact zeros of the given function.

20. $f(x) = 3^{2x} + 3^x - 6$ $x \approx 0.631$
21. $f(y) = (y + 2)(y + 1)^2(y - 3)$ $y = \{-2, -1, 3\}$
22. $h(z) = z^3 + 9z^2 + 20z$ $z = \{-5, -4, 0\}$
23. $f(x) = \cos^2 x - \cos x$ (for $0 \leq x \leq 2\pi$)

In 24 and 25, use chunking to solve the given equation. 24) $x = 26$ or $x = 6/5$

24. $(\log_5(x - 1))^2 - \log_5(x - 1) = 2$
25. $e^{4x} - 4e^{2x} = 12$ $x \approx 0.896$

23) $x = \left\{0, \frac{\pi}{2}, \frac{3\pi}{2}, 2\pi\right\}$

Objective D: *Solve inequalities algebraically.* *(Lessons 3-5, 3-7, 3-8, 3-9)*

In 26–28, solve the inequality for all real number solutions.

26. $x^3 + x^2 > 2x$ $-2 < x < 0,\ x > 1$
27. $|w + 2| \leq 3$ $-5 \leq w \leq 1$
28. $|3z + 1| > 2$ $z < -1,\ z > \frac{1}{3}$
29. Solve $2x^2 + 4x < 70$ and graph the solutions on a number line. See below.
30. Solve $(3x + 1)(x - 2) > 0$ using the indicated method. See below.
    a. Sign of a Product Property
    b. Test-Point Method
31. Solve $5^t < 5^{2t + 1}$. $t > -1$

14) $t = \frac{5}{7}, t = 1$

29) $-7 < x < 5$

-8 -6 -4 -2 0 2 4 6 x

30a, b) $\left\{x: x < -\frac{1}{3}, x > 2\right\}$

Additional Answers, pages 218–219

15. $f \cdot g: x \rightarrow (-x^3)(\ln x)$; domain: $\{x: x > 0\}$

$\frac{f}{g}: x \rightarrow -\frac{\ln x}{x^3}$; domain: $\{x: x > 0\}$

$f \circ g: x \rightarrow \ln(-x^3)$; domain: $\{x: x < 0\}$

$g \circ f: x \rightarrow -(\ln x)^3$; domain: $\{x: x > 0\}$

16. $f \cdot g: x \rightarrow \frac{x - 6}{x}$; domain: $\{x: x \neq 0\}$

$\frac{f}{g}: x \rightarrow 1 - \frac{6}{x}$; domain: $\{x: x \neq 0, x \neq 6\}$

$f \circ g: x \rightarrow \frac{1}{x - 6}$; domain: $\{x: x \neq 6\}$

$g \circ f: x \rightarrow \frac{1}{x} - 6$; domain: $\{x: x \neq 0\}$

33. a. The second step, where both sides of the equation were divided by x^3, is incorrect. This step is valid only if $x \neq 0$, but $x = 0$ is a solution to this equation.

34. a. No. $h(2) = h(-2) = 16$, but $2 \neq -2$.

b. No, it is not a reversible operation because it is not a 1-1 function.

PROPERTIES DEAL WITH THE PRINCIPLES BEHIND THE MATHEMATICS.

Objective E: *Analyze the reversibility of steps used in solving equations and inequalities.* *(Lessons 3-3, 3-5)*

32. Which of the following procedures can result in a nonreversible step? b, c
- (a) adding the same number to both sides of an equation
- (b) squaring both sides of an equation
- (c) dividing both sides of an equation by a quantity containing a variable
- (d) multiplying both sides of an equation by a nonzero number
- (e) All of the above are nonreversible steps.

33. a. Find the error in the solution of $x^5 - x^4 = 2x^3$. See margin.

$$x^5 - x^4 = 2x^3$$
$$\Rightarrow \quad x^2 - x = 2$$
$$\Rightarrow \quad x^2 - x - 2 = 0$$
$$\Rightarrow \quad (x-2)(x+1) = 0$$
$$\Rightarrow \quad x = 2 \text{ or } x = -1$$

b. Correct the solution to find all real numbers for which $x^5 - x^4 = 2x^3$. $x = \{-1, 0, 2\}$

34. a. Is the function $h: t \rightarrow t^4$ a 1-1 function? Explain. See margin.

b. Use your answer to part **a** to determine whether or not raising both sides of an equation to the fourth power is a reversible operation. See margin.

35. In each step replace ? by $\Leftrightarrow$ for a reversible step or by $\Rightarrow$ for a nonreversible step.

$$\sqrt{2-x} = x - 2$$

- **a.** ? $\Rightarrow$ $\quad 2 - x = (x-2)^2$
- **b.** ? $\Leftrightarrow$ $\quad 2 - x = x^2 - 4x + 4$
- **c.** ? $\Leftrightarrow$ $\quad x^2 - 3x + 2 = 0$
- **d.** ? $\quad (x-2)(x-1) = 0$ $\Leftrightarrow$
- **e.** ? $\Leftrightarrow$ $\quad x - 2 = 0$ or $x - 1 = 0$
- **f.** ? $\Leftrightarrow$ $\quad x = 2$ or $x = 1$

36. *True or false.* If f is an increasing function, then applying f to both sides of $g(x) < h(x)$ preserves the sense of the inequality. True

Objective F: *Identify and prove properties of inverse functions.* *(Lessons 3-2, 3-5)*

In 37 and 38, prove that the two functions are inverses. 37–39) See margin.

37. $f: z \rightarrow z^{3/5}$ and $g: z \rightarrow z^{5/3}$

38. $h: x \rightarrow (\log x) + 7$ and $m: x \rightarrow 10^{x-7}$ $\forall x > 0$

39. Explain why every decreasing function has an inverse function.

Objective G: *Identify continuous functions and their properties, such as the Intermediate Value Theorem.* *(Lesson 3-4)*

40. Let g be the function defined by $g(x) = \frac{1}{x+2}$.

a. Find $g(-3)$. -1

b. Find $g(-1)$. 1

c. Does g have a zero between -1 and -3? Explain. See below.

41. Tell whether the function $f: x \rightarrow \lfloor 2x \rfloor$ is continuous on the given interval.

a. $[1, 2]$ No **b.** $\left[1, 1\frac{1}{2}\right]$ No

c. $\left[1, \frac{1}{4}\right]$ Yes

42. Suppose h is a continuous function on the interval $[a, b]$. If $h(a) < 0$ and $h(b) > 0$, then what conclusion can you draw about a zero of h? *h* has a zero between *a* and *b*.

43. Consider the function $f: x \rightarrow 2e^{-x^2} - 1$.

a. Graph the function to determine how many real zeros it has. a, b) See margin.

b. For each zero, find the two consecutive integers between which it is located.

44. a. How many solutions does the equation $\sin x = \frac{2}{5} \ln x$ have? 3

b. Between which two consecutive integers does each solution lie? $[2, 3], [7, 8], [8, 9]$

40c) No. g is not continuous on the interval $[-3, -1]$ because it is undefined at -2. The Intermediate Value Theorem does not apply.

It is effective to ask students which questions they still do not understand and use the day or days as a total class discussion of the material which the class finds most difficult.

Assessment

Evaluation The *Assessment Sourcebook* provides six forms of the Chapter 3 Test. Forms A and B present parallel versions in a short-answer format. Forms C and D offer performance assessment. The fifth test is Chapter 3 Test, Cumulative Form. About 50% of this test covers Chapter 3, 25% of it covers Chapter 2, and 25% of it covers Chapter 1. In addition to these tests, Comprehensive Test Chapters 1–3 gives roughly equal attention to all chapters covered thus far.

For information on grading, see *General Teaching Suggestions: Grading* in the *Professional Sourcebook,* which begins on page T20 in the Teacher's Edition.

37. $(f \circ g)(x) = (z^{5/3})^{3/5} = z$;
$(g \circ f)(x) = (z^{3/5})^{5/3} = z$.
Since $f \circ g = g \circ f = I$, f and g are inverse functions.

38. $(h \circ m)(x) = \log(10^{x-7}) + 7 = x - 7 + 7 = x$; $(m \circ h)(x) = 10^{\log x + 7 - 7} = 10^{\log x} = x$.
Since $h \circ m = m \circ h = I$, h and m are inverse functions.

39. By definition, a decreasing function f is such that for all $x_1 < x_2$, $f(x_1) > f(x_2)$. Hence, for $x_1 \neq x_2$, $f(x_1) \neq f(x_2)$. Therefore, f is 1-1 and has an inverse.

43. a.

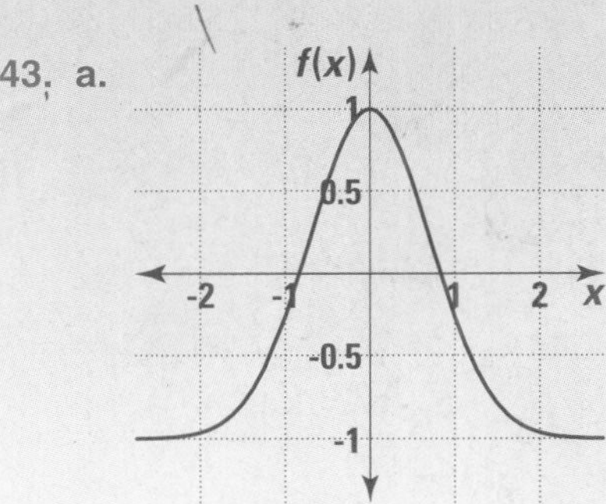

b. [-1, 0] and [0, 1]

Feedback After students have taken the test for Chapter 3 and you have scored the results, return the tests to students for discussion. Class discussion of the questions that caused trouble for the most students can be very effective in identifying and clarifying misunderstandings. You might want to have them write down the items they missed and work, either in groups or at home, to correct them. It is important for students to receive feedback on every chapter test, and we recommend that students see and correct their mistakes before proceeding too far into the next chapter.

Additional Answers

49. b.

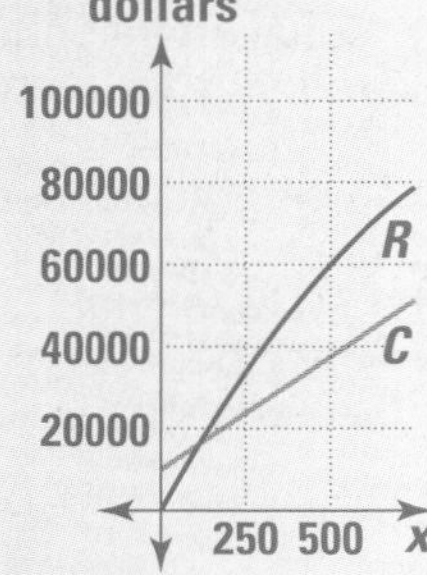

c.

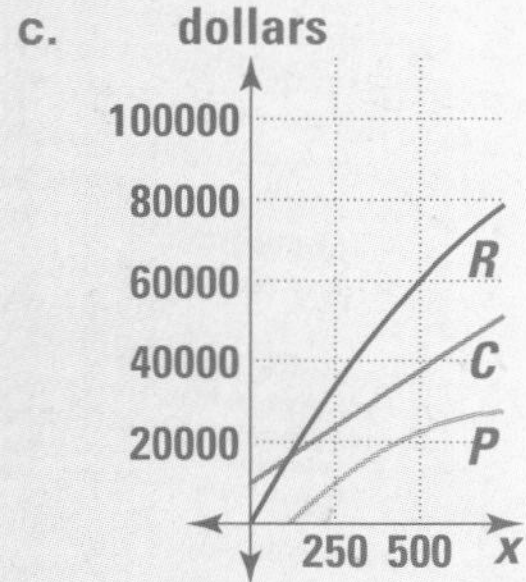

USES DEAL WITH APPLICATIONS OF MATHEMATICS IN REAL SITUATIONS.

Objective H: *Apply equation-solving techniques to real-world problems.* (*Lessons 3-3, 3-4, 3-6*)

45. The formula $v = (c\sqrt{3})/2$

$$m = m_0\left(\frac{1}{\sqrt{1 - \left(\frac{v}{c}\right)^2}}\right)$$

relates the mass of an object at rest, m_0, to its mass m when traveling at a velocity v. (c represents the speed of light.) Determine the velocity, as a function of the speed of light, when the traveling mass is twice the mass at rest.

46. The weight w_h (in kg) of an object at altitude h (in km) above Earth's surface satisfies

$$w_h = \left(\frac{r}{r + h}\right)^2 w_0$$

where w_0 is the weight at sea level and r is the radius of Earth (about 6400 km). At what altitude would a person weigh $\frac{1}{4}$ of his sea level weight? $h = 6400$ km

47. If a ball is dropped from a height of 50 feet, its height h (ft) at any time t (sec) is given by the equation $t \approx 1.369$ sec

$$h(t) = -16t^2 + 50.$$

At what time is the ball at a height of 20 feet?

48. Slowtown has a population of 3500 and is losing people at the rate of 150 per year. Boomtown has a population of 1500 and is growing 5% per year. In about how many years will the two towns have the same population? about 8 years

model city from the computer game Sim City

Objective I: *Use arithmetic operations on functions to find formulas which model realistic situations.* (*Lessons 3-1, 3-2*)

49. An assembly line has the capacity to fill orders for up to 750 television sets per day to be sold by a nationwide department store chain. For each day the assembly line is in operation, the

fixed costs are \$10,000 for line operators, equipment depreciation, and maintenance. The cost of the components used to assemble each television set is \$55. The televisions are sold to the department store at a price of \$150 minus a sales incentive discount of \$$t$ per television, where t is 6% of the number of televisions per day sold to the chain. a) See below.

a. Find formulas for the following.

- **i.** the total cost function C
- **ii.** the selling price function S
- **iii.** the total revenue function R
- **iv.** the total profit function P

b. Sketch the graphs of functions C and R on the same coordinate axes. See margin.

c. Use subtraction of ordinates to sketch function P. See margin.

a) i) C: $x \to 10000 + 55x$
ii) S: $x \to 150 - 0.06x$
iii) R: $x \to S(x) \cdot x = 150x - 0.06x^2$
iv) P: $x \to R - C = -0.06x^2 + 95x - 10000$

50. b.

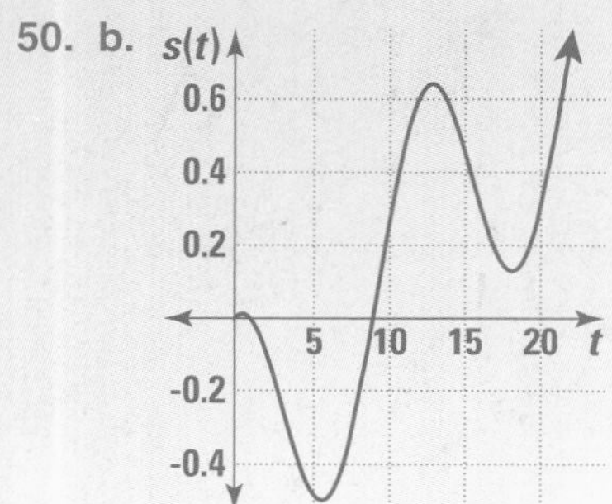

53. possible

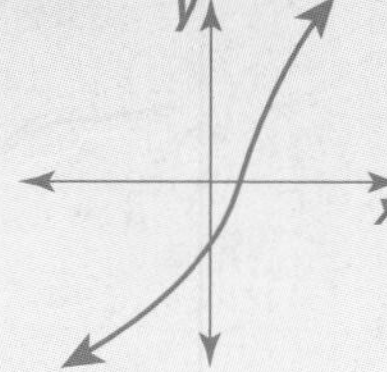

54. Not possible. The function shown is not 1-1 so it does not have an inverse.

CHAPTER THREE

50. At time $t = 0$, an oil tanker is in a harbor with its deck level with the pier. It is being unloaded, which causes the ship to rise .05 meters per minute. At the same time the wave action raises and lowers the ship according to the formula $h = .4 \cos (.5t)$, where h is the height in meters after t minutes.

a. Write a formula for s, where $s(t)$ is the height above or below the pier after t minutes. **See below.**

b. Graph s. **See margin.**

c. Explain why this model can be used only over a short period of time. **The ship's height will no longer increase once it is completely unloaded.**

a) $s(t) = 0.05t \pm 0.4 \cos (0.5t) - 0.4$

Objective J: *Use inequalities to solve real-world problems.* *(Lessons 3-5, 3-9)*

51. Suppose the ball in Question 47 is thrown upward with an initial velocity of 48 ft/sec. Then its height at any time t (in seconds) is given by the equation $h(t) = -16t^2 + 48t + 50$. Find the times when the ball is higher than 18 feet above the ground. **$0 \le t \le 3.56$**

52. A pollster reports that 58% of Americans favor a law that is pending in Congress. The margin of error is 2%.

a. Write an absolute value inequality that describes the true percentage p of Americans who are in favor of the legislation. **$|p - 0.58| < 0.02$**

b. Solve your inequality in part **a** for p. **$0.56 < p < 0.60$**

REPRESENTATIONS DEAL WITH PICTURES, GRAPHS, OR OBJECTS THAT ILLUSTRATE CONCEPTS.

Objective K: *Graph functions obtained from other functions by function operations or inverses.* *(Lessons 3-1, 3-2, 3-5)*

In 53 and 54, a graph of a function f is given. If possible, sketch the graph of f^{-1}. If not possible, explain why not. **53, 54) See margin.**

53.

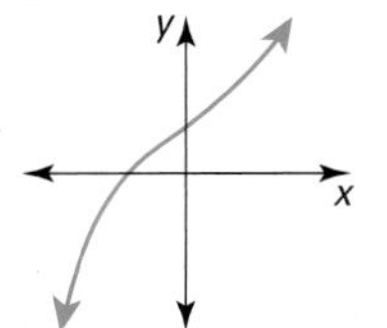

possible

54.

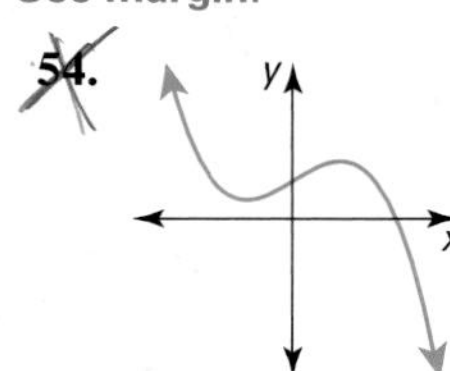

not possible

55. Graph $f: x \rightarrow \sin x$ and $g: x \rightarrow x$ on the same axes. **See margin.**

a. Use addition of ordinates to graph $f + g$.

b. Use multiplication of ordinates to graph $f \cdot g$.

c. Use the properties of f and g to explain the differences in the graphs of $f + g$ and $f \cdot g$.

In 56–58, let $f(x) = \sin x$, $g(x) = \sin 2x$, $h(x) = \frac{1}{x}$, and $k(x) = x$. Sketch graphs of the function over the interval $0 < x < 2\pi$. **See margin.**

56. $h \cdot f$ 57. $h - k$ 58. $g + k$

Objective L: *Find an equation of a graph after a transformation.* *(Lesson 3-8)*

59. The circle $x^2 + y^2 = 1$ is transformed by $S_{3,1/3}$ and then $T_{2,-5}$. **See margin.**

a. Find the equation of the image under $S_{3,1/3}$.

b. Find the equation of the final image.

60. Give an equation in x and y for $\begin{cases} x = .4 \cos t \\ y = 2 \sin t - 1 \end{cases}$ **See below.**

61. Find the zeros of $a(x) = x^2 - 4$ and use them to find the zeros of $a(x + 7)$. **-5, 9**

60) $\frac{x^2}{0.16} + \frac{(y+1)^2}{4} = 1$

Objective M: *Use graphs to approximate zeros of functions and solve equations and inequalities.* *(Lessons 3-4, 3-8)*

62. *Multiple choice.* The x-coordinates of the intersection point of the graphs $y = f(x)$ and $y = g(x)$ are solutions of which of the following equations? ***d***

(a) $f(x) = g(x)$ (b) $f(x) - g(x) = 0$

(c) $|g(x) - f(x)| = 0$ (d) all of these

63. Find an interval of length .05 that contains a solution for the equation $x^3 + 3x^2 - 2 = x^2 - 4x + 5$. **Sample: $.975 \le x \le 1.025$**

64. Approximate the zeros of the function $f(x) = e^{x^2} - 2$ to within .02 of their actual value. **$x \approx \pm 0.83$**

Setting Up Lesson 4-1

Homework Assign Lesson 4-1 to be read and at least the Questions Covering the Reading to be completed.

Additional Answers

56. $(h \cdot f)(x)$

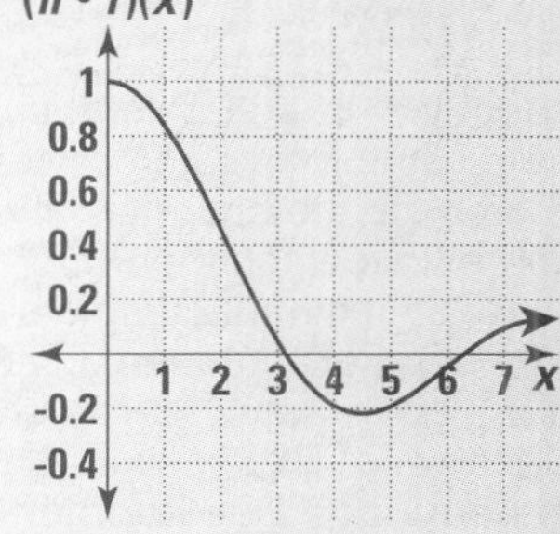

57.

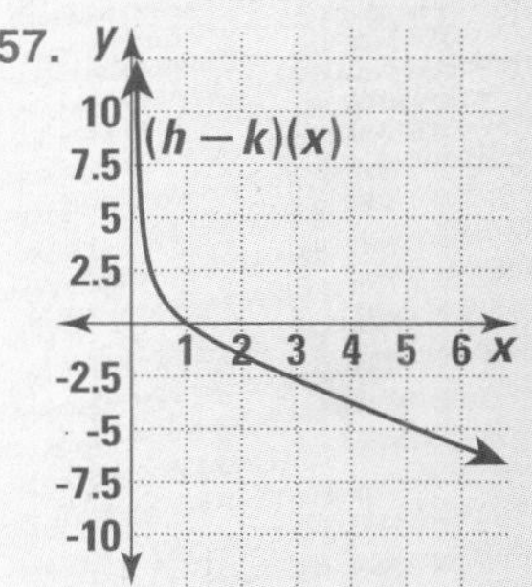

58.

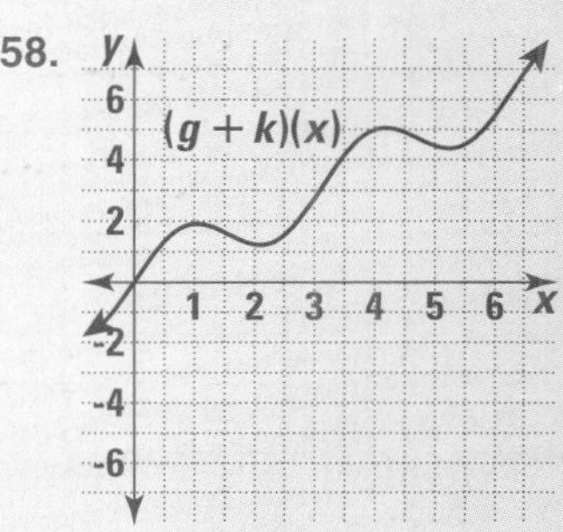

59. a. $\frac{x^2}{9} + 9y^2 = 1$

b. $\frac{(x-2)^2}{9} + 9(y+5)^2 = 1$

55. a.

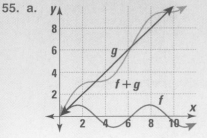

b.

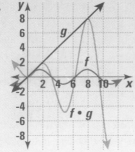

c. Because the range of $\sin x$ is [-1, 1], $x + \sin x$ is bounded by the lines $y = x + 1$ and $y = x - 1$. Similarly, $x \sin x$ is bounded by the lines $y = x$, $y = -x$.

Adapting to Individual Needs

The student text is written for the vast majority of students. The chart at the right suggests two pacing plans to accommodate the needs of your students. Students in the Full Course should complete the entire text by the end of the year. Students in the Minimal Course will spend more time when there are quizzes and more time on the Chapter Review. Therefore, these students may not complete all of the chapters in the text.

Options are also presented to meet the needs of a variety of teaching and learning styles. For each lesson, the Teacher's Edition provides a section entitled *Adapting to Individual Needs.* This section regularly includes **Optional Activities, Challenge** problems, **English Language Development** suggestions, and suggestions for providing **Extra Help.** The Teacher's Edition also frequently includes an **Error Alert,** an **Extension,** and an **Assessment** alternative. The options available in Chapter 4 are summarized in the chart below.

Chapter 4 Pacing Chart

Day	Full Course	Minimal Course
1	4-1	4-1
2	4-2	4-2
3	4-3	4-3
4	4-4	4-4
5	Quiz*; 4-5.	Quiz*; begin 4-5.
6	4-6	Finish 4-5.
7	4-7	4-6
8	Self-Test	4-7
9	Review	Finish
10	Test*	Self-Test
11		Review
12		Review
13		Test*

*in the Teacher's Resource File

In the Teacher's Edition...

Lesson	Optional Activities	Extra Help	Challenge	English Language Development	Error Alert	Extension	Cooperative Learning	Ongoing Assessment
4-1	●	●	●	●	●	●	●	Written
4-2	●	●	●		●	●		Written
4-3	●	●	●		●		●	Written
4-4	●	●	●		●	●	●	Quiz
4-5	●	●	●		●	●		Written
4-6	●	●	●		●	●		Oral
4-7	●	●	●		●	●		Written

In the Additional Resources...

	In the Teacher's Resource File							
Lesson	Lesson Masters	Teaching Aids*	Answer Masters	Technology Sourcebook	Assessment Sourcebook	Visual Aids**	Technology	Explorations Software
4-1	4-1	32, 34, 35	4-1			32, 34, 35, AM		
4-2	4-2	32	4-2	Calc 5		32, AM		4-2
4-3	4-3	32, 36, 37	4-3	Calc 6		32, 36, 37, AM		
4-4	4-4	32, 38	4-4		Quiz	32, 38, AM		
In-class Activity	4-5		4-5			AM		
4-5	4-5	33	4-5			33, AM		4-5
4-6	4-6	33, 39, 40	4-6			33, 39, 40, AM		4-6
4-7	4-7	33, 41, 42	4-7	Calc 7		33, 41, 42, AM		
End of chapter					Tests			

*Teaching Aids are pictured on pages 222C and 222D.

**Visual Aids provide transparencies for all Teaching Aids and all Answer Masters.

Also available is the Study Skills Handbook which includes study-skill tips related to reading, note-taking, and comprehension.

Integrating Strands and Applications

	4-1	4-2	4-3	4-4	4-5	4-6	4-7
Mathematical Connections							
Number Sense	●	●	●	●	●	●	●
Algebra	●	●	●	●			●
Logic and Reasoning	●	●	●		●	●	●
Patterns and Functions	●	●	●	●	●	●	●
Discrete Mathematics		●			●	●	
Interdisciplinary and Other Connections							
Music					●		
Science	●	●			●		●
Social Studies	●	●			●	●	
Multicultural	●	●					
Technology	●	●	●		●	●	●
Consumer	●	●			●		

Teaching and Assessing the Chapter Objectives

Chapter 4 Objectives (Organized into the SPUR catetgories—Skills, Properties, Uses, and Representations)	**Lessons**	**Progress Self-Test Questions**	**Chapter Review Questions**	**In the Teacher's Resource File** Chapter Test, Forms A and B	Chapter Test, Forms C	D
Skills						
A: Find quotients and remainders using the Quotient-Remainder Theorem for integers or polynomials.	4-2	1	1–7	1	2	X
B: Divide polynomials.	4-3	3	8–14	3	2	X
C: Determine the congruence of integers in a given modulus.	4-5	8	15–20	8	1	
D: Factor polynomials over the reals.	4-1, 4-4, 4-7	12	21–28	13	2	X
E: Use factoring or the Factor Theorem to solve polynomial equations.	4-4	6	29–34	6	3	
Properties						
F: Justify properties of factors of integers or factors of polynomials.	4-1	2, 16	35–42	4		X
G: Use the properties of congruence of integers in a given modulus to rewrite sentences.	4-5	9	43–48	9		
H: Use the Remainder Theorem, Factor Theorem, or Quotient-Remainder Theorem to describe characteristics of given polynomials.	4-2, 4-3, 4-4	4, 5	49–54	7, 10		X
I: Use proof by contradiction.	4-7	17	55–59	16		
J: Use the Factor Search Theorem and the Fundamental Theorem of Arithmetic in determining prime numbers and prime factorizations.	4-7	10, 11	60–67	11, 15	6	X
Uses						
K: Use the Quotient-Remainder Theorem to solve applied problems.	4-2	1	68–71	1	5	
L: Use modular arithmetic to solve applied problems.	4-5	7	72–75	14		
Representations						
M: Represent numbers in other bases and perform addition in base 2.	4-6	13, 14, 15	76–83	2, 5, 12	4	

Assessment Sourcebook
Quiz for Lessons 4-1 through 4-4
Chapter 4 Test, Forms A–D
Chapter 4 Test, Cumulative Form

TestWorks CD-ROM

TEACHING AID 32

Warm-up
Lesson 4-1

Consider those six-digit integers of the form $\underline{a\ b\ c\ a\ b\ c}$. (One such integer is 497497.) Explain why every such integer is divisible by 7.

Warm-up
Lesson 4-2

What is the remainder when 438 is divided by 27?

Warm-up
Lesson 4-3

1. Use polynomial long division to find the remainder when $2x^3 - 11x^2 + 4x - 12$ is divided by $x + 5$.
2. Let $P(x) = 2x^3 - 11x^2 + 4x - 12$. Verify that the answer to *Warm-up* Question 1 equals $P(-5)$.

Warm-up
Lesson 4-4

Find the remainder when $2x^3 + 5x^2 - 4$ is divided by each polynomial.

1. $x - 2$
2. $x + 4$
3. $x + 2$
4. Are any of the divisors in 1–3 factors of the given polynomial? If so which divisors.

TEACHING AID 33

Warm-up
Lesson 4-5

Find a number whose remainder when divided by 7 is 6. Find a number whose remainder when divided by 7 is 3. Multiply these numbers together. What is the remainder when their product is divided by 7? Share your results with a classmate. Must you get the same answer?

Warm-up
Lesson 4-6

A number has hundreds digit *h*, tens digit *t*, and units digit *u*.

1. What is the value of the number?
2. What is the value of the number formed by reversing the digits.
3. Show that the difference of the number and the number formed by reversing the digits is divisible by 11.

Warm-up
Lesson 4-7

1. How many digits does $2^{1{,}000{,}000} - 1$ have in base 10?
2. Explain why $2^{1{,}000{,}000} - 1$ is not a prime number.

TEACHING AID 34
Lesson 4-1

Definitions and Basic Theorems of Divisibility I

Definition

Suppose that n and d are integers and $d \neq 0$. ***d* is a factor of *n*** if and only if there is an integer *q* such that $n = q \cdot d$.

Definition

Suppose that $n(x)$ and $d(x)$ are polynomials and d is not the zero function. ***d(x)* is a factor of *n(x)*** if and only if there exists a polynomial $q(x)$ such that $n(x) = q(x) \cdot d(x)$.

Theorem (Transitive Property of Integer Function)

For all integers *a*, *b*, and *c*, if *a* is a factor of *b* and *b* is a factor of *c*, then *a* is a factor of *c*.

Theorem (Factor of an Integer Sum)

For all integers *a*, *b*, and *c*, if *a* is a factor of *b* and *a* is a factor of *c*, then *a* is a factor of *b* + *c*.

TEACHING AID 35
Lesson 4-1

Definitions and Basic Theorems of Divisibility II

Theorems

For all polynomials $a(x)$, $b(x)$, and $c(x)$:

Transitive Property of Polynomial Factors

If $a(x)$ is a factor of $b(x)$ and $b(x)$ is a factor of $c(x)$, then $a(x)$ is a factor of $c(x)$.

Factor of a Polynomial Sum Theorem

If $a(x)$ is a factor of $b(x)$ and $a(x)$ is a factor of $c(x)$, then $a(x)$ is a factor of $b(x) + c(x)$.

Theorem (Factor of an Integer Product)

For all integers *m*, *n*, and *p*, if *m* is a factor of *n*, then *m* is a factor of $n \cdot p$.

TEACHING AID 36
Lesson 4-3

Long Division of Polynomials

$$
\begin{array}{r}
3x^2 - 6x + 7 \\
2x + 1\overline{)6x^3 - 9x^2 + 8x + 1} \\
6x^3 + 3x^2 \\
\hline
-12x^2 + 8x + 1 \\
-12x^2 - 6x \\
\hline
14x + 1 \\
14x + 7 \\
\hline
-6
\end{array}
$$

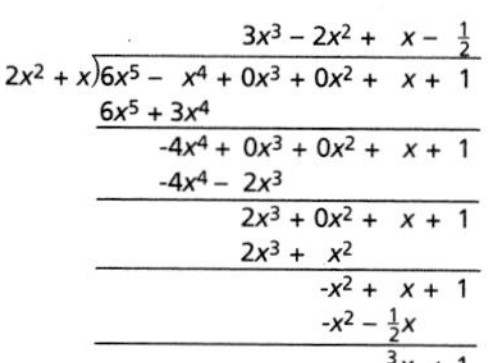

TEACHING AID 37
Lesson 4-3

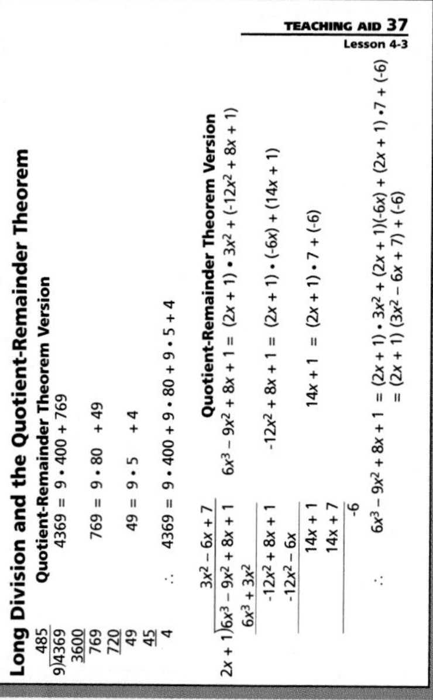

Long Division and the Quotient-Remainder Theorem

$$
\begin{array}{r}
485 \\
9\overline{)4369} \\
3600 \\
\hline
769 \\
720 \\
\hline
49 \\
45 \\
\hline
4
\end{array}
$$

Quotient-Remainder Theorem Version

$4369 = 9 \cdot 400 + 769$

$769 = 9 \cdot 80 + 49$

$49 = 9 \cdot 5 + 4$

$\therefore 4369 = 9 \cdot 400 + 9 \cdot 80 + 9 \cdot 5 + 4$

$$
\begin{array}{r}
3x^2 - 6x + 7 \\
2x + 1\overline{)6x^3 - 9x^2 + 8x + 1} \\
6x^3 + 3x^2 \\
\hline
-12x^2 + 8x + 1 \\
-12x^2 - 6x \\
\hline
14x + 1 \\
14x + 7 \\
\hline
-6
\end{array}
$$

Quotient-Remainder Theorem Version

$6x^3 - 9x^2 + 8x + 1 = (2x + 1) \cdot 3x^2 + (-12x^2 + 8x + 1)$

$-12x^2 + 8x + 1 = (2x + 1) \cdot (-6x) + (14x + 1)$

$14x + 1 = (2x + 1) \cdot 7 + (-6)$

$\therefore 6x^3 - 9x^2 + 8x + 1 = (2x + 1) \cdot 3x^2 + (2x + 1)(-6x) + (2x + 1) \cdot 7 + (-6)$
$= (2x + 1)(3x^2 - 6x + 7) + (-6)$

TEACHING AID 38
Lesson 4-4

Question 8

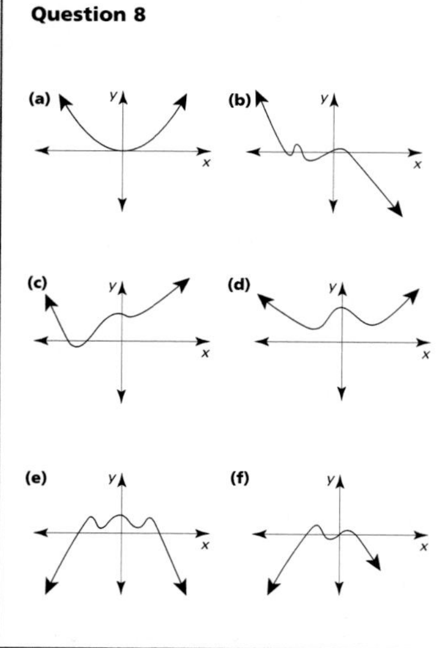

TEACHING AID 39
Lesson 4-6

Integers in Base 10 and Base 2

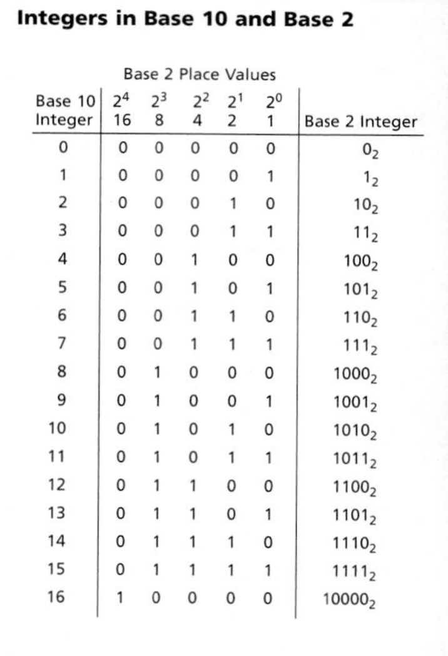

	Base 2 Place Values					
Base 10 Integer	2^4 16	2^3 8	2^2 4	2^1 2	2^0 1	Base 2 Integer
0	0	0	0	0	0	0_2
1	0	0	0	0	1	1_2
2	0	0	0	1	0	10_2
3	0	0	0	1	1	11_2
4	0	0	1	0	0	100_2
5	0	0	1	0	1	101_2
6	0	0	1	1	0	110_2
7	0	0	1	1	1	111_2
8	0	1	0	0	0	1000_2
9	0	1	0	0	1	1001_2
10	0	1	0	1	0	1010_2
11	0	1	0	1	1	1011_2
12	0	1	1	0	0	1100_2
13	0	1	1	0	1	1101_2
14	0	1	1	1	0	1110_2
15	0	1	1	1	1	1111_2
16	1	0	0	0	0	10000_2

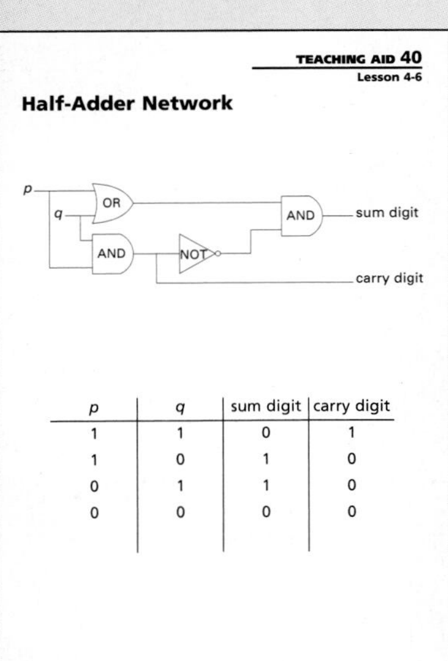

TEACHING AID 40
Lesson 4-6

Half-Adder Network

p	q	sum digit	carry digit
1	1	0	1
1	0	1	0
0	1	1	0
0	0	0	0

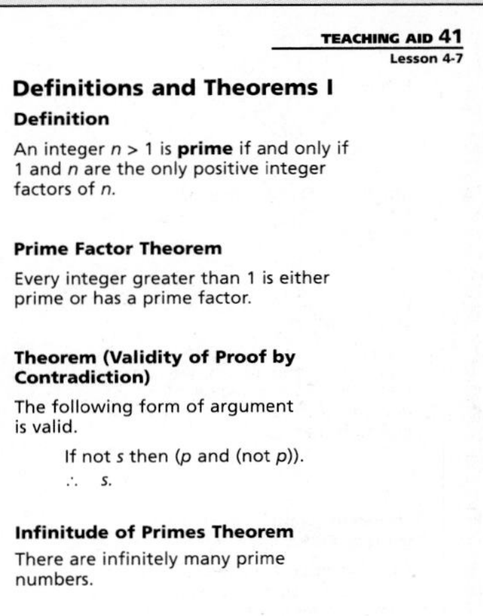

TEACHING AID 41
Lesson 4-7

Definitions and Theorems I

Definition

An integer $n > 1$ is **prime** if and only if 1 and n are the only positive integer factors of n.

Prime Factor Theorem

Every integer greater than 1 is either prime or has a prime factor.

Theorem (Validity of Proof by Contradiction)

The following form of argument is valid.

If not s then (p and (not p)).
$\therefore$ s.

Infinitude of Primes Theorem

There are infinitely many prime numbers.

Factor Search Theorem

If an integer n has no prime factors between 1 and $\sqrt{n}$ inclusive, then n is prime.

TEACHING AID 42
Lesson 4-7

Definitions and Theorems II

Fundamental Theorem of Arithmetic

Suppose that n is an integer and that $n > 1$. Then either n is a prime number or n has a prime factorization which is unique except for the order of the factors.

Definition

A polynomial $p(x)$ with degree $n \geq 1$ is **prime over the real numbers** if and only if the only polynomial factors of $p(x)$ with real coefficients and leading coefficient 1 are constants or constant multiples of $p(x)$.

Unique Factorization Theorem for Polynomials

Suppose that $p(x)$ is a polynomial with integer coefficients. Then either $p(x)$ is prime over the real numbers or $p(x)$ has a factorization into polynomials prime over the reals which is unique except for the order of the factors or multiplications by real constants.

Chapter Opener

Pacing

All lessons in this chapter are designed to be covered in one day. At the end of the chapter, you should plan to spend 1 day to review the Progress Self-Test, 1–2 days for the Chapter Review, and 1 day for a test. You may wish to spend a day on projects, and possibly a day is needed for quizzes and the In-class Activity. This chapter should therefore take 10–13 days. Spending more than 15 days on this chapter is not recommended; there is ample opportunity to review ideas in later chapters.

Using Pages 222–223

It may come as a surprise to students that the National Security Agency is the largest employer of mathematicians in the United States. Many of these people work on the mathematical theory of codes. The reason for this is that the interception and transcription of coded messages is considered essential for national defense. British intelligence intercepted German coded messages early in World War II. These messages were constructed by machine with a very complicated code that the Germans thought would be impossible to decipher. British mathematicians and cryptologists, after much effort, broke the code. It is felt by many that the outcome of the war might have been different had this code not been broken.

CHAPTER 4

222

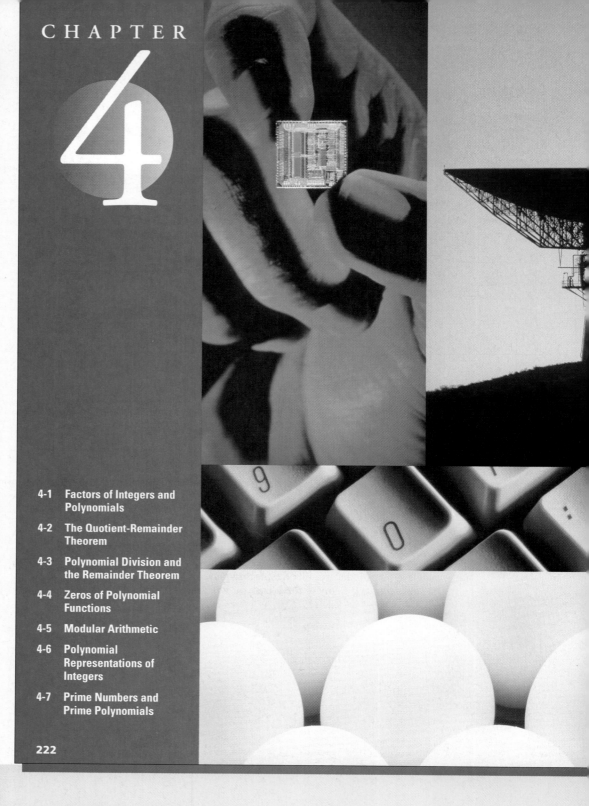

Chapter 4 Overview

Integers and polynomials over a field (such as the field of real numbers or the field of complex numbers) have much in common. Structurally, with the operations of addition and multiplication, they are both rings. For each, there is a Quotient-Remainder Theorem. Some integers and some polynomials can be factored over particular domains; others cannot and are prime over that domain. When integers are represented in base 10, that representation is an abbreviation for a polynomial in the number 10. Thus it is natural to discuss these ideas together. By discussing relationships for both integers and polynomials, it is hoped that students will utilize the ideas from one to help with the other. Note that the study of integers is considered part of discrete mathematics, while the study of polynomials involves continuous functions.

Although polynomials are built up through addition or subtraction of powers of a particular number, the operation that is the theme of this chapter is division. In Lesson 4-1, factors are introduced for integers and polynomials. Lesson 4-2 asks what happens when one integer or polynomial is not afactor of another and presents the Quotient-Remainder Theorem.

Lessons 4-3 and 4-4 are devoted to the division of polynomials. First, long division and the Remainder Theorem are discussed.

Integers and Polynomials

Codes have been used to send secret messages for many centuries. The history and development of codes is tied to mathematics, statistics, and computing. Early secret codes were simple substitutions of one letter for another. Julius Caesar is said to have used the following type of code to send battle plans to his troops (using the Latin alphabet, of course).

A B C D E F G H I J K L M N O P Q R S T U V W X Y Z
D E F G H I J K L M N O P Q R S T U V W X Y Z A B C

The message "ATTACK" would be written by substituting the corresponding letters in the second row: "DWWDFN." In the mathematical language of modular arithmetic, a subject that you will study in this chapter, the position $m(x)$ of the encoded letter for the letter in position x of the alphabet would be

$$m(x) = x + 3 \pmod{26}.$$

Codes are still important in national defense. In fact, the largest employer of mathematicians in the United States is the National Security Agency, the part of the Department of Defense responsible for ensuring the security of U.S. communications.

The need for secure coding systems now extends beyond the military to the needs of business to keep records and electronic messages safe from prying eyes, and to ensure privacy. Modern codes are based on factoring very large integers into two primes. If the primes are each about 75 digits in length, their product will have about 150 digits. At this time, prime codes based on 150-digit numbers seem to be relatively safe. The problem is to find 75-digit primes. This is not an easy task, even with high-speed computers, so mathematicians have built new mathematical theories, techniques, and programs which extend many of the ideas you will study in this chapter.

Photo Connections

The photo collage makes real-world connections to the content of the chapter: integers and polynomials.

Computer Chip: A microprocessor is a computer chip, a half-inch square that can hold over 33 million characters. Computer chips process information in binary form, a topic discussed in Lesson 4-6.

Satellite: Man-made satellites are used in such things as scientific research, weather prediction, communication, navigation, and collecting military data. Transferring sensitive data via satellite necessitates secure coding systems, which is discussed on this page.

Keyboard: When a character is typed on a computer keyboard, electronic circuits translate the character into bits (binary digits). Students write numbers in binary form in Lesson 4-6.

Eggs: Egg-carton arrays can be used to demonstrate factors and products, a topic presented in Lesson 4-1, and to illustrate the Quotient-Remainder Theorem, which is discussed in Lesson 4-2.

Presidential Podium: In their inaugural address, presidents of the United States set an agenda for their first 100 days in office. In Lesson 4-5, students are given the date of an inaugural address and they use modular arithmetic to determine the day of the week the 100-day period will end.

Chapter 4 Projects

At this time, you might want to have students look over the projects on pages 273–274.

Then the Factor Theorem and its applications to the number of zeros of a polynomial are covered.

The next two lessons of the chapter return to the discrete mathematics of integers. By the Quotient-Remainder Theorem for Integers, if an integer is divided by n, there are n possible remainders. Each of these gives rise to a congruence class modulo that integer n. Lesson 4-5 discusses modular arithmetic, which is based on those remainders. Lesson 4-6 presents a connection between polynomials and integers of a different sort, namely that the representation of an integer m in base x is a shorthand for the value of a polynomial in x. Lesson 4-7 brings the two themes together again, discussing prime numbers and an analogue, prime polynomials over a field. Indirect proof is analyzed and exemplified by Euclid's proof of the infinitude of the primes.

There is work with proof-writing throughout the chapter. Students are expected to be able to do proofs of divisibility in this chapter. Some of the proofs involve numbers of various congruence classes, such as even and odd integers, or those of the form $3k + 1$. Others involve proving that, for all integer arguments, the values of a particular polynomial are divisible by a particular number. Students should begin to develop proficiency with indirect proof.

Lesson 4-1

Objectives

D Factor polynomials over the reals.
F Justify properties of factors of integers or factors of polynomials.

Resources

From the ***Teacher's Resource File***

- Lesson Master 4-1
- Answer Master 4-1
- Teaching Aids
  32 Warm-up
  34 Definitions and Basic Theorems of Divisibility I
  35 Definitions and Basic Theorems of Divisibility II

Additional Resources

- Visuals for Teaching Aids 32, 34, 35

Teaching Lesson 4-1

Warm-up

Consider those six-digit integers of the form *a b c a b c*. (One such integer is 497497.) Explain why every such integer is divisible by 7.
Every integer of the form *a b c a b c* is the product of 1001 and *a b c*. 1001 = 7 • 143, so every integer of the form *a b c a b c* is the product of 7, 143, and *a b c*. Consequently, by the definition of divisible, every integer of the form *a b c a b c* is divisible by 7. (Note that the above proof can be shortened somewhat by using the Transitive Property of Integer Factors.)

LESSON 4-1

Factors of Integers and Polynomials

Factor Factory. *Arrays such as this one with bars of glycerin soap can be used to demonstrate factors and products. The numbers of rows and columns are factors of the number of items in the array.*

Integers and polynomials do not look alike. Integers are simply numbers, while polynomials are a special type of expression. For a given nonnegative integer n, a **polynomial** is an expression of the form $a_nx^n + a_{n-1}x^{n-1} + \ldots + a_1x + a_0$, with $a_n \neq 0$. The numbers $a_0, a_1, \ldots, a_{n-1}$, and a_n are the **coefficients** of the polynomial, and n is its **degree**. If the polynomial is called $p(x)$, and all the a_i are from a particular set S, then we say that $p(x)$ is a **polynomial over S**. For example,

$$p(x) = 6x^3 + 2x^2 - x - 4$$

is a polynomial of degree 3 over the set of integers.

Although integers and polynomials do not look alike, you will see throughout this chapter that they have many structural similarities. Consider division. You can always divide a given integer n by another integer d, provided that $d \neq 0$. However, the result may not be an integer. If the result is an integer, d is said to be a *factor* of n.

1 **Definition**
Suppose that n and d are integers and $d \neq 0$. **d is a factor of n** if and only if there is an integer q such that $n = q \cdot d$.

Other phrases with the same meaning are **n is a multiple of d, n is divisible by d,** and **d is a divisor of n**. The letter q is chosen in the definition because q is the **quotient** when n is divided by d.

For example, 8 is a factor of 56 because there is an *integer q*, namely 7, such that

$$56 = q \cdot 8.$$

Lesson 4-1 Overview

Broad Goals The corresponding properties of factors of integers and polynomials are discussed.

Perspective Divisibility is treated in two different contexts: the system of integers and the system of polynomials. Students may be familiar with the facts presented in this lesson, but this may be the first time they have seen these facts presented with attention to the language used.

This care is necessary in order to prove the various theorems about divisibility in the lesson and in order for students to have the wherewithal to write proofs of divisibility.

Emphasize that throughout this chapter, students will see pairs of analogous properties of integers and polynomials. You might begin making a list of these properties: definitions of factor, multiple, and divisor; transitive property of factors; factor of a sum.

The finding of factors of large numbers is now a vocational activity for some and a recreational activity for others. A large number to be factored will be announced on the Internet and people will be organized to use their computers to try factors of a particular type. Together this enables all possible factors to be tried more quickly than if only one computer was attacking the problem, and it has resulted in the factorization of some large composite numbers.

Similarly, -117 is a multiple of 13 because $-117 = -9 \cdot 13$, and 5 is a factor of -5 because $-5 = -1 \cdot 5$. However, 4 is not a factor of 58 because there is no integer q such that

$$58 = q \cdot 4.$$

There is a solution to this equation, but the solution is not an integer.

Example 1

For all integers m and n:

a. Is 3 a factor of $3m - 6n$?

b. Is $7m^2n^3$ a multiple of mn^5?

Solution

a. Yes. Because $3m - 6n = 3(m - 2n)$, and $m - 2n$ is an integer for all integers m and n.

b. When $m = 2$ and $n = 3$, $7m^2n^3 = 756$ and $mn^5 = 486$. So $7m^2n^3$ is not always a multiple of mn^5.

The preceding definition of *d is a factor of n* specifically excludes the possibility that d is equal to 0, because division by 0 is not defined. Thus, 0 is not a factor of any integer.

From the definition of polynomials, the degree of a **constant polynomial** $p(x) = k \neq 0\ \forall\ x$ is 0. This definition does not include the **zero function** defined by $p(x) = 0\ \forall\ x$ because the leading coefficient of a polynomial function is required to be nonzero. However, it is convenient to think of the zero function as being a polynomial function with no assigned degree.

The words associated with factoring integers are also used with polynomials. Notice the similarity of the definitions.

❷ **Definition**

Suppose that $n(x)$ and $d(x)$ are polynomials and d is not the zero function. ***d*(*x*) is a factor of *n*(*x*)** if and only if there exists a polynomial $q(x)$ such that $n(x) = q(x) \cdot d(x)$.

Example 2

Is $x + 15$ a factor of $x^2 - 225$?

Solution

Yes, because $x^2 - 225 = (x + 15)(x - 15)$. Here $n(x) = x^2 - 225$ and $d(x) = x + 15$. The quotient is the polynomial $q(x) = x - 15$.

The form

$$p(x) = a_nx^n + a_{n-1}x^{n-1} + \ldots + a_1x + a_0$$

used in the definition of polynomial is called the **expanded form** of $p(x)$. Polynomials can also be written in **factored form**. For example,

$$P(x) = \left(x - \tfrac{3}{2}\right)\left(x + \tfrac{1}{2}\right)$$

is a factored form of

$$P(x) = x^2 - x - \tfrac{3}{4}.$$

Notes on Reading

The definitions and theorems of divisibility in this lesson are on **Teaching Aids 34-35.**

❶ In the definition of factor, the letter d is chosen to suggest divisor, the letter q to suggest quotient. In the Quotient-Remainder Theorem (Lesson 4-2) these letters are again used along with r to suggest remainder.

❷ In the definition of factor for polynomials, you may have to remind students that the quotient $q(x)$ could be a polynomial of degree zero, that is, a constant polynomial. In **Example 1a,** it is also the case that $m - 2n$ is a factor of $3m - 6n$, because $3m - 6n = 3(m - 2n)$.

Optional Activities

Activity 1 Cooperative Learning

After discussing **Question 7,** you might have students **work in groups** to extend the reasoning and proof to polynomials. That is, have them prove the Factor of a Polynomial Product Theorem: For all polynomials $m(x)$, $n(x)$, and $p(x)$, if $m(x)$ is a factor of $n(x)$, then $m(x)$ is a factor of $n(x) \cdot p(x)$. [Since $m(x)$ is a factor of $n(x)$, $n(x) = q(x) \cdot m(x)$ by definition. So, $n(x) \cdot p(x) = [q(x) \cdot m(x)] \cdot p(x)$. By using the commutative and associative properties, $n(x) \cdot p(x) = m(x) \cdot [q(x) \cdot p(x)]$. Since $q(x) \cdot p(x)$ is a polynomial, $m(x)$ is a factor of $n(x) \cdot p(x)$.]

Activity 2 Multicultural Connection

After discussing **Question 23,** students may enjoy researching *perfect, abundant,* and *deficient* numbers. Suggest that they look for references in various cultures. For example, the ancient Greeks believed that the world was created in 6 days because 6 is a perfect number, and Hrotsvitha, a 10th-century nun from Saxony, gave the ages of three women as "a defective even number, a defective odd number, and an abundant number."

❸ It is worthwhile to discuss the proof of the Transitive Property of Factor Theorem in class, along with **Question 7,** as students are expected to be able to write a proof like it. Note that the closure property of multiplication is used in the proof although it has not been explicitly stated.

You might ask: Why is there no Factor of a Polynomial Difference Theorem? [$p(x) - q(x) = p(x) + (-q(x))$, which is the sum of polynomials or their opposites. If $q(x)$ is divisible by a polynomial, so is its opposite $-q(x)$. So, because any subtraction can be converted in this way to an addition, no separate theorem is needed.]

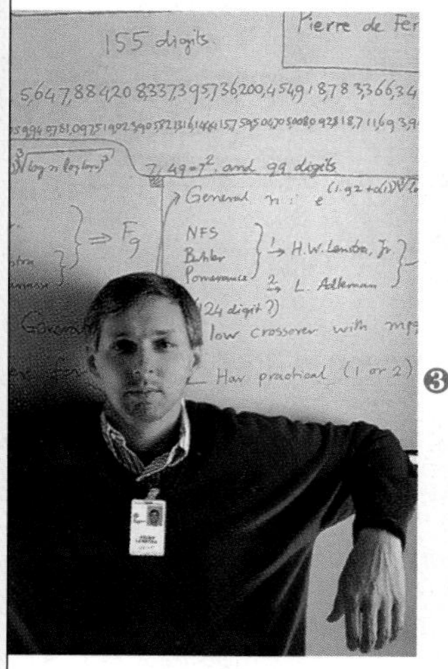

PIN numbers and other numbers used to protect financial transactions depend on the inability of people to factor large numbers. By displaying the factors of a 155-digit number, Arjen Lenstra showed that larger numbers would be needed.

This factored form of $P(x)$ clearly identifies the zeros, $\frac{3}{2}$ and $-\frac{1}{2}$, of the function P, while the expanded form clearly displays the degree.

Now we return to properties of factors. By division, you can verify that 13 is a factor of 1001, and 1001 is a factor of 364,364. Can you explain why 13 is then a factor of 364,364? Here is the general theorem and its proof.

Theorem (Transitive Property of Integer Factors)
For all integers a, b, and c, if a is a factor of b and b is a factor of c, then a is a factor of c.

❸ **Proof**
Suppose that a, b, and c are integers such that a is a factor of b and b is a factor of c. Then there are integers m and n such that

$$b = a \cdot m \text{ and } c = b \cdot n$$

by the definition of factor. It follows that

$$c = b \cdot n = (a \cdot m) \cdot n = a \cdot (m \cdot n)$$

because multiplication is associative. The product $m \cdot n$ is an integer, so by the definition of factor, a is a factor of c.

Another key property of factors has to do with the factor of a sum. Since 13 is a factor of 1001 and of 52, is it a factor of their sum, 1053?

Theorem (Factor of an Integer Sum)
For all integers a, b, and c, if a is a factor of b and a is a factor of c, then a is a factor of $b + c$.

Proof
We begin the proof. You are asked to complete the proof in the Questions.
Suppose a, b, and c are any integers such that a is a factor of b and a is a factor of c. By the definition of factor, there exist integers q and r such that $b = a \cdot q$ and $c = a \cdot r$.

Example 3

Disprove the following conjecture.

∀ integers a, b, and c, if c is a factor of a · b, then c is a factor of a or c is a factor of b.

Analysis
Only one counterexample is needed to disprove the conjecture. The conjecture is false if and only if its negation is true. The negation of the given statement is

∃ integers a, b, and c such that c is a factor of a · b, and c is not a factor of a, and c is not a factor of b.

▶

Adapting to Individual Needs

Extra Help
Example 3 provides an opportunity to recall what it means to find a counterexample to a universal statement, and to review ∃ and ∀. Notice the form of the conjecture: *∀ a,b,c, if p(a,b,c), then (q(a,b,c) or r(a,b,c)). The negation is ∃ a,b,c such that p(a,b,c) and not(q(a,b,c) or r(a,b,c)).* The last, by De Morgan's Laws, is equivalent to not-*q*(*a*,*b*,*c*) and not-*r*(*a*,*b*,*c*), which is the form of the negation in the solution.

English Language Development
The words *division, divide, divisor, dividend, divisible,* and *divisibility* look very similar yet have different meanings. Make sure that students use them accurately. Division is the binary operation; divide is the action verb of the operation; the divisor and dividend are the two inputs into that operation; if the quotient is in the system, then the dividend is said to be divisible by the divisor. Lastly, divisibility is the study of being divisible.

Challenge
Have students use polynomials and supply these proofs.

1. Prove that the product of two consecutive even integers is one less than the square of the odd integer between them. [Let $2n$ and $2n + 2$ be two consecutive even integers. $(2n)(2n + 2) = 4n^2 + 4n = 4n^2 + 4n + 1 - 1 = (2n + 1)^2 - 1$.]

Try to think of integers that make this negation true. Pick a and b with a common factor, say 2. Let $a = 12$ and $b = 16$. Then $ab = 192$. Can you find a factor of 192 which is not a factor of 12 and not a factor of 16? When you do, this is what you might write.

Solution

Let $a = 12$, $b = 16$, and $c =$ _?_. Note that _?_ is a factor of $12 \cdot 16 = 192$ but _?_ is not a factor of 12 and _?_ is not a factor of 16. Thus c is a factor of $a \cdot b$ but c is not a factor of a and c is not a factor of b. Hence, the conjecture is false.

Activity

Find an appropriate value for c. **See Question 9 on page 228.**

Factors of polynomials have properties which correspond to the theorems on page 226 about factors of integers.

Theorems
For all polynomials $a(x)$, $b(x)$, and $c(x)$:
Transitive Property of Polynomial Factors
If $a(x)$ is a factor of $b(x)$ and $b(x)$ is a factor of $c(x)$, then $a(x)$ is a factor of $c(x)$.
Factor of a Polynomial Sum Theorem
If $a(x)$ is a factor of $b(x)$ and $a(x)$ is a factor of $c(x)$, then $a(x)$ is a factor of $b(x) + c(x)$.

For instance, $x^3 - 1 = (x - 1)(x^2 + x + 1)$, so $x^2 + x + 1$ is a factor of $x^3 - 1$. From factoring the difference of the two sequences, $x^3 - 1$ is a factor of $x^6 - 1$. Consequently, by the Transitive Property of Polynomial Factors, $x^2 + x + 1$ is a factor of $x^6 - 1$.

Example 4

Let $a(x) = x - 2$, $b(x) = x^2 - 4$ and $c(x) = x^2 + 8x - 20$.

a. Show that $a(x)$ is a factor of $b(x)$ and of $c(x)$.
b. Show that $b(x) + c(x)$ can be expressed as $a(x) \cdot$ (some polynomial).

Solution

a. $b(x) = x^2 - 4 = (x + 2)(x - 2) = (x + 2) \cdot a(x)$
$c(x) = x^2 + 8x - 20 = (x + 10)(x - 2) = (x + 10) \cdot a(x)$
Thus, $a(x)$ is a factor of both $b(x)$ and $c(x)$.

b. To show that $x - 2$ is a factor of $b(x) + c(x)$, first express $b(x)$ and $c(x)$ in factored form.

$$b(x) + c(x) = (x^2 - 4) + (x^2 + 8x - 20)$$
$$= (x + 2)(x - 2) + (x + 10)(x - 2)$$

Now factor out the common factor.

$$= [(x + 2) + (x + 10)](x - 2)$$
$$= (2x + 12)(x - 2)$$

Thus,

$$b(x) + c(x) = a(x) \cdot (2x + 12).$$

Additional Examples

1. For all integers m and n:
   a. Is 17 a factor of 171177? **No**
   b. Is $11m^5n^2$ a factor of $m^{10}n^4$? **No**
2. Is $x - 7$ a factor of $x^2 - 49$? Explain your answer. **Yes; $x^2 - 49 = (x + 7)(x - 7)$**
3. Disprove the following conjecture. *$\forall$ integers a, b, and c, if c is a factor of a and c is a factor of b, then c is a factor of a $\div$ b.* **A counterexample is when $a = 100$, $b = 50$, $c = 10$. 10 is a factor of 100, and 10 is a factor of 50, but 10 is not a factor of $2 = \frac{100}{50}$.**
4. Let $p(x) = x + 3$, $q(x) = x^2 + 7x + 12$, and $r(x) = x^2 - 5x - 24$.
   a. Show that $p(x)$ is a factor of $q(x)$ and of $r(x)$. **$q(x) = (x + 3)(x + 4)$, $r(x) = (x + 3)(x - 8)$**
   b. Show that $q(x) + r(x)$ can be expressed as $p(x) \cdot$ (some polynomial). **$q(x) + r(x) = (x + 3)(2x - 4)$**

2. Prove that the product of two consecutive odd integers is one less than the square of the even integer between them. [Let $2n + 1$ and $2n + 3$ be two consecutive odd integers. $(2n + 1)(2n + 3) = 4n^2 + 8n + 3 = 4n^2 + 8n + 4 - 1 = (2n + 2)^2 - 1$]

3. Combine the statements of Challenges 1 and 2 into one statement and prove it. [If two integers differ by 2, then their product is 1 less than the square of the integer between them. Let n and $n + 2$ be the integers. $n(n + 2) = n^2 + 2n = (n^2 + 2n + 1) - 1 = (n + 1)^2 - 1$]

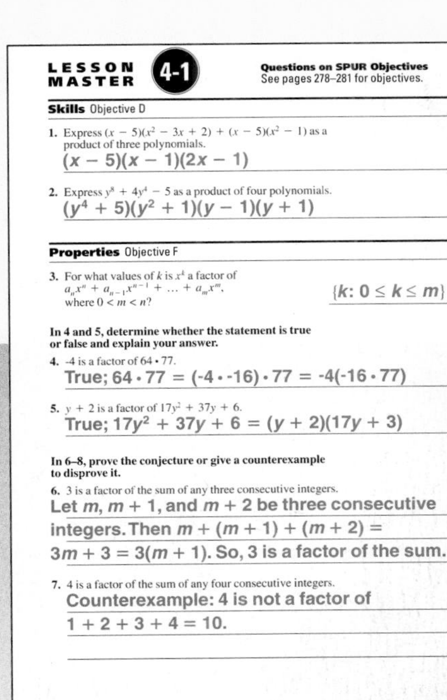
LESSON MASTER 4-1
Questions on SPUR Objectives
See pages 278–281 for objectives.

Skills Objective D

1. Express $(x - 5)(x^2 - 3x + 2) + (x - 5)(x^2 - 1)$ as a product of three polynomials.
   $(x - 5)(x - 1)(2x - 1)$
2. Express $y^8 + 4y^4 - 5$ as a product of four polynomials.
   $(y^4 + 5)(y^2 + 1)(y - 1)(y + 1)$

Properties Objective F

3. For what values of k is x^k a factor of $a_nx^n + a_{n-1}x^{n-1} + \ldots + a_mx^m$, where $0 < m < n$?
   $\{k: 0 \le k \le m\}$

In 4 and 5, determine whether the statement is true or false and explain your answer.

4. -4 is a factor of $64 \cdot 77$.
   True; $64 \cdot 77 = (-4 \cdot -16) \cdot 77 = -4(-16 \cdot 77)$
5. $y + 2$ is a factor of $17y^2 + 37y + 6$.
   True; $17y^2 + 37y + 6 = (y + 2)(17y + 3)$

In 6–8, prove the conjecture or give a counterexample to disprove it.

6. 3 is a factor of the sum of any three consecutive integers.
   Let m, $m + 1$, and $m + 2$ be three consecutive integers. Then $m + (m + 1) + (m + 2) = 3m + 3 = 3(m + 1)$. So, 3 is a factor of the sum.
7. 4 is a factor of the sum of any four consecutive integers.
   Counterexample: 4 is not a factor of $1 + 2 + 3 + 4 = 10$.

Notes on Questions

Questions 1–4 Reading Mathematics Remind students to use the definition of *factor* carefully. For instance, it is incorrect use of language to say that 11 is a factor of 132 because $\frac{132}{11} = 12$. The correct reason should be stated as "11 is a factor of 132 because $132 = 12 \cdot 11$."

Question 6 The operations do not have to be performed completely to answer these questions, though **part d** needs to be worked out in some detail before one sees that the terms with degree 10 add to zero.

Question 7 Discuss this theorem along with the proof of the Transitivity of Factors Theorem. You can call upon different students to supply the missing phrases. Activity 1 in *Optional Activities* on page 225 extends this question.

Question 11 Error Alert Students may not see at first why this conjecture is false. As a hint, you could remind them that, for example, both 9 and -9 are factors of 63. After students complete the exercise, challenge them to reword the conjecture to make it true. [$\forall$ integers a and b, if a is divisible by b and b is divisible by a, then $|a| = |b|$.]

Question 15 Some students will probably need to be reminded of the definition of *factorial*.

Question 17 Students who are having difficulty should think of $(8x - 1)(4x + 3)$ as a chunk.

3) True; there exists an integer, $nm + 3n$, such that $2n(2m + 6) = (m + 3) \cdot 4n = (nm + 3n) \cdot 4$.

5) (1) If d is a factor of n, then there is an integer q such that $n = q \cdot d$.
(2) If there is an integer q such that $n = q \cdot d$, then d is a factor of n.
Statement (1) is used to justify the substitution of $a \cdot m$ for b and $b \cdot n$ for c. (2) is used to conclude that a is a factor of c.

7a) a factor
b) $n = m \cdot q$
c) $m \cdot q$
d) $(q \cdot p)$
e) $q \cdot p$
f) m is a factor of $n \cdot p$

8) By substitution, $b + c = a \cdot q + a \cdot r$, which equals $a(q + r)$ by The Distributive Property. Since q and r are integers, $(q + r)$ is an integer. Then by the definition of factor, a is a factor of $(b + c)$.

We care about factors of polynomials for two major reasons. First, just as factors of integers help us understand how integers are related, factors of polynomials are also important in understanding how polynomials are related. Second, factors of polynomials determine the zeros of the polynomials and thus help us solve polynomial equations and inequalities. Before we turn to these ideas in Lesson 4-4, we take a more detailed look at division of integers in Lesson 4-2.

QUESTIONS

Covering the Reading

In 1–4, determine whether the statement is true or false and explain your answer.

1. 11 is a factor of 132. True; there exists an integer, 12, such that $132 = 12 \cdot 11$.
2. 17 is a multiple of 17. True; there exists an integer, 1, such that $17 = 1 \cdot 17$.
3. For any integers n and m, 4 is a factor of $2n(2m + 6)$. See left.
4. $n - 6$ is a factor of $n^2 - 17n + 66$. True; there exists a polynomial, $n - 11$, such that $n^2 - 17n + 66 = (n - 11)(n - 6)$.
5. Write the two conditional statements contained in the definition of *d is a factor of n*. Explain how each direction of the definition is used in the proof of the Transitive Property of Integer Factors Theorem. See left.
6. Find the degree of the following polynomials.
   a. $(4y^{10} - 3y^8 + 4)(y^2 + 7y + 2)$ 12
   b. $(4y^{10} - 3y^8 + 4) + (y^2 + 7y + 2)$ 10
   c. $(4y^{10} - 3y^8 + 4) - (y^{10} - 5y^4 + 7)$ 10
   d. $(4y^{10} - 3y^8 + 4) + 2(y^6 - 2y^{10})$ 8
7. Consider the following theorem.

> **Theorem (Factor of an Integer Product)**
> For all integers m, n, and p, if m is a factor of n, then m is a factor of $n \cdot p$.

Fill in the blanks in the proof of this theorem. See left.

Suppose m, n, and p are any integers such that m is __a.__ of n. By the definition of factor, there exists an integer q such that __b.__. Then

$n \cdot p =$ __c.__ $\cdot\, p$ by substitution
$= m \cdot$ __d.__ by the Associative Property

Therefore, by the definition of factor and because __e.__ is an integer, __f.__.

8. Complete the proof of the Factor of an Integer Sum Theorem. See left.
9. Write your answer to the Activity in this lesson. Sample: 96
10. Let $a(x) = x - 6$, $b(x) = 2x^2 - 12x$, and $c(x) = x^2 - 3x - 18$.
    a. Show that $a(x)$ is a factor of both $b(x)$ and $c(x)$. a, b) See margin.
    b. Show that $b(x) + c(x)$ can be expressed as $a(x) \cdot$ (some polynomial).
    c. What theorem is illustrated by parts **a** and **b**? The Factor of a Polynomial Sum Theorem

Additional Answers

10. a. $a(x)$ is a factor of $b(x)$ because $2x^2 - 12x = 2x \cdot (x - 6) = 2x \cdot a(x)$.
$a(x)$ is a factor of $c(x)$ because $x^2 - 3x - 18 = (x + 3)(x - 6) = (x + 3) \cdot a(x)$.
b. $3x^2 - 15x - 18 = (3x + 3)(x - 6) = (3x + 3) \cdot a(x)$

12. Suppose that $a(x)$, $b(x)$, and $c(x)$ are polynomials such that $a(x)$ is a factor of $b(x)$ and $b(x)$ is a factor of $c(x)$. By the definition of factor, there exist polynomials $n(x)$ and $m(x)$ such that $b(x) = m(x) \cdot a(x)$ and $c(x) = n(x) \cdot b(x)$. By substitution $c(x) = n(x) \cdot b(x) = n(x) \cdot (m(x) \cdot a(x)) = (n(x) \cdot m(x)) \cdot a(x)$ because polynomial multiplication is associative. Since polynomials are closed under multiplication, $(n(x) \cdot m(x))$ is a polynomial; so, by the definition of factor, $a(x)$ is a factor of $c(x)$.

13. d. The degree of a polynomial is determined by its term of greatest degree. The product of a polynomial of degree n and a polynomial of degree m will have a term of greatest degree of the form $(a_n \cdot b_m) \cdot x^{n+m}$ so the product has degree $n + m$. If the individual

Applying the Mathematics

11b) ∃ integers a and b such that a is divisible by b and b is divisible by a and $a \neq b$.

13b) The degree of the product of two polynomials is equal to the sum of the degrees of the individual polynomials. The degree of the sum of two polynomials is less than or equal to the maximum of the degrees of the individual polynomials.

11. Consider the conjecture:
∀ *integers a and b, if a is divisible by b and b is divisible by a, then* $a = b$.
a. Disprove this conjecture by giving a counterexample. Sample: $a = 2$, $b = -2$
b. Write the negation of this conjecture. See left.

12. Use the proof of the Transitive Property of Integer Factors Theorem as a guide to prove the Transitive Property of Polynomial Factors Theorem. See margin.

13. a. If $s(x) = x^4 + 3x^2 + 8$ and $t(x) = x^2 - x - 1$, find the degree of $s(x) \cdot t(x)$ and $s(x) + t(x)$. degree 6; degree 4
b. Make a conjecture concerning the degree of the sum or product of two polynomials. See left.
c. Check your conjecture with the sum $t(x) + (-t(x))$ and modify it if necessary. The conjecture does not need to be modified.
d. Justify your conjecture. See margin.

14. Let $f(x) = x^3 + 1$ and $g(x) = x^7 + 2x^6 + x^4 - x^3 - 3$. If $f(x) \cdot h(x) = g(x)$, what is the degree of $h(x)$? 4

15. If m is any integer that is greater than 3, must $m!$ be divisible by 3? Why or why not? (Hint: Try to write $m!$ as $3 \cdot$ (some integer).) Yes. See margin.

16. Prove: *For any integer n, the sum of the three consecutive integers n, n + 1, and n + 2 is divisible by 3.* See margin.

17. Write the polynomial $p(x) = (8x - 1)(4x + 3)x + (8x - 1)(4x + 3)5$
a. in factored form. $(8x - 1)(4x + 3)(x + 5)$
b. in expanded form. $32x^3 + 180x^2 + 97x - 15$

18. Express $x^4 - 81$ as a product of three polynomials. $(x - 3)(x + 3)(x^2 + 9)$

Review

19a) domain: all real numbers, range: $\{y : y \geq 3\}$
c) neither

19. Consider the graph of $f(x) = (x - 2)^2 + 3$ at the right. a, c) See left.
a. Identify the domain and range of f.
b. Over what interval is the function increasing? $\{x : x \geq 2\}$
c. Is this function even, odd, or neither?
d. This graph can be obtained from the graph of $y = x^2$ by what translation? *(Lessons 2-1, 2-2, 2-4, 3-8)* $T_{2,3}$

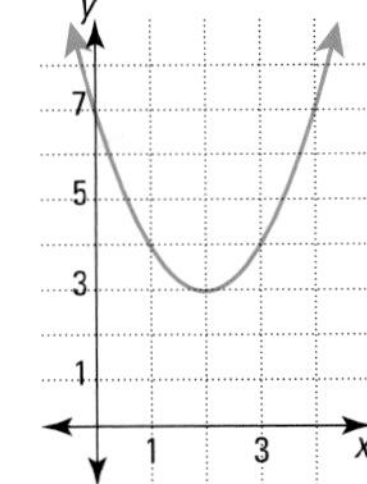

20. a. Sketch the graph of the sequence t defined by the rule $t_n = \frac{3n}{n+2}$ for all positive integers n. See margin.
b. Find $\lim_{n \to \infty} t_n$. *(Lessons 2-4, 2-8)* 3

21. Write the negation of the following statement using one of DeMorgan's Laws:

b is divisible by a, or c is divisible by a. *(Lesson 1-3)*

b is not divisible by a and c is not divisible by a.

Additional Answers

15. Yes, $m! = m \cdot (m - 1) \cdot (m - 2) \cdot \ldots \cdot 4 \cdot 3 \cdot 2 \cdot 1$. Because the integers are closed under multiplication, $n = m \cdot (m - 1) \cdot (m - 2) \ldots \cdot 4 \cdot 3 \cdot 2 \cdot 1$ is an integer. Substituting, we have $m! = n \cdot 3$. Thus, by the definition of factor, $m!$ is divisible by 3.

16. For any integer n, the sum $n + (n + 1) + (n + 2) = 3n + 3$. By the distributive law, $3n + 3 = (n + 3) \cdot 3$. Since the integers are closed under addition, $n + 3$ is an integer. Thus, by the definition of factor, the sum of any three consecutive integers is divisible by 3.

20. a.

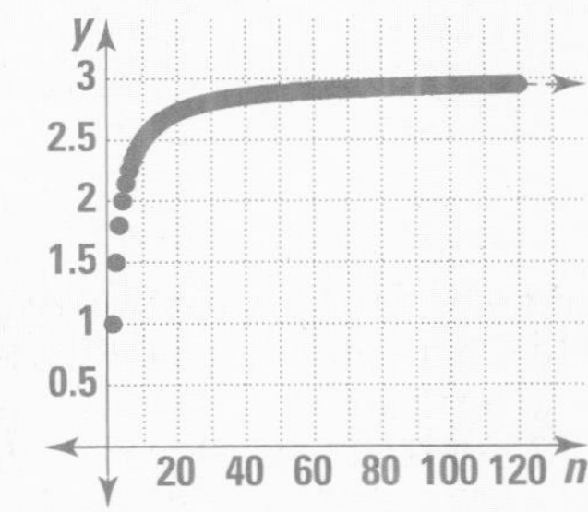

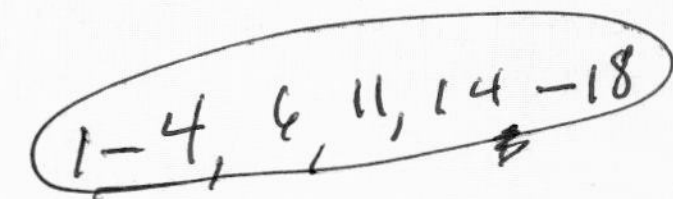

polynomials are both of degree n, their sum will have a term of greatest degree of the form $(a_n + b_n) \cdot x^n$ making the sum a degree n polynomial—unless $a_n = -b_n$ in which case the degree will be less than n. If the individual polynomials are not of the same degree, the larger degree being n, then the term of the greatest degree of the sum will be $a_n \cdot x^n$ making the sum of degree n.

Notes on Questions

Question 23 History Connection Over 2200 years ago, Euclid found four examples of perfect numbers: 6, 28, 496, and 8128. The fifth perfect number, 33,550,336, was not discovered until 1500 years later. Activity 2 in *Optional Activities* on page 225 asks students to research *perfect, abundant,* and *deficient* numbers.

Question 24 This idea is also discussed in the *Extension.*

Follow-up for Lesson 4-1

Practice

For more questions on SPUR Objectives, use **Lesson Master 4-1** (shown on page 227).

Assessment

Written Communication Have students write the theorems of this lesson and provide an example of each one. [Students show understanding of the Transitive Property for integer or polynomial factors as well as the properties about factors of an integer or polynomial sum.]

Extension

You might ask students to take note of the parallel between the degree of a product of polynomials and the logarithm of a product of integers, extending the idea of **Question 24.** The reason for this parallel is that for an integer N, $\log N$ is approximately the number of decimal digits in N. In other words, $\log N$ is approximately the degree of N when N is written as a polynomial in powers of 10. More exactly, for an integer N, the number of decimal digits in N is $\lfloor \log N \rfloor + 1$ and the degree of N when written as a polynomial in powers of ten is $\lfloor \log N \rfloor$. In Lesson 4-6, you can use this to relate logarithms to other bases and integers written in different bases.

22. a. Write a logical expression that corresponds to the following network.

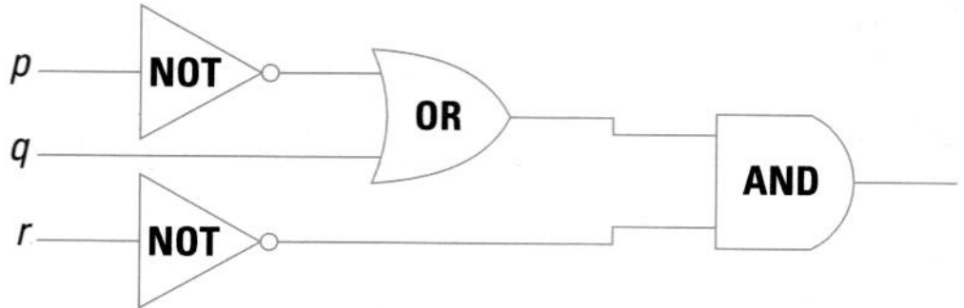

((not p) or q) and not r

b. Find the output if $p = 0$, $q = 1$, and $r = 0$. *(Lesson 1-4)* 1

Exploration

23. A positive integer n is a **perfect number** if n equals the sum of its proper divisors, those divisors less than n. Thus, 6 is a perfect number because $6 = 1 + 2 + 3$; 1, 2, and 3 are the proper divisors of 6. The next perfect number is less than 50. What is this number? $28 = 1 + 2 + 4 + 7 + 14$

24. The degree of a polynomial has much in common with the number of digits of an integer. What theorems about integers correspond to the results from Question 13**a** about the degrees of sums and products of polynomials? If two integers have n and m digits, respectively, and if they have the same sign, then the number of digits in their sum is either the larger of m and n or the larger of $m + 1$ and $n + 1$. If the two integers have opposite signs, then the number of digits in the sum is less than or equal to the larger of m and n. If both integers are nonzero, then the number of digits in their product is either $m + n - 1$ or $m + n$.

LESSON

4-2 The Quotient-Remainder Theorem

Sitting Pretty. *The Fox Theater, built in Atlanta, GA, in 1929, is a National Historic Landmark. Refurbished and updated in 1975, it is now the scene of many concerts. See Example 1.*

Lesson 4-1 examined the division of one integer or polynomial by another that is a factor of the first. This lesson explores division of two integers or polynomials in which one is not necessarily a factor of the other. There are two ways of looking at the division of two such integers, say 43 by 8. As *rational number division*, the quotient is $\frac{43}{8}$, or 5.375, which is a single rational number, but not an integer. As *integer division*, the quotient is 5 and the remainder is 3. Integer division requires two numbers for its description but has the advantage that no new numbers other than integers need to be used.

The following situation applies integer division.

Example 1

Tickets to a certain concert are first offered to ticket brokers in lots of 200. Only tickets not bought by the brokers are sold directly to the general public. The concert hall has 4566 seats. What is the maximum number of tickets that can be purchased by brokers? What is the minimum number of tickets that will be offered for sale to the general public?

Solution

To answer this question, we divide 4566 by 200 to get a quotient of 22 and a remainder of 166. Thus, the maximum number of tickets that can be purchased by brokers is $22 \cdot 200 = 4400$, and the minimum number of tickets to be sold directly to the general public is 166.

$$\begin{array}{r} 22 \leftarrow \text{quotient} \\ 200\overline{)4566} \\ \underline{400} \\ 566 \\ \underline{400} \\ 166 \leftarrow \text{remainder} \end{array}$$

Lesson 4-2

Objectives

A Find quotients and remainders using the Quotient-Remainder Theorem for Integers or Polynomials.
H Use the Quotient-Remainder Theorem for Polynomials to describe characteristics of given polynomials.
K Use the Quotient-Remainder Theorem to solve applied problems.

Resources

From the ***Teacher's Resource File***
- Lesson Master 4-2
- Answer Master 4-2
- Teaching Aid 32: Warm-up
- Technology Sourcebook Calculator Master 5

Additional Resources
- Visual for Teaching Aid 32
- Exploration 4-2

Teaching Lesson 4-2

Warm-up

What is the remainder when 438 is divided by 27? 6

Notes on Reading

Because students have known about quotients and remainders since 4th grade, they may need to be convinced of the importance of the Quotient-Remainder Theorem. The reasons for discussing it are given in the *Perspective*.

Lesson 4-2 Overview

Broad Goals This lesson is devoted to explaining the Quotient-Remainder Theorem for negative as well as positive integers, and to showing how the theorem suggests a partitioning of the integers into sets of integers with equal remainders. The idea of the theorem itself is then shown to apply also to polynomials, and gives insight into their end behavior.

Perspective There are two ways to divide one integer by another, say 32 by 5. In *integer division,* the quotient is 6 and the remainder is 2. That is the division students first learned. In *rational number division,* the quotient is 6.4. Similarly, there are two ways of dividing polynomials. There is *polynomial division,* in which $x^2 - 2$ divided by $x - 1$ is $x + 1$ with a remainder of -1. There is *rational expression division,* in which the quotient is $x + 1 + \frac{-1}{x-1}$.

The Quotient-Remainder Theorem for integers (when an integer n is divided by an integer d, there is a unique integer quotient q and an integer remainder less than d) has been known to students since they studied division in elementary school.

The Quotient-Remainder Theorems for integers and polynomials are important

(Overview continues on page 232.)

➊ The restriction that $0 \leq r < d$ in the Quotient-Remainder Theorem is important not only for guaranteeing the uniqueness of q and r. This expression provides the basis for the modular arithmetic that will be discussed in the Lesson 4-5. Make sure that students understand this concept. You may want to discuss **Examples 1–3** in class, paying special attention to **Example 3.** It is probably a good idea to have students work out several more examples of a similar nature in class, like the *Additional Examples* on page 234.

Or, you could write

$$4566 = \underbrace{22 \cdot 200}_{\text{22 groups of 200}} + \underbrace{166}_{\text{166 left over}}$$

The number left over (166) is less than the size of the groups (200) because if 200 or more were left over, another group could be formed.

This idea is generalized in the Quotient-Remainder Theorem for Integers. In words, this theorem says that when *any* integer n (even a negative one) is divided by *any* positive integer d, there is an **integer quotient** q and a nonnegative **integer remainder** r that is less than d. This is called **integer division** of n by d.

➊ **Quotient-Remainder Theorem for Integers**
If n is an integer and d is a positive integer, then there exist unique integers q and r such that

$$n = q \cdot d + r \text{ and } 0 \leq r < d.$$

$27 = 2 \cdot 12 + 3$

It follows immediately from the Quotient-Remainder Theorem that if n is an integer and d is a positive integer,

d is a factor of n if and only if the remainder r obtained by applying the Quotient-Remainder Theorem to n and d equals zero.

Note that the Quotient-Remainder Theorem gives the result of an integer division as a pair of integers: a quotient and a remainder (which might be zero). Thus it expresses the result of integer division in terms of the integers. Of course, you can also think of the integers n and d as real numbers and form their real number quotient. The result of the rational number division of n by d is the single rational number $\frac{n}{d}$.

The restriction $0 \leq r < d$ in the Quotient-Remainder Theorem guarantees that the values of q and r will be unique. That is, for any given choice of n and d, there is only one pair of integers q and r such that $n = q \cdot d + r$ and $0 \leq r < d$. For instance, if $n = 4566$ and $d = 200$, then each of the equations

$$4566 = 20 \cdot 200 + 566$$
$$4566 = 21 \cdot 200 + 366$$
$$4566 = 22 \cdot 200 + 166$$

is true. But only the third equation (with $q = 22$ and $r = 166$) satisfies the restriction $0 \leq r < d$.

LESSON MASTER 4-2

Questions on SPUR Objectives
See pages 278–281 for objectives.

Skills Objective A

In 1 and 2, values for n and d are given. Find the values of q and r as defined in the Quotient-Remainder Theorem for Integers.

1. $n = 61{,}302$, $d = 179$ — $q = 342$, $r = 84$
2. $n = -173$, $d = 11$ — $q = -16$, $r = 3$

3. When the polynomial $p(x) = x^5 + 2x^4 + 3x^2 + 3x + 1$ is divided by $x^3 + 1$, the quotient is $x^2 + 2x$.
   a. Find the remainder. — $2x^2 + x + 1$
   b. Write $p(x)$ in the form of the Quotient-Remainder Theorem for Polynomials.
   $(x^2 + 2x)(x^3 + 1) + 2x^2 + x + 1$

Properties Objective H

In 4 and 5, $d > 0$ and $n = q \cdot d + r$ in accordance with the Quotient-Remainder Theorem for Integers.

4. Suppose that q is negative.
   a. What can be said about n? — n is negative
   b. What can be said about r? — $0 \leq r < d$
5. Suppose that q is a factor of n.
   a. What can be said about d? — d is a factor of n
   b. What can be said about r? — $r = 0$
6. Suppose that $d = 11$ and $r = 9$.
   a. Give a possible positive value of n. — Sample: $n = 20$
   b. Give a possible negative value of n. — Sample: $n = -2$

Lesson 4-2 Overview, continued.

because they enable a division of integers that is discussed without reference to decimals or fractions and a division of polynomials that is discussed without reference to rational expressions. By considering the remainders when dividing by n, the theorems partition the integers into n distinct subsets. We show the benefits of this partition in Lesson 4-5.

Notice the analogies between integers and polynomials: integer division and rational number division correspond to polynomial division and rational expression division. The former of each pair results in a quotient and remainder that are both in the system. The latter of each pair results in a quotient that is outside the system unless the dividend is evenly divisible by the divisor.

Example 2

Use a calculator to determine integers q and r that satisfy the conditions of the Quotient-Remainder Theorem when $n = 8714$ and $d = 73$.

Solution

If you perform the division $8714 \div 73$ on a calculator, a number like 119.3698630 will appear on your display. This tells you that **q, the integer quotient of 8714 divided by 73, is 119.** What is the remainder, r?

To find r, note that because

$$n = q \cdot d + r,$$
$$r = n - q \cdot d.$$

So in this case,

$$r = 8714 - 119 \cdot 73,$$
$$= 27.$$

Thus $q = 119$ and $r = 27$.

Check

We need to check that $n = d \cdot q + r$ and whether $0 \le r < d$. Does $8714 = 119 \cdot 73 + 27$? Yes. Is $0 \le 27 < 73$? Yes.

When n is negative, you must take extra care to obtain the correct values for q and r.

Example 3

If $n = -16$ and $d = 3$ find values of q and r so that $n = q \cdot d + r$ and $0 \le r < d$.

Solution

If you divide -16 by 3 on a calculator, you obtain a number like -5.333333333 on your display. You may be tempted to conclude that $q = -5$ (by ignoring the decimal part). Unfortunately, this conclusion is wrong.

You need to find integers q and r for which

$$-16 = q \cdot 3 + r \quad \text{and} \quad 0 \le r < 3.$$

Because of the second condition, *r must be nonnegative*. Therefore, $q \cdot 3$ must be less than -16. This means you must take $q = -6$. Then

$$-16 = q \cdot 3 + r$$
$$= (-6) \cdot 3 + r$$
$$= -18 + r$$

and so $r = 2$.

Polynomial Division

The preceding results for the division of integers have the following analogs for the division of polynomials.

Technology Many computer languages allow variables to be declared as integer variables and allow integer division to be performed on such variables. Check your language to see how integer arithmetic is handled. In one version of BASIC available to us, the integer division of 5 by 2 gives the correct quotient of 2, but the integer division of -5 by 2 gives the incorrect quotient of -2. Students who have a background in programming may be asked to write a program using real number division along with the function INT to compute the integers q and r in the Quotient-Remainder Theorem. One such program is shown below.

```
10 INPUT "Please enter the
   integer N.";N
20 INPUT "Please enter the
   integer D.";D
30 LET Q=INT(N/D)
40 LET R=N–Q*D
50 PRINT N;"=";Q;"*";D;"+";R
60 END
```

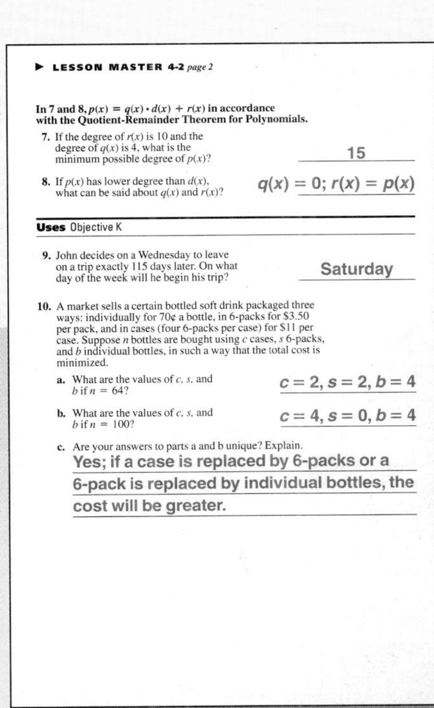

▶ LESSON MASTER 4-2 *page 2*

In 7 and 8, $p(x) = q(x) \cdot d(x) + r(x)$ in accordance with the Quotient-Remainder Theorem for Polynomials.

7. If the degree of $r(x)$ is 10 and the degree of $q(x)$ is 4, what is the minimum possible degree of $p(x)$? **15**

8. If $p(x)$ has lower degree than $d(x)$, what can be said about $q(x)$ and $r(x)$? **$q(x) = 0$; $r(x) = p(x)$**

Uses Objective K

9. John decides on a Wednesday to leave on a trip exactly 115 days later. On what day of the week will he begin his trip? **Saturday**

10. A market sells a certain bottled soft drink packaged three ways: individually for 70¢ a bottle, in 6-packs for \$3.50 per pack, and in cases (four 6-packs per case) for \$11 per case. Suppose n bottles are bought using c cases, s 6-packs, and b individual bottles, in such a way that the total cost is minimized.

a. What are the values of c, s, and b if $n = 64$? **$c = 2, s = 2, b = 4$**

b. What are the values of c, s, and b if $n = 100$? **$c = 4, s = 0, b = 4$**

c. Are your answers to parts a and b unique? Explain. **Yes; if a case is replaced by 6-packs or a 6-pack is replaced by individual bottles, the cost will be greater.**

Optional Activities

Activity 1 Technology Connection
Materials: Explorations software

You may wish to have students use *Exploration 4-2, The Quotient-Remainder Theorem,* to introduce polynomial division. This program demonstrates the step-by-step process of polynomial long division. To divide a polynomial (of degree ≤ 4) by another polynomial (of degree ≤ 3), students can enter the coefficients for each term of the polynomials.

Activity 2 You might extend the discussion of **Question 12** by asking these questions.

1. Compile your answers to **part b.** What do you notice about the numbers. [They are terms of an arithmetic sequence where the difference is 13.]
2. Write a formula for all possible answers to **part b**. [$n = 13q + 4$, where q is any integer]
3. Give all possible answers to **parts c and d.** [c. $n = 13q$; d. $26 \le n \le 38$]

Additional Examples

1. Letter boxes 5 inches wide are placed on a shelf that is 10 feet 3 inches long. How many boxes will fit? How much space will be left over? **24 boxes will fit; there will be 3 inches left over.**

In 2 and 3, determine integers q and r that satisfy the conditions of the Quotient-Remainder Theorem for the given values of n and d.

2. $n = 6784$ and $d = 93$. **$q = 72$, $r = 88$; $6784 = 72 \bullet 93 + 88$ and $0 \le 38 < 93$.**
3. $n = -38$ and $d = 5$. **$q = -8$, $r = 2$; $-38 = (-8)5 + 2$ and $0 \le 2 < 5$.**
4. Find the quotient and remainder when $2m^3 + 4m^2 - 7m + 19$ is divided by m^2. What does this tell you about the end behavior of the function f with $f(m) = \frac{2m^3 + 4m^2 - 7m + 19}{m^2}$. **Quotient $2m + 4$; remainder $-7m + 19$; end behavior is like that of $g(m) = 2m + 4$, so that line is an oblique asymptote to the graph of the function.**

Consider the division of the polynomial $x^5 - x^3 - 2x$ by $x^2 - 3$. One type of division of polynomials is *rational expression division*, in which the quotient is $\frac{x^5 - x^3 - 2x}{x^2 - 3}$. This is analogous to rational number division in that there is a single expression as an answer, but that expression is a rational expression, not a polynomial. You will study this type of expression in Chapter 5.

The other type of division of polynomials is analogous to integer division. It is called **polynomial division**. In the polynomial division of $p(x) = x^5 - x^3 - 2x$ by $d(x) = x^2 - 3$, the quotient is $x^3 + 2x$ and the remainder is $4x$. Note that the quotient $q(x) = x^3 + 2x$ and the remainder $r(x) = 4x$ satisfy

$$p(x) = q(x) \cdot d(x) + r(x).$$

That is,

$$x^5 - x^3 - 2x = (x^3 + 2x)(x^2 - 3) + 4x.$$

Also note that the degree of $r(x)$, which is 1, is less than the degree of $d(x)$, which is 2. This example illustrates the fact that a version of the Quotient-Remainder Theorem holds true for polynomials. Given any polynomials $p(x)$ and $d(x)$ with $d(x)$ not the zero polynomial, $p(x)$ can be divided by $d(x)$ to obtain a quotient $q(x)$ and a remainder $r(x)$. For integer division, the remainder must be a smaller number than the divisor. For polynomial division, the remainder polynomial either must have smaller degree than the divisor polynomial or must be the zero polynomial. (Recall that the zero polynomial has no degree.)

Quotient-Remainder Theorem for Polynomials
If $p(x)$ is a polynomial and $d(x)$ is a nonzero polynomial, then there exist unique polynomials $q(x)$ and $r(x)$ such that for all numbers x,
(1) $p(x) = q(x) \cdot d(x) + r(x)$
and (2) either degree of $r(x) <$ degree of $d(x)$
or $r(x)$ is the zero polynomial.
The polynomial $q(x)$ is called the **quotient** and $r(x)$ is called the **remainder** for the division of $p(x)$ by $d(x)$.

The Quotient-Remainder Theorem for Polynomials can be used to analyze the end behavior of a function.

Example 4

Determine the end behavior of the function $f(x) = \frac{3x^2 - 2x + 1}{x - 1}$.

Solution

Note that $f(x) = \frac{p(x)}{d(x)}$, where

$$p(x) = 3x^2 - 2x + 1 \quad \text{and} \quad d(x) = x - 1$$

are polynomials. In the form of the Quotient-Remainder Theorem for Polynomials, that is,

$$p(x) = q(x) \cdot d(x) + r(x)$$
$$3x^2 - 2x + 1 = (3x + 1)(x - 1) + 2$$

Optional Activities

Activity 3 Technology Connection
You might wish to assign *Technology Sourcebook, Calculator Master 5*. In this activity, students use graphs and tables on a graphics calculator to investigate The Remainder Theorem. Students rewrite quotients of functions in the form of The Remainder Theorem and determine remainders without performing long division.

Activity 4 Multicultural Connection
The ancient Egyptians developed a method of division in which the quotient was found by successively doubling the divisor. The Babylonians multiplied the dividend by the reciprocal of the divisor. A method closer to the long division we know today, the "scratch method," was probably brought to Europe from India by the Arabs. You might have interested students investigate methods of dividing as they were developed through the ages.

Adapting to Individual Needs

Extra Help
As extra reinforcement that $p(x) = q(x) \bullet d(x) + r(x)$, have students do the actual multiplication and addition in specific cases. For example, in the polynomial division illustrated on page 234 above the Quotient-Remainder Theorem for Polynomials, have students show their work to verify that $x^5 - x^3 - 2x = (x^3 + 2x)(x^2 - 3) + 4x$. Similarly, in **Example 4,** have them verify that $3x^2 - 2x + 1 = (3x + 1)(x + 1) + 2$.

Divide both sides of this equation by $d(x) = x - 1$ to obtain

$$f(x) = \frac{3x^2 - 2x + 1}{x - 1} = 3x + 1 + \frac{2}{x - 1}.$$

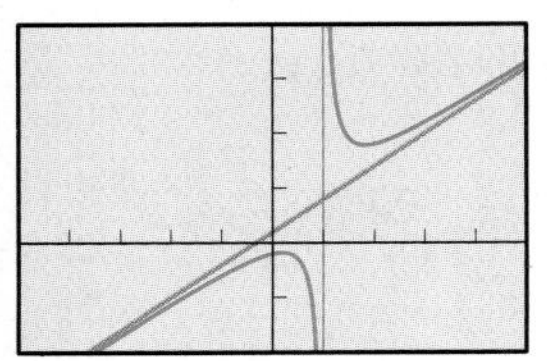

$-5 \le x \le 5$, x-scale = 1
$-10 \le y \le 20$, y-scale = 5

Note that as $x \to \infty$ or $x \to -\infty$, the term $\frac{2}{x-1}$ approaches 0. Consequently, for values of x that are large in magnitude, the values of the function $f(x)$ are very close to the values of the much simpler linear function $L(x) = 3x + 1$. In particular, $\lim_{x\to\infty} f(x) = \lim_{x\to\infty} (3x + 1) = \infty$ and $\lim_{x\to-\infty} f(x) = \lim_{x\to-\infty} (3x + 1) = -\infty$.

Check

Graph the functions f and L. At the left the graphs are in the window $-5 \le x \le 5$, $-10 \le y \le 20$. We see that f is quite close to L at both ends of the x-axis.

Caution: In the check to Example 4, the apparent vertical line through $x = 1$ is not part of the graph of f. It is an error due to the fact that the graphing calculator plots a discrete function h that approximates f. The graph of h joins the large positive value of f at the pixel just to the right of $x = 1$ to the negative value of f at the pixel just to the left of 1.

The next two lessons explore other useful consequences of the Quotient-Remainder theorems for integers and polynomials.

QUESTIONS

Covering the Reading

1a) If Ms. Smith makes 43 copies, she will have 1¢ left.

1. Ms. Smith wants to make copies of a map to a picnic location but finds she has only \$1.30 in her pocket, and copies cost 3¢ a piece. To determine how many copies she can make, she performs the division at the right. **a) See left.**

$$\begin{array}{r} 43 \\ 3\overline{)130} \\ \underline{12} \\ 10 \\ \underline{9} \\ 1 \end{array}$$

   a. Provide a meaning for 43 and 1 in the context of this problem.
   b. Match the numbers 3, 43, 130, and 1 with n, q, r, and d in the Quotient-Remainder Theorem for Integers. **See below.**
   c. Rewrite the long division shown at the right in the form provided in the Quotient-Remainder Theorem for Integers.
   $130 = 43 \cdot 3 + 1$ b) $n = 130$, $d = 3$, $q = 43$, $r = 1$

2. Find and correct the error in the integer division at the right. Use the Quotient-Remainder Theorem for Integers to explain why the error is, in fact, an error. **The division is in error because the remainder (12) is greater than the divisor (6). The correct division is $60 = 7 \cdot 8 + 4$.**

$$\begin{array}{r} 6 \\ 8\overline{)60} \\ \underline{48} \\ 12 \end{array}$$

In 3–6, integers n and d are given. **a.** With d as divisor, find the rational number quotient. **b.** Find integers q and r that satisfy the conditions of the Quotient-Remainder Theorem for Integers. **3, 4) See left.**

3a) 12.4
b) $q = 12$, $r = 2$

4a) -7.25
b) $q = -8$, $r = 3$

3. $n = 62$, $d = 5$
4. $n = -29$, $d = 4$
5. $n = 1063$, $d = 38$
   a) 27.9736 ...
   b) $q = 27$, $r = 37$
6. $n = 78{,}312$, $d = 66$
   a) 1186.5454 ...
   b) $q = 1186$, $r = 36$

Notes on Questions

Question 1 History Connection In 1938 Chester Carlson invented a method for coping documents that did not require using a liquid. The process was called *xerography* from Greek words meaning *dry* and *writing.* After World War II, the Haloid Company perfected xerography. In 1961, the company changed its name to the Xerox Corporation.

Question 2 This is an important question for relating the Quotient-Remainder Theorem and the familiar long division algorithm.

Question 4 Error Alert Students who miss **part b** should study **Example 3** again.

Adapting to Individual Needs

Challenge

Have students answer the following as a preview to Chapter 5.

1. When $p(x) = x^3 + x^2 - 5x + 3$ is divided by $d(x) = x - 1$, the quotient is $q(x) = x^2 + 2x - 3$ and the remainder is 0. Does that mean that $\frac{p(x)}{d(x)} = q(x)$ for all x? If your answer is yes, justify it; if your answer is no, give a corrected statement. [No; the left side is not defined at $x = 1$, but the right side is. So, $\frac{x^3 + x^2 - 5x + 3}{x - 1} = x^2 + 2x - 3$, provided $x \ne 1$.]
2. Explain why graphing $y = \frac{p(x)}{d(x)}$ and $y = q(x)$ from the above question on a automatic grapher does not help answer the question. Stated generally, if $p(x)$ is divided by $d(x)$, yielding a quotient of $q(x)$ with a remainder of 0, does $f(x) = \frac{p(x)}{d(x)}$ have the same graph as $g(x) = q(x)$? [Almost, but no; $f(x)$ has holes where $d(x) = 0$. At all other places, the graphs agree. Most automatic graphers do not show the holes.]

Notes on Questions

Question 7 If you have not done so already, point out that analogies between integers and polynomials are a theme of this chapter.

Question 12 This question is important for preparing students for Lesson 4-5. It is extended in Activity 2 in the *Optional Activities* on page 233.

Questions 13–16 The answers to the divisions in these related questions are not the object of this question but still might be discussed. For each question which has an answer of "integer" you could ask if $\lfloor \frac{n}{d} \rfloor$ or $\lceil \frac{n}{d} \rceil$ is the better answer. For instance, in **part a,** the answer is $\lfloor \frac{n}{d} \rfloor$. If the question asked "How many buses are needed," the answer could be either $\lfloor \frac{n}{d} \rfloor$ or $\lfloor \frac{n}{d} \rfloor + 1$, depending on whether there is a requirement that all students be bused.

7) (integer division, polynomial division), (rational number division, rational expression division)

11a) $(x - 12)(x + 3) + 56 = x^2 - 9x + 20$

12a) 0, 1, 2, 3, 4, 5, 6, 7, 8, 9, 10, 11, 12
b) any value of the form $q \cdot 13 + 4$ (for example, 17, 30, 43)
c) any value of the form $q \cdot 13$ (for example, 13)
d) any value of the form $2 \cdot 13 + r$, $0 \le r < 13$ (for example, 27)

17c) $22150 = 8 \cdot 2500 + 2150$; the quotient is 8, the remainder is 2150.

7. Pair the analogous terms: rational expression division, integer division, polynomial division, rational number division. See left.

8. When $x^5 + x^3 - x + 3$ is divided by $x^2 - 1$, the quotient is $x^3 + 2x$. Find the remainder and its degree. $r(x) = x + 3$, degree = 1

9. When the polynomial $p(x) = x^3 - x^2 + x - 1$ is divided by $d(x) = x + 2$, the quotient is $q(x) = x^2 - 3x + 7$.
a. Find the remainder. $r(x) = -15$
b. Write $p(x)$ in the form of the Quotient-Remainder Theorem for Polynomials. $x^3 - x^2 + x - 1 = (x^2 - 3x + 7)(x + 2) - 15$

10. Use your calculator to find the quotient and remainder when -18,743 is divided by 436. $q = -43$, $r = 5$

11. a. Verify that the function h with

$$h(x) = \frac{x^2 - 9x + 20}{x + 3}$$

can be rewritten as

$$h(x) = x - 12 + \frac{56}{x + 3}.$$ See left.

b. Use the result of part **a** to analyze the end behavior of h. As $x \to \pm\infty$, the values of $h(x)$ become closer and closer to those of the linear function $L(x) = x - 12$.

Applying the Mathematics

12. An integer n is divided by 13. See left.
a. What are the possible remainders?
b. Find 3 different values for n for which the remainder is 4.
c. Find a value for n for which the remainder is 0.
d. Find a value for n for which the integer quotient is 2.

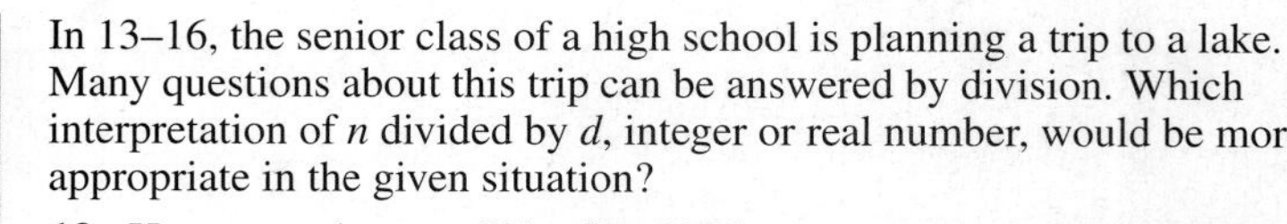

In 13–16, the senior class of a high school is planning a trip to a lake. Many questions about this trip can be answered by division. Which interpretation of n divided by d, integer or real number, would be more appropriate in the given situation?

13. How many buses will be filled if there are n people going and each bus can hold d persons? integer

14. If the lake is n miles away and the buses can go d miles an hour, how long will the ride to the lake take? real number

15. If each person drinks n bottles of soda and there are d bottles in a case, how many full cases of soda will be drunk? integer

16. If the temperature is rising n degrees per minute and it will take d minutes to get to the lake, how much warmer will it be there than it was when the bus ride began? not a division problem

17. Martin gets a bonus point for each \$2500 worth of computer sales he makes. Last month his computer sales totaled \$22,150.
a. How many points did Martin earn? 8 points
b. On how much in sales did Martin fail to earn points? \$2150
c. Relate your answers to parts **a** and **b** to the Quotient-Remainder Theorem for Integers. See left.

In 18 and 19, *true or false*. Justify your answer.

18. 93 is divisible by 5. **False.** $93 = 18 \cdot 5 + 3$

19. $x^2 + x + 1$ is a factor of $x^3 + x^2 + x + 1$. **False.** $x^3 + x^2 + x + 1 = x \cdot (x^2 + x + 1) + 1$

Review

20. Prove: $\forall$ *integers a and b, if a is divisible by b, then a^2 is divisible by b^2.* *(Lesson 4-1)* **See left.**

In 21–23, write the expression as a polynomial in expanded form. *(Lesson 4-1)*

21. $(3x^2 + 4x - 8)(x^3 - 1)$ $3x^5 + 4x^4 - 8x^3 - 3x^2 - 4x + 8$

22. $(z^6 + z^3 + 1)(z^2 + z + 1)$ $z^8 + z^7 + z^6 + z^5 + z^4 + z^3 + z^2 + z + 1$

23. $\left(y + \frac{1}{2}\right)^3 - \left(y - \frac{1}{2}\right)^3$ $3y^2 + \frac{1}{4}$

24. The formula

$$m = m_0\left(\frac{1}{\sqrt{1 - \frac{v^2}{c^2}}}\right)$$

relates the mass of an object at rest (m_0) to its mass when traveling at velocity v and the speed of light c. At what percentage of the speed of light should an object be moving to have its mass at rest tripled? *(Lesson 3-3)* $(2\sqrt{2})/3 \approx 94.3\%$

25. Lookouts on two naval vessels, about 2 miles apart, spot a disabled boat off the port side. One lookout spots the boat at an angle of 42° with the line connecting the naval vessels. The other lookout spots the boat at an angle of 28° with the same line.

a. Which naval vessel is closer to the disabled boat? **See below.**

b. How much closer is it? *(Lesson 2-6)* $\approx$ **0.4 mi**

a) The vessel that spotted the boat at an angle of 42°

26. Analyze the function f defined by $f(x) = 2^{1-x}$. Discuss its domain, range, end behavior, and any intervals on which it is increasing or decreasing. *(Lessons 2-1, 2-2, 2-3, 2-4)* **See left.**

27. Write the contrapositive of the following statement:

If the temperature stays below 28°F, the citrus crop will be ruined. *(Lesson 1-5)* **If the citrus crop is not ruined, the temperature did not stay below 28°.**

Exploration

28. The Quotient-Remainder Theorem for Integers can be generalized to include the case when $d < 0$. We modify the algorithm as follows: If n and $d \neq 0$ are integers, then there exist unique integers q and r such that $n = q \cdot d + r$ and $0 \leq r < |d|$.
For each n, d pair, find the corresponding q, r pair.

a. $n = 17$ $d = 3$ $q = 5, r = 2$
b. $n = 17$ $d = -3$ $q = -5, r = 2$
c. $n = -17$ $d = 3$ $q = -6, r = 1$
d. $n = -17$ $d = -3$ $q = 6, r = 1$

20) Suppose we have integers a and b such that a is divisible by b. Then by the definition of factor, there is an integer q such that $a = q \cdot b$. Squaring both sides gives $a^2 = (q \cdot b)^2 = q^2 \cdot b^2$. Since integer multiplication is closed, q^2 is an integer. Therefore, by the definition of factor, a^2 is divisible by b^2.

26) domain: all reals; range: all reals greater than 0; continously decreasing over its entire domain; $\lim_{x\to\infty} = 0$, $\lim_{x\to-\infty} = \infty$

Follow-up for Lesson 4-2

Practice

For more questions on SPUR Objectives, use **Lesson Master 4-2** (shown on pages 232–233).

Assessment

Written Communication Have students **work in pairs**. Ask each student to make up a problem like **Question 17** (including **parts a, b, and c**). Then have students solve their partner's problem. [Students use the Quotient-Remainder Theorem to analyze and solve applied problems.]

Extension

Project Update Project 1, *Casting Out Nines*, on page 273, relates to the content of this lesson.

Setting Up Lesson 4-3

Questions 1–2 should be discussed in order to provide an opportunity to view long division as an algorithm. In this view, note the prevalence of the threesome *subtract, divide, and multiply,* in that order. This is exactly what is done in the long division algorithm for polynomials.

Lesson 4-3

Objectives

B Divide polynomials
H Use the Remainder Theorem and Quotient-Remainder Theorem to describe characteristics of given polynomials.

Resources

From the ***Teacher's Resource File***
- Lesson Master 4-3
- Answer Master 4-3
  Teaching Aids
  32 Warm-up
  36 Long Division of Polynomials
  37 Long Division and the Quotient-Remainder Theorem
- Technology Connection
  Calculator Master 6

Additional Resources
- Visuals for Teaching Aids 32, 36, 37

Teaching Lesson 4-3

Warm-up

1. Use polynomial long division to find the remainder when $2x^3 - 11x^2 + 4x - 12$ is divided by $x + 5$.
   Quotient: $2x^2 - 21x + 109$
   Remainder: -557
2. Let $P(x) = 2x^3 - 11x^2 + 4x - 12$. Verify that the answer to Warm-up 1 equals $P(-5)$. $P(-5) = 2(-5)^3 - 11(-5)^2 + 4(-5) - 12 = -557$

Notes on Reading

Reading Mathematics In this lesson, it is particularly useful to read with pencil in hand, carrying out the steps in the long divisions. This is, of course, a good habit to acquire for reading any kind of mathematics, but it is especially important for following an algorithm such as the long division algorithm.

LESSON

4-3 Polynomial Division and the Remainder Theorem

The Quotient-Remainder Theorem for Polynomials states that if a polynomial $p(x)$ is divided by a nonzero polynomial $d(x)$, then there exist unique polynomials $q(x)$ and $r(x)$ such that

(1) $p(x) = q(x) \cdot d(x) + r(x)$

and

(2) either $r(x)$ is the zero polynomial or the degree of $r(x)$ is less than the degree of $d(x)$.

The statement of this theorem does not indicate how to determine $q(x)$ and $r(x)$. However, these polynomials can be found by a long division procedure for polynomials. In this lesson, we carefully discuss polynomial long division and show how it and its counterpart, integer long division, follow from their respective Quotient-Remainder theorems.

A Step-by-Step Look at Polynomial Long Division

We will begin with a detailed description of the long division procedure for dividing the polynomial $p(x) = 6x^3 - 9x^2 + 8x + 1$ by $d(x) = 2x + 1$.

Step 1:

$$\begin{array}{r} 3x^2 \\ 2x + 1 \overline{)\, 6x^3 - 9x^2 + 8x + 1} \\ \underline{6x^3 + 3x^2} \\ -12x^2 + 8x + 1 \end{array}$$

Divide the leading term, $6x^3$, by the leading term $2x$. $\frac{6x^3}{2x} = 3x^2$. This makes $3x^2$ the leading term in the quotient. Now multiply $3x^2$ by $2x + 1$ and subtract from $6x^3 - 9x^2 + 8x + 1$.

Step 2:

$$\begin{array}{r} 3x^2 - 6x \\ 2x + 1 \overline{)\, 6x^3 - 9x^2 + 8x + 1} \\ \underline{6x^3 + 3x^2} \\ -12x^2 + 8x + 1 \\ \underline{-12x^2 - 6x} \\ 14x + 1 \end{array}$$

Divide the new leading term, $-12x^2$, by $2x$. $\frac{-12x^2}{2x} = -6x$. This makes $-6x$ the second term in the quotient. Multiply $-6x$ by $2x + 1$ and subtract from $-12x^2 + 8x + 1$.

Step 3:

$$\begin{array}{r} 3x^2 - 6x + 7 \\ 2x + 1 \overline{)\, 6x^3 - 9x^2 + 8x + 1} \\ \underline{6x^3 + 3x^2} \\ -12x^2 + 8x + 1 \\ \underline{-12x^2 - 6x} \\ 14x + 1 \\ \underline{14x + 7} \\ -6 \end{array}$$

Continue the process. $\frac{14x}{2x} = 7$. Thus 7 is the third term in the quotient. Multiply 7 by $2x + 1$ and subtract from $14x + 1$. The degree of -6 is less than the degree of $2x + 1$, so the division is finished.

Lesson 4-3 Overview

Broad Goals Students are expected to be proficient at long division of polynomials, a review topic for all. The Remainder Theorem is introduced in this lesson.

Perspective Students who have used prior UCSMP materials will have seen long division of polynomials in *Functions, Statistics, and Trigonometry,* the course preceding this one. Other students may not have studied long division of polynomials for as long as four years. A refresher is good for all.

The Remainder Theorem was justified informally in Lesson 4-2; here it is proved formally.

Unlike traditional series, UCSMP students do not study division of polynomials in their first or second year of algebra. They will have seen long division of polynomials first in *Functions, Statistics, and Trigonometry.*

The quotient is $q(x) = 3x^2 - 6x + 7$ and the remainder is $r(x) = -6$. You can check that the division is correct by observing that

$$\begin{array}{ccccc} p(x) & = & q(x) & \cdot\ d(x) & +\ r(x) \\ 6x^3 - 9x^2 + 8x + 1 & = & (3x^2 - 6x + 7) & (2x + 1) & + (-6). \end{array}$$

By dividing both sides of this equation by $2x + 1$, the result of the long division procedure may be written in the rational form

$$\frac{6x^3 - 9x^2 + 8x + 1}{2x + 1} = 3x^2 - 6x + 7 + \frac{-6}{2x + 1}.$$

Polynomial Long Division as You Would Write It

Because we rewrote each step when doing the next step, the long division on the previous page is truly long. Example 1 shows what your paper might look like on a difficult problem. In it some of the coefficients in the polynomial $p(x)$ are zero, so you need to fill in the zero coefficients for all the missing powers of the variable.

Example 1

Divide $p(x) = 6x^5 - x^4 + x + 1$ by $d(x) = 2x^2 + x$ using long division.

Solution

In the polynomial $p(x)$ the coefficients of x^3 and x^2 are zero. So in using the long division procedure, it is helpful to write $p(x)$ as $6x^5 - x^4 + 0x^3 + 0x^2 + x + 1$. The division is shown below.

1

$$\begin{array}{r|l} & 3x^3 - 2x^2 + x - \frac{1}{2} \\ \hline 2x^2 + x & 6x^5 - x^4 + 0x^3 + 0x^2 + x + 1 \\ & \underline{6x^5 + 3x^4} \\ & -4x^4 + 0x^3 + 0x^2 + x + 1 \\ & \underline{-4x^4 - 2x^3} \\ & 2x^3 + 0x^2 + x + 1 \\ & \underline{2x^3 + x^2} \\ & -x^2 + x + 1 \\ & \underline{-x^2 - \frac{1}{2}x} \\ & \frac{3}{2}x + 1 \end{array}$$

Think: $\frac{6x^5}{2x^2} = 3x^3$. Multiply $3x^3$ by $2x^2 + x$ and subtract.

Think: $\frac{-4x^4}{2x^2} = -2x^2$. Multiply $-2x^2$ by $2x^2 + x$ and subtract.

Think: $\frac{2x^3}{2x^2} = x$. Multiply x by $2x^2 + x$ and subtract.

Think: $\frac{-x^2}{2x^2} = -\frac{1}{2}$. Multiply $-\frac{1}{2}$ by $2x^2 + x$ and subtract.

The degree of $\frac{3}{2}x + 1$ is less than the degree of $2x^2 + x$, so the division is complete.

Therefore $q(x) = 3x^3 - 2x^2 + x - \frac{1}{2}$ and $r(x) = \frac{3}{2}x + 1$.

Check

Does $p(x) = q(x) \cdot d(x) + r(x)$?

$6x^5 - x^4 + x + 1 \stackrel{?}{=} \left(3x^3 - 2x^2 + x - \frac{1}{2}\right)(2x^2 + x) + \left(\frac{3}{2}x + 1\right)$

$6x^5 - x^4 + x + 1 \stackrel{?}{=} 6x^5 + 3x^4 - 4x^4 - 2x^3 + 2x^3 + x^2 - x^2 - \frac{1}{2}x + \frac{3}{2}x + 1$

$6x^5 - x^4 + x + 1 \stackrel{?}{=} 6x^5 - x^4 + x + 1$. Yes.

It may help to do an integer long division parallel to a polynomial long division. Point out similarities and differences as you do the two divisions simultaneously.

Step 3 on page 238 and the long division in **Example 1** are shown on **Teaching Aid 36.**

Discuss **Example 1** with the class. When the dividend polynomial has terms with zero coefficients, or when there is a fraction in the quotient, students frequently have trouble. Note the use of the Quotient-Remainder Theorem in the check.

1 You may wish to review the following characteristics of the display of polynomial long division:

1. Both dividend and divisor should be written in decreasing powers of the variable.
2. "Missing" powers should be represented by 0 times the variable to that power.
3. Quotient terms should be placed over like terms in the dividend.
4. Unlike integer division, keep bringing down the entire leftover dividend.
5. Avoid adding unlike terms!
6. The division is over when the degree of the divisor is more than the degree of the remaining dividend.

Having quotient terms placed over like terms in the dividend parallels long division in arithmetic. It also clearly indicates when the division is over, since there is no room for any quotient term after the constant. Some books do this differently; they instruct students to place quotient terms as far left as possible. Either way is acceptable; the important thing is that the work be well-organized and legible.

Optional Activities

Activity 1 Technology Connection
You might want to use *Technology Sourcebook, Calculator Master 6.* Students use a programmable calculator to run and edit a program that divides polynomials by binomials.

Activity 2 Writing Even after they have seen the proof, students often find it rather mysterious or magical that the remainder R in the polynomial division $p(x)$ by $x - c$ is equal to $p(c)$. Have them verify the Quotient-Remainder Theorem with several examples and then write an explanation, in their own words, why the theorem is true.

❷ The long division example shown here and the Quotient-Remainder Theorem are on **Teaching Aid 37**.

Example 2 is a simple application of the Remainder Theorem.

Additional Examples

1. Divide $p(x) = 6x^6 - 20x^5 - 7x^4 + 9x^3 - x^2 - 2x + 7$ by $d(x) = 3x^2 + 2x$ using the long division method. Quotient $= 2x^4 - 8x^3 + 3x^2 + x - 1$ Remainder $= 7$
2. Find the remainder when $p(y) = y^6 - 7y^4 - 18y^2 + 5y - 3$ is divided by $y - 3$. 12

Notes on Questions

Question 1 Students should use the Quotient-Remainder Theorem to answer this question.

Questions 2, 3, 5, and 6 Advise students to check their work using the Quotient-Remainder Theorem. This is analogous to the way they probably learned to check long division arithmetic problems in elementary school.

Written in its rational form, the division of Example 1 shows that

$$\frac{6x^5 - x^4 + x + 1}{2x^2 + x} = 3x^3 - 2x^2 + x - \frac{1}{2} + \frac{\frac{3}{2}x + 1}{2x^2 + x}.$$

❷ Why Does Long Division Work?

To answer this question, first consider the integer division of 4369 by 9.

$$\begin{array}{r} 485 \\ 9\overline{)4369} \\ \underline{3600} \\ 769 \\ \underline{720} \\ 49 \\ \underline{45} \\ 4 \end{array}$$

Quotient-Remainder Theorem Version

$$\begin{aligned} 4369 &= 9 \cdot 400 + 769 \\ 769 &= 9 \cdot 80 + 49 \\ 49 &= 9 \cdot 5 + 4 \\ \therefore\ 4369 &= 9 \cdot 400 + 9 \cdot 80 + 9 \cdot 5 + 4 \\ &= 9 \cdot 485 + 4 \end{aligned}$$

Consider now how the algorithm relates to the first example of long division of polynomials in this lesson, $p(x) = 6x^3 - 9x^2 + 8x + 1$ divided by $d(x) = 2x + 1$.

$$\begin{array}{r} 3x^2 - 6x + 7 \\ 2x + 1\overline{)6x^3 - 9x^2 + 8x + 1} \\ \underline{6x^3 + 3x^2 \qquad\qquad} \\ -12x^2 + 8x + 1 \\ \underline{-12x^2 - 6x \quad} \\ 14x + 1 \\ \underline{14x + 7} \\ -6 \end{array}$$

Quotient-Remainder Theorem Version

$$\begin{aligned} 6x^3 - 9x^2 + 8x + 1 &= (2x + 1) \cdot 3x^2 + (-12x^2 + 8x + 1) \\ -12x^2 + 8x + 1 &= (2x + 1) \cdot (-6x) + (14x + 1) \\ 14x + 1 &= (2x + 1) \cdot 7 + (-6) \\ \therefore\ 6x^3 - 9x^2 + 8x + 1 &= (2x + 1) \cdot 3x^2 + (2x + 1)(-6x) + (2x + 1) \cdot 7 + (-6) \\ &= (2x + 1)(3x^2 - 6x + 7) + (-6) \end{aligned}$$

Thus, with both integers and polynomials, the long division procedure involves repeated application of the Quotient-Remainder Theorem.

The Remainder Theorem

The Quotient-Remainder Theorem for Polynomials has an important consequence when the divisor is of the form $d(x) = x - c$. Then the remainder is a particularly nice constant.

> **The Remainder Theorem**
> If a polynomial $p(x)$ of degree $n \geq 1$ is divided by $x - c$, then the remainder is the constant $p(c)$. That is,
> $$p(x) = q(x)(x - c) + p(c).$$

Adapting to Individual Needs

Extra Help

When subtracting in polynomial long division, advise students not to physically change the signs of the subtrahend. Students who do this often find that they cannot check their work because they cannot tell if what is written is one of the immediate products or its opposite.

Challenge

Have students find the quotient of $a^2x^3 + (5a^2b + ab)x^2 + (ab^3 + 5ab^2)x + b^4$ divided by $ax + b$. $[ax^2 + 5abx + b^3]$

Proof

Since $p(x)$ is divided by $x - c$, the Quotient-Remainder Theorem guarantees the existence of polynomials $q(x)$ and $r(x)$ such that

$$p(x) = q(x)(x - c) + r(x)$$

and either $0 \leq$ degree of $r(x) <$ degree of $(x - c)$ or $r(x) = 0$ for all x. Because the degree of $x - c$ is 1, it follows that either the degree of $r(x)$ is 0 or $r(x)$ is 0. In either case, $r(x)$ has a constant value, call it R. Thus for all x,

$$p(x) = q(x)(x - c) + R.$$

Since this equation is true for all x, it must be true when $x = c$. So

$$p(c) = q(c)(c - c) + R.$$

$$p(c) = R$$

This says that the remainder R is the constant $p(c)$. That is, for all x,

$$p(x) = q(x)(x - c) + p(c).$$

Thus the Remainder Theorem says that certain remainders are values of the polynomial $p(x)$.

Example 2

Let $p(x) = x^5 - 3x^4 + 8x^2 - 9x + 27$.

Find the remainder when $p(x)$ is divided by $x + 2$.

Solution

In this case, $x - c = x + 2$, so $c = -2$. Then, according to the Remainder Theorem, the remainder is $p(-2)$.

$$p(-2) = (-2)^5 - 3(-2)^4 + 8(-2)^2 - 9(-2) + 27$$
$$= -32 - 48 + 32 + 18 + 27$$
$$= -3$$

In Lesson 4-4 you will see how the Remainder Theorem helps in finding zeros of polynomial functions.

QUESTIONS

Covering the Reading

1. If a polynomial of degree 15 is divided by a polynomial of degree 5, then what is the maximum degree of the remainder? $r(x) = x + 3$; degree: 1

In 2 and 3, use long division to find the quotient $q(x)$ and the remainder $r(x)$ when $p(x)$ is divided by $d(x)$.

2. $p(x) = 3x^2 + 2x + 4$, $d(x) = x - 2$ $q(x) = 3x + 8$, $r(x) = 20$
3. $p(x) = x^5 - 3x^3 + x + 1$, $d(x) = x^3 - 1$
$q(x) = x^2 - 3$, $r(x) = x^2 + x - 2$

LESSON MASTER 4-3

Questions on SPUR Objectives
See pages 278–281 for objectives.

Skills Objective B

In 1 and 2, use long division to find the quotient $q(x)$ and remainder $r(x)$ when $p(x)$ is divided by $d(x)$.

1. $p(x) = x^5 + x^4 - x^3 - 3x^2 - 2x$, $d(x) = x^2 + x + 1$
$q(x) =$ $x^3 - 2x - 1$
$r(x) =$ $x + 1$
2. $p(x) = 3x^3 + 7x^2 + 11x + 6$, $d(x) = x + \frac{1}{3}$
$q(x) =$ $3x^3 - 6x + 9$
$r(x) =$ 3
3. What is the height of a rectangular box, if the bottom of the box measures $(m + 6)$ inches by $(m + 4)$ inches and the volume of the box in cubic inches is $m^3 + 7m^2 - 6m - 72$? $(x - 3)$ in.

Properties Objective H

4. Consider the polynomials $p(x) = x^6 - 9x^4 - x^2 + 9$ and $d(x) = x^2 + 1$.
   a. Use long division to find the quotient $q(x)$ and remainder $r(x)$ when $p(x)$ is divided by $d(x)$.
   $q(x) =$ $x^4 - 10x^2 + 9$
   $r(x) =$ 0
   b. Divide the quotient found in part b by $x^2 - 9$.
   $x^2 - 1$
   c. Using the results of parts a and b, express $p(x)$ as a product of five polynomials.
   $(x^2 + 1)(x + 1)(x - 1)(x + 3)(x - 3)$
   d. Find the values of $p(1)$, $p(-1)$, $p(3)$, $p(-3)$.
   $p(1)$ 0 $p(-1)$ 0 $p(3)$ 0 $p(-3)$ 0
5. If $f(x)$ is a polynomial, $f(-3) = 5$, and the quotient is $x^2 + x + 1$ when $f(x)$ is divided by $x + 3$, what is $p(x)$?
$x^3 + 4x^2 + 4x + 8$
6. *Multiple choice.* If $p(x)$ is divided by $x + \frac{7}{2}$, the remainder is given by which of the following? c
(a) $p(7)$ (b) $p\left(\frac{7}{2}\right)$ (c) $p\left(-\frac{7}{2}\right)$ (d) $p(2)$

Notes on Questions

Question 4 Refer back to Lesson 2-4 and remind students that this answer means that the end behavior of the graph of h is the same as the end behavior of the quotient polynomial q, where $q(x) = 3x - 1$. You can verify this result by asking students to graph h and q. The distance between h and q for any value of x is $\frac{r(x)}{d(x)}$, and this distance approaches 0 as $x \to \infty$. This provides a graphical way to check any long division of polynomials.

Question 14 This question provides a lead-in to the Factor Theorem discussed in Lesson 4-4. The Factor Theorem enables the result to be shown without long division.

Question 16 Error Alert Students may have trouble keeping track of the subtractions if the terms of the dividend are not written in order of decreasing powers of x: $x^3 + 0x^2y + 0xy^2 + y^3$. You may want to have students practice with $x^4 + y^4$. Alternately, it is possible to avoid writing down the missing terms if enough room is left for the intermediate products in the long division.

Question 17 What seems to be a complicated result is a direct consequence of the Quotient-Remainder Theorem for Integers.

Question 22 Emphasize that it is the *form* that is being judged here, not the result. The conclusion is a true statement, but that is not the question.

Question 23 This exploration points out one of the few times where direct substitution into variable expressions does not parallel all of the arithmetic. The reason here is that the remainder polynomials can have negative and noninteger values. Yet, in all cases, the Quotient-Remainder Theorem works.

4) $3x^3 - x^2 + 1 = (3x - 1)(x^2 + 1) + (-3x + 2)$, which can be rewritten in the desired form.

6) $q(x) = \frac{5}{2}x^2 + \frac{3}{4}$,
$r(x) = \frac{1}{2}x^2 + \frac{3}{4}x - \frac{7}{4}$

12) $h(x) = \left(7 + \frac{-18}{2x + 1}\right)$

13) As $x \to \pm\infty$, the values of $f(x)$ become closer and closer to those of the function $q(x) = 3x^3 - 2x^2 + x - \frac{1}{2}$.

14) By the Remainder Theorem, since $p(2) = 0$, $(x - 2)$ is a factor.

15) $(x^2 - x - 1) \cdot (x^2 + x + 1) = x^4 - x^2 - 2x - 1$. Both $(x^2 - x - 1)$ and $(x^2 + x + 1)$ are factors of $x^4 - x^2 - 2x - 1$.

4. Use long division to show that

$$h(x) = \frac{3x^3 - x^2 + 1}{x^2 + 1}$$

can be rewritten as

$$h(x) = 3x - 1 + \frac{2 - 3x}{x^2 + 1}.$$

See left.

5. Without using long division, find the remainder when $p(x) = 3x^5 - x^3 + 4x - 3$ is divided by $x + 1$.
By the Remainder Theorem, $r(x) = p(-1) = 9$.

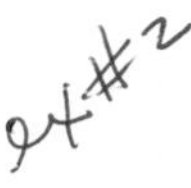

Applying the Mathematics

6. Use long division to find the quotient and remainder when $p(x) = 5x^5 - x^3 + 3x^2 - 1$ is divided by $d(x) = 2x^3 - x + 1$. **See left.**

In 7 and 8, find the remainder when $a^4 + 8a^3 - 10a^2 + 15$ is divided by the given polynomial.

7. $a + 2$ **$p(-2) = -73$**

8. $a - 4$ **$p(4) = 623$**

9. Suppose $x^3 + x^2 - x + 2$ is divided by $x - 13$.

a. What is the remainder? **2355**

b. What value of the function $p: x \to x^3 + x^2 - x + 2$ does the remainder indicate? **$p(13)$**

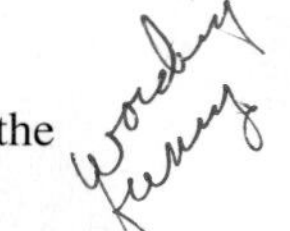

10. A polynomial $p(x)$ is divided by $x - 2$ to obtain a polynomial $q(x)$ with degree 5 and a remainder of 0. Find a number r so that $P(r) = 0$. **$p(2) = 0$**

In 11 and 12, a function is described by the indicated formula. Find another formula for the function by using long division.

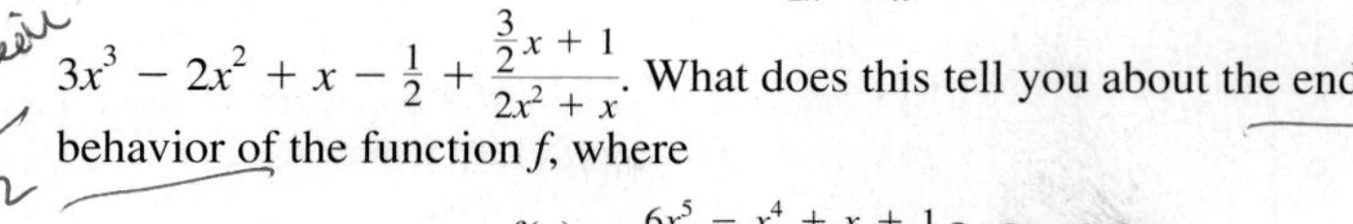

11. $f(x) = \frac{x^2 + 4x - 21}{x - 3}$
$f(x) = (x + 7)$; $x \neq -3$

12. $h(x) = \frac{14x - 11}{2x + 1}$ **See left.**

13. Example 1 of this lesson enables $\frac{6x^5 - x^4 + x + 1}{2x^2 + x}$ to be rewritten as $3x^3 - 2x^2 + x - \frac{1}{2} + \frac{\frac{3}{2}x + 1}{2x^2 + x}$. What does this tell you about the end behavior of the function f, where

$$f(x) = \frac{6x^5 - x^4 + x + 1}{2x^2 + x}?$$ **See left.**

In 14 and 15, recall that $d(x)$ is a factor of $p(x)$ if $p(x) = q(x) \cdot d(x)$ for some polynomial $q(x)$. That is, dividing $p(x)$ by $d(x)$ gives a remainder of zero.

14. Show that $x - 2$ is a factor of $5x^3 - 4x^2 - 10x - 4$. **See left.**

15. Show that $x^2 + x + 1$ is a factor of $x^4 - x^2 - 2x - 1$ and find another factor. **See left.**

16. Let $p(x) = x^3 + y^3$ and $d(x) = x + y$. **a) $x^3 + 0x^2y + 0xy^2 + y^3$**

a. Rewrite $p(x)$ to show zero coefficients for the missing powers of the variables. (Hint: The missing terms are of the form x^ny^m for positive integer values of m and n less than 3, and $m + n = 3$.)

b. Find the quotient and remainder when $p(x)$ is divided by $d(x)$.
$q(x) = x^2 - xy + y^2$, $r(x) = 0$

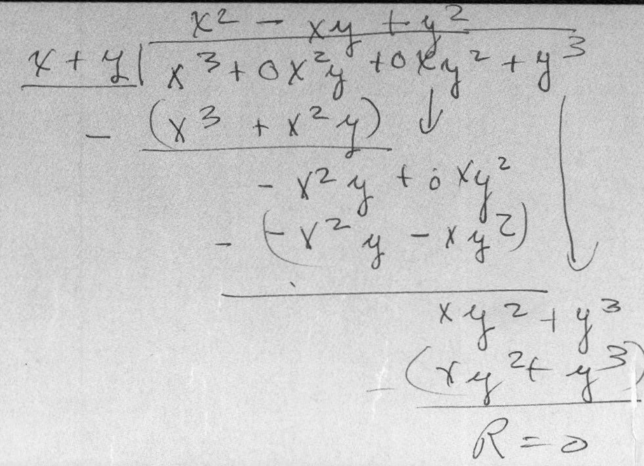

Review

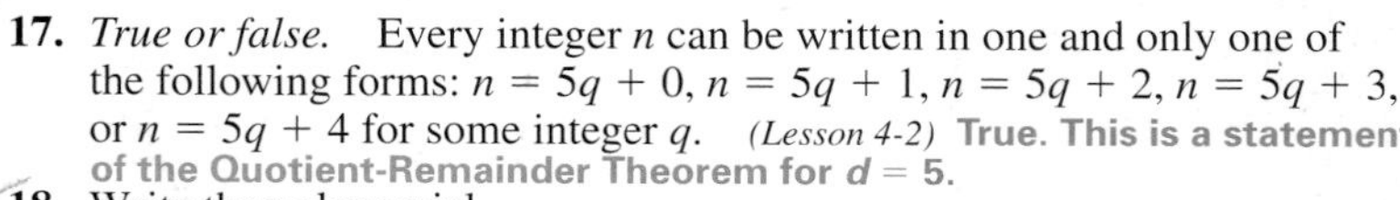

17. *True or false.* Every integer n can be written in one and only one of the following forms: $n = 5q + 0$, $n = 5q + 1$, $n = 5q + 2$, $n = 5q + 3$, or $n = 5q + 4$ for some integer q. *(Lesson 4-2)* **True. This is a statement of the Quotient-Remainder Theorem for $d = 5$.**

18. Write the polynomial $(x - 5)^2 (x + 3)^4 (x + 7)^3 - (x - 5)^3 (x + 3)^4 (x + 7)$ in factored form. *(Lesson 4-1)* $(x - 5)^2(x + 3)^4(x + 7)(x^2 + 13x + 54)$

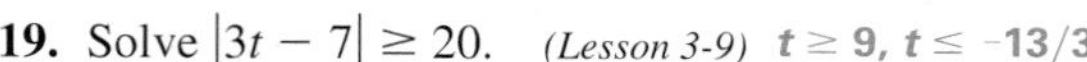

19. Solve $|3t - 7| \geq 20$. *(Lesson 3-9)* $t \geq 9, t \leq -13/3$

20. Use chunking to find all real number solutions to $x^{10} - 9x^5 + 20 = 0$. *(Lesson 3-6)* $5^{(1/5)} \approx 1.38$, $4^{(1/5)} \approx 1.32$

21b) $A(s) = \frac{2160}{s} + 2s^2$

c) The minimum is at $s \approx 8.14$, $h \approx 8.14$.

$7.5 \leq x \leq 8.5$, x-scale = 0.1
$397.8 \leq y \leq 399.4$, y-scale = 0.2

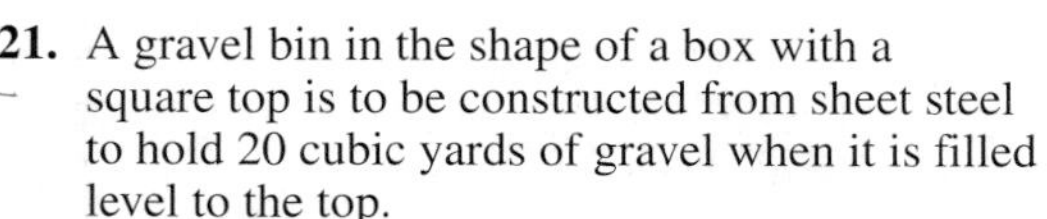

21. A gravel bin in the shape of a box with a square top is to be constructed from sheet steel to hold 20 cubic yards of gravel when it is filled level to the top.

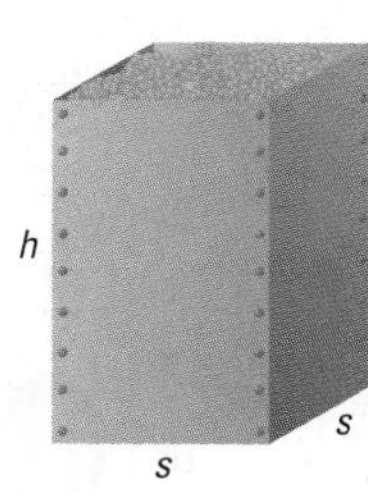

a. If each of the four sides of the bin has width s feet and height h feet, express the height as a function of the width. $h = 540/s^2$

b. Express the total number of square feet of sheet steel needed to construct the bin and top as a function of s. Call your function A. **See left.**

c. Use an automatic grapher to graph the function A and use this graph to estimate the dimensions of the bin that require the least sheet steel for its construction. **See left.**

d. Analyze the behavior of A as a function of s as $s \to 0$ and as $s \to \infty$. *(Lessons 2-2, 2-4)* $\lim_{s \to 0^+} A(s) = \infty$; $\lim_{s \to \infty} A(s) = \infty$

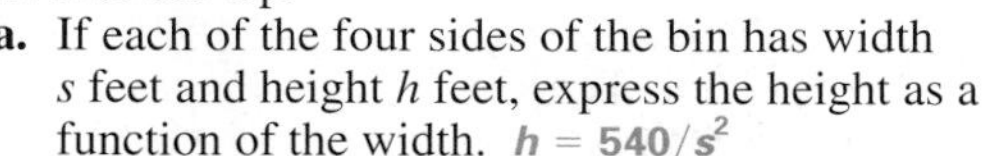

22) Invalid. This is an example of the converse error. As a counterexample, observe that $2 \cdot 10$ is divisible by 4 but not by 6.

22. Decide if the following argument is valid or invalid. Justify your answer.

If an integer n is divisible by 6, then 2n is divisible by 4.
2 · 6144 is divisible by 4.
∴ *6144 is divisible by 6.* *(Lessons 1-6, 1-7)*

See left.

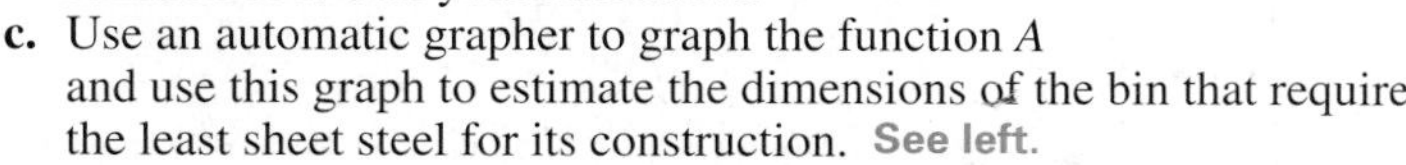

Exploration

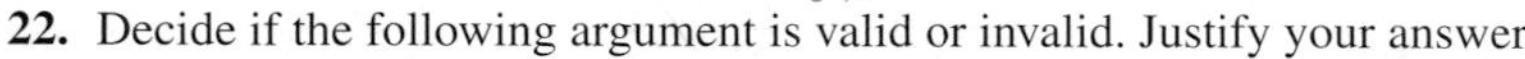

23. Try to check each of the two long division examples in this lesson by substituting a number for x and performing the numerical division. Describe what happens. **In general, when $n(x) = q(x) \cdot d(x) + r(x)$ and $n(a) = q \cdot d(a) + r$ for some value a, $q(a) \neq q$ and $r(a) \neq r$. In Example 1, $n(x) = 6x^5 - x^4 + x + 1$, $d(x) = 2x^2 + x$, $q(x) = 3x^3 - 2x^2 + x - \frac{1}{2}$, and $r(x) = \frac{3}{2}x + 1$. At $x = 5$, $q(5) = 329.5$, $r(5) = 8.5$ but $n(5) = 18131$ and $d(5) = 55$, so $n(5) = 329 \cdot d(5) + 36$. In Example 2, $n(x) = x^5 - 3x^4 + 8x^2 - 9x + 27$, $d(x) = x + 2$, $q(x) = x^4 - 5x^3 + 10x^2 - 12x + 15$, and $r(x) = -3$. At $x = 2$, $q(2) = 7$, $r(2) = -3$ but $n(2) = 25$ and $d(2) = 4$, so $n(2) = 6 \cdot d(2) + 1$.**

Follow-up for Lesson 4-3

Practice

For more questions on SPUR Objectives, use **Lesson Master 4-3** (shown on page 241).

Assessment

Written Communication Have students **work in pairs.** Ask each student to write a polynomial $p(x)$ with degree ≥ 2 and a binomial $d(x)$ of the form $x - c$. Have students exchange papers and (1) use division to find the quotient and remainder when $p(x)$ is divided by $d(x)$, and (2) verify that the Remainder Theorem works in this case. [Students divide polynomials and verify the Remainder Theorem.]

Setting Up Lesson 4-4

When discussing **Question 14,** point out that in Lesson 4-4 students will learn a way to show the result without using long division.

Lesson 4-4

Objectives

D Factor polynomials over the reals.
E Use factoring or the Factor Theorem to solve polynomial equations.
H Use the Factor Theorem to describe characteristics of given polynomials.

Resources

From the ***Teacher's Resource File***
- Lesson Master 4-4
- Answer Master 4-4
- Assessment Sourcebook: Quiz for Lesson 4-1 through 4-4
- Teaching Aids
  32 Warm-up
  38 Question 8

Additional Resources
- Visuals for Teaching Aids 32, 38

Teaching Lesson 4-4

Warm-up

Find the remainder when $2x^3 + 5x^2 - 4$ is divided by each polynomial.
1. $x - 2$ 32
2. $x + 4$ -52
3. $x + 2$ 0
4. Are any of the divisors in 1–3 factors of the given polynomial? If so which divisors. Yes; $x + 2$

LESSON

4-4 Zeros of Polynomial Functions

The Factor Theorem

Suppose c is a real or complex number, and p is a given polynomial function. Then:

1. c is a *zero* of p if and only if $p(c) = 0$. (Definition of zero)
2. $p(c)$ is the remainder when the polynomial $p(x)$ is divided by $x - c$. (Remainder Theorem)

By combining these two facts, we obtain the following result, a theorem with useful applications.

The Factor Theorem
For all polynomials $p(x)$, $x - c$ is a factor of $p(x)$ if and only if $p(c) = 0$, that is, if and only if c is a zero of $p(x)$.

Steps of a proof of the Factor Theorem are given in Question 1.

Finding Factors by Using the Factor Theorem

The Factor Theorem enables powerful theorems to be deduced about factoring.

Example 1

Prove: For all positive integers n, $x - a$ is a factor of $x^n - a^n$.

Solution

Proof: Let $p(x) = x^n - a^n$. From the Factor Theorem, $x - a$ is a factor of $p(x)$ if $p(a) = 0$. But $\forall$ n, $p(a) = a^n - a^n = 0$. Thus $\forall$ n, $x - a$ is a factor of $p(x) = x^n - a^n$.

The Factor Theorem can also be applied when the factor is linear but not of the form $x - c$. In fact, for all polynomials $p(x)$ and numbers a, b with $a \neq 0$, $(ax - b)$ is a factor of $p(x)$ if and only if $\left(x - \frac{b}{a}\right)$ is a factor of $p(x)$, because $ax - b = a\left(x - \frac{b}{a}\right)$. Therefore, by the Factor Theorem, $(ax - b)$ is a factor of $p(x)$ if and only if $p\left(\frac{b}{a}\right) = 0$.

Example 2

Show that $2x + 3$ is a factor of the polynomial

$$p(x) = 2x^4 - x^3 - 4x^2 - x - 6.$$

Lesson 4-4 Overview

Broad Goals This lesson covers the Factor Theorem and uses it to deduce the maximum number of zeros that a polynomial of degree n can have.

Perspective The Factor Theorem follows immediately from the Remainder Theorem. It roughly says that a polynomial "contains" each of its zeros in the form of a linear factor. Since a polynomial of degree n cannot have more than n linear factors, it has at most n zeros and so its graph can cross a particular horizontal line at most n times.

In the preceding paragraph, we write of "zeros of a polynomial" rather than "zeros of a polynomial function." This use of the word "zero" is common with polynomials, and we employ it throughout the chapter. In the UCSMP series, the Factor Theorem is found in *Advanced Algebra,* and in *Functions, Statistics, and Trigonometry.*

In *Advanced Algebra,* a completely different proof of the "if part" of the Factor Theorem is given, using the Graph-Translation Theorem. If 0 is a solution to a polynomial equation $f(x) = 0$, then the graph of the function $f: x \to f(x)$ contains (0, 0) and the constant term of the polynomial is 0, so x is a factor of $f(x)$. Now any polynomial function p with a zero c contains $(c, 0)$, so it is the image of such a function f under the translation c units to the right. By the

Solution

The polynomial $2x + 3$ is a factor of $p(x)$ if and only if $p\left(-\frac{3}{2}\right) = 0$.
By entering $p\left(-\frac{3}{2}\right) = 2\left(-\frac{3}{2}\right)^4 - \left(-\frac{3}{2}\right)^3 - 4\left(-\frac{3}{2}\right)^2 - \left(-\frac{3}{2}\right) - 6$ into your calculator or by simplifying this expression, you can check that $p\left(-\frac{3}{2}\right) = 0$.
Therefore, $(2x + 3)$ is a factor of $p(x)$.

Locating Zeros by Using the Factor Theorem

The Factor Theorem is a useful tool for determining exact values of zeros of a polynomial. Suppose you are able to show that c is a zero of $p(x)$. Then $x - c$ is a factor of $p(x)$. To find other zeros of $p(x)$, divide $p(x)$ by $x - c$ to obtain the quotient polynomial $q(x)$. Other zeros of $p(x)$ can then be found by finding the zeros of $q(x)$. This is usually an easier task because $q(x)$ has one less degree than $p(x)$. This procedure is justified by the following theorem.

❶ **Theorem**
If c_1 is a zero of a polynomial $p(x)$ and if c_2 is a zero of the quotient polynomial $q(x)$ obtained when $p(x)$ is divided by $x - c_1$, then c_2 is a zero of $p(x)$.

Proof
Since c_1 is a zero of a polynomial $p(x)$, then by the Factor Theorem

$$p(x) = q(x)(x - c_1).$$

Since c_2 is a zero of the quotient $q(x)$, $q(c_2) = 0$.
Thus $p(c_2) = q(c_2)(c_2 - c_1) = 0 \cdot (c_2 - c_1)$. So $p(c_2) = 0$.

Example 3 is typical of how the above theorem is used to locate zeros of polynomial functions.

Example 3

Find all zeros of the function p, where $p(x) = 6x^3 - 17x^2 - 31x + 12$.

Solution

We wish to find all values of x such that $p(x) = 0$. First find one zero, either by graphing or using a table.

x	$p(x)$
-4	-520
-3	-210
-2	-42
-1	20
0	12
1	-30
2	-70
3	-72
4	0

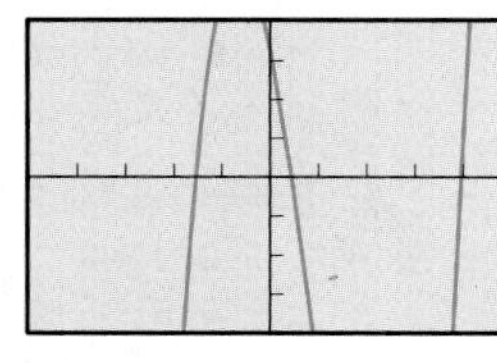

$-5 \le x \le 5$, x-scale = 1
$-20 \le y \le 20$, y-scale = 5

Either process shows that $p(4) = 0$, so $x - 4$ is a factor.

Notes on Reading

Example 1 immediately shows the power of the Factor Theorem; factors of polynomials can be obtained without dividing and sometimes without even much substitution.

Example 2 uses the fact that when $a \ne 0$, $q(x)$ is a factor of $p(x)$ if and only if $aq(x)$ is a factor of $p(x)$.

❶ The idea of this theorem is that dividing $p(x)$ by $x - c_1$ "divides out" the zero c_1 from $p(x)$. Any zeros that are still left must be zeros of the original polynomial $p(x)$. This result can sometimes be used to find all zeros of a polynomial if some of the zeros are already known, as **Example 3** illustrates.

To clarify the theorem, you might want to carry out the solutions to a polynomial equation in its entirety. For instance,
Let $p(x) = x^4 - 4x^3 - x^2 + 16x - 12$.
The zero 1 is easy to find.
Dividing by $x - 1$,
$p(x) = (x - 1)(x^3 - 3x^2 - 4x + 12)$.
Now 2 is a zero of the quotient polynomial. So, after division,
$x^3 - 3x^2 - 4x + 12 =$
$(x - 2)(x^2 - x - 6)$.
The new quotient polynomial has -2 as a zero, and dividing gives
$x^2 - x - 6 = (x + 2)(x - 3)$.
Thus the original polynomial
$p(x) = (x - 1)(x - 3)(x + 2)(x - 2)$.

Remind students that they have already seen another case where one solution to an equation was used to find other solutions. With trigonometric equations, if they knew one solution to $\sin x = k$, then another solution was found by using $\sin(\pi - x) = \sin x$ and all others were found by adding 2π to these solutions.

Graph-Translation Theorem, an equation for p can be found by putting $x - c$ in place of x in the formula for $f(x)$ and so $x - c$ is a factor of $p(x)$. The proof of the "only if" part is as is found in this lesson.

In the first edition of this book, we included a discussion of synthetic division. While synthetic division is a cute topic, it is our opinion that synthetic division is not important enough to be part of the objectives of this course. It is however, an appropriate topic for a student project.

Optional Activities

Cooperative Learning After discussing the lesson, you might give students the following information about a polynomial function and ask them to draw a possible graph. Compare the graphs students draw to discuss alternate possibilities.

1. of degree 3 with more than one x-intercept.
2. of degree 4 that crosses the x-axis exactly twice.

(Optional Activities continue on page 246.)

❷ Since a polynomial of degree n can have no more than n linear factors, it can have no more than n zeros. In order to prove that it has exactly n zeros, we need to know that every polynomial has at least one zero. This theorem, whose proof is beyond the scope of this course, is discussed in Lesson 8-8, after we have discussed complex numbers. This will assuage those students who are unhappy with the "imprecision" of the "number of Zeros of a Polynomial" Theorem.

❸ **Error Alert** This theorem considers how many times *any* horizontal line, not just the x-axis, can cross the graph of a polynomial. If students have trouble understanding this, discuss **Question 8** with them.

In general, a problem of the type in **Example 4** is solved by looking for the maximum number of times that some horizontal line intersects the graph of $y = p(x)$.

Additional Examples

1. For any positive integer n, show that $x - 1$ is a factor of $p(x) = x^{2n} - 1$. **For all n, $p(1) = 1^{2n} - 1 = 0$, so, by the Factor Theorem, $x - 1$ is a factor of $x^{2n} - 1$.**
2. Show that $3x - 2$ is a factor of $p(x) = 3x^4 + 4x^3 - 19x^2 + 7x + 2$. **Since $p(\frac{2}{3}) = 0$, $x - \frac{2}{3}$ is a factor of $p(x)$. $\therefore 3(x - \frac{2}{3})$ is a factor of $p(x)$. $\therefore 3x - 2$ is also a factor of $p(x)$.**

The given equation can be factored: $(3x - 1)(2x + 3) = 0$.

Thus $x = \frac{1}{3}$ **or** $x = -\frac{3}{2}$.

Check $x = \frac{1}{3}$ **in**

$6x^3 - 17x^2 - 31x + 12 =$

$6\left(\frac{1}{27}\right) - 17\left(\frac{1}{9}\right) - 31\left(\frac{1}{3}\right) + 12 = -\frac{324}{27} + 12 =$

$-12 + 12 = 0.$

Check $x = -\frac{3}{2}$

$6\left(-\frac{27}{8}\right) - 17\left(\frac{9}{4}\right) - 31\left(-\frac{3}{2}\right) + 12 = -\frac{48}{4} + 12 = 0.$

Divide $6x^3 - 17x^2 - 31x + 12$ by $x - 4$. The long division process is self-checking since we know the remainder is 0.

$$\begin{array}{r|l} & 6x^2 + 7x - 3 \\ x - 4 & 6x^3 - 17x^2 - 31x + 12 \\ & 6x^3 - 24x^2 \\ \hline & 7x^2 - 31x + 12 \\ & 7x^2 - 28x \\ \hline & -3x + 12 \\ & -3x + 12 \\ \hline \end{array}$$

Thus $p(x) = 6x^3 - 17x^2 - 31x + 12 = (x - 4)(6x^2 + 7x - 3)$.

By the Zero Product Property, if $p(x) = 0$, either $x - 4 = 0$ or $6x^2 + 7x - 3 = 0$. Solving $6x^2 + 7x - 3 = 0$ yields the other two zeros of p.

Activity

Solve the quadratic equation $6x^2 + 7x - 3 = 0$ and check that its solutions are zeros of the function p in Example 3. See left.

Example 3 shows that because you know the Quadratic Formula, you need to know only one solution to a cubic equation in order to obtain the other two.

How Many Zeros Does a Polynomial Function Have?

Now imagine beginning with a polynomial $p(x)$ of degree n and repeatedly dividing by $x - c$ for each zero c of $p(x)$. Each division reduces the degree of the current polynomial by 1. So the process of repeated division can have at most n steps (in which case it would end with a polynomial of degree 0). This reasoning justifies the following theorem.

❷ **Theorem (Number of Zeros of a Polynomial)**
A polynomial of degree n has at most n zeros.

This theorem provides a test of the possible shape of a graph of a polynomial $y = p(x)$ with real coefficients. Because the real zeros of a polynomial p with real coefficients are the x-intercepts of the graph of p, the graph of a polynomial of degree n with real coefficients cannot cross the x-axis more than n times. In fact, it cannot cross any horizontal line $y = k$ more than n times. This can be proved easily.

❸ **Theorem**
Let $p(x)$ be a polynomial of degree $n \geq 1$ with real coefficients. The graph of $y = p(x)$ can cross any horizontal line $y = k$ *at most* n times.

3. of degree 5 with no maxima or minima.
4. with 2 maxima and 1 minimum.
5. of degree 2 with no real zeros.
6. degree 3 with no real zeros.
[Sample graphs for Questions 1, 2, 3, and 5 are shown at the right. For the polynomial in Question 4, see graph 2; a graph for the polynomial in Question 6 is not possible.]

1.
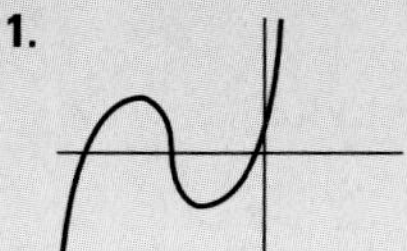

2.
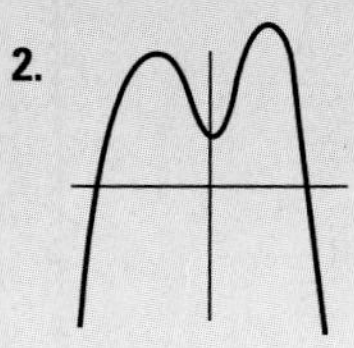

3.
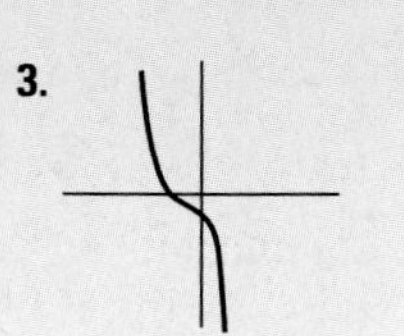

5.
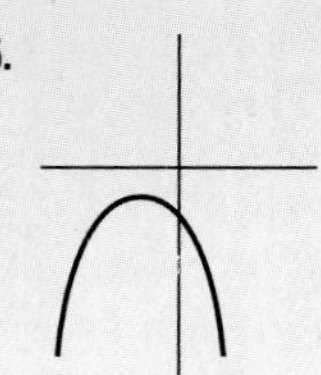

Adapting to Individual Needs

Extra Help
Point out in **Example 3** that it is possible to start with one of the other zeros, -1.5 or $\frac{1}{3}$. Then the division would have resulted in a different quadratic whose solutions are the other two zeros. This is similar to the factorization of integers into primes: the prime factorization of any number yields one set of factors regardless of which factor is found first.

Proof

Suppose that $p(x)$ is a polynomial with degree $n \geq 1$. The points of intersection of the graph of $y = p(x)$ and the horizontal line $y = k$ are the solutions of the equation $p(x) = k$. In other words, they are the zeros of a new polynomial $f(x) = p(x) - k$. This means that the number of points of intersection equals the number of zeros of the polynomial $f(x)$. Because the polynomials $p(x)$ and $f(x)$ only differ by the constant k, the degree of $f(x)$ is the same as the degree, n, of $p(x)$. By the theorem on the number of zeros of a polynomial, f has at most n zeros. It follows that the graph of $y = p(x)$ can cross the horizontal line $y = k$ at most n times.

Example 4

Suppose $p(x)$ is a polynomial whose graph is shown at the right. What is the smallest possible value for the degree of $p(x)$?

p(x)
y
y = k
x

Solution

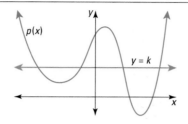

The polynomial $p(x)$ crosses some horizontal line $y = k$ four times. Hence, the degree of $p(x)$ must be at least 4.

The preceding theorem can be interpreted geometrically in terms of the maximum number of *critical points* that can occur in the graph of a polynomial: If we think of a **critical point** in the graph as a point at which the graph changes from that of an increasing function to that of a decreasing function, or vice versa, then the theorem states that a polynomial $p(x)$ of degree $n \geq 1$ with real coefficients can have at most $n - 1$ critical points in its graph. However, the degree does not indicate the exact number of critical points. For instance, the graph of $y = x^{10}$ looks quite a bit like the flattened parabola $y = x^2$, each having one critical point at (0, 0).

QUESTIONS

Covering the Reading

1. Give the justification for each step in this proof of the Factor Theorem.
   Step 1: $x - c$ is a factor of $p(x) \Leftrightarrow$ the remainder is 0 when $p(x)$ is divided by $x - c$.
   Step 2: $\Leftrightarrow p(c) = 0$.
   Step 3: $\Leftrightarrow c$ is a zero of p.
   See left.
2. Without dividing, how can you tell that $t - 5$ has to be a factor of $t^4 - 5t - 600$? See left.
3. Determine if $p(x)$ has $3x + 1$ as a factor.
   a. $p(x) = 9x^4 - 19x^2 - 2$ No
   b. $p(x) = 9x^4 - 19x^2 + 2$ Yes

1) Step 1: definition of factor
Step 2: The Remainder Theorem
Step 3: definition of zero

2) $t^4 - 5t - 600$ evaluated at $t = 5$ is 0. By the Factor Theorem, we can conclude that $t - 5$ is a factor of $t^4 - 5t - 600$.

3. Given that $\frac{2}{3}$ is a solution to $3x^3 - 11x^2 - 15x + 14 = 0$, find the other solutions.
   $\frac{3 + \sqrt{37}}{2}, \frac{3 - \sqrt{37}}{2}$
4. What is the smallest possible degree for the polynomial function whose graph is shown below?

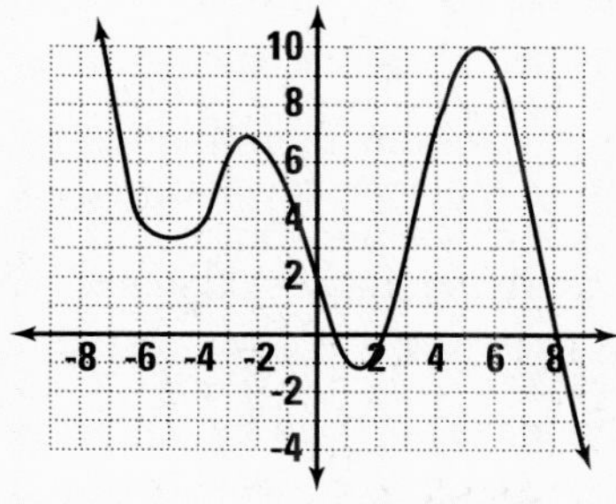

The line $y = 4$ intersects the graph 5 times, so the degree is at least 5.

Notes on Questions

Question 3 This question extends the idea of **Example 2**: If $a \neq 0$, then dividing $p(x)$ by $q(x)$ gives the same remainder as does dividing $p(x)$ by $aq(x)$ because $p(x) = q(x) \cdot d(x) + r(x) = aq(x)\frac{d(x)}{a} + r(x)$.

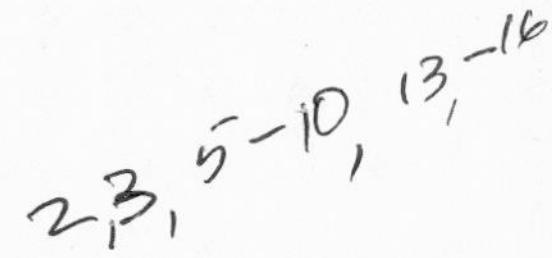

Adapting to Individual Needs

Challenge

Have students explore the Factor Theorem with nonreal zeros. In each of the following exercises, have them use only the Factor Theorem to explain if $x - c$ is a factor of $p(x)$.

1. $x + i$; $x^3 + 2x^2 + x + 2$.
   [Yes; since $p(-i) = 0$]
2. $x - 2i$; $x^3 + 2x^2 - 4x + 8$.
   [No; since $p(2i) = -16i \neq 0$]
3. $x - i$; $x^{96} - 2x^{20} + 1$.
   [Yes; since $p(i) = 0$]

LESSON MASTER 4-4

Questions on SPUR Objectives
See pages 278–281 for objectives.

Skills Objective D

1. Factor the polynomial $3x^6 - 39x^4 + 108x^2$ completely over the reals.
   $3x^2(x - 2)(x + 2)(x - 3)(x + 3)$

Skills Objective E

2. **a.** Show that -1 is a zero of the polynomial $g(x) = 6x^3 - 5x^2 - 46x - 35$.
   $g(-1) = 6(-1)^3 - 5(-1)^2 - 46(-1) - 35 =$
   $-6 - 5 + 46 - 35 = 0$
   b. Find the remaining real zeros of $g(x)$. $-\frac{5}{3}, \frac{7}{2}$
3. Given that $x - 4$ is a factor of $p(x) = x^4 - 23x^2 + 18x + 40$ and that -1 is a zero of $p(x)$, find all real zeros of $p(x)$. -5, -1, 2, 4
4. Given that $t^2 + 1$ is a factor of $f(t) = t^5 - 3t^4 - 39t^3 - 3t^2 - 40t$, find all real zeros of $f(t)$. -5, 0, 8

Properties Objective H

5. *Multiple choice.* If the graph of the equation $y = p(x)$, where $p(x)$ is a polynomial function, crosses the line $y = b$ five times, which of the following statements is not necessarily correct? b
   (a) $p(x)$ has degree at least 5.
   (b) $p(x)$ has 5 real zeros.
   (c) $f(x) = p(x) - b$ has 5 real zeros.
   (d) $f(x) = p(x) - b$ has degree at least 5.
6. Suppose that $g(x)$, $h(x)$, and $k(x)$ are all factors of the polynomial $f(x)$. If 5 is a zero of $g(x)$, -5 and 2 are zeros of $h(x)$, and -2 is a zero of $k(x)$, find a polynomial of degree 4 that is a factor of $f(x)$.
   Sample: $(x - 5)(x + 5)(x - 2)(x + 2) =$
   $x^4 - 29x^2 + 100$
7. Fill in the blanks in the following sentence. If $ax + b$ is a factor of $p(x)$, then $-\frac{b}{a}$ is a zero of $p(x)$, provided that $a \neq 0$.

Notes on Questions

Question 6b Because each division results in a polynomial of one degree less, two divisions (using -1 and 3) will produce a quotient polynomial of degree two. The quadratic formula then provides the remaining zeros.

Question 8 Teaching Aid 38 shows these six graphs.

Question 10 This use of the Factor Theorem, that we are able to prove that infinitely many terms of a sequence are composite, may surprise many students.

Question 12 In this question, the uniqueness part of a theorem is proven useful in modeling and in numerical analysis: Given $n + 1$ points in the *xy*-plane, if there is no polynomial of degree $n - 1$ that contains them, then there exists a unique polynomial of degree n which contains them. For instance, 3 points, no 2 of them collinear, determine a parabola with a vertical line of symmetry.

4) When n is an odd positive integer, $c^n + d^n$ has a zero at $c = -d$. By the Factor Theorem, $(c + d)$ is a factor of $c^n + d^n$.

8) These are the only graphs in which a horizontal line can be drawn that crosses the graph more than 4 times.

10b) Since $x - a$ is a factor of $x^n - a^n$, $4 - 1 = 3$ is always a factor of $4^n - 1$. Hence, no value of $4^n - 1 > 3$ can be prime.

11a) $p(x)$ intersects the line $y = x$ whenever $p(x) = x$ or $p(x) - x = 0$. Since $p(x)$ is a third degree polynomial, the polynomial $p_1(x) = p(x) - x$ is also a third degree polynomial and thus has, at most, three zeros. Therefore, $p(x)$ intersects $y = x$ at, at most, three points.

4. Suppose that c and d are integers with $c + d \neq 0$, and that n is any odd positive integer. Use the Factor Theorem to prove that $c + d$ is a factor of $c^n + d^n$.
See left.

5. Given that -2 is a zero of the polynomial $p(y)$ defined by $p(y) = 6y^3 + 11y^2 - 17y - 30$, find the remaining zeros of $p(y)$.
$y = -3/2$, $y = 5/3$

6. a. Show that -1 and 3 are zeros of the polynomial $p(x)$ defined by $p(x) = x^4 - 5x^2 - 10x - 6$. $p(-1) = 0$, $p(3) = 0$

b. Find the remaining zeros of $p(x)$. $x = -1 + i$, $x = -1 - i$

7. A polynomial $p(x)$ is divided by $x - 2$ to obtain a polynomial $q(x)$ with a remainder of 0. $q(x)$ has degree 5 and a zero at $x = -3$.

a. Give two zeros of $p(x)$. $x = 2$, $x = -3$

b. Give two factors of $p(x)$. $(x - 2)$, $(x + 3)$

c. What is the maximum number of zeros that $p(x)$ can have? 6

d. What is the remainder when $q(x)$ is divided by $x + 3$? 0

8. Which of the following *cannot* be the shape of the graph of a polynomial of degree 4 with real coefficients? Explain your answer. b and e. See left.

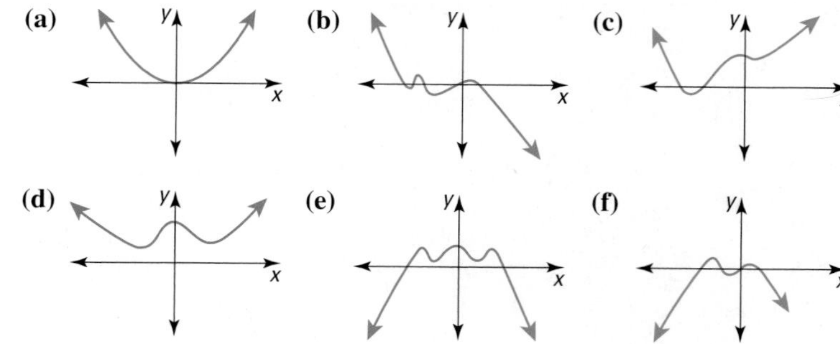

Applying the Mathematics

9. Find the three real solutions to the equation $4x^3 + 63x^2 + 38x - 105 = 0$.
$x = -(7/4)$, $x = -15$, $x = 1$

10. Suppose $S_n = 4^n - 1$. **a.** Give the first five terms of the sequence. **b.** Use Example 1 to explain why no term after the first is a prime number.
a) {3, 15, 63, 225, 1032} b) See left.

11. a. If $p(x)$ is a polynomial of degree 3, explain why the graph of $y = p(x)$ cannot cross the line $y = x$ more than 3 times. (Hint: Consider the polynomial $p_1(x) = p(x) - x$ and use the idea in the proof of the last theorem in this lesson.) See left.

b. Generalize part **a** to arbitrary polynomials $p(x)$ of degree $n \geq 2$.
See margin.

12. Prove that if the graphs of two polynomials $p_1(x)$ and $p_2(x)$ of degree n intersect at more than n points, then $p_1(x)$ and $p_2(x)$ are identical. (Hint: Consider the polynomial $p(x) = p_1(x) - p_2(x)$ and use the theorem on the number of zeros of a polynomial.) See margin.

13. The zeros of a fourth degree polynomial function p are 0, -4, $\frac{2}{3}$, and $\frac{1}{5}$. Write a formula for $p(x)$ in $a_4x^4 + a_3x^3 + a_2x^2 + a_1x + a_0$ form, where the a_i are all integers.
$p(x) = 15x^4 + 47x^3 - 50x^2 + 8x + 0$

248

Additional Answers

11. b. A polynomial of degree $n \geq 2$ will intersect the line $y = x$ in, at most, n points.

12. Suppose we have two polynomials of degree n, $p_1(x)$ and $p_2(x)$, that intersect at more than n points. Because polynomial addition is closed, $p(x) = p_1(x) + -p_2(x)$ is also a polynomial. Assume $p(x)$ is the not the zero polynomial. Because the degree of the sum of two polynomials is less than or equal to the larger of the degrees of the two polynomials, the degree of $p(x)$ is $\leq n$. By the Number of Zeros Theorem, $p(x)$ has at most n zeros. Therefore, $p_1(x)$ and $p_2(x)$ intersect in, at most, n points—contradicting our initial assumption. Therefore, $p(x)$ must equal 0, and hence, $p_1(x)$ must equal $p_2(x)$.

Review

14. Long division of the polynomial $x^4 - x^3 + x - 1$ by the polynomial $x^2 + 1$ is displayed below. Express this result in terms of the polynomials $p(x)$, $d(x)$, $q(x)$, $r(x)$ of the Quotient-Remainder Theorem for Polynomials. *(Lesson 4-3)*

$$\begin{array}{r|l} & x^2 - x - 1 \\ x^2 + 1 & x^4 - x^3 + 0x^2 + x - 1 \\ & x^4 \qquad + x^2 \\ \hline & -x^3 - x^2 + x - 1 \\ & -x^3 \qquad - x \\ \hline & -x^2 + 2x - 1 \\ & -x^2 \qquad - 1 \\ \hline & 2x \end{array}$$

$x^4 - x^3 + x - 1 = (x^2 - x - 1) \cdot (x^2 + 1) + 2x$

15. Find the quotient and remainder when

$$x^4 + 7x^3 - 2x + 1$$

is divided by $x + 3$. *(Lesson 4-3)* $q(x) = x^3 + 4x^2 - 12x + 34$, $r(x) = -101$

16. Factor: $(2x + y)(x + 3y)^2(x - y)^3 + (x - 4y)(x + 3y)(x - y)^4$. *(Lesson 4-1)* $(x - y)^3(x + 3y)(3x^2 + 2xy + 7y^2)$

17) $S_{1, \frac{1}{4}}$ followed by $T_{-6, -2}$

17. Give a rule for the rubberband transformation that maps the graph of $y = x^3$ onto the graph of $y = \frac{1}{4}(x + 6)^3 - 2$. *(Lesson 3-8)* See left.

18b)

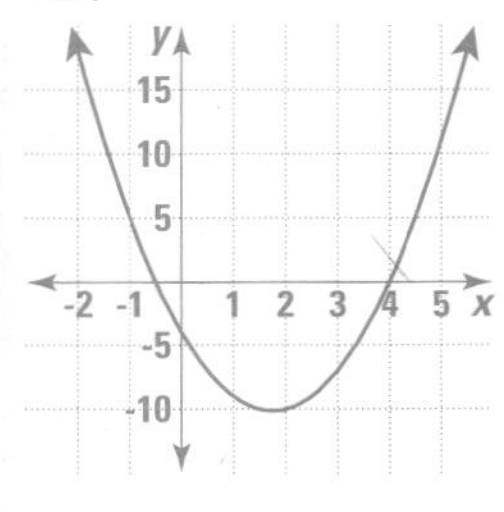

18. Solve the inequality $(2x + 1)(x - 4) < 0$.
   a. algebraically $-(1/2) < x < 4$
   b. graphically *(Lessons 3-5, 3-7)* See left.

19. Use the Intermediate Value Theorem to find an interval between two consecutive integers that contains a zero of the function g defined by $g(x) = x^5 - 4x^2 + 6$. *(Lesson 3-4)* $-2 < x < -1$

20a) f: $\{x : x \geq -2\}$, g: $\{x : x \neq 0\}$

20. Let $f: x \rightarrow \sqrt{x + 2}$ and $g: x \rightarrow \frac{1}{x^2}$.
   a. Identify the domains of f and g. See left.
   b. Find a formula for $g \circ f(x)$. $g \circ f(x) = 1/(x + 2)$
   c. Identify the domain of $g \circ f$. $\{x : x > -2\}$
   d. Explain why f has an inverse but g does not. *(Lessons 2-1, 3-2)* f is 1-1 but g is not.

21. a. Write the negation of the following statement:

   $\exists$ *x such that* $\log_2 x < 0$. $\forall x, \log_2 x \geq 0$

   b. Which is true, the statement or its negation? *(Lessons 1-1, 1-2)* the statement

Exploration

22. A polynomial is of degree 9.
   a. What is the largest number of relative maxima that it can have? 4
   b. What is the largest number of relative minima that it can have? 4
   c. Find an equation for a polynomial of degree 9 that verifies your answer to either part **a** or part **b**.
   $p(x) = x(x - 4)(x - 3)(x - 2)(x - 1)(x + 1)(x + 2)(x + 3)(x + 4)$

Follow-up Lesson 4-4

Practice

For more questions on SPUR Objectives, use **Lesson Master 4-4** (shown on page 247).

Assessment

Quiz A quiz covering Lessons 4-1 through 4-4 is provided in the *Assessment Sourcebook*.

Extension

Refer students to **Question 4.** Ask them to use the Factor Theorem to determine whether $c - d$ is a factor of $c^n - d^n$, if n is a positive even integer. [Yes.] Ask them to determine whether $c + d$ and $c - d$ are factors of $c^n - d^n$ if n is a positive odd integer. [$c + d$ is not; $c - d$ is.]

Project Update Project 4, *An Algorithm for Solving Cubic Equations,* on page 274, is related to the content of this lesson.

Setting Up Lesson 4-5

Do the In-class Activity on page 250 before discussing Lesson 4-5.

In-class Activity

Resources

From the ***Teacher's Resource File***

- Answer Master 4-5

The partitioning of the integers into three subsets, the focus of this activity, is important background for Lesson 4-5. These subsets become the equivalence classes for arithmetic modulo 3. It is worth the time to make certain that students understand that every integer is an element of exactly one of the congruence classes *R*1, *R*2, or *R*0.

In Parts 5 and 6, one way to summarize what students find is to write addition and multiplication tables for the sets *R*0, *R*1, and *R*2.

+	***R*0**	***R*1**	***R*2**
***R*0**	*R*0	*R*1	*R*2
***R*1**	*R*1	*R*2	*R*0
***R*2**	*R*2	*R*0	*R*1

*	***R*0**	***R*1**	***R*2**
***R*0**	*R*0	*R*0	*R*0
***R*1**	*R*0	*R*1	*R*2
***R*2**	*R*0	*R*2	*R*1

Introducing Lesson 4-5

Modular Arithmetic

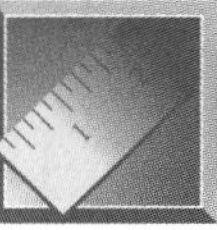

IN-CLASS ACTIVITY

Suppose you divide an integer n by 3. The Quotient-Remainder Theorem for Integers says that the quotient q and remainder r must satisfy

$$n = 3q + r$$

and that $0 \leq r < 3$. This explains why the remainder in division by 3 can be only 0, 1, or 2.

1 Let $R0$ = the set of integers whose remainder after division by 3 is 0. Let $R1$ = the set of integers whose remainder after division by 3 is 1. Let $R2$ = the set of integers whose remainder after division by 3 is 2. List ten of the elements of each of the sets $R0$, $R1$, and $R2$. Include both positive and negative integers in each set. **See margin.**

2 What happens if you add an element of $R1$ to an element of $R2$? Try this a few times. Then choose and, if necessary, complete the sentence below which describes your results.

(a) The sum is always in the set _?_. ***R*0**

(b) The sum is sometimes in the set _?_, sometimes in _?_, but never in _?_.

(c) The sum may be in any of the three sets.

3 Answer part 2 if you add an element of $R0$ to an element of $R2$. **(a) always in set *R*2**

4 Answer part 2 if you add an element of $R1$ to an element of $R1$. **(a) always in set *R*2**

5 Try part 2 with other sums and summarize what you find. **See margin.**

6 What happens if you *multiply* an element of $R2$ by an element of $R1$? Try this a few times. Then choose and, if necessary, complete the sentence below which describes your results.

(a) The product is always in the set _?_. ***R*2**

(b) The product is sometimes in the set _?_, sometimes in _?_, but never in _?_.

(c) The product may be in any of the three sets.

7 Try part 6 with other products and summarize what you find. **See margin.**

Additional Answers

1. Sample:
   $R0 = \{..., -12, -9, -6, -3, 0, 3, 6, 9, 12, 15, ...\}$
   $R1 = \{..., -11, -8, -5, -2, 1, 4, 7, 10, 13, 16, ...\}$
   $R2 = \{..., -10, -7, -4, -1, 2, 5, 8, 11, 14, 17, ...\}$
5. The values in Rn are given by $3a + n$, where a is any integer and $0 \leq n \leq 2$. The sum of any value from Rn plus any value from Rm is $(3a + n) + (3b + m) = 3 \cdot (a + b) + (n + m)$. When this sum is divided by 3, it has a fixed remainder: $n + m$ (or $n + m - 3$ if $n + m \geq 3$). Thus, such sums are always members of a single set.
7. Following the notation used in problem 5, the product of any value from Rn and any value from Rm is $(3a + n) \cdot (3b + m) = 9ab + 3bn + 3am + nm$. When this product is divided by 3, it has a fixed remainder: nm (or $nm - 3$ if $nm \geq 3$). Thus, such products are always members of a single set.

LESSON

4-5 Modular Arithmetic

Mod Placesetting. *Analog clocks provide examples of arithmetic modulo 12.*

In the chapter opener, we mentioned that codes can be constructed using *modular arithmetic*.

This arithmetic was developed by the great German mathematician Karl Friedrich Gauss (1777–1855). Gauss described the technique in his book *Disquisitiones Arithmeticae* ("Inquiries about Arithmetic"), published in 1801, in which he laid the foundation for the modern theory of numbers. This arithmetic is based on the Quotient-Remainder Theorem for Integers discussed in Lesson 4-2.

Sets of Remainders after Division by 3

In the In-class Activity you worked with sets of remainders after integer division by 3. One set is the set of integers with remainder 0, a second set is the set of integers with remainder 1, and the third set is the set of integers with remainder 2. We call these sets $R0$, $R1$, and $R2$.

The elements of $R0$ all have the form $3k$, for some integer k.

$$R0 = \{\ldots, -6, -3, 0, 3, 6, 9, 12, 15, 18, 21, \ldots\}$$

$R1$ consists of all the integers of the form $3k + 1$ for some integer k.

$$R1 = \{\ldots, -5, -2, 1, 4, 7, 10, 13, 16, 19, 22, \ldots\}$$

The elements of $R2$ all have the form $3k + 2$ for some integer k.

$$R2 = \{\ldots, -4, -1, 2, 5, 8, 11, 14, 17, 20, 23, \ldots\}$$

The Quotient-Remainder Theorem states that every integer is an element of exactly one of the sets $R0$, $R1$, or $R2$.

Lesson 4-5

Objectives

C Determine the congruence of integers in a given modulus.
G Use the properties of congruence of integers in a given modulus to rewrite sentences.
L Use modular arithmetic to solve applied problems.

Resources

From the ***Teacher's Resource File***
- Lesson Master 4-5
- Answer Master 4-5
- Teaching Aid 33: Warm-up

Additional Resources
- Visual for Teaching Aid 33
- Exploration 4-5

Teaching Lesson 4-5

Warm-up

Find a number whose remainder when divided by 7 is 6. Find a number whose remainder when divided by 7 is 3. Multiply these numbers together. What is the remainder when their product is divided by 7? Share your results with a classmate. Must you get the same answer? **Sample: 13; 10; the remainder, when 130 is divided by 7 is 4; the result should always be the same.**

Lesson 4-5 Overview

Broad Goals The definition and basic properties of modular arithmetic are presented here, with applications to check digits and to finding rightmost digits of certain numbers.

Perspective There are a number of reasons for discussing modular arithmetic here. (1) It is an immediate application of the Quotient-Remainder Theorem. (2) We later use the language of modular arithmetic to describe properties of the trigonometric functions. (For example, the solutions to the equation $\sin x = \frac{1}{2}$ can be described as $\{x: x = \frac{\pi}{6} \pm 2n\pi$ or $x = \frac{5\pi}{6} \pm 2n\pi$, for any integer $n\}$ or as $\{x: x \equiv \frac{\pi}{6} \pmod{2\pi}$ or $x \equiv \frac{5\pi}{6} \pmod{2\pi}$, for any integer $n\}$.) (3) There are some interesting problems that can be solved using congruences, and there are interesting applications. (4) Modular arithmetic is an idea that all college students of mathematics or computer science are expected to know.

Notes on Reading

❶ Some books define $a \equiv b \pmod{m}$ if and only if m is a factor of $a - b$. This is our Congruence Theorem. To make the Congruence Theorem more meaningful to students you may want to have students choose two elements from the set $R2$ and check that their difference is divisible by 3.

The starting point for generalizing the definition of congruence to noninteger values of m is the Congruence Theorem. For noninteger values of m we define $a \equiv b \pmod{m}$ if and only if $a - b$ is an integer multiple of m. So, for instance, $\frac{17\pi}{4} \equiv \frac{\pi}{4} \pmod{2\pi}$ because $\frac{17\pi}{4} - \frac{\pi}{4} = 4\pi$, which is an integer multiple of 2π.

Error Alert Watch for students who confuse the divisor and remainder in the notation. Modulo 5 means the divisor is 5, not the remainder. To discuss a remainder of 5 we use $R5$.

In the day-of-week discussion in **Example 1,** some students may suggest the following alternative. Dividing 100 by 7 leaves a remainder of 2. Two days after Thursday is Saturday. Thus the solution is Saturday.

You will probably have to explain **Example 3.** An alternate method is to find the last 2 digits of 17^9 by hand. When this is done, people ignore all but the last two digits of the multiplications.

We call 3 the **modulus** or **mod** for these sets. If two integers a and b are in the same set, we say that a and b are **congruent modulo 3,** and we write $a \equiv b \pmod 3$, read "a is congruent to b mod 3." For instance, both -2 and 19 are in $R1$, so $-2 \equiv 19 \pmod 3$. Because all multiples of 3 are in $R0$, $420 \equiv -15 \equiv 0 \pmod 3$. We call the sets **congruence classes modulo 3.**

Congruence with Moduli Other Than 3

The Quotient-Remainder Theorem for Integers implies that if d is any positive integer, then *any* integer n can be written uniquely as

$$n = dk + r,$$

where k is an integer and r is one of the d integers

$$0, 1, \dots, d - 1.$$

This means that the set of all integers can be partitioned into d disjoint subsets. One of the subsets consists of all integers n which have remainder $r = 0$ when divided by d; a second subset consists of all integers n which have a remainder $r = 1$ when divided by d; and so on. For example, if $d = 7$, the set of all integers is partitioned into seven disjoint subsets, $R0, \dots R6$, according to their remainder after division by 7. Elements of these subsets are congruent modulo 7. In general, the congruence of numbers is defined as follows.

❶ **Definition**
Let a and b be integers and let m be a positive integer. We say that ***a* is congruent to *b* modulo *m*,** denoted $a \equiv b \pmod{m}$, if and only if a and b have the same integer remainder when they are divided by m.

Presidential Plans.
President Franklin Delano Roosevelt addressing a joint session of Congress

Example 1

A tradition among politicians that dates back at least to President Franklin D. Roosevelt is to set an agenda for changes that they promise to enact in the first 100 days that they are in office. Suppose in an inaugural address on Thursday, January 20, 2005, a politician promises to accomplish an agenda for change in the next 100 days, starting with that day. Use modular arithmetic to determine the day of the week on which the 100-day period will end.

Solution

The number of a day of the week repeats just as remainders do. So identify Sunday as 1, Monday as 2, Tuesday as 3, and so on. We want to know what day of the week is 100 days after Thursday, which is 5. This translates to solving the equation $(x \equiv 5 + 100) \pmod 7$ for a number between 1 and 7. Since $x \equiv 105 \pmod 7$, divide 105 by 7 to find the remainder. The remainder is 0, so 100 days after Thursday, January 20, 2005, is a Saturday.

Optional Activities

Activity 1 Technology Connection
Materials: Explorations software

Students may use Exploration 4-5, *Modular Arithmetic,* to do the In-class Activity prior to Lesson 4-5. Students choose a modulus from 2 to 16 and two integers. A table of congruence classes and two equations showing the quotient and remainder for that modulus appear. Students may also add, subtract, or multiply two integers and see the results.

Activity 2 You might use this activity while discussing the lesson. Have students examine the ISBN numbers on several books and verify the check digits. This activity will help them practice (and remember!) that the remainder must always be positive, even though the dividend may be negative.

Activity 3 You might use this activity with **Question 19.** Ask students to extend the pattern to M_k as suggested in the Notes on the Questions. For M_k, ask them to determine the period, range, and intercepts of the function. [The period is k; the range is $0 \le y \le k - 1$, where y is an integer; x-intercepts occur at nk, where n is any integer; 0 is the only y-intercept.]

When Are Numbers Congruent Modulo *m*?

When two numbers a and b are congruent modulo m, then there exist integer quotients q_1 and q_2 with the same remainder r such that

$$a = mq_1 + r$$

and

$$b = mq_2 + r.$$

Because the remainder r is the same in both equations, when one equation is subtracted from the other, r disappears.

$$a - b = m(q_1 - q_2)$$

Also, because $q_1 - q_2$ is an integer, m is a factor of $a - b$. So if two integers are congruent mod m, then m is a factor of their difference. Conversely, it can be shown that if m is a factor of the difference $a - b$ of two integers a and b, then a and b are congruent modulo m. This leads to the following theorem.

Congruence Theorem
$\forall$ integers a and b and positive integers m, $a \equiv b \pmod{m}$ if and only if m is a factor of $a - b$.

For instance, consider the modulus 12. By the congruence theorem, two integers are congruent modulo 12 if their difference is divisible by 12. Thus $31 \equiv 7 \pmod{12}$ because $31 - 7 = 24$ and 24 is divisible by 12. By repeatedly adding or subtracting 12, you can find all the integers that are congruent to 7 modulo 12.

7, 19, 31, 43, . . . and -5, -17, -29, -41, . . .

The modulus 12 explains *clock arithmetic*, that is, 7 hours after 6:00 is 1:00 because $6 + 7 \equiv 1 \pmod{12}$.

Modular Arithmetic and Check Digits

When people enter or copy information, mistakes are made. In today's world, with so much information stored in computers, an error of just a single digit or number may mean that a company does not realize that you paid your bill, or you will receive an item different from the one you ordered by mail, or the wrong emergency vehicle is dispatched to an accident. To catch errors, many identification numbers (such as credit card numbers or billing numbers) have extra digits called *check digits*. The check digit is a code number determined in some mathematical way from the other digits in the identification number. Almost all check digits are calculated using modular arithmetic.

Example 2

Books published since 1972 are assigned ten-digit International Standard Book Numbers (ISBN). The first 9 digits give information; the last digit is a check digit. The check digit is determined by multiplying the first nine digits by 10, 9, 8, 7, 6, 5, 4, 3, and 2, respectively. The opposite of the sum of these products must be congruent to the check digit modulo 11. (A check digit of X means 10.) Fill in the correct check digit for 0-07-062341-____.

Technology Symbol manipulator programs, like *Mathematica* or *Derive*, display all the decimal places of numbers like 17^9, and so provide an alternate way of doing questions like those in **Example 3,** or a check.

When working mod m you should encourage students to replace any integer by the smallest nonnegative integer to which it is congruent whenever possible. This greatly simplifies calculations mod m. **Example 3** shows the power of this technique.

The idea of multiples of nonintegers, as discussed at the top of page 256, will bother some students and can lead to a lively class discussion.

Adapting to Individual Needs

Extra Help
As you discuss the Properties of Congruence, emphasize that there is no Division Property of Congruence. You might want to ask students to discuss the reasonableness of this. Some students might simply offer a counterexample; others might note that while the set of integers is closed over addition, subtraction, and multiplication, it is not closed over division.

LESSON MASTER 4-5
Questions on SPUR Objectives
See pages 278–281 for objectives.

Skills Objective C

1. Name two elements in each of the congruence classes modulo 5.
Sample: $R_0 = \{0, 5\}$, $R_1 = \{1, 6\}$, $R_2 = \{2, 7\}$, $R_3 = \{3, 8\}$, $R_4 = \{4, 9\}$

In 2 and 3, give the smallest positive integer that makes the congruence true.

2. $m \equiv 11 \bmod 5$ __1__
3. $x \equiv -9 \pmod{21}$ __12__

4. Consider the congruence classes $R_0, R_1, R_2, \ldots R_{10}$ for integers modulo 11.
   a. If you add an element of R_1 to an element of R_{10}, which class contains the sum? __R_0__
   b. If you multiply an element of R_4 and an element of R_7, which class contains the product? __R_6__

Properties Objective G

5. If a "special leap year" is defined as a year divisible by 4 but not divisible by 100, express any special leap year y as a solution to congruence sentences.
$y \equiv 0 \pmod{4}$ and $y \not\equiv 0 \pmod{100}$

6. If $m \equiv 3 \pmod{14}$ and $n \equiv 7 \pmod{14}$, write a congruence statement for
   a. $m - n$ $m - n \equiv 10 \pmod{14}$
   b. mn. $mn \equiv 7 \pmod{14}$

Uses Objective L

7. Find the last three digits of 11^{12}. __721__

8. The first 11 digits of the Universal Product Code (UPC) for a product give information; the last digit is the *Modulo 10 Check Character.* To calculate this check digit, add the values in the even-numbered positions of the first 11 digits starting from right to left. Then multiply this sum by 3, and add the product and the sum of the values in the odd-numbered positions. The check digit is the least number that when added to the above result gives a number that is a multiple of 10. Find the check digit for each number.
   a. 0-212000-15577-? __8__
   b. 0-87547-36720-? __5__

Additional Examples

1. Use modular arithmetic to explain why, if no leap year day intervenes, a date that falls on Monday this year will fall on Wednesday two years from now. **$730 \equiv 2 \pmod 7$, so when 730 days are added, it is like adding 2 to the day of the week.**
2. Using the ISBN check digit formula as given in **Example 2** of this lesson, fill in the correct check digit for 0-688-03118-__?__ **Sum of products = $0 \bullet 0 + 6 \bullet 9 + 8 \bullet 8 + \ldots + 1 \bullet 3 + 8 \bullet 2 = 212$. $-212 \pmod{11} \equiv 8 \pmod{11}$. Thus the check digit is 8.**
3. Find the last three digits of 19^9. **779**

Solution

Calculate the sum of the products.

$0 \cdot 10 + 0 \cdot 9 + 7 \cdot 8 + 0 \cdot 7 + 6 \cdot 6 + 2 \cdot 5 + 3 \cdot 4 + 4 \cdot 3 + 1 \cdot 2 = 128$

Now determine the smallest positive integer congruent to -128 mod 11.

Doing integer division of -128 by 11, -128 = 11(-12) + 4. So the quotient is -12 and the remainder is 4. Thus the check digit should be 4.

As you should have found in the In-class Activity, addition and multiplication behave in a consistent way with respect to congruence modulo m. Consider the following congruent numbers mod 3.

$$11 \equiv 8 \pmod 3$$
$$7 \equiv 19 \pmod 3$$

Add the numbers on the two sides and congruence (modulo 3) is maintained.

$$18 \equiv 27 \pmod 3$$

Similarly, subtract. $\quad 4 \equiv -11 \pmod 3$

Also, multiply. $\quad 77 \equiv 152 \pmod 3$

Congruences (modulo 3) are obtained for both subtraction and multiplication. The following theorem says that these results hold in general.

Theorem (Properties of Congruence)
Let a, b, c, and d be any integers and let m be a positive integer.
If $a \equiv b \pmod m$ and $c \equiv d \pmod m$, then

$a + c \equiv b + d$	$\pmod m$	Addition Property of Congruence
$a - c \equiv b - d$	$\pmod m$	Subtraction Property of Congruence
$ac \equiv bd$	$\pmod m$	Multiplication Property of Congruence

Proof
Addition Property of Congruence

Suppose $a \equiv b \pmod m$ and $c \equiv d \pmod m$.
Using the Congruence Theorem,

m is a factor of $a - b$ and m is a factor of $c - d$.

Thus there exist integers k_1 and k_2 such that

$$a - b = k_1 m \quad \text{and} \quad c - d = k_2 m.$$

Using the Addition Property of Equality,

$$(a - b) + (c - d) = k_1 m + k_2 m.$$

Adapting to Individual Needs

Challenge

Have students answer each of the following questions in the language of modular arithmetic.

1. Describe the x-intercepts of $y = \sin x$. $[x \equiv 0 \pmod \pi]$
2. Describe the asymptotes of $y = \tan x$. $[x \equiv \frac{\pi}{2} \pmod \pi]$
3. Solve: $\cos^2 x - \cos x - 2 = 0$. $[x \equiv \pi \pmod{2\pi}]$
4. Simplify i^n, where $i = \sqrt{-1}$ and n is any integer. $[i^n = 1$, if $n \equiv 0 \pmod 4$; $i^n = i$, if $n \equiv 1 \pmod 4$; $i^n = -1$, if $n \equiv 2 \pmod 4$; $i^n = -i$, if $n \equiv 3 \pmod 4)]$

From the Associative and Commutative Properties of Addition and from the Distributive Property,

$$(a + c) - (b + d) = (k_1 + k_2)m$$

Because $k_1 + k_2$ is an integer, m is a factor of $(a + c) - (b + d)$. So $a + c \equiv b + d \pmod{m}$ by the Congruence Theorem. The other parts of the theorem can be proved in a similar way.

Thus the congruence classes modulo m form a finite number system with many of the properties of the integers.

Using Modular Arithmetic to Study Large Numbers

When a large number such as 17^9 is calculated with a scientific calculator, the answer is an estimate in scientific notation. We got $1.1859 \cdot 10^{11}$ with one calculator and $1.185878765 \cdot 10^{11}$ with another. In normal decimal notation, these numbers are 118,590,000,000 and 118,587,876,500. Suppose that you wanted to obtain the exact value of 17^9. You can do this if you knew the last three digits of 17^9.

Observe that two integers a and b have the same last three digits in their decimal representation if and only if the decimal representation of $a - b$ ends in three zeros; that is, if and only if $a \equiv b \pmod{1000}$. So, modulo 1000, each integer is congruent to the integer formed by its three right digits.

Example 3

Find the last three digits of 17^9.

Solution

We need to find the smallest positive number in the congruence class (mod 1000) that is congruent to 17^9. We can do this by repeatedly applying the Multiplication Property of Congruence.

$$17 \equiv 17 \pmod{1000}$$
$$17^2 \equiv 289 \pmod{1000}$$

We use a calculator and reduce the number whenever possible so that the calculator will not give an answer in scientific notation.

$$17^3 = 4913 \equiv 913 \pmod{1000}$$
$$\Rightarrow 17^6 = 17^3 \cdot 17^3 \equiv 913 \cdot 913 \pmod{1000}$$
$$\Rightarrow 17^6 \equiv 833569 \equiv 569 \pmod{1000} \quad \text{because } 913 \cdot 913 = 833569$$
$$17^9 = 17^3 \cdot 17^6 \equiv 913 \cdot 569 \pmod{1000}$$
$$\Rightarrow 17^9 \equiv 519497 \equiv 497 \pmod{1000} \quad \text{because } 913 \cdot 569 = 519497$$

Thus the final three digits of 17^9 are 497. Combining this information with that of the second calculator approximation of 17^9, we find the exact value of 17^9 to be 118,587,876,497.

255

Notes on Questions

Question 5 Ask if students have noticed that the day of their birthday "migrates" by one day each non-leap year. Ask what happens during a leap year? [It migrates two days.] Ask if it is different for pre-March versus post-February birth dates? [Yes, pre-February 29th acts like the previous year.]

Question 12 Notice that the parts of this question are done in completely different ways. The first part can be gotten from a calculator directly. The second part should be done using modular arithmetic.

Question 16 Some students may do this problem by looking at the 2-digit endings of small powers of 4. There are 10 different 2-digit endings that repeat. They are, in order, 04, 16, 64, 56, 24, 96, 84, 36, 44, 76, and then the cycle repeats.

Question 19 A generalization is easy to make. If $M_k(n)$ is the smallest nonnegative integer congruent to n modulo k, then the graph of M_k is periodic with period k.

Question 20b Some students may say that all real numbers with the same decimal part are in the same congruence class modulo 1. This is a fine answer.

Question 26 Music Connection Meredith Wilson's musical *The Unsinkable Molly Brown,* was based on the life of Margaret Tobin Brown, a wealthy and eccentric turn-of-the-century Denver socialite. Molly Brown became a heroine during the sinking of the Titanic when she took charge of a lifeboat and offered support to others.

Many statements can be rephrased in the language of modular arithmetic. For instance,

x is an odd integer

means that x is of the form $2k + 1$, which means that x leaves a remainder of 1 when divided by 2. This can be written

$$x \equiv 1 \pmod{2}.$$

Modular arithmetic can be extended so that any real number is a modulus. For instance, the modulus 2π is often used with the circular functions. Thus $\frac{17\pi}{4} \equiv \frac{\pi}{4} \pmod{2\pi}$ because 2π is a factor of $\frac{17\pi}{4} - \frac{\pi}{4} = 4\pi$.

QUESTIONS

Covering the Reading

In 1–3, consider the congruence classes $R0$, $R1$, and $R2$ modulo 3.

1. In what set is the number 4321? $R1$

2. In what set is -42? $R0$

3. An integer of the form $3k + 1$ is in which of these sets? $R1$

4. a. How is the sentence $x \equiv y \pmod{4}$ read?
b. Describe the congruence classes modulo 4.
a, b) See left.

4a) x is congruent to y modulo 4

b) There are four disjoint sets: $Rk = \{x : x = 4 \cdot n + k$ for any integer $n\}$ for $k = 0, 1, 2, 3$.

5. Bill's birthday falls on a Sunday this year. On what day will it fall next year, 365 days later? (This assumes there is no leap year day in between.) Monday

6. *True or false.*
a. $139 \equiv 59 \pmod{10}$ True **b.** $139 \equiv 59 \pmod{9}$ False **c.** $139 \equiv 59 \pmod{4}$ True

In 7–10, give the smallest positive value that makes the congruence true.

7. $x \equiv 97 \pmod{5}$ 2

8. $y \equiv 46 \pmod{30}$ 16

9. $n \equiv 736 \pmod{360}$ 16

10. $z \equiv -1 \pmod{10}$ 9

11. The ISBN code for this book was 0-673-45914-__?__, where the blank is the check digit. Fill in the blank. 4

12. a. Give the last three digits of 18^{10}. 624 **b.** Give the first three digits of 18^{10}. 357

13. Describe a situation about time that is related to the fact that $9 + 5 \equiv 2 \pmod{12}$. Five hours after 9:00 it is 2:00.

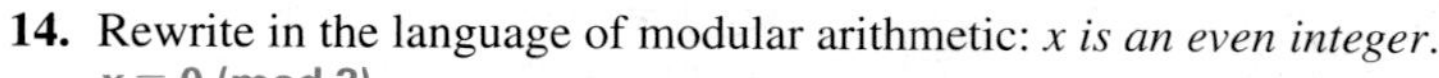

Applying the Mathematics

14. Rewrite in the language of modular arithmetic: *x is an even integer.* $x \equiv 0 \pmod{2}$

15. In geometry, rotations differing by 360° are considered equal. How can this be described in the language of modular arithmetic? See left.

15) Sample: $x + 360 \equiv x \pmod{360}$

16. Find the last two digits of 4^{2001}. 04

Additional Answers

17. By the Quotient-Remainder Theorem, for any integer n there exist unique integers q and r such that $n = q \cdot 3 + r$ where $0 \le r < 3$. If $r = 0$, then, by definition, n is divisible by 3. If $r \ne 0$, either $r = 1$ so $n + 2 = q \cdot 3 + r + 2 = q \cdot 3 + 3$ or $r = 2$ so $n + 1 = q \cdot 3 + r + 1 = q \cdot 3 + 3$. So one of the three consecutive integers, n, $n + 1$, or $n + 2$ is divisible by 3.

18. Suppose $a \equiv b \pmod{m}$ and $c \equiv d \pmod{m}$. The Congruence Theorem requires that m be a factor of both $a - b$ and $c - d$. Therefore, by the definition of factor, there exist integers k_1 and k_2 such that $a - b = k_1m$ and $c - d = k_2m$. By the Subtraction Property of Equality, $(a - b) - (c - d) = k_1m - k_2m$. By the Associative and Commutative Properties of Subtraction and the Distributive Property $(a - c) - (b - d) = (k_1 - k_2)m$. Because integers are closed under subtraction, $(k_1 - k_2)$ is an integer. Therefore, by definition, m is a factor of $(a - c) - (b - d)$. Therefore, by the Congruence Theorem, $(a - c) \equiv (b - d) \pmod{m}$.

19a)

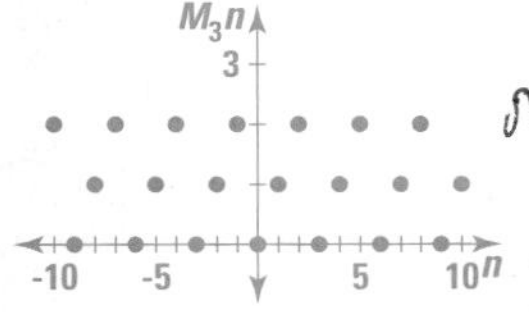

20a) $\{x : x = \pi + n \text{ for all integers } n\}$

25a)

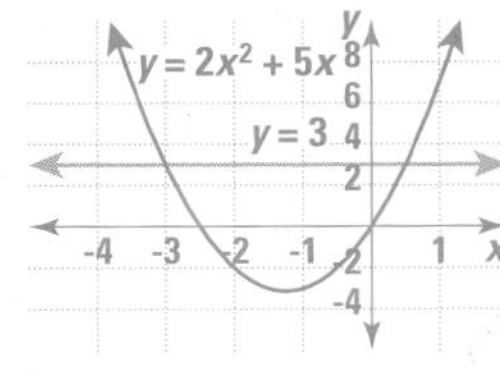

21) $v = -\frac{1}{2}$, $v = -1 + i$, $v = -1 - i$

17. Explain why exactly one of every three consecutive integers is divisible by 3. See margin.

18. Prove the Subtraction Property of Congruence. See margin.

19. Let $M_3(n)$ be the smallest nonnegative integer congruent to n (mod 3).
a. Graph the function M_3 for the interval of integers [-10, 10]. See left.
b. What is the period of this function? 3

20. Consider the real numbers modulo 1.
a. Which numbers are in the same congruence class as π? See left.
b. Generalize part **a** to complete the following sentence: Two real numbers are congruent modulo 1 if and only if ___?___. their difference is an integer

Review

21. $2x + 1$ is a factor of $2x^3 + 5x^2 + 6x + 2$. Use this information to find all solutions to the equation $2v^3 + 5v^2 + 6v + 2 = 0$. *(Lessons 4-3, 4-4)* See left.

22. $x^9 - 4x^8 + 3x^6 - 12x^5 - x + 4 = (x - 4) \cdot q(x)$ for some polynomial $q(x)$. *(Lessons 4-1, 4-2, 4-3)*
a. What is the degree of $q(x)$? 8
b. Write $q(x)$ in expanded form. $x^8 + 3x^5 - 1$

23. Consider the polynomial $p(a) = (2a + 5)^3 - (2a)^3 - 125$.
a. Write in expanded form. a) $60a^2 + 150a$
b. Write in factored form. $30a(2a + 5)$
c. Solve $p(a) = 0$. *(Lesson 4-1)* c) $a = 0, a = -\frac{5}{2}$

24. Prove the following conjecture or disprove by finding a counterexample. *(Lesson 4-1)* See margin.

$\forall$ positive integers a, b, and c, if a divides b and a divides b + c, then a divides c.

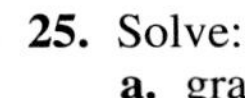

25. Solve: $2x^2 + 5x \geq 3$.
a. graphically See left.
b. algebraically *(Lessons 3-3, 3-7)* $x \leq -3, x \geq \frac{1}{2}$

26. Determine whether the following argument is valid or invalid. Justify your answer. valid by the Law of Detachment

If a ship hits an iceberg, then it sinks.
The Titanic hit an iceberg.
$\therefore$ *The Titanic sank.* *(Lessons 1-6, 1-7)*

27. Simplify. *(Previous course)*
a. $\frac{6x^5}{2x^3}$ $3x^2$
b. $\frac{8y^8}{4y^4}$ $2y^4$
c. $\frac{10z^3}{z}$ $10z^2$

TITANIC
WHITE STAR LINE
The World's Largest Liner
SOUTHAMPTON ~ NEW YORK
VIA CHERBOURG & QUEENSTOWN

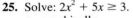

An original travel poster for the maiden and only voyage of the Titanic, *1912*

Exploration

28. Two nonzero numbers are reciprocals of one another if their product is 1. Similarly, for a given modulus, two congruence classes are reciprocals if their product is the multiplicative identity. In modulo 3, does each congruence class $R0$, $R1$, and $R2$ have a reciprocal? If so, find these reciprocals; if not, why not? Repeat the same investigation for the congruence classes $R0$, $R1$, $R2$, and $R3$ modulo 4. See margin.

Follow-up for Lesson 4-5

Practice

For more questions on SPUR Objectives, use **Lesson Master 4-5** (shown on page 253).

Assessment

Written Communication Have students **work in pairs**. Ask each student to determine a large power that cannot be shown in normal decimal notation on a calculator. Then have students follow the strategy of **Example 3** to find the exact digits in their partner's number. [Students use modular arithmetic to determine the decimal notation of very large numbers.]

Extension

You can extend **Question 28** by having students make multiplication tables for the integers modulo 3, mod 4, mod 5, and mod 6. The tables will show that, in every modulus, the number 1 is an identity for multiplication. In mod 4 and mod 6 there are nonzero elements that have no reciprocals (no number whose product with them is 1), but in mod 3 and mod 5 every element has a reciprocal. These algebraic systems can help to heighten the meaning of multiplicative identities and inverses.

Project Update Project 1, *Casting Out Nines,* Project 3, *Solving Modular Equations,* and Project 5, *Gauss,* on pages 273–274, relate to the content of this lesson.

24. Assume that a, b, and c are any positive integers such that a divides b and a divides $(b + c)$. Then by the definition of factor, there exist integers q_1 and q_2 such that $b = q_1 \cdot a$ and $(b + c) = q_2 \cdot a$. By the Subtraction Property of Equality $c = (b + c) - b = q_2 \cdot a - q_1 \cdot a$. Using the Distributive Property, this can be written as $c = (q_2 - q_1) \cdot a$. Since $q_2 - q_1$ is an integer, by the definition of factor, a divides c.

28. For the system of congruence classes modulo 3, both $R1$ and $R2$ are their own reciprocals, since $R1 \cdot R1 = R1$ and $R2 \cdot R2 = R2$. $R0$ does not have a reciprocal, since $R0 \cdot Rn = R0 \neq R1$, for $n = 0, 1$, and 2. For the system of congruence classes modulo 4, both $R1$ and $R3$ are their own reciprocals, since $R1 \cdot R1 = R1$ and $R3 \cdot R3 = R1$. $R2$ does not have a reciprocal, since $R2 \cdot R0 = R0$, $R2 \cdot R1 = R2$, $R2 \cdot R2 = R0$, and $R2 \cdot R3 = R2$. Similarly $R0$ does not have a reciprocal.

Lesson 4-6

Objectives

M Represent numbers in other bases and perform addition in base 2.

Resources

From the ***Teacher's Resource File***
- Lesson Master 4-6
- Answer Master 4-6
- Teaching Aids
  - 33 Warm-up
  - 39 Integers in Base 10 and Base 2
  - 40 Half-Adder Network

Additional Resources
- Visuals for Teaching Aids 33, 39, 40
- Exploration 4-6

Teaching Lesson 4-6

Warm-up

A number has hundreds digit *h*, tens digit *t*, and units digit *u*.

1. What is the value of the number? $100h + 10t + u$
2. What is the value of the number formed by reversing the digits? $100u + 10t + h$
3. Show that the difference of the number and the number formed by reversing the digits is divisible by 11. Difference $= (100h + 10t + u) - (100u + 10t + h) = 99h - 99u = 99(h - u) = 11 \cdot 9 \cdot (h - u)$, so the difference is divisible by 11. (Notice that the proof shows that the difference is not only divisible by 11, but it is divisible by 99.)

LESSON

4-6 Polynomial Representations of Integers

Bits of Art. *Modern computer monitors can display hundreds, thousands, or millions of distinct colors specified as 8-bit, 16-bit, or 32-bit color. The programs governing these displays are most efficient if numbers are written in a base that is a power of 2.*

When an integer, say 3407, is written in base 10, you mentally register that 3 is the thousands digit, 4 is the hundreds digit, and so on, and that the value of the number is the sum of the products of the coefficients with the place values. In polynomial language, the digits 3, 4, 0, and 7 are the coefficients of the polynomial $p(x) = 3x^3 + 4x^2 + 7$ evaluated at $x = 10$:

$$p(10) = 3 \cdot 10^3 + 4 \cdot 10^2 + 0 \cdot 10^1 + 7 \cdot 10^0 = 3407.$$

More generally, if an integer in base 10 has thousands digit T, hundreds digit h, tens digit t, and units digit u, then its value equals the polynomial *in 10*,

$$T \cdot 10^3 + h \cdot 10^2 + t \cdot 10 + u.$$

This is often written as $1000T + 100h + 10t + u$, which disguises its origin as a polynomial.

Bases other than 10 are frequently used in mathematics and its applications. For example, digital computers use **base 2 (binary)**, **base 8 (octal)**, and **base 16 (hexadecimal)** representations for internal storage and processing of data.

Binary or base 2 representation is especially appropriate for the representation of the input and output of internal computer components or memory locations that can be in one of two states, which can be thought of as On or Off and denoted by the digits 1 or 0, respectively. These states are called *bits*. In base 2, a number is the value $p(2)$ of a polynomial in 2 with coefficients that are either 0 or 1. For example, the integer 20 written in base 2 is 10100 because

$$20 = 1 \cdot 2^4 + 0 \cdot 2^3 + 1 \cdot 2^2 + 0 \cdot 2^1 + 0 \cdot 2^0.$$

Lesson 4-6 Overview

Broad Goals In this lesson students learn how to represent integers in bases other than base 10, and see the logic that a computer uses to add in base 2.

Perspective The first part of the lesson discusses the representation of an integer as a polynomial "in (base) 10." The second part of the lesson deals with other bases, concentrating on base 2 (binary) because that is the base most often used in computer science and other applications.

Students should be able to convert from one base to another and should be able to add integers written in binary. The last part of the lesson discusses the logical mechanism by which a computer adds, a mechanism dependent on base 2.

An important advantage of binary representation is the simplicity of its arithmetic, as is summarized in the addition and multiplication tables below.

Binary Addition Table

+	0	1
0	0	1
1	1	10

Binary Multiplication Table

×	0	1
0	0	0
1	0	1

To avoid confusion, whenever we write a number in a base other than our ordinary base 10 system, a subscript will be used to indicate the base. Also, commas are *not* used in numbers in any base other than 10.

Notice that octal or base 8 representation uses the integers 0, 1, 2, 3, 4, 5, 6, 7 as its digits and as the coefficients in its polynomial representation. For example, the integer 20 in base 8 is

$$20 = 2 \cdot 8^1 + 4 \cdot 8^0 = 24_8.$$

Because $2^3 = 8$, octal representation can be obtained from binary representation by partitioning the binary representation into groups of three.

$$20 = 10100_2 = \left|\ \underset{2}{10}\ \right|\ \underset{4}{100}\ \left| = 24_8\right.$$

Hexadecimal or base 16 representation uses the sixteen "digits"

0, 1, 2, 3, 4, 5, 6, 7, 8, 9, A, B, C, D, E, F

in its polynomial representation. For example, the integer 20 in base 16 is

$$20 = 1 \cdot 16^1 + 4 \cdot 16^0 = 14_{16}.$$

Hexadecimal representation can be obtained from binary representation by partitioning the latter into groups of 4 (because $2^4 = 16$).

$$20 = 10100_2 = \left|\ \underset{1}{1}\ \right|\ \underset{4}{0100}\ \left| = 14_{16}\right.$$

The binary, octal, and hexadecimal representations of the integers from 0 to 16 are given in the following table.

Integer	Base 2 Place Values 2^4 16	2^3 8	2^2 4	2^1 2	2^0 1	Base 2 Integer	Octal Integer	Hexadecimal Integer
0	0	0	0	0	0	0_2	0_8	0_{16}
1	0	0	0	0	1	1_2	1_8	1_{16}
2	0	0	0	1	0	10_2	2_8	2_{16}
3	0	0	0	1	1	11_2	3_8	3_{16}
4	0	0	1	0	0	100_2	4_8	4_{16}
5	0	0	1	0	1	101_2	5_8	5_{16}
6	0	0	1	1	0	110_2	6_8	6_{16}
7	0	0	1	1	1	111_2	7_8	7_{16}
8	0	1	0	0	0	1000_2	10_8	8_{16}
9	0	1	0	0	1	1001_2	11_8	9_{16}
10	0	1	0	1	0	1010_2	12_8	A_{16}
11	0	1	0	1	1	1011_2	13_8	B_{16}
12	0	1	1	0	0	1100_2	14_8	C_{16}
13	0	1	1	0	1	1101_2	15_8	D_{16}
14	0	1	1	1	0	1110_2	16_8	E_{16}
15	0	1	1	1	1	1111_2	17_8	F_{16}
16	1	0	0	0	0	10000_2	20_8	10_{16}

Notes on Reading

Weaned exclusively on base 10, students may find working in other bases confusing. You may wish to represent the same number in bases 2, 3, 4 , 5, and 10. Discuss which digits are allowed for each base. Note the similarity of place values in various bases. All share a right-most place value of one. In the hexadecimal (base 16) system used in some computer languages, extra digits needed to be invented. Ask why.

You may wish to recall the *Extension* in Lesson 4-1 (page 230) about $\log_b N$ approximating the number of digits in the base *b* representation of *N*. This fact helps explain why the logarithm to the base 2 is so important in computer science.

Technology Students may be interested to know that computers store all kinds of data in binary form. Occasionally programmers need to see the contents of certain memory locations. When the contents of memory are printed, it is represented in hexadecimal notation so that it is easy to read. The programmer knows that two hexadecimal digits are equal to one byte and, from this, is able to determine the size of memory.

Some advanced scientific and graphing calculators can represent and perform arithmetic on numbers in binary, octal, and hexadecimal. If you are using such calculators in your class, you should consult the owner's manual to see how to work with binary and hexadecimal numbers.

Optional Activities

Activity 1 Technology Connection
Materials: Explorations software

Students may use Exploration 4-6, *Base Notation,* as an alternative to **Examples 1–2.** Students can choose representation or conversion in any base from 2 to 16. They can input a number in the given base and see their number converted to base 10. Or they can input a number in base 10 and see the number converted to their chosen base.

Activity 2 You might use this activity after discussing the half-adder example on page 262. Have students verify that the sum digit network corresponds to *(p or q) and (not(p and q))*. [See table at right.]

p	*q*	*p or q*	*p and q*	*not(p and q)*	result
1	1	1	1	0	0
1	0	1	0	1	1
0	1	1	0	1	1
0	0	0	0	1	0

(Optional Activities continue on page 260.)

Students may wonder about other arithmetic operations on binary integers. The subtraction algorithm familiar to students can be mimicked to subtract binary integers but computers perform the operation in quite a different way. Multiplication as done by computers is even more difficult. However, the special case of multiplication by powers of 2 has properties like those of multiplying by 10 in base 10. To multiply by 2 you simply "shift left one bit." For example, the result of multiplying 101100101_2 by 2 is 1011001010_2.

Error Alert The table of base ten and base two integers at the bottom of page 259 should be explained carefully. Many students will incorrectly call 10_2 "ten" and 100_2 "one hundred." Do not let them be careless. It will interfere with their understanding. **Teaching Aid 39** shows this table.

In general, the digits in the base b representation of a number are the coefficients of a polynomial in b whose value is that number.

Definition

A number is written in **base b notation,**

$$(d_n\, d_{n-1} \ldots d_1\, d_0)_b,$$

if and only if each digit d_i is a particular integer from 0 through $b - 1$, and the value of the number is

$$d_n \cdot b^n + d_{n-1} \cdot b^{n-1} + \ldots + d_1 \cdot b^1 + d_0 \cdot b^0.$$

Example 1 illustrates how the definition can be used to find the base 10 representation of a number expressed in another base.

Example 1

Find the base 10 representation for the number 101011_2.

Solution

Use the definition and simplify. This number is in base 2, so $b = 2$ in the definition. Also, there are six digits, so $n = 5$.

$$\begin{aligned} 101011_2 &= 1 \cdot 2^5 + 0 \cdot 2^4 + 1 \cdot 2^3 + 0 \cdot 2^2 + 1 \cdot 2^1 + 1 \cdot 2^0 \\ &= 32 + 0 + 8 + 0 + 2 + 1 \\ &= 43 \end{aligned}$$

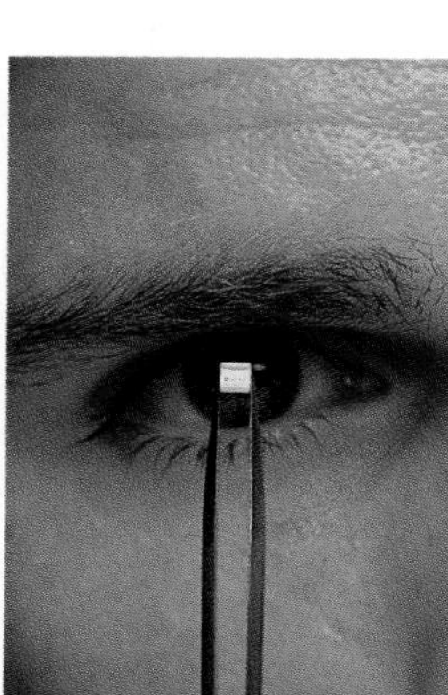

A modern computer chip of the size pictured can hold over 32 megabytes, or about 33,554,432 characters.

Computers process numbers in binary form. Bits are organized into groups of eight called **bytes**. Example 1 shows that 43_{10} can be stored in one computer byte as 00101011.

To change a number in base 10 to another base, you can use division. Example 2 shows how to do this.

Example 2

Write 397 in base 2.

Solution

The largest power of 2 that is less than or equal to 397 is $2^8 = 256$. Write down successive Quotient-Remainder Theorem representations $p = q \cdot d + r$, starting with $p = 397$, $q = 256$, and continuing with p equal to the successive remainders and q equal to the successively lower powers of 2.

$2^8 = 256$:	$397 = 1 \cdot 256 + 141$
$2^7 = 128$:	$141 = 1 \cdot 128 + 13$
$2^6 = 64$:	$13 = 0 \cdot 64 + 13$
$2^5 = 32$:	$13 = 0 \cdot 32 + 13$
$2^4 = 16$:	$13 = 0 \cdot 16 + 13$
$2^3 = 8$:	$13 = 1 \cdot 8 + 5$
$2^2 = 4$:	$5 = 1 \cdot 4 + 1$
$2^1 = 2$:	$1 = 0 \cdot 2 + 1$
$2^0 = 1$:	$1 = 1 \cdot 1 + 0$

$397 = 110001101_2$

Optional Activities

Activity 3 In **Example 1,** ask students to convert 101011_2 to base 4, base 8, and base 16 by partitioning the number into groups of 2 digits, 3 digits, and 4 digits. Students can check their results by using the definition of base b notation and simplifying. [For base 4 conversion, partition as $10|10|11 = 223_4$. For base 8 conversion, partition as $101|011 = 53_8$. For hexadecimal conversion, partition as $10|1011 = 2B_{16}$. To check: $2(4)^2 + 2(4)^1 + 3(4)^0 = 43$; $5(8)^1 + 3(8)^0 = 43$; $2(16)^1 + 11(16)^0 = 43$. Note that B becomes 11 in the conversion to base 10.] You could extend this activity to **Questions 5-6** on page 262.

Activity 4 This activity can be used after discussing the lesson. Have students consider numeration base (-2), which can convert positive or negative integers into binary numbers. Ask them to convert:

1. $10011_{(-2)}$ and $1101_{(-2)}$ into base 10. [15; -5]

2. t10 and -31 into base (-2). [11110; 100001]

Base 10 notation is more compact than binary, but base 2 has a computational advantage. You only need four facts to add any binary numbers. These facts are $0 + 0 = 0$; $0 + 1 = 1$; $1 + 1 = 10_2$; and $1 + 1 + 1 = 11_2$.

Example 3

Perform the base 2 addition at the right.

$$\begin{array}{r} 1\ 1\ 1\ 0_2 \\ +\quad 1\ 1\ 1_2 \\ \hline \end{array}$$

Solution

Just as in base 10, addition is usually done from right to left.

In the 2^0 or 1s place: $0 + 1 = 1 = 1_2$, so you write the 1 in the 2^0 place of the sum row.

$$\begin{array}{r} 1\ 1\ 1\ 0_2 \\ +\quad 1\ 1\ 1_2 \\ \hline 1_2 \end{array}$$

In the 2^1 or 2s place: $1 + 1 = 2 = 10_2$, so you write the 0 in the 2s place of the sum row and carry the 1 to the top of the 2^2 place column. (The carried 1 represents 2 groups of 2, which equals 1 group of 4, or 2^2.)

$$\begin{array}{r} {}^{1} \\ 1\ 1\ 1\ 0_2 \\ +\quad 1\ 1\ 1_2 \\ \hline \boxed{1}0\ 1_2 \end{array}$$

In the 2^2 or 4s place: $1 + 1 + 1 = 3 = 11_2$, so you write a 1 in the 2^2 place of the sum row and carry the other 1 to the 2^3 place column. (The carried 1 represents 2 groups of 4, which equals 1 group of 8, or 2^3.)

$$\begin{array}{r} {}^{1\ 1} \\ 1\ 1\ 1\ 0_2 \\ +\quad 1\ 1\ 1_2 \\ \hline \boxed{1}1\ 0\ 1_2 \end{array}$$

In the 2^3 or 8s place: $1 + 1 = 2 = 10_2$, so you write a 0 in the 2^3 place and carry the other 1 to the 2^4 place column. (The carried 1 represents 2 groups of 8, which equals 1 group of 16, or 2^4.)

$$\begin{array}{r} {}^{1\ 1\ 1} \\ 1\ 1\ 1\ 0_2 \\ +\quad 1\ 1\ 1_2 \\ \hline \boxed{1}0\ 1\ 0\ 1_2 \end{array}$$

In the 2^4 or 16s place: bring the one down.

$$\begin{array}{r} {}^{1\ 1\ 1} \\ 1\ 1\ 1\ 0_2 \\ +\quad 1\ 1\ 1_2 \\ \hline 1\ 0\ 1\ 0\ 1_2 \end{array}$$

The sum is 10101_2.

Check

In base 10, the addends are 14 and 7. So the sum should be 21. Check that $10101_2 = 21_{10}$:

$$1 \cdot 2^4 + 0 \cdot 2^3 + 1 \cdot 2^2 + 0 \cdot 2^1 + 1 = 21.$$

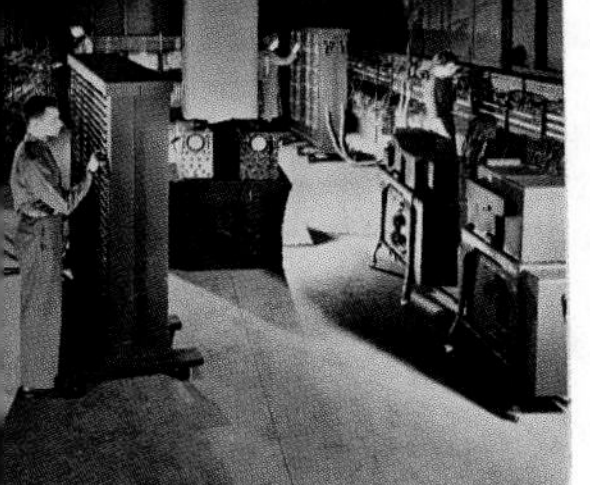

ENIAC, the first computer

In the early days of computers, programmers had to write numbers in binary format to code their machines and to enter data. Today, systems programmers, who write computer programs which can be run on a computer's central processing unit without decoding, often write programs using octal and hexadecimal representation. As we have seen, these bases are important because they are powers of 2 and because it is easy to convert numbers in them to and from base 2.

You now have the tools to understand the mechanisms by which a computer performs addition. Digital computers use several networks, one of which is a **half-adder**. A half-adder takes two binary digits as input and produces the two digits of their sum as output. (The sum $1_2 + 0_2$ can be

Adapting to Individual Needs

Extra Help

Some students may have difficulty following the conversion from binary to either octal or hexadecimal notation as discussed above the table on page 259. You may need to provide more detail. First, point out that the partitioning begins at the right. The number of digits in the partition matches the power: Three for $2^3 = 8$ and 4 for $2^4 = 16$. (You might ask how to convert to base 4 using this method: Partition the binary number into groups of 2 because $4 = 2^2$.) Have students notice that the left-most partition might have less digits than the others. Then convert each group as if it were a separate binary number by adding powers of 2. For example, in the right-most partition in the octal conversion,
$100 = 1 \cdot 2^2 + 0 \cdot 2^1 + 0 \cdot 2^0 = 4$.
This digit, 4, is the right-most octal digit.

LESSON MASTER 4-6 Questions on SPUR Objectives
See pages 278–281 for objectives.

Representations Objective M

In 1 and 2, find the base-2 representation of the number.

1. 38 100110_2 2. 111 1101111_2

In 3–6, find the base-10 representation of the number.

3. 1100011_2 99 4. 100001_2 33

5. 327_8 215 6. $BF21_{16}$ 48,929

7. Express 100 in base n where

a. $n = 2$. 1100100_2 b. $n = 5$. 400_5

c. $n = 8$. 144_8 d. $n = 6$. 244_6

In 8 and 9, perform the indicated addition and then verify your answer by finding the base 10 representations of the numbers.

8. $101_2 + 1110_2$ = 10011_2 $101_2 = 5$; $+\ 1110_2 = +\ 14$; $10011_2 = 19$

9. $1110110_2 + 100111_2$ = 10011101_2 $1110110_2 = 118$; $+\ 100111_2 = +\ 39$; $10011101_2 = 159$

When discussing the half-adder network, reassure students that they are not expected to become computer designers in this course. The purpose of this example is to tie together concepts in number representation and logic with computer design. **Teaching Aid 40** contains the network and truth table for the half-adder.

Additional Examples

1. Give the base 10 representation for the number 11011011_2. 219
2. Write 289 in base 2. 100100001_2
3. Perform the base 2 addition below.

$$\begin{array}{r} 1\ 0\ 1\ 1\ 0\ 1\ 1_2 \\ +\ \ 1\ 0\ 1\ 1\ 1\ 0_2 \\ \hline 1\ 0\ 0\ 1\ 0\ 0\ 1_2 \end{array}$$

Notes on Questions

Question 9 Ask students to calculate $\log_2 72$ and compare this to the answers to **parts a and b.** [For any positive integer x, $\log_2 x$ is one less than the number of digits in the base 2 representation of x.]

Question 15 Think of what you get by adding one to 11111_2.

Question 16 Ask how to tell if an integer written in base 3 is even or odd. [Because of the result in the Challenge below, the number is even if and only if the sum of its digits is even.]

thought of as having a two-digit value by writing $1_2 + 0_2 = 01_2$.) A half-adder network is shown below.

Half-Adder Network

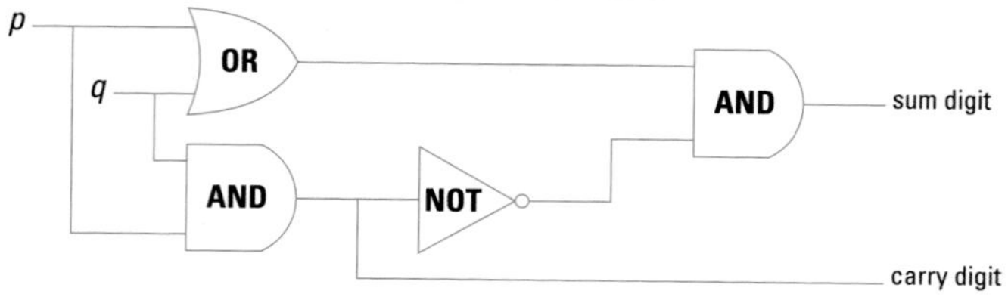

p
q
OR
AND
NOT
AND
sum digit
carry digit

p	q	sum digit	carry digit
1	1	0	1
1	0	1	0
0	1	1	0
0	0	0	0

The variables p and q represent the digits to be added, and they are in State 0 or State 1. Trace through the network and determine the output when 1 and 0 are added. (This is the second row of the table at the left.) Then $p = 1$ and $q = 0$. Notice that the network gives two outputs—the sum digit and the carry digit. For the sum digit, the OR gate outputs a 1 and sends it to the upper AND gate. Along the lower path, the AND gate outputs a 0 which is reversed to a 1 by the NOT gate. Because the input to the upper AND gate is two 1s, its output, the sum digit, is 1. For the carry digit, the output of the lower AND gate is 0, so 0 is the carry digit.

This analysis also describes the third row of the input-output table; the other rows are completed in a similar way.

Notice that the half-adder network can be viewed as the combination of two networks. The *carry digit* network is the simpler one and corresponds to the logical expression *p and q*. The *sum digit* network is more complicated, but, as you can check for yourself, corresponds to *(p or q) and (not(p and q))*.

The half-adder can only be used to compute the sum of the ones digits of two binary numbers. But when adding the other digits you must take carrying into account. This requires the use of a network called a *full-adder*. We leave the discussion of full-adders to a computer science course.

QUESTIONS

Covering the Reading

1. Write the number $6 \cdot 10^9 + 2 \cdot 10^5 + 3 \cdot 10^2$ in base 10. 6000200300
2. *Multiple choice.* What is the correct way to read 10_2? d
   (a) ten (b) ten base two
   (c) one zero two (d) one zero base two
3. Why is it incorrect to write the base 2 representation of 8 as 200_2? 2 is not a digit in base 2.
4. Find the binary, octal, and hexadecimal representations of the positive integer 63. 111111_2, 77_8, $3F_{16}$

In 5–8, find the base 10 representation of the number.

5. 111_2 7
6. 110010_2 50
7. 567_8 375
8. $A4_{16}$ 164

Adapting to Individual Needs

Challenge

Have students prove that an integer is divisible by 9 if and only if the sum of its digits in base 10 is divisible by 9. [Let the number have digits $a_n a_{n-1} \ldots a_1 a_0$, so that its value is $a_n 10^n + a_{n-1} 10^{n-1} + \ldots a_1 \cdot 10 + a_0$. Since $10 \equiv 1 \pmod 9$, for all k, $10k \equiv 1 \pmod 9$, and so for all k $a_k 10^k \equiv a_k \pmod 9$. Thus the value of the number is congruent to $a_n + a_{n-1} + \ldots + a_1 + a_0$, which is the sum of its digits. But a number is divisible by 9 if and only if it is congruent to 0 (mod 9). Thus, if the sum of its digits is congruent to 0 (mod 9), the value of the number is divisible by 9. More generally, a number is divisible by $b - 1$ if and only if the sum of its digits in its base b representation is divisible by $b - 1$. This can be proved by an argument similar to that in the preceding paragraph. Replace 10 by b and 9 by $b - 1$.)]

9. a. How many digits are in the base 2 representation of 72? (Hint: Write integer powers of 2 as in Example 2.) 7

b. Find the base 2 representation of 72. 1001000_2

c. Check your result in part **b** by expanding the base 2 representation with appropriate powers of 2. $2^6 + 2^3 = 72$

10. Find the decimal (base 10), octal, and hexadecimal representations of the integer whose binary representation is 10101101_2.
173, 255_8, AD_{16}

11. a. How many addition facts do you need to add in base 2? 4

b. How many addition facts do you need to add in base 10? 100

In 12 and 13, perform the indicated additions.

12. $10111_2 + 11010_2$ = 110001_2

13. $11011_2 + 1010_2$ = 100110_2

14. Refer to the half-adder network at the end of the lesson. Let $p = 0$ and $q = 0$. Trace through the network and determine the sum and carry digits. Show that your results agree with the entries in the fourth row of the input-output table. See left.

14) Carry digit is the output of the lower AND gate, which is 0. Since the output of the OR gate is 0 and is one of the inputs to the upper AND gate, the sum digit, which is the output of that gate, is also 0.

Applying the Mathematics

15. *Multiple choice.* Which of the following equals the base 10 representation of 11111_2? $2^5 - 1$

(a) 2^6 (b) $2^6 - 1$ (c) 2^5 (d) 2^{5-1} (e) $2^5 - 1$

16. How can you tell just by looking at a base 2 representation whether the number is even or odd?
It is even if the last digit is 0 and odd if that digit is 1.

17. In 1995, the total federal debt was about 4,921,000,000,000 dollars. This takes 13 digits to write. How many digits would be in the base 2 representation of the debt? 43

18. a. What digits are allowed in the base 3 representation of an integer?

b. Determine the base 10 representation for 1201_3. 46

c. Find the base 3 representation for 46. 1201_3

a) 0, 1, 2

19. Create addition and multiplication tables for base 8. See margin.

Review

20. Name 5 elements in each of the congruence classes modulo 5. *(Lesson 4-5)*
See left.

20) $R0$: -10, -5, 0, 5, 10
$R1$: -9, -4, 1, 6, 11
$R2$: -8, -3, 2, 7, 12
$R3$: -7, -2, 3, 8, 13
$R4$: -6, -1, 4, 9, 14

21. Find the smallest positive integer that makes the congruence true.

a. $x \equiv 87 \pmod{15}$ $x = 12$ **b.** $y \equiv -3 \pmod{7}$ *(Lesson 4-5)* $y = 4$

22. Find all solutions to $136t = 18t^3 + 7t^2 + 15$. (Hint: Graph to find one solution.) *(Lesson 4-4)* $t = \frac{1}{9}$, $t = \frac{5}{2}$, $t = -3$

23. Show that $5x + 2$ is a factor of the polynomial $p(x) = 5x^3 + 22x^2 + 53x + 18$. *(Lesson 4-3)*
$5x^3 + 22x^2 + 53x + 18 = (x^2 + 4x + 9)(5x + 2)$

Question 17 As in **Question 9,** suggest $\log_2$ as being helpful.

Social Studies Connection The national debt cannot rise above the *national debt ceiling.* However, Congress can, and does, raise the ceiling. There was a surplus in only 8 of the years between 1936 and 1995.

Additional Answers

19.

+	0	1	2	3	4	5	6	7
0	0	1	2	3	4	5	6	7
1	1	2	3	4	5	6	7	10
2	2	3	4	5	6	7	10	11
3	3	4	5	6	7	10	11	12
4	4	5	6	7	10	11	12	13
5	5	6	7	10	11	12	13	14
6	6	7	10	11	12	13	14	15
7	7	10	11	12	13	14	15	16

•	0	1	2	3	4	5	6	7
0	0	0	0	0	0	0	0	0
1	0	1	2	3	4	5	6	7
2	0	2	4	6	10	12	14	16
3	0	3	6	11	14	17	22	25
4	0	4	10	14	20	24	30	34
5	0	5	12	17	24	31	36	43
6	0	6	14	22	30	36	44	52
7	0	7	16	25	34	43	52	61

Follow-up for Lesson 4-6

Practice

For more questions on SPUR Objectives, use **Lesson Master 4-6** (shown on page 261).

Assessment

Oral Communication Write down a three-digit number given in decimal notation. Have the student explain each step in the conversion to binary notation as either you or the student performs the computations. Then repeat the process by beginning with a 6- or 7-digit binary number and converting to decimal notation. [Students convert numbers between binary and decimal notation.]

Extension

Ask students to write addition and multiplication tables for base 2:

+	0	1
0	0	1
1	1	0

•	0	1
0	0	0
1	0	1

You might compare this to the base 10 tables that students learned in elementary school.

Project Update Project 1, *Casting Out Nines,* on page 273, relates to the content of this lesson.

25) Suppose m is any integer. When m is divided by 4, the possible remainders are 0, 1, 2, 3. By the Quotient-Remainder Theorem, there exists an integer k such that $m = 4k$, or $m = 4k + 1$, or $m = 4k + 2$, or $m = 4k + 3$.

24. Use long division to find the quotient $q(x)$ and remainder $r(x)$ when $p(x) = 2x^3 - 3x^2 + 4x - 6$ is divided by $d(x) = x - 1.25$. *(Lesson 4-3)* $q(x) = 2x^2 - .5x + 3.375$, $r(x) = -1.78125$

25. Use the Quotient-Remainder Theorem to show that every integer m can be written in one of the following forms:

$$m = 4k,\ m = 4k + 1,\ m = 4k + 2, \text{ or } m = 4k + 3$$

for some integer k. *(Lesson 4-2)* See left.

26. Use your calculator to find the quotient and remainder when 64,942 is divided by 98. *(Lesson 4-1)* $q = 662$, $r = 66$

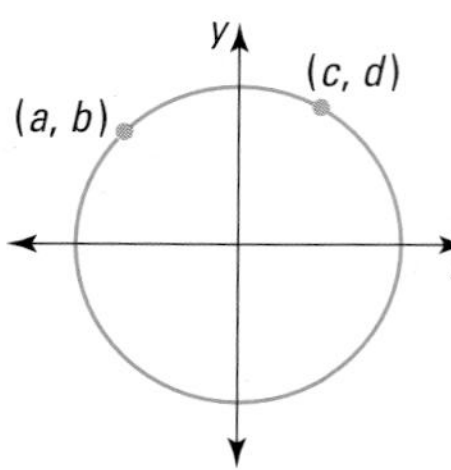

27. Which letter on the unit circle at the left could stand for each of the following? *(Lesson 2-6)*

a. $\cos\left(\frac{3\pi}{4}\right)$ *a* **b.** $\sin\left(\frac{\pi}{3}\right)$ *d* **c.** $\cos 60°$ *c* **d.** $\sin\left(\frac{3\pi}{4}\right)$ *b*

28. Determine whether the statement is logically equivalent to

If figure ABC is a right triangle, then it has exactly two acute angles.

a. *If ABC has exactly two acute angles, then it is a right triangle.*
b. *If ABC does not have exactly two acute angles, then it is not a right triangle.* Yes (contrapositive)
c. *If ABC is not a right triangle, then it does not have exactly two acute angles.* *(Lesson 1-5)* No (inverse error)

a) No (converse error)

29. *True or false.* If false, give a counterexample.

$$\forall \text{ real numbers } x,\ |x| = x. \quad \textit{(Lesson 1-1)}$$

False. $|-1| \neq -1$

30. The equation $d = .044v^2 + 1.1v$ estimates the distance d in feet that it takes to stop a car traveling at v miles per hour. At what speed(s) is the stopping distance 50 feet? *(Lesson 3-4)* ≈ 23 mph

Stopping Distance? *On October 15, 1997, near Gerlach, Nevada, RAF pilot Andy Green drove the Thrust SSC at a record-breaking average speed of 763.035 mph (Mach 1.02).*

Exploration

31. a. Show that $\frac{1}{3} = .010101\ldots_2 = .\overline{01}_2$. See left.
b. Find the base 2 representation for $\frac{1}{7}$. $0.001001\ldots_2$
c. Find the base 2 representation for $\frac{1}{5}$. $0.00110011\ldots_2$

31a) $0.0101\ldots_2 = 2^{-2} + 2^{-4} + 2^{-6} + \ldots = \frac{2^{-2}}{1 - 2^{-2}} = \frac{1}{3}$

LESSON

4-7

Prime Numbers and Prime Polynomials

Prime Needs. *Supercomputers make finding very large prime numbers possible. This one is capable of 60 billion calculations per second. The heat created by its processors is removed by liquid immersion cooling.*

In this chapter, you have seen many similarities and connections between integers and polynomials. We end with a discussion of "primeness" of each. Recall the definition of prime number.

> **Definition**
> An integer $n > 1$ is **prime** if and only if 1 and n are the only positive integer factors of n.

For example, 53 is prime because its only positive integer factors are 1 and 53. But 54 is not prime because 6 is a factor of 54. If n is not prime, then either $n \leq 1$ or $n = d \cdot q$, where both d and q are positive integers greater than 1. With $n = 54$, d and q could be 6 and 9 or 3 and 18 or 2 and 27. Notice that the factors d and q are smaller than n and they themselves either are prime or can be factored.

Prime numbers have long been important in pure mathematics. Until recently, it was thought that prime numbers had few practical applications. However, as we pointed out in the opening of this chapter, with the advent of electronic computing, prime numbers have been used to develop codes that are very difficult to break. As computers have become faster and mathematicians have developed better algorithms for factoring large numbers, larger and larger primes are needed.

The largest prime known (as of this writing) is $2^{2976221} - 1$. It was found on August 24, 1997, by Gordon Spence using a program written by George Woltman. Because $\log (2^{2976221} - 1) = 895931.79\ldots$, this number is larger than 10^{895931} and has 895,932 digits in base 10. The universe is not old enough for all integers between 1 and $2^{2976221} - 1$ to have been checked

Lesson 4-7

Objectives

D Factor polynomials over the reals.
I Use proof by contradiction.
J Use the Factor Search Theorem and the Fundamental Theorem of Arithmetic in determining prime numbers and prime factorizations.

Resources

From the ***Teacher's Resource File***

- Lesson Master 4-7
- Answer Master 4-7
- Teaching Aids
  - 33 Warm-up
  - 41 Definitions and Theorems I
  - 42 Definitions and Theorems II
- Technology Sourcebook
  Calculator Master 7

Additional Resources

- Visuals for Teaching Aids 33, 41, 42

Teaching Lesson 4-7

Warm-up

1. How many digits does $2^{1,000,000} - 1$ have in base 10? **301,030**
2. Explain why $2^{1,000,000} - 1$ is not a prime number. **$2^{1,000,000} - 1$ is of the form $x^2 - 1$, where $x = 2^{500,000}$. Since $x^2 - 1 = (x - 1)(x + 1)$, $2^{1,000,000} - 1 = (2^{500,000} + 1)(2^{500,000} - 1)$. Thus $2^{1,000,000} - 1$ has factors other than itself and 1, and so it is not prime.**

Lesson 4-7 Overview

Broad Goals This lesson formalizes the factoring of integers and polynomials that students have done in previous courses. The infinitude of primes is proved by contradiction (the way Euclid did it) and the versions of unique factorization into prime factors for integers and polynomials are explained.

Perspective Some books use the term *irreducible polynomial* similar to the way we use *prime polynomial.* We use prime polynomial to emphasize the common features of integers and polynomials.

Although we define polynomials as prime only over the reals, you could replace *real* by *rational* or, for that matter, by any field.

The only polynomials that are prime over the complex numbers are polynomials of degree 1, because any quadratic can be factored into linear factors if complex coefficients are allowed. For instance, $x^2 + 1 = (x - i)(x + i)$.

Because there is no natural order relation on the set of polynomials, there is no standard prime factorization for polynomials. The factors may be written in any order.

for factors, even if a trillion trillion numbers could be checked each second. Obviously Woltman knew some efficient testing techniques.

A first step toward efficiency is found by using the Prime Factor Theorem.

Prime Factor Theorem
Every integer greater than 1 is either prime or has a prime factor.

❶ **Proof**
The argument is indirect. Suppose that there is an integer that neither is prime nor has a prime factor. Then there would be a smallest integer n greater than 1 that neither is prime nor has a prime factor. Since n is not prime, it can be factored. So

$$n = n_1 \cdot n_2,$$

where n_1 and n_2 are integers smaller than n. Because $n_1 < n$ and n is the smallest integer greater than 1 that neither is prime nor has a prime factor, n_1 must either be prime or have a prime factor. But if n_1 has a prime factor, so does n. (Look back at Question 7 of Lesson 4-1.) So n_1 must be prime. But then n has a prime factor, which contradicts the supposition. Consequently, the supposition is false, and the statement of the Prime Factor Theorem must be true.

The reasoning used above to prove the Prime Factor Theorem is an example of a *proof by contradiction*.

In general, *proof by contradiction* works in the following way: Let s be the statement you want to prove. You reason from *not s* until you deduce a statement of the form *p and (not p)*, which is a contradiction. From this you conclude that *not s* is false, which means that s is true. The Latin name for this form of argument is **reductio ad absurdum**, literally meaning "reducing to an absurdity." The following theorem guarantees that Proof by Contradiction is a valid form of argument.

Theorem (Validity of Proof by Contradiction)
The following form of argument is valid.

If not s then (p and (not p)).
$\therefore$ *s.*

Proof
To prove the validity of this argument, we must prove that the conditional $(\sim s \Rightarrow (p \text{ and } \sim p)) \Rightarrow s$ is always true. This is shown by the truth table below.

s	p	$\sim s$	$\sim p$	p and $\sim p$	$\sim s \Rightarrow (p \text{ and } \sim p)$	$(\sim s \Rightarrow (p \text{ and } \sim p)) \Rightarrow s$
T	T	F	F	F	T	T
T	F	F	T	F	T	T
F	T	T	F	F	F	T
F	F	T	T	F	F	T

Notes on Reading

The definitions and theorems in this lesson are on **Teaching Aids 41-42.**

In the Infinitude of Primes Theorem, the integer $n + 1$ obtained in the proof (1 more than the product of the first m primes) is pointed out as being either prime or having a prime factor larger than any prime on the list. Students may think that the latter possibility does not occur and that $n + 1$ is prime for all m. For instance, $2 \cdot 3 + 1$, $2 \cdot 3 \cdot 5 + 1$, $2 \cdot 3 \cdot 5 \cdot 7 + 1$, and $2 \cdot 3 \cdot 5 \cdot 7 \cdot 11 + 1$ are all prime. However, $2 \cdot 3 \cdot 5 \cdot 7 \cdot 11 \cdot 13 + 1 = 30031 = 59 \cdot 509$. Let n_p be 1 more than the product of primes less than or equal to p. Then, among the primes less than 11,213, it is known that n_p is prime only for $p = 2, 3, 5, 7, 11$ (the cases mentioned above), and 31, 379, 1019, 1021, and 2657.

When discussing the largest prime that has been found to date, you might mention that on most calculators, the number of digits in $2^{2976221} - 1$ cannot be found by taking its common logarithm. However, subtracting 1 does not change the number of digits in this number (it is not an integer power of 10), and we can use properties of logs to find the number of digits in $2^{2976221}$.

Optional Activities

Activity 1 Technology Connection
In Technology Sourcebook, Calculator Master 7, students use a programmable calculator to explore prime numbers, related number theory, and applications to security codes.

Activity 2 You might ask students familiar with programming to write programs that will determine if a number n is prime by testing different sets of positive integers as factors such as those below. Have students enter a large test integer and compare the computing times each test takes.

1. all the positive integers up to $n - 1$
2. all the positive integers up to $\frac{n}{2}$
3. all the positive integers up to $\sqrt{n}$

The search for large primes is greatly facilitated by the Prime Factor Theorem because it means that we need check only for *prime* factors when we are testing whether a given large number is prime or not.

A prime number larger than any given known prime always exists because it has long been established that there are infinitely many primes. The earliest known proof of the infinitude of primes is in Book 9 of the 13 books of Euclid's *Elements*, which was written about 250 B.C. The proof by contradiction given below is a version of the one presented by Euclid, but it has been put into today's mathematical language and notation.

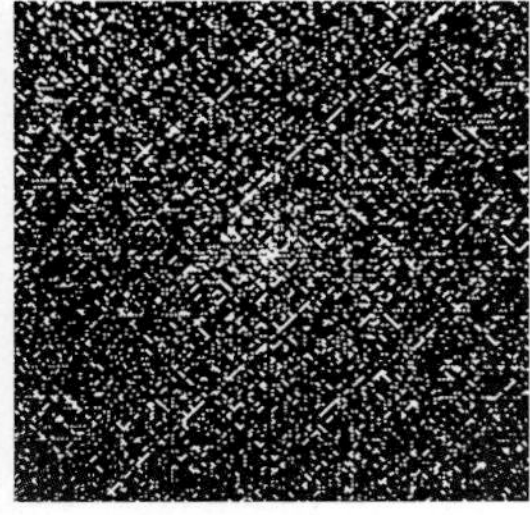

This is a computer-generated grid showing primes (white dots) as a spiral of integers from 1 to about 65,000.

Infinitude of Primes Theorem
There are infinitely many prime numbers.

Proof

Let *s*: There are infinitely many prime numbers.
Suppose *not s*: There are finitely many prime numbers.
Because there is a finite number, say *m*, of primes, they can be listed from smallest to largest:

$$p_1 = 2,\ p_2 = 3,\ p_3 = 5,\ \ldots,\ p_m.$$

Multiply these primes to get a new number

$$n = p_1\, p_2\, p_3 \cdot \ldots \cdot p_m.$$

Now consider the next consecutive integer, $n + 1$. Since $n + 1$ is larger than the assumed largest prime p_m, it is not prime. By the Prime Factor Theorem, $n + 1$ must have a prime factor, say *p*. Then *p*, being prime, must be on the list of all primes given at the start of the proof. Now *n* is the product of all the primes on the list, and so *p* is a factor of *n*. Also, *p* is a factor of $n + 1$. Hence *p* is a factor of the difference $(n + 1) - n$, which equals 1. Because the only positive integer factor of 1 is 1, *p* must equal 1. But *p* is a prime number and all prime numbers are greater than 1. Thus we have arrived at a contradiction: $p = 1$ and $p > 1$. Hence the assumption *not s* is false. So *s* is true: there are infinitely many prime numbers.

We have already seen that to test whether a given integer *n* is prime, we need only check if it has a prime factor. However, it is not necessary to check all prime numbers less than *n* as a factor of *n*. For example, if $n = 391$ and *d* is a prime factor of 391, then $391 = d \cdot q$ and $q > 1$. If both *d* and *q* are greater than $\sqrt{391}$, then $d \cdot q > 391$. But that's impossible. Thus, if 391 is not prime, at least one of its factors must be less than or equal to $\sqrt{391}$. In general, to test whether *n* is prime, you need search only the prime numbers less than or equal to $\sqrt{n}$. All this is summarized in the following theorem.

Factor Search Theorem
If an integer *n* has no prime factors between 1 and $\sqrt{n}$ inclusive, then *n* is prime.

❶ We use the word *suppose* in indirect proofs where many people use the synonym *assume*, because *suppose* conveys a better impression of an idea that is utilized for only a brief period of time. Also, we do not wish to confuse statements from which we reason in an indirect proof with properties we assume throughout an entire course.

Activity 3 History Connection At the time the first edition of this book, was being published (1990), the largest known prime was $2^{216091} - 1$, which contained 65,050 digits. In the months between the printing of the second edition of the student's book and the printing of this teacher's edition, a new largest prime, $2^{3021377} - 1$, was discovered on January 27, 1998, by a team led by Roland Clarkson, George Woltman, and Scott Kurowski. Have interested students investigate the current largest known prime. At the time of printing, one could check this web site: http://www.utm.edu/research/primes/largest.html

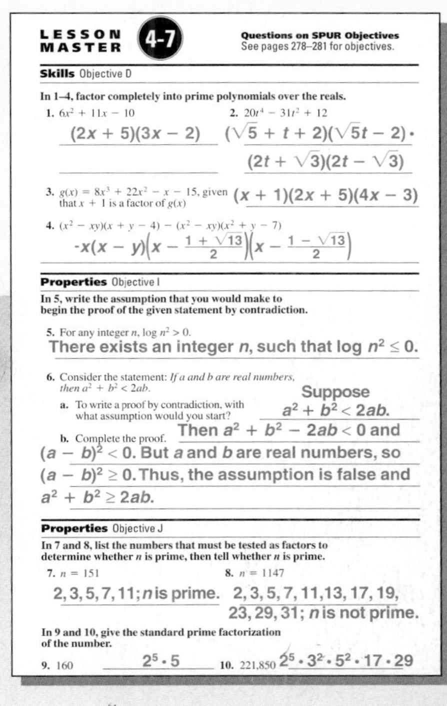

LESSON MASTER 4-7

Questions on SPUR Objectives
See pages 278–281 for objectives.

Skills Objective D

In 1–4, factor completely into prime polynomials over the reals.

1. $6x^2 + 11x - 10$ $(2x + 5)(3x - 2)$
2. $20t^4 - 31t^2 + 12$ $(\sqrt{5} + t + 2)(\sqrt{5}t - 2) \cdot (2t + \sqrt{3})(2t - \sqrt{3})$
3. $g(x) = 8x^3 + 22x^2 - x - 15$, given that $x + 1$ is a factor of $g(x)$ $(x + 1)(2x + 5)(4x - 3)$
4. $(x^2 - xy)(x + y - 4) - (x^2 - xy)(x^2 + y - 7)$ $-x(x - y)\left(x - \frac{1 + \sqrt{13}}{2}\right)\left(x - \frac{1 - \sqrt{13}}{2}\right)$

Properties Objective I

In 5, write the assumption that you would make to begin the proof of the given statement by contradiction.

5. For any integer *n*, $\log n^2 > 0$. There exists an integer *n*, such that $\log n^2 \leq 0$.
6. Consider the statement: *If a and b are real numbers, then* $a^2 + b^2 < 2ab$.
   a. To write a proof by contradiction, with what assumption would you start? Suppose $a^2 + b^2 < 2ab$.
   b. Complete the proof. Then $a^2 + b^2 - 2ab < 0$ and $(a - b)^2 < 0$. But *a* and *b* are real numbers, so $(a - b)^2 \geq 0$. Thus, the assumption is false and $a^2 + b^2 \geq 2ab$.

Properties Objective J

In 7 and 8, list the numbers that must be tested as factors to determine whether *n* is prime, then tell whether *n* is prime.

7. $n = 151$ 2, 3, 5, 7, 11; *n* is prime.
8. $n = 1147$ 2, 3, 5, 7, 11, 13, 17, 19, 23, 29, 31; *n* is not prime.

In 9 and 10, give the standard prime factorization of the number.

9. 160 $2^5 \cdot 5$
10. 221,850 $2^5 \cdot 3^2 \cdot 5^2 \cdot 17 \cdot 29$

❷ Students undoubtedly will have seen the Fundamental Theorem of Arithmetic before. The uniqueness of the factorization perhaps is something that some will not have realized. This can be demonstrated by beginning the factorization of 24 in two different ways: $24 = 8 \cdot 3$ and $24 = 4 \cdot 6$. The ultimate factorization is the same since $8 \cdot 3 = 2^3 \cdot 3$ and $4 \cdot 6 = 2^2 \cdot 2 \cdot 3 = 2^3 \cdot 3$.

Additional Examples

The proofs of the Infinitude of Primes Theorem and the Factor Search Theorem are indirect. Some other statements which you might have students prove through indirect proofs are:

1. There is no largest even integer. Let *s*: There is no largest even integer. Suppose *not s*: There is a largest even integer. Then this integer can be written as $2m$. But the integer $2m + 2$ is larger than $2m$, and it is even, since $2m + 2 = 2(m + 1)$. Hence *not s* leads to a false statement. So *not s* is false, and *s* must be true.
2. If a function *f* is increasing on a set *S* and if $f(x_1) = f(x_2)$, then $x_1 = x_2$. Let *s*: If *f* is increasing and $f(x_1) = f(x_2)$, then $x_1 = x_2$. Suppose *not s*: *f* is increasing, $f(x_1) = f(x_2)$ and $x_1 \neq x_2$. Since $x_1 \neq x_2$, then $x_1 < x_2$ or $x_1 > x_2$. Since *f* is increasing, if $x_1 < x_2$, then $f(x_1) < f(x_2)$. And also, if *f* is increasing, if $x_1 > x_2$, then $f(x_1) > f(x_2)$. Consequently, in both cases, $f(x_1) \neq f(x_2)$. Hence *not s* leads to a contradiction of itself, a false statement. So *not s* is false, and *s* must be true.]

Specifically, to test whether 391 is prime, it is necessary only to test its divisibility by primes between 1 and $\sqrt{391} \approx 19.77$, that is, the numbers 2, 3, 5, 7, 11, 13, 17, and 19.

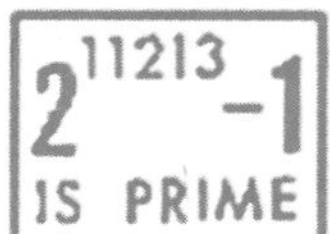

Finding the largest known prime number is a matter of pride. The University of Illinois in 1963 announced its achievement on the mathematics department's postage meter.

Prime numbers are often thought of as the *building blocks* of the positive integers because it can be proved that every integer $n > 1$ either is prime or can be written as a product of prime factors. For example, 29 and 41 are primes, while $26 = 2 \cdot 13$ and $36 = 2 \cdot 2 \cdot 3 \cdot 3 = 2^2 \cdot 3^2$ are products of prime factors.

If $n > 1$ is not a prime number, then a representation of n as a product of primes is called a **prime factorization** of n. For example,

$$2 \cdot 2 \cdot 3 \cdot 7, \quad 7 \cdot 2 \cdot 3 \cdot 2, \text{ and } 2^2 \cdot 3 \cdot 7$$

are all prime factorizations of 84. The following theorem states that the only way two prime factorizations of an integer can differ from each other is in the order in which the factors are written. This result is so important that it is called the *Fundamental Theorem of Arithmetic*. The proof of the complete result is beyond the level of this course, but parts of the theorem are proved in Chapter 7.

❷ **Fundamental Theorem of Arithmetic**
Suppose that n is an integer and that $n > 1$. Then either n is a prime number or n has a prime factorization which is unique except for the order of the factors.

Thus, according to this theorem, if you first notice that 11 is a factor of 1001, and someone else first notices that 7 is a factor, the ultimate prime factorizations you both get will be the same.

Among the different prime factorizations of an integer $n > 1$ that is not prime, there is one and only one in which

(a) all like factors are combined using exponents;
(b) the prime factors are arranged in increasing order of magnitude.

This factorization is called the **standard prime factorization** of n. For example, the standard prime factorization of 60 is $60 = 2^2 \cdot 3 \cdot 5$ and that of 231 is $231 = 3 \cdot 7 \cdot 11$.

Now consider polynomials. Like integers, polynomials can be factored. For instance,

$$\begin{aligned} 4x^4 - 56x^2 + 180 &= 4(x^4 - 14x^2 + 45) \\ &= 4(x^2 - 9)(x^2 - 5) \\ &= 4(x + 3)(x - 3)(x^2 - 5). \end{aligned}$$

A polynomial is not considered to be *completely* factored unless all its factors are prime. How can you determine if a polynomial is prime? After all, $x^2 - 5$ could be factored into $(x + \sqrt{5})(x - \sqrt{5})$.

Adapting to Individual Needs

Extra Help

Some students should benefit from a discussion of the Factor Search Theorem. This can be illustrated by factoring a number such as $21021 = 3 \cdot 7^2 \cdot 11 \cdot 13$. By the Factor Search Theorem, you first have to check for prime factors up to $\sqrt{21021} \approx 144$. After finding that 3 is a factor, however, the problem is reduced to factoring $\sqrt{7007}$. Now it is necessary to check factors only up to $\sqrt{7007} \approx 83$. Continuing in this way you find that only a small number of primes need to be checked.

Definition
A polynomial $p(x)$ with degree $n \geq 1$ is **prime over the real numbers** if and only if the only polynomial factors of $p(x)$ with real coefficients and leading coefficient 1 are constants or constant multiples of $p(x)$.

So, factored into prime factors over the real numbers,

$$4x^4 - 56x^2 + 180 = 4(x + 3)(x - 3)(x + \sqrt{5})(x - \sqrt{5}).$$

You may recall from earlier work that if a, b, and c are real numbers, then $ax^2 + bx + c$ is factorable if and only if $b^2 - 4ac \geq 0$. Thus, over the real numbers, $x^2 + 1$ is a prime polynomial, as is $3x^2 - 9x + 12$.

A natural question to ask is whether there is a theorem for polynomials like the Fundamental Theorem of Arithmetic for integers. That is, is the prime factorization of a polynomial over the real numbers unique except for order? For example, consider the polynomial $p(x) = x^8 - 1$. Because $p(1) = 0$, $x - 1$ is a factor. The quotient is $q_1(x) = x^7 + x^6 + x^5 + x^4 + x^3 + x^2 + x + 1$ and there is no remainder.

$$x^8 - 1 = (x - 1)(x^7 + x^6 + x^5 + x^4 + x^3 + x^2 + x + 1) = (x - 1)\,q_1(x)$$

But $p(-1) = 0$ also, so $x + 1$ is also a factor.

$$x^8 - 1 = (x + 1)(x^7 - x^6 + x^5 - x^4 + x^3 - x^2 + x - 1) = (x + 1)\,q_2(x)$$

If there is unique factorization into primes, then $q_1(x)$ and $q_2(x)$ must each be factorable. This is, in fact, what happens.

$$\begin{aligned} x^8 - 1 &= (x - 1)\,q_1(x) \\ &= (x - 1)(x + 1)(x^6 + x^4 + x^2 + 1) \\ &= (x - 1)(x + 1)(x^2 + 1)(x^4 + 1) \end{aligned}$$

Factoring $q_2(x)$ yields the same factorization of $x^8 - 1$.

$$\begin{aligned} x^8 - 1 &= (x + 1)\,q_2(x) \\ &= (x + 1)(x - 1)(x^6 + x^4 + x^2 + 1) \\ &= (x + 1)(x - 1)(x^2 + 1)(x^4 + 1) \quad \text{as above.} \end{aligned}$$

However, neither is a prime factorization over the reals, because $(x^4 + 1) = (x^2 + \sqrt{2}x + 1)(x^2 - \sqrt{2}x + 1)$. A prime factorization of $x^8 - 1$ over the reals is thus

$$(x + 1)(x - 1)(x^2 + 1)(x^2 + \sqrt{2}x + 1)(x^2 - \sqrt{2}x + 1)$$

and it seems to be a unique factorization. In general, there is unique factorization of a polynomial into prime polynomials over the reals as long as constant multiples are ignored.

Unique Factorization Theorem for Polynomials
Suppose that $p(x)$ is a polynomial with integer coefficients. Then either $p(x)$ is prime over the real numbers or $p(x)$ has a factorization into polynomials prime over the reals which is unique except for the order of the factors or multiplications by real constants.

3. If p is prime and n^2 is divisible by p, then n is divisible by p.
Let s: If p is prime and n^2 is divisible by p, then n is divisible by p. Suppose *not s*: p is prime, n^2 is divisible by p, and n is not divisible by p. Since n is not divisible by p, n does not have p as a factor in its prime factorization. Consequently, $n^2 = n \cdot n$ does not have p as a factor in its prime factorization. Hence n^2 is not divisible by p. Hence *not s* leads to a contradiction of itself, a false statement. So *not s* is false, and s must be true. (You may want to demonstrate Additional Example 3 for specific values of p first. For instance, let $p = 13$ and $n^2 = 8281 \equiv 0 \pmod{13}$. Then $n = 91$, which is divisible by p. The general result will be used in Lesson 5-6 in proofs that certain numbers are irrational.)

Adapting to Individual Needs

Challenge
Have students answer one the following questions.

1. Explore the following "prime number generators". You might want to use a computer program to aid in some of the factoring.
   a. Consider the polynomial $p(x) = x^2 - x + 41$. For how many integers 1 to n is $p(n)$ a prime number? [$n = 41$ is the first composite.]
   b. Take the product of the first n prime integers and add 1. Does this generate another prime number? [Yes, until you get to $2 \cdot 3 \cdot 5 \cdot 7 \cdot 11 \cdot 13 + 1$ which is composite. See the Teaching Notes on p. 266.]
2. List the prime integers between 1 and 100. Suppose an integer is picked at random between 1 and 100. What is the probability that it is prime? [$\frac{1}{4}$]
3. Goldbach's conjecture states that every even integer greater than 4 is the sum of 2 odd primes. Do you think this conjecture is true? [Answers will vary.]

In the next chapter, you will see that the factorization of polynomials helps in understanding the behavior of the functions known as rational functions.

QUESTIONS

Covering the Reading

1. Write the smallest 15 prime numbers. 2, 3, 5, 7, 11, 13, 17, 19, 23, 29, 31, 37, 41, 43, 47

2. Before $2^{2976221} - 1$ was found to be prime, the largest known prime was $2^{1398269} - 1$, which was discovered in 1996. How many digits does this number have? 420,921 digits

From the side, the two-pronged African oryx looks like the legendary unicorn.

3. You know $1 \neq 2$. Suppose you can prove the following.

   If there are unicorns, then $1 = 2$.
   $1 \neq 2$.

   What conclusion can you draw? There are no unicorns.

4. Consider the statement: *There is no largest positive integer.*
   a. To write a proof by contradiction, with what assumption should you start the proof? There exists a largest positive integer.
   b. If you let n be the largest positive integer, what can you say about $n + 1$? $n + 1$ cannot be an integer.
   c. Use your results from parts **a** and **b** to complete the proof by contradiction. See left.

4c) Since n and 1 are integers and the integers are closed under addition, $n + 1$ must be an integer. This contradicts part b. Therefore, our initial assumption must be false. Therefore, there is no largest positive integer.

5. Refer to the proof of the Infinitude of Primes Theorem.
   a. What number n was constructed from the primes?
   b. What was the contradiction derived from the assumption?
   $p = 1$ and $p > 1$ a) the product of all the primes

6. *True or false.* If n is an integer and p is a prime factor of $n + 1$, then p is not a factor of n. True

7. a. To determine if 783 is prime, what is the largest number that must be tested to see if it is a factor of 783? $\sqrt{783}$
   b. Is 783 prime? No

8. Give the standard prime factorization of 480. $2^5 \cdot 3 \cdot 5$

In 9–11, give a prime factorization of the polynomial over the reals.

9. $3x^2 - 33x - 72$ $3(x^2 - 11x - 24)$

10. $9y^{100} - y^{98}$ $y^{98}(3y - 1)(3y + 1)$

11. $z^2 - 17$ $(z - \sqrt{17})(z + \sqrt{17})$

12. John noticed that $x^2 + 1$ is a factor of $p(x) = x^4 + x^3 + x^2 + x$. Joan noticed that -1 is a zero of p. Jan noticed only that x is a factor. Put all this information together to factor $p(x)$. $x(x + 1)(x^2 + 1)$

Additional Answers

15. Assume ∃ a number n which is the largest multiple of 5. Then, by the definition of multiple, $n = 5m$, where m is an integer. Because the integers are closed under addition, $m + 1$ is an integer. Because the integers are closed under multiplication, $5(m + 1)$ is an integer which, by the definition of multiple, is a multiple of 5. By the distributive law, $5(m + 1) = 5m + 5$ which is an integer larger than $5m = n$. This contradicts the assumption that n is the largest multiple of 5. Therefore, this assumption is false, so there is no largest multiple of 5.

Applying the Mathematics

13. *True or false.* The only common positive integer factor of two consecutive integers is 1. True

14. Every prime number greater than 2 is an odd number. Explain why. See left.

In 15 and 16, give a proof by contradiction.

15. There is no largest multiple of 5. See margin.

16. There is no smallest positive real number. See margin.

In 17 and 18, give the prime factorization of the polynomial over the reals.

17. $x^4 - 13x^2 + 36$ $(x + 2)(x - 2)(x + 3)(x - 3)$

18. $6 - 12y^4 + 6y^8$ $6(y^2 + 1)^2(y + 1)^2(y - 1)^2$

19. a. One factor of $x^3 - 39x + 70$ is $x - 2$. Determine the other factor. a) $x^2 + 2x - 35$

b. Write $x^3 - 39x + 70$ as the product of three prime factors over the reals. $(x - 2)(x - 5)(x + 7)$

c. Find all solutions to $x^3 - 39x = -70$. $x = 2$, $x = 5$, $x = -7$

20. Use the Fundamental Theorem of Arithmetic to argue that 11 is not a factor of 1,000,000,000. See left.

14) If $n > 2$ and n is even, then n cannot be a prime because it has 2 as a factor.

20) The prime factorization of $1{,}000{,}000{,}000 = 2^9 \cdot 5^9$. Since the Fundamental Theorem of Arithmetic guarantees this factorization is unique, and 11 is prime, 11 cannot be a factor.

25b) period $= \frac{1}{60}$ sec, amplitude = 15 amperes

c) $c(t) = 15 \sin(120\pi t)$

Review

21. Write the base 10 representation of 101100_2. *(Lesson 4-6)* 44

22. *Multiple choice.* Which of the following is the base 2 representation of 257? c

(a) 1111111_2 (b) 11111111_2

(c) 100000001_2 (d) 10000001_2 *(Lesson 4-6)*

23. Suppose $x \equiv 4 \pmod 6$ and $y \equiv 3 \pmod 6$.

a. What can be deduced about xy? $xy \equiv 12 \pmod 6 \equiv 0 \pmod 6$

b. Give two instances of the conclusion you made for part **a.** *(Lesson 4-5)* $10 \cdot 9 = 90 \equiv 0 \pmod 6$; $16 \cdot 15 = 240 \equiv 0 \pmod 6$

24. Provide a proof of the following statement used in the proof of the Infinitude of Primes Theorem:

If p is a factor of a and p is a factor of b, then p is a factor of a − b. *(Lesson 4-1)*

See margin.

current, 15, 0, -15, $\frac{1}{60}$, $\frac{2}{60}$, time

25. Residential electricity is called AC for "alternating current" because the direction of current flow alternates through a circuit. At the left is a graph of current (in amperes) as a function of time (in seconds).

a. What type of function has a graph like this one? sine function

b. Identify the period and amplitude of this graph. See left.

c. Write an equation for current as a function of time. See left.

d. Find the current produced at 0.10 seconds. *(Lessons 2-6, 3-8)* 0 amperes

26. Solve: $\sqrt{3x - 8} = \frac{1}{2}x$. *(Lesson 3-3)* $x = 4$, $x = 8$

27. Is the sine function even, odd, or neither? *(Lesson 2-6)* odd

Notes on Questions

Question 17 Error Alert Students sometimes forget to look first for a common monomial factor. In this case, they can think of x^2 as a chunk.

Question 18 Some students may notice first that 6 is a factor; others may notice first that the polynomial is quadratic in y^4 (that is, with y^4 as a chunk).

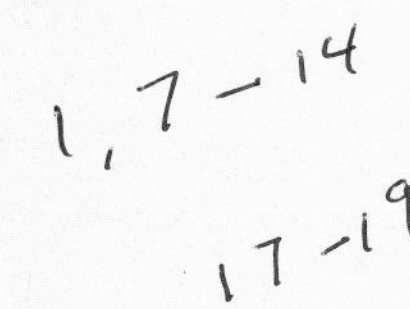

16. Assume ∃ a number x which is the smallest positive real number. Since the real numbers are closed under multiplication, $\frac{1}{2}x$ is a real number. Furthermore, because both $\frac{1}{2}$ and x are positive, $\frac{1}{2}x$ is positive. However, $\frac{1}{2}x$ is less than x. This contradicts the assumption that x is the smallest positive real number. Therefore, this assumption is false, so there is no smallest positive real number.

24. Assume for integers a, b, and p that p is a factor of both a and b. Then ∃ integers m and n such that $a = mp$ and $b = np$, by definition of factor. So $a - b = mp - np = (m - n)p$, by the distributive law. Since $m - n$ is an integer by closure properties, p is a factor of $a - b$.

Notes on Questions

Question 31 Students may be surprised to learn that there is a place on the Internet where one can learn about the latest work with primes. The reason is that primes have both theoretical and recreational appeal.

Follow-up for Lesson 4-7

Practice

For more questions on SPUR Objectives, use **Lesson Master 4-7** (shown on page 267).

Assessment

Written Communication Have students determine whether the following conjecture is true or false. Ask them to include an example to support their conclusion. If n is prime, then $2n + 1$ is prime. [The conjecture is not true. 7 is prime, but $2 \cdot 7 + 1 = 15$ is not.]

Extension

Because of the Factor Theorem, if a quadratic with real coefficients has real zeros, then it can be factored over the reals. For instance, the zeros of $3x^2 - 2x - 4 = 0$ are $\frac{1 \pm \sqrt{13}}{3}$, which implies that

$3x^2 - 2x - 4 =$

$3\left(x - \frac{1 \pm \sqrt{13}}{3}\right)\left(x - \frac{1 \pm \sqrt{13}}{3}\right)$.

Ask students to make up other quadratics with irrational zeros and to give their prime factorizations over the reals.

Project Update Project 2, *Cryptography,* on page 273, relates to the content of this lesson.

28. A manufacturer needs to construct a box with a square base, no top, and a volume of 544 in^3 and wants to use as little material as possible in constructing the box.

a. Express the height of the box as a function of the length of the side of the base. $h = 544/s^2$

b. Express the surface area of the box as a function of the length of the base. $A(s) = s^2 + 2176/s$

c. Use an automatic grapher to find the dimensions of the box that would require the least amount of material for construction. *(Lesson 2-2)* $s \approx 10.29$ inches, $h \approx 5.14$ inches

29. Prove: $\forall$ *integers n, if n^2 is odd, then n is odd.* (Hint: Consider the contrapositive.) *(Lessons 1-5, 1-8)* See left.

29) Assume n is an even integer. Then by the definition of even, $n = 2 \cdot m$ for some integer m. Therefore $n^2 = (2m)^2 = 2m \cdot 2m = 2(2m^2)$ because integer multiplication is associative. Therefore, by the definition of an even number, if n is even, then n^2 is even. Consequently, by the Law of the Contrapositive, if n^2 is not even, then n is not even.

Exploration

30. Pick a rate (primes per second) at which you think a computer can test a number to determine whether it is prime. With the rate you pick, how many years would it have taken to test all primes less than the square root of the largest prime number known? How fast a rate would be needed to test the number $10^{100,000} + 1$ if the computer were operating all day and night for a century? Answers will vary.

31. Search the Internet to find out whether the largest known prime is still the one mentioned in this lesson. Answers will vary.

PROJECTS 4 CHAPTER FOUR

A project presents an opportunity for you to extend your knowledge of a topic related to the material of this chapter. You should allow more time for a project than you do for a typical homework question.

1 Casting Out Nines

Prior to the time when calculators were widely available, a procedure called casting out nines was commonly used to check arithmetic calculations done by hand. Here is a statement of the casting-out-nines check for multiplication.

Suppose that c is the computed result for the multiplication of two positive integers, a and b. Let r, s, and t be the smallest positive integers congruent modulo 9 to the sums of the digits of a, b, and c, respectively. If c is correct (i.e., if $a \cdot b = c$), then $r \cdot s \equiv t \pmod{9}$.

a. Cast out nines to check each of the following stated products.

$$247 \times 4731 = 1{,}158{,}557$$
$$277 \times 569 = 157{,}613$$

Carefully state the conclusions that you can draw from your check. Now check these calculations with your calculator.

b. Use the properties of congruence for multiplication and addition to prove the following results.

i. For all positive integers n, $10^n \equiv 1 \pmod{9}$.

ii. If $a_0, a_1, \ldots, a_n$ are n nonnegative integers, then
$(a_n 10^n + a_{n-1} 10^{n-1} + \ldots + a_1 10 + a_0) \equiv (a_n + a_{n-1} + \ldots + a_1 + a_0) \pmod{9}$.

c. Use the result in part **b** to explain the casting out nines check for multiplication.

d. Develop a procedure of casting out nines for checking the sums of positive integers.

2 Cryptography

Prime numbers and modular arithmetic are frequently used tools in the study of cryptography. Look in an index of periodicals or search the Internet to find one or more articles dealing with this topic and write a report. Some possible journals are *Scientific American*, *Science*, and *Byte*.

3 Solving Modular Equations

a. Any solution to the equation $ax \equiv b \pmod{d}$ must be congruent to one of the integers $0, 1, 2, \ldots, d-1$. To determine whether any solutions exist, find the greatest common factor (GCF) of a and d: GCF$\{a, d\} = k$. The fact is that if b is divisible by k, then there are k solutions in the set $\{0, 1, 2, \ldots, d-1\}$. If b is not divisible by k, then there are no solutions. For instance, the equation $6x \equiv 10 \pmod{8}$ has two solutions in the set $\{0, 1, 2, \ldots, 7\}$ because GCF $\{6, 8\} = 2$, and 10 is divisible by 2. The solutions are $x = 3$ and $x = 7$. Determine the number of solutions that exist in each case and then find the solutions, if any.

i. $5x \equiv 8 \pmod{12}$ **ii.** $3x \equiv 12 \pmod{9}$
iii. $4x \equiv 5 \pmod{6}$ **iv.** $6x \equiv 24 \pmod{12}$

Chapter 4 Projects

The projects relate chiefly to the content of the lessons of this chapter as follows:

Project	Lesson(s)
1	4-2, 4-5, 4-6
2	4-7
3	4-5
4	4-4
5	4-5

1 Casting Out Nines Solutions for **part b** of this project can be found in the notes to Lesson 4-6.

2 Cryptography Your high school library may have books on codes which could be used as references for this report.

3 Solving Modular Equations This project is quite mathematical; it provides an algorithm for finding the greatest common factor of two integers without finding their prime factorizations.

Possible Responses

1. a. $247 \times 4731 = 1{,}158{,}557$ becomes $4 \times 6 \equiv 5 \pmod{9}$, which is false. Hence, 1,158,557 cannot be the correct product. $277 \times 569 = 157{,}613$ becomes $7 \times 2 \equiv 5 \pmod{9}$. Hence, 157,613 may be the correct product.

   b. i. Because 9 is a factor of $(10 - 1)$, we know that $10 \equiv 1 \pmod{9}$. Then, by the multiplication property of congruence, $10 \cdot 10 = 10^2 \equiv 1 \cdot 1 \equiv 1 \pmod{9}$ and $10^2 \cdot 10 = 10^3 \equiv 1 \cdot 1 \pmod{9}$, and so on. Consequently, $10^n \equiv 1 \pmod{9}$.

   ii. Clearly, $a_n \equiv a_n \pmod{9}$. Then by the result of part i. and the multiplication property of congruence, we have $a_n \cdot 10^n \equiv a_n \cdot 1 \equiv a_n \pmod{9}$. Then by the addition property of congruence $a10^n + b10^m \equiv a + b$. Therefore, $a_n 10^n + a_{n-1}10^{n-1} + \ldots + a_1 10 + a_0 \equiv a_n + a_{n-1} + \ldots + a_1 + a_0 \pmod{9}$.

   c. The remainder of an integer represented in quotient-remainder form is the smallest number congruent to the represented integer. Consider two integers a and b. By the Quotient-Remainder Theorem, $a = 9q_a + r_a$ so $a \equiv r_a \pmod{9}$.

(Responses continue on page 274.)

4 An Algorithm for Solving Cubic Equations This algorithm can work for all polynomials; students might try the algorithm on other polynomials.

5 Gauss It is easy to find information about Gauss, as he is famous in both mathematics and physics.

Additonal Responses, page 273–274

Project 1 continued

Because of part *b*, $a \equiv$ (sum of the digits of $a) \equiv r_a$ (mod 9). Similar reasoning shows that $b \equiv$ (sum of the digits of $b) \equiv r_b$ (mod 9). By the multiplication property of congruence and by part *b*, $a \cdot b \equiv$ (sum of the digits of $a \cdot b) \equiv r_a r_b$ (mod 9).

d. Let the integer *c* be the computed result of adding integers *a* and *b*. Let *r*, *s*, and *t* be the smallest integers congruent modulo 9 to the sums of the digits of *a*, *b*, and *c*, respectively. If *c* is correct, then $r + s \equiv t$ (mod 9).

2. Some possible sources are
   a. "The Mathematics of Public-Key Cryptography" Martin E. Hellman, *Scientific American,* Aug. 1979, pp. 146–152
   b. *Applied Cryptography, 2nd Edition,* Bruce Schneier, John Wiley and Sons Inc., New York (1996)
   c. *Decrypted Secrets,* Friedrich L. Bauer, Springer-Verlag, Berlin-Heidelberg (1997)
   d. *The Codebreakers. The Story of Secret Writing,* David Kahn, Macmillan Publishing, (1967)
   e. The WWW site www.yahoo.com has a list of cryptography-related sites.
   f. The Usenet group sci.crypt has an excellent FAQ (frequently asked questions) with lots of information and an extensive bibliography.

(continued)

Identify those numbers *d* which yield exactly one solution for every equation $ax \equiv b \pmod{d}$, $a \not\equiv 0$.

b. Take a value of *d* in part **a**. Explore the solution of quadratic equations $ax^2 + bx + c \equiv 0 \pmod{d}$. Establish criteria for the solvability of quadratics in this system.

4 An Algorithm for Solving Cubic Equations

Write a computer program or use a calculator to follow the algorithm below to solve $5x^3 + 4x^2 - 551x + 110 = 0$. This algorithm approximates all zeros of a cubic equation; it merges bisection (Chapter 3, Project 3), polynomial division (Lesson 4-3), and the Quadratic Formula. (Hint: Try first to find the solution between -2 and 2.)

Algorithm: given $p(x) = ax^3 + bx^2 + cx + d$.

a. Evaluate $p(t)$ for values of *t* until you find a value t_1 that gives a positive remainder, and a value t_2 which gives a negative remainder.

b. Use bisection to generate a sequence of values $t_3, t_4, \ldots$ which causes the remainders to approach zero. (Stop when you get within .001 of zero, that is, when $|p(t_n)| < .001$.)

c. The value t_n is an approximation to one of the zeros. Use long division by $x - t_n$ to find the coefficients of a quadratic $q(x)$, called the *reduced polynomial*. Use the Quadratic Formula to estimate the real zeros, if any, of $q(x)$. These will be estimates of the other two zeros of $p(x)$.

5 Gauss

Carl Friedrich Gauss (1777–1855) introduced the theory of congruences modulo *d* in a book entitled *Disquisitiones Arithmeticae*. Use an encyclopedia, a biography, or a history of mathematics book to learn more about the discoveries made by this remarkable mathematician. Write a short report about what you find.

3. a. i. $k = \text{GCF}(5, 12) = 1$, $\frac{b}{k} = \frac{8}{1} = 8$. There is one solution in the set {0, 1, ..., 11}: $x = 4$

ii. GCF(3, 9) = 3, $\frac{b}{k} = \frac{12}{3} = 4$. There are three solutions in the set {0, 1, ..., 8}: $x = \{1, 4, 7\}$

iii. GCF(4, 6) = 2, $\frac{b}{k} = \frac{5}{2} = 2.5$. There are no solutions in the set {0, 1, ..., 5}.

iv. GCF(6, 12) = 5, $\frac{b}{k} = \frac{24}{6} = 4$. There are six solutions in the set {0, 1, ..., 11}: $x = (0, 2, 4, 6, 8, 10\}$

b. If *d* is prime and $d \neq a$, then there will be exactly one solution for every equation of the form $ax \equiv b \pmod{d}$ $a \neq 0$.

SUMMARY

The operation of division is fundamental in mathematics. This chapter relates integer division to division of polynomials, to the development of modular arithmetic, to the solution of polynomial equations, and to the examination of the theory of prime numbers.

Just as $n = q \cdot d$ means that q and d are factors of n, so $n(x) = q(x) \cdot d(x)$ means that the polynomials $q(x)$ and $d(x)$ are factors of $n(x)$. When an integer n is divided by d, there is a unique integer quotient q and remainder r such that $n = q \cdot d + r$ and $0 \le r < d$. Similarly, when a polynomial $n(x)$ is divided by $d(x)$, there is a unique polynomial quotient $q(x)$ and remainder $r(x)$ such that $n(x) = q(x) \cdot d(x) + r(x)$, and either the degree of $r(x)$ is less than the degree of $d(x)$ or $r(x)$ is the zero polynomial. These are the Quotient-Remainder theorems for integers and polynomials. Because of the similarity of the integer and polynomial versions of the Quotient-Remainder Theorem, there are many analogous properties for integers and polynomials.

Just as you can use long division to compute the quotient and remainder when an integer n is divided by an integer d, you can use an analogous algorithm of long division to compute the quotient and remainder when a polynomial $p(x)$ is divided by $d(x)$. If $d(x) = x - c$, then the remainder equals $p(c)$. If $p(c) = 0$, then $x - c$ is a factor of $p(x)$. Thus, the Factor Theorem, enables many polynomial equations to be solved.

Pick a particular divisor d, and group numbers together whose remainders are equal when divided by d. This produces an arithmetic modulo d. Modular arithmetic has simple applications to calendars and codes.

Electronic computing devices operate using binary logic, and they apply that logic to perform arithmetic on numbers represented in base 2 (binary) notation. Computers also use base 8 (octal) and base 16 (hexadecimal) representations of numbers. The Quotient-Remainder Theorem gives a method for changing any base 10 representation of a number into a different base. Addition in different bases can be performed using algorithms similar to those of base 10 arithmetic.

Prime numbers are those positive integers greater than 1 that are not divisible by any positive integer other than 1 and themselves. There are an infinite number of primes. Determining whether a number is prime can be very difficult for large numbers. However, it is possible to prove that there are an infinite number of primes, and to facilitate the search for large primes with the Prime Factor Theorem and the Factor Search Theorem.

The proofs of the Infinitude of Primes and the Prime Factor theorems use a method of indirect reasoning called proof by contradiction. To prove a statement s using proof by contradiction, start by supposing *not s* and show that this leads to a contradiction.

Summary

The Summary gives an overview of the entire chapter and provides an opportunity for students to consider the material as a whole. Thus, the Summary can be used to help students relate and unify the concepts presented in the chapter.

Additional Responses, page 274

5. Student's reports may include some of the following information:
   a. proved the Fundamental Theorem of Algebra (4 different ways),
   b. co-invented the electromagnetic telegraph,
   c. anticipated non-Euclidean geometry by papers on surface theory,
   d. first to construct a regular polygon of 17 sides
   e. proved every positive integer is the sum of three triangular numbers,
   f. invented the heliotrope,
   g. contributed to astronomy, geodesy, and electricity.

4.

t	$p(t)$
-2	1188
2	-936
0	110
1	-432
0.5	163.87
0.25	-27.422
0.125	41.197
0.1875	6.8611
0.21875	-10.288
0.20313	-1.7149
0.19531	2.5727

t	$p(t)$
0.19922	0.42875
0.20117	0.64209
0.2002	0.10976
0.19971	0.15915
0.19995	0.027440
0.20007	0.038416
0.20001	-0.005488
0.19998	0.010976
0.2	0.

$t = \frac{1}{5}$ is a root. Long division gives the quotient as $5(x^2 + x - 110) = 5(x - 10)(x + 11)$. Therefore the roots are $x = \{-11, \frac{1}{5}, 10\}$.

Vocabulary

Terms, symbols, and properties are listed by lesson to provide a checklist of concepts a student must know. Emphasize to students that they should read the vocabulary list carefully before starting the Progress Self-Test. If students do not understand the meaning of a term, they should refer back to the indicated lesson.

CHAPTER FOUR

VOCABULARY

Below are the most important terms and phrases for this chapter. You should be able to give a definition and a specific example of each and a precise definition for those marked with an asterisk (*).

Lesson 4-1
polynomial
coefficients
degree
polynomial over *S*
* factor, divisor
multiple
quotient
constant polynomial
zero function
expanded/factored form of a polynomial
Transitive Property of Integer Factors
Factor of an Integer Sum Theorem
Transitive Property of Polynomial Factors
Factor of a Polynomial Sum Theorem
Factor of an Integer Product Theorem
perfect number

Lesson 4-2
rational number division
integer division
integer quotient
integer remainder
Quotient-Remainder Theorem for Integers
polynomial division
rational expression division
Quotient-Remainder Theorem for Polynomials
polynomial quotient
remainder
polynomial

Lesson 4-3
long division of polynomials
The Remainder Theorem

Lesson 4-4
zero of a polynomial
Factor Theorem
Number of Zeros of a Polynomial Theorem
critical points

Lesson 4-5
modulus, mod
≡, is congruent to
* congruent modulo *m*
congruence classes
Congruence Theorem
Properties of Congruence Theorem

Lesson 4-6
base 2 (binary)
base 8 (octal)
base 16 (hexadecimal)
* base *b* notation
half-adder

Lesson 4-7
* prime
Prime Factor Theorem
Validity of Proof by Contradiction Theorem
Infinitude of Primes Theorem
Factor Search Theorem
prime factorization
Fundamental Theorem of Arithmetic
standard prime factorization
prime over the real numbers
Unique Factorization Theorem for Polynomials

PROGRESS SELF-TEST

2, 17) See margin. 1c, 7, 9, 10, 14, 16) See below.

Take this test as you would take a test in class. You will need an automatic grapher. Then check the test yourself using the solutions at the back of the book.

1. A bottling company packages bottles in 8-packs. If 145,230 bottles are prepared in one day, determine each. a) 18,153

a. the number of 8-packs that can be packaged

b. the number of bottles left unpackaged 6

c. Relate your answers to parts **a** and **b** to the Quotient-Remainder Theorem.

2. Prove: *If n, p, and m are integers and n is a factor of m, then n is a factor of p · m.*

3. Use long division to find the quotient $q(x)$ and the remainder $r(x)$ when $p(x) = 3x^4 - 19x^3 + 36x^2 - 32x + 15$ is divided by $d(x) = x^2 - 4x$.

$q(x) = 3x^2 - 7x + 8$, $r(x) = 15$

1c) $145230 = 18153 \cdot 8 + 6$. The quotient is 18153. The remainder is 6.

7) 2624

9) n is a factor of $(a - 5)$.

10) $3^2 \cdot 7 \cdot 13$

14) 1011_2

16) Let $a = 5$, $b = 12$. $a^2 - 1 = 24$ and 12 is a factor of 24. However, 12 is not a factor of either $(a - 1) = 4$ or $(a + 1) = 6$.

4. *True or false.* $x - 4$ is a factor of $2x^3 - 3x^2 - 10x + 6$. False

5. A polynomial of degree 4 has at most how many zeros? 4

6. Find all the zeros of $p(x) = 12x^3 + 34x^2 - 26x - 20$. $x = 1, x = -\frac{1}{2}, x = -\frac{10}{3}$

7. There are 2^{50} ways to answer a true-false test with 50 questions. Find the last four digits of 2^{50}.

8. Give the smallest positive integer solution to $y \equiv 151 \pmod{11}$. $151 \equiv 8 \pmod{11}$

9. If $a \equiv 5 \pmod{n}$, how are a and n related?

10. Give the standard prime factorization of 819.

11. *True or false.* For all positive integers m, if m is not divisible by any prime number less than $\sqrt{m}$, then m is prime. False

12. Give the prime factorization of $7x^4 - 3x^3 - 4x^2$ over the set of polynomials with real coefficients. $x^2(7x + 4)(x - 1)$

13. Write the base 2 representation of 33. 100001_2

14. Add: $101_2 + 110_2$. Give your answer in base 2.

15. Write the base 10 representation of 312_5. 82

16. Find a counterexample to show that the following statement is false. *For all integers a and b, if b is a factor of $a^2 - 1$, then b is a factor of either a + 1 or a − 1.*

17. Use a proof by contradiction to prove the following statement: *There is no largest even integer.*

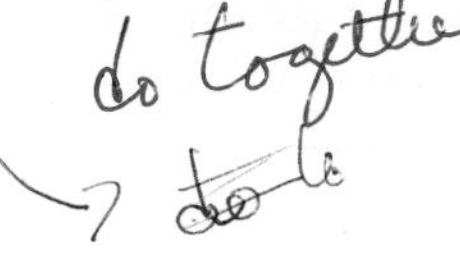

Progress Self-Test

For the development of mathematical competence, feedback and correction, along with the opportunity to practice, are necessary. The Progress Self-Test provides the opportunity for feedback and correction; the Chapter Review provides additional opportunities and practice. We cannot overemphasize the importance of these end-of-chapter materials. It is at this point that the material "gels" for many students, allowing them to solidify skills and understanding. In general, student performance should be markedly improved after these pages.

Assign the Progress Self-Test as a one-night assignment. Worked-out *solutions* for all questions are in the Selected Answers section of the student book. Encourage students to take the Progress Self-Test honestly, grade themselves, and then be prepared to discuss the test in class.

Advise students to pay special attention to those Chapter Review questions (pages 278–281) that correspond to questions missed on the Progress Self-Test.

Additional Answers

2. Let n, p, and m be integers such that n is a factor m. If n is a factor of m, then, by the definition of factor, $m = kn$ for some integer k. This means that $pm = p(kn) = (pk)n$ by the associative law. Since p and k are integers and the integers are closed under multiplication, pk is an integer. Therefore, by definition, n is a factor of pm.

17. Assume n is largest even integer. Since n is even, $n = 2m$ for some integer m. Since m is an integer, $m + 1$ is an integer because the integers are closed under addition. Since the integers are also closed under multiplication, $2(m + 1)$ is also an integer. Since $(m + 1)$ is an integer, by the definition of factor, $2(m + 1)$ is divisible by 2 and, so, is even. By the distributive law $2(m + 1) = 2m + 2 > 2m = n$. contradicting the initial assumption that n is the largest even integer. Therefore, there is no largest even integer.

CHAPTER FOUR

Chapter 4 Review

Resources

From the ***Teacher's Resource File***
- Answer Master for Chapter 4 Review
- Assessment Sourcebook: Chapter 4 Test, Forms A–D Chapter 4 Test, Cumulative Form

Additional Resources
- TestWorks CD-ROM

The main objectives for the chapter are organized in the Chapter Review under the four types of understanding this book promotes—Skills, Properties, Uses, and Representations.

Whereas end-of-chapter material may be considered optional in some texts, in UCSMP *Precalculus and Discrete Mathematics* we have selected these objectives and questions with the expectation that they will be covered. Students should be able to answer these questions with about 85% accuracy after studying the chapter.

You may assign these questions over a single night to help students prepare for a test the next day, or you may assign the questions over a two-day period. If you work the questions over two days, then we recommend assigning the *evens* for homework the first night so that students get feedback in class the next day, then assigning the *odds* the night before the test, because answers are provided to the odd-numbered questions.

CHAPTER REVIEW

Questions on SPUR Objectives

SPUR stands for **S**kills, **P**roperties, **U**ses, and **R**epresentations. The Chapter Review questions are grouped according to the SPUR Objectives for this chapter.

SKILLS DEAL WITH THE PROCEDURES USED TO GET ANSWERS.

Objective A: *Find quotients and remainders using the Quotient-Remainder theorem for integers or polynomials.* *(Lesson 4-2)*

In 1 and 2, given the pair of integers n and d, find integers q and r as defined in the Quotient-Remainder Theorem.

1. $n = 81$, $d = 15$ $q = 5, r = 6$

2. $n = 47$, $d = 9$ $q = 5, r = 2$

In 3 and 4, for each pair of integers n and d, use a calculator to determine integers q and r that satisfy the Quotient-Remainder Theorem.

3. $n = 7865$, $d = 94$ $q = 83, r = 63$

4. $n = -15{,}758$, $d = 45$ $q = -351, r = 37$

5. Use a calculator to help in finding an exact remainder for $1{,}739{,}541 \div 859$. 66

6. When $x^7 + 2x^5 - x^3 + x^2 + 7$ is divided by $x^2 + 2$, the quotient is $x^5 - x + 1$. Find the remainder and its degree. $2x + 5$; 1

7. Find a real number a that makes the following true: $y^2 - 12y + 9 = (y + a)(y - 7) - 26$ $a = -5$

Objective B: *Divide polynomials.* *(Lesson 4-3)*

In 8–14, find the quotient $q(x)$ and the remainder $r(x)$ when $p(x)$ is divided by $d(x)$. 8–14) See margin.

8. $p(x) = 3x^3 + 8x^2 - 33x + 18$, $d(x) = x + 5$

9. $p(x) = 35x^3 - 19x^2 + 11x - 9$, $d(x) = 5x^2 + 3x + 2$

10. $p(x) = x^5 + 7x^4 + 12x^3 + 5$, $d(x) = x^2 + 4x$

11. $p(x) = 6x^3 - 13x^2 - 6x + 6$, $d(x) = 3x^2 + x - 1$

12. $p(x) = x^4 - 7x^3 + 3x^2 - 4x + 9$, $d(x) = x + 1$

13. $p(x) = 5x^3 + x - 4$, $d(x) = x - 6$

14. $p(x) = x^5 + x^4 - x^3 + x^2 - x - 3$, $d(x) = x + \frac{1}{2}$

Objective C: *Determine the congruence of integers in a given modulus.* *(Lesson 4-5)*

In 15–18, give the smallest positive integer which makes the congruence true.

15. $x \equiv 214 \pmod 7$ 4

16. $y \equiv -1 \pmod{13}$ 12

17. $z \equiv 1000 \pmod{11}$ 10

18. $t \equiv -482 \pmod{25}$ 1

19. Consider the congruence classes $R0$, $R1$, $R2, \ldots, R11$ for integers modulo 12. If you add an element from $R9$ to an element in $R5$, which set contains the sum? $R2$

20. Suppose $x \equiv 3 \pmod 8$ and $y \equiv -9 \pmod 8$. What is the smallest positive integer congruent to $x + y \pmod 8$? 2

Objective D: *Factor polynomials over the reals.* *(Lessons 4-1, 4-4, 4-7)* 21–28) See margin.

In 21–28, factor completely into prime polynomials over the reals.

21. $5x^2 - 5y^2$

22. $9t^2 + 45t + 54$

23. $3x^3 + x^2 - 10x$

24. $4y^4 - 37y^2 + 9$

25. $18v^4 + 60v^2 + 50$

26. $w^4 - z^4$

27. $(2x + 1)^2(x - 4) + (2x + 1)(3x - 5)$

28. $(7t - 2)^2(8t + 1)(5t - 6) - (7t - 2)(8t + 1)^2(6t + 1)$

Objective E: *Use factoring or the Factor Theorem to solve polynomial equations.* *(Lesson 4-4)* 29) 3, $\frac{1}{14}(-3 + \sqrt{37})$, $\frac{1}{14}(-3 - \sqrt{37})$

29. Given that $x - 3$ is a factor of $p(x) = 7x^3 - 18x^2 - 10x + 3$, find all real zeros of $p(x)$.

30. Given that $2x + 5$ is a factor of $f(x) = 24x^3 + 34x^2 - 59x + 15$, find all real zeros of $f(x)$. $-\frac{5}{2}, \frac{3}{4}, \frac{1}{3}$

Additional Answers

8. $q(x) = 3x^2 - 7x + 2$, $r(x) = 8$
9. $q(x) = 7x - 8$, $r(x) = 21x + 7$
10. $q(x) = x^3 + 3x^2$, $r(x) = 5$
11. $q(x) = 2x - 5$, $r(x) = x + 1$
12. $q(x) = x^3 - 8x^2 + 11x - 15$, $r(x) = 24$
13. $q(x) = 5x^2 + 30x + 181$, $r(x) = 1082$
14. $q(x) = x^4 + \frac{1}{2}x^3 - \frac{5}{4}x^2 + \frac{13}{8}x - \frac{29}{16}$, $r(x) = -\frac{67}{32}$
21. $5(x - y)(x + y)$
22. $9(t + 2)(t + 3)$
23. $x(3x - 5)(x + 2)$
24. $(2y - 1)(2y + 1)(y - 3)(y + 3)$
25. $2(3v^2 + 5)^2$
26. $(w^2 + z^2)(w + z)(w - z)$
27. $(2x + 1)(2x^2 - 4x - 9)$
28. $(7t - 2)(8t + 1)(-13t^2 - 66t + 11)$
33. Because $x^3 - x^2 - x - 2 = (x - 2)(x^2 + x + 1)$ *and* $x^2 + x + 1$ has no real zeros, 2 is the only real number with this property.
35. True; $90 = 5 \cdot 18$.
36. False; $156 = 17 \cdot 9 + 3$.
37. True; if a and b are even, then $a = 2m$, $b = 2n$ for some integers n, m. Then $2a + 2b = 4m + 4n = 4(m + n)$ by the distributive law. Because the integers are closed under addition, $m + n$ is an integer. Therefore, by the definition of factor, $2a + 2b$ is divisible by 4.
38. Let n be an odd integer. Because it is odd, $n = 2m + 1$ for some integer m. Then $n^2 + n = (2m + 1)^2 + (2m + 1) = 4m^2 + 6m + 2 =$

31. By graphing, Phyllis found that 2 and -3 are zeros of $14x^4 - 15x^3 - 128x^2 + 159x + 90$. Find the other two zeros. $-\frac{3}{7}, \frac{5}{2}$

32. By graphing, find two zeros of $f: x \rightarrow 15x^4 - 67x^3 - 54x^2 + 312x + 64$. Then use these zeros to find the other two zeros. $-2, -\frac{1}{5}, \frac{8}{3}, 4$

33. The number 2 has the property that its 3rd power equals 2 more than the sum of its 1st and 2nd powers. Use factoring to show that no other real number has this property. See margin.

34. Find all solutions to $4h^4 - 45h^2 + 11 = 0$. $-\sqrt{11}, -\frac{1}{2}, \frac{1}{2}, \sqrt{11}$

PROPERTIES DEAL WITH THE PRINCIPLES BEHIND THE MATHEMATICS.

35–38, 40–42, 51) See margin.

Objective F: *Justify properties of factors of integers or factors of polynomials.* *(Lesson 4-1)*

In 35–37, determine whether the statement is *true or false*. Explain your answer.

35. 18 is a factor of 90. True

36. 156 is divisible by 9. False

37. $2a + 2b$ is divisible by 4 if a and b are even integers. True

38. Prove: *For all odd integers n, $n^2 + n$ is divisible by 2.*

39. Which of the following expressions are divisible by 6 if a is divisible by 3? b, c, e

(a) $6 + a$ (b) $2a$ (c) $4a$

(d) $3a^2$ (e) $6 - 2a$

In 40 and 41, prove the conjecture or find a counterexample to disprove it.

40. *For all integers a, b, c, and d, if $a = b - c$ and a and c are divisible by d, then b is divisible by d.*

41. *For all integers a, if a is odd, then $a^3 - 1$ is divisible by 4.*

42. Prove that the number one greater than the product of any two consecutive odd integers is divisible by 4.

Objective G: *Use the properties of congruence of integers in a given modulus to rewrite sentences.* *(Lesson 4-5)*

43. If $x \equiv y \pmod{11}$, what can you conclude about $x - y$? 11 is a factor of $x - y$.

In 44 and 45, rewrite in the language of congruences.

44. x is a multiple of 5. $x \equiv 0 \pmod 5$

45. If $\sin x = -\frac{1}{2}$, then $x = \frac{7\pi}{6} + 2\pi k$ or $x = \frac{11\pi}{6} + 2\pi k$ for some integer k.

$x \equiv \frac{7\pi}{6} \pmod{2\pi}$ or $x \equiv \frac{11\pi}{6} \pmod{2\pi}$

In 46 and 47, suppose $c \equiv 5 \pmod{11}$ and $d \equiv 7 \pmod{11}$. What congruence statement can you write for the expression?

46. $c - d$ See below. **47.** cd $cd \equiv 2 \pmod{11}$

48. In a listing of students in a school, the tops of the columns start with the 1st, 13th, 25th, 37th, 49th, . . . student. Let x stand for the number of a student. Write a congruence that indicates that student is at the top column of a page. $x \equiv 1 \pmod{12}$ 46) $c - d \equiv -2 \pmod{11}$

Objective H: *Use the Remainder Theorem, Factor Theorem, or Quotient-Remainder Theorem to describe characteristics of given polynomials.* *(Lessons 4-2, 4-3, 4-4)* 49, 50) See below.

49. In the Quotient-Remainder Theorem, given polynomials $n(x)$ and $d(x)$, what are the restrictions on $r(x)$ if $n(x) = q(x) \cdot d(x) + r(x)$?

50. If the degree of $p(x)$ is 5, the degree of $q(x)$ is d, and the degree of their product is 10, find d.

51. Use long division to show that $x^4 - 3$ is a factor of $x^6 + 2x^5 - 7x^4 - 3x^2 - 6x + 21$.

52. *Multiple choice.* When $p(x) = 4x^5 - 7x^3 + 2x^2 + 1$ is divided by $x + 5$, the remainder is given by which of the following? d

(a) $p(x + 5)$ (b) $p(x - 5)$

(c) $p(5)$ (d) $p(-5)$.

53. If 7 is a zero of $p(x)$, then __?__ is a factor of $p(x)$. $(x - 7)$

54. If p is a polynomial of degree 7, then p can have at most __?__ zeros. 7

49) Either $r(x)$ is the zero polynomial or the degree of $r(x)$ is less than the degree of $d(x)$.

50) $d = 5$

It is effective to ask students which questions they still do not understand and use the day or days as a total class discussion of the material which the class finds most difficult.

Assessment

Evaluation The Assessment Sourcebook provides five forms of the Chapter 4 Test. Forms A and B present parallel versions in a short-answer format. Forms C and D offer performance assessment. The fifth test is Chapter 4 Test, Cumulative Form. About 50% of this test covers Chapter 4, 25% of it covers Chapter 3, and 25% of it covers earlier chapters.

For information on grading, see *General Teaching Suggestions: Grading* in the *Professional Sourcebook,* which begins on page T20 in the Teacher's Edition.

Additional Answers

51.

$$\begin{array}{r} x^2 + 2x - 2 \\ x^4 - 3\overline{)x^6 + 2x^5 - 7x^4 - 3x^2 - 6x + 21} \\ \underline{x^6 \qquad\qquad\qquad - 3x^2 \qquad\qquad} \\ 2x^5 - 7x^4 \qquad - 6x + 21 \\ \underline{2x^5 \qquad\qquad\qquad - 6x \qquad} \\ -7x^4 \qquad\qquad + 21 \\ \underline{-7x^4 \qquad\qquad + 21} \\ 0 \end{array}$$

$2(2m^2 + 3m + 1)$ by the distributive law. Because the integers are closed under both multiplication and addition, $2m^2 + 3m + 1$ is an integer. ∴ by the definition of factor, 2 is a factor of $n^2 + n$. Since a number is even if it is divisible by 2, $n^2 + n$ is even.

40. Let a, b, c, and d be any integers such that a and c are divisible by d and $a = b - c$. Then ∃ integers r and s such that $a = d \cdot r$ and $c = d \cdot s$ by definition. Then, $b = a + c = d \cdot r + d \cdot s = d(r + s)$. Since $(r + s)$ is an integer by closure properties, b is divisible by d.

41. This is false. For example, $3^3 - 1$ is not divisible by 4.

42. Let a be an odd integer. Then for some integer n, $a = 2n + 1$. The next higher odd integer is $a + 2 = 2n + 3$. The number one greater than the product of two consecutive odd integers is then $a(a + 2) + 1 = (2n + 1)(2n + 3) + 1 = 4n^2 + 8n + 4 = 4(n^2 + 2n + 1)$ by the distributive law. Because the integers are closed under both multiplication and addition, $n^2 + 2n + 1$ is an integer. Therefore, by the definition of factor, the number one greater than product of two consecutive odd integers is divisible by 4.

Feedback After students have taken the test for Chapter 4 and you have scored the results, return the tests to students for discussion. Class discussion of the questions that caused trouble for the most students can be very effective in identifying and clarifying misunderstandings. You might want to have them write down the items they missed and work, either in groups or at home, to correct them. It is important for students to receive feedback on every chapter test, and we recommend that students see and correct their mistakes before proceeding too far into the next chapter.

Objective I: *Use proof by contradiction.* *(Lesson 4-7)* 55–58) See margin.

In 55 and 56, write the assumption that you would make to begin the proof of the given statement by contradiction.

55. *There is no smallest integer.*

56. *For all primes p, if p is a factor of n^2, then p is a factor of n.*

57. Use proof by contradiction to prove the statement in Question 55.

58. Give Euclid's proof of the infinitude of the primes.

59. If n_p is one more than the product of all the primes from 2 to p, inclusive, what is n_{11}? 2311

Objective J: *Use the Factor Search Theorem and the Fundamental Theorem of Arithmetic in determining prime numbers and prime factorizations.* *(Lesson 4-7)*

60. *True or false.* To determine if 653 is prime, you only need to check if 653 is divisible by the prime numbers between 1 and 26. True

61. How many primes must be tested to determine whether 227 is prime? six (2, 3, 5, 7, 11, 13)

62. Only primes less than what number must be tested to determine whether 1,000,001 is prime? 1001

63. *Multiple choice.* Which is true about the largest prime? a

(a) There is no largest prime.

(b) The largest known prime has fewer than 500,000 digits.

64. *Multiple choice.* Which of the following is the standard prime factorization of 2352? c

(a) $2 \cdot 2 \cdot 2 \cdot 2 \cdot 3 \cdot 7 \cdot 7$

(b) $7^2 \cdot 3 \cdot 2^4$

(c) $2^4 \cdot 3 \cdot 7^2$

(d) $2^2 \cdot 2^2 \cdot 3 \cdot 7^2$

In 65–67, determine if the given integer is prime. If it is not prime, write the standard prime factorization of it.

65. 653 Prime **66.** 551 $19 \cdot 29$ **67.** 8430 $2 \cdot 3 \cdot 5 \cdot 281$

USES DEAL WITH APPLICATIONS OF MATHEMATICS IN REAL SITUATIONS.

Objective K: *Use the Quotient-Remainder Theorem to solve applied problems.* *(Lesson 4-2)*

68. A computer printer prints 66 lines per page. A document with 5789 lines is printed.

a. How many pages are needed? 88

b. How many lines are on the last page? 47

c. Write an equation in the form

$$5789 = pq + r$$

to describe the situation. $5789 = 66 \cdot 87 + 47$

69. Once around a track is 400 meters. If a runner wants to run 5.5 miles, find the number of complete laps and the number of meters that must be run. Use the fact that 1 mile is about 1609 meters. 22 laps, 49.5 m left

55. Assume there exists a smallest integer.

56. Assume that there exists a prime p that is a factor of n^2, but not a factor of n.

57. Assume that n is the smallest integer. Because the integers are closed under addition, $n - 1$ is also an integer. Since $n - 1 < n$, n cannot be the smallest integer. This is a contradiction. Therefore, there is no smallest integer.

58. Assume there are finitely many prime numbers. They can be listed from smallest to largest: $p_1 = 2$, $p_2 = 3$, ..., p_m. Multiply these: $n = p_1p_2p_3 \ldots p_m$. Consider the integer $n + 1$. Since $n + 1$ is larger than the assumed largest prime p_m, it is not prime. By the prime Factor Theorem, $n + 1$ must have a prime factor, p, on the list of primes. Then p is a factor of both n and $n + 1$. It is also a factor of the difference $(n + 1) - n = 1$. Therefore, p must equal 1. But p is a prime number, so p cannot equal 1. This contradiction proves that the original assumption is false. Hence, there are infinitely many prime numbers.

70. Emily is a frequent flyer with an airline and earns a free ticket for every 40,000 miles credited to her account. She has 387,500 miles credited to her account.

a. How many free tickets did she earn? 9

b. How many credited miles can be applied to her next free ticket? 27,500

c. Relate your answers in parts **a** and **b** to the Quotient-Remainder Theorem.
$387{,}500 = 9 \cdot 40{,}000 + 27{,}500$

71. Consider a 365-day year in which all months have the same number of days. How many months would be in a year? How many days would be in a month?
73 months of 5 days, 5 months of 73 days, 365 months of 1 day, or 1 month of 365 days

Objective L: *Use modular arithmetic to solve applied problems.* *(Lesson 4-5)* 72) 5625

72. There are 5^{30} ways to answer a 30-question multiple-choice test with 5 choices for each question. Write the last 4 digits of this number.

73. A calculator displays 7^{19} in scientific notation as $1.13989 \cdot 10^{16}$. Find the last 3 digits of this number. 143

In 74 and 75, find the check digit for the ISBN number.

74. 0-939765-04-_?_ 7

75. 0-7216-1983-_?_ 5

REPRESENTATIONS DEAL WITH PICTURES, GRAPHS, OR OBJECTS THAT ILLUSTRATE CONCEPTS.

Objective M: *Represent numbers in other bases and perform addition in base 2.* *(Lesson 4-6)*

In 76 and 77, write the base 2 representation of the number.

76. 65 1000001_2 **77.** 165 10100101_2

In 78 and 79, write the base 10 representation of the number.

78. 11111_2 31 **79.** 101010_2 42

In 80 and 81, perform the indicated addition and then verify your answer by finding the base 10 representations of the numbers. See below.

80. $10101_2 + 11010_2$ **81.** $11111_2 + 11111_2$

82. *Multiple choice.* Which of the following is evenly divisible by 4? d

(a) 1001_2 (b) 1010_2
(c) 1011_2 (d) 1100_2

83. In base 2, how can you quickly tell if a number is divisible by 16? In base 2, a number divisible by 16 ends in 0000.

80) 101111_2; 21 + 26 = 47

81) 111110_2; 31 + 31 = 62

Adapting to Individual Needs

The student text is written for the vast majority of students. The chart at the right suggests two pacing plans to accommodate the needs of your students. Students in the Full Course should complete the entire text by the end of the year. Students in the Minimal Course will spend more time when there are quizzes and more time on the Chapter Review. Therefore, these students may not complete all of the chapters in the text.

Options are also presented to meet the needs of a variety of teaching and learning styles. For each lesson, the Teacher's Edition provides a section entitled *Adapting to Individual Needs.* This section regularly includes **Optional Activities, Challenge** problems, **English Language Development** suggestions, and suggestions for providing **Extra Help.** The Teacher's Edition also frequently includes an **Error Alert,** an **Extension,** and an **Assessment** alternative. The options available in Chapter 5 are summarized in the chart below.

Chapter 5 Pacing Chart

Day	Full Course	Minimal Course
1	5-1	5-1
2	5-2	5-2
3	5-3	5-3
4	5-4	5-4
5	Quiz*; 5-5	Quiz*; begin 5-5.
6	5-6	Finish 5-5.
7	5-7	5-6
8	Quiz*; 5-8	5-7
9	5-9	Quiz*; begin 5-8.
10	Self-Test	Finish 5-8.
11	Review	5-9
12	Test*	Self-Test
13		Review
14		Review
15		Test*

*in the Teacher's Resource File

In the Teacher's Edition...

Lesson	Optional Activities	Extra Help	Challenge	English Language Development	Error Alert	Extension	Cooperative Learning	Ongoing Assessment
5-1	●	●	●		●	●		Oral
5-2	●		●		●	●	●	Written
5-3	●	●	●		●	●		Written
5-4	●	●	●		●	●		Quiz
5-5	●		●		●	●	●	Written
5-6	●	●	●			●	●	Written
5-7	●	●	●		●	●		Quiz
5-8	●	●	●		●	●		Oral
5-9	●	●	●		●	●		

In the Additional Resources...

	In the Teacher's Resource File							
Lesson	Lesson Masters	Teaching Aids*	Answer Masters	Technology Sourcebook	Assessment Sourcebook	Visual Aids**	Technology	Explorations Software
5-1	5-1	43	5-1			43, AM		
5-2	5-2	43	5-2			43, AM		
5-3	5-3	43, 46	5-3			43, 46, AM		
5-4	5-4	44, 47, 48	5-4		Quiz	44, 47, 48, AM		5-4
5-5	5-5	44, 49	5-5	Calc 8		44, 49, AM		
5-6	5-6	44	5-6			44, AM		
5-7	5-7	45, 50, 51	5-7		Quiz	45, 50, 51, AM		5-7
In-class Activity			5-8					
5-8	5-8	45	5-8	Calc 9		45, AM		
5-9		45, 52	5-9	Comp 2		45, 52, AM	Graphic Art software	
End of chapter					Tests			

*Teaching Aids are pictured on pages 282C and 282D.

**Visual Aids provide transparencies for all Teaching Aids and all Answer Masters.

Also available is the Study Skills Handbook which includes study-skill tips related to reading, note-taking, and comprehension.

Integrating Strands and Applications

	5-1	5-2	5-3	5-4	5-5	5-6	5-7	5-8	5-9
Mathematical Connections									
Number Sense	●	●	●	●	●	●	●	●	●
Algebra	●	●	●	●	●	●	●	●	●
Geometry	●					●	●	●	●
Measurement				●				●	●
Logic and Reasoning	●	●			●	●		●	●
Probability					●				
Patterns and Functions	●	●	●	●	●	●	●	●	●
Interdisciplinary and Other Connections									
Art						●			●
Science			●		●	●		●	●
Social Studies		●							●
Multicultural						●		●	
Technology		●	●	●	●	●	●	●	●
Career					●				
Consumer	●			●			●	●	
Sports							●	●	

Teaching and Assessing the Chapter Objectives

				In the Teacher's Resource File		
Chapter 5 Objectives (Organized into the SPUR catetgories—Skills, Properties, Uses, and Representations)	**Lessons**	**Progress Self-Test Questions**	**Chapter Review Questions**	**Chapter Test, Forms A and B**	**Chapter Test, Forms C**	**D**
Skills						
A: Simplify rational expressions.	5-2	1, 2	1-13		2	X
B: Identify numbers as rational or irrational.	5-1, 5-6	4	14-21		1	
C: Simplify expressions involving radicals.	5-6	6	22-27		4	
D: Identify rational functions and their domains.	5-4, 5-7	7	28-33		3	
E: Solve rational equations.	5-8	11	34-38		5	X
Properties						
F: Prove properties of rational and irrational numbers.	5-1, 5-6	5	39-47		1	
G: Use limit notation to describe the behavior of rational functions.	5-4, 5-5	8, 9	48-57			
H: Classify discontinuities as essential or removable.	5-4, 5-7	10	58-61		3	
Uses						
I: Apply rational expressions and rational equations.	5-1, 5-2, 5-8	3	62-65			X
Representations						
J: Graph rational functions.	5-3, 5-4, 5-5	9	66-68			
K: Relate the limit of a function to its graph, and find equations for its asymptotes.	5-3, 5-4, 5-5, 5-7	16	69-72		6	
L: Use right triangles or graphs to find values of the tangent, cotangent, secant, and cosecant functions.	5-7	12, 13, 14, 15	73-80			

Assessment Sourcebook
Quiz for Lessons 5-1 through 5-4
Quiz for Lessons 5-5 through 5-7

Chapter 5 Test, Forms A–D

TestWorks CD-ROM

Teaching Aids

TEACHING AID 43

Warm-up

Lesson 5-1

When it is m minutes after 5:00 and not yet 5:30, the minute hand on a clock will have rotated $6m$ degrees clockwise from straight up, and the hour hand will have rotated $\frac{m}{2}$ degrees clockwise from the 5:00 position.

1. What is the origin of the fraction $\frac{m}{2}$?
2. What is the measure of the angle between the hour hand and the minute hand? Write this measure as a single fraction.
3. At what time will the minute hand cross the hour hand?

Warm-up

Lesson 5-2

Write the sum $\frac{a}{b} + \frac{c}{d} - \frac{e}{f}$ as a single fraction, and check your answer.

Warm-up

Lesson 5-3

Compare the graphs of $y = \frac{1}{x^2}$ and $y = \frac{1}{x^4}$. Name two ways in which they are alike, and tell how they are different.

TEACHING AID 44

Warm-up

Lesson 5-4

You fill up your car's gas tank with 14.3 gallons of gas when its odometer shows 12345.6 miles, and you fill it up again with 13.7 gallons when its odometer shows 12698.4 miles. How many miles per gallon is your car getting?

Warm-up

Lesson 5-5

Give an equation for a function f such that $\lim_{x \to \infty} f(x) = 6$.

Warm-up

Lesson 5-6

1. Find a recursive formula for the first four terms of the sequence $\frac{3}{2}, \frac{7}{5}, \frac{17}{12}, \frac{41}{29}, \frac{99}{70}, \ldots$
2. Use your formula to obtain the next few terms of the sequence. Does the sequence seem to have a limit? If so, conjecture what that limit is?

TEACHING AID 45

Warm-up

Lesson 5-7

In right triangle ABC, there are six possible ratios of sides.

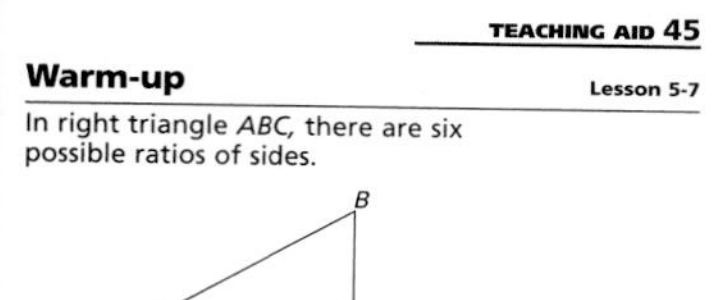

1. Write these six ratios.
2. Match these ratios with the following six numbers: sin A, cos A, tan A, cot A, sec A, and csc A.

Warm-up

Lesson 5-8

A trucker drives 25 miles from city A to city B in 40 minutes. The trucker wants to drive the 20 miles from city B to city C so as to average 55 mph for the entire trip. Is this possible? At what average speed must the trucker travel from city B to city C?

Warm-up

Lesson 5-9

Define each term.

1. Unit fraction
2. Regular polygon
3. Regular polyhedron

TEACHING AID 46

Lesson 5-3

Graph of $f(x) = \frac{1}{x}$

$f(x) = \frac{1}{x}$

$\lim_{x \to 0^+} f(x) = \infty$

Additional Examples

1. Consider the function f with rule $f(x) = \frac{1}{x-3} + 2$, where $x \neq 3$, graphed here.

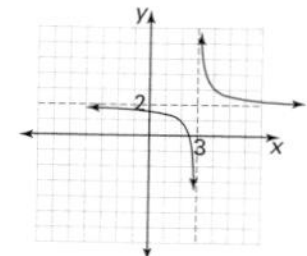

   a. Give an equation for the vertical asymptote to the graph.
   b. Use limit notation to describe the behavior of the function near this asymptote.

2. a. Describe the behavior of the function $g: x \to \frac{-5}{x^4}$ as x approaches 0.
   b. Graph g.

TEACHING AID 47

Lesson 5-4

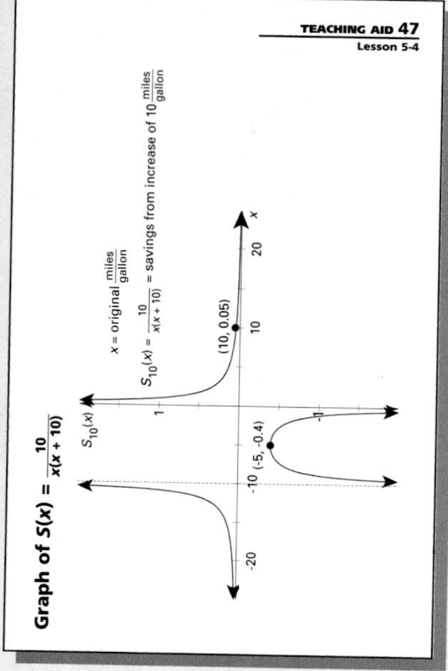

TEACHING AID 48

Lesson 5-4

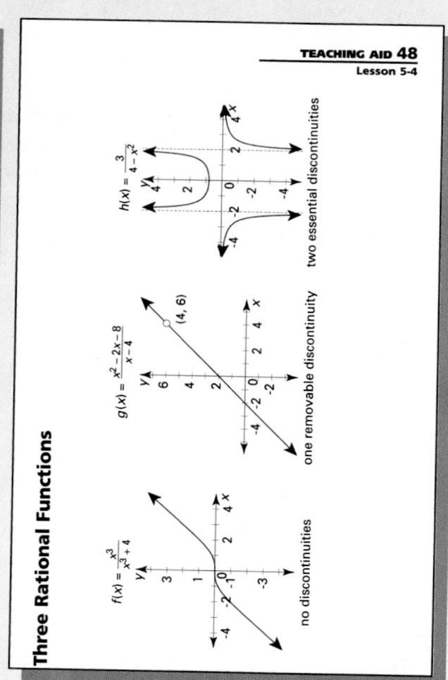

TEACHING AID 49

Lesson 5-5

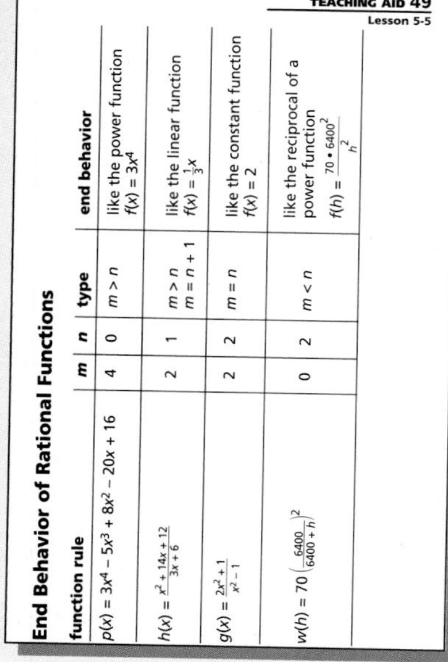

End Behavior of Rational Functions

function rule	m	n	type	end behavior
$p(x) = 3x^4 - 5x^3 + 8x^2 - 20x + 16$	4	0	$m > n$	like the power function $f(x) = 3x^4$
$h(x) = \frac{x^2 + 14x + 12}{3x + 6}$	2	1	$m > n$ $m = n + 1$	like the linear function $f(x) = \frac{1}{3}x$
$g(x) = \frac{2x^2 + 1}{x^2 - 1}$	2	2	$m = n$	like the constant function $f(x) = 2$
$w(h) = 70\left(\frac{6400}{6400 + h}\right)^2$	0	2	$m < n$	like the reciprocal of a power function $f(h) = \frac{70 \cdot 6400^2}{h^2}$

TEACHING AID 50

Lesson 5-7

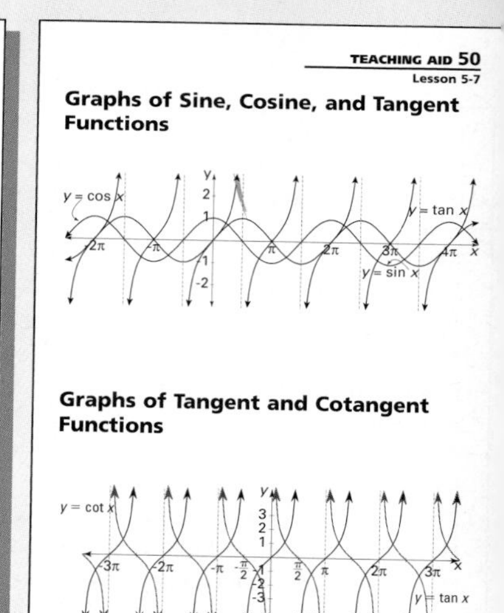

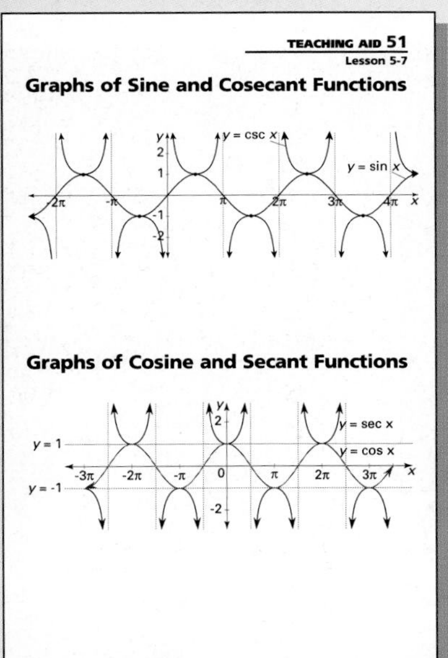
TEACHING AID 51
Lesson 5-7
Graphs of Sine and Cosecant Functions
y = csc x
y = sin x
y
2
1
-1
-2
-2π
-π
π
2π
3π
4π
x
Graphs of Cosine and Secant Functions
y = sec x
y = cos x
y = 1
y = -1
y
2
-2
-3π
-2π
-π
0
π
2π
3π
x

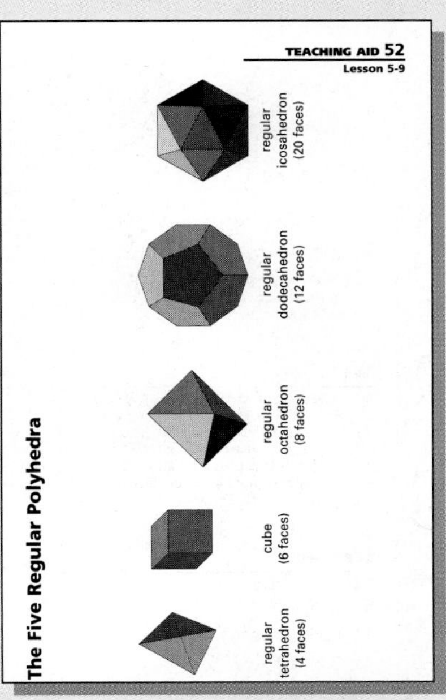
TEACHING AID 52
Lesson 5-9
The Five Regular Polyhedra
regular icosahedron (20 faces)
regular dodecahedron (12 faces)
regular octahedron (8 faces)
cube (6 faces)
regular tetrahedron (4 faces)

Chapter Opener

Pacing

All lessons in this chapter are designed to be covered in one day. At the end of the chapter, you should plan to spend 1 day to review the Progress Self-Test, 1–2 days for the Chapter Review, and 1 day for a test. You may wish to spend a day on projects, and possibly a day is needed for quizzes and the In-class Activity. This chapter should therefore take 12–15 days. Spending more than 15 days on this chapter is not recommended; there is ample opportunity to review ideas in later chapters.

Using Pages 282–283

You might wish to clarify the terms to be used in this chapter by putting the terms into two columns, as we do on this page.

arithmetic	algebra
integer	polynomial
prime number	prime polynomial
set of integers	set of polynomials
closed under +, −, and •, but not ÷	closed under +, −, and •, but not ÷
integer division	polynomial division
rational number	rational expression
quotient of integers	quotient of polynomials
irrational number	nonrational expression

CHAPTER 5

Chapter 5 Overview

In this chapter, the system of rational numbers is used to build student understanding of rational functions. Irrational numbers and some nonrational functions are used both for contrast and because they are important in their own right. It is useful to think of the following pairs of terms as analogous:

1. *rational expression* (an indicated quotient of two polynomials) and *fraction* (an indicated quotient of two integers);
2. *rational function* (a function that can be expressed as the quotient of two polynomial functions) and *rational number* (a number that can be written as the quotient of two integers);
3. *nonrational function* (a real function that is not a rational function) and *irrational number* (a real number that is not a rational number)

The chapter can be thought of as having three parts. The first two lessons provide the groundwork for the study of rational functions. In Lessons 5-1 and 5-2, there is work with operations on rational numbers and expressions.

The next three lessons study rational functions themselves. The simplest rational functions (other than polynomial functions) are the reciprocals of power functions, that is, those functions with rules of the form

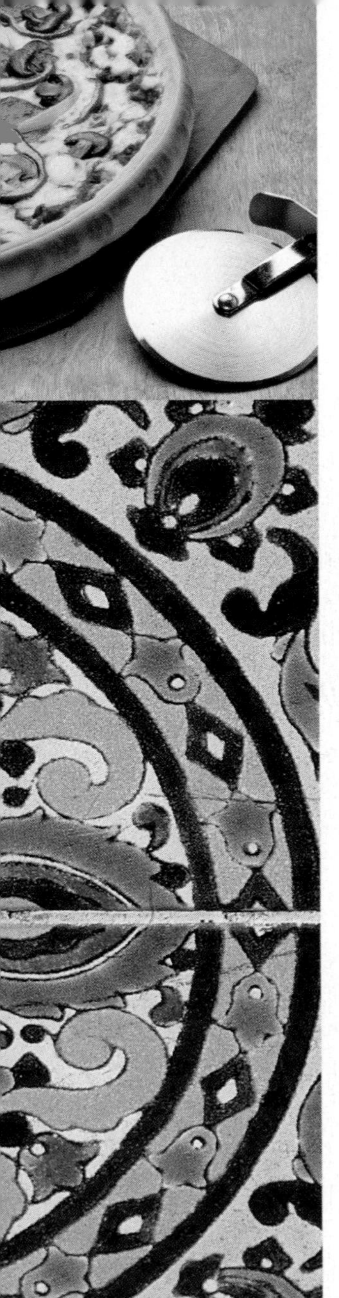

Rational Numbers and Rational Functions

As you saw in the last chapter, the systems of integers and polynomials have much the same structure. Any integer or polynomial is either prime or can be factored into a product of primes.

29 is prime.	$x^2 + 6$ is prime.
$80 = 2^4 \cdot 5$	$x^4 + x^3 + 4x^2 + 9x + 5 =$ $(x + 1)^2(x^2 - x + 5)$

In each system, the operations of addition, subtraction, and multiplication are closed.

$29 + 80$, $29 - 80$, and $29 \cdot 80$ are integers.	$(x^2 + 6) + (x^4 + x^3 + 4x^2 + 9x + 5)$, $(x^2 + 6) - (x^4 + x^3 + 4x^2 + 9x + 5)$, and $(x^2 + 6)(x^4 + x^3 + 4x^2 + 9x + 5)$ are polynomials.

There is a Quotient-Remainder Theorem that enables a division problem to be treated without leaving the system.

$80 = 29 \cdot 2 + 22$	$x^4 + x^3 + 4x^2 + 9x + 5 =$ $(x^2 + 6)(x^2 + x - 2) + (3x + 17)$

However, division is not closed, and expressing the quotient of two elements often requires going outside the system.

$\frac{80}{29} = 2 + \frac{22}{29}$ is not an integer.	$\frac{x^4 + x^3 + 4x^2 + 9x + 5}{x^2 + 6} = x^2 + x - 2 + \frac{3x + 17}{x^2 + 6}$ is not a polynomial.

The quotient of two integers is a *rational number*; the quotient of two polynomials is a *rational expression*. The irrational number $\frac{\sqrt{3}}{2}$ arises often as the length of a side in a triangle or other polygon. The nonrational expression $\frac{1000}{1 + 999e^{-3t}}$ is found in the study of epidemics. This chapter studies rational and irrational numbers, rational and nonrational expressions, and their related equations, functions, and applications.

Notice how there is a smooth transition of the material from Chapter 4 (the first six entries in the table) to the material of this chapter (the last two rows).

Photo Connections

The photo collage makes real-world connections to the content of the chapter: rational numbers and rational functions.

Greece: The ancient Greeks knew of five different regular polyhedra. In Lesson 5-9, a proof is given that there are no other regular polyhedra.

Pizza: In Lesson 5-1, rational expressions are used to find how much of one whole pizza a student ate.

Car: One way to keep the cost of operating a car down is to increase fuel efficiency. The amount that can be saved is discussed in Lesson 5-4.

Tessellating Tiles: In Lesson 5-9, a problem involving unit fractions is used to determine which regular polygons will tessellate.

Boat: In Lesson 5-8, rational equations are used to find the average speed of a speedboat relative to still water.

Chapter 5 Projects

At this time, you might want to have students look over the projects on pages 340–341.

$f(x) = \frac{k}{x^n}$. These are studied in Lesson 5-3. In Lessons 5-4 and 5-5, the behavior of rational functions is discussed. In Lesson 5-6, irrational numbers are defined and dealt with. Some irrational numbers appear in fractions, of course, and the operations with fractions can be used with them.

The last three lessons apply the ideas of the earlier part of the chapter. The tangent, cotangent, secant, and cosecant functions are nonrational functions that are defined as reciprocals or quotients of sine and cosine functions. Thus some of the ideas of reciprocal functions and rational functions (such as vertical asymptotes) apply to them in much the same way that ideas about fractions can be used with irrational numbers. These are discussed in Lesson 5-7. Lesson 5-8 covers the solving of equations of the form $f(x) = g(x)$, where both are rational expressions. These kinds of equations appear naturally from discussions of rational functions. Lesson 5-9 deals with unit fractions and their surprising relationship to the determination of those regular polygons that will tessellate the plane and to the determination of regular polyhedra.

The mathematics of this chapter is beautiful but was relatively inaccessible to students before the days of automatic graphers.

Lesson 5-1

Objectives

B Identify numbers as rational or irrational.
F Prove properties of rational and irrational numbers.
I Apply rational expressions and rational equations.

Resources

From the ***Teacher's Resource File***
- Lesson Master 5-1
- Answer Master 5-1
- Teaching Aid 43: Warm-up

Additional Resources
- Visual for Teaching Aid 43

Teaching Lesson 5-1

Warm-up

When it is m minutes after 5:00 and not yet 5:30, the minute hand on a clock will have rotated $6m$ degrees clockwise from straight up, and the hour hand will have rotated $\frac{m}{2}$ degrees clockwise from the 5:00 position.

1. What is the origin of the fraction $\frac{m}{2}$? **In 60 minutes the hour hand moves 30°. Since it is moving at a constant rate, in m minutes it moves $\frac{m}{2}$ degrees.**
2. What is the measure of the angle between the hour hand and the minute hand? Write this measure as a single fraction. $150 + \frac{m}{2} - 6m = \frac{300 - 11m}{2}$
3. At what time will the minute hand cross the hour hand? **When $m = \frac{300}{11}$, i.e., when the time is $\frac{300}{11}$ minutes after the hour, at $5{:}27\frac{3}{11}$.**

LESSON

5-1 Rational Numbers

A number that can be written as a ratio of two integers is said to be *rational*.

> **Definition**
> A real number r is **rational** if and only if there exist integers a and b $(b \neq 0)$ such that $r = \frac{a}{b}$.

Rational numbers are not always written as fractions. However, if you can express a given number as a ratio of two integers, that number must be rational. For example, since $-0.283 = \frac{-283}{1000}$, there is a way to write -0.283 as a ratio of integers, and so -0.283 is rational. $1\frac{3}{5}$ is rational because $1\frac{3}{5} = \frac{8}{5}$. 0 is rational because 0 can be written as $\frac{0}{1}$. On the other hand, $\frac{\sqrt{2}}{2}$ is a ratio, but not a ratio of two integers. In Lesson 5-6 you will see that $\frac{\sqrt{2}}{2}$ is not a rational number.

The rational numbers are **closed** with respect to addition, subtraction, and multiplication. That is, the sum, difference, and product of any two rational numbers is rational.

Adding Rational Numbers

Example 1

Show that the sum of any two rational numbers is a rational number.

Solution

Suppose that r and s are any two rational numbers. Then there exist integers a, b, c, and d with $b \neq 0$ and $d \neq 0$ such that $r = \frac{a}{b}$ and $s = \frac{c}{d}$. So

$$
\begin{aligned}
r + s &= \frac{a}{b} + \frac{c}{d} \\
&= \frac{a}{b} \cdot \frac{d}{d} + \frac{b}{b} \cdot \frac{c}{d} && \text{Multiplication Property of 1} \\
&= \frac{ad}{bd} + \frac{bc}{bd} && \text{Multiplication of Fractions} \\
&= \frac{ad + bc}{bd} && \text{Distributive Property}
\end{aligned}
$$

Because sums and products of integers are integers, $ad + bc$ and bd are integers. Furthermore, $bd \neq 0$ because neither b nor d is 0. Hence $\frac{ad + bc}{bd}$ is a ratio of integers, meaning that $r + s$ is a rational number.

Lesson 5-1 Overview

Broad Goals This lesson gives the mathematical underpinnings of work with rational expressions, by examining the addition, multiplication, and division of rational numbers in general. It is the first of two consecutive lessons with concentrated practice in the manipulation of rational expressions.

Perspective The biggest difficulty with the understanding of the definition of *rational number* is that a number is rational independent of the way it looks. For example, the rational number $\frac{9}{4}$ is rational in all of its other forms, including 2.25, $\sqrt{\frac{81}{16}}$, 1.5^2, $\frac{9\pi}{4\pi}$, and $2 + \frac{1}{4}$. On the other hand, a *rational expression* is a written form. We do not consider the expression $\sqrt{(x + 5)^4}$ to be a rational expression even though it is identically equal (for all real values of x) to $(x + 5)^2$.

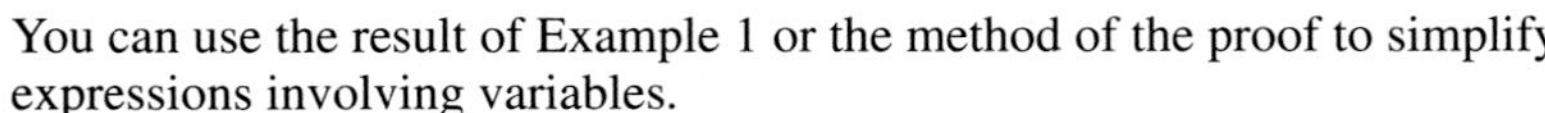

You can use the result of Example 1 or the method of the proof to simplify expressions involving variables.

Example 2

A group of N students ordered one sausage pizza and one pepperoni pizza of the same size. They divided the sausage pizza evenly. Since two students did not want any pepperoni pizza, they divided that one into $N - 2$ pieces. Suppose a student ate one piece of each kind of pizza. Expressed as a fraction of one whole pizza, how much pizza did that student eat?

Solution

One piece of the sausage pizza is $\frac{1}{N}$ of one pizza; one piece of the pepperoni pizza is $\frac{1}{N-2}$ of one pizza. **So the student ate a total of $\frac{1}{N} + \frac{1}{N-2}$ of one whole pizza.** Since $N > 2$, these expressions are defined for all values of N possible in this situation. Add the rational expressions.

$$\frac{1}{N} + \frac{1}{N-2} = \frac{1}{N} \cdot \frac{N-2}{N-2} + \frac{1}{N-2} \cdot \frac{N}{N} \quad \text{Multiplication Property of 1}$$

$$= \frac{N-2}{N^2 - 2N} + \frac{N}{N^2 - 2N} \quad \text{Multiplication of Fractions}$$

$$= \frac{2N-2}{N^2 - 2N} \quad \text{Distributive Property}$$

Thus **the total amount eaten by the student is $\frac{2N-2}{N^2 - 2N}$ of one whole pizza.**

Check

Suppose $N = 10$. If there were 10 students, then the student ate $\frac{1}{10}$ of the sausage pizza and $\frac{1}{8}$ of the pepperoni pizza. $\frac{1}{10} + \frac{1}{8} = \frac{8}{80} + \frac{10}{80} = \frac{18}{80} = \frac{9}{40}$.

Now substitute 10 for N in the answer. $\frac{2N-2}{N^2 - 2N} = \frac{2 \cdot 10 - 2}{10^2 - 2 \cdot 10} = \frac{18}{80}$. It checks.

Identities Involving Rational Expressions

The above steps show that, $\forall N$ with $N \neq 0$ and $N \neq 2$, $\frac{1}{N} + \frac{1}{N-2} = \frac{2N-2}{N^2 - 2N}$. That is, when N is replaced by any number other than 0 or 2, the expressions on both sides have the same value. Such an equation is called an *identity*.

Definition

An **identity** is an equation that is true for all values of the variables for which both sides are defined. The set of all such values is called the **domain of the identity**.

In the context of Example 2, the domain of N is the set of integers greater than 2.

Notes on Reading

Example 1 proves that the set of rational numbers is closed under addition. It is obvious that the product of two rational numbers is a rational number, since $\frac{a}{b} \cdot \frac{c}{d} = \frac{ac}{bd}$. Since both addition and multiplication in the set of rational numbers satisfy the associative, commutative, and distributive properties, and have identities and inverses, the set of rational numbers is a field. As a result, the set is closed under subtraction and division (except for division by zero). **Example 3** shows that the set of rational numbers is also closed under division.

In **Example 2,** to check whether $\frac{1}{N} - \frac{1}{N-2} = \frac{2N-2}{N^2 - 2N}$ is an identity, you can have a computer (program or spreadsheet) generate a table of values for $N = 1, 2, 3, \ldots$ and the expression on each side of the identity. Graphing the two sides, with $f(x) = \frac{1}{x} - \frac{1}{x-2}$ and $g(x) = \frac{2x-2}{x^2 - 2x}$ may also be illuminating. Remind students that the domain of the identity in the situation of **Example 2** is the set of integers $N > 2$, but the solution demonstrates that the identity is true for all real values of N for which the expressions are defined, that is, for all real numbers except 0 or 2.

The analogy between rational numbers and rational expressions is used in this lesson to explain the techniques used to manipulate rational expressions. However, the theme of logic is still maintained by putting the manipulations in the context of proving identities. Usually, students are introduced to the word *identity* when they study trigonometry, but they have actually been proving identities from the time that they first learned to simplify algebraic expressions.

Optional Activities

If your students have never learned how to find the simple fraction equal to a repeating decimal, you might do this activity at the conclusion of the lesson. It will simplify the reading of Lesson 5-6.

1. Write $.\overline{3}$ as a ratio of two integers.
[$10x = 3.333\ldots$
$x = .333\ldots$
$9x = 3$
$x = \frac{3}{9} = \frac{1}{3}$]
2. Repeat Question 1 for $.\overline{27}$.
[$100x = 27.272727\ldots$
$x = .272727\ldots$
$99x = 27$
$x = \frac{27}{99} = \frac{3}{11}$]
3. Use the answer to Question 2 to determine the simple fraction equal to $86.00\overline{27}$.
[$86 + .001 \cdot \frac{3}{11} = 86 + \frac{3}{11000} = \frac{946003}{11000}$]

❶ Another method for dividing fractions is to multiply both numerator and denominator by the reciprocal of the divisor.

$$\frac{\frac{2}{3}}{\frac{4}{5}} = \frac{\frac{2}{3} \cdot \frac{5}{4}}{\frac{4}{5} \cdot \frac{5}{4}} = \frac{\frac{10}{12}}{\frac{20}{20}} = \frac{\frac{10}{12}}{1} = \frac{10}{12} = \frac{5}{6}$$

Additional Examples

1. Show that the product of two rational numbers is a rational number. **Any two rational numbers can be denoted as $\frac{a}{b}$ and $\frac{c}{d}$, where a, b, c, and d are integers with $b \neq 0$ and $d \neq 0$. $\frac{a}{b} \cdot \frac{c}{d} = \frac{ac}{bd}$ (multiplication of fractions), which is a rational number by the definition of rational number, because the integers are closed under multiplication and because $bd \neq 0$ since both $b \neq 0$ and $d \neq 0$.**
2. One vegetarian and two mixed-meat submarine sandwiches were ordered for a party. Of the N students at the party, three would eat only vegetarian and two only mixed-meat subs. The vegetarian sub was sliced into $N - 2$ equal sandwiches and the mixed-meat sub into $N - 3$ equal sandwiches. If Horacio eats one of each kind of sandwich, what fraction of one whole submarine sandwich has he eaten? $\frac{2N-5}{(N-2)(N-3)}$

Complex Fractions

When the numerator or denominator of a fraction includes a fraction, the original fraction is called **complex**. (This is a different use of the word "complex" than occurs in the term *complex number*.)

❶ To simplify complex numerical fractions such as $\frac{\frac{2}{3}}{\frac{4}{5}}$, you may use one of two methods. One method is to replace the division $\frac{a}{b}$ by the equivalent multiplication $a \cdot \frac{1}{b}$.

Method (1): $\frac{\frac{2}{3}}{\frac{4}{5}} = \frac{2}{3} \div \frac{4}{5} = \frac{2}{3} \cdot \frac{1}{\frac{4}{5}} = \frac{2}{3} \cdot \frac{5}{4} = \frac{10}{12} = \frac{5}{6}$

A second method is to multiply both numerator and denominator by a number designed to clear the fractions.

Method (2): $\frac{\frac{2}{3}}{\frac{4}{5}} = \frac{\frac{2}{3} \cdot 15}{\frac{4}{5} \cdot 15} = \frac{10}{12} = \frac{5}{6}$

The set of rational numbers is closed under division whenever division is allowed.

Example 3

Prove: If r and s are rational numbers ($s \neq 0$), then $\frac{r}{s}$ is rational.

Solution

Let r be $\frac{a}{b}$ where a, b are integers and $b \neq 0$. Let $s = \frac{c}{d}$ where c and d are integers, $d \neq 0$.

Then $\frac{r}{s} = \frac{\frac{a}{b}}{\frac{c}{d}} = \frac{\frac{a}{b}}{\frac{c}{d}} \cdot 1 = \frac{\frac{a}{b} \cdot bd}{\frac{c}{d} \cdot bd} = \frac{ad}{bc}$.

ad is an integer, and bc is an integer not equal to zero ($c \neq 0$ since $s \neq 0$). Therefore $\frac{ad}{bc}$ is a rational number.

Example 4

a. In Example 2, what is the ratio of the area of a larger slice to the area of a smaller slice?
b. When will the ratio in sizes be too close to 1 to notice (say less than 1.1)?

Solution

a. The larger piece is in the pizza that is cut into fewer slices. Its area is $\frac{1}{N-2}$ of a pizza. The smaller area is $\frac{1}{N}$ of a pizza, so the ratio of areas is $\frac{\frac{1}{N-2}}{\frac{1}{N}}$.

$$\frac{\frac{1}{N-2}}{\frac{1}{N}} = \frac{1}{N-2} \div \frac{1}{N} = \frac{1}{N-2} \cdot \frac{N}{1} = \frac{N}{N-2}$$

Adapting to Individual Needs

Extra Help

Point out to students that a rational expression such as $\frac{2x(4-a)}{y(a-4)}$ is not simplified. Remind them that $(4 - a) = -1(a - 4)$. Then show how this allows us to write the expression with identical common factors and continue simplifying: $\frac{2x(4-a)}{y(a-4)} = \frac{-2x(a-4)}{y(a-4)} = -\frac{2x}{y}$.

Additional Answers, page 287

4. Suppose r and s are any two rational numbers. By definition, there exist integers a, b, c, and d, where $b \neq 0$ and $d \neq 0$ such that $r = \frac{a}{b}$ and $s = \frac{c}{d}$. So, $r - s = \frac{a}{b} - \frac{c}{d}$

$= \frac{a}{b} \cdot \frac{d}{d} - \frac{c}{d} \cdot \frac{b}{b}$ Mult. Prop. of 1

$= \frac{ad}{bd} - \frac{cb}{bd}$ Mult. of fractions

$= \frac{ad - cb}{bd}$ Add. of fractions

Since by closure properties the product of two integers and the difference between two integers are integers, $ad - cb$ and bd are integers. Also, $bd \neq 0$ since $b \neq 0$ and $d \neq 0$. Therefore, since $\frac{ad - cb}{bd}$ is a ratio of integers, $r - s$ is a rational number by definition.

b. We need to solve $\frac{N}{N-2} < 1.1$.
Since $N > 2$, $N - 2 > 0$ and so $N - 2$ is positive. Consequently, multiplying both sides of the inequality keeps the sense of the inequality.

$N < 1.1(N - 2)$	M_{N-2}
$N < 1.1N - 2.2$	Distributive Property
$N - 1.1N < -2.2$	$A_{-1.1N}$
$-.1N < -2.2$	Distributive Property
$N > 22$	M_{-10}

Thus it would take splitting the pizza among 22 people in order for the area of the larger slice to be too close to the area of the smaller slice to notice the difference (less than 10%).

QUESTIONS

Covering the Reading

In 1–3, *true or false*. If false, give a counterexample.

1. Every rational number is an integer. False; counterexample: $\frac{2}{3}$ is a rational number, but it is not an integer.
2. All integers are rational numbers. True
3. $\forall$ integers N, $1 + \frac{1}{N} = \frac{N+1}{N}$. False; counterexample: $N = 0$

4. Prove: The difference of any two rational numbers is a rational number. See margin.
5. Find the difference in the areas of the sausage and pepperoni pizza slices in Example 2. See margin.

In 6–13, all variables represent integers. Write each expression as a single rational number. Indicate the domain of the expression. See left.

6. $1 + \frac{K}{N}$
7. $N + \frac{K}{N}$
8. $N + \frac{K}{N^2}$
9. $\frac{1}{M-1} + \frac{M-1}{M-2}$
10. $\frac{1}{(N+K)^2}$
11. $1 - \frac{1}{K+1}$
12. $K - \frac{1}{K+1}$
13. $\frac{1}{a-1} + \frac{1}{a}$
14. *Multiple choice.* Which is *not* a complex fraction? b
   (a) $\frac{\frac{1}{2}}{\frac{1}{M}}$ (b) $\frac{1+N}{1-N}$ (c) $\frac{Q}{1-\frac{1}{Q}}$

In 15–17, each variable represents an integer. Write the complex expression as a single rational number.

15. $\frac{1}{1-\frac{1}{a}}$ $\frac{a}{a-1}$
16. $\frac{\frac{2}{b}}{\frac{3}{a}}$ $\frac{2a}{3b}$
17. $\frac{\frac{8}{a^2}}{\frac{4}{a}}$ $\frac{2}{a}$

6) $\frac{N+K}{N}$ $\{N: N \neq 0\}$

7) $\frac{N^2+K}{N}$ $\{N: N \neq 0\}$

8) $\frac{N^3+K}{N^2}$ $\{N: N \neq 0\}$

9) $\frac{M^2 - M - 1}{M^2 - 3M + 2}$
$\{M: M \neq 1 \text{ and } M \neq 2\}$

10) $\frac{1}{N^2 + 2NK + K^2}$
$\{N: N = -K\}$

11) $\frac{K}{K+1}$ $\{K: K \neq -1\}$

12) $\frac{K^2 + K - 1}{K+1}$
$\{K: K \neq -1\}$

13) $\frac{2a-1}{a^2-a}$
$\{a: a \neq 0 \text{ and } a \neq 1\}$

3. Suppose that you have allocated m minutes to do your mathematics homework each night. On one night, after reading for 15 minutes, you have n questions to answer. On a second night, after reading for 20 minutes, you have half as many questions to answer. What is the ratio of the average amount of time per question on the first night to the average amount of time per question on the second night? Write this ratio as a single fraction.
$\frac{m-15}{n} \div \frac{m-20}{\frac{1}{2}n} = \frac{m-15}{2(m-20)}$

Notes on Questions

Questions 6–13 The meaning of direction "Simplify." depends on its context. For some situations, the expressions as given might be the simplest. Yet usually, for rational expressions, "simplify" implies writing the expression as a simple fraction in lowest terms. Students need to focus on what the end result is to be when the instruction is "simplify."

Question 6 Error Alert Some students exclude zeros of the numerator from the domain. Remind them that while division *by* zero is not defined, division *into* zero always produces a quotient of zero.

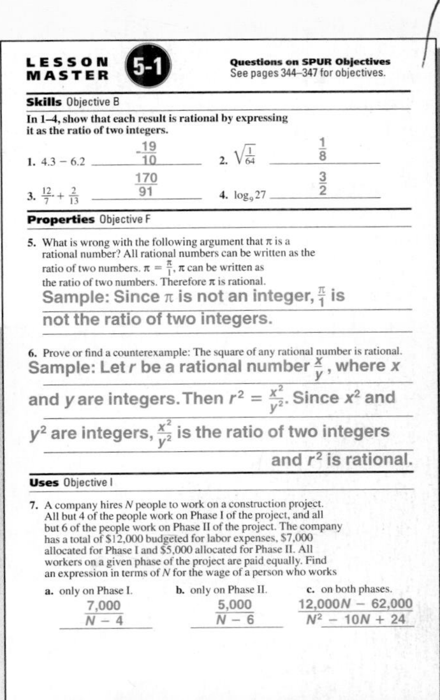

LESSON MASTER 5-1 **Questions on SPUR Objectives**
See pages 344–347 for objectives.

Skills Objective B

In 1–4, show that each result is rational by expressing it as the ratio of two integers.

1. $4.3 - 6.2$ $-\frac{19}{10}$
2. $\sqrt{\frac{1}{64}}$ $\frac{1}{8}$
3. $\frac{12}{7} + \frac{2}{13}$ $\frac{170}{91}$
4. $\log_9 27$ $\frac{3}{2}$

Properties Objective F

5. What is wrong with the following argument that π is a rational number? All rational numbers can be written as the ratio of two numbers. $\pi = \frac{\pi}{1}$, π can be written as the ratio of two numbers. Therefore π is rational.
Sample: Since π is not an integer, $\frac{\pi}{1}$ is not the ratio of two integers.

6. Prove or find a counterexample: The square of any rational number is rational.
Sample: Let r be a rational number $\frac{x}{y}$, where x and y are integers. Then $r^2 = \frac{x^2}{y^2}$. Since x^2 and y^2 are integers, $\frac{x^2}{y^2}$ is the ratio of two integers and r^2 is rational.

Uses Objective I

7. A company hires N people to work on a construction project. All but 4 of the people work on Phase I of the project, and all but 6 of the people work on Phase II of the project. The company has a total of $12,000 budgeted for labor expenses, $7,000 allocated for Phase I and $5,000 allocated for Phase II. All workers on a given phase of the project are paid equally. Find an expression in terms of N for the wage of a person who works
a. only on Phase I. $\frac{7{,}000}{N-4}$
b. only on Phase II. $\frac{5{,}000}{N-6}$
c. on both phases. $\frac{12{,}000N - 62{,}000}{N^2 - 10N + 24}$

5. The sausage pizza is cut into N pieces, the area of each slice is $\frac{1}{N}$ of a pizza. The pepperoni pizza is cut into $N - 2$ pieces, the area of each slice is $\frac{1}{N-2}$ of a pizza. Since the sausage pizza is cut into more pieces, its slices are smaller than those of the pepperoni pizza. The difference in the areas of the sausage and pepperoni slices is:

$$\frac{1}{N-2} - \frac{1}{N} = \frac{1}{N-2}\left(\frac{N}{N}\right) - \frac{1}{N}\left(\frac{N-2}{N-2}\right) = \frac{N}{N^2-2N} - \frac{N-2}{N^2-2N} = \frac{2}{N^2-2N}$$ of a pizza.

Notes on Questions

Question 30 The pattern ($4n$, $4n^2 - 1$, $4n^2 + 1$) will generate Pythagorean triples in which the hypotenuse is 2 units longer than a leg. A pattern generating *all* Pythagorean triples with no common factors is ($x^2 - y^2$, $2xy$, $x^2 + y^2$).

Follow-up for Lesson 5-1

Practice

For more questions on SPUR Objectives, use **Lesson Master 5-1** (shown on page 287).

Assessment

Oral Communication Have students apply both methods for simplifying complex fractions to either **Question 16** or **Question 17.** Then have students justify the method they prefer. [Students correctly use both methods.]

Extension

As an extension of **Question 20,** ask students to find the ratio of the area of a larger slice to the area of a smaller slice. $\left[\frac{N+2}{N-2}\right]$ Ask when the ratio in sizes will be too close to 1 to notice (say less than 1.1). [Solve $\frac{N+2}{N-2} < 1.1$. $N > 42$. So if the pizza were split among 42 people, the area of the larger and smaller slices would be within 10% of each other.] Before solving, have students guess whether N will be less than or greater than 22, the answer found in **Example 4.**

Project Update Project 5, *Rational Zeros of Polynomials*, on page 341, relates to the content of this lesson.

Applying the Mathematics

18. Show that the average of two rational numbers is rational. See margin.

19. Prove that between any two rational numbers there exists a rational number. See margin.

20. One of the students sharing the pizzas pointed out that it was not fair to the two students that did not like the second pizza. Each student should get two pieces of pizza. So she said that the favorite pizza should be divided into $N + 2$ pieces. What fraction of a whole pizza would each student then eat? See margin.

In 21 and 22, write the complex fraction as a simple fraction and give all restrictions on the variable.

21. $\dfrac{\frac{1}{(x + h^2)}}{\frac{1}{x^2}}$ $\quad \frac{x^2}{x + h^2}$ $\quad x \neq -h^2$ and $x \neq 0$

22. $\dfrac{5 - \frac{1}{x^3}}{\frac{4}{x^3} - 2}$ $\quad \frac{5x^3 - 1}{4 - 2x^3}$ $\quad x \neq \sqrt[3]{2}$

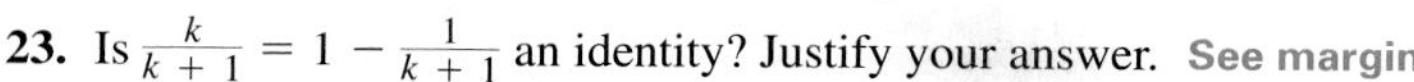

23. Is $\frac{k}{k+1} = 1 - \frac{1}{k+1}$ an identity? Justify your answer. See margin.

In 24 and 25, write as a simple fraction and check your answer.

24. $\frac{A^2}{N+3} + \frac{A^2}{N-3}$ See margin.

25. $\frac{K}{K+1} \cdot \frac{K+1}{K+2} \cdot \frac{K+2}{K+3} \cdot \frac{K+3}{K+4}$ See margin.

Review

y | $g: x \to 4e^{-(x-2.5)^2}$ | 4 | 2 | 2 | 4 | x

26a) domain: $\{x: 0 \le x \le 5\}$ range: $\{y: 0 \le y \le 4\}$

26. Refer to the graph of g at the left. *(Lessons 2-1, 2-2, 2-3)*
   a. Identify the domain and range of the function. See left.
   b. Identify the maximum value of the function. $y = 4.0$
   c. Identify the interval on which the function is increasing. [0, 2.54]

27. a. What is the contrapositive of this statement? See margin.

If n^2 is an even integer, so is n.

   b. Prove the contrapositive. See margin.
   c. Is the original statement true? *(Lessons 1-5, 1-8)* yes

28. Give the negation of the universal conditional $\forall$ *x, if p(x), then q(x).* *(Lesson 1-2)* $\exists$ x such that $p(x)$ and not $q(x)$.

29. a. Give the slope of the line through (d, $2d$) and ($3d$, $4d$). 1
   b. Generalize the result of part **a.** *(Previous course)* A line with slope = 1 will be 45° from the x-axis.

Exploration

30. A Pythagorean triple is a set of three integers that can be the lengths of the three sides of a right triangle.

3, 4, 5 and 9, 40, 41

are two examples. Sines and cosines of all angles in these triangles are rational. Find three other Pythagorean triples in which two sides are consecutive integers. Try to find a pattern to generate infinitely many Pythagorean triples. See margin.

Adapting to Individual Needs

Challenge

Have students give the first six terms of the sequence defined by

$$a_1 = 1$$
$$a_{k+1} = 1 + \frac{1}{a_k} \text{ for } k \ge 1.$$

[1, 2, $\frac{3}{2}$, $\frac{5}{3}$, $\frac{8}{5}$, $\frac{13}{8}$, ... Note the connection with the Fibonacci sequence.]

Additional Answers
18–20, 23–25, 27a, b, 30. See Additional Answers at the back of this book.

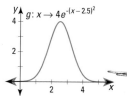

LESSON

5-2

Rational Expressions

This symbol manipulator shows the work for Solution 2 of Example 1.

What Is a Rational Expression?

The pizza problem of Example 2 of the last lesson showed that

$$\forall \text{ integers } N \text{ with } N \neq 0 \text{ and } N \neq 2, \frac{1}{N} + \frac{1}{N-2} = \frac{2N-2}{N^2-2N}.$$

Because all the properties used in adding the fractions are properties of real numbers, this statement holds for real numbers as well. For example, it holds for the value π.

$$\frac{1}{\pi} + \frac{1}{\pi - 2} = \frac{2\pi - 2}{\pi^2 - 2\pi}$$

So the universal statement applies over a larger domain.

$$\forall \text{ real numbers } x, x \neq 0, x \neq 2, \frac{1}{x} + \frac{1}{x-2} = \frac{2x-2}{x^2-2x}.$$

The numerators and denominators of the fraction, $1, x, x-2, 2x-2$, and $x^2 - 2x$ are all polynomials. Just as the quotient of two integers is called a rational number, so the quotient of two polynomials is called a rational expression.

Definition
An algebraic expression $r(x)$ is said to be a **rational expression** if and only if it has the form $r(x) = \frac{p(x)}{q(x)}$, where $p(x)$ and $q(x)$ are polynomials (with $q(x)$ not the zero polynomial.)

You saw in Chapter 4 that the arithmetic of polynomials is similar to that of integers. A similar analogy holds between the arithmetic of rational expressions and the arithmetic of rational numbers.

Lesson 5-2

Objectives

A Simplify rational expressions.
I Apply rational expressions and rational equations.

Resources

From the ***Teacher's Resource File***
- Lesson Master 5-2
- Answer Master 5-2
- Teaching Aid 43: Warm-up

Additional Resources
- Visual for Teaching Aid 43

Teaching Lesson 5-2

Warm-up

Write the sum $\frac{a}{b} + \frac{c}{d} - \frac{e}{f}$ as a single fraction, and check your answer.

$\frac{adf + bcf - bde}{bdf}$; let $a = 2$, $b = 3$, $c = 4$, $d = 5$, $e = 6$, and $f = 7$. Then the original expression has the value $\frac{2}{3} + \frac{4}{5} - \frac{6}{7}$, which equals $\frac{64}{105}$, and the answer has the value $\frac{70 + 84 - 90}{105}$, which also equals $\frac{64}{105}$.

Notes on Reading

Students who have studied from UCSMP texts in previous years may have had less experience with algebraic manipulations like those in this lesson. However, our research indicates that teachers feel that almost all students, regardless of background or ability, can benefit from additional practice like that provided. Few students perform at the level teachers would like, but do not blame this on the students. These are the most difficult manipulations in elementary mathematics, and even experienced *teachers* have to concentrate to get right answers.

Lesson 5-2 Overview

Broad Goals This lesson focuses on rational expressions that are a little more complicated than those in Lesson 5-1, and on fractions that require factoring to be placed in lowest terms.

Perspective Dealing with rational expressions is very similar to dealing with arithmetic fractions. They are added, subtracted, multiplied, and divided following the same rules, and they are considered to be in lowest terms if the numerator and denominator have no common factor. Rational expressions, however, have two additional concerns: there may be values of the variable for which a given expression is undefined (the domain of the expression); and two expressions are equal if and only if they are equal for every value of the variable for which they are defined (the notion of identity). So one has to examine excluded values.

❶ The symbol manipulator Solution 2 to **Example 1** is significant because one does not enter the command to add. Rather, one enters a command for a common denominator.

Error Alert As you discuss material like that following **Example 1,** watch for students who want to remove matching addends, such as the x^2 in the numerator and denominator of $\frac{x^2 + 5x + 6}{x^2 - 4}$.

Example 2 is contrived to show that it is possible for factoring to help in converting a complicated expression to quite a simple one.

Examples 3–4 are not so contrived. Expressions like these occur rather often in calculus when one is dealing with derivatives. Specifically, **Example 4** uses manipulative skills to simplify a difference quotient.

Example 1

a. Show that $\frac{5}{x-2} + \frac{6}{x^2-1}$ can be written as a rational expression.

b. Write your final result as a universal statement.

Solution 1

a. The common denominator is $(x - 2)(x^2 - 1)$. Rewrite each rational expression with the common denominator.

$$\frac{5}{x-2} + \frac{6}{x^2-1} = \frac{5}{x-2} \cdot \frac{x^2-1}{x^2-1} + \frac{6}{x^2-1} \cdot \frac{x-2}{x-2}$$
$$= \frac{5x^2-5}{(x-2)(x^2-1)} + \frac{6x-12}{(x^2-1)(x-2)}$$
$$= \frac{5x^2-5+6x-12}{(x-2)(x^2-1)}$$
$$= \frac{5x^2+6x-17}{x^3-2x^2-x+2}$$

The numerator is a polynomial and the denominator is a polynomial, so the expression is a rational expression.

b. The denominator cannot be 0, so $x - 2 \neq 0$ and $x^2 - 1 \neq 0$. So x cannot be 2, 1, or -1. Thus

$$\forall x \neq 2, x \neq 1, x \neq -1, \quad \frac{5}{x-2} + \frac{6}{x^2-1} = \frac{5x^2+6x-17}{x^3-2x^2-x+2}.$$

❶ **Solution 2**

Use a symbol manipulator. We enter

```
comDenom(5/(x – 2) + 6/(x^2 – 1))
```

on our symbol manipulator. The screen shows the answer given by Solution 1.

Check

Let $x = 5$. Then the original expression has the value $\frac{5}{3} + \frac{6}{24}$, or $\frac{46}{24}$. The answer has the value $\frac{5 \cdot 5^2 + 6 \cdot 5 - 17}{5^3 - 2 \cdot 5^2 - 5 + 2} = \frac{138}{72}$, which equals $\frac{46}{24}$.

Rewriting Rational Expressions in Lowest Terms

As with a numerical fraction, a rational expression is in **lowest terms** if its numerator and denominator have no common factor.

Hence

$\frac{x^2 + 5x + 6}{x^2 - 4}$ is not in lowest terms

because the polynomials factor as

$\frac{(x + 2)(x + 3)}{(x + 2)(x - 2)}$, showing a common factor of $(x + 2)$.

You may show the quotient 1 by placing slashes through the identical factors.

$$\frac{\cancel{(x + 2)}(x + 3)}{\cancel{(x + 2)}(x - 2)}$$

Optional Activities

Cooperative Learning You may wish to use this activity after discussing **Example 3.** In groups of 3 or 4, have each student write a complex rational expression (such as those in **Questions 15–16**) at the top of a piece of paper and perform the first manipulation in the simplification process. Then have students pass their papers one person to the right. That person should read the problem shown on the paper, check the previous step performed, and perform the next step. Students should continue passing the papers around until all problems are satisfactorily simplified and checked. This type of cooperative learning is sometimes called "a roundtable."

There are no further factors of numerator and denominator, so

$\frac{x^2 + 5x + 6}{x^2 - 4}$ reduced to lowest terms is $\frac{x + 3}{x - 2}$.

You may state that these form an identity by listing the full set of excluded values. In the original expression, $x^2 - 4 \neq 0$, so $x \neq 2$ and $x \neq -2$.

$$\forall \text{ real numbers } x, x \neq 2, x \neq -2, \quad \frac{x^2 + 5x + 6}{x^2 - 4} = \frac{x + 3}{x - 2}$$

or, shorter, $\frac{x^2 + 5x + 6}{x^2 - 4} = \frac{x + 3}{x - 2}$ when $x \neq 2$ and $x \neq -2$.

You should be careful to recognize all excluded values. Thus examine the original expression, not just the answer. For instance, if you just look at $\frac{x + 3}{x - 2}$, you would think $x \neq 2$ is the only restriction on x. However, in the original expression, $x \neq -2$ also. Later you will see that both restrictions play a role in graphing.

Example 2

a. Multiply $\frac{a^2 + 5a + 6}{a^2 - 3a - 10}$ by $\frac{a^2 - 25}{a + 3}$.

b. State restrictions on the answer.

Solution

a. Factor the numerators and denominators and multiply.

$$\frac{a^2 + 5a + 6}{a^2 - 3a - 10} \cdot \frac{a^2 - 25}{a + 3} = \frac{(a + 3)(a + 2)}{(a - 5)(a + 2)} \cdot \frac{(a - 5)(a + 5)}{(a + 3)}$$
$$= a + 5$$

b. The original denominators cannot be zero. So $a \neq 5$, $a \neq -2$, and $a \neq -3$.

Check

When $a = 2$, the original expression has value $\frac{20}{-12} \cdot \frac{-21}{5} = 7$, which is the value of $a + 5$ when $a = 2$.

Complex fractions involving rational expressions can be rewritten as quotients of two rational expressions. The methods are the same as those involved with rational numbers.

Example 3

Write as a rational expression in lowest terms:

$$\frac{x}{1 - \frac{1}{x - 1}}$$

Solution

First list restrictions. $x - 1 \neq 0$ so $x \neq 1$.

$$1 - \frac{1}{x - 1} \neq 0 \Rightarrow 1 \neq \frac{1}{x - 1} \Rightarrow x - 1 \neq 1 \Rightarrow x \neq 2.$$

▶

Additional Examples

1. Simplify $\frac{2x^2 - 5x - 3}{x^2 - 9}$.
   $\frac{2x + 1}{x + 3}$ when $x \neq 3$ or $x \neq -3$
2. a. Multiply $\frac{a^2 + 6a + 8}{a^2 - 5a - 14} \cdot \frac{a - 7}{a^2 - 16}$.
   $\frac{1}{a - 4}$
   b. State restrictions on a.
   $a \neq 7$, $a \neq -2$, $a \neq 4$, and $a \neq -4$.
3. A graph of $f(x) = x^2$ for $x > 0$ is shown below. What is the slope of the line connecting the point $(x, f(x))$ and $(x + h, f(x + h))$?

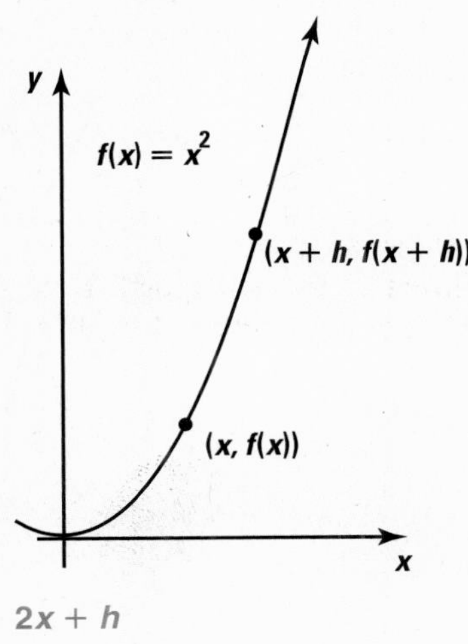

$2x + h$

Adapting to Individual Needs

Challenge

Show that $\frac{4 - a}{x(x - a)} - \frac{4 - x}{x^2 - ax} = \frac{1}{x}$ is an identity by transforming the expression on the left side into that on the right. What is the domain of the identity?

[left side $= \frac{4 - a}{x(x - a)} - \frac{4 - x}{x(x - a)} = \frac{4 - a - (4 - x)}{x(x - a)} = \frac{x - a}{x(x - a)} = \frac{1}{x}$;
$\{x\colon x \neq 0 \text{ and } x \neq a\}$]

You could ask students to check that this equation is an identity by graphing the left and right sides for two different values of a.

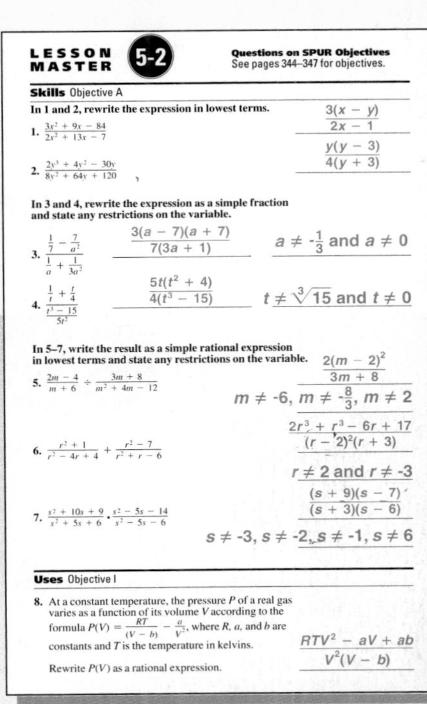

LESSON MASTER 5-2 — Questions on SPUR Objectives
See pages 344–347 for objectives.

Skills Objective A

In 1 and 2, rewrite the expression in lowest terms.

1. $\frac{3x^2 + 9x - 84}{2x^2 + 13x - 7}$ — $\frac{3(x - y)}{2x - 1}$
2. $\frac{2y^3 + 4y^2 - 30y}{8y^2 + 64y + 120}$ — $\frac{y(y - 3)}{4(y + 3)}$

In 3 and 4, rewrite the expression as a simple fraction and state any restrictions on the variable.

3. $\frac{\frac{1}{7} - \frac{7}{a^2}}{\frac{1}{a} + \frac{1}{3a^2}}$ — $\frac{3(a - 7)(a + 7)}{7(3a + 1)}$ — $a \neq -\frac{1}{3}$ and $a \neq 0$
4. $\frac{\frac{1}{t} + \frac{t}{4}}{\frac{t^3 - 15}{5t^2}}$ — $\frac{5t(t^2 + 4)}{4(t^3 - 15)}$ — $t \neq \sqrt[3]{15}$ and $t \neq 0$

In 5–7, write the result as a simple rational expression in lowest terms and state any restrictions on the variable.

5. $\frac{2m - 4}{m + 6} \div \frac{3m + 8}{m^2 + 4m - 12}$ — $\frac{2(m - 2)^2}{3m + 8}$; $m \neq -6$, $m \neq -\frac{8}{3}$, $m \neq 2$
6. $\frac{r^2 + 1}{r^2 - 4r + 4} + \frac{r^2 - 7}{r^2 + r - 6}$ — $\frac{2r^3 + r^3 - 6r + 17}{(r - 2)^2(r + 3)}$; $r \neq 2$ and $r \neq -3$
7. $\frac{s^2 + 10s + 9}{s^2 + 5s + 6} \cdot \frac{s^2 - 5s - 14}{s^2 - 5s - 6}$ — $\frac{(s + 9)(s - 7)}{(s + 3)(s - 6)}$; $s \neq -3$, $s \neq -2$, $s \neq -1$, $s \neq 6$

Uses Objective I

8. At a constant temperature, the pressure P of a real gas varies as a function of its volume V according to the formula $P(V) = \frac{RT}{(V - b)} - \frac{a}{V^2}$, where R, a, and b are constants and T is the temperature in kelvins.
   Rewrite $P(V)$ as a rational expression. — $\frac{RTV^2 - aV + ab}{V^2(V - b)}$

Multiply numerator and denominator by $x - 1$.

$$\frac{x}{1 - \frac{1}{x-1}} \cdot \frac{(x-1)}{(x-1)} = \frac{x(x-1)}{(x-1) - \frac{(x-1)}{(x-1)}}$$
$$= \frac{x(x-1)}{x-1-1}$$
$$= \frac{x^2 - x}{x - 2}$$

So $$\frac{x}{1 - \frac{1}{x-1}} = \frac{x^2 - x}{x-2} \quad \text{for } x \neq 2, x \neq 1.$$

Example 4

A part of the graph of $f(x) = \frac{1}{x^2}$ for $x > 0$ is shown at the right. Give the slope of the segment connecting the points $(x, f(x))$ and $(x + h, f(x + h))$ as a simple fraction in lowest terms.

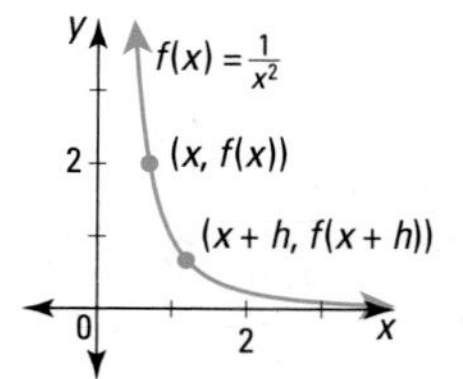

Solution

The slope is

$$\frac{f(x+h) - f(x)}{(x+h) - x} = \frac{\frac{1}{(x+h)^2} - \frac{1}{x^2}}{h} \quad \text{if } h \neq 0, x + h \neq 0, x \neq 0$$
$$= \left(\frac{1}{(x+h)^2} - \frac{1}{x^2}\right) \cdot \frac{1}{h}$$
$$= \left(\frac{x^2}{(x+h)^2x^2} - \frac{(x+h)^2}{(x+h)^2x^2}\right) \cdot \frac{1}{h}$$
$$= \frac{x^2 - (x+h)^2}{hx^2(x+h)^2}$$

This is already a simple fraction. Now we work to put it in lowest terms.

$$= \frac{x^2 - (x^2 + 2xh + h^2)}{hx^2(x+h)^2}$$
$$= \frac{-2xh - h^2}{hx^2(x+h)^2}$$
$$= \frac{h(-2x - h)}{hx^2(x+h)^2}$$
$$= \frac{-2x - h}{x^2(x+h)^2}$$

The restrictions are $h \neq 0$, $x \neq 0$, and $x + h \neq 0$. But $x + h \neq 0$ means that $x \neq -h$. Therefore the slope of the segment between $(x, f(x))$ and $(x + h, f(x + h))$ is

$$\frac{-2x - h}{x^2(x+h)^2} \quad \text{if } h \neq 0, x \neq 0, \text{ and } x \neq -h.$$

Additional Answers, page 293

1. $$\frac{1}{x} + \frac{1}{x-2} = \frac{2x-2}{x^2-2x} \text{ for } x = e$$
$$\frac{1}{e} + \frac{1}{e-2} = \frac{2e-2}{e^2-2e}$$
$$\frac{1}{e} \cdot \frac{e-2}{e-2} + \frac{1}{e-2} \cdot \frac{e}{e} =$$
$$\frac{e-2}{e^2-2e} + \frac{e}{e^2-2e} =$$
$$\frac{2e-2}{e^2-2e} = \frac{2e-2}{e^2-2e}$$

Check

Because identities work for all values of the variables for which both sides are defined, when you check you always have a large choice of values to substitute for the variables. Let $x = 2$ and $h = 3$. This yields the points (2, .25) and (5, .04) on the graph. The slope of the segment containing them is $\frac{0.04 - 0.25}{5 - 2}$ or -0.07. The final expression gives the value $\frac{-2 \cdot 2 - 3}{4 \cdot 25} = \frac{-7}{100}$, which checks.

QUESTIONS

Covering the Reading

1. Show that $\frac{1}{x} + \frac{1}{x-2} = \frac{2x-2}{x^2-2x}$ when $x = e$. **See margin.**

In 2–4, tell whether the expression is a rational expression, and give the restrictions on real numbers in its domain. **See left.**

2. $\frac{x + \sqrt{x}}{1 - \sqrt{x}}$

3. $\frac{y^2 - 25}{3y - 7}$

4. $\frac{5x + 9}{x^3 - 2x^2 - 3x}$

5. Write $\frac{2x^2 + 5x - 7}{7x^2 - 5x - 2}$ in lowest terms. **See left.**

In 6–11, rewrite each expression as a rational expression in lowest terms. Write an identity for each. **See margin.**

6. $\frac{1}{x+5} - \frac{1}{x-5}$

7. $\frac{a}{a+1} + \frac{1}{a+3}$

8. $\frac{p^2 - 4p + 3}{4p^2 - 1} \cdot \frac{2p+1}{p^2 - 3p}$

9. $\frac{\frac{x^2 - 25}{x - 1}}{x - 5}$

10. $\frac{2}{x-5} + \frac{3}{x^2 - 25}$

11. $\frac{2y + 6}{y^2 - 2y - 24} \cdot \frac{y - 6}{y + 3}$

12. To do Question 6 with a symbol manipulator, what might you enter? **See left.**

13. The graph of $f(x) = \frac{1}{x}$ for $x > 0$ is shown below. Write the slope of $\overline{AB}$ as a simple fraction. **See margin.**

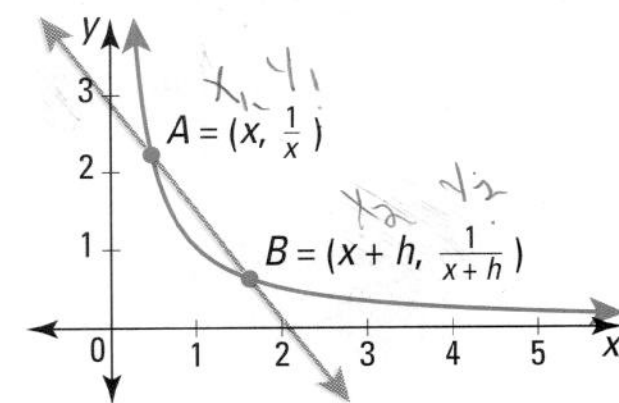

In 14–17, write the complex fraction as a simple fraction and give all restrictions on the variable.

14. $\frac{\frac{3}{4}}{\frac{2}{x}}$ **$\frac{3x}{8}$; $x \neq 0$**

15. $\frac{\frac{3}{y+1}}{\frac{2}{y}}$ **$\frac{3y}{2y+2}$; $y \neq 0$ and $y \neq -1$**

16. $\frac{2 + \frac{1}{x^2}}{1 - \frac{1}{x^2}}$ **See left.**

17. $1 - \frac{1}{1 + \frac{a}{1-a}}$ **a; $a \neq 1$**

2) No, the expression contains non-integer powers of the variable.

3) Yes, $x \neq \frac{7}{3}$

4) Yes, $x \neq -1$, $x \neq 0$, and $x \neq 3$

5) $\frac{2x^2 + 5x - 7}{7x^2 - 5x - 2} = \frac{(2x + 7)\cancel{(x - 1)}}{(7x + 2)\cancel{(x - 1)}} = \frac{2x + 7}{7x + 2}$

12) com Denom $\left(\frac{1}{(x + 5)} - \frac{1}{(x + 5)}\right)$

16) $\frac{2x^2 + 1}{x^2 - 1}$; $x \neq \pm 1$ and $x \neq 0$

Notes on Questions

Question 1 It might surprise students that if they estimate the values of the three fractions using 2.718 for *e*, the two sides of the equation will have identical values. They might think that the exact value of *e* is needed. You might ask why the exact value is not needed for the check. (Since the equation is an identity, it is true for *all* real numbers for which the expressions are defined. Thus it is true for any estimate of *e*.)

Question 12 If you have a symbol manipulator, you might see what it does if the command "Subtract" is entered.

Question 13 Discuss this question, since this function is the subject of the beginning of Lesson 5-3. Make certain that students remember its entire graph, not just the part with $x > 0$ that is shown here. As with **Example 4**, this question anticipates the study of the derivative (Chapter 9). Doing some of these manipulations now decreases the quantity of "new" material to be mastered later.

6. $\frac{1}{x+5} - \frac{1}{x-5} = \frac{-10}{x^2 - 25}$ when $x \neq -5$ and $x \neq 5$

7. $\frac{a}{a+1} + \frac{1}{a+3} = \frac{a^2 + 4a + 1}{a^2 + 4a + 3}$ when $a \neq -3$ and $a \neq -1$

8. $\frac{p^2 - 4p + 3}{4p^2 - 1} \cdot \frac{2p + 1}{p^2 - 3p} = \frac{\cancel{(p - 3)}(p - 1)}{\cancel{(2p + 1)}(2p - 1)} \cdot \frac{\cancel{(2p + 1)}}{p\cancel{(p - 3)}} = \frac{p - 1}{2p^2 - p}$ when $p \neq -\frac{1}{2}$, $p \neq 0$, $p \neq \frac{1}{2}$ and $p \neq 3$

9. $\frac{\frac{x^2 - 25}{x - 1}}{x - 5} = \frac{(x + 5)\cancel{(x - 5)}}{(x - 1)} \cdot \frac{1}{\cancel{(x - 5)}}$ $= \frac{x + 5}{x - 1}$ when $x \neq 1$ and $x \neq 5$

10. $\frac{2}{x - 5} + \frac{3}{x^2 - 25} = \frac{2x + 13}{x^2 - 25}$ when $x \neq \pm 5$

11. $\frac{2y + 6}{y^2 - 2y - 24} \cdot \frac{y - 6}{y + 3} = \frac{2}{y + 4}$ when $x \neq -4$, $x \neq -3$ and $x \neq 6$

13. $\frac{\frac{1}{x + h} - \frac{1}{x}}{x + h - x} = \frac{\frac{1}{x + h} \cdot \frac{x}{x} - \frac{1}{x} \cdot \frac{x + h}{x + h}}{h}$ if $h \neq 0$, $x \neq 0$, and $x \neq -h$ $= \left(\frac{x}{x^2 + hx} - \frac{x + h}{x^2 + hx}\right) \div h$ $= -\frac{h}{x^2 + hx} \cdot \frac{1}{h}$ $= -\frac{1}{x^2 + hx}$

Notes on Questions

Question 25 Social Studies Connection In 1996, 182,661,000,000 pieces of mail were processed by the U.S. Postal Service. Included in this amount are 10,126,000,000 periodicals. (Source: *Statistical Abstract of the United States 1997*)

Question 29 You might wish to graph $y = g(x) + k$ for some small value of k to distinguish the graphs of f and g.

Follow-up for Lesson 5-2

Practice

For more questions on SPUR Objectives, use **Lesson Master 5-2** (shown on page 291).

Assessment

Written Communication Have students **work in pairs.** Ask each student to write a rational expression like the two given in **Example 1, part a.** Have the students independently write the sum of these two rational expressions as a rational expression in lowest terms and give restrictions on real numbers in the domain. Then have partners compare results. [Students write, simplify, and determine restrictions for rational expressions.]

Extension

Question 17 is reminiscent of continued fractions. A small research project on using continued fractions to approximate mathematical constants or functions may be appropriate. Ask students to find x, the value of the infinite continued fraction $x = 1 + \frac{1}{1 + \frac{1}{1 + \ldots}}$.
[$x = 1 + \frac{1}{x}$ and $x > 0$, so $x = \frac{1 + \sqrt{5}}{2}$.]

Project Update Project 6, *Simpson's Paradox,* on page 341, relates to the content of this lesson.

Applying the Mathematics

18. Given that 11 is a zero of the numerator of $\frac{67x^2 + x - 6x^3 - 132}{x^2 + 12x - 6x^3}$, rewrite this fraction in lowest terms. $\frac{x - 11}{x}$ $x \neq \frac{-4}{3}$, $x \neq 0$, and $x \neq \frac{3}{2}$

Review

19. Prove that the reciprocal of a rational number is rational. *(Lesson 5-1)* See margin.

In 20–24, each variable represents an integer. Write each expression as a ratio of two integers. *(Lesson 5-1)*

20. $\frac{H}{K^2} + H$ $\frac{H + HK^2}{K^2}$

21. $\frac{7x}{2x + 1} - 3$ $\frac{x - 3}{2x + 1}$

22. $\frac{\frac{9}{a^2} - 1}{a - 3}$ $\frac{-(3 + a)}{a^2}$

23. $\frac{12K^3}{5} \cdot \frac{15}{K^3}$ 36

24. $\frac{1 - \frac{1}{x}}{1 + \frac{1}{x^2}}$ $\frac{x^2 - x}{x^2 + 1}$

25. An organization has 400 envelopes to stuff and mail.
   a. If this job is split among N people, how many envelopes will each have to stuff and mail? $400/N$
   b. If two more people help, how many fewer envelopes will each person have to stuff and mail? *(Lesson 5-1)* $\frac{400}{N} - \frac{400}{N + 2} = \frac{800}{N^2 + 2N}$

26. Use chunking to solve for x: $e^{2x} - 5e^x + 6 = 0$. *(Lesson 3-6)* See left.

27. Simplify without using a calculator: $(7\sqrt{2})^2$. *(Previous course)* $(7\sqrt{2})^2 = 49 \cdot 2 = 98$

28. a. Name two similarities among the graphs of the even power functions $y = x^2, y = x^4, y = x^6, \ldots, y = x^{2n}$.
   b. Name two differences between the graphs of the even power functions $y = x^2, y = x^4, y = x^6, \ldots, y = x^{2n}$ and the graphs of the odd power functions $y = x^3, y = x^5, y = x^7, \ldots, y = x^{2n+1}$. *(Previous course)*
See left.

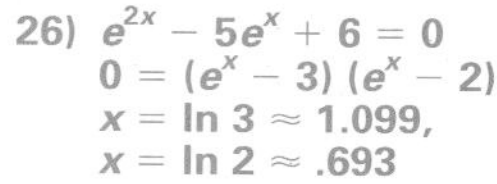

26) $e^{2x} - 5e^x + 6 = 0$
$0 = (e^x - 3)(e^x - 2)$
$x = \ln 3 \approx 1.099$,
$x = \ln 2 \approx .693$

28a) All graphs open up and have minumum points at (0, 0).

b) Odd power functions include negative values and have no upper or lower limits. Even power functions have minumum equal to 0, and include no negative values.

Exploration

29. Use an automatic grapher to plot
$$f(x) = \frac{1}{x - 2} + \frac{1}{x^2 - 1}$$
and the function
$$g(x) = \frac{x^2 + x - 3}{x^3 - 2x^2 - x + 2}.$$
Choose a viewing window that enables you to see relative maxima and minima, end behavior, and behavior close to zero. How do the functions compare? The functions are identical. Relative maxima: (-1.097, -1.486); Relative minimum: none; $\lim_{x \to \infty} f(x) = \lim_{x \to -\infty} g(x) = 0$. The functions do not exist when $x = 2m$, $x = 1$, or $x = -1$.

Additional Answers

19. Suppose that r is any rational numbers. Then there exist integers a and b with $a \neq 0$ and $b \neq 0$ so that $r = \frac{a}{b}$.
$r = \frac{a}{b}$ $\quad \frac{1}{r} = \frac{1}{\frac{a}{b}}$ $\quad \frac{1}{r} = \frac{b}{a}$
$\frac{b}{a}$ must be a rational number since it is the ratio of two integers.

Setting Up Lesson 5-3

Point out that the function in **Example 4** is the reciprocal of the power function f defined by $f(x) = x^2$. The function in **Question 13** can also be considered as a reciprocal of a power function, and it is utilized to begin Lesson 5-3.

LESSON

5-3

Reciprocals of the Power Functions

The intensity of light at various distances can be described by an inverse square law. *See page 296.*

At the right is the familiar graph of the function f defined by $f(x) = \frac{1}{x}$. Both the domain and the range of f are the set of nonzero real numbers. The graph is a hyperbola with two branches, one in the first quadrant and one in the third quadrant.

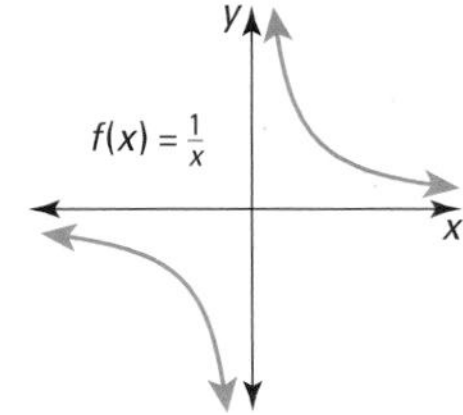

The function f is different in two respects from polynomial functions. First, it is not continuous on any interval that contains $x = 0$ but is continuous everywhere else. Second, as x gets closer and closer to 0, the graph of f gets closer and closer to the y-axis, which is its *vertical asymptote*.

The behavior of this function near $x = 0$ can be used to analyze many other functions and their graphs, so it will be analyzed in detail. Consider the part of the graph in the first quadrant near the y-axis, in orange at the right. As x approaches 0 *from the right*, the function values get larger and larger. For instance, when $x = 0.5$, $f(x) = 2$, but when $x = 0.05$, $f(x) = 20$, and when $x = 0.0001$, $f(x) = 10{,}000$. The values of the function can be made as large as desired simply by taking x close enough to 0. You are familiar with this idea; it is the idea of limit. The only difference here is that x is approaching a particular value (0) from a particular direction (the right). We write

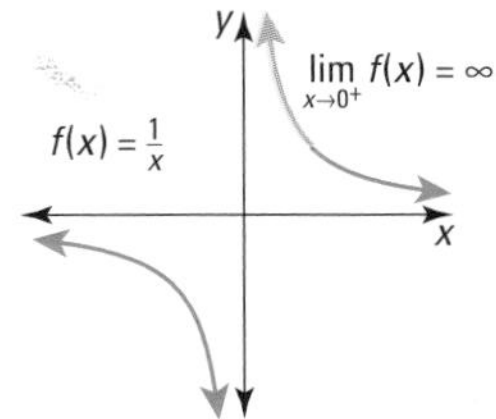

$$\lim_{x\to 0^+} \frac{1}{x} = \infty,$$

which is read "the limit of $\frac{1}{x}$ as x approaches 0 from the right is positive infinity."

Lesson 5-3

Objectives

J Graph rational functions.
K Relate the limit of a function to its graph, and find equations for its asymptotes.

Resources

From the ***Teacher's Resource File***
- Lesson Master 5-3
- Answer Master 5-3
- Teaching Aids
  43 Warm-up
  46 Graph of $f(x) = \frac{1}{x}$ to show limits/Additional Examples

Additional Resources
- Visuals for Teaching Aids 43, 46

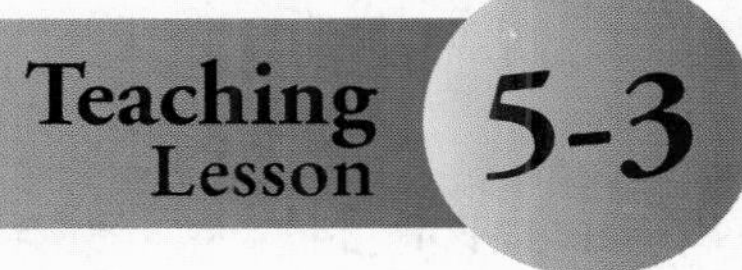

Teaching Lesson 5-3

Warm-up

How are the graphs of $y = \frac{1}{x^2}$ and $y = \frac{1}{x^4}$ alike? How are they different?
Sample: The graphs are both above the x-axis and symmetric to the y-axis. The graph of $y = \frac{1}{x^4}$ is closer to the x-axis and y-axis than the graph of $y = \frac{1}{x^2}$.

Lesson 5-3 Overview

Broad Goals This lesson studies the functions with equations $f: x \to \frac{k}{x^n}$, the reciprocals of the power functions. Students are expected to be able to describe the end behavior of these functions and the behavior of these functions near the y-axis using limit notation.

Perspective The functions $f: x \to \frac{k}{x}$, whose graphs are hyperbolas, and the functions $f: x \to \frac{k}{x^2}$, which represent inverse square laws, are familiar examples of the reciprocals of the power functions $f: x \to \frac{k}{x^n}$. Other than the polynomial functions, these are the simplest rational functions. An analysis of their behavior near asymptotes and their end behavior helps in understanding more complicated rational functions. The first of these functions is odd, and all odd power functions have the same symmetry and same end behavior. The second of these functions is even, and all even power functions have the same symmetry and same end behavior.

Notes on Reading

The graph of $f(x) = \frac{1}{x}$ is shown on **Teaching Aid 46.** Students should have encountered the word *asymptote* in earlier courses. The initial discussion of asymptotes begins in a concrete way with a function that is quite familiar to UCSMP students. If your students have never studied the graph of $y = \frac{k}{x}$, or are unfamiliar with the term *hyperbola*, then you probably want to begin by graphing a number of equations of this form with different values of k. For this, a table of values is helpful. Consider the part of the graph in the first quadrant that is near the y-axis. The table below gives some values of $\frac{1}{x}$ for positive values of x near zero.

x	1	0.5	0.1	0.01
$\frac{1}{x}$	1	2	10	100

x	0.001	0.0001	10^{-10}
$\frac{1}{x}$	1000	10,000	10^{10}

Observe that as x gets closer to 0 from the right, the function values get larger and larger; they increase without bound. This means that the value of the function can be made as large as desired by simply taking x close enough to 0. (For example, to obtain $f(x) > 1000$, take $0 < x < .001$.) We describe this behavior by writing $\lim_{x \to 0^+} \frac{1}{x} = \infty$.

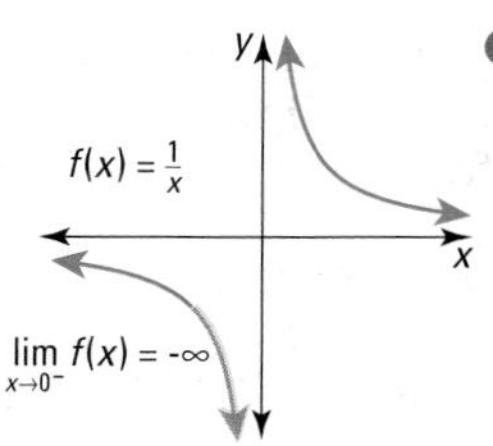

❶ The behavior of the part of the graph of f that is near the y-axis in the third quadrant can be analyzed in a similar way. Note that as x gets closer to 0 *from the left*, the values of $\frac{1}{x}$ are negative and get smaller and smaller (though larger and larger in absolute value). They can be made as small as desired by taking x close enough to 0. For instance, to make $\frac{1}{x} < -25{,}000$, choose a value of x between -0.00004 and 0. We write

$$\lim_{x \to 0^-} \frac{1}{x} = -\infty,$$

which is read "the limit of $\frac{1}{x}$ as x approaches 0 from the left is negative infinity."

Notice the two new symbols in this limit notation.

$x \to a^-$	$x \to a^+$
x approaches a from the left.	x approaches a from the right.

This notation is used to define a vertical asymptote.

Definition
The line $x = a$ is a **vertical asymptote** to the graph of a function f if and only if $\lim_{x \to a^+} f(x) = \infty$ or $\lim_{x \to a^+} f(x) = -\infty$ or $\lim_{x \to a^-} f(x) = \infty$ or $\lim_{x \to a^-} f(x) = -\infty$.

Example 1

At the left is graphed the function h defined for all real numbers $x \neq 4$ by the rule $h(x) = \frac{1}{x-4}$.

a. Determine an equation for the vertical asymptote.

b. Use the limit notation to describe the behavior of the function near the vertical asymptote.

Solution

By the Graph-Translation Theorem the graph of $h(x) = \frac{1}{x-4}$ is the image of the graph of $f(x) = \frac{1}{x}$ under a translation which moves points four units to the right; that is, under the translation $T_{4,0}$.

a. $f(x) = \frac{1}{x}$ has a vertical asymptote at $x = 0$. The translation shifts the asymptote for the image four units to the right. Hence, an equation for the vertical asymptote to the graph of h is $x = 4$.

❷ **b.** The domain consists of all real values except $x = 4$. The limit notation reflects the translation by replacing $x \to 0^+$ and $x \to 0^-$ with $x \to 4^+$ and $x \to 4^-$, respectively.

$$\lim_{x \to 4^+} h(x) = \infty \quad \text{and} \quad \lim_{x \to 4^-} h(x) = -\infty.$$

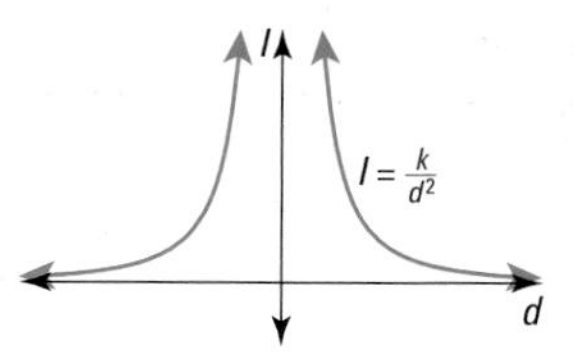

Many physical phenomena obey the *inverse square laws*. That is, one quantity varies as the reciprocal of the square of another. (Do not confuse this multiplicative inverse with an inverse function.) For instance, the intensity of light I varies inversely as the square of the distance d of the observer from it, that is, $I = \frac{k}{d^2}$. A graph of the function $f: d \to \frac{k}{d^2}$ is at the left.

Optional Activities

Activity 1 After discussing **Question 8,** have students generalize the answers to this question. That is, for all reciprocals of odd power functions, $y = \frac{1}{x^{2n+1}}$, ask students to determine the domain, range, end behavior, behavior as $x \to 0$, and the intervals on which the function is increasing and decreasing. [Both domain and range are all nonzero real numbers; $\lim_{x \to \infty} \frac{1}{x^{2n+1}} = 0$, $\lim_{x \to -\infty} \frac{1}{x^{2n+1}} = 0$; $\lim_{x \to 0^+} \frac{1}{x^{2n+1}} = \infty$, $\lim_{x \to 0^-} \frac{1}{x^{2n+1}} = -\infty$; the function is decreasing on its entire domain.] As an extension of this activity, ask students to perform the same analysis for all reciprocals of even power functions, $y = \frac{1}{x^{2n}}$.

Activity 2 You may wish to make this suggestion to your students at the beginning of the lesson. If students have automatic graphers that they can take outside of class, remind them to verify the graphs as they read. This will pay off in the next few lessons.

Think of the light source as being at the origin. If you travel along the x-axis from left to right, then the graph illustrates quite well what happens to the intensity of the light. When you are far left from the origin, the light is dim and the intensity is low. As you near the origin from the left, the light becomes more intense until at the origin it is blinding. Then as you continue past the origin to the right, the light again becomes less intense. The function is not continuous at the origin. The behavior at the origin can be described by

$$\lim_{d \to 0^-} \frac{k}{d^2} = \infty \quad \text{and} \quad \lim_{d \to 0^+} \frac{k}{d^2} = \infty.$$

The functions $f: x \to y$ with $y = \frac{a}{x}$ and $y = \frac{a}{x^2}$ are the simplest examples of the reciprocals of the power functions. Like the power functions themselves, reciprocals of the odd power functions all have similar behavior, and reciprocals of the even power functions also behave similarly. However, the reciprocals of the odd powers and the reciprocals of the even powers behave differently from each other.

Example 2

a. Describe the behavior of the function $f: x \to \frac{-3}{x^5}$ as x approaches 0.

b. Graph f.

Solution

a. As x approaches 0 from the left, x^5 is negative and becomes closer and closer to 0 itself. Thus $f(x) = \frac{-3}{x^5}$ increases without bound in the positive direction. So $\lim_{x \to 0^-} f(x) = \infty$. As x approaches 0 from the right, x^5 is positive and approaches 0. Thus $f(x) = \frac{-3}{x^5}$ is negative and its magnitude increases without bound. So $\lim_{x \to 0^+} f(x) = -\infty$.

b. To graph this function, you need to know its end behavior: $\lim_{x \to \infty} f(x) = 0$ and $\lim_{x \to -\infty} f(x) = 0$. Using the end behavior and the behavior near the vertical axis, you can see that the graph resembles a reflection image of the hyperbola that opened this lesson, but its curve hugs the horizontal axis more tightly and the vertical axis less tightly.

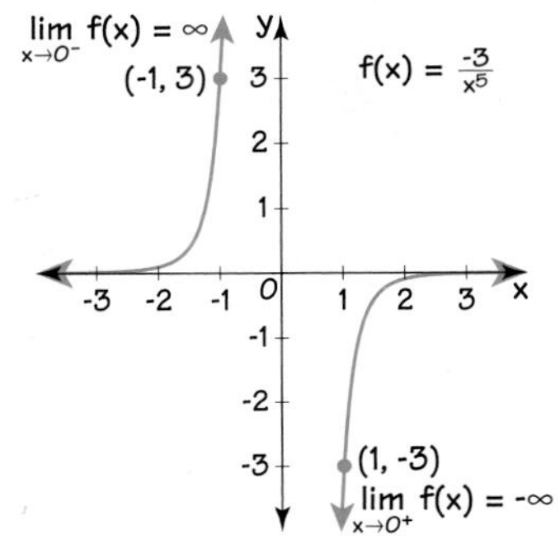

You can check the graphs of Examples 1 and 2 with an automatic grapher, but beware that some automatic graphers do not handle vertical asymptotes well. For this reason, you should be sure to dot or color any asymptotes when you put a graph on paper.

❶ The table below gives values of the function for negative values of x near zero.

x	-1	-0.1	-0.01	-0.001
$\frac{1}{x}$	-1	-10	-100	-1000

x	-0.0001	-10^{-10}
$\frac{1}{x}$	-10,000	-10^{10}

We describe this behavior by writing $\lim_{x \to 0^-} (\frac{1}{x}) = -\infty$.

Example 1 uses the Graph-Translation Theorem to analyze the hyperbola with equation $y = \frac{1}{x - 4}$. Note that all aspects of the graph of $y = \frac{1}{x}$ are translated to the right 4 units, so the analysis is rather easy.

❷ In dealing with limit notation, make sure students do not confuse this notation with function mapping notation. Here, the notation $x \to 4$ means x *approaches* 4 while the notation $f: x \to 4$ means the function f *maps* x to the number 4, that is $f(x) = 4$.

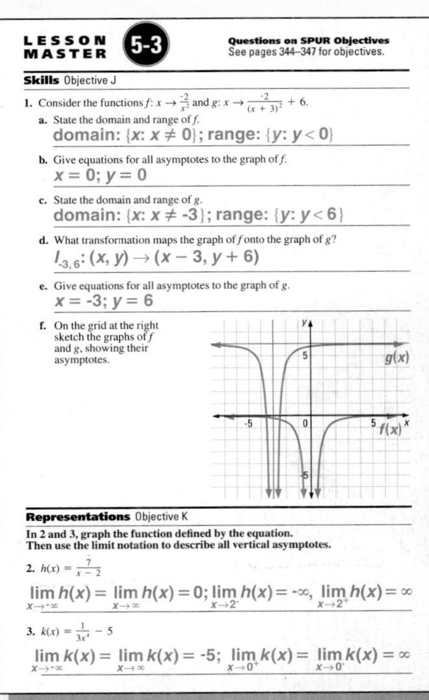

LESSON MASTER 5-3

Questions on SPUR Objectives
See pages 344–347 for objectives.

Skills Objective J

1. Consider the functions $f: x \to \frac{-2}{x^2}$ and $g: x \to \frac{-2}{(x + 3)^2} + 6$.

a. State the domain and range of f.
domain: $\{x: x \neq 0\}$; range: $\{y: y < 0\}$

b. Give equations for all asymptotes to the graph of f.
$x = 0$; $y = 0$

c. State the domain and range of g.
domain: $\{x: x \neq -3\}$; range: $\{y: y < 6\}$

d. What transformation maps the graph of f onto the graph of g?
$T_{-3,6}: (x, y) \to (x - 3, y + 6)$

e. Give equations for all asymptotes to the graph of g.
$x = -3$; $y = 6$

f. On the grid at the right sketch the graphs of f and g, showing their asymptotes.

Representations Objective K

In 2 and 3, graph the function defined by the equation. Then use the limit notation to describe all vertical asymptotes.

2. $h(x) = \frac{7}{x - 2}$

$\lim_{x \to -\infty} h(x) = \lim_{x \to \infty} h(x) = 0$; $\lim_{x \to 2^-} h(x) = -\infty$, $\lim_{x \to 2^+} h(x) = \infty$

3. $k(x) = \frac{1}{3x^4} - 5$

$\lim_{x \to -\infty} k(x) = \lim_{x \to \infty} k(x) = -5$; $\lim_{x \to 0^+} k(x) = \lim_{x \to 0^-} k(x) = \infty$

Error Alert Make sure students understand that $x \to 0^+$ means x approaches 0 from the right. It certainly does not mean "positive zero," as some students assume. In general, however, caution that the raised + does not mean that x necessarily takes positive values. $x \to -5^+$ means x approaches -5 from the right and such values of x are negative (-4.9, -4.99, -4.999, etc.).

In discussing **Example 2,** note that only the sign of the constant numerator has an effect on the behavior of the function as $x \to 0$, for the absolute value of the fraction gets larger and larger regardless of the value of the numerator.

Additional Examples

Additional Examples 1–2 are on **Teaching Aid 46.**

1. Consider the function f with rule $f(x) = \frac{1}{x-3} + 2$, where $x \neq 3$, graphed here.

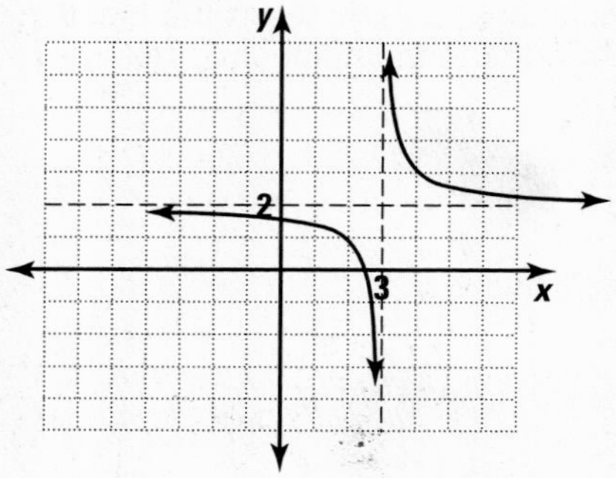

   a. Give an equation for the vertical asymptote to the graph. $x = 3$
   b. Use limit notation to describe the behavior of the function near this asymptote. $\lim_{x\to 3^+} f(x) = \infty$, and $\lim_{x\to 3^-} f(x) = -\infty$

2. a. Describe the behavior of the function $g: x \to \frac{5}{x^4}$ as x approaches 0. $\lim_{x\to 0^-} g(x) = \infty$, and $\lim_{x\to 0^+} g(x) = \infty$;
   b. Graph g.

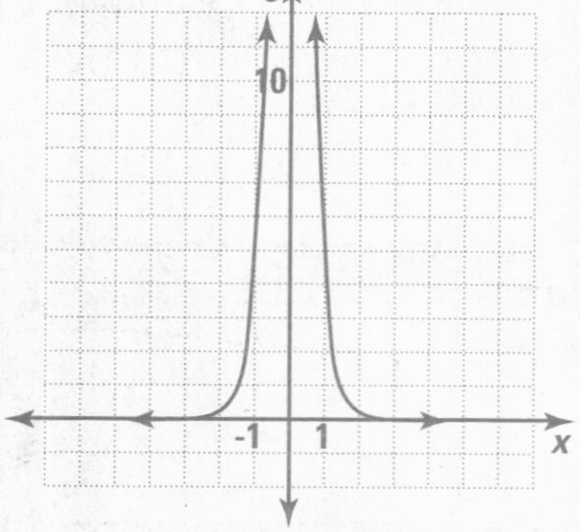

QUESTIONS

Covering the Reading

In 1–3, refer to the sentence $\lim_{x\to 3^+} f(x) = \infty$.

1. *True or false.* The sentence indicates that as $x \to 3^+$ the function values get larger and larger, increasing without bound. True

2. *Multiple choice.* Which of the following is a correct way to read "$x \to 3^+$"? d
   (a) x is to the right of 3
   (b) x is to the left of 3
   (c) x approaches 3
   (d) x approaches 3 from the right
   (e) x approaches 3 from the left

3. Sketch a graph of a function f with this property. See left.

3)

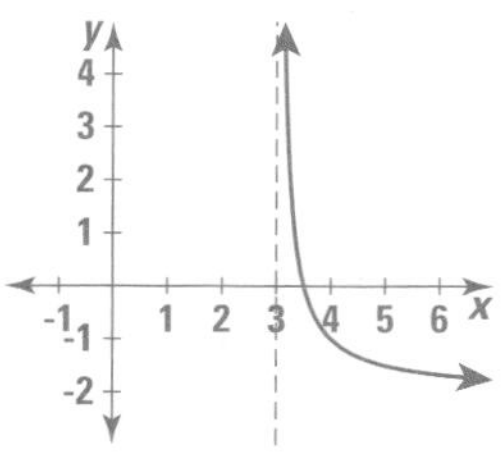

4. Explain in words and draw a graph of a function f with the indicated property. See margin.
   a. $\lim_{x\to 0^-} f(x) = -\infty$
   b. $\lim_{x\to 0^-} f(x) = \infty$

5. Consider the function h defined by the rule $h(x) = \frac{1}{x+6}$.
   a. The graph of the function h can be considered as the translation image of $f: x \to \frac{1}{x}$ under what translation? $T_{6,0}$
   b. Determine the equation for the vertical asymptote to the graph of h. b) $x = -6$
   c. Describe the behavior of h near its vertical asymptote using limit notation. $\lim_{x\to -6^+} h(x) = +\infty$ and $\lim_{x\to -6^-} h(x) = -\infty$

6. Consider the inverse square function f graphed at the right.

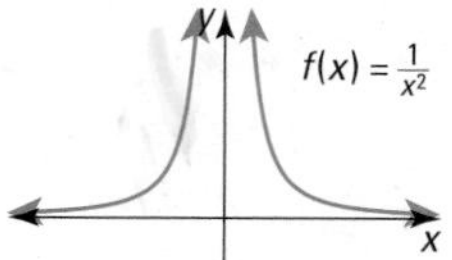

   a. *True or false.* $\lim_{x\to 0^+} f(x) = \infty$. True
   b. *True or false.* $\lim_{x\to 0^-} f(x) = -\infty$. False
   c. Write an equation for the vertical asymptote to the graph of f. $x = 0$
   d. Determine the values of x that make each sentence true.
      i. $f(x) > 400$ $-0.5 < x < 0.5$
      ii. $f(x) > 250{,}000$ $-.002 < x < .002$

7. a. Describe the behavior of the function $g: t \to \frac{5}{t^4}$ as t approaches 0.
   b. Describe the end behavior of g.
   c. Graph g.
   See left.

7a) $\lim_{t\to 0^+} g(t) = \infty$ and $\lim_{t\to 0^-} g(t) = \infty$

b) $\lim_{t\to\infty} g(t) = 0$ and $\lim_{t\to -\infty} g(t) = 0$

c)

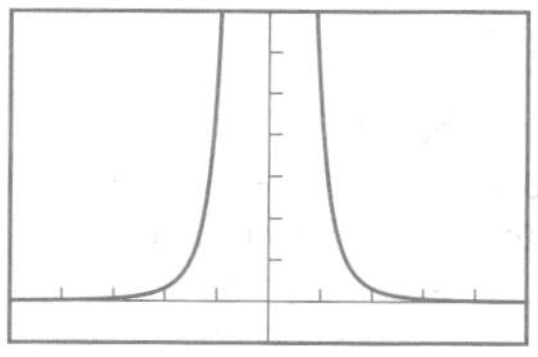

$-5 \le x \le 5$, x-scale = 1
$-1 \le y \le 7$, y-scale = 1

Applying the Mathematics

8. Consider the function f defined by $f(x) = \frac{1}{x^3}$. See margin.
   a. Give its domain and range.
   b. Indicate when it is increasing and when it is decreasing.
   c. Describe its end behavior by using limit notation.
   d. Describe its behavior as $x \to 0$ by using limit notation.
   e. Tell whether f is odd or even.
   f. Graph the function.

Adapting to Individual Needs

Extra Help

Compare the symmetry in the graph of $f(x) = \frac{1}{x}$ shown at the beginning of the lesson with that of the graph of $f(x) = \frac{1}{x^2}$, as pictured in **Question 6.** Discuss in general $f(x) = ax^n$ where n is a nonzero integer and $a \neq 0$. Remind students that odd functions receive their name because when the exponent n is odd, as in $f(x) = 2x^3$ or $f(x) = -3x^{-5} = -\frac{3}{x^5}$, the graph of f is symmetric around the origin. On the other hand, when the exponent n is even, as in $f(x) = 5x^4$ or $f(x) = 3x^{-2} = \frac{3}{x^2}$, $f(x) = f(-x)$ for all x and f is symmetric to the y-axis.

10a)

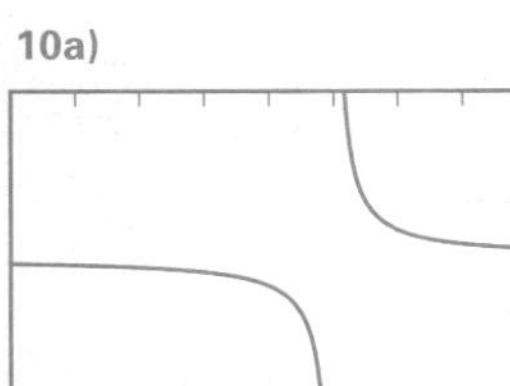

$-16 \le x \le 0$, x-scale = 2
$-6 \le y \le 0$, y-scale = 2

11a) $\frac{4}{x-3}$
b) $x \ne 3$

12a) $\frac{a}{2a+5}$
b) $a \ne \frac{1}{3}$, $a \ne -2$, and $a \ne \frac{-5}{2}$

13a) $-x$
b) $x \ne 0$

14a) $\frac{1}{3-x}$
b) $x \ne 0$

17a) $f \circ g = t^2 - 2t$
b) domain: the set of real numbers

18a) $\frac{f}{g} = t + 1$
b) domain: $\{t: t \ne 1\}$

9. On the average, Mars is about 1.5 times as far from the Sun as Earth is. Compare the brightness of the Sun as seen from Mars with its brightness as seen from Earth. The Sun's brightness seen from Earth is 2.25 times the brightness seen from Mars.

10. a. Graph h, where $h(y) = \frac{1}{y+6} - 3$. See left.

b. To what graph of this lesson is the graph of h congruent? The graph of $h(x) = \frac{1}{x-4}$ given in Example 1.

Review

In 11–14, an operation on two rational expressions is described. See left.

a. Write the answer as a quotient of polynomials.

b. State all restrictions on the variable. *(Lesson 5-2)*

11. $\frac{7}{3-x} + \frac{11}{x-3}$

12. $\frac{a^2+2a}{3a^2+5a-2} \cdot \frac{6a^2+13a-5}{4a^2+20a+25}$

13. $\frac{\frac{1}{x} - \frac{2}{x}}{\frac{1}{x^2}}$

14. $\frac{\frac{1}{x} + \frac{3}{x^2}}{\frac{9}{x^2} - 1}$

15. a. Write $2^{\frac{x}{2}} \cdot 2^{\frac{1}{x}}$ as a power of 2. $2^{\left(\frac{x^2+2}{2x}\right)}$

b. What value(s) of x are impossible? *(Previous course, Lesson 5-2)* $x \ne 0$

16. Prove: $\forall$ integers a, b, and c, if a is a factor of b, and a is a factor of $b + c$, then a is a factor of c. (Hint: $c = (b + c) - b$). *(Lesson 4-1)* See margin.

In 17 and 18, an operation on functions is given. See left.

a. Write a rule for the resulting function if $f: t \to t^2 - 1$ and $g: t \to t - 1$.

b. Give the domain of the resulting function. *(Lessons 2-1, 3-1, 3-5)*

17. $f \circ g$ **18.** $\frac{f}{g}$

Exploration

19. Some automatic graphers use lines to connect the points they actually compute so that the resulting graph looks continuous. When a function has vertical asymptotes, this can cause problems. The graph at the right shows the result of using such an automatic grapher with $f(x) = \frac{-1}{x+1} + 2$.

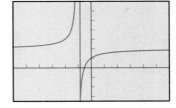

$-6 \le x \le 6$, x-scale = 1
$-3.5 \le y \le 7$, y-scale = 1

a. Use the techniques you learned in the lesson to determine the behavior of f as $x \to -1^+$ and as $x \to -1^-$. If it is appropriate, use limit notation to describe the behavior.

b. Use an automatic grapher to sketch a graph of f. How does your graph compare to the one above? Use your grapher to prepare a table of values of the function from $x = -5$ to $x = 5$. What does the table show?

See margin.

Notes on Questions

Question 6d These are ideas that students will see more formally in a calculus course. Make sure students can answer this question algebraically.

Question 12 Remind students that restrictions on the variable include restrictions necessary before any operations have been performed.

Question 19 Use this question as a springboard to discuss limitations of technology. Some automatic graphers display asymptotes as if they were part of a graph. Few, if any, show points of discontinuity. Large domain and range value settings hide local behavior while small ones reveal little about global or end behavior.

Make certain students see that the vertical line that appears on the graph in this question was meant to connect the highest point on the left branch with the lowest point on the right branch. Automatic graphers may sometimes give a deceiving result. Hence, students must not rely only on the technology but must apply mathematical understanding to interpret results correctly.

Practice

For more questions on SPUR Objectives, use **Lesson Master 5-3** (shown on page 297).

Assessment

Written Communication Have students draw the graph of the reciprocal of a power function of their own choosing. Then have them describe the end behavior and the behavior near asymptotes using both limit notation and ordinary written language. [Students graph the reciprocal of a power function and describe it using the concept and notation of limits.]

Extension

Where does the graph of the power function $y = x^n$, $n \in \{1, 2, 3, \ldots\}$, intersect the graph of its reciprocal function? [If n is odd, at (1,1) and (-1,-1); if n is even, at (1,1) and (-1,1).]

Adapting to Individual Needs

Challenge

Have students answer the following.

1. Which reciprocal power functions are self-inverses? [$y = \frac{1}{x}$]
2. The graphs of $y = \frac{1}{x^n}$, where n is odd, all look similar. How does your answer to Question 1 show one difference? [The graph of $y = \frac{1}{x}$ is the only one that is symmetric to the line $y = x$.]

Additional Answers

4, 8, 16, 19. See Additional Answers at the back of this book.

Lesson 5-4

Objectives

D Identify rational functions and their domains.
G Use limit notation to describe the behavior of rational functions.
H Classify discontinuities as essential or removable.
J Graph rational functions.
K Relate the limit of a function to its graph, and find equations for its asymptotes.

Resources

From the ***Teacher's Resource File***
- Lesson Master 5-4
- Answer Master 5-4
- Assessment Sourcebook: Quiz for Lessons 5-1 through 5-4
- Teaching Aids
  44 Warm-up
  47 Graph of $S(x) = \frac{10}{x(x+10)}$
  48 Three Rational Functions

Additional Resources
- Visuals for Teaching Aids 44, 47, 48
- Exploration 5-4

Teaching Lesson 5-4

Warm-up

You fill up your car's gas tank with 14.3 gallons of gas when its odometer shows 12345.6 miles, and you fill it up again with 13.7 gallons when its odometer shows 12698.4 miles. How many miles per gallon is your car getting? **≈ 25.8; note that the information 14.3 is not needed**

Notes on Reading

This lesson, rather long in its reading section, has three parts. The first two pages motivate the definition of *rational function*. Then there is a half page in which examples and properties of rational functions are discussed. The last page and a half are devoted to a discussion of discontinuities.

LESSON 5-4 Rational Functions

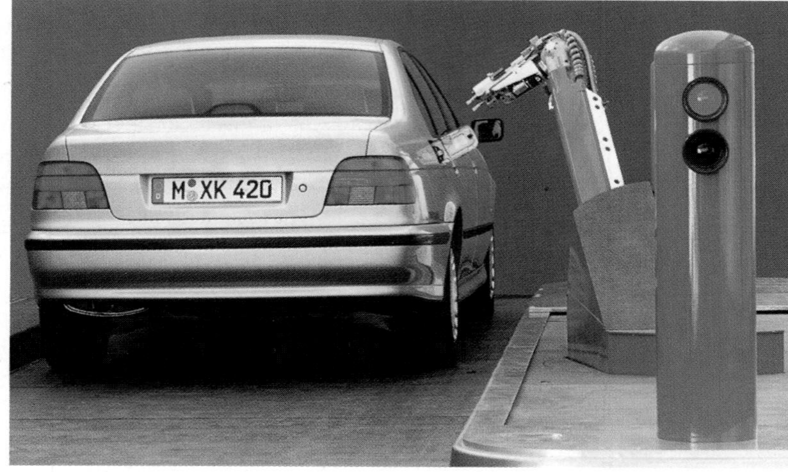

What a Gas! *This robotic gas pump can fill the tank of a passenger vehicle in under 2 minutes. No special training is required to operate it.*

Saving Money by Increasing Gas Efficiency

When a car gets better gas mileage, it is less expensive to run. But how much will be saved? If gas mileage increases from $15\frac{\text{mi}}{\text{gal}}$ to $25\frac{\text{mi}}{\text{gal}}$, will that save more, less, or the same amount of money as increasing from $10\frac{\text{mi}}{\text{gal}}$ to $20\frac{\text{mi}}{\text{gal}}$?

❶ Clearly the amount saved depends on how many miles the car is driven and on the cost per gallon of gas. Suppose that a gallon of gas costs \$1.25 and a car is driven 10,000 miles in a year. The problem can be analyzed by using unit analysis.

$$\frac{\text{cost}}{\text{year}} = \frac{\text{miles}}{\text{year}} \cdot \frac{\text{cost}}{\text{mile}} = \frac{\text{miles}}{\text{year}} \cdot \frac{\text{cost}}{\text{gal}} \cdot \frac{\text{gal}}{\text{mile}},$$

where the last unit is the reciprocal of miles per gallon. Thus if C is the total cost in a year, then at $25\frac{\text{mi}}{\text{gal}}$,

$$C = 10{,}000\frac{\text{mi}}{\text{yr}} \cdot 1.25\frac{\$}{\text{gal}} \cdot \frac{1}{25}\frac{\text{gal}}{\text{mi}} = \$500.$$

Similarly, at $15\frac{\text{mi}}{\text{gal}}$,

$$C = 10{,}000\frac{\text{mi}}{\text{yr}} \cdot 1.25\frac{\$}{\text{gal}} \cdot \frac{1}{15}\frac{\text{gal}}{\text{mi}} \approx \$833.$$

Thus the increase in gas mileage from $15\frac{\text{mi}}{\text{gal}}$ to $25\frac{\text{mi}}{\text{gal}}$ saves \$833 − \$500 = \$333 per year.

The General Savings Function from Increased Efficiency

Although any comparison of costs could be done by arithmetic, using the procedures described above, it is more efficient to use algebra. Then the comparison can be done quickly.

Lesson 5-4 Overview

Broad Goals This lesson discusses the graphs of rational functions, in particular, examining their discontinuities.

Perspective A rational function is a function f such that $f(x) = \frac{p(x)}{q(x)}$ for all x in its domain, and p and q are polynomial functions. The behavior of rational functions is highly dependent on the zeros of q, for at these points the function is not continuous.

The lesson analyzes the two types of discontinuities: removable discontinuities, where the zero of q is also a zero of p and the function can be made continuous by the insertion of a single point; and essential discontinuities, where there is a vertical asymptote to the graph at the zero.

The words *discontinuity* and *singularity* are often used interchangeably by mathematicians.

Example 1

Suppose a car is driven d miles a year and gas costs g dollars a gallon. If fuel efficiency increases from $x\frac{\text{mi}}{\text{gal}}$ to $(x + a)\frac{\text{mi}}{\text{gal}}$, what is the amount saved?

Solution

Following the analysis on page 300, the cost at $x\frac{\text{mi}}{\text{gal}}$ is $\frac{dg}{x}$. The cost at $(x + a)\frac{\text{mi}}{\text{gal}}$ is $\frac{dg}{x + a}$. Thus **the amount saved is** $\frac{dg}{x} - \frac{dg}{x + a}$. **Rewriting it as a rational expression gives**

$$\frac{dg(x + a) - dgx}{x(x + a)} = \frac{dga}{x(x + a)}.$$

By substituting into $\frac{dga}{x(x + a)}$, the amount saved can be determined for any values of d, g, x, and a. For instance, to determine the amount $S(x)$ saved in an increase in fuel efficiency from $15\frac{\text{mi}}{\text{gal}}$ to $25\frac{\text{mi}}{\text{gal}}$ when a car is driven 10,000 miles and gas costs \$1.25, set $d = 10{,}000$, $g = \$1.25$, and $a = 10$. Then when $x = 15$,

$$S(x) = \frac{dga}{x(x + a)} = \frac{10000 \cdot 1.25 \cdot 10}{15(15 + 10)} \approx \$333$$

which checks with our previous computation.

The general savings function S with $S(x) = \frac{dga}{x(x + a)}$ allows you to analyze different situations. The constant dg is the magnitude of a vertical scale change from the parent function S_a with

$$S_a(x) = \frac{a}{x(x + a)}.$$

For an increase of efficiency of $10\frac{\text{mi}}{\text{gal}}$, the parent is

$$S_{10} = \frac{10}{x(x + 10)}.$$

The domain of the fuel efficiency x for this situation is reasonably $\{x: 0 \leq x \leq 50\}$. But the graph has an interesting shape when $x < 0$, so we show a graph when $-20 \leq x \leq 25$.

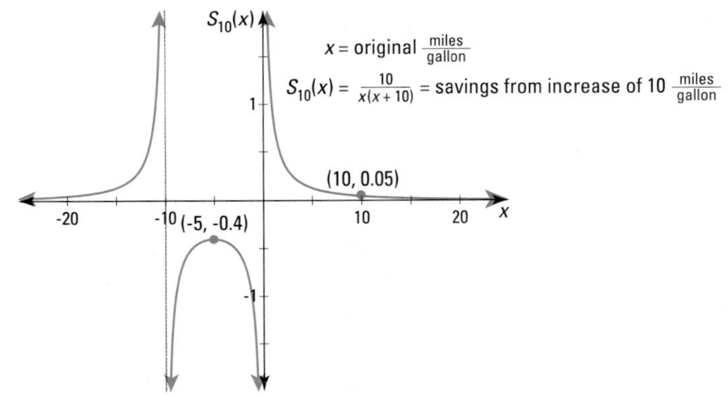

❶ *Dimensional analysis,* the arithmetic of units, is a powerful way of telling whether a formula is correct or not. While having units come out properly is no guarantee of correctness, incorrect units in the final answer are a very strong indicator that the answer is wrong. Students with previous UCSMP experience should be familiar with these ideas.

Following **Example 1**, at first we let S be the amount saved. Then, to emphasize that S depends on x, the fuel efficiency of the car (in miles per gallon), the variable S becomes $S(x)$. This may confuse students, but it is very common practice in mathematics and its applications. They may have seen the practice before with geometry formulas such as $A = \pi r^2$, which when written as a function, becomes $A(r) = \pi r^2$.

If one only graphed S for positive values of x, one might think that the graph is a rubberband transformation image of the inverse square graph. By graphing the function for a broader domain, we see that there are two asymptotes and the graph is reflection-symmetric to the line $x = -5$.

The fact that $S(x)$ decreases as x increases illustrates the law of diminishing returns. Converting to percents may be helpful. While a change in gas efficiency from 10 mpg to 20 mpg is an increase of 100%, a change from 100 mpg to 110 mpg is only 10%. In each case the absolute change is 10 mpg, but the relative changes are much different. The graph is shown on **Teaching Aid 47.**

Optional Activities

Activity 1 Technology Connection
Materials: *Explorations* software

Students may use *Exploration 5-4, A General Savings Function*, as an alternative to **Example 1** in Lesson 5-4. Two graphs of the rational function that represents savings derived from increasing fuel efficiency are shown. By exploring the algebraic and graphical results for different values, students observe how increasing fuel efficiency effects savings.

Activity 2 As an assessment covering just this lesson, you can give students or small groups of students the following tasks.

1. a. Write an equation for a rational function f that has a removable discontinuity at $x = 3$.
[Sample: $f(x) = \frac{x^2 - x - 6}{x - 3}\ \forall\ x \neq 3$]

b. Define your function at $x = 3$ to make it continuous. [$f(3) = 5$]

2. a. Write an equation for a rational function g that has essential discontinuities at $x = -4$ and $x = 1$.
[Sample: $g(x) = \frac{1}{(x + 4)(x - 1)}$]

b. Graph your function.
[Graph shown on page 302.]

(Optional Activities continue on page 302.)

We assert that the formulas $r(x) = \frac{x^2 + 5}{\cos x + 2}$ and $s(x) = \frac{\sqrt{x - 1} + 3}{x^2 - 9}$ do not define rational functions, but we do not prove this. In fact, it is quite difficult to prove these results. However, though they are not rational functions, they can be estimated over any closed interval in which they are defined to as close as one demands by rational functions.

In **Example 2**, the discontinuity is removable because 4 is a zero (and thus $x - 4$ is a factor) of multiplicity 1 of both the denominator and numerator. If 4 were a zero of the denominator and not the numerator, there would be an essential discontinuity. Note that this discontinuity can only be removed by defining $g(4) = 6$. If you defined $g(4) = 3$, then the function g is still not continuous at $x = 4$.

In **Example 3**, there is also an essential discontinuity at $x = -2$. To dramatize the vertical asymptotes $x = -2$ and $x = 2$ of this example, you might use the trace feature of an automatic grapher. With domain $-6 \le x \le 6$ and range $-10 \le y \le 10$, have students note carefully the values of $h(x)$ as they trace from $x = -6$ to $x = 6$. Special attention should be paid near $x = -2$ and $x = 2$. The jumps are somewhat spectacular as one "crosses" these two values.

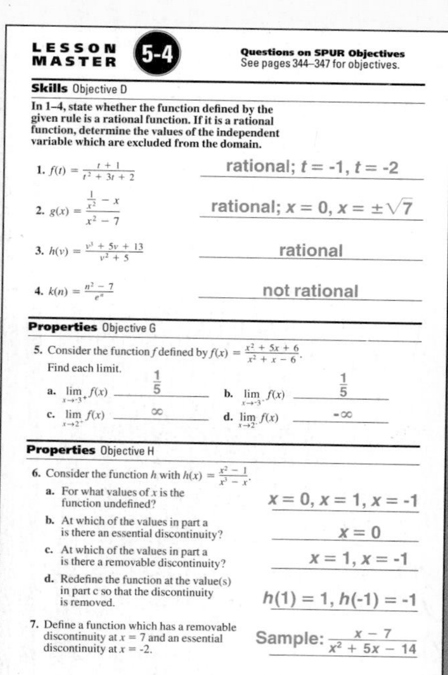
LESSON MASTER 5-4 **Questions on SPUR Objectives** See pages 344–347 for objectives.

Skills Objective D

In 1–4, state whether the function defined by the given rule is a rational function. If it is a rational function, determine the values of the independent variable which are excluded from the domain.

1. $f(t) = \frac{t + 1}{t^2 + 3t + 2}$ rational; $t = -1, t = -2$
2. $g(x) = \frac{\frac{1}{x^2} - x}{x^2 - 7}$ rational; $x = 0, x = \pm\sqrt{7}$
3. $h(v) = \frac{v^3 + 5v + 13}{v^2 + 5}$ rational
4. $k(n) = \frac{n^2 - 7}{e^n}$ not rational

Properties Objective G

5. Consider the function f defined by $f(x) = \frac{x^2 + 5x + 6}{x^2 + x - 6}$. Find each limit.
   a. $\lim_{x \to -3^+} f(x)$ $\frac{1}{5}$
   b. $\lim_{x \to -3^-} f(x)$ $\frac{1}{5}$
   c. $\lim_{x \to 2^+} f(x)$ ∞
   d. $\lim_{x \to 2^-} f(x)$ $-\infty$

Properties Objective H

6. Consider the function h with $h(x) = \frac{x^2 - 1}{x^3 - x}$.
   a. For what values of x is the function undefined? $x = 0, x = 1, x = -1$
   b. At which of the values in part a is there an essential discontinuity? $x = 0$
   c. At which of the values in part a is there a removable discontinuity? $x = 1, x = -1$
   d. Redefine the function at the value(s) in part c so that the discontinuity is removed. $h(1) = 1, h(-1) = -1$
7. Define a function which has a removable discontinuity at $x = 7$ and an essential discontinuity at $x = -2$. Sample: $\frac{x - 7}{x^2 + 5x - 14}$

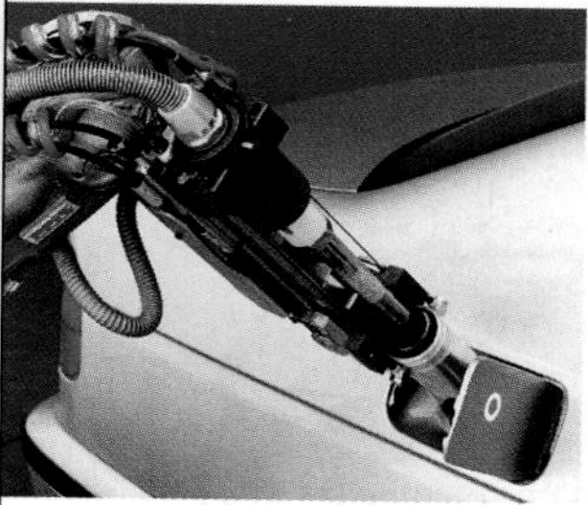

a close-up view of the nozzle of the robotic gas pump on page 300

Amount saved $= \frac{dga}{x(x + a)}$. The amount saved when increasing from $10\frac{mi}{gal}$ to $20\frac{mi}{gal} = \frac{dg \cdot 10}{10(20)} = \frac{dg}{20}$. The amount saved when increasing from $15\frac{mi}{gal}$ to $25\frac{mi}{gal} = \frac{dg \cdot 10}{15(25)} = \frac{10dg}{375}$. The ratio is: $\frac{\frac{dg}{20}}{\frac{10dg}{375}} = \frac{375}{200} \approx 2$

Notice that, when $x > 0$, as x increases the values of S decrease. Thus the savings from increasing efficiency by $10\frac{mi}{gal}$ are greater when the original miles per gallon x is poor (when x is small) than when it is good (when x is large). You can verify this by substitution.

Activity

Show that an increase from $10\frac{mi}{gal}$ to $20\frac{mi}{gal}$ saves almost twice as much as an increase from $15\frac{mi}{gal}$ to $25\frac{mi}{gal}$. See left.

Examples of Rational Functions

The function S is an example of a *rational function*, a function whose formula can be written as a rational expression.

Definition
A function f is a **rational function** if and only if for all values of x in the domain of f, $f(x) = \frac{p(x)}{q(x)}$, where $p(x)$ and $q(x)$ are polynomials.

All polynomial functions are rational functions. For example, if f is defined by $f(x) = x^2 - 2x - 15$, then $f(x) = \frac{x^2 - 2x - 15}{1}$, and since 1 is a constant polynomial function, f is rational. Also, all reciprocals of polynomial functions are rational. However, the formulas $r(x) = \frac{x^2 + 5}{\cos x + 2}$ and $s(x) = \frac{\sqrt{x - 1} + 3}{x^2 - 9}$ do not define rational functions because it is not possible to find any polynomial functions whose quotients equal either of these. (Proving this is beyond the scope of this book.)

Because the sum, difference, product, and quotient of two rational expressions can be written as rational expressions, the sum, difference, product, and quotient of two rational functions are rational functions. For instance, $f(x) = \frac{9}{x + 2} + x^3$ defines a rational function because $f = g + h$, where $g(x) = \frac{9}{x + 2}$ and $h(x) = x^3$. You can verify this by adding the rational expressions.

$$f(x) = g(x) + h(x) = \frac{9}{x + 2} + x^3 = \frac{9}{x + 2} + \frac{x^3(x + 2)}{x + 2}$$
$$= \frac{x^4 + 2x^3 + 9}{x + 2}$$

Thus $f(x)$ is a quotient of polynomials and so f is a rational function. Notice that f is defined for all real numbers $x \neq -2$.

2. b.

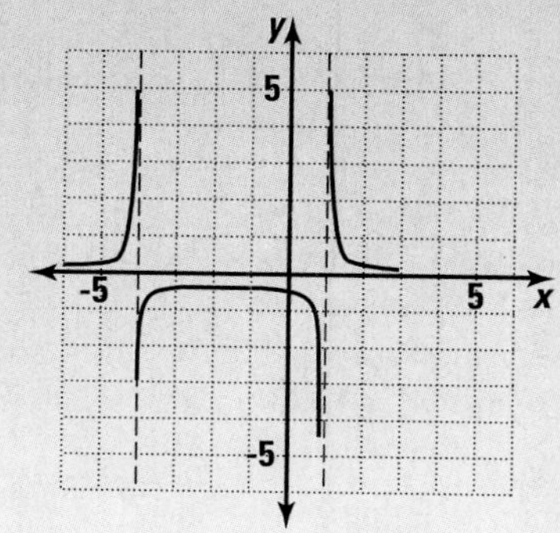

3. a. Write an equation for a rational function h that has an essential discontinuity at $x = -2$ and a removable discontinuity at $x = 10$. [Sample: $h(x) = \frac{x - 10}{(x + 2)(x - 10)}$.]
   b. Identify all asymptotes to the graph of h. [vertical asymptote is $x = -2$; horizontal asymptote is the x-axis]

Discontinuities of Rational Functions

The domain of a rational function has a great bearing on its shape. If p and q are polynomial functions, and $f(x) = \frac{p(x)}{q(x)}$, then the domain of $f = \frac{p}{q}$ is the set of all real numbers x such that $q(x) \neq 0$. At points where $q(x) = 0$, f is undefined and can have *discontinuities* of two types:

(i) a vertical asymptote, as when $x = 2$ or $x = -2$ in h below,

or, **(ii)** a hole in the graph, as when $x = 4$ in the graph of g below.

Some rational functions have no discontinuities, as is the case with function f below. The function g is said to have a **removable discontinuity** at a point x because the graph of g has a hole at x but is otherwise continuous on an interval around x. The discontinuity is called removable because the function could be made continuous by redefining its value at that one point. On the other hand, changing the value of the function at a single point cannot remove the discontinuity at a vertical asymptote, as you can see in the graph of h. A discontinuity that cannot be removed by insertion of a single point is called an **essential discontinuity**.

❷

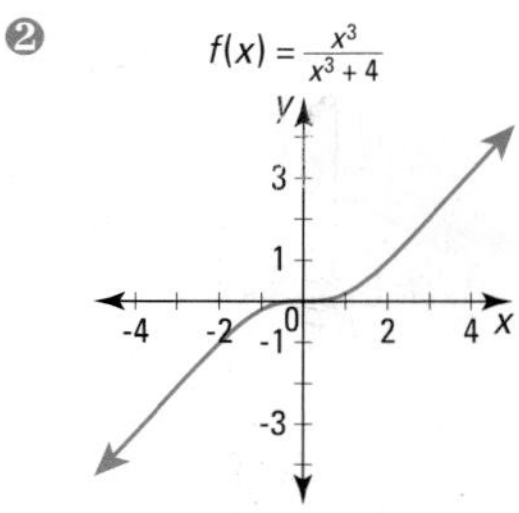

no discontinuities

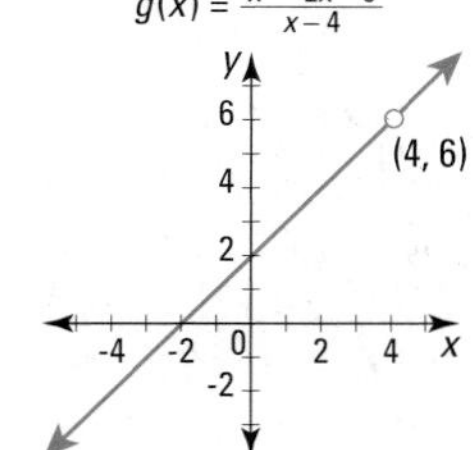

one removable discontinuity

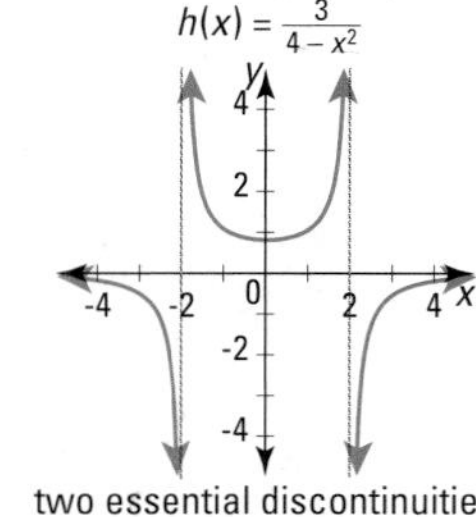

two essential discontinuities

The following examples illustrate how a study of the discontinuities of a function can be used to sketch its graph.

Example 2

a. Determine the location of the discontinuity of the function g above.
b. Explain why the discontinuity is removable.

Solution

a. A discontinuity exists at $x = 4$ because this is where the function is undefined.

b. Notice that the formula for g is not in lowest terms.
$\frac{x^2 - 2x - 8}{x - 4} = \frac{(x + 2)(x - 4)}{x - 4} = x + 2$, provided $x \neq 4$. Thus, the graph of g is the line $y = x + 2$ everywhere except at $x = 4$ where it has a hole. Since $x + 2 = 6$ when $x = 4$, this hole is located at (4, 6). If we were to define $g(4) = 6$, then the hole would be filled in. Thus the discontinuity is removable.

A spreadsheet or short program can also describe what is happening to the function h in **Example 3**. Numerically "zoom in" near $x = -2$ and $x = 2$ to show students the numerical behavior of function h near its asymptotes. A sample BASIC program follows:

```
10 FOR X = 1 TO 3 STEP.1
20 PRINT X, 3/(4 – X^2)
30 NEXT X
```

By using smaller STEP values the behavior can be seen closer and closer to the asymptote $x = 2$.

❷ These three graphs are shown on **Teaching Aid 48.**

Error Alert In the Discontinuity Theorem, emphasize that for $x = c$ to be a vertical asymptote, two conditions must be true: $p(c) \neq 0$; and $q(c) = 0$. Some students focus exclusively on solving $q(x) = 0$ and assume that all its zeros determine vertical asymptotes. A few students may use zeros of $p(x)$ for vertical asymptotes. A student who can correctly sketch the graphs of $y = \frac{1}{x - 2}$ and $y = \frac{x^2 - 4}{x - 2}$ probably knows the difference between an asymptote and a hole in a graph.

Mention the use of the Factor Theorem related to the Discontinuity Theorem. If $p(c) = 0$ and $q(c) = 0$, then $x - c$ is a factor of both $p(x)$ and $q(x)$.

Activity 3 You may wish to extend **Questions 9–10** by asking students to write as many limit statements as they can for these questions. This activity will reinforce the notation from the last lesson as well as, possibly, anticipate the content of the next lesson. [**Question 9:** $\lim_{y \to -5/3^+} f(y) = \infty$, and $\lim_{y \to -5/3^-} f(y) = -\infty$; a few students may notice that $\lim_{y \to \infty} f(y) = \frac{1}{3}$, and $\lim_{y \to -\infty} f(y) = \frac{1}{3}$.

Question 10: $\lim_{x \to 1^+} f(x) = \infty$ and $\lim_{x \to 1^-} f(x) = -\infty$; also $\lim_{x \to -1^+} f(x) = -\infty$ and $\lim_{x \to -1^-} f(x) = \infty$; a few students may notice that $\lim_{x \to \infty} f(x) = \lim_{x \to -\infty} f(x) = 2$.]

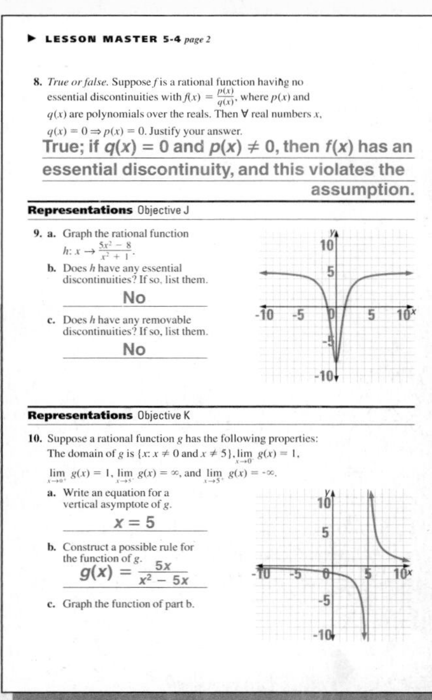

▸ **LESSON MASTER 5-4** *page 2*

8. *True or false.* Suppose f is a rational function having no essential discontinuities with $f(x) = \frac{p(x)}{q(x)}$, where $p(x)$ and $q(x)$ are polynomials over the reals. Then $\forall$ real numbers x, $q(x) = 0 \Rightarrow p(x) = 0$. Justify your answer.
True; if $q(x) = 0$ and $p(x) \neq 0$, then $f(x)$ has an essential discontinuity, and this violates the assumption.

Representations Objective J

9. a. Graph the rational function $h: x \to \frac{5x^2 - 8}{x^2 + 1}$.
b. Does h have any essential discontinuities? If so, list them.
No
c. Does h have any removable discontinuities? If so, list them.
No

Representations Objective K

10. Suppose a rational function g has the following properties: The domain of g is $\{x: x \neq 0 \text{ and } x \neq 5\}$, $\lim_{x \to 0^-} g(x) = 1$, $\lim_{x \to 0^+} g(x) = 1$, $\lim_{x \to 5^-} g(x) = \infty$, and $\lim_{x \to 5^+} g(x) = -\infty$.
a. Write an equation for a vertical asymptote of g.
$x = 5$
b. Construct a possible rule for the function of g.
$g(x) = \frac{5x}{x^2 - 5x}$
c. Graph the function of part b.

Additional Examples

1. Suppose a local commuter train travels the m miles between two cities at an average speed of x miles per hour and an express train covers the same distance at an average of $x + a$ miles per hour. How much time is saved taking the express train instead of the local? $\frac{m}{x} - \frac{m}{x+a}$ or $\frac{ma}{x(x+a)}$
2. a. Determine the location(s) of the removable discontinuities of the function f with $f(x) = \frac{2x^3 - 18x}{x^2 - 9}$. at $x = 3$ and $x = -3$
   b. How can these discontinuities be moved? Define $f(3) = 6$ and $f(-3) = -6$.
3. Show that $g(x) = \frac{4}{x^2 - x - 6}$ has essential discontinuities at $x = -2$ and at $x = 3$.
   $\lim_{x \to -2^-} g(x) = \infty \neq$
   $\lim_{x \to -2^+} g(x) = -\infty$, and
   $\lim_{x \to 3^-} g(x) = -\infty \neq$
   $\lim_{x \to 3^+} g(x) = \infty$.

Notes on Questions

Question 1 Consumer Connection In 1994, the average number of miles driven per car in the U.S. was 11,372 and the average miles per gallon of gas was 21.5 miles. (Source: *Statistical Abstract of the United States 1997.*)

Questions 7–8 Urge students first to decide whether the discontinuity is removable or essential, and then use the automatic grapher to test their answer.

Caution! If a function has a removable discontinuity and you graph it with an automatic grapher, the graph may look as if it has no hole. When you sketch the graph on paper, be sure to indicate the hole.

If your automatic grapher includes a table generator, the values on the table may alert you to a discontinuity. A table for $g(x)$ is shown below. The abbreviation "undef" (for "undefined") indicates the discontinuity at $x = 4$.

x	g(x)
2.5	4.5
3	5
3.5	5.5
4	undef
4.5	6.5
5	7

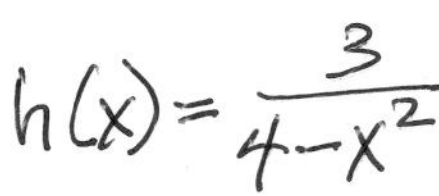

Example 3

Show that function h on page 303 has an essential discontinuity at $x = 2$.

Solution

As $h \to 2^+$, $4 - x^2$ is negative, so $h(x) = \frac{3}{4 - x^2}$ is negative. And since $4 - x^2 \to 0$ as $x \to 2^+$, $\lim_{x \to 2^+} h(x) = -\infty$. Thus it is impossible to define $h(2)$ so as to make h continuous. Hence h has a discontinuity at $x = 2$ that is essential.

The function g in Example 2 has a hole at $x = 4$. Since $x - 4$ is a factor of both the numerator and denominator of $g(x)$, both of those are zero when $x = 4$. This idea can be used to distinguish between holes and asymptotes.

Discontinuity Theorem
Given a rational function f with $f(x) = \frac{p(x)}{q(x)}$, where $p(x)$ and $q(x)$ are polynomials over the reals: If $\exists$ a real number c such that $q(c) = 0$ but $p(c) \neq 0$, then f has an essential discontinuity when $x = c$, and the line $x = c$ is a vertical asymptote to the graph of f.

If both $q(c) = 0$ and $p(c) = 0$, then you should factor out $x - c$ from the numerator and denominator of $f(x)$. If the resulting rational function is defined when $x = c$, then there is a removable discontinuity at $x = c$. This is what happened in Example 2. If the resulting function is still not defined at $x = c$ and $x - c$ is not a factor of the remaining numerator and denominator, analyze the new function for discontinuities.

Finally, note that a nonrational function may have an essential discontinuity without an asymptote. For instance, the floor function $f: x \to \lfloor x \rfloor$ has an essential discontinuity at each integer, but it has no asymptotes.

Adapting to Individual Needs

Extra Help
Some students, especially those who have not used UCSMP materials in previous courses, may have difficulty with the unit analysis at the beginning of the lesson. Explain that once the unit for the cost per year is written as a rate $\frac{\text{cost}}{\text{year}}$, the other units must be written in such a way that some of the terms "cancel," leaving only $\frac{\text{cost}}{\text{year}}$ as the result.

Show them this "canceling" in both equations.

$\frac{\text{cost}}{\text{year}} = \frac{\text{miles}}{\text{year}} \cdot \frac{\text{cost}}{\text{mile}}$

$\frac{\text{cost}}{\text{year}} = \frac{\text{miles}}{\text{year}} \cdot \frac{\text{cost}}{\text{gal}} \cdot \frac{\text{gal}}{\text{mile}}$

The last rate $\frac{\text{gal}}{\text{mile}}$, might be particularly troublesome. Show that if miles per gallon instead of its reciprocal is used, the result would not be the desired rate $\frac{\text{cost}}{\text{year}}$.

$\frac{\text{miles}}{\text{year}} \cdot \frac{\text{cost}}{\text{gal}} \cdot \frac{\text{mile}}{\text{gal}} = \frac{\text{miles}^2 \cdot \text{cost}}{\text{year}^2 \cdot \text{gal}}$

QUESTIONS

Covering the Reading

In 1 and 2, refer to Example 1.

1. Suppose a person drives 15,000 miles a year and a gallon of gas costs \$1.20 on average. How much would this person save by driving a car that gets $30\frac{\text{mi}}{\text{gal}}$ over one that gets $20\frac{\text{mi}}{\text{gal}}$? \$300

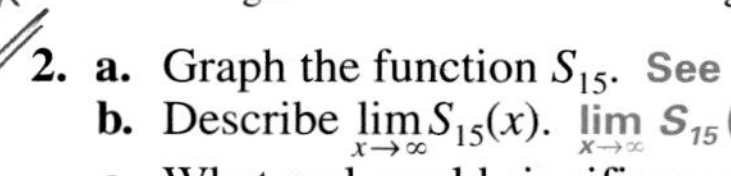

2a)

$-2.5 \le x \le 45$, x-scale = 10
$-0.02 \le y \le 0.07$, y-scale = 0.01

c) The greater the initial gas mileage, the less the savings for an increase of 15 mpg.

2. a. Graph the function S_{15}. See left.
   b. Describe $\lim_{x\to\infty} S_{15}(x)$. $\lim_{x\to\infty} S_{15}(x) = 0$
   c. What real-world significance does the answer to part **b** have? See left.

In 3–5, determine if the function defined by the given formula is a rational function. If it is, determine its domain. Yes, $\{x: x \neq -1\}$

3. $g(x) = \frac{x^2}{x+1} - \frac{x}{x+1}$

4. $f(z) = \sqrt{z^2 + 1}$ No

5. $h(x) = -3x^4 + 2x^3 - 7x^2 + x$ Yes, domain: the set of real numbers.

6. The function $f: x \to \frac{1}{x^2}$ graphed below has a discontinuity at $x = 0$. Is this discontinuity removable or essential? essential

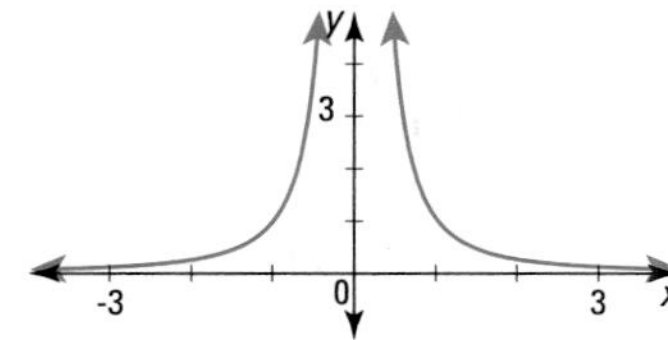
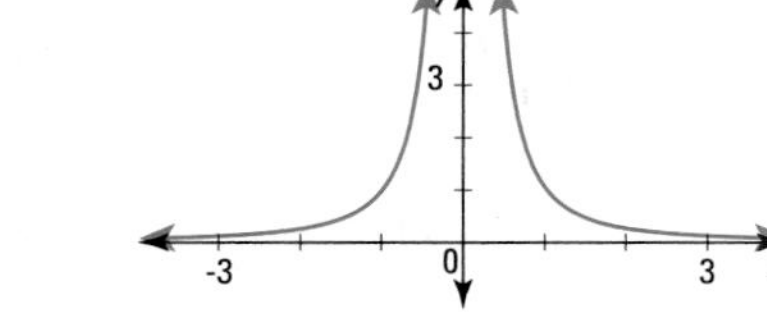

7b)

7. The function g defined by $g(u) = \frac{3u + 30}{u + 10}$ has a discontinuity at $u = -10$.
   a. Is this discontinuity removable or essential? removable
   b. Graph g. See left.

8. *True or false.* The function f defined by $f(t) = \frac{t(t-1)}{(t-1)^2}$ has a removable discontinuity at $t = 1$. False

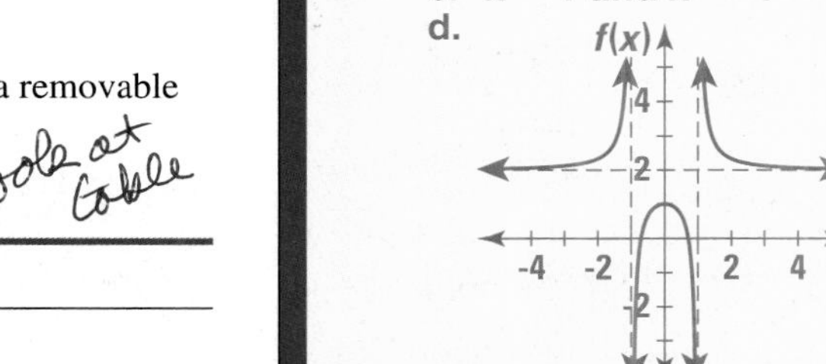

Applying the Mathematics

In 9–11, a formula for a function f is given. See margin.
   a. Determine the domain of f.
   b. Classify its discontinuities.
   c. Find equations of its vertical asymptotes.
   d. Sketch a rough graph of f. (Mark holes or asymptotes wherever they occur.)

9. $f(y) = \frac{y+2}{3y+5}$

10. $f(x) = \frac{2x^2 - 1}{x^2 - 1}$

11. $f(k) = \frac{2k+3}{k^2+9}$

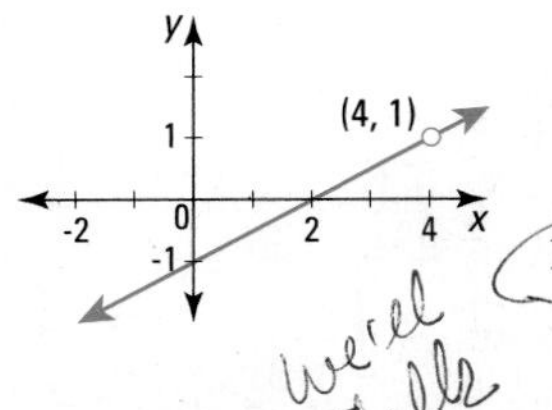

12. Write an equation for the function f whose graph is a line with a hole in it, as shown at the left. $y = \frac{x^2 - 6x + 8}{2x - 8}$

Questions 9–11 Again advise students that the use of an automatic grapher should be the last step—not the first!

Question 12 The numerator and denominator of the rational expression in the formula could be multiplied by any nonzero real number, or by any expression which does not have the value zero except when $x = 4$.

Additional Answers

9. a. $\{y: y \neq -\frac{5}{3}\}$
   b. essential
   c. $y = -\frac{5}{3}$
   d.

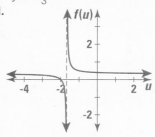

10. a. $\{x: x \neq 1 \text{ and } x \neq -1\}$
    b. essential
    c. $x = 1$ and $x = -1$
    d.

11. a. the set of real numbers
    b. none
    c. none
    d.

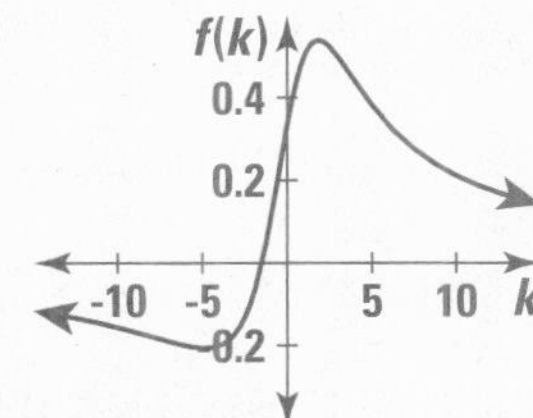

Adapting to Individual Needs

Challenge

Have students answer the following.

1. Find $f^{-1}(x)$.
   a. $f(x) = \frac{4x+2}{x-4}$ $[f^{-1}(x) = \frac{4x+2}{x-4}]$
   b. $f(x) = \frac{3x-1}{2x-3}$ $[f^{-1}(x) = \frac{3x-1}{2x-3}]$
   c. If $f(x) = \frac{ax+b}{cx+d}$ is self-inverse, what must be true about a, b, c, and d? [$a = -d$; b and c can be anything.]

2. Suppose $C(x) = 20x^2 + 3x + 960$ is a cost function which gives the total cost for making x items in one day. Write a rational function that gives the average cost per item for making x items in a day. $\left[\text{Avg. Cost} = \frac{20x^2 + 3x + 960}{x}\right]$ Use the graph to determine the number of items to make each day that would give the minimum average cost. [about 7 items]

Notes on Questions

Question 14 Ask students for a function f that satisfies the given condition. Sample: $f: x \to \frac{-1}{x-7}$.

Question 17b Students should recall that e is not rational.

Question 21b This can be done by trial and error, or by making a table.

Question 23 Have students predict the vertical asymptotes.

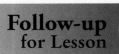

Follow-up for Lesson 5-4

Practice

For more questions on SPUR Objectives, use **Lesson Master 5-4** (shown on pages 302–303).

Assessment

Quiz A quiz covering Lesson 5-1 through 5-4 is provided in the *Assessment Sourcebook.*

Extension

Students have now seen discontinuities in the form of vertical asymptotes, holes in a graph, and jumps, as in a step function. Ask students if the discontinuities of a step function are removable or essential? [Essential, because the insertion of a single value cannot result in a continuous function]

Project Update Project 3, *A Family of Functions,* and Project 4, *Fuel Efficiency,* on page 340, relate to the content of this lesson.

Additional Answers

15. a. domain: $\{x: x \neq 0\}$; range: $\{y: y > 0\}$

b. $\lim_{x\to0^+} h(x) = \infty$; $\lim_{x\to0^-} h(x) = \infty$

c. $\lim_{x\to\infty} h(x) = 0$; $\lim_{x\to-\infty} h(x) = 0$.

d. $\forall\, x,\ h(-x) = \frac{5}{(-x)^4} = \frac{5}{x^4} = h(x)$

e.

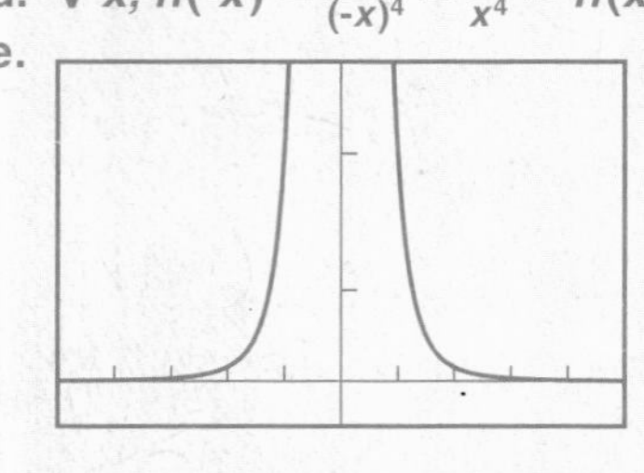

$-5 \le x \le 5$, x-scale = 1
$-1 \le y \le 7$, y-scale = 3

13) $g(x)$ is a function with a removable discontinuity at $x = 1$. Since $\lim_{x\to1} g(x) = \lim_{x\to\infty} (x+5) = 6$, redefining $g(1) = 6$ makes $g(x)$ continuous for all x.

14) The limit of $f(x)$ as x approaches 7 from the right is negative infinity.

17a) $\left(1 + \frac{1}{1000}\right)^{1000} = \frac{(1001)^{1000}}{(1000)^{1000}}$, rational

20a) $x = \frac{7}{5}$ or $x = -\frac{11}{5}$

b) $x \le -\frac{11}{5}$ or $x \ge \frac{7}{5}$

electric car, 1997

13. Let g be the function defined by

$$g(x) = \begin{cases} \frac{x^2+4x-5}{x-1} & \text{if } x \neq 1 \\ 6 & \text{if } x = 1. \end{cases}$$

Explain why g is a continuous function. See left.

Review

14. Explain, in words, the meaning of $\lim_{x\to7^+} f(x) = -\infty$. *(Lesson 5-3)* See left.

15. Consider the function h defined by $h(x) = \frac{5}{x^4}$. See margin.

a. Give the domain and range of h.

b. Describe the behavior of h as $x \to 0$.

c. Describe the end behavior of h using limit notation.

d. Prove that h is even. algebra

e. Graph the function. *(Lessons 2-1, 2-4, 5-3)*

16. Express the following sum as a single fraction. Assume a and b are integers and that $a \neq b$.

$$\frac{9}{a-b} + \frac{21}{b-a} + \frac{7}{4a-4b} \quad \frac{-41}{4(a-b)}$$

(Lesson 5-1)

17. Determine whether the value of each expression below is a rational number. *(Lessons 2-7, 5-1)*

a. $\left(1 + \frac{1}{1000}\right)^{1000}$ See left. **b.** $\lim_{n\to\infty}\left(1 + \frac{1}{n}\right)^n$ irrational

18. Find the base 10 representation of 111001_2. *(Lesson 4-6)* 57

19. Use long division to find the quotient and remainder when $p(x) = x^5 + 3x^4 + 3x^3 + x^2 + 4x - 10$ is divided by $d(x) = x^2 + 1$. *(Lesson 4-3)* $q(x) = x^3 + 3x^2 + 2x - 2$; $r(x) = 2x - 8$

20. Solve over the set of real numbers. See left.

a. $|5x + 2| = 9$ **b.** $|5x + 2| \ge 9$ *(Lesson 3-9)*

21. a. Use the Intermediate Value Theorem to show that the equation $\cos x = .2x^2$ has a solution in the interval from 1 to 1.5.

b. Find an interval of length .01 that contains this solution. *(Lesson 3-4)* See margin.

22. Write the negation of the statement. *(Lessons 1-2, 1-5)* See margin.

a. *If the duplicating machine works, then it is Sunday.*

b. *The car is American made and it is not an electric car.*

Exploration

23. a. Graph f when $f(x) = \frac{1}{x-1} + \frac{1}{x^2} + \frac{1}{x+1}$. See margin.

b. Experiment with other functions that have discontinuities. Copy the equations and graphs of the ones that you find most interesting. Answers will vary.

21–23a. See Additional Answers at the back of this book.

Setting Up Lesson 5-5

As you discuss the graphs of the rational functions in this lesson, note that we concentrate here on the behavior at the vertical asymptotes. At the same time, mention that the end behavior of many of these functions seems predictable, and that this is discussed in the next lesson.

LESSON

5-5

End Behavior of Rational Functions

Astronaut Shannon Lucid is shown floating in the Space Shuttle Atlantis while returning from 188 days aboard the Russian Space Station Mir in 1996. It took her some time to recover from the effects of prolonged weightlessness. See page 312.

With an automatic grapher, you can rather easily determine the behavior of a rational function on any interval. The Discontinuity Theorem enables you to determine any asymptotes of the function, and so tells you if it will have unusual behavior far away from the x-axis. Still, neither of these helps determine the end behavior of the function.

Since graphs of rational functions have many possible shapes, it would seem to be a very difficult task to determine the end behaviors of all rational functions. This lesson is devoted to explaining and proving a theorem which shows that the task is not so difficult at all: the end behavior of any rational function is the same as that of one of three functions: a power function, a constant function, or the reciprocal of a power function.

The End Behavior of Polynomial Functions

We first analyze polynomial functions, in some ways the simplest of the rational functions. (Polynomial functions are to rational functions as integers are to rational numbers.)

Consider the polynomial function p defined by

$$p(x) = 3x^4 - 5x^3 + 8x^2 - 20x + 16.$$

❶ Factor out x^4. This complicates the expression for $p(x)$ but simplifies the analysis of its end behavior.

$$p(x) = \left(3 + \frac{-5}{x} + \frac{8}{x^2} + \frac{-20}{x^3} + \frac{16}{x^4}\right)x^4$$

The end behavior of p is the behavior of $p(x)$ as $|x| \to \infty$. With a calculator, you can see how close $3 + \frac{-5}{x} + \frac{8}{x^2} + \frac{-20}{x^3} + \frac{16}{x^4}$ is to 3 when $|x|$ is large.

Lesson 5-5

Objectives

G Use limit notation to describe the behavior of rational functions.
J Graph rational functions.
K Relate the limit of a function to its graph, and find equations for its asymptotes.

Resources

From the ***Teacher's Resource File***
- Lesson Master 5-5
- Answer Master 5-5
- Teaching Aids
  44 Warm-up
  49 End Behavior of Rational Functions Table
- Technology Sourcebook
  Calculator Master 8

Additional Resources
- Visuals for Teaching Aids 44, 49

Teaching Lesson 5-5

Warm-up

Give an equation for a function f such that $\lim_{x\to\infty} f(x) = 6$.

Sample: $f(x) = \frac{1}{x} + 6$; This is equivalent to $f(x) = \frac{6x+1}{x}$. It is likely that the functions given by students will be rational functions.

Notes on Reading

❶ To determine the end behavior of a polynomial, the polynomial is written as a product of its leading power and the rest of the polynomial. This will be a new kind of factoring for most students, and some students are likely to need help with the

Lesson 5-5 Overview

Broad Goals The end behavior of rational functions (including polynomial functions) is given. Students should be able to explain these end behaviors through algebraic arguments and with graphs.

Perspective Polynomial functions and rational functions have a symbiotic relationship with regard to end behavior. The behavior of the simplest rational functions (the reciprocals of the power functions) is critical in determining the end behavior of polynomial functions. In turn, the end behavior of polynomial functions is needed for analyzing the end behavior of more complicated rational functions. When we speak of end behavior of a function (not necessarily a rational function), there are three possible levels of discourse. At the broadest level, there is the question of the limiting value of the function as $x \to \infty$ or as $x \to -\infty$. There are only four possibilities for such a limit: (1) such a value may exist; (2) the function may become larger than any number you might choose, so that the limit is said to be ∞, (3) the function may become smaller than any number you might choose, so that the limit is said to be $-\infty$, or (4) the function may vacillate and there is no limit at all. In the case of rational functions, all but (4) can occur.

(Overview continues on page 308.)

algebra involved. By factoring out x to the highest power, emphasize that $p(x)$ has been rewritten in a way that facilitates analyzing its behavior as $|x| \to \infty$, because when f is the reciprocal of a power function, $\lim_{x\to\infty} f(x) = \lim_{x\to-\infty} f(x) = 0$. The key point to make is that when $|x|$ is large, the leading term's behavior dominates the behavior of the entire polynomial function.

❷ Note that even though p and q: $x \to 3x^4$ have the same behavior, the values of $p(x)$ and $q(x)$ do not get closer and closer to each other as $x \to \infty$. In fact, $p(x) - q(x) = 5x^3 - 8x^2 + 20x - 16$, so the absolute value of their difference gets larger and larger as $|x| \to \infty$. In general, two functions p and q have the same end behavior if and only if $\lim_{x\to\infty} \frac{p(x)}{q(x)} = \lim_{x\to-\infty} \frac{p(x)}{q(x)} = 1$. You might liken this to the tossing of a fair coin.

x	$3 + \frac{-5}{x} + \frac{8}{x^2} + \frac{-20}{x^3} + \frac{16}{x^4}$	$p(x)$	$3x^4$	$\frac{p(x)}{3x^4}$
50	2.90304	1.814×10^7	$1.875 \cdot 10^7$	0.9677
100	2.95078	2.951×10^8	$3.000 \cdot 10^8$	0.9836
500	2.99003	1.869×10^{11}	$1.875 \cdot 10^{11}$	0.9967
1000	2.99501	2.995×10^{12}	$3.000 \cdot 10^{12}$	0.9983
10,000	2.99950	3.000×10^{16}	$3.000 \cdot 10^{16}$	0.9998
-50	3.10336	1.940×10^7	$1.875 \cdot 10^7$	1.0345
-100	3.05082	3.051×10^8	$3.000 \cdot 10^8$	1.0169
-500	3.01003	1.881×10^{11}	$1.875 \cdot 10^{11}$	1.0033
-1000	3.00501	3.005×10^{12}	$3.000 \cdot 10^{12}$	1.0017
-10,000	3.00500	3.001×10^{16}	$3.000 \cdot 10^{16}$	1.0002

❷ As $|x|$ gets larger, $p(x) = \left(3 + \frac{-5}{x} + \frac{8}{x^2} + \frac{-20}{x^3} + \frac{16}{x^4}\right)x^4$ does not get closer and closer to $3x^4$, but the ratio $\frac{p(x)}{3x^4}$ of these polynomials gets closer and closer to 1. Thus the end behavior of p is the same as the end behavior of the power function $3x^4$. That is, $\lim_{x\to\infty} p(x) = \infty$ and $\lim_{x\to-\infty} p(x) = \infty$.

In general, suppose that p is a polynomial function of degree n defined by

$$p(x) = a_n x^n + a_{n-1} x^{n-1} + \ldots + a_1 x + a_0.$$

When $x \neq 0$, this polynomial can be rewritten in the following equivalent (and unusual) form by factoring out x^n.

$$p(x) = \left(a_n + \frac{a_{n-1}}{x} + \frac{a_{n-2}}{x^2} + \ldots + \frac{a_1}{x^{n-1}} + \frac{a_0}{x^n}\right)x^n$$

As x gets farther and farther from the origin, the terms

$$\frac{a_{n-1}}{x}, \frac{a_{n-2}}{x^2}, \ldots, \frac{a_1}{x^{n-1}}, \frac{a_0}{x^n}$$

get closer to 0. In fact, $a_n + \frac{a_{n-1}}{x} + \frac{a_{n-2}}{x^2} + \ldots + \frac{a_1}{x^{n-1}} + \frac{a_0}{x^n}$ is approximately equal to a_n for values of x far to the left or right of the origin. Hence when $|x|$ is large, the ratio of the values of

$$p(x) = \left(a_n + \frac{a_{n-1}}{x} + \frac{a_{n-2}}{x^2} + \ldots + \frac{a_1}{x^{n-1}} + \frac{a_0}{x^n}\right)x^n$$

and $a_n x^n$ come arbitrarily close to the value 1.

Therefore, far to the left or right of the origin, the graph of p will behave much like the graph of the power function q defined by $q(x) = a_n x^n$. Consequently, the graphs of p and q display the same end behavior even though they may be quite different for values of x relatively close to the origin. It follows that you can determine the end behavior of any polynomial function from its degree and its leading coefficient!

That is, *the end behavior of a polynomial function is the same as the end behavior of its leading term.*

The processes used to determine the end behavior of polynomial functions can be extended to any rational functions. Notice how many techniques there are for determining end behavior.

Lesson 5-5 Overview, continued

At a more specific level, we are concerned with the speed with which a given function approaches its end behavior. The speed is described by identifying a simpler function whose end behavior is the same as the given function. This is the sense of end behavior found in the table on page 312, in the End Behavior of Rational Functions Theorem. There we note that the end behavior of a rational function f: $x \to \frac{p(x)}{q(x)}$ is the same as the end behavior of the function defined as the quotient of the leading terms of the polynomials p and q. If the degree of p is greater than the degree of q, then the end behavior is the same as that of a polynomial. If the degree of p equals the degree of q, then there is a horizontal asymptote to the graph. If the degree of p is less than the degree of q, then the end behavior is the same as that of one of the reciprocals of the power functions studied in Lesson 5-3.

A third level of discourse, in between the first two, is to note a class of functions similar to the behavior of a given function. For instance, an algorithm might be said to take "polynomial time," by which is meant that as the complexity of the problem n increases, the end behavior of the number of steps $p(n)$ required for the algorithm is the same as that of some polynomial.

The End Behavior of a Rational Function with Equal Degrees in Numerator and Denominator

Example 1

Describe the end behavior of the function g defined by the formula

$$g(x) = \frac{2x^2 + 1}{x^2 - 1}.$$

Solution 1

Use a calculator or computer to generate a table of values of $g(x)$ for large values of x. From the table, it seems that $\lim_{x\to\infty} g(x) = 2$.

x	2	5	10	100	1000
$g(x) = \frac{2x^2+1}{x^2-1}$	3	2.125	2.0303	2.0003	2.000003

Since g is an even function, it is symmetric to the y-axis, so it appears that $\lim_{x\to-\infty} g(x) = \lim_{x\to\infty} g(x) = 2$.

Solution 2

Divide the numerator and denominator of the formula by the highest power of the independent variable that appears in the denominator. In this case, divide by x^2.

$$g(x) = \frac{2x^2+1}{x^2-1} = \frac{\frac{2x^2+1}{x^2}}{\frac{x^2-1}{x^2}} = \frac{2+\frac{1}{x^2}}{1-\frac{1}{x^2}}$$

For values of x far to the left or to the right of the origin, $\frac{1}{x^2}$ is negligibly small, and so the values of $g(x)$ become arbitrarily close to $\frac{2}{1} = 2$. In limit notation, this is written

$$\lim_{x\to-\infty} g(x) = \lim_{x\to\infty} g(x) = \lim_{x\to\infty}\left(\frac{2+\frac{1}{x^2}}{1-\frac{1}{x^2}}\right) = \lim_{x\to-\infty}\left(\frac{2+\frac{1}{x^2}}{1-\frac{1}{x^2}}\right) = 2.$$

Therefore, the line $y = 2$ is a horizontal asymptote for the function.

Solution 3

Use long division.

$$\begin{array}{r} 2 \\ x^2-1\overline{)2x^2+1} \\ \underline{2x^2-2} \\ 3 \end{array}$$

The long division shows that $g(x) = \frac{2x^2+1}{x^2-1} = 2 + \frac{3}{x^2-1}$. Since $x^2 - 1$ grows without bound as $x \to \infty$, $\lim_{x\to\infty} \frac{3}{x^2-1} = 0$. Thus $\lim_{x\to\infty} g(x) = \lim_{x\to\infty}\left(2 + \frac{3}{x^2-1}\right) = \lim_{x\to-\infty} g(x) = 2.$

▶

Generally, as the coin is tossed more, the absolute difference between the numbers of heads and tails tends to increase, but the ratio of heads to tails approaches 1.

Consequently, when we write $p(x) \approx a_nx^n$, we do not mean that the absolute difference $|p(x) - a_nx^n|$ is small; in fact, it becomes arbitrarily large as x grows in magnitude. Instead, we mean that this difference relative to the absolute value of the polynomial, $\frac{|p(x) = a_nx^n|}{|p(x)|}$, becomes small. This can be seen by noting that this relative difference is the absolute value of a rational function whose numerator has smaller degree than its denominator. Thus the relative difference approaches zero as x grows in magnitude.

However, in **Example 2,** the function h does get closer and closer to the line $y = \frac{1}{3}x + 4$.

You might point out that the method of Solution 1 of **Example 1** is quite limited because you may not be able to see the limit from the table of values. For instance, should f be such that $f(x) = \frac{3x^2+1}{7x^2-1}$, it is likely not to be obvious from a table that $\lim_{x\to\infty} f(x) = \lim_{x\to-\infty} f(x) = \frac{3}{7}$.

Optional Activities

Activity 1 Technology Connection
You might wish to assign *Technology Sourcebook, Calculator Master 8.* In this activity, students use graphs and tables on a graphics calculator to examine various types of rational functions in order to categorize their local and end behavior. Students link their observations back to the equations for the functions and make conclusions about which parts of the equations produce certain behavior.

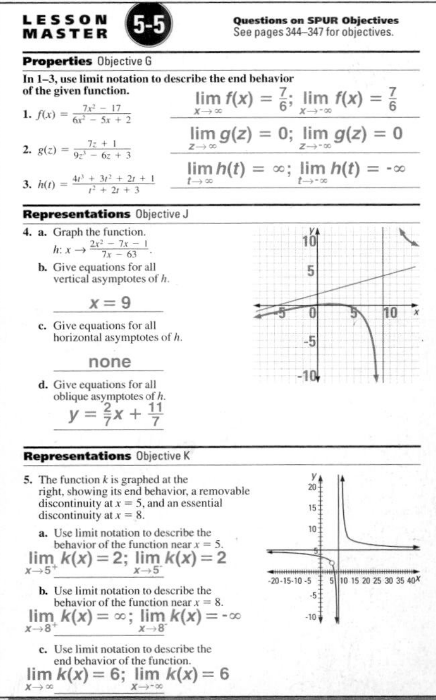
LESSON MASTER 5-5

Questions on SPUR Objectives
See pages 344–347 for objectives.

Properties Objective G

In 1–3, use limit notation to describe the end behavior of the given function.

1. $f(x) = \frac{7x^2 - 17}{6x^2 - 5x + 2}$ $\lim_{x\to\infty} f(x) = \frac{7}{6}$; $\lim_{x\to-\infty} f(x) = \frac{7}{6}$

2. $g(z) = \frac{7z + 1}{9z^2 - 6z + 3}$ $\lim_{z\to\infty} g(z) = 0$; $\lim_{z\to-\infty} g(z) = 0$

3. $h(t) = \frac{4t^3 + 3t^2 + 2t + 1}{t^2 + 2t + 3}$ $\lim_{t\to\infty} h(t) = \infty$; $\lim_{t\to-\infty} h(t) = -\infty$

Representations Objective J

4. a. Graph the function. $h: x \to \frac{2x^2 - 7x - 1}{7x - 63}$.

b. Give equations for all vertical asymptotes of h. $x = 9$

c. Give equations for all horizontal asymptotes of h. none

d. Give equations for all oblique asymptotes of h. $y = \frac{2}{7}x + \frac{11}{7}$

Representations Objective K

5. The function k is graphed at the right, showing its end behavior, a removable discontinuity at $x = 5$, and an essential discontinuity at $x = 8$.

a. Use limit notation to describe the behavior of the function near $x = 5$. $\lim_{x\to5^+} k(x) = 2$; $\lim_{x\to5^-} k(x) = 2$

b. Use limit notation to describe the behavior of the function near $x = 8$. $\lim_{x\to8^+} k(x) = \infty$; $\lim_{x\to8^-} k(x) = -\infty$

c. Use limit notation to describe the end behavior of the function. $\lim_{x\to\infty} k(x) = 6$; $\lim_{x\to-\infty} k(x) = 6$

In the method of Solution 2 of **Example 1**, emphasize that the divisor is the highest power of the independent variable in the denominator. Many students will prefer thinking of multiplying both numerator and denominator by $\frac{1}{x^2}$ (rather than dividing by x^2). Then apply the distributive property to in effect divide each term of the expression by x^2. First analyze numerator and denominator of $\frac{2+\frac{1}{x^2}}{1-\frac{1}{x^2}}$ separately as $|x| \to \infty$, then divide to get the quotient. Implicit (you may wish to make it explicit) is the theorem that the limit of a quotient is the quotient of the limits.

Error Alert Some students may incorrectly extend the method of Solution 2 of **Example 1** to analyzing end behavior of polynomial functions, by incorrectly writing $f(x) = 5x^4 + 3x^2 + 7x + 8$ as $f(x) = 5 + \frac{2}{x^2} + \frac{7}{x^3} + \frac{8}{x^4}$ and concluding that $\lim_{|x| \to \infty} f(x) = 5$.

In Solution 3 to **Example 1**, implicit in $\lim_{|x| \to \infty}\left(2 + \frac{2}{x^2 - 1}\right) = 2$ is the theorem that is often paraphrased "the limit of a sum is the sum of the limits." Some students have trouble with $\lim_{|x| \to \infty} 2 = 2$.

Example 2 shows another reason for dividing polynomials. Considered as polynomial division, the quotient is a function whose end behavior is identical to that of the given rational function. You could interpret earlier examples of long division in terms of nonlinear asymptotes of rational functions. For instance, the long division at the beginning of Lesson 4-3 gave $\frac{6x^3 - 9x^2 + 8x + 1}{2x + 1} = 3x^2 - 6x + 7 + \frac{-6}{2x+1}$. Thinking of the left side of this equation as a formula for a rational function, its end behavior is the same as that of the parabola $y = 3x^2$, and in fact it gets closer and closer to the parabola $y = 3x^2 - 6x + 7$.

Students should be able to apply the End Behavior of Rational Functions Theorem without mindless memorization. It is valid regardless of whether $m < n$, $m = n$, or $m > n$. Students should fully understand the derivation of the table shown on page 312. That table is shown on **Teaching Aid 49.**

Solution 4

A graph of g is shown at the right. The graph confirms that the end behavior is described by $\lim_{x \to \infty} g(x) = \lim_{x \to -\infty} g(x) = 2$.

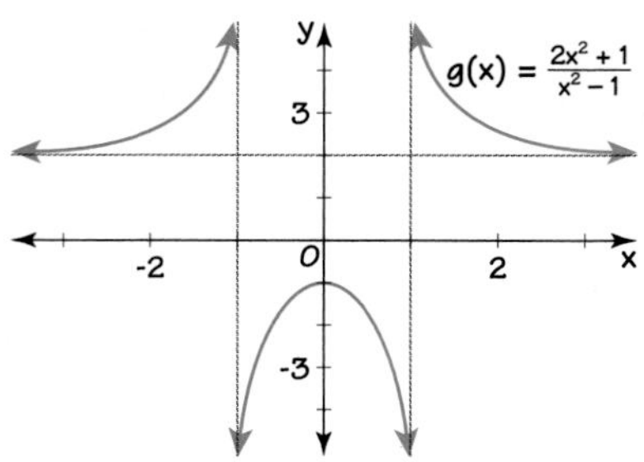

The End Behavior of a Rational Function with Numerator of Greater Degree

Solution 3 to Example 1 illustrates how long division can be used to express a function in a form that permits the behavior as $x \to \infty$ and as $x \to -\infty$ to be quickly determined. This can be done with any rational function in which the degree of the numerator is greater than the degree of the denominator.

Example 2

Let h be the function defined by $h(x) = \frac{x^2 + 14x + 12}{3x + 6}$.

a. Rewrite $h(x)$ as a quotient plus remainder term.

b. Use the results from part **a** to discuss the behavior of h as $x \to \infty$ and as $x \to -\infty$.

Solution

a. Use long division.

$$\begin{array}{r} \frac{1}{3}x + 4 \\ 3x + 6\overline{)x^2 + 14x + 12} \\ \underline{x^2 + 2x} \\ 12x + 12 \\ \underline{12x + 24} \\ -12 \end{array}$$

Therefore,

$$h(x) = \frac{1}{3}x + 4 + \frac{-12}{3x + 6}.$$

b. Notice that as $x \to \infty$ and as $x \to -\infty$, $\frac{-12}{3x+6}$ gets arbitrarily close to 0. It follows that the values of $h(x)$ get arbitrarily close to the values of $\frac{1}{3}x + 4$. That is,

$$\lim_{x \to \infty} h(x) = \lim_{x \to \infty}\left(\frac{1}{3}x + 4 + \frac{-12}{3x+6}\right) = \lim_{x \to \infty}\left(\frac{1}{3}x + 4\right) = \infty,$$

$$\lim_{x \to -\infty} h(x) = \lim_{x \to -\infty}\left(\frac{1}{3}x + 4 + \frac{-12}{3x+6}\right) = \lim_{x \to -\infty}\left(\frac{1}{3}x + 4\right) = -\infty.$$

Optional Activities

Activity 2 Writing To summarize the lesson, ask students to examine the following four "cases" of rational functions and describe the general end behavior of these functions: (a) the numerator has degree two more than the denominator; (b) the numerator has degree one more than the denominator; (c) the degrees of the numerator and denominator are equal; (d) the numerator has degree one less than the denominator. Encourage them to give an example of a function for each description and to describe the end behavior in general. [Sample: for part (a), $y = \frac{2x^3 - 1}{x}$; these functions will have end behavior like the power function $y = x^2$, meaning that $\lim_{|x| \to \infty} y = \infty$ if the leading coefficients of the numerator and denominator are both positive or both negative; if the leading coefficients have different signs, then $\lim_{|x| \to \infty} y = -\infty$.]

In Example 2, the line $y = \frac{1}{3}x + 4$ is called an **oblique asymptote** to the graph of h. Below, the function h and its oblique asymptote are plotted. On the graph at the left, the x- and y-axes have the same scale. The center and right graphs show the effects of zooming out along the x-axis. Notice that for very large values of $|x|$, the graph of h gets closer and closer to the line $y = \frac{1}{3}x + 4$.

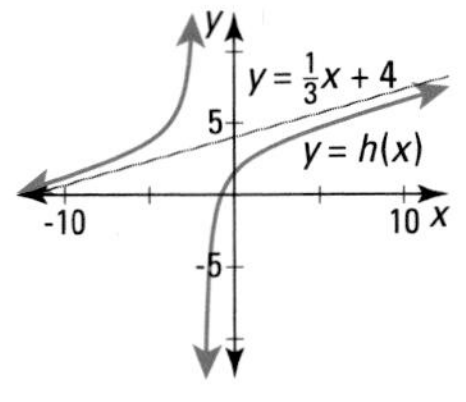

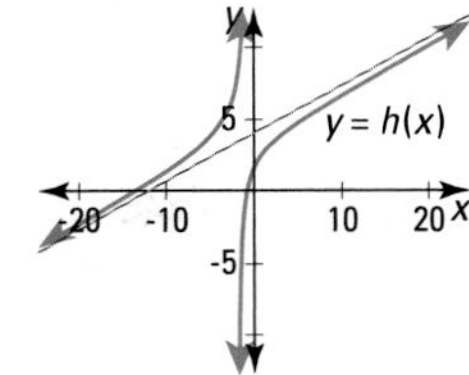

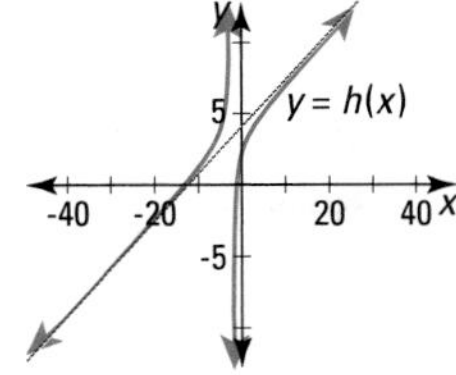

The General Theorem

From the polynomial example that began this lesson and from Example 1, perhaps you have already conjectured the general pattern. When a rational function is written as a quotient of polynomials, its end behavior is determined by dividing the leading terms of the polynomials.

Theorem (End Behavior of Rational Functions)

Suppose $f(x) = \frac{a_m x^m + \ldots + a_1 x + a_0}{b_n x^n + \ldots + b_1 x + b_0}$ $\forall$ real numbers x for which the denominator is nonzero, where the a_i and b_i are real numbers $\forall$ i, $a_m \neq 0$, and $b_n \neq 0$. Then the end behavior of f is the same as the end behavior of the function g defined $\forall$ x by $g(x) = \frac{a_m}{b_n}x^{m-n}$.

Proof

Rewrite the formula for $f(x)$ by factoring x^m from the numerator and factoring x^n from the denominator.

$$f(x) = \frac{\left(a_m + \frac{a_{m-1}}{x} + \frac{a_{m-2}}{x^2} + \ldots + \frac{a_1}{x^{m-1}} + \frac{a_0}{x^m}\right)x^m}{\left(b_n + \frac{b_{n-1}}{x} + \frac{b_{n-2}}{x^2} + \ldots + \frac{b_1}{x^{n-1}} + \frac{b_0}{x^n}\right)x^n}$$

As $|x|$ gets larger and larger, all the terms in the parentheses approach zero except a_m and b_n, which remain constant. Thus

$$\lim_{x\to\infty} f(x) = \frac{a_m x^m}{b_n x^n} \quad \text{and} \quad \lim_{x\to-\infty} f(x) = \frac{a_m x^m}{b_n x^n}.$$

Dividing the powers of x,

$$\lim_{x\to\infty} f(x) = \frac{a_m}{b_n}x^{m-n} \quad \text{and} \quad \lim_{x\to-\infty} f(x) = \frac{a_m}{b_n}x^{m-n}.$$

Regarding **Example 3,** a more general formula for weight as a function of planet radius and height above the planet is provided in **Question 9.**

Additional Examples

1. Describe the end behavior of the function f defined by the formula $f(x) = \frac{5x^4 + 3x^2 + 8}{2x^4 + 7x^2 + 1}$.
   Because f is an even function, $\lim_{x\to-\infty} f(x) = \lim_{x\to\infty} f(x) = \lim_{x\to\infty} \frac{5x^4 + 3x^2 + 8}{2x^4 + 7x^2 + 1} = \lim_{x\to\infty} \frac{5 + \frac{3}{x^2} + \frac{8}{x^4}}{2 + \frac{7}{x^2} + \frac{1}{x^4}} = \frac{5}{2}$ or 2.5.
2. Let h be the function h defined by $h(x) = \frac{3x^2 + 5x - 9}{2x + 6}$.
   a. Rewrite h using long division.
   $h(x) = \frac{3}{2}x - 2 + \frac{3}{2x + 6}$
   b. Discuss the behavior of h as $x \to \infty$ and as $x \to -\infty$.
   $\lim_{x\to\infty} h(x) = \infty$,
   $\lim_{x\to-\infty} h(x) = -\infty$.
   The graph of h approaches the line $y = \frac{3}{2}x - 2$.
3. Describe the end behavior of the function $m(h) = 100\left(\frac{1740}{1740 + h}\right)^2$.
   The end behavior is the same as that of the reciprocal of an inverse square function, so $\lim_{h\to\infty} m(h) = 0$; $\lim_{h\to-\infty} m(h) = 0$
   This formula gives the weight of an object that is h kilometers above the surface of our moon.
4. Describe the end behavior of the function f, where $f(x) = \frac{10(x + 3)^2}{(x - 4)^3}$.
   The end behavior is the same as that of the function g, where $g(x) = \frac{10}{x}$, so $\lim_{x\to\infty} f(x) = \lim_{x\to-\infty} f(x) = 0$.

Notes on Questions

Question 1 Error Alert The small amount of space between the parentheses of "(?)x^3" leads some students erroneously to think that the answer is a single digit or variable.

Question 4 For automatic graphing, wise selection of domain and range is critical. Try the window $-30 \le x \le 30$ and $-0.5 \le y \le 0.75$. Many students think of an asymptote as a line that a graph approaches, but never touches. They are distressed to see the graph of $f(x) = \frac{2x+3}{x^2+9}$ crossing its horizontal asymptote $y = 0$ at the point (-1.5, 0). This problem provides an excellent opportunity to purify their understanding of asymptotes.

Questions 6–7 Invite students to use an automatic grapher to graph these. Suggest settings of $-100 \le x \le 100$ and $-500 \le y \le 500$. The end behaviors will be nicely illustrated.

Question 9 Science Connection You may have to emphasize that $w(0)$ represents the weight at the planet's surface and *h,* not *r,* is the independent variable since, for a given planet, *r* is fixed. Dieters wishing to feel good should have their initial weigh-in on a beautiful ocean beach and their second weigh-in on the peak of Mount McKinley, or, better yet, Mount Everest. (We ignore the equipment the dieter will have to carry up the mountain.)

(Notes on Questions continue on page 314.)

Example 3

Describe the end behavior of the function w defined by $w(h) = 70\left(\frac{6400}{6400+h}\right)^2$.

Solution

Write the formula as a quotient of polynomials. Notice that the polynomial in the denominator is expanded and written in decreasing order of the exponents.

$$w(h) = \frac{70 \cdot 6400^2}{h^2 + 12800h + 6400^2}$$

The numerator is a constant polynomial $p(h) = 70 \cdot 6400^2$. The denominator is a quadratic expression $q(h) = h^2 + 12800h + 6400^2$. The end behavior of w is the same as the end behavior of

$$g: h \rightarrow \frac{70 \cdot 6400^2}{1} \cdot \frac{1}{h^2} = \frac{70 \cdot 6400^2}{h^2}.$$

This is an inverse square function whose end behavior you should know.

$$\lim_{h\to\infty} w(h) = \lim_{h\to\infty} g(h) = 0 \text{ and } \lim_{h\to-\infty} w(h) = \lim_{h\to-\infty} g(h) = 0.$$

The function of Example 3 may seem exotic, but it is not. If an astronaut weighs 70 kg on the surface of Earth, $w(h)$ is the astronaut's weight h kilometers above the surface. $\lim_{h\to\infty} w(h)$ is what happens to the weight as the person goes farther and farther from the surface. The astronaut's weight approaches zero, which is called weightlessness.

The four specific functions in this lesson illustrate major cases of the End Behavior of Rational Functions Theorem.

function rule	*m*	*n*	type	end behavior
$p(x) = 3x^4 - 5x^3 + 8x^2 - 20x + 16$	4	0	$m > n$	like the power function $f(x) = 3x^4$
$h(x) = \frac{x^2 + 14x + 12}{3x + 6}$	2	1	$m > n$, $m = n + 1$	like the linear function $f(x) = \frac{1}{3}x$
$g(x) = \frac{2x^2 + 1}{x^2 - 1}$	2	2	$m = n$	like the constant function $f(x) = 2$
$w(h) = 70\left(\frac{6400}{6400+h}\right)^2$	0	2	$m < n$	like the reciprocal of a power function $f(h) = \frac{70 \cdot 6400^2}{h^2}$

Adapting to Individual Needs

Challenge

Have students answer the following, given that $p(x)$ and $q(x)$ are polynomials.

1. When does $y = \frac{p(x)}{q(x)}$ not have a vertical asymptote? [If $q(x)$ has no real zeros that are not zeros of $p(x)$.]
2. When does $y = \frac{p(x)}{q(x)}$ not have a horizontal asymptote? [If $q(x)$ is a constant.]
3. *True or False.* The graph of $y = \frac{p(x)}{q(x)}$ does not cross its horizontal asymptote? If true, explain why; if false, give a counterexample. [False; sample: $y = \frac{x}{x^2 - 3x + 2}$]

1) $4 - \frac{11}{x} + \frac{6}{x^2} - \frac{2}{x^3}$

3b) The end behavior of r is like the function $f(x) = \frac{1}{3}$; $\lim_{x\to\infty} r(x) = \frac{1}{3}$, $\lim_{x\to-\infty} r(x) = \frac{1}{3}$.

4) The end behavior of f is like the function $g(k) = \frac{2}{k}$; $\lim_{k\to\infty} f(k) = 0$, $\lim_{k\to-\infty} f(k) = 0$.

5) The end behavior of g is like the function $f(x) = x^4$; $\lim_{x\to\infty} g(x) = \infty$, $\lim_{x\to-\infty} g(x) = -\infty$

QUESTIONS

Covering the Reading

1. Fill in the parentheses: $4x^3 - 11x^2 + 6x - 2 = (?)\, x^3$. See left.

2. Consider the polynomial function p with $p(x) = 6 - 4x^5 + 2x^3$.

a. What is the leading term of $p(x)$? $-4x^5$

b. The end behavior of p is like that of which power function? $f(x) = -4x^5$

3. Consider the graph of the rational function r with

$$r(x) = \frac{2x^2 + 9x - 11}{6x^2 + 3}.$$

a. Describe all asymptotes. $y = \frac{1}{3}$

b. Describe the end behavior of r. See left.

4. Give the end behavior of the function f with $f(k) = \frac{2k + 3}{k^2 + 9}$. (Note: You were asked to analyze this function in Question 11 of Lesson 5-4.) See left.

5. Give the end behavior of See left.

$$g: x \to \frac{7x^8 - 12x^7 - 6x^6 - 9x^5 + 4x^3 - 12x + 1000}{7x^4 + 6x^3 - 2x^2}.$$

6. Use long division to find the oblique asymptote for the graph of the function t with equation $t(w) = \frac{6w^2 - 8w + 4}{2w + 1}$. $t = 3w - \frac{11}{2}$

7. Use long division to show that the end behavior of $h: v \to \frac{4v^3 + 3v^2 + 8v - 2}{2v - 1}$ is like the end behavior of a polynomial of degree 2. See margin.

8. a. If you weigh 70 kg on the surface of Earth, how much will you weigh in an airplane 11 km above the surface? ≈ 149.5 lb, 69.76 kg

b. An astronaut who weighs 70 kg on the surface of Earth has what weight in a space shuttle 190 km above the surface? ≈ 141.4 lb, 66.02 kg

c. When astronauts went to the moon, how much did Earth's gravitation contribute to their weight halfway there, about 375,000 km above the surface of Earth? ≈ 0.05 lb, 0.08 kg

Applying the Mathematics

9. A more general formula for the weight w of an object in kilograms h km above the surface of a planet is $w(h) = w(0)\left(\frac{r}{r + h}\right)^2$, where r is the radius of a planet. If an object weighed 45 kg on the surface of Mars, whose radius is about 3200 km, graph what its weight would be at all altitudes above the surface. See left.

9)

$-2500 \le x \le 12500$, x-scale = 2500
$-25 \le y \le 125$, y-scale = 25

10. Give a formula for a function f which has a vertical asymptote at $x = 5$, contains the point (1, 2), and has end behavior like the function $g: x \to \frac{3}{x^3}$.
Sample: $f(x) = \frac{3x - 11}{x^3(x - 5)}$

Follow-up for Lesson 5-5

Practice

For more questions on SPUR Objectives, use **Lesson Master 5-5** (shown on page 309).

Assessment

Written Communication Have students **work in pairs.** Ask each to define a polynomial function. Call one $p(x)$ and the other $q(x)$. One partner should determine the end behavior of the rational function $\frac{p(x)}{q(x)}$ and the other partner do the same for $\frac{q(x)}{p(x)}$. Then have students compare results and verify them on an automatic grapher. [Students describe the end behavior of rational functions.]

Extension

Have students make up a question similar to **Question 10.** They should write a possible answer to their question on a separate piece of paper and then exchange questions with a partner. Have them write a solution to their partner's question and again exchange and check their partner's answer. This activity may emphasize that there are many functions that can satisfy certain conditions.

Project Update Project 3, *A Family of Functions*, on page 340, relates to the content of this lesson.

Additional Answers

7.
$$\begin{array}{r} 2v^2 + \frac{5}{2}v + \frac{21}{4} \\ 2v - 1\overline{)4v^3 + 3v^2 + 8v - 2} \\ \underline{4v^3 - 2v^2 \qquad\qquad} \\ 5v^2 + 8v - 2 \\ \underline{5v^2 - \frac{5}{2}v \qquad} \\ \frac{21}{2}v - 2 \\ \underline{\frac{21}{2}v - \frac{21}{4}} \\ \frac{13}{4} \end{array}$$

Notes on Questions

Question 13 This function is interesting because of its possession of one removable and one essential discontinuity. Using the window $-5 \le x \le 5$ and $-5 \le y \le 5$ and the trace mode, some calculators display no y value for $x = 3$. The hole at $(3, \frac{5}{7})$ is actually visible because one pixel on the graph is not activated.

Question 15 This is another question that will help prepare students for the derivative in calculus.

Question 19 These are simple review questions in preparation for Lesson 5-7.

Question 20 This question is closely related to the In-class Activity preceding Lesson 5-8, and it is discussed at the beginning of that lesson. You can discuss this question in some detail instead of doing that activity. In general, if someone has gone from A to B at speed x and returned at speed y, then, unless $x = y$, the average speed is not $\frac{x+y}{2}$ because it takes longer to go at the slower speed. This question shows that if $y = 20$ mph, then there are certain average speeds for the round trip that are not possible.

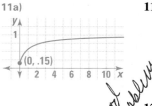

11a) [graph: y-axis with 1; x-axis 2, 4, 6, 8, 10; point (0, .15)]

13a) $z = 3$

b) $t(z) = \frac{z^2 - z - 6}{z^2 + z - 12} = \frac{(z-3)(z+2)}{(z-3)(z+4)} = \frac{z+2}{z+4}$ ∴ $t(z)$ is always undefined at $z = -4$.

20a) The total distance traveled is $2d$. The first average speed is 20 mph and the second is x mph. Since the distance traveled either way, d, is equal, the two rates divided into d will give the total time spent. When this value is divided into $2d$ the average speed is obtained.

b) $\frac{40xd}{xd + 20d}$

11. In Mr. Ease's class, all points on quizzes and tests are combined to come up with a student's final grade. Viola only got 3 of 20 points possible on the first quiz. Suppose Viola does not miss any point for the rest of the year. Let x be the number of points after the first quiz and $r(x)$ be the total fraction of points Viola has earned. See left.

a. Graph r.

b. What does the end behavior of r tell you about this situation? As the number of total points increases, Viola's grade approaches 100%

12. Let s be the sequence defined by $s_n = \frac{7n+11}{4n-3}$. Find $\lim_{n\to\infty} s_n$. $\frac{7}{4}$

Review

13. Consider the function t defined by $t(z) = \frac{z^2 - z - 6}{z^2 + z - 12}$. See left.

a. Determine the location of the removable discontinuity of function t.

b. Show that t has an essential discontinuity at $z = -4$. *(Lesson 5-4)*

14. Write $3x + 1 + \frac{2}{3x-1}$ as a ratio of two polynomials. *(Lesson 5-2)* $\frac{9x^2+1}{3x-1}$

15. Consider the function $f: x \to \frac{4}{x}$. Find the slope of the segment joining $\left(x, \frac{4}{x}\right)$ to $\left(x + h, \frac{4}{x+h}\right)$. *(Lesson 5-1)* $\frac{-4}{x(x+h)}$, $x \ne 0$, $h \ne 0$, and $x \ne -h$

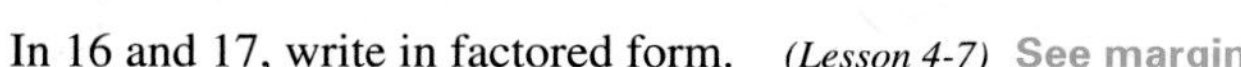

In 16 and 17, write in factored form. *(Lesson 4-7)* See margin.

16. $(x + 11)^2(x - 5)^3(x + 2) + (x + 11)^3(x - 5)^2(x + 2)^2$

17. $(3t - 7y)^4(8t + 5y)^3 - (3t - 7y)^3(8t + 5y)^4(t + y)$

18. Solve $e^{2x} + 6e^x + 8 = 0$. *(Lesson 3-6)* $x = \ln 4 \approx 1.386$ and $x = \ln 2 \approx .6931$

19. Evaluate without using a calculator. *(Previous course, Lesson 2-6)*

a. $\sin \frac{\pi}{4}$ $\frac{\sqrt{2}}{2}$

b. $\cos \frac{2\pi}{3}$ $-\frac{1}{2}$

c. $\sin \frac{3\pi}{2}$ -1

d. $\cos \frac{7\pi}{6}$ $-\frac{\sqrt{3}}{2}$

Exploration

20. Suppose you travel a distance d (in miles) at an average speed of 20 mph and travel back at x mph.

a. Explain why your average speed is $\frac{2d}{\frac{d}{20} + \frac{d}{x}}$. See left.

b. Write the expression from part **a** as a simple rational expression in lowest terms. See left.

c. Let $f(x)$ equal your answer from part **b**. What is $\lim_{x\to\infty} f(x)$? What real-world interpretation does the limit have? $\lim_{x\to\infty} f(x) = 40$; the return trip approaches 40 mph.

Additional Answers

16. $(x + 11)^2(x - 5)^2(x + 2)(x^2 + 14x + 17)$

17. $(3t - 7y)^3(8t + 5y)^3(-8t^2 + 3t - 7y - 13ty - 5y^2)$

LESSON

5-6

Irrational Numbers

This 6th century B.C. Greek bowl depicts a boat that may be similar to the one mentioned by Proclus.

The Discovery of Irrational Numbers

The diagram at the right shows an isosceles right triangle with sides of lengths 1, 1, and x. By the Pythagorean Theorem,

$$x^2 = 1^2 + 1^2 = 2,$$

and so

$$x = \sqrt{2}.$$

Pythagoras, after whom the Pythagorean Theorem is named, led a group of philosophers in Greece during the sixth century B.C. For many years, the Pythagoreans believed that all natural phenomena could be explained in terms of the natural numbers 1, 2, 3, ... One part of their belief was that any number could be expressed as a ratio of two natural numbers. In the triangle pictured above, this would mean that the length of the hypotenuse, which is $\sqrt{2}$, could be expressed as $\frac{a}{b}$ for some natural numbers a and b.

However, despite their belief that $\sqrt{2}$ should be rational, the Pythagoreans, who were very clever mathematicians, proved otherwise. They proved that $\sqrt{2}$ could not be written as a ratio of two natural numbers. Such numbers were called **irrational** because they could not be understood as obtainable from ratios of integers. This discovery shook the very foundations of their belief system and created a major crisis in their group. Proclus, a Greek mathematician who lived about 1000 years later, wrote, "It is told that those who first brought out the irrationals from concealment into the open perished in a shipwreck, to a man."

Lesson 5-6

Objectives

B Identify numbers as rational or irrational.
C Simplify expressions involving radicals.
F Prove properties of rational and irrational numbers.

Resources

From the ***Teacher's Resource File***
- Lesson Master 5-6
- Answer Master 5-6
- Teaching Aid 44: Warm-up

Additional Resources
- Visual for Teaching Aid 44

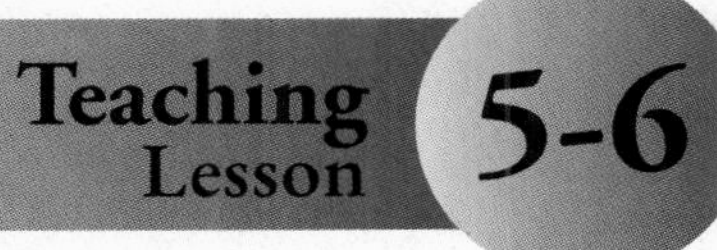

Teaching Lesson 5-6

Warm-up

1. Find a recursive formula for the first four terms of the sequence $\frac{3}{2}, \frac{7}{5}, \frac{17}{12}, \frac{41}{29}, \frac{99}{70}, \ldots$.
   Let the nth term be $s_n = \frac{a_n}{b_n}$. Then $s_{n+1} = \frac{a_{n+1}}{b_{n+1}} = \frac{2b_n + a_n}{b_n + a_n}$.
2. Use your formula to obtain the next few terms of the sequence. Does the sequence seem to have a limit? If so, conjecture what that limit is. **The limit of the sequence is $\sqrt{2}$. These terms are known as convergents to $\sqrt{2}$; they are the simple fractions with smallest numerators and denominators that get as close as they do to $\sqrt{2}$.**

Lesson 5-6 Overview

Broad Goals This lesson reviews some ideas about irrational numbers, those real numbers that are not rational. The proof that $\sqrt{2}$ is irrational, and proofs concerning the results of combining rational and irrational numbers, are used as vehicles to practice the writing of indirect proofs. The decimal representations of rational and irrational numbers are discussed. The lesson closes with work on rationalizing denominators of certain fractions representing irrational numbers.

Perspectives History Connection Regarding the discovery of the irrationality of $\sqrt{2}$, Howard Eves writes (*History of Mathematics,* 6th ed., Saunders College Publishing, 1990, page 84) "so great was the logical scandal that efforts were made for a while to keep the matter secret. One legend has it that the Pythagorean Hippasus perished at sea for his impiety in disclosing the secret to outsiders, or was banished from the Pythagorean community and a tomb was erected for him as though he was dead."

The application of *modus tollens* to show that π is irrational can be detailed as follows:

(Overview continues on page 316.)

Notes on Reading

To help students understand the proof that $\sqrt{2}$ is irrational, you might review the "Proof by Contradiction" Theorem in Lesson 4-7. Draw a vertical line on the board. To its left, write the form of the proof by contradiction argument as in that lesson. To its right, summarize the corresponding steps of the proof that $\sqrt{2}$ is irrational. Take time out to remind students why "a^2 is even $\Rightarrow$ a is even" is true.

Proving that $\sqrt{2}$ Is Irrational

The most common proof that $\sqrt{2}$ is irrational is an indirect proof, specifically, a proof by contradiction. It makes use of the fact that, if the square of an integer is even, then the integer itself must be even, which was to be proved in Question 27 of Lesson 5-1. The proof also makes use of the fact that any fraction can be written in lowest terms, with no factors greater than 1 common to both the numerator and the denominator.

Theorem (The Irrationality of $\sqrt{2}$)
$\sqrt{2}$ is irrational.

Analysis
The statement to be proved is

s: $\sqrt{2}$ *is irrational.*

The proof starts by assuming ~*s*; in other words, by assuming

~*s*: $\sqrt{2}$ *is a rational number.*

Then a contradiction is deduced. The existence of this contradiction will imply that the assumption is false and hence that *s* is true.

Proof
Assume $\sqrt{2}$ is a rational number. Then $\sqrt{2}$ can be expressed as a ratio of integers $\frac{a}{b}$ where $b \neq 0$ and $\frac{a}{b}$ is written in lowest terms. That is, a and b have no integer factors greater than 1 in common.

	$\sqrt{2} = \frac{a}{b}$	supposition
$\Rightarrow$	$2 = \frac{a^2}{b^2}$	Apply the squaring function to both sides.
$\Rightarrow$	$2b^2 = a^2$	M_{b^2}

But since $2b^2 = a^2$, by the definition of even, a^2 is even. Hence, as seen earlier, a is even. By the definition of even, then $a = 2k$ for some integer k. Now we show that b must also be even:

$2b^2 = (2k)^2$	Substitute $2k$ for a.
$2b^2 = 4k^2$	Power of a Product Property
$b^2 = 2k^2$	$M_{1/2}$

But since $b^2 = 2k^2$, b^2 is even; thus b is even. Now it has been deduced that both a and b are even, and so they must have a common factor of 2. Consequently, on the one hand a and b have no factors in common greater than 1, and on the other hand, they have a common factor of 2. This contradiction shows that the assumption that $\sqrt{2}$ is a rational number is false. Therefore, $\sqrt{2}$ is not a rational number.

The irrationality of $\sqrt{3}$, $\sqrt{5}$, $\sqrt{6}$, $\sqrt{7}$, $\sqrt{8}$, $\sqrt{10}$, $\sqrt{11}$, $\sqrt{12}$, $\sqrt{13}$, $\sqrt{14}$, $\sqrt{15}$, and $\sqrt{17}$ was proved by Theodorus of Cyrene around 390 B.C. (You will be asked to prove the irrationality of some of these square

Lesson 5-6 Overview, continued

The first premise $p(x) \Rightarrow q(x)$ is what Lambert already has proved: *If* x *is a nonzero rational number, then* tan x *is irrational.* Let $x = \frac{\pi}{4}$. Then the second premise ~$q(c)$ is: *tan* $\frac{\pi}{4}$ *is rational.* This premise is certainly true, because tan $\frac{\pi}{4} = 1$. ∴ we can conclude ~$p(c)$: $\frac{\pi}{4}$ *is irrational or zero.* Since we know $\frac{\pi}{4} \neq 0$, $\frac{\pi}{4}$ must be irrational.

Using $\frac{\pi}{4}$ is irrational to conclude that π is irrational requires the following theorem. *The quotient (or product) of an irrational and a rational number is irrational.* This can be proved by the method of **Example 1.**

roots in the Questions.) In general, it can be proved that for any integer n, if n is not a perfect square, then $\sqrt{n}$ is irrational. The proofs use the same idea as in the proof on page 316. In each proof you need to make use of the following theorem:

If n^2 is divisible by a prime p, then n is divisible by p.

Of course, if n is a perfect square, then $\sqrt{n}$ is an integer and thus rational.

Decimals Which Represent Rational Numbers

Consider the *terminating decimal* 73.5906. By multiplying and dividing this number by 10^4, we find that $73.5906 = \frac{735906}{10000}$. Thus 73.5906 can be written as a ratio of integers, and so it is a rational number. In general, every **terminating decimal** is of the form

$$a_n10^n + \ldots + a_1 \cdot 10 + a_0 + a_{-1}10^{-1} + a_{-2}10^{-2} + \ldots + a_{-m}10^{-m},$$

where all the a_i, from a_n to a_{-m}, are digits from 0 to 9. Multiplying and dividing this number by 10^m rewrites it as a ratio of integers.

Activity

What is this ratio? See margin on page 320.

Consider the *infinite repeating decimal* $4.6\overline{901} = 4.6901901901\ldots$. This decimal, too, can be written as a quotient of integers. You have likely seen this before.

Let	$x = 4.6\overline{901}$.	
Then	$10^3x = 4690.1\overline{901}$.	Can you see why 10^3 was chosen?
So	$10^3x - x = 4685.5$	A_{-x}
	$(10^3 - 1)x = 4685.5$	Distributive Property
	$x = \frac{4685.5}{10^3 - 1} = \frac{4685.5}{999}$	$M_{\frac{1}{10^3-1}}$
	$= \frac{46855}{9990}$	$M_{\frac{10}{10}}$

By a similar method, any infinite repeating decimal can be shown to represent a rational number. Consequently:

Theorem

If a real number x can be written as a terminating or infinite repeating decimal, then x is a rational number.

Decimals for Irrational Numbers

Because $\sqrt{2}$ is irrational, it follows from the above theorem (by *modus tollens*, the Law of Indirect Reasoning) that its decimal expansion is neither terminating nor repeating. The value 1.4142136 that you might see when you use a calculator is simply an approximation.

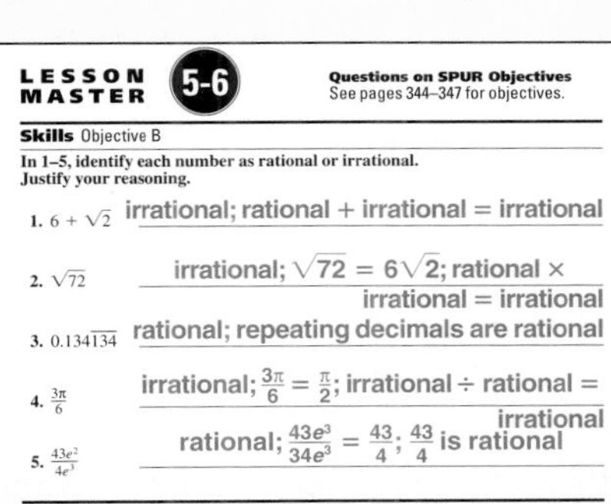
LESSON MASTER 5-6

Questions on SPUR Objectives
See pages 344–347 for objectives.

Skills Objective B

In 1–5, identify each number as rational or irrational. Justify your reasoning.

1. $6 + \sqrt{2}$ irrational; rational + irrational = irrational
2. $\sqrt{72}$ irrational; $\sqrt{72} = 6\sqrt{2}$; rational × irrational = irrational
3. $0.134\overline{134}$ rational; repeating decimals are rational
4. $\frac{3\pi}{6}$ irrational; $\frac{3\pi}{6} = \frac{\pi}{2}$; irrational ÷ rational = irrational
5. $\frac{43e^2}{4e^3}$ rational; $\frac{43e^3}{34e^3} = \frac{43}{4}$; $\frac{43}{4}$ is rational

Skills Objective C

In 6–9, rationalize the denominator.

6. $\frac{7}{3 - \sqrt{2}}$ $\sqrt{2} + 3$
7. $\frac{\sqrt{5}}{7 - \sqrt{10}}$ $\frac{7\sqrt{5} + 5\sqrt{2}}{39}$
8. $\frac{\sqrt{3} + 2}{\sqrt{5} - 1}$ $\frac{\sqrt{15} + 2\sqrt{5} + \sqrt{3} + 2}{4}$
9. $\frac{13}{1 - \sqrt{3}}$ $\frac{-13 - 13\sqrt{3}}{2}$

Properties Objective F

10. Prove or find a counterexample: The square root of any irrational number is irrational.
Sample: Assume the square root is rational. Then $\sqrt{x} = \frac{a}{b}$, where a and b are integers, then $x = \frac{a^2}{b^2}$. Since the square of an integer is an integer, a^2 and b^2 are both integers. Thus x is rational, which is a contradiction. So, the square root of any irrational number is irrational.

Optional Activities

As an extension of **Question 20,** ask students how they can determine whether a simple fraction will be a repeating or terminating decimal. [If the denominator is any multiple or product of 1, 2, 4, 5, 8, the decimal will terminate. If the denominator is any multiple or product of 3, 6, 7, 9, *or a product of these numbers with 1, 2, 4, 5, 8,* then the decimal will repeat. You may want to start this activity by asking which single digit integer denominators produce terminating decimals and which produce repeating decimals.]

Notes on Reading

❶ This discussion mentions the most accurate approximation of π to date. Approximations like these are made using formulas that themselves are not easy to derive. You may be able to find recent results on the Internet.

❷ The creation of an irrational number $x = 0.1010010001\ldots$ that is not a square root illustrates a method of creating an infinite number of decimal representations of irrational numbers. Some students, however, confuse a pattern with a repeating cycle. They are not necessarily the same. The building of an irrational number as a decimal expansion relies on creating a pattern that lacks repetition. For variety, consider $x = 0.1234567891011121314\ldots$, which is irrational, but with a different pattern than $0.1010010001\ldots$.

In **Example 2,** to convince students that multiplying a number of the form $c + \sqrt{d}$ by its conjugate will always eliminate the square root, show the multiplication:
$(c + \sqrt{d})(c - \sqrt{d}) =$
$c^2 + c\sqrt{d} - c\sqrt{d} + \sqrt{d^2} = c^2 - d)$

In rationalizing denominators, a common error is to use the denominator as its own conjugate, thinking that, if a and b are rational, then just as the square of $\sqrt{a}$ is rational, so the square of $\sqrt{a} + b$ will be rational.

In 1761, Johann Heinrich Lambert proved that if x is a nonzero rational number, then e^x and $\tan x$ are irrational. Thus $e^1 = e$ is irrational. Also, using *modus tollens*, since $\tan \frac{\pi}{4} = 1$, a rational number, then $\frac{\pi}{4}$ is irrational. So π is irrational. The values of $\frac{22}{7}$ and 3.14 that you may have used for π are just approximations. Even your calculator only gives an approximation.

❶ In 1997, 51 billion decimal places of π were calculated by Yasumasa Kanada of the University of Tokyo.

Recall from Lesson 3-10 that Cantor proved that the set of rational numbers is countable and the set of real numbers is uncountable. Thus there are more irrational numbers than rational numbers. You can generate irrational numbers quite easily by recalling that the converse of the above theorem is also true. If x is rational, then its decimal expansion is either terminating or repeating. It follows that irrational numbers are exactly those numbers whose decimal expansions neither terminate nor repeat.

❷ For instance, let $x = 0.1010010001\ldots$

The number of 0s between successive 1s keeps increasing by 1.

The decimal expansion of x neither terminates nor repeats; hence x must be an irrational number.

Properties Involving Irrational Numbers

Proof by contradiction is often used to prove properties involving irrational numbers. Example 1 illustrates such a proof.

Example 1

Prove by contradiction: The sum of a rational number and an irrational number is an irrational number.

Solution

Let p be the statement to be proved. Write p formally as follows.

p: $\forall$ real numbers r and q, if r is rational and q is irrational, then r + q is irrational.

Start the proof by assuming $\sim p$. In other words, assume

$\sim$p: $\exists$ real numbers r and q such that r is rational and q is irrational and r + q is rational.

Then reason to a contradiction. Here is what you could write.

Proof

Assume the negation of the statement to be proved. That is, assume there is a rational number r and an irrational number q whose sum is a rational number, call it s. Then

$$r + q = s$$
$$q = s - r.$$

Adapting to Individual Needs

Extra Help

Some students may need a review of the strategy shown on page 317 for writing an infinite repeating decimal as a quotient of integers. The key to the process is in the second line of the work. Be sure students understand that both sides are multiplied by 10^n, where n is the number of digits in the repetend.

As was shown in Lesson 5-1, Question 4, the difference of two rational numbers is also rational. Since s and r are rational, q is rational. This contradicts the part of the assumption that states q is irrational. Hence, the assumption as a whole is false; this means the original statement is true. That is, the sum of any rational number and any irrational number is an irrational number.

Notice, however, that the sum of two irrational numbers can be a rational number. For instance, $11 + \sqrt{3}$ and $11 - \sqrt{3}$ are irrational (by Example 1), yet their sum is 22. These two irrationals also have the property that their product is rational. As you know, $\forall$ real numbers x and y,

$$(x + y)(x - y) = x^2 - y^2.$$

Here $$(11 + \sqrt{3})(11 - \sqrt{3}) = 121 - 3 = 118.$$

In general, if c is an integer or the square root of an integer and d is an integer, then $c + \sqrt{d}$ and $c - \sqrt{d}$ are called **conjugates**, and their product is the integer $c^2 - d$.

In the Questions, you are asked to prove that when a nonzero rational number is divided by an irrational number, the quotient is irrational. If the divisor is of the form $a + \sqrt{b}$, then multiplying the numerator and denominator of the fraction by the conjugate of the denominator removes the square root from the denominator. This process is called **rationalizing the denominator**.

Example 2

Rationalize the denominator of $\frac{4}{5 - \sqrt{7}}$.

Solution

Multiply both numerator and denominator by $5 + \sqrt{7}$, the conjugate of $5 - \sqrt{7}$.

$$\begin{aligned}\frac{4}{5-\sqrt{7}} &= \frac{4}{5-\sqrt{7}} \cdot \frac{5+\sqrt{7}}{5+\sqrt{7}}\\ &= \frac{20+4\sqrt{7}}{25-7}\\ &= \frac{20+4\sqrt{7}}{18}\\ &= \frac{2(10+2\sqrt{7})}{2\cdot 9}\\ &= \frac{10+2\sqrt{7}}{9}\end{aligned}$$

Before the days of calculators and computers, rationalizing the denominator helped in evaluating expressions involving square roots. It was much easier to approximate $\frac{10 + 2\sqrt{7}}{9}$ (requiring division by 9) than to approximate $\frac{4}{5 - \sqrt{7}}$ (requiring division by an infinite decimal). Today, calculators and computers do the arithmetic, and rationalizing the denominator is ordinarily done to prepare the way for further computations.

Additional Examples

1. Prove by contradiction: The product of a nonzero rational number and an irrational number is irrational. **Assume there is a nonzero rational number r and an irrational number t such that $rt = s$ is rational. Then $t = \frac{r}{s}$. But the quotient of two nonzero rational numbers is a rational number. This contradicts the assumption that t is irrational. So the assumption is false. Thus the product of a nonzero rational number and an irrational number is irrational.**
2. Rationalize the denominator of $\frac{2 + \sqrt{3}}{7 + \sqrt{5}}$. $\frac{14 - 2\sqrt{5} + 7\sqrt{3} - \sqrt{15}}{44}$

Adapting to Individual Needs

Challenge

Have students answer the following.

1. Show that the set of irrational numbers is uncountable. [Assuming it is countable implies that the set of real numbers is countable because it is the union of two countable sets.]
2. Explain why the converse of the second theorem in this lesson is also true. [When a is divided by b to get a decimal, there are only b possible remainders. If the remainder is 0, the decimal terminates. If it is never 0, the remainders will eventually repeat thus causing a repeating quotient.]

Notes on Questions

Questions 1–3 A Venn diagram can be used to picture the relations among the sets.

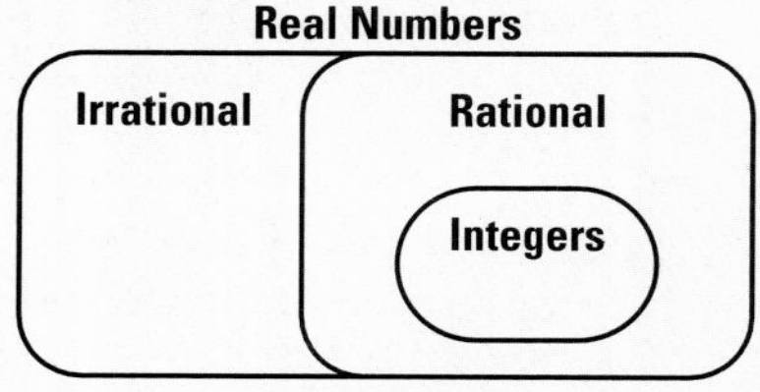

Question 5 Students should be able to generalize the proof to prove that for any prime number p, $\sqrt{p}$ is irrational.

Question 14 The rewriting can be checked with a calculator. The expression has the approximate value 3.174092.

Questions 15–16: Clarify that "any two" could refer to the same number used twice.

Question 17 Some students may have seen this result before. It is important and should be discussed.

Question 18 There are two obvious generalizations, one true and one not true. In general, $\sqrt{n} - \sqrt{n-1}$ and $\sqrt{n} + \sqrt{n-1}$ are reciprocals. This is easy to prove; just multiply the two expressions. However, in general, $\sqrt{a} - \sqrt{b}$ and $\sqrt{a} + \sqrt{b}$ are not reciprocals.

Question 20 Although this question is a review, it is directly related to the content of this lesson.

5b) a^2 and a have a factor of 3.

d) b^2 and b have a factor of 3.

7a) irrational; The decimal expansion neither terminates nor repeats.

b) rational; The decimal expansion repeats.

c) rational; The decimal expansion terminates.

13c) $\frac{10}{5+\sqrt{3}} \approx 1.4854315$ and $\frac{25-5\sqrt{3}}{11} \approx 1.4854315$

QUESTIONS

Covering the Reading

In 1–3, *true or false*.

1. $\exists$ a real number which is irrational. True
2. Some irrational numbers can be expressed as a ratio of integers. False
3. If a number is a real number, then it is either rational or irrational. True
4. In doing a proof by contradiction, what is the first assumption you make? Assume the negation of the original statement.
5. Use the proof of the irrationality of $\sqrt{2}$ as a model to complete the steps below in the proof that $\sqrt{3}$ is irrational.
   a. Let $\sqrt{3} = \frac{a}{b}$, where a and b are integers with $b \neq 0$ and $\frac{a}{b}$ is in lowest terms. Square both sides and solve for a^2. $a^2 = 3b^2$
   b. What does your result in part **a** imply about a^2? about a? See left.
   c. Let $a = 3k$ for some integer k. Substitute $3k$ for a in part **a** and solve the result for b^2. $b^2 = 3k^2$
   d. What does your result in part **c** imply about b^2? about b? See left.
   e. Show that the results from parts **b** and **d** lead to a contradiction. Use this contradiction to finish the proof. See margin.
6. **a.** Is $\sqrt{4}$ a rational number? Why or why not? Yes, $\sqrt{4} = \frac{2}{1}$.
   b. Is $\sqrt{4}$ an irrational number? Why or why not? No, 2 is a rational number.
7. Determine whether each decimal expansion represents a rational or an irrational number. Explain. See left.
   a. .313113111311113 . . . **b.** $.\overline{31}$ **c.** .31

   The number of 1s between successive 3s keeps increasing by 1.
8. What result did you obtain for the Activity on page 317? See margin.
9. Write 730.4810 as a ratio of integers. $\frac{7{,}304{,}810}{10{,}000}$
10. Write $730.48\overline{10}$ as a ratio of integers. $\frac{3{,}651{,}881}{4950}$
11. *True or false.* e^2 is irrational. True
12. Use Example 1 as a model to prove the following statement: See margin.

    $\forall$ *real numbers x and y, if x is rational and y is irrational, then $\frac{x}{y}$ is irrational.*
13. **a.** Give the conjugate of $5 + \sqrt{3}$. $5 - \sqrt{3}$
    b. Rationalize the denominator of $\frac{10}{5+\sqrt{3}}$. $\frac{25-5\sqrt{3}}{11}$
    c. Check your answer to part **b** by finding decimal approximations to each fraction. See left.
14. Rationalize the denominator of $\frac{4\sqrt{5}+6}{3\sqrt{5}-2}$. $\frac{72+26\sqrt{5}}{41}$

Additional Answers

5. e. Both a and b have a common factor of 3. However, at the beginning of the proof, $\frac{a}{b}$ is assumed in lowest terms, thus having no common factors. There is an inherent contradiction, so the negated statement is false, and the original statement ($\sqrt{3}$ is irrational) must be true.

8. $\frac{a_n 10^{m+n} + \ldots + a_1 10^{m+1} + a_0 10^m + a_{-1} 10^{m-1} + a_{-2} 10^{m-2} + \ldots + a_{-m} 10^0}{10^m}$

12. Assume the negation of the original statement is true. Thus, there is a rational number x and an irrational number y whose quotient $\frac{x}{y}$ is rational. Then since the quotient of x and y is rational, both x and y must be rational, but this contradicts the assumption that y is irrational.

Applying the Mathematics

15) False; counterexample: π and $3 - \pi$ sum to 3, which is rational.

16) False; counterexample: Let $a = \sqrt{2}$ and $b = \sqrt{8}$. Then, $a \cdot b = \sqrt{2} \cdot \sqrt{8} = \sqrt{16} = 4$, but 4 is a rational number.

17a) when $b^2 - 4ac$ is zero or a perfect square

b) when $b^2 - 4ac > 0$ and not a perfect square

In 15 and 16, *true or false*. If false, give a counterexample. See left.

15. *The sum of any two irrational numbers is an irrational number.*

16. *The product of any two irrational numbers is an irrational number.*

17. Recall the Quadratic Formula $x = \frac{-b \pm \sqrt{b^2 - 4ac}}{2a} \Leftrightarrow ax^2 + bx + c = 0$ and $a \neq 0$. Suppose a, b, and c are all rational numbers. See left.

a. When will x be rational? **b.** When will x be irrational?

18. Prove that the reciprocal of $\sqrt{7} + \sqrt{6}$ is $\sqrt{7} - \sqrt{6}$. See margin.

Review

19. The end behavior of $w: z \rightarrow \frac{6z^4 - 4z^3 + 2z + 1}{11z^5 + 2}$ is the same as the end behavior of what simpler function? *(Lesson 5-5)* $\frac{6}{11z}$

$$\begin{array}{r} .53703 \\ 54\overline{)29.00000} \\ 27\,0 \\ \hline 2\,00 \\ 1\,62 \\ \hline 380 \\ 378 \\ \hline 20 \\ 0 \\ \hline 200 \end{array}$$

20. The long division at the left converts the rational number $\frac{29}{54}$ to a decimal. The remainder at each step of the division is in blue.

a. Use the Quotient-Remainder Theorem to explain why, after 54 steps or less, some integer (here, 20) must repeat as the remainder.

b. What effect does the repetition of a remainder have on the decimal expansion of $\frac{29}{54}$?

c. How do parts **a** and **b** serve to explain why the decimal expansion of every rational number is terminating or repeating?

d. What is the decimal equal to $\frac{29}{54}$? *(Lessons 4-2, 5-1)*

See margin.

In 21 and 22, rewrite the expression as a single rational expression. *(Lesson 5-2)*

21. $\frac{3}{x} + \frac{3x}{x - 4}$ See left. **22.** $\frac{t + 1}{t - 1} - \frac{t - 1}{t + 1}$ See left.

21) $\frac{3(x^2 + x - 4)}{x(x - 4)}$; $x \neq 0$, $x \neq 4$

22) $\frac{4t}{t^2 - 1}$; where $t \neq \pm 1$

23. For what values is $\cos x = 0$? *(Lesson 2-6)* $\frac{n\pi}{2}$; where n is an odd integer

24. The electrical circuit at the right is a parallel circuit with resistances R_1 and R_2. The total resistance, R, is given by the formula

$$R = \frac{1}{\frac{1}{R_1} + \frac{1}{R_2}}.$$

[Circuit diagram: resistors R_1 and R_2 in parallel]

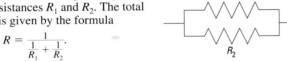

Find a single fraction that expresses the value of R. *(Lesson 5-2)*

$R = \frac{R_1 R_2}{R_1 + R_2}$

Exploration

25. Investigate the terms *algebraic number* and *transcendental number*. How do these relate to rational and irrational numbers? A number is said to be algebraic if it is a root of some polynomial having rational coefficients; otherwise it is said to be transcendental.

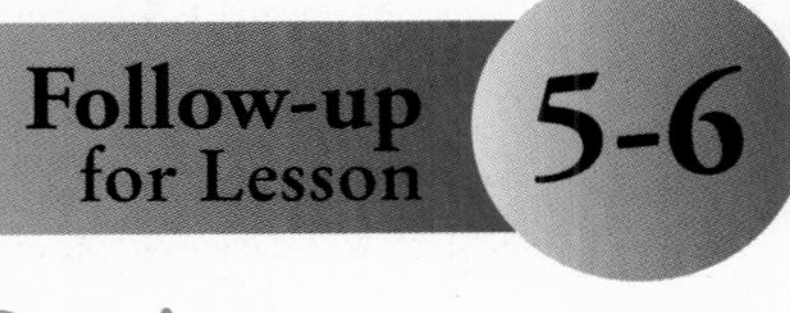

Follow-up for Lesson 5-6

Practice

For more questions on SPUR Objectives, use **Lesson Master 5-6** (shown on page 317).

Assessment

Written Communication Have students **work in pairs.** Ask each to write a problem like **Question 13b** or **14.** Then have students complete their partner's problem and check their answers as instructed in **Question 13c**. [Students use conjugates to rationalize denominators.]

Extension

In some situations, rationalizing the numerator is appropriate. Define a function f by the rule $f(x) = \sqrt{x}$ for all $x > 0$. In calculus, limits such as the following must be computed: $\lim_{h \to 0} \frac{f(2 + h) - f(2)}{h}$. What is this limit?

$[\frac{f(2 + h) - f(2)}{h} = \frac{\sqrt{2 + h} - \sqrt{2}}{h}$

$= \frac{\sqrt{2 + h} - \sqrt{2}}{h} \cdot \frac{(\sqrt{2 + h} + \sqrt{2})}{(\sqrt{2 + h} + \sqrt{2})}$

$= \frac{1}{(\sqrt{2 + h} + \sqrt{2})}$

Therefore,

$\lim_{h \to 0} \frac{f(2 + h) - f(2)}{h} = \lim_{h \to 0} \frac{1}{(\sqrt{2 + h} + \sqrt{2})}$

$= \frac{1}{2\sqrt{2}}$.]

Project Update Project 1, *Irrationality of π,* and Project 2, *An Unusual Sequence,* on page 340, relate to the content of this lesson.

18. reciprocal of $\sqrt{7} + \sqrt{6} = \frac{1}{\sqrt{7} + \sqrt{6}} = \frac{1}{\sqrt{7} + \sqrt{6}} \cdot \frac{\sqrt{7} - \sqrt{6}}{\sqrt{7} - \sqrt{6}} = \frac{\sqrt{7} - \sqrt{6}}{7 - 6} = \frac{\sqrt{7} - \sqrt{6}}{1} = \sqrt{7} - \sqrt{6}$

20. a. The Quotient-Remainder Theorem states that the remainder r for this division is an integer in the range $0 \leq r < 54$. Therefore, after 54 steps at least one remainder must repeat since there are only 54 unique remainders.

b. The number of steps taken before repeat of the remainder is equal to the number of digits in the repeating number sequence in the decimal expansion. Each time the remainder repeats, the repeating digit sequence is begun again.

c. The Quotient-Remainder Theorem requires the remainder to be an integer r in the range $0 \leq r < d$ for any long division. Hence, after d steps there must be a zero or a repeated remainder. If there is a zero remainder, then the decimal expansion terminates. If there is a repeated remainder, then the decimal expansion is repeating.

d. $\frac{29}{54} = 0.5\overline{370}$

Lesson 5-7

Objectives

D Identify rational functions and their domains.

H Classify discontinuities as essential or removable.

K Relate the limit of a function to its graph, and find equations for its asymptotes.

L Use right triangles or graphs to find values of the tangent, cotangent, secant, and cosecant functions.

Resources

From the ***Teacher's Resource File***

- Lesson Master 5-7
- Answer Master 5-7
- Assessment Sourcebook: Quiz for Lesson 5-5 through 5-7
- Teaching Aids
  45 Warm-up
  50 Graphs of Sine, Cosine, and Tangent Functions, and Tangent and Cotangent Functions
  51 Graphs of Sine and Cosecant Functions and Cosine and Secant Functions

Additional Resources

- Visuals for Teaching Aids 45, 50, 51
- Exploration 5-7

Teaching Lesson 5-7

Warm-up

In right triangle *ABC*, there are six possible ratios of sides.

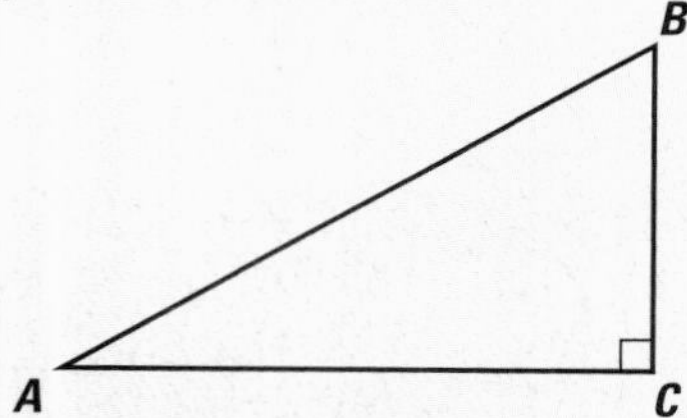

1. Write these six ratios. See below.
2. Match these ratios with the following six numbers: sin *A*, cos *A*, tan *A*, cot *A*, sec *A*, and csc *A*. $\sin A = \frac{BC}{AB}$, $\cos A = \frac{AC}{BC}$, $\tan A = \frac{BC}{AC}$, $\cot A = \frac{AC}{BC}$, $\sec A = \frac{BC}{AC}$, $\csc A = \frac{AB}{BC}$

LESSON

5-7 The Tangent, Cotangent, Secant, and Cosecant Functions

Quotients and Reciprocals of the Sine and Cosine Functions

You can create a rational function by using the reciprocal of a polynomial function or by dividing one polynomial function by another. Similarly, new trigonometric functions can be obtained by using the reciprocal of the sine function or cosine function or by dividing one of these functions by the other. These four functions are not rational functions but they can be analyzed by using many of the techniques you have seen in the previous lessons. Their names should be familiar to you from previous courses.

Definitions

For any real number *x*:

the **tangent** of $x = \textbf{tan}\ x = \frac{\sin x}{\cos x}$ provided $\cos x \neq 0$.

the **cotangent** of $x = \textbf{cot}\ x = \frac{\cos x}{\sin x}$ provided $\sin x \neq 0$.

the **secant** of $x = \textbf{sec}\ x = \frac{1}{\cos x}$ provided $\cos x \neq 0$.

the **cosecant** of $x = \textbf{csc}\ x = \frac{1}{\sin x}$ provided $\sin x \neq 0$.

Each of these definitions defines a trigonometric function whose domain is the set of all real numbers except those for which the denominator is 0. For instance, the **tangent function** is the function tan: $x \rightarrow \tan x$, $x \neq (2n + 1)\frac{\pi}{2}$ for any integer *n*.

Calculating Values of These Functions

From the definitions, values of each function can be calculated. For instance,

$$\cot\frac{\pi}{6} = \frac{\cos\frac{\pi}{6}}{\sin\frac{\pi}{6}} = \frac{\frac{\sqrt{3}}{2}}{\frac{1}{2}} = \sqrt{3} \approx 1.732 \text{ and } \sec 68° = \frac{1}{\cos 68°} \approx 2.67.$$

Also, from the definitions, some values of the functions can be obtained by using right triangles. For instance, in the triangle below,

$$\tan\theta = \frac{\sin\theta}{\cos\theta} = \frac{\frac{\text{side opposite }\theta}{\text{hypotenuse}}}{\frac{\text{side adjacent to }\theta}{\text{hypotenuse}}} = \frac{\text{side opposite }\theta}{\text{side adjacent to }\theta} = \frac{4}{5}.$$

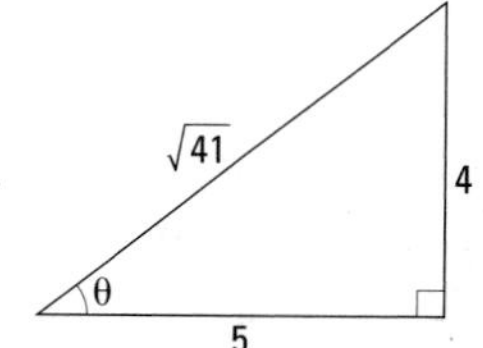

Lesson 5-7 Overview

Broad Goals The properties of the sine and cosine functions are put together with those of the rational functions to review the basic properties of the tangent, cotangent, secant, and cosecant functions.

Perspective Although trigonometric functions are not rational functions, they share some properties with the functions studied in Lessons 5-4 and 5-5. The secant and cosecant functions are reciprocal functions of the sine and cosine, and the tangent and cotangent functions are quotients of the sine and cosine. All of these functions have essential discontinuities at the zeros of either the sine or the cosine functions.

The Graphs of the Secant and Cosecant Functions

With rational functions, when a value of x causes the denominator to be 0, there is a discontinuity. The same is true for these trigonometric functions. Consider the cosecant function. Because $\sin x = 0$ when x is a multiple of π, the cosecant function is not defined when x is a multiple of π.

At each value of x where $\sin x = 0$ there is a vertical asymptote to the cosecant function. Notice also that the two functions have the same values when $\sin x = 1$ or when $\sin x = -1$. This is because the numbers 1 and -1 equal their reciprocals. This information that we have determined so far is shown below.

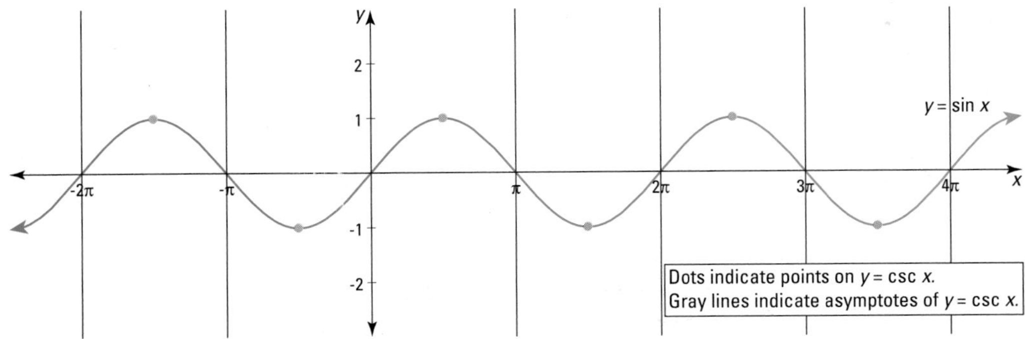

When a number is positive, its reciprocal is positive, and when a number is negative so is its reciprocal. Thus the sine and cosecant are positive at the same time and negative at the same time. As the sine gets closer to zero, the cosecant gets farther away from zero. And since the sine is periodic with period 2π, the cosecant is periodic also. This information allows the
❶ rest of a sketch of the graph to be made.

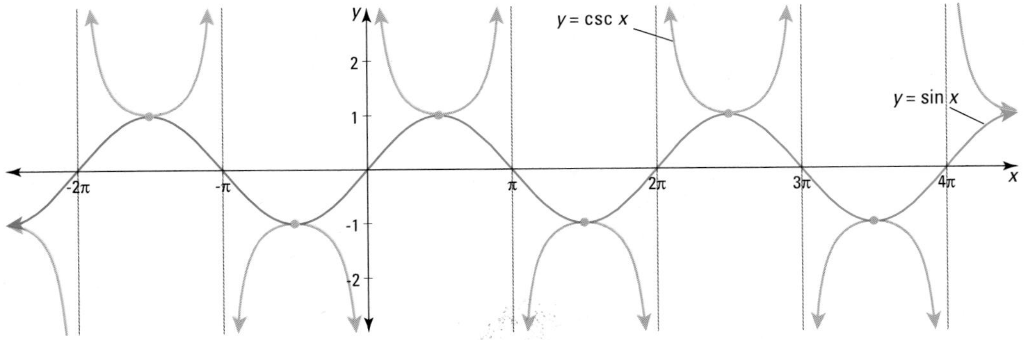

The graph of the secant function is related in a similar way to the graph of the cosine.

Notes on Reading

❶ To assist students in understanding the graph of $y = \csc x$, you might begin with a discussion of the trend in values of $\frac{1}{x}$ as x itself increases and as x decreases. Then use a calculator or computer to prepare a table as below (x in radians, not degrees).

x	$\sin x$	$\csc x$
0	0	not defined
.1	.09983	10.01669
.2	.19867	5.03349
.	.	.
.	.	.
.	.	.
1.5	.99749	1.00251
$\frac{\pi}{2}$	1	1
1.6	.99957	1.00043
1.7	.99166	1.00841
.	.	.
.	.	.
.	.	.
3.1	.04158	24.04964
π	0	not defined

Graph both $y = \sin x$ and $y = \csc x$ simultaneously. **Teaching Aid 51** contains these graphs. This can also be done quite effectively on some calculators by setting the graphing mode to "Simul" (simultaneous).

Optional Activities

Technology Connection
Materials: Explorations software

You may use *Exploration 5-7, Reciprocals of Trigonometric Functions,* to introduce the reciprocal trigonometric functions. Choosing a trigonometric function and its reciprocal shows both functions on the same graph. You can choose an x-coordinate for a point in the domain of the function and demonstrate the corresponding points on both functions.

Adapting to Individual Needs

Extra Help
You may want to emphasize that there are a few names and abbreviations that can be troublesome when discussing reciprocals of trigonometric functions. Have students note that the abbreviation for *cosecant* is *csc,* not the first three letters, as this would be the same as the abbreviation *cos* for *cosine.* Also, warn students not to mismatch *sine* with *secant* and *cosine* with *cosecant.*

Challenge
Have students answer the following: If θ is the measure of the angle between two lines of slopes m_1 and m_2, show that $\tan\theta = \frac{m_2 - m_1}{1 + m_1 m_2}$. [If θ_1 and θ_2 are the angles of elevation of each line, then $\theta = \theta_1 - \theta_2$. So $\tan\theta = \tan(\theta_1 - \theta_2) = \frac{\tan\theta_1 - \tan\theta_2}{1 + \tan\theta_1 \tan\theta_2} = \frac{m_2 - m_1}{1 + m_1 m_2}$.]

❷ To help students understand the behavior of the graph of $y = \tan x$, you might begin with a brief analysis of signs and values of sine and cosine.

$y = \sin x$

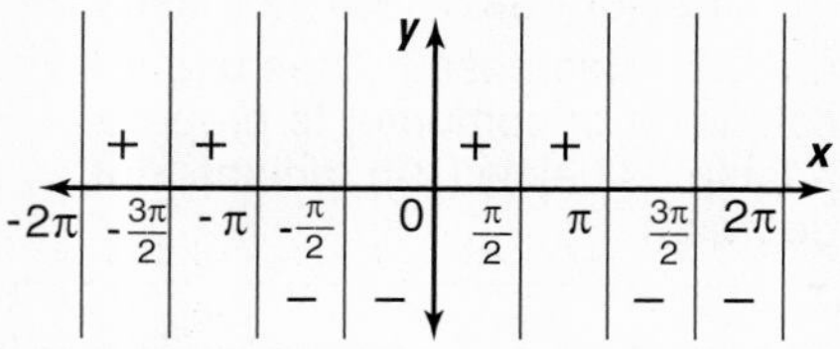

$y = \cos x$

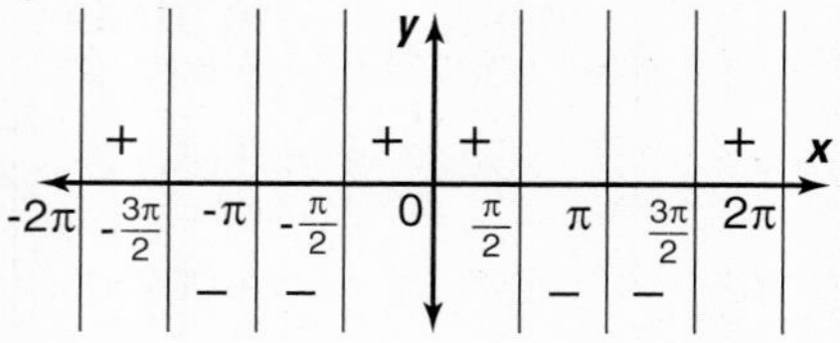

Now, think of the quotient of numbers in these intervals. The signs of the quotients are ruled by whether the numbers divided have the same sign or different signs.

$y = \frac{\sin x}{\cos x} = \tan x$

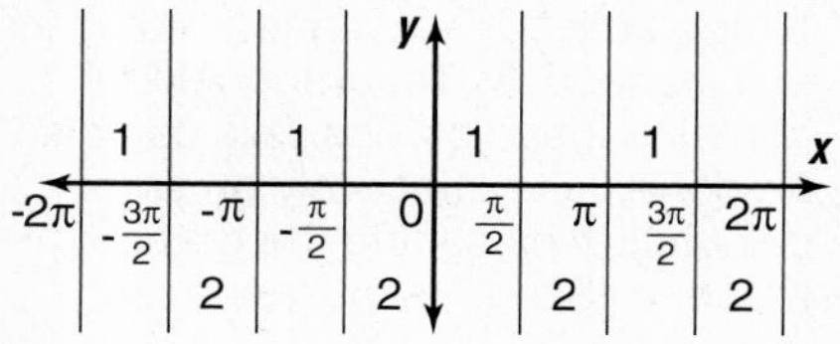

Then discuss values of $\frac{\sin x}{\cos x}$ as $\sin x$ and $\cos x$ increase and/or decrease. The graphs of all three functions are shown on **Teaching Aid 50.**

Error Alert Because $x^{-1} = \frac{1}{x}$, some students may assume that the $\sin^{-1}$, $\cos^{-1}$, and $\tan^{-1}$ keys on a calculator are for reciprocals of these functions. Warn them that this is definitely not the case. Inverse trigonometric functions are discussed in Lesson 6-7.

The Graph of the Tangent Function

The graphs of the tangent and cotangent functions have quite a different shape than any graphs you have yet seen in this book. First, since $\tan x = \frac{\sin x}{\cos x}$, $\tan x$ is not defined when $\cos x = 0$, that is, when x is an odd multiple of $\frac{\pi}{2}$. Second, by the definition, $\tan x = 0$ if and only if $\sin x = 0$. So the x-intercepts are the multiples of π. Third, the tangent is positive when the sine and cosine have the same sign and it is negative when the sine and cosine have opposite signs. A graph of the ❷ tangent function, in green below, exhibits all of these properties.

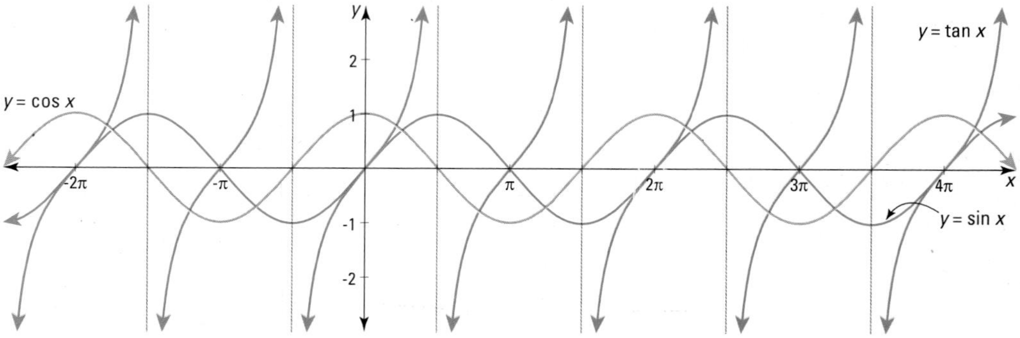

A surprise is that the graph has period π. This is proved in the next chapter.

Activity

a. For what values of x is $\cot x$ not defined?
b. Graph the cotangent function $y = \cot x$. See Question 6, page 325.

QUESTIONS

Covering the Reading

1. If $\sin x = .8$ and $\cos x = .6$, give the values of $\tan x$, $\cot x$, $\sec x$, and $\csc x$. $\tan x = \frac{4}{3}$; $\cot x = \frac{3}{4}$; $\sec x = \frac{5}{3}$; $\csc x = \frac{5}{4}$

2. Describe the function value in terms of the sides of the right triangle as named in the drawing. See margin.

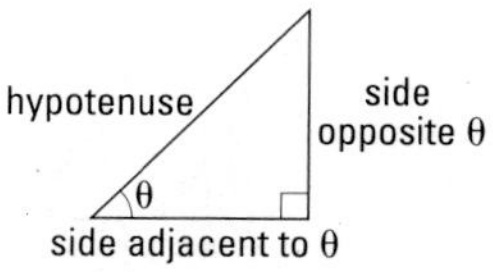

a. $\tan\theta$ **b.** $\cot\theta$
c. $\sec\theta$ **d.** $\csc\theta$

3. Use the triangle at the right. Find each value.

a. $\tan\theta$ $\frac{1}{2}$ **b.** $\cot\theta$ 2
c. $\sec\theta$ $\frac{\sqrt{5}}{2}$ **d.** $\csc\theta$ $\sqrt{5}$

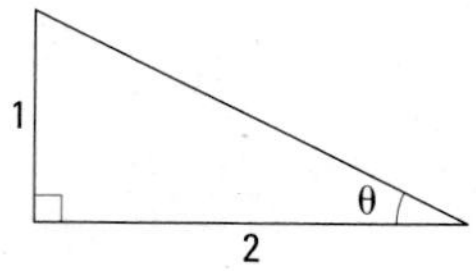

Additional Answers

2. a. $\tan\theta = \frac{\text{side opposite } \theta}{\text{side adjacent to } \theta}$

b. $\cot\theta = \frac{\text{side adjacent to } \theta}{\text{side opposite } \theta}$

c. $\sec\theta = \frac{\text{hypotenuse}}{\text{side adjacent to } \theta}$

d. $\csc\theta = \frac{\text{hypotenuse}}{\text{side opposite } \theta}$

8. d.

	$\frac{\pi}{6}$	$\frac{\pi}{4}$	$\frac{\pi}{3}$
sin	$\frac{1}{2}$	$\frac{\sqrt{2}}{2}$	$\frac{\sqrt{3}}{2}$
cos	$\frac{\sqrt{3}}{2}$	$\frac{\sqrt{2}}{2}$	$\frac{1}{2}$
tan	$\frac{\sqrt{3}}{3}$	1	$\sqrt{3}$
cot	$\sqrt{3}$	1	$\frac{\sqrt{3}}{3}$
sec	$\frac{2\sqrt{3}}{3}$	$\sqrt{2}$	2
csc	2	$\sqrt{2}$	$\frac{2\sqrt{3}}{3}$

11. a. The area of triangle ABO is $\frac{1}{2}(AB)h$. The area of the regular n-gon is the sum of the areas of n congruent triangles, $n \cdot \frac{1}{2}(AB)h$. $m\angle AOB = \frac{2\pi}{n}$. The altitude h splits $\angle AOB$ into two angles measuring $\frac{\pi}{n}$. $\tan\left(\frac{\pi}{n}\right) = \frac{\frac{1}{2}AB}{h}$. $AB = 2h\tan\frac{\pi}{n}$. The area of the n-gon is $n \cdot \frac{1}{2}(2h\tan\frac{\pi}{n})h = nh^2\tan\frac{\pi}{n}$.

5b)

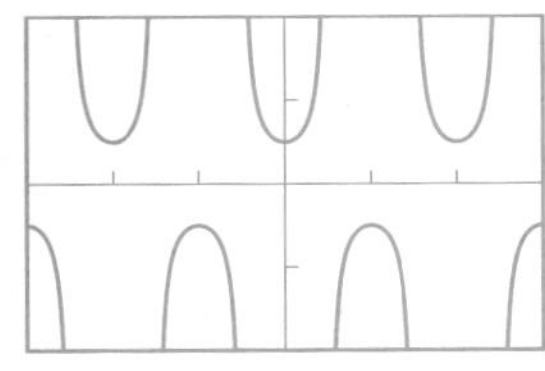

$-3\pi \le x \le 3\pi$, x-scale $= \pi$
$-4 \le y \le 4$, y-scale $= 2$

6a) $x \ne n\pi$, n is an integer

b)

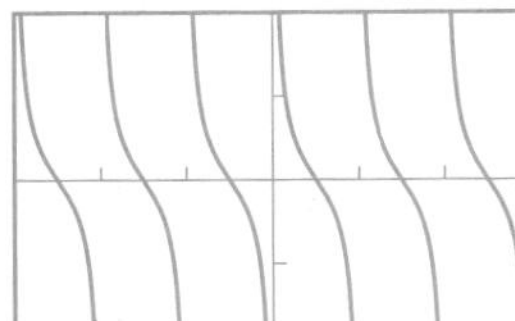

$-3\pi \le x \le 3\pi$, x-scale $= \pi$
$-4 \le y \le 4$, y-scale $= 2$

7) Sample: $(0,0)$, $\left(\frac{\pi}{6}, \frac{\sqrt{3}}{3}\right)$, $\left(\frac{\pi}{4}, 1\right)$, $\left(\frac{\pi}{3}, \sqrt{3}\right)$

10) $\tan\left(-\frac{\pi}{4}\right) = -1$; $\cot\left(-\frac{\pi}{4}\right) = -1$; $\sec\left(-\frac{\pi}{4}\right) = \sqrt{2}$; $\csc\left(-\frac{\pi}{4}\right) = -\sqrt{2}$

12b) Sine is an odd function and cosine is an even function.

4. A graph of the cosecant function is in this lesson. Identify four points on this graph with $0 \le x \le 2\pi$. Sample: $\left(\frac{\pi}{4}, \sqrt{2}\right)$, $\left(\frac{\pi}{2}, 1\right)$, $\left(\frac{3\pi}{4}, \sqrt{2}\right)$, $\left(\frac{3\pi}{2}, -1\right)$

5. **a.** For what values of x is sec x not defined? $x = \frac{\pi}{2} + n\pi$, n is an integer

b. Graph the secant function $y = \sec x$. See left.

6. Give your answers for the Activity in this lesson. See left.

7. Identify four points on the graph of $y = \tan x$ with $0 \le x \le \frac{\pi}{2}$. See left.

8. Consider the six trigonometric functions sine, cosine, tangent, cotangent, secant, and cosecant. c) sin and cos

a. Which are even functions, which are odd, which are neither?

b. Which are rational functions? none

c. Which are continuous functions over the set of all real numbers?

d. Make a table of values of these functions for the domain values $\frac{\pi}{6}$, $\frac{\pi}{4}$, and $\frac{\pi}{3}$. See margin.

a) sin, csc, tan, and cot are odd functions; cos and sec are even functions

Applying the Mathematics

9. *Multiple choice.* If p and q are real numbers and $p = \frac{q}{\sin x}$, then $p = \underline{\ ?\ }$.

(a) $q \tan x$ (b) $q \cot x$ (c) $q \sec x$ (d) $q \csc x$

d

10. Give the values of tan x, cot x, sec x, and csc x when $x = -\frac{\pi}{4}$. See left.

11. Suppose that $\overline{AB}$ is a side of a regular n-gon inscribed in circle O and suppose that h is the distance from O to $\overline{AB}$. See margin.

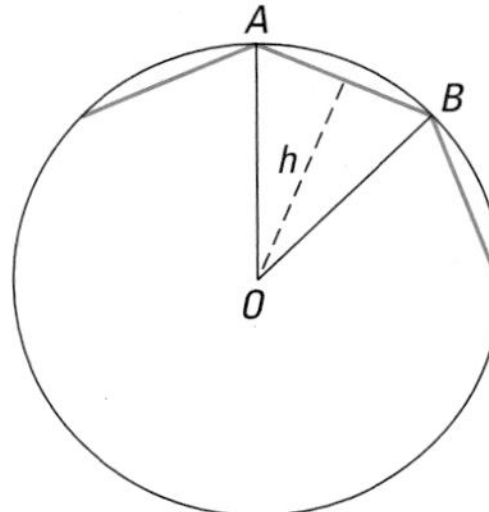

a. Prove that the area of the polygon is $nh^2 \tan \frac{\pi}{n}$.

b. Check the formula for the case where $\overline{AB}$ is a side of a square in a circle with radius 6.

12. Here is a proof that the tangent function is an odd function. Justify each conclusion.

a. For all real numbers x in the domain of the tangent function, $\tan(-x) = \frac{\sin(-x)}{\cos(-x)}$ definition of tangent

b. $= \frac{-\sin x}{\cos x}$ See left.

c. $= -\tan x$ definition of tangent

d. $\therefore$ The tangent function is an odd function. Transitive Property of Equality and definition of odd function

Additional Examples

Students are asked to graph $y = \sec x$ and $y = \cot x$ in **Questions 5–6** of this lesson. They are also appropriate additional examples.

Notes on Questions

Question 2 For students familiar with the SOHCAHTOA (SineOppositeHypotenuse, CosineAdjacentHypotenuse, TangentOppositeAdjacent) mnemonic for remembering the right triangle definitions of sin, cos, and tan, CHOSHACAO is the corresponding mnemonic for csc, sec, and cot relative to a right triangle.

Questions 5–6 It is particularly helpful for students to keep in mind that if a number is positive, so is its reciprocal. Thus the graphs of $y = \tan x$ and $y = \cot x$ are above the x-axis for the same values of x.

Question 9 A major historical reason for the use of the cotangent, secant, and cosecant functions was to avoid having to divide by decimals. This question shows how any division by sin x can be converted into a multiplication by another trigonometric function.

11. b. Let the radius, r, be 6 and $n = 4$. Then $AB = 6\sqrt{2}$, and $h = 3\sqrt{2}$ by the Pythagorean Theorem. Using the formula from part a, the area is $4(3\sqrt{2})^2 \tan \frac{\pi}{4} = 72$. The area of the square is $(AB)^2 = (6\sqrt{2})^2 = 72$ and so the formula checks.

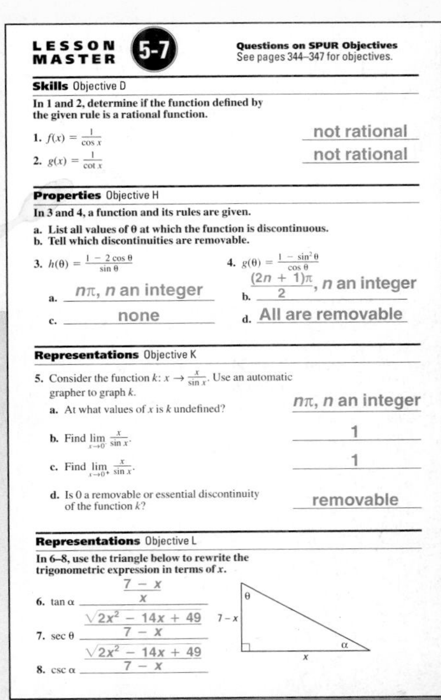

LESSON MASTER 5-7 — Questions on SPUR Objectives. See pages 344–347 for objectives.

Skills Objective D

In 1 and 2, determine if the function defined by the given rule is a rational function.

1. $f(x) = \frac{1}{\cos x}$ not rational
2. $g(x) = \frac{1}{\cot x}$ not rational

Properties Objective H

In 3 and 4, a function and its rules are given.
a. List all values of θ at which the function is discontinuous.
b. Tell which discontinuities are removable.

3. $h(\theta) = \frac{1 - 2\cos\theta}{\sin\theta}$ a. $n\pi$, n an integer c. none
4. $g(\theta) = \frac{1 - \sin^2\theta}{\cos\theta}$ b. $\frac{(2n+1)\pi}{2}$, n an integer d. All are removable

Representations Objective K

5. Consider the function $k: x \to \frac{x}{\sin x}$. Use an automatic grapher to graph k.
a. At what values of x is k undefined? $n\pi$, n an integer
b. Find $\lim_{x\to 0^-} \frac{x}{\sin x}$. 1
c. Find $\lim_{x\to 0^+} \frac{x}{\sin x}$. 1
d. Is 0 a removable or essential discontinuity of the function k? removable

Representations Objective L

In 6–8, use the triangle below to rewrite the trigonometric expression in terms of x.

6. $\tan\alpha$ $\frac{7-x}{x}$
7. $\sec\theta$ $\frac{\sqrt{2x^2 - 14x + 49}}{7-x}$
8. $\csc\alpha$ $\frac{\sqrt{2x^2 - 14x + 49}}{7-x}$

Follow-up for Lesson 5-7

Practice

For more questions on SPUR Objectives, use **Lesson Master 5-7** (shown on page 325).

Assessment

Quiz A quiz covering Lesson 5-5 through 5-7 is provided in the *Assessment Sourcebook.*

Extension

The cosine, cotangent, and cosecant are called *cofunctions,* that is, functions of the complement. They received their names because for all x, function (x) = cofunction $(\frac{\pi}{2} - x)$ for radians and function (x) = cofunction $(90 - x)$ for degrees. (**Question 20** shows this graphically.) Thus $\sin(x) = \cos(\frac{\pi}{2} - x)$, etc. For this reason, in any trigonometric identity involving only the single argument x, you can switch $\sin x$ with $\cos x$, $\tan x$ with $\cot x$, and $\sec x$ with $\csc x$ to obtain a (possibly different) identity. For instance, the cofunction counterpart to $\tan^2 x + 1 = \sec^2 x$ is $\cot^2 x + 1 = \csc^2 x$. Have students find other identities and their cofunction counterpart identities.

15a)

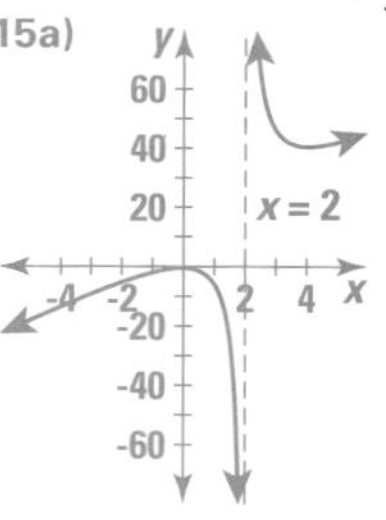

b) $\lim_{x \to 2^+} f(x) = \infty$

$\lim_{x \to 2^-} f(x) = -\infty$

c) $\lim_{x \to \infty} 5x + 10 = \infty$

$\lim_{x \to -\infty} 5x + 10 = -\infty$

Pilot Knob, CA

18b) All increasing functions are 1-1 functions, so the inverse of $\log_5 x$ could be used to simplify the equation without changing the solutions.

Review

13. Rationalize the denominator: $\frac{6}{\sqrt{10} + 5}$. *(Lesson 5-6)* $\frac{-2\sqrt{10} + 10}{5}$

14. Use limit notation to describe the end behavior of

$g: y \to \frac{7y^3 + 2y - 1}{8y^3 + 5y^2 + 11y}$. *(Lesson 5-5)* $\lim_{y \to \infty} g(y) = \frac{7}{8}$; $\lim_{y \to -\infty} g(y) = \frac{7}{8}$

15. a. Sketch a graph of $f(x) = \frac{5x^2 + 1}{x - 2}$. See left.

b. Use limit notation to describe the behavior of the function near $x = 2$.

c. Use limit notation to describe the end behavior. *(Lessons 5-4, 5-5)*

16. Find the smallest nonnegative integer that satisfies each congruence.

a. $y \equiv 17 \pmod{2}$ **b.** $t \equiv 1000 \pmod{11}$ *(Lesson 4-5)*

See margin.

17. Use chunking to solve $e^{2x} - 4e^x + 3 = 0$. *(Lesson 3-6)*

$x = \ln 3$ or $x = 0$

18. a. Solve over the set of real numbers: $-1 < x < 4$

$$\log_5 (x^2 + 2) < \log_5 (3x + 6).$$

b. The function $f: x \to \log_5 x$ is an increasing function. How was this fact used in answering part **a**? *(Lesson 3-5)* See below left.

19. One mountain peak is 10 miles due east of another. A hiker locates the first mountain peak at an angle of 65° W of N, and the second at an angle of 32°N of E. How far is the hiker from each mountain peak? *(Previous course)*
See margin.

Exploration

20. Use the diagram of a unit circle at the right. All six trigonometric values of θ can be represented by lengths of segments in this unit circle diagram. Match the values in the left column with the appropriate lengths in the right column.

a. cos θ iv (i) *AC*
b. sin θ i (ii) *BF*
c. tan θ ii (iii) *DE*
d. cot θ iii (iv) *OA*
e. sec θ vi (v) *OD*
f. csc θ v (vi) *OF*

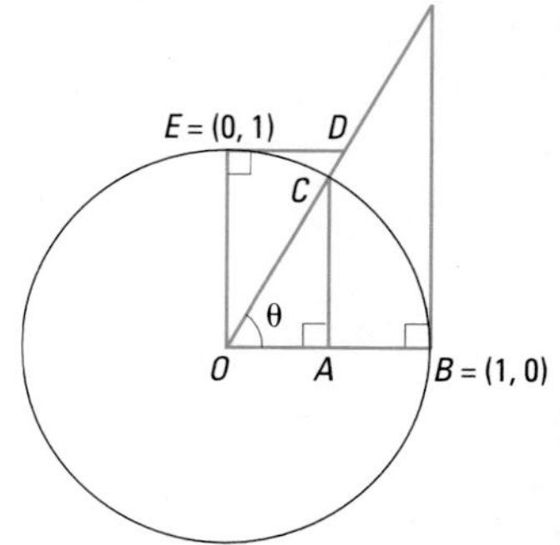

326

Additional Answers

16. a. $17 = 8 \cdot 2 + 1$. So $17 \equiv 1 \pmod{2}$; $y = 1$

b. $1000 = 90 \cdot 11 + 10$, so $1000 \equiv 10 \pmod{11}$; $t = 10$

19. [Diagram: triangle A, B, C with AB = 10; angles 25°, 32°, 65°, 58°, 25°, 32°; sides b, a]

$\frac{b}{\sin 32°} = \frac{10}{\sin 123°}$

$b = \frac{10 \sin 32°}{\sin 123°} \approx \frac{(10)(.5299)}{.8387} \approx 6.32$

$\frac{a}{\sin 25°} = \frac{10}{\sin 123°}$

$a = \frac{10 \sin 25°}{\sin 123°} \approx \frac{(10)(.4226)}{.8387} \approx 5.04$

The hiker is ≈ 6.32 miles from the first and ≈ 5.04 miles from the second.

Introducing Lesson 5-8

Average Rates

IN-CLASS ACTIVITY

Good activity

Suppose a plane has a speed of $450\frac{mi}{hr}$ in still air. When it flies with a $50\frac{mi}{hr}$ tailwind, then its speed over land is $(450 + 50)\frac{mi}{hr}$, or $500\frac{mi}{hr}$. When it flies against a $50\frac{mi}{hr}$ wind (called a headwind), its speed is $(450 - 50)\frac{mi}{hr}$.

1 Suppose cities A and B are 100 miles apart. How long will it take for this plane to travel from A to B with the $50\frac{mi}{hr}$ wind? **.2 hour = 12 minutes**

2 How long will it take for this plane to travel back from B to A against the same wind? **.25 hour = 15 minutes**

3 **a.** Calculate the **average speed** for the entire trip by dividing the total distance by the total time. **444.44 $\frac{mi}{hr}$**
b. Compare the average speed with the speed of the plane in still air. **average speed < speed in still air**

4 Repeat parts 1–3 with the same plane and same wind but with two cities that are d miles apart. **See below.**

south coast of Kauai, HI

4) $\frac{d}{400}$; $\frac{d}{500}$; $\frac{2d}{\frac{900d}{20{,}000}} = \frac{400d}{9d} = 444.44\ \frac{mi}{hr}$;
average speed < speed in still air

In-class Activity

Resources

From the ***Teacher's Resource File***
- Answer Master 5-8

If you have discussed **Question 20** of Lesson 5-5 in some detail, then it is not necessary to do this In-class Activity.

The purpose of this brief In-class Activity is given in the first sentence of Lesson 5-8. You might want to add the following question. Suppose a person travels from A to B at an average speed x, and back at an average speed y. What is the person's average speed for the entire trip? $\left[\frac{2}{\frac{1}{x}+\frac{1}{y}}\right.$, which equals $\left.\frac{2xy}{x+y}.\right]$

This number is called the **harmonic mean** of x and y. It is the reciprocal of the means of the reciprocals of x and y.

Lesson 5-8

Objectives

E Solve rational equations.
I Apply rational expressions and rational equations.

Resources

From the ***Teacher's Resource File***
- Lesson Master 5-8
- Answer Master 5-8
- Teaching Aid 45: Warm-up
- Technology Sourcebook Calculator Master 9

Additional Resources
- Visual for Teaching Aid 45

Teaching Lesson 5-8

Warm-up

A trucker drives 25 miles from city *A* to city *B* in 40 minutes. The trucker wants to drive the 20 miles from city *B* to city *C* so as to average 55 mph for the entire trip. Is this possible? At what average speed must the trucker travel from city *B* to city *C*? **Yes, but he would have to average 132 mph for the trip from city *B* to city *C*. So it is possible but not legal.**

Notes on Reading

Example 1 is given to motivate why one would ever want to solve a rational equation. While for a single situation the value of *A* would be known, the advantage of treating a more general problem is that a more significant conclusion can be reached. That conclusion is found in the paragraph following the example.

LESSON

5-8 *Rational Equations*

These camels are in Cairo, Egypt. Camels can run at a speed of over 20 mph.

The purpose of the In-class Activity is to have you see that the average speed for a round trip is not found by taking the mean of the speeds each way. The reason for this is that it takes different lengths of *time* to travel the same distance at different speeds. If a trip had you traveling for the same amount of time at two different speeds, then you would have traveled different distances at each speed, but you could average the speeds to get your average speed for the entire trip. A specific example can show how the average speed for a round trip is related to the speeds each way.

Suppose you go to a place d miles away averaging $20\frac{\text{mi}}{\text{hr}}$. Then it has taken $\frac{d}{20}$ hours. If you come back averaging $b\frac{\text{mi}}{\text{hr}}$, then it has taken $\frac{d}{b}$ hours. The average rate A equals $\frac{\text{total distance}}{\text{total time}}$. That is,

$$A = \frac{d + d}{\frac{d}{20} + \frac{d}{b}}.$$

It is instructive to solve this equation for b.

Example 1

If a person goes to a place at $20\frac{\text{mi}}{\text{hr}}$ and has an average speed of A for the entire trip, what is the speed b going back?

Solution

The equation to be solved for b is the one above: $A = \frac{d + d}{\frac{d}{20} + \frac{d}{b}}$. First, change the complex fraction into a simple fraction.

$$A = \frac{d + d}{\frac{d}{20} + \frac{d}{b}} = \frac{2d}{d\left(\frac{1}{20} + \frac{1}{b}\right)} = \frac{2 \cdot 20b}{\left(\frac{1}{20} + \frac{1}{b}\right) \cdot 20b} = \frac{40b}{b + 20}$$

Lesson 5-8 Overview

Broad Goals Algebraic manipulation with rational expressions is applied to the solution of equations involving these expressions.

Perspective As the objectives for this lesson suggest, the main idea here is a skill—the solving of rational equations. Four examples are given. In each, multiplication of both sides by the least common denominator is a key step.

Approach the determination of the LCD in a systematic way rather than by an arbitrary rule. Focus on the reason for finding this expression: this one expression must have enough factors so that when each term in the equation is multiplied by it, each product is a polynomial.

A key point to make concerns the reversibility of steps. As with some of the equations in Chapter 3, a step used in solving may not be reversible, so all potential solutions must be checked to see if they actually are solutions.

Now the equation can be solved rather easily.

$$\begin{aligned} A(b + 20) &= 40b && M_{b+20} \\ Ab + 20A &= 40b && \text{Distributive Property} \\ 20A &= 40b - Ab && A_{-Ab} \\ 20A &= (40 - A)b && \text{Distributive Property} \\ \frac{20A}{40 - A} &= b && M_{\frac{1}{40-A}} \end{aligned}$$

An examination of the answer in Example 1 shows an interesting result: there is no positive value for b if $A \geq 40$. The interpretation for this situation is as follows: If you go some place at $20\frac{\text{mi}}{\text{hr}}$, you cannot average $40\frac{\text{mi}}{\text{hr}}$ for the total trip. The physical reason for this is that, in going a distance d at $20\frac{\text{mi}}{\text{hr}}$, you have already used up all the time that it would take to go a distance $2d$ at $40\frac{\text{mi}}{\text{hr}}$.

The equation in Example 1 has rational expressions on both sides. Such an equation is called a **rational equation**. Rational equations are solved by using the same properties as any other equation.

Example 2 is motivated by equations like $\frac{1}{3} + \frac{1}{6} = \frac{1}{2}$ and $\frac{1}{5} + \frac{1}{20} = \frac{1}{4}$ in which the reciprocal of a positive integer is the sum of the reciprocals of two other integers.

Example 2

Are there any rational numbers x, $x + 1$, and $x + 2$ such that the reciprocal of the smallest number is the sum of the reciprocals of the others?

Solution

The problem asks you to solve

$$\frac{1}{x} = \frac{1}{x + 1} + \frac{1}{x + 2}.$$

To do this, multiply both sides by the least common multiple of the denominators, called the least common denominator (LCD). The LCD here is $x(x + 1)(x + 2)$.

$$x(x + 1)(x + 2) \cdot \frac{1}{x} = x(x + 1)(x + 2)\left(\frac{1}{x + 1} + \frac{1}{x + 2}\right)$$
$$(x + 1)(x + 2) = x(x + 2) + x(x + 1)$$
$$x^2 + 3x + 2 = x^2 + 2x + x^2 + x$$

Add $-x^2 - 3x$ to each side.

$$2 = x^2$$

So $x = \sqrt{2}$ or $x = -\sqrt{2}$. Hence the only real numbers that satisfy the equation are

$$\sqrt{2},\ \sqrt{2} + 1, \text{ and } \sqrt{2} + 2$$

and

$$-\sqrt{2},\ -\sqrt{2} + 1, \text{ and } \sqrt{2} + 2.$$

None of these is rational, so the answer to the question is no.

It is easy to get confused when solving rational equations. This confusion stems from the fact that solving such equations involves multiplying both sides by a variable quantity, which is not a reversible step. The following is true for all a, b, and c (even for $c = 0$):

$$a = b \Rightarrow ac = bc.$$

However, the converse is true only for $c \neq 0$:

$$ac = bc \text{ and } c \neq 0 \Rightarrow a = b,$$

or, alternatively,

$$ac = bc \Rightarrow c = 0 \text{ or } a = b.$$

Thus in **Examples 2 and 3,**

$$\frac{1}{x} = \frac{1}{x + 1} + \frac{1}{x + 2}$$
$$\Rightarrow x = \sqrt{2} \text{ or } x = -\sqrt{2} \text{ and}$$
$$1 + \frac{8}{x^2 - 14} = \frac{1}{x - 4}$$
$$\Rightarrow x = 4 \text{ or } x = -3.$$

but the converses of the above implications are not necessarily true.

Ask students to find the nonreversible step in **Examples 2–3.** In **Example 2,** the nonreversible step occurs when both sides of the equation are multiplied by $x(x + 1)(x + 2)$. This multiplier equals 0 when $x = 0$, $x = -1$, or $x = -2$. Since it is found that $x = \sqrt{2}$ and $x = -\sqrt{2}$, the multiplier causes no problem, and both $\sqrt{2}$ and $-\sqrt{2}$ lead to solutions. In **Example 3,** the nonreversible step occurs when both sides are multiplied by $(x + 4)(x - 4)$. This multiplier equals 0 when $x = 4$, so a problem is caused, and $x = 4$ is found not to be a solution.

Optional Activities

Activity 1 Technology Connection
You might wish to assign *Technology Sourcebook, Calculator Master 9.* In this activity, students use a graphics calculator to solve complex rational equations. Students analyze a situation where a trucker needs to determine his speed during different legs of a journey in order to maintain a 55 mph average speed.

Activity 2 Students may solve **Question 17** using the Law of Sines, but they may also use their knowledge of special triangles in geometry to solve the problem. Ask them to demonstrate this alternate solution. [Let $BC = x$ and $AB = x + 1$. Draw the altitude from B to AC, thereby splitting the triangle into a 30°-60°-90° triangle and a 45°-45°-90° triangle. The legs of the 45°-45°-90° triangle are each $\frac{x\sqrt{2}}{2}$, and twice this amount equals AB. So $x\sqrt{2} = x + 1$. Therefore $BC = \sqrt{2} + 1$ and $AB = \sqrt{2} + 2$.]

Error Alert In **Examples 2–3,** and in most rational equations, fractions are removed from the equation by multiplying by the LCD. A common error is to forget to multiply *every* term in the rational equation by the LCD. This is especially true in a problem such as **Example 3,** where one term, the 1, is not a fraction.

In **Example 4,** the multiplication by $4(r + 3)(r - 3)$ does not cause any problem for the solution of the rational equation since neither -3 nor 3 is found to be a potential solution. Yet, still one of the solutions is discarded because it is not appropriate for the original situation.

Additional Examples

1. Notice that $\frac{1}{2} + \frac{1}{3} = 1 - \frac{1}{2 \cdot 3}$. Are there any other consecutive integers that fit this pattern; in other words, are there any other consecutive integers n and $n + 1$ such that $\frac{1}{n} + \frac{1}{(n+1)} = 1 - \frac{1}{n(n+1)}$?
   No. The above equation leads to $n = 2$ or $n = -1$, but -1 is not in the domain of the equation.
2. Solve $\frac{2x-1}{x+3} + \frac{1}{x^2+x-6} = \frac{4-x}{x-2}$.
   $x = 3$ or $x = -1$
3. Solve $\frac{3}{x+2} + \frac{12}{x^2-4} = \frac{1}{2-x}$.
   There is no solution.

In Example 2, both sides of the original equation were multiplied by an expression containing a variable. Multiplying both sides of an equation by an expression which contains a variable is not a reversible step when the value of the expression is zero. Therefore, if the solutions had been rational, we would have had to check that the values obtained were, in fact, solutions to the original equation. Example 3 shows the danger of not checking.

Example 3

Solve $1 + \frac{8}{x^2 - 16} = \frac{1}{x - 4}$.

Solution

To find the LCD, factor all denominators:

$$1 + \frac{8}{(x+4)(x-4)} = \frac{1}{x-4}.$$

The LCD is $(x + 4)(x - 4)$. Now multiply both sides by the LCD.

$$(x+4)(x-4)\left(1 + \frac{8}{(x+4)(x-4)}\right) = (x+4)(x-4)\left(\frac{1}{x-4}\right)$$

$\Rightarrow$	$(x+4)(x-4) + 8 = x + 4$	Distribute on left side and multiply on right side.
$\Leftrightarrow$	$x^2 - 16 + 8 = x + 4$	Distributive Property
$\Leftrightarrow$	$x^2 - x - 12 = 0$	A_{-x-4}
$\Leftrightarrow$	$(x-4)(x+3) = 0$	Distributive Property
$\Leftrightarrow$	$x - 4 = 0$ or $x + 3 = 0$	Zero-Product Property
$\Leftrightarrow$	$x = 4$ or $x = -3$	A_4 and A_{-3}

This work shows that if x is a solution to the given equation, then x = 4 or x = -3. But x = 4 in the original equation makes the denominators zero. Thus 4 is not a solution. If you substitute -3 for x in the original equation, you get

$$1 + \frac{8}{(-3)^2 - 16} = \frac{1}{-3-4} \Leftrightarrow 1 + \frac{8}{-7} = -\frac{1}{7},$$

which is true. Therefore, -3 is the only solution to this equation.

As with all problem solving, if you find potential solutions by solving an equation, you must check that the solutions make sense in the original problem, not just in the equation. The next example again involves rates.

Example 4

The current in a river was estimated to be 3 mph. A speedboat went downstream 6 miles and came 6 miles back in 15 minutes. What was the average speed of the speedboat relative to still water? ▸

Adapting to Individual Needs

Extra Help

In **Example 1,** some students might prefer to change the complex fraction into a simple one by "inverting and multiplying." Explain that to do this, the denominator of the original complex fraction must be written as a single fraction. You might want to discuss this approach and point out that the result is the same.

$$\frac{d+d}{\frac{d}{20}+\frac{d}{b}} = \frac{2d}{\frac{db+20d}{20b}} = \frac{2d}{1} \cdot \frac{20b}{db+20d} = \frac{40b}{b+20}$$

Solution

Let r be the average speed (in miles per hour) of the speedboat in still water. Then going downstream the speedboat traveled at a rate $r + 3$, and returning it traveled at a rate $r - 3$. Since rate $= \frac{\text{distance}}{\text{time}}$ in general, time $= \frac{\text{distance}}{\text{rate}}$. Substitution of the given information for d and r indicates that the time going is $\frac{6}{r+3}$ and the time returning is $\frac{6}{r-3}$. Since the total time is $\frac{1}{4}$ hour,

$$\frac{6}{r+3} + \frac{6}{r-3} = \frac{1}{4}.$$

Multiply both sides by the LCD, which is $4(r + 3)(r - 3)$.

$$4(r+3)(r-3)\left(\frac{6}{r+3} + \frac{6}{r-3}\right) = \frac{1}{4} \cdot 4(r+3)(r-3)$$

$$24(r-3) + 24(r+3) = (r+3)(r-3)$$

$$24r - 72 + 24r + 72 = r^2 - 9$$

$$0 = r^2 - 48r - 9$$

$$r = \frac{48 \pm \sqrt{2304 + 36}}{2}$$

$$= \frac{48 \pm \sqrt{2340}}{2}$$

$$= 24 \pm \sqrt{585}$$

So $r = 24 + \sqrt{585} \approx 48.2$ or $r = 24 - \sqrt{585} \approx -0.2$

Since we assume r is positive (the speedboat was going forward), the solution -0.2 to the equation is not considered a solution to the problem. The speedboat was traveling at about 48.2 miles per hour.

QUESTIONS

Covering the Reading

1. If you travel to a place averaging $70\frac{\text{km}}{\text{hr}}$ and come back averaging $30\frac{\text{km}}{\text{hr}}$, what is your average speed for the entire trip? 42 ~~mph~~ km/hr.

2. Suppose a small plane travels at a speed of 300 mph in still air. If it flies with a 30 mph tailwind going to its destination and against a 20 mph headwind coming back, what will its average speed be for the trip? 303 mph

3. If a person travels to a place at $20\frac{\text{mi}}{\text{hr}}$, how fast must the person travel on the way back if their average speed for the entire trip is the following?
   a. $20\frac{\text{mi}}{\text{hr}}$ 20 mph **b.** $30\frac{\text{mi}}{\text{hr}}$ 60 mph **c.** $40\frac{\text{mi}}{\text{hr}}$ not possible **d.** $50\frac{\text{mi}}{\text{hr}}$ not possible

4. Consider the rational equation $\frac{2x+9}{x^2-25} + \frac{1}{x+5} = \frac{x+11}{4x+20}$.
   a. Find the least common denominator. $4(x + 5)(x - 5)$
   b. Without solving the equation, give two numbers that are not solutions to the equation. $x = 5$ and $x = -5$

4. Consider the situation of **Example 4.** If upstream flooding increased the current's rate by 2 mph, what would the still water speed of the speedboat have to be to make the same round trip in 15 minutes?
$\frac{6}{r+5} + \frac{6}{r-5} = \frac{1}{4}$
$\Rightarrow r^2 - 48r - 25 = 0$
$\Rightarrow r = 24 + \sqrt{601} \approx 48.52$ mph
With s as the speed of the river, the equation of Additional Example 4 and that of Example 4 are of the form $r^2 - 48r - s^2 = 0$.

Adapting to Individual Needs

Challenge

Ask students to answer the following: When does $\frac{1}{a} + \frac{1}{b} = \frac{1}{c}$ have integer solutions? [when $ac = b$ and $a = c + 1$]

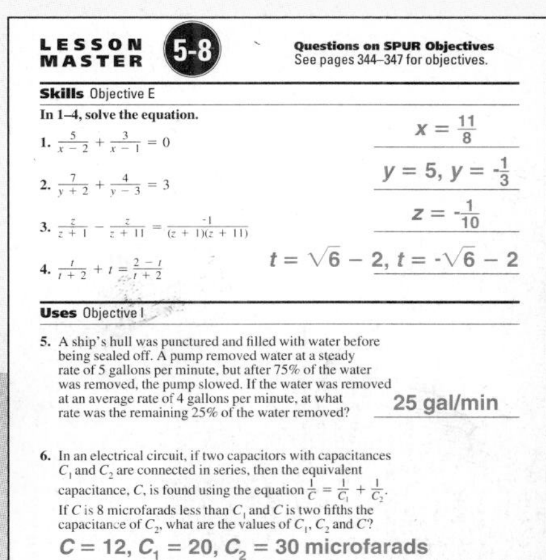

LESSON MASTER 5-8 **Questions on SPUR Objectives** See pages 344–347 for objectives.

Skills Objective E

In 1–4, solve the equation.

1. $\frac{5}{x-2} + \frac{3}{x-1} = 0$ $x = \frac{11}{8}$
2. $\frac{7}{y+2} + \frac{4}{y-3} = 3$ $y = 5, y = -\frac{1}{3}$
3. $\frac{z}{z+1} - \frac{z}{z+11} = \frac{-1}{(z+1)(z+11)}$ $z = -\frac{1}{10}$
4. $\frac{t}{t+2} + t = \frac{2-t}{t+2}$ $t = \sqrt{6} - 2, t = -\sqrt{6} - 2$

Uses Objective I

5. A ship's hull was punctured and filled with water before being sealed off. A pump removed water at a steady rate of 5 gallons per minute, but after 75% of the water was removed, the pump slowed. If the water was removed at an average rate of 4 gallons per minute, at what rate was the remaining 25% of the water removed? 25 gal/min

6. In an electrical circuit, if two capacitors with capacitances C_1 and C_2 are connected in series, then the equivalent capacitance, C, is found using the equation $\frac{1}{C} = \frac{1}{C_1} + \frac{1}{C_2}$. If C is 8 microfarads less than C_1 and C is two fifths the capacitance of C_2, what are the values of C_1, C_2 and C?
$C = 12, C_1 = 20, C_2 = 30$ microfarads

Notes on Questions

Question 5 This is a different sort of question than students are accustomed to encountering, and it may confuse some students. Go back to the definition of "equivalent equations" as having the same solutions.

Questions 7–10 Remind students to check potential solutions back into the original rational equations.

Question 17 This question requires the use of the Law of Sines. Encourage students to rationalize the denominators in their answers.

Question 18 Dimensional analysis is helpful.

hours $\cdot \frac{\text{parts}}{\text{hour}}$ = parts

Since 120 parts are needed in all,

x hours $\cdot$ 120 $\frac{\text{parts}}{\text{hour}}$ +

x hours $\cdot$ 240 $\frac{\text{parts}}{\text{hour}}$ = 120 parts.

Question 27 There are many ways to approach this problem.

a. using logarithms
b. using an automatic grapher
c. using a calculator and the guess-and-check method.

5b) No: the first equation is undefined when $x = 2$, but $x = 2$ is a solution of the second equation.

6) No; there are no rational numbers x, $x + 2$, and $x + 4$, but there are irrational solutions $\{\sqrt{8}, \sqrt{8} + 2, \sqrt{8} + 4\}$ and $\{-\sqrt{8}, -\sqrt{8} + 2, -\sqrt{8} + 4\}$

11b) Yes, the current decreases the length of travel about 0.05 miles every 15 minutes.

13) your average speed returning is 0 mph.

14) If you go someplace at 20 mph, you cannot average 40 mph for the total trip.

15) Your return rate does not depend on distance traveled.

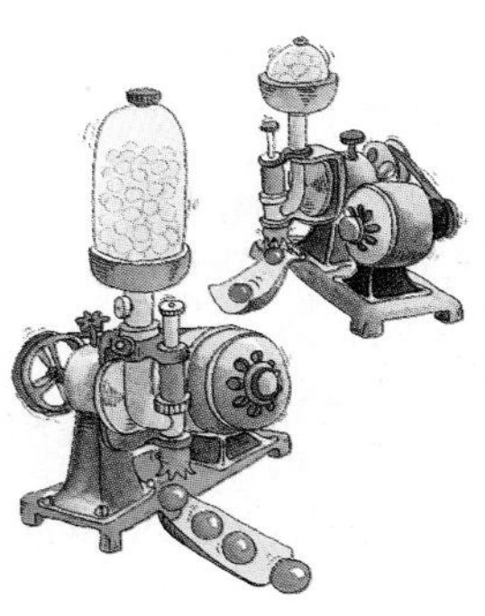

5. Determine whether or not the equations are equivalent.

a. $\frac{x}{x-1} + \frac{3}{x-1} = \frac{5}{x-1}$; $x + 3 = 5$ Yes

b. $\frac{x}{x-2} + \frac{3}{x-2} = \frac{5}{x-2}$; $x + 3 = 5$ See left.

6. Are there any rational numbers x, $x + 2$, and $x + 4$ such that the reciprocal of the smallest number is the sum of the reciprocals of the other two?

In 7–10, solve.

7. $\frac{4}{2x} + \frac{2}{3x} = \frac{1}{6}$ $x = 16$

8. $\frac{3}{x+1} + 2 = \frac{5}{x+1}$ $x = 0$

9. $\frac{12}{x-2} - \frac{6}{x-3} = 1$ $x = 5$ or $x = 6$

10. $\frac{t+5}{t+1} + \frac{3}{t-3} = \frac{-16}{t^2 - 2t - 3}$ $t = -4$

11. Refer to Example 4.

a. If there were no current, how fast would the speedboat have been going?

b. Did the current affect how far the speedboat could go in 15 minutes?

a) 48 mph b) See left.

12. A commuter flight travels into a 60 mph headwind and returns, going 150 miles out and coming 150 miles back in 2 hours.

a. How fast would the plane have gone in still air? ≈ 171 mph

b. How far could the plane have gone in 2 hours had there been no wind? ≈ 342 miles

Applying the Mathematics

In 13–15, refer to Example 1. Give the physical interpretation of each mathematical fact. See left.

13. $b \neq 0$

14. $\lim_{A \to 40^+} b = \infty$

15. There is no d in the final equation.

16. In an electrical circuit, the equivalent resistance, R, of two resistors, R_1 and R_2, connected in parallel is given by the equation

$$\frac{1}{R} = \frac{1}{R_1} + \frac{1}{R_2}.$$

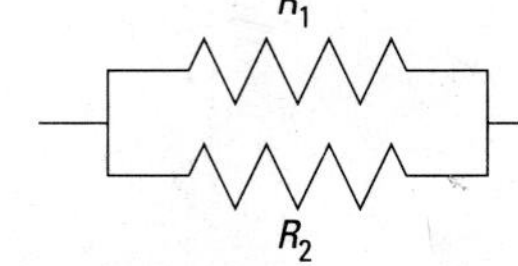

a. If $R_1 = 5$ ohms and $R_2 = 6$ ohms, find R. $R \approx 2.73$ ohms

b. If R is known to be 4 ohms and R_1 is 6 ohms, find R_2. $R_2 \approx 12$ ohms

17. In $\triangle ABC$, $\overline{AB}$ is one unit longer than $\overline{BC}$. Determine exact values for the lengths of $\overline{BC}$ and $\overline{AB}$. $BC = \sqrt{2} + 1$; $AB = \sqrt{2} + 2$

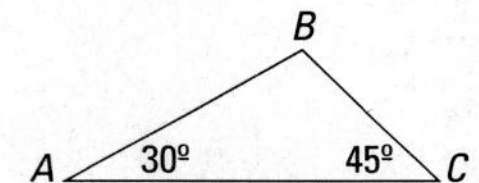

18. A manufacturing company has an old machine that produces 120 parts per hour. If the company buys a new machine that makes twice as many parts per hour, how long will it take the two machines to make 120 parts if they work together? (Hint: You may wish to let x = the number of hours the machines run.) 20 minutes

19. Suppose that you travel 10 miles at r miles per hour, 20 miles at 4 mph less than r, and 30 miles at 4 mph faster than r. Write your average speed as a rational expression in r. $\frac{3(r^3 - 16r)}{3r^2 - 2r - 8}$

Review

20. If $\sin x = .28$ and $\cos x = .96$, give the values of $\tan x$ and $\cot x$. *(Lesson 5-7)*
$\tan x = 7/24$; $\cot x = 24/7$

21. Give the values of $\sec x$ and $\csc x$ when $x = \frac{5\pi}{6}$. *(Lesson 5-7)*
$\sec x = -1.15$; $\csc x = 2$

22. a. Write the negation: See left.
The decimal expansion of x is terminating or the decimal expansion of x is repeating.

b. Write the contrapositive: See left.
If x is a rational number, then the decimal expansion of x is terminating or repeating.

c. Use the result in part **b** to determine whether the given number is rational or irrational.

i. $.\overline{78}$ rational

ii. .7878878887 . . . (The number of 8s between successive 7s keeps increasing by 1.) *(Lessons 1-2, 1-5, 5-6)* not rational

22a) *The decimal expansion of x is not terminating and the decimal expansion of x is not repeating.*
b) *If the decimal expansion of x is not terminating or repeating, then x is not a rational number.*

23. Rationalize the denominator: $\frac{6}{\sqrt{10}}$. *(Lesson 5-6)* $\frac{3\sqrt{10}}{5}$

24. Let f be the rational function defined by $f(x) = \frac{2x^2 - x - 3}{x - 2}$. The end behavior of f is like the end behavior of what simpler function? *(Lesson 5-5)*
$2x + 3$

25. a. Describe the behavior of $f(x) = \frac{10}{x^5}$ as x approaches 0.

b. Describe the end behavior of f. *(Lesson 5-3)*
See left.

25a) $\lim_{x\to 0^+} f(x) = \infty$; $\lim_{x\to 0^-} f(x) = 0$;
b) $\lim_{x\to \infty} f(x) = 0$; $\lim_{x\to -\infty} f(x) = 0$

26. a. Show that $\frac{16x^2 - 4}{8x + 4}$ simplifies to $2x - 1$.

b. Give any restrictions on the variable. *(Lesson 5-2)*
See left.

26a) $\frac{16x^2 - 4}{8x + 4} = \frac{4(4x^2 - 1)}{4(2x + 1)} = \frac{4(2x + 1)(2x - 1)}{4(2x + 1)} = 2x - 1$
b) $x \neq -\frac{1}{2}$

27. If a deposit doubles in value in 10 years when compounded quarterly, find the interest rate. *(Lesson 2-7)* 7.0%

28. What can be concluded using all these statements? *(Lesson 1-6)*
If the legislature passes this bill, the governor will veto it.
If the governor vetoes this bill, the legislature will override the veto.
The legislature did not override this veto.
The legislature did not pass this bill.

Exploration

29. Consider the equation

$$\frac{ax - 1}{x^2 - 1} = \frac{1}{x - 1}.$$

a. Solve for x. $x = \frac{2}{a - 1}$

b. Find three values of a for which there is no value of x that satisfies the equation. $a = 1, a = -1, a = 3$

c. Find a when $x = 4$. $a = \frac{3}{2}$

Practice
For more questions on SPUR Objectives, use **Lesson Master 5-8** (shown on page 331).

Assessment
Oral Communication Have students show how they solved and checked one of **Questions 7–10** and explain each step in their work. [Students solve rational equations.]

Extension
Project Update Project 6, *Simpson's Paradox,* on page 341, relates to the content of this lesson.

Lesson 5-9

Resources

From the ***Teacher's Resource File***

- Answer Master 5-9
- Technology Sourcebook
- Teaching Aids
  45 Warm-up
  52 The Five Regular Polyhedra
- Technology Sourcebook
  Computer Master 2

Additional Resources

- Visuals for Teaching Aids 45, 52
- Graphic art software

Teaching Lesson 5-9

Warm-up

Define each term.

1. Unit fraction A fraction of the form $\frac{1}{n}$, where n is a positive integer.
2. Regular polygon A convex polygon whose sides are all the same length and whose angles are all the same measure.
3. Regular polyhedron A convex polyhedron whose faces are all congruent regular polygons with the same number of sides.

LESSON

5-9 *Tessellating Polygons and Regular Polyhedra*

Two motif system VI[B], variant 1, November, 1942, *one of Escher's many studies of tessellations*

A **unit fraction** is a fraction of the form $\frac{1}{n}$, where n is a positive integer. Thus $\frac{1}{2}, \frac{1}{3}, \frac{1}{4}, \ldots$ are the unit fractions. A **regular polygon** is a convex polygon whose sides are all the same length and whose angles are all the same measure. Equilateral triangles and squares are regular polygons, and there can be regular polygons of any number of sides. Since the sum of the measures of the angles of a convex polygon is $(n - 2)180°$, each angle of a regular polygon has measure $\frac{(n-2)180°}{n}$.

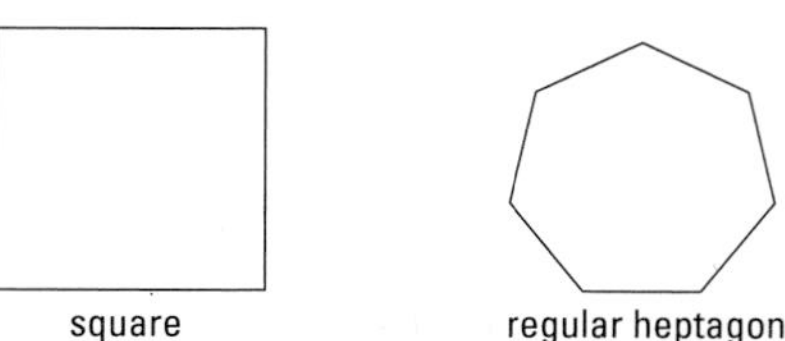

A **tessellation** is a covering of the plane with congruent copies of the same region, with no holes and no overlaps. There are many possible shapes for that region; each is called a **fundamental region** for the tessellation. One of the many famous tessellations of the Dutch artist Maurits Escher (1898–1972) is shown above.

It would not seem that unit fractions, regular polygons, and tessellations are related, but they are. Their relationship arises from trying to answer the following problem.

Lesson 5-9 Overview

Broad Goals This reading lesson applies rational equations to determine which regular polygons tessellate and which regular polyhedra are possible.

Perspective As the artist Maurits Escher has so dramatically shown, tessellations can be constructed from figures of many varieties and forms. But only three regular polygons tessellate: the equilateral triangle, square, and hexagon. In this lesson, the proof of that result is shown to be equivalent to the solving of the Diophantine equation $\frac{1}{n} + \frac{1}{s} = \frac{1}{2}$. There are only five regular polyhedra: the regular tetrahedron, cube, regular octahedron, regular dodecahedron, and regular icosahedron. The proof of this result is shown to be equivalent to the solving of the related Diophantine equation $\frac{1}{n} + \frac{1}{s} > \frac{1}{2}$.

Thus this reading lesson covers some beautiful mathematics related to the solving of rational equations and illustrates the ability to use mathematics from one branch to solve significant problems in another branch.

part of a wall of the Dome of the Rock, Jerusalem

Problem 1

Which regular polygons can be fundamental regions for a tessellation?

Analysis

From floor tiles and designs, and perhaps from earlier mathematics courses, you may be familiar with tessellations having equilateral triangles, squares, and regular hexagons as fundamental figures. They are drawn here. So the question is: Are tessellations possible with any other regular polygons?

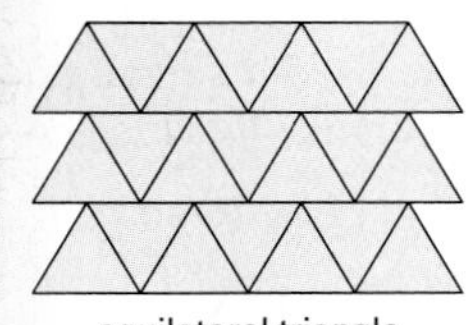
equilateral triangle tessellation

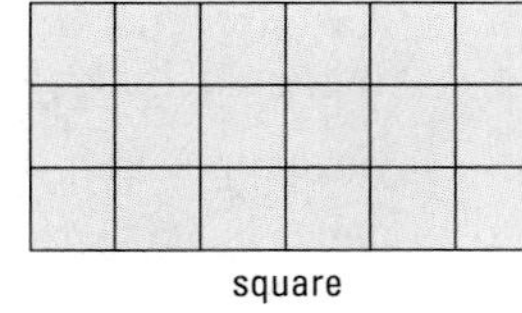
square tessellation

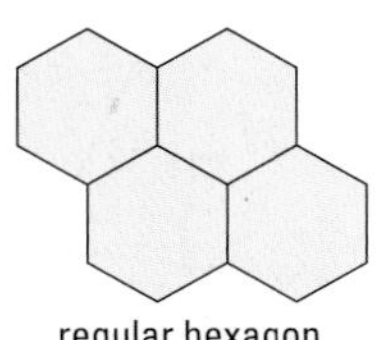
regular hexagon tessellation

Now let us consider a problem involving unit fractions. It seems to be an unrelated digression, but it is not.

Problem 2

Write $\frac{1}{2}$ as the sum of two unit fractions.

Solution

Restated, this problem asks for a pair of positive integers n and s such that $\frac{1}{2} = \frac{1}{n} + \frac{1}{s}$. If this is so, then at least one of $\frac{1}{n}$ and $\frac{1}{s}$ must be as great as $\frac{1}{4}$. (Short proof by contradiction: If both are less than $\frac{1}{4}$, then adding them yields a sum that is less than $\frac{1}{2}$, and that contradicts the condition of the problem.)

Thus either $\frac{1}{n} \geq \frac{1}{4}$ or $\frac{1}{s} \geq \frac{1}{4}$.

Suppose $\frac{1}{n} \geq \frac{1}{4}$. Then multiplying both sides by $4n$ gives $4 \geq n$. Since n is a positive integer, $n = 1, 2, 3,$ or 4. To find s, substitute these values for n.

when $n = 1$: $\frac{1}{2} = \frac{1}{1} + \frac{1}{s}$ This implies $s = -2$, which is not allowed.
when $n = 2$: $\frac{1}{2} = \frac{1}{2} + \frac{1}{s}$ This implies $\frac{1}{s} = 0$, which is impossible.
when $n = 3$: $\frac{1}{2} = \frac{1}{3} + \frac{1}{s}$ This implies $s = 6$.
when $n = 4$: $\frac{1}{2} = \frac{1}{4} + \frac{1}{s}$ This implies $s = 4$.

Because n and s can be interchanged in the original equation, the same reasoning can be applied with them interchanged. So, when $s = 3$, then $n = 6$, and when $s = 4$, then $n = 4$ (which was found the first time). There are thus three solutions to the equation $\frac{1}{2} = \frac{1}{n} + \frac{1}{s}$:

$$(n, s) = (3, 6) \qquad (n, s) = (4, 4) \quad \text{or} \quad (n, s) = (6, 3).$$

The answer to Problem 2 enables us to solve Problem 1.

Notes on Reading

Art Connection The walls of many mosques are decorated with tessellations and other geometric designs because Islam forbids placing pictures of people in its religious houses. This practice placed Islam in direct opposition to Eastern Orthodoxy, a religion in which icons of saints are worshiped.

Finding equivalent problems in very different contexts is quite exciting and very important, because it means that no new mathematics needs to be invented for a new problem. When Descartes invented analytic geometry, he thought that because he could now find an algebraic equivalent to every geometry problem, every geometry problem would be able to be solved. He had a little too much faith in algebra, but he was correct in that many problems that are very difficult to solve geometrically have easier algebraic solutions.

Equivalent problems may not look at all alike. **Problems 1–2,** and the problems of **Questions 8–9** are all equivalent. They are all equivalent to solving $\frac{1}{2} = \frac{1}{n} + \frac{1}{s}$.

Point out that equivalent problems are not like alternate solutions to problems. They are alternate problems to solve!

The method of solving **Problem 2** is one of considering and exhausting all possible cases. There are exactly three ways to write $\frac{1}{2}$ as the sum of two positive unit fractions: $\frac{1}{3} + \frac{1}{6}$, $\frac{1}{4} + \frac{1}{4}$, $\frac{1}{6} + \frac{1}{3}$. This implies $(n, s) =$ (3, 6) or (4, 4) or (6, 3). Some students will fail to make that connection!

Optional Activities

Activity 1 Technology Connection
You might want to consider using *Technology Sourcebook, Computer Master 2.* In this activity, students use graphic art software to create original Escher-style tessellations based on transformations of the equilateral triangle, rectangle, and other polygons.

Activity 2 After discussing the definition of *unit fraction,* have students find all pairs of unit fractions whose sum is $\frac{1}{3}$ and ask them to explain how they know they have them all. [$\frac{1}{4}$ and $\frac{1}{12}$, $\frac{1}{6}$ and $\frac{1}{6}$; at least one of the unit fractions must be as large as $\frac{1}{6}$ because otherwise their sum will not be large enough to be $\frac{1}{3}$.] Then ask students if there are any unit fractions that are the sum of two other unit fractions in more than three ways. [Yes. Sample: $\frac{1}{6} = \frac{1}{12} + \frac{1}{12} = \frac{1}{8} + \frac{1}{24} = \frac{1}{9} + \frac{1}{18} = \frac{1}{7} + \frac{1}{42} = \frac{1}{10} + \frac{1}{15}$.]

To help explain why there are only three possibilities for regular polygons fitting around a vertex, a table of measures of each angle of a regular n-gon will help.

n	$\frac{180(n-2)}{n}$
3	60
4	90
5	108
6	120

When there are more than 6 sides, the measure of each angle is too large to allow three polygons to meet.

For **Problem 3,** the argument that each angle of a face polygon must be less than $\frac{360}{s}$ may not be intuitively obvious. Although pictures of the polyhedra are in the book and on **Teaching Aid 52,** they usually do not suffice. Building straw or pipe cleaner models will help, or bring in models of the regular polyhedra.

Additional Examples

The product of a pair of integers is positive and equal to twice their sum. Find the possible pairs of integers.
Let m and n be the integers. Then $mn = 2(m + n)$, from which $mn = 2m + 2n$. Dividing both sides by $2mn$, the equation $\frac{1}{2} = \frac{1}{n} + \frac{1}{m}$ results. So this problem, too, is equivalent to Problems 1–2 in the lesson. So the pairs of integers are 4 and 4, and 3 and 6.

(Notes on Questions begin on page 338.)

Think of what happens at the vertex P of a polygon in a tessellation. Either P is the vertex of other polygons (as in the square or regular hexagon tessellations drawn on page 335) or the vertex lies on a side of other polygons (as in the equilateral triangle tessellation drawn on page 335).

The vertex can lie on a side of other polygons only when an angle of the regular polygon is a factor of 180°, because all the angles formed must be congruent. There are no factors of 180° between 90° and 180°, so this can occur only for squares and equilateral triangles.

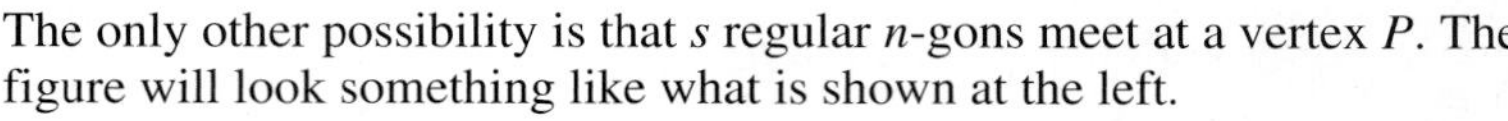

The only other possibility is that s regular n-gons meet at a vertex P. The figure will look something like what is shown at the left.

Since there are s angles at point P, and the sum of the measures of these angles is 360°, each has measure $\frac{360°}{s}$. And since these are angles of regular n-gons, each angle must also have measure $\frac{(n-2)180°}{n}$. Thus n and s are integer solutions to the equation

$$\frac{(n-2)180°}{n} = \frac{360°}{s},$$

where $s \geq 3$ (at least 3 polygons must meet at a vertex) and $n \geq 3$ (a polygon has at least 3 sides). Divide both sides by 180°.

$$\frac{n-2}{n} = \frac{2}{s}$$

Rewrite the fraction on the left side as the difference of two fractions.

$$1 - \frac{2}{n} = \frac{2}{s}$$

Divide both sides by 2.

$$\frac{1}{2} - \frac{1}{n} = \frac{1}{s}$$

Adding $\frac{1}{n}$ to both sides yields the equation of Problem 2. That equation has only three solutions: $(n, s) = (3, 6)$, $(n, s) = (4, 4)$, and $(n, s) = (6, 3)$. Now we see that each of those solutions determines a geometric configuration.

$(n, s) = (3, 6)$ means that the polygons are triangles (3-gons) with 6 meeting at each vertex.
$(n, s) = (4, 4)$ means that the polygons are squares (4-gons) with 4 meeting at each vertex.
$(n, s) = (6, 3)$ means that the polygons are hexagons (6-gons) with 3 meeting at each vertex.

So, at most three regular polygons can be fundamental regions for a tessellation. The drawings on page 335 show that all three are possible.

Now consider regular polyhedra, again recalling some terminology. A **regular polyhedron** (plural **polyhedra**) is a convex polyhedron whose faces are all congruent regular polygons. The ancient Greeks knew of five different regular polyhedra. They are pictured on page 337.

Adapting to Individual Needs

Extra Help
Some students might be confused by the conclusion that equilateral triangles can tessellate the plane, six meeting at each vertex, when the picture on page 336 does not show this specific configuration. They will sketch this configuration in **Question 1.** In **Question 2** they will draw a configuration of squares different from that shown on page 335. Your students might find it interesting that only one arrangement is possible with hexagons. Invite them to experiment until they are convinced.

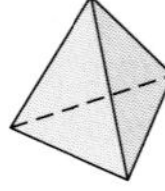
regular tetrahedron (4 faces)

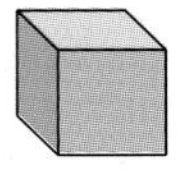
cube (6 faces)

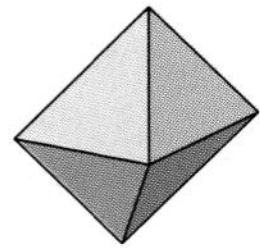
regular octahedron (8 faces)

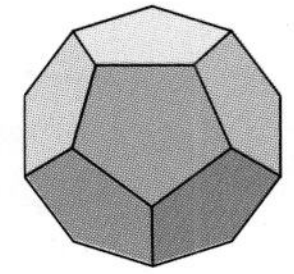
regular dodecahedron (12 faces)

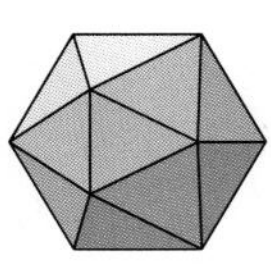
regular icosahedron (20 faces)

The question is: Do regular polyhedra exist that were unknown to the Greeks?

Problem 3

How many regular polyhedra are there?

Solution

This problem is related to the first two in the following way. Think of looking at a regular polyhedron from above one of its corners.

side of n-gon

$< \frac{360°}{s}$

s edges at each vertex

You see a number of edges (call it s) of the polyhedron radiating from the corner, forming equal angles. The edges are not all in the same plane, so the sum of the measures of these angles must be less than 360°, and thus the measure of each angle must be less than $\frac{360°}{s}$. If the angle is an interior angle of an n-gon, then its measure is, as before, $\frac{(n-2)180°}{n}$. So Problem 3 reduces to finding integers n and s such that $n \geq 3$ and $s \geq 3$ and

$$\frac{(n-2)180°}{n} < \frac{360°}{s}.$$

This sentence is identical to the equation to be solved in Problem 2 except that there is a $<$ sign where there was an $=$ sign. By the same steps used in solving the equation, the above sentence is equivalent to

$$\frac{1}{2} < \frac{1}{n} + \frac{1}{s}.$$

Now we must have $\frac{1}{n} > \frac{1}{4}$ or $\frac{1}{s} > \frac{1}{4}$; so $n < 4$ or $s < 4$, otherwise their sum will not be greater than $\frac{1}{2}$. But by the conditions of the problem, $n \geq 3$ and $s \geq 3$. Thus either $s = 3$ or $n = 3$. Because $(n, s) = (3, 6)$ makes the sum of the reciprocals equal to $\frac{1}{2}$, it follows that s can only be 3, 4, or 5 when $n = 3$.

$$\frac{1}{2} < \frac{1}{3} + \frac{1}{3} \qquad \frac{1}{2} < \frac{1}{3} + \frac{1}{4} \qquad \frac{1}{2} < \frac{1}{3} + \frac{1}{5}$$

The analysis is similar when n and s are switched. When $s = 3$, n can only be 3, 4, or 5.

Consequently, there are only 5 pairs of numbers (n, s) that satisfy the inequality $\frac{1}{2} < \frac{1}{n} + \frac{1}{s}$. They are (3, 3), (3, 4), (3, 5), (4, 3), and (5, 3). Each solution refers to a particular regular polyhedron. For instance, $(n, s) = (3, 4)$ means 4 triangles (3-gons) meet at each vertex of the polyhedron. This is the regular octahedron, with 8 faces. In the Questions, you are asked to match each of the other solutions with its polyhedron.

So the Greeks knew of all the regular polyhedra. There are no others.

Follow-up for Lesson 5-9

Extension

History Connection The ancient Egyptians strove to express all fractions as sums of unit fractions. Students interested in history may be invited to explore the mathematics of ancient Egypt.

There are many interesting problems related to unit fractions. For instance, have students find a general pattern in the following:

$\frac{1}{12} + \frac{1}{4} = \frac{1}{3}$

$\frac{1}{20} + \frac{1}{5} = \frac{1}{4}$

Then ask students if the generalization they found is true.

[$\frac{1}{n(n+1)} + \frac{1}{n+1} = \frac{1}{n}$ is a true generalization.]

Adapting to Individual Needs

Challenge

Have students derive a formula for the area of a regular n-gon with sides of length x. [By connecting a line segment from each vertex to the center, every regular n-gon becomes the sum of n isosceles triangles, each with an area of $\frac{1}{4}x^2 \cot \frac{180°}{n}$. So the total area is $\frac{1}{4}nx^2 \cot \frac{180°}{n}$.]

Notes on Questions

Questions 1–2 Each of these tessellations is different than the one shown in the lesson. Invite students to do tessellations that combine two regular polygons with different numbers of sides. (Strips of equilateral triangles and squares can form a tessellation. If one tries to tessellate regular octagons, there are holes into which squares fit.)

Question 12 A visit to a well-equipped physics lab will provide the equipment needed to demonstrate the relationship $\frac{1}{o} + \frac{1}{i} = \frac{2}{r}$ described in this question. As an extension of this question, ask students if they can design an experiment to approximate the radius of the spherical mirror.

Question 15 Invite students to write a new function whose graph is identical to that of $y = h(x)$, but with two exceptions: removable discontinuities at $x = -3$ and at $x = 7$.
$\left[f(x) = \frac{(x + 2)(x + 3)(x - 7)}{(x^2 - 25)(x + 3)(x - 7)}\right]$

Question 16b Error Alert A student who indicates x cannot be 4 is confusing 0 in the numerator (which is possible) with 0 in the denominator (which is not possible).

Problem 1 is a geometry problem and Problem 2 is an arithmetic problem, yet they can both be solved using the same algebra. Problems which can be solved using the same mathematics are called *equivalent problems.* Equivalent problems demonstrate the power, unity, and internal consistency of mathematics.

QUESTIONS

Covering the Reading

1. Draw a tessellation of equilateral triangles in which each vertex of any triangle is a vertex of five others. See left.
2. Draw a tessellation of squares in which each vertex of every square is a vertex of only one other square. See left.
3. Find all pairs of unit fractions whose denominators are greater than or equal to 3 and whose sum is greater than $\frac{5}{11}$. See margin.
4. Solve for t: $\frac{1}{t} + \frac{1}{3} = \frac{1}{2}$. $t = 6$
5. Let a_n = the measure of an angle of a regular n-gon, for $n \geq 3$.
   a. Give a formula for a_n in terms of n. See left.
   b. Compute the first five terms of the sequence a. See left.
   c. What is $\lim_{n \to \infty} a_n$? (Hint: Think of the sequence as a discrete rational function.) $180°$
6. **a.** How many regular polyhedra are there? 5
   b. How many of these were known to the ancient Greeks? all 5
7. Match each solution (n, s) to the inequality $\frac{1}{n} + \frac{1}{s} < \frac{1}{2}$ with its corresponding regular polyhedron. See margin.
   a. (3, 3) **b.** (3, 4) **c.** (3, 5) **d.** (4, 3) **e.** (5, 3)
8. Consider this problem: Find all rectangles with integer sides whose area and perimeter are numerically equal. Show that this problem is equivalent to Problems 1 and 2 in this lesson. See margin.
9. Consider this problem: For which positive integers $n > 2$ is $n - 2$ a factor of $2n$? Show that this problem is equivalent to Problems 1 and 2 in this lesson. See margin.

1)

2)

5a) $a_n = \frac{(n - 2)180°}{n}$

b) $60°, 90°, 108°, 120°, 128\frac{4}{7}°$

Review

10. An insurance company has a machine that can write a batch of checks in 2 hours. The company buys a new machine capable of writing the same batch of checks in $\frac{3}{4}$ hour. If both machines work simultaneously, how long will it take the company to write a batch of checks? *(Lesson 5-8)* $\frac{6}{11}$ of an hour

antique check writer

Additional Answers

3. $(\frac{1}{3}, \frac{1}{3}), (\frac{1}{3}, \frac{1}{4}), (\frac{1}{3}, \frac{1}{5}), (\frac{1}{3}, \frac{1}{6}), (\frac{1}{3}, \frac{1}{7}), (\frac{1}{3}, \frac{1}{8}),$
   $(\frac{1}{4}, \frac{1}{3}), (\frac{1}{4}, \frac{1}{4}), (\frac{1}{5}, \frac{1}{3}), (\frac{1}{6}, \frac{1}{3}), (\frac{1}{7}, \frac{1}{3}), (\frac{1}{8}, \frac{1}{3})$
7. a. regular tetrahedron
   b. regular octahedron
   c. regular icosahedron
   d. cube
   e. regular dodecahedron
8. The area of a rectangle is its length times its width, lw. Its perimeter is then $2l + 2w$. By setting these equal, the problem is to find positive integers l and w such that $lw = 2l + 2w$. Dividing both sides by $2lw$ (which is nonzero) yields $\frac{lw}{2lw} = \frac{2l + 2w}{2lw}$, which simplifies to $\frac{1}{2} = \frac{1}{w} + \frac{1}{l}$. This is equivalent to the equation in Problem 2, which is also equivalent to Problem 1.
9. Let n be an integer greater than 2. Suppose $(n - 2)$ is a factor of $2n$. Then $2n = (n - 2)k$ for some integer k. Then $\frac{2n}{n - 2} = k$, since $n \neq 2$. By taking the reciprocal, $\frac{n - 2}{2n} = \frac{1}{k}$. So $\frac{1}{2} - \frac{1}{n} = \frac{1}{k}$, or $\frac{1}{2} = \frac{1}{k} + \frac{1}{n}$. This is equivalent to the equation in Problem 2, which is equivalent to Problem 1.

11. The *relative error* in a measurement is usually reported as a percent and given by $\left|\frac{x - x_m}{x}\right|$, where x is the true value of a quantity and x_m is its measured value. Suppose a machine makes ball bearings whose diameter should be 2.8 cm. If the relative error can be at most 2%, find the acceptable values for the measured diameter. *(Lessons 3-9, 5-8)* 2.744 cm $< x <$ 2.85 cm

12. The diagram below shows a spherical mirror with center C and radius r. A light ray from a point on an object O reflects off the mirror and passes through an image point I. The relationship among the image distance i, the object distance o, and the radius r can be approximated by

$$\frac{1}{o} + \frac{1}{i} = \frac{2}{r}.$$

Suppose a spherical mirror has radius 5 cm.

a. If an object is located at a distance of 15 cm from the mirror, find the image distance. 3 cm

b. Where should the object be placed so that the image distance is twice the object distance? *(Lesson 5-8)* 3.75 cm from the mirror

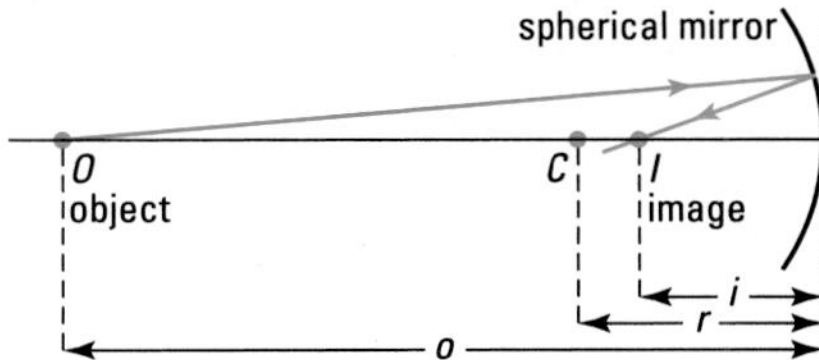

13. Find tan x, cot x, sec x, and csc x if $x = \frac{5\pi}{3}$. *(Lesson 5-7)* See left.

13) $\tan\frac{5\pi}{3} = -\sqrt{3}$; $\cot\frac{5\pi}{3} = \frac{-\sqrt{3}}{3}$; $\sec\frac{5\pi}{3} = 2$; $\csc\frac{5\pi}{3} = \frac{-2\sqrt{3}}{3}$

14. Rationalize the denominator: $\frac{20}{\sqrt{10} - 6}$. *(Lesson 5-6)* $-\frac{10\sqrt{10} + 60}{13}$

15. Let the function h be defined by $h(x) = \frac{x + 2}{x^2 - 25}$. See margin.

a. Identify the domain of h.

b. Describe the behavior of h near any vertical asymptotes.

c. Describe the end behavior of h by using limit notation.

d. Identify all x- and y-intercepts.

e. Sketch a graph of the function. *(Lessons 2-1, 5-4, 5-5)*

16. a. Show that $\frac{5x^2 + 3x - 2}{7x^2 + 8x + 1} \cdot \frac{7x^2 - 27x - 4}{5x^2 + 8x - 4}$ simplifies to $\frac{x - 4}{x + 2}$.

b. State any restrictions on the variable. *(Lesson 5-1)*

See left.

16a $\frac{5x^2 + 3x - 2}{7x^2 + 8x + 1} \cdot \frac{7x^2 - 27x - 4}{5x^2 + 8x - 4} = \frac{(5x - 2)(x + 1)}{(7x + 1)(x + 1)} \cdot \frac{(7x + 1)(x - 4)}{(5x - 2)(x + 2)} = \frac{x - 4}{x + 2}$

b) $x \neq -\frac{1}{7}$, $x \neq -1$, $x \neq \frac{2}{5}$, and $x \neq -2$

17. Find the standard prime factorization of 4388. *(Lesson 4-7)* $2^2 \cdot 1097$

18. Prove: ∀ *integers p and q, if 4 is a factor of p and q is even, then 8 is a factor of p · q.* *(Lessons 1-8, 4-1)* See margin.

Exploration

19. What are the *semi-regular polyhedra*? See margin.

Additional Answers

15. a. $\{x: x \neq 5 \text{ and } x \neq -5\}$

b. near $x = 5$:
$\lim_{x\to5^-} h(x) = -\infty$;
$\lim_{x\to5^+} h(x) = +\infty$

near $x = -5$,
$\lim_{x\to5^-} h(x) = -\infty$;
$\lim_{x\to5^+} h(x) = +\infty$

c. $\lim_{x\to-\infty} h(x) = 0$;
$\lim_{x\to+\infty} h(x) = 0$

d. x-intercept: $(-2, 0)$;
y-intercept: $(0, -\frac{2}{25})$

e.

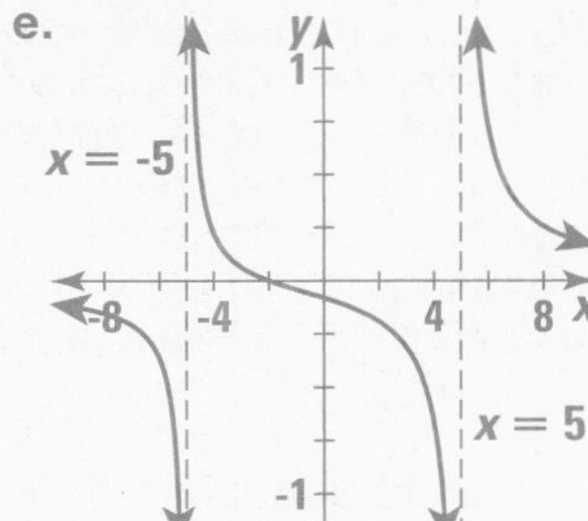

18. Suppose p and q are integers such that 4 is a factor of p, and q is even. By definition, there exist integers r and s such that $p = 4r$ and $q = 2s$. Then $pq = (4r)(2s) = 8(rs)$. Since rs is an integer by closure properties, 8 is a factor of pq by definition.

19. If two or more different regular polygons are allowed as faces, there are 13 polyhedra for which each vertex is surrounded by the same arrangement of polygons. These are called semi-regular polyhedra, and they are convex.

Chapter 5 Projects

The projects relate chiefly to the content of the lessons of this chapter as follows:

Project	Lesson(s)
1	5-6
2	5-6
3	5-4, 5-5
4	5-4
5	5-1
6	5-2, 5-8

1 Irrationality of Pi If a student has written about π in previous years, either this project should be discouraged or it should require a more advanced look at the history. The student might wish to include continued fraction estimates of π, as well as the way that trigonometric identities are used to obtain many decimal places of π.

2 An Unusual Sequence This is a straightforward project.

3 A Family of Functions Students should be encouraged to try values of *a* and *b* that are similar, far apart, have small absolute values, and that have large absolute values in order to consider the possibilities.

4 Fuel Efficiency This is a popular project. To put it at the level of *Precalculus and Discrete Mathematics,* you may wish to require that the table be graphed and that equations be derived.

A project presents an opportunity for you to extend your knowledge of a topic related to the material of this chapter. You should allow more time for a project than you do for a typical homework question.

1 Irrationality of π

In Lesson 5-6, it was mentioned that π was shown to be irrational in 1761. However, there have been attempts in the United States to legislate a value for π that would make π rational. Find some references that review the history of π. Write a short report on π's history. Be sure to include information about the state(s) that tried to legislate a value for π and about some of the attempts to find π's decimal expansion.

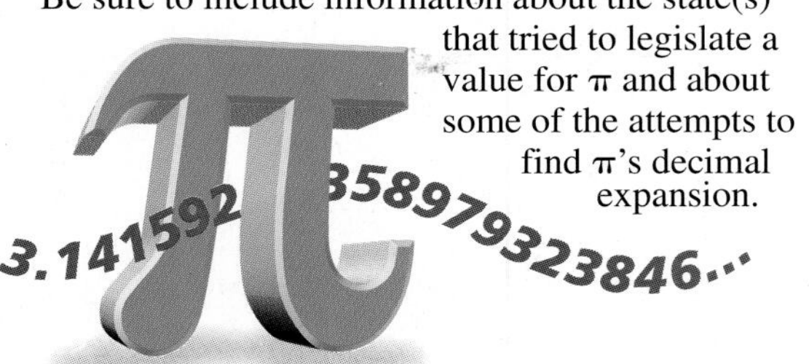

2 An Unusual Sequence

a. Approximate the value of:

i. $\sqrt{2 + \sqrt{2}}$

ii. $\sqrt{2 + \sqrt{2 + \sqrt{2}}}$

iii. $\sqrt{2 + \sqrt{2 + \sqrt{2 + \dots}}}$.

b. Approximate the value of $\sqrt{6 + \sqrt{6 + \sqrt{6 + \dots}}}$.

c. Approximate the value of $x = \sqrt{a + \sqrt{a + \sqrt{a + \dots}}}$ for various other values of *a*.

d. Use the data from parts **a–c** to conjecture a relationship between *x* and *a*.

e. Use the fact that $x = \sqrt{a + x}$ to prove the relationship you conjectured in part **d**.

3 A Family of Functions

Consider the family of real functions of the form $f: x \to \frac{x^2 + a}{x^2 + b}$ for all possible real values of *a* and *b*. Find pairs of values of *a* and *b* that yield the least and most zeros of *f* and all numbers of zeros in between. Do the same for asymptotes. Write up your results in a report that displays the various possible graphs of *f*.

4 Fuel Efficiency

Research to find the gas mileage obtained by current cars and estimate a cost per gallon in your area. Make a table of amounts a person could save in a year in gas costs by driving some particular cars over others; have the table include a variety of miles driven in a year.

Possible Responses

1. See Additional Answers at the back of this book.
2. a. i. ≈ 1.8478
   ii. ≈ 1.9616
   iii. Continuing the pattern from parts i and ii yields the values 1.9904, 1.9976, ...; so the values seem to approach 2.

   b. Using the approach in part a, the sequence generated is 2.9068, 2.9844, 2.9974, ...; so the values seem to approach 3.

   c. sample: $a = 0$, $x = 0$
   $a = 8$, $x \approx 3.37$
   $a = 10$, $x \approx 3.7$
   $a = 20$, $x \approx 5$

   d. If the points (a, x) are plotted on a graph, they appear to lie on the parabola $a = x^2 - x$. So a reasonable conjecture is that *x* is a solution to the equation $x^2 - x - a = 0$ or that $x = \sqrt{a + x}$.

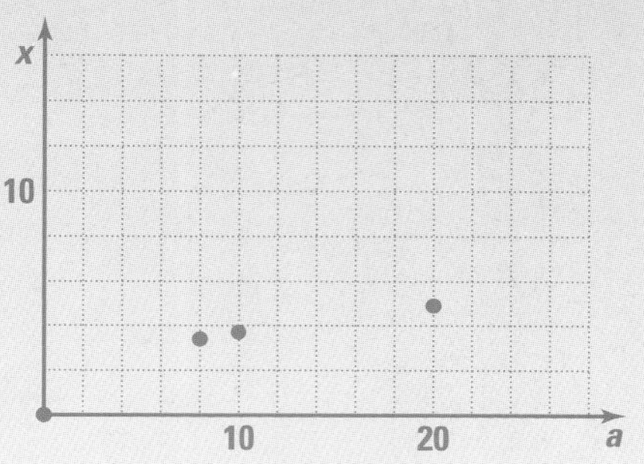

Rational Zeros of Polynomials

a. Suppose that a_0, a_1, a_2, a_3 are integers with $a_3 \neq 0$ and that p is the polynomial function defined by

$$p(x) = a_3x^3 + a_2x^2 + a_1x + a_0.$$

Suppose that m and k are positive integers with no common factors.

i. Show that the equation $p\left(\frac{m}{k}\right) = 0$ can be rewritten in the form
$m(a_3m^2 + a_2mk + a_1k^2) = -a_0k^3$.

ii. Use the result of part **i** to show that m must be a factor of the constant coefficient a_0 of p.

iii. Show that the equation $p\left(\frac{m}{k}\right) = 0$ can also be rewritten in the form
$a_3m^3 = -k(a_2m^2 + a_1mk + a_0k^2)$.

iv. Use the result of part **iii** to show that k must be a factor of the leading coefficient a_3 of p.

b. i. Generalize the results in parts **ii** and **iv** above to prove the following result.

> **Rational Zero Theorem**
> Suppose that p is a polynomial function with integer coefficients:
> $p(x) = a_nx^n + a_{n-1}x^{n-1} + \ldots + a_1x + a_0,\ a_n \neq 0.$
> If $r = \frac{m}{k}$ is a rational number in lowest terms that is a zero of p, then m is a factor of the constant coefficient a_0 and k is a factor of the leading coefficient a_n.

ii. List all possible candidates for rational zeros of the polynomial p defined by
$p(x) = 6x^4 - 7x^3 + 8x^2 - 7x + 2.$

iii. Determine if p has any rational zeros and then find all remaining zeros of p.

6 Simpson's Paradox

Consider two baseball players' batting averages from the first half and second half of the season. (Each player was injured for part of the season.)

Player (1)	At-bats	Hits	Average
First half	200	60	.300
Second half	50	10	.200

Player (2)	At-bats	Hits	Average
First half	50	17	.340
Second half	200	45	.225

a. Calculate the average for each player for the season.

b. Which player had the higher average for the first half? Which for the second half? Which for the season?

c. The conflicting results in part **b** show that these data exemplify **Simpson's paradox**. Read about this paradox in some other place and obtain another example.

d. Explain why Simpson's paradox is possible.

5 Rational Zeros of Polynomials Some teachers like to teach the theorem that is in this project, and by so doing take it out of consideration for students as a project. If you have time, this is a beautiful theorem to discuss. It also can be used to show that certain numbers are irrational. For instance, the theorem shows that the only candidates for rational zeros to $x^7 - 2 = 0$ are 1, -1, 2 and -2. But a zero to this equation is $\sqrt[7]{2}$. Since $\sqrt[7]{2}$ does not equal any of the possible rational zeros, it cannot be rational.

6 Simpson's Paradox This project illustrates the perils of combining data.

Project 3, continued

$a > 0$, $b > 0$, $a \neq b$; 1 asymptote, no zeros

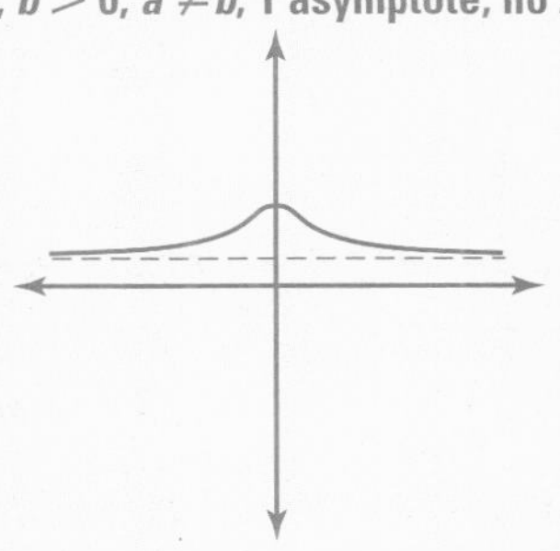

$a = 0$, $b > 0$; 1 asymptote, 1 zero

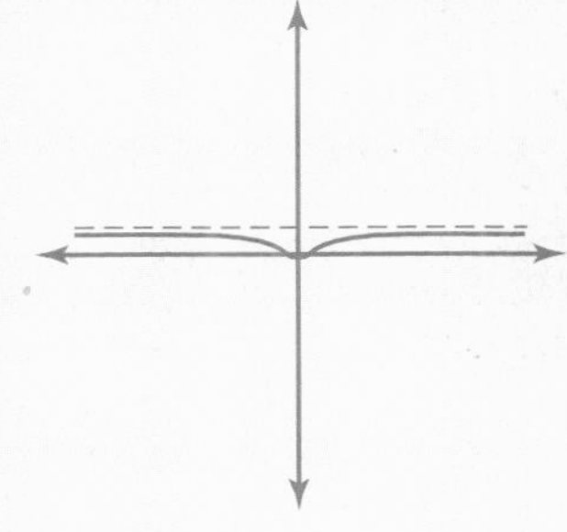

$a < 0$, $b > 0$; 1 asymptote, 2 zeros

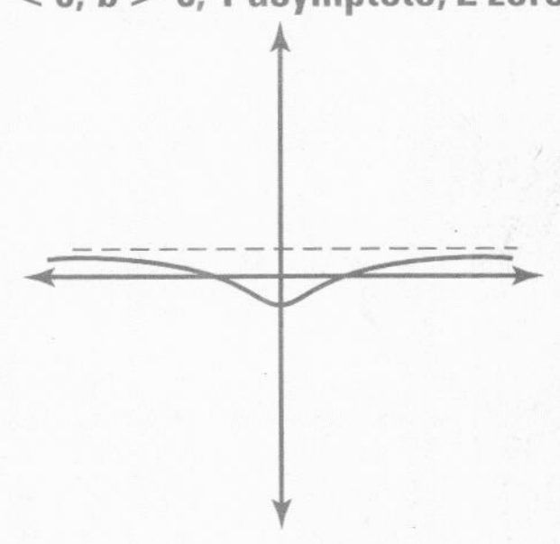

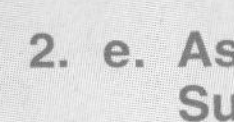

2. e. Assume that $x = \sqrt{a + x}$. Substituting $\sqrt{a + x}$ for x yields: $x = \sqrt{a + \sqrt{a + x}}$. Repeating the same substitution in the new equation yields: $x = \sqrt{a + \sqrt{a + \sqrt{a + x}}}$. If this process is repeated indefinitely, the result is

$$x = \sqrt{a + \sqrt{a + \sqrt{a + \sqrt{a + \ldots}}}}$$

3. **$a = b$; 0 asymptotes, no zeros**

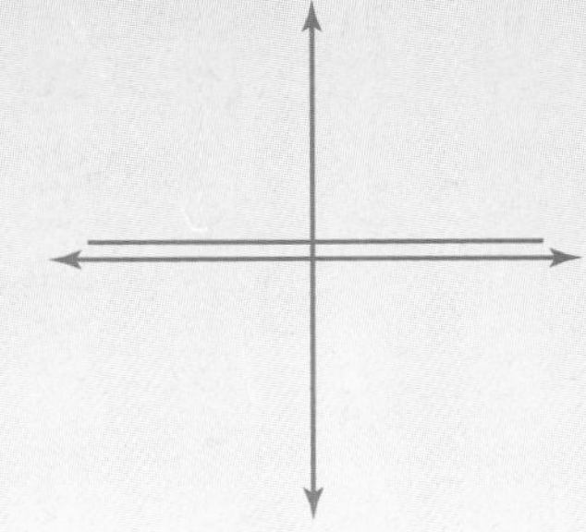

(Responses continue on page 242.)

Summary

The Summary gives an overview of the entire chapter and provides an opportunity for students to consider the material as a whole. Thus, the Summary can be used to help students relate and unify the concepts presented in the chapter.

Vocabulary

Terms, symbols, and properties are listed by lesson to provide a checklist of concepts a student must know. Emphasize to students that they should read the vocabulary list carefully before starting the Progress Self-Test. If students do not understand the meaning of a term, they should refer back to the indicated lesson.

Additional Responses, pages 340–341

Project 3, continued

$a > 0$, $b = 0$; 2 asymptotes, no zeros

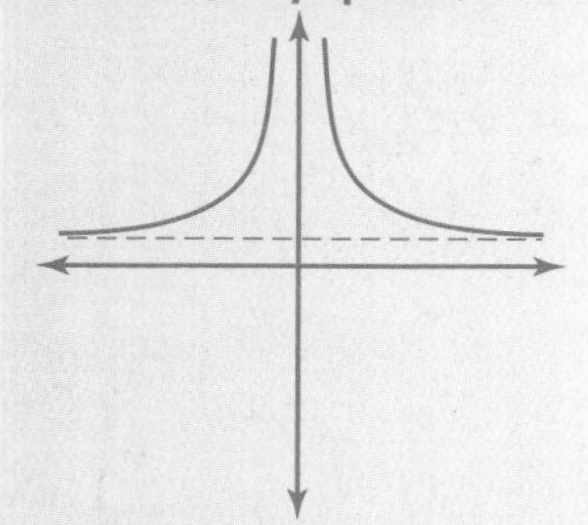

$a < 0$, $b = 0$; 2 asymptotes, 2 zeros

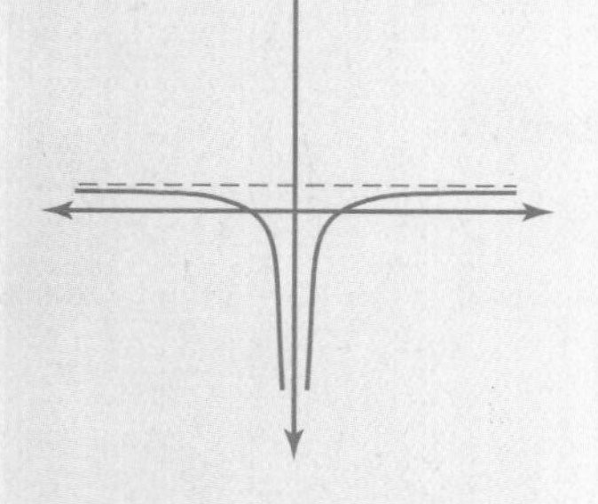

SUMMARY

Chapter 4 studied properties of integers and extended these properties to polynomials. This chapter continues this idea by studying rational numbers and relating their properties to the behavior of rational functions. Irrational numbers and nonrational functions are also studied.

Rational numbers are those real numbers that can be expressed as a ratio of integers $\frac{a}{b}$ where $b \neq 0$. Any infinite repeating decimal can be expressed as a ratio of integers. Hence, any finite decimal or any infinite repeating decimal is a rational number.

Those real numbers that cannot be expressed as a ratio of integers are called irrational numbers. For any integer n, $\sqrt{n}$ is irrational if and only if n is not a perfect square. Any decimal expansion that neither terminates nor repeats represents an irrational number.

A rational function is a function of the form $f(x) = \frac{p(x)}{q(x)}$, where $p(x)$ and $q(x)$ are polynomials and $q(x)$ is not zero. Such functions can be roughly sketched by considering the end behavior of the function as well as the behavior of the function near vertical asymptotes. Discontinuities, or breaks in the graph, may be either removable or essential.

The end behavior of a rational function $f(x) = \frac{a_m x^m + \ldots + a_1 x + a_0}{b_n x^n + \ldots + b_1 x + b_0}$ is the same as the end behavior of the function $g(x) = \frac{a_m}{b_n}x^{m-n}$. If $m > n$, then the end behavior of the rational function is the same as the end behavior of a power function. If $m < n$, then the end behavior is the same as that of a reciprocal of a power function. If $m = n$, then $y = \frac{a_m}{b_n}$ is a horizontal asymptote to the graph of the function.

Four trigonometric functions, defined in terms of sine and/or cosine, are also studied in this chapter. These nonrational functions are

$$\text{when } \cos x \neq 0,\ \tan x = \frac{\sin x}{\cos x} \text{ and } \sec x = \frac{1}{\cos x}$$

$$\text{and when } \sin x \neq 0,\ \cot x = \frac{\cos x}{\sin x} \text{ and } \csc x = \frac{1}{\sec x}.$$

The graphs of these functions can be obtained by considering where the sine and cosine functions are positive, negative, or zero.

Rational equations can be solved by multiplying both sides of the equation by the least common denominator. The logic of equation solving that you studied in Chapter 3 can be used to determine when this multiplication is reversible and when it is not.

VOCABULARY

Below are the most important terms and phrases for this chapter. You should be able to give a definition and a specific example of each and a precise definition for those marked with an asterisk (*).

Lesson 5-1
* rational number
closed
identity
domain of an identity
complex fraction

Lesson 5-2
* rational expression
lowest terms

Lesson 5-3
$\lim_{x \to a^-}$, $\lim_{x \to a^+}$
vertical asymptote

Lesson 5-4
* rational function
* removable discontinuity
* essential discontinuity
Discontinuity Theorem

Lesson 5-5
oblique asymptote
End Behavior of Rational Functions Theorem

Lesson 5-6
irrational number
terminating decimal
* conjugates
rationalizing the denominator

Lesson 5-7
* tangent, tan x
* cotangent, cot x
* secant, sec x
* cosecant, csc x

Lesson 5-8
average speed
rational equation

$a > 0$, $b < 0$; 3 asymptotes, no zeros

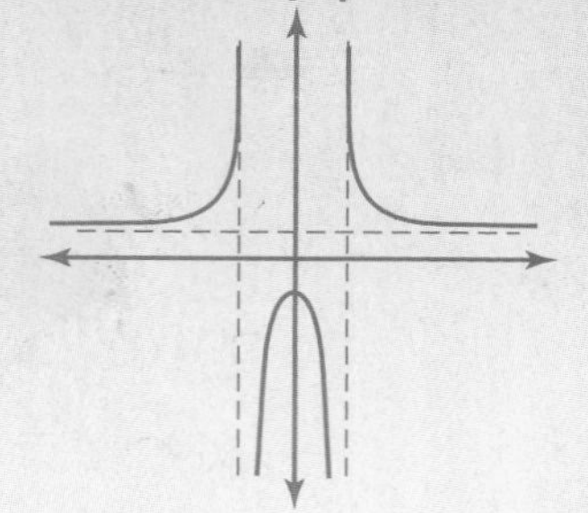

$b < 0$, $a = 0$; 3 asymptotes, 1 zero

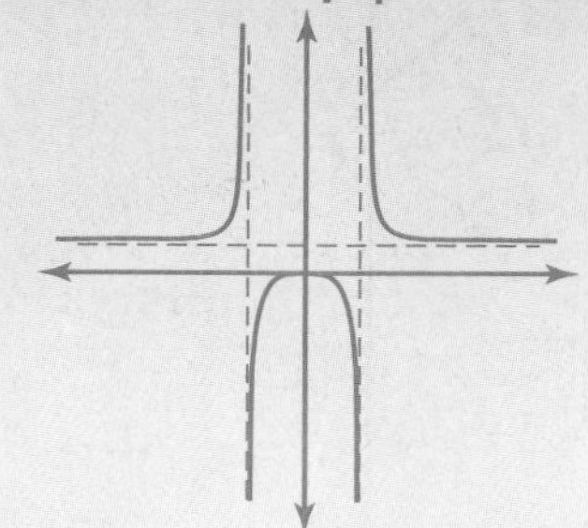

$a < 0$, $b < 0$, $a \neq b$; 3 asymptotes, 2 zeros

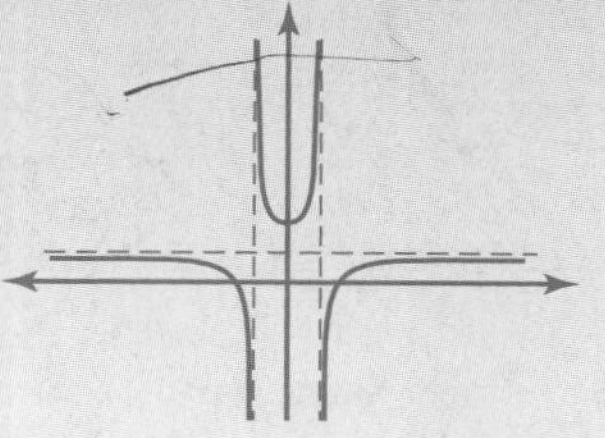

4–6. See Additional Answers at the back of this book.

PROGRESS SELF-TEST

1, 2b, 5–9, 14) See margin.

Directions: Give yourself 40 minutes to take this test. Check the test yourself using the answers at the end of this book.

1. a. Write as a single fraction in lowest terms.
$$\frac{6x}{(x+3)(x+1)} + \frac{2x}{(x+2)(x+1)}$$
   b. State any restrictions on the variable.

2. a. Write as a simple fraction in lowest terms.
$$\frac{2t^2 - t - 1}{3t^2 - 2t - 5} \cdot \frac{3t^2 + 7t - 20}{t^2 + 3t - 4} \quad \frac{2t+1}{t+1}$$
   b. State any restrictions on the variable.

3. The diagram below illustrates one situation with a converging lens of focal length f.

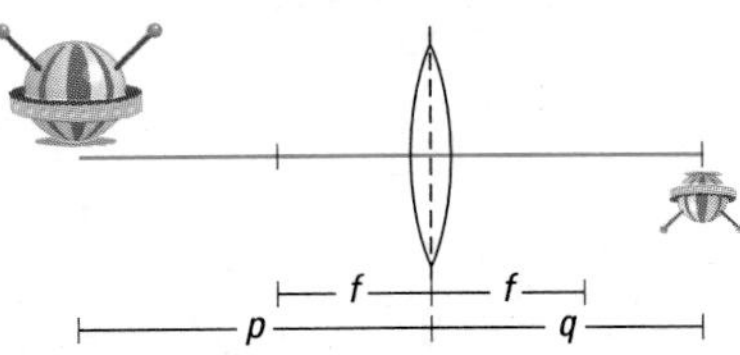

If an object is placed at a distance p from the center of the lens, its image is located at a distance q from the center, and the distances p, q, and f are related by the equation
$$f = \frac{1}{\frac{1}{p} + \frac{1}{q}}.$$
Express f as a simple fraction. $\frac{pq}{p+q}$

4. Identify each of the following numbers as rational (R) or irrational (I).
   a. $\frac{10}{6}$ R b. $\sqrt{24}$ I c. $\sqrt{49} + 3$ R d. $7.\overline{63}$ R
   e. .464664666466664 . . . (pattern continues with 6s increasing in number between the 4s) I

5. Prove that $\sqrt{11}$ is irrational.

6. Rationalize the denominator: $\frac{8}{10 - \sqrt{5}}$.

7. Identify each function as rational or not. Justify your reasoning.
   a. $h(z) = \frac{2z+1}{\sqrt{z^2+1}}$ b. $g(t) = \frac{t^2 + 2t - 4}{\cos t}$
   c. $f(x) = \frac{4x^3 - 1}{3x^2 - 2x + 7}$
   d. Describe the end behavior of each of the rational functions you have identified.

8. Write in words: $\lim_{x \to 2^-} f(x) = \infty$.

9. Consider the function $g: x \to \frac{3x+6}{x-2}$.
   a. Describe the behavior of the function as $x \to 2^+$.
   b. Describe the behavior of the function as $x \to 2^-$.
   c. Use limit notation to describe the end behavior of g.
   d. Sketch a graph of g.

10. For the function in Question 9, is $x = 2$ an essential discontinuity, a removable discontinuity, or neither? essential discontinuity

11. Solve for y: $\frac{2}{y-1} + \frac{3y}{y+4} = 3$.
    $y = 2$

In 12 and 13, find the indicated value.

12. $\tan \frac{2\pi}{3}$ $-\sqrt{3}$

13. $\cot \frac{\pi}{4}$ 1

14. Sketch a graph of $y = \tan x$ over the interval $-2\pi \le x \le 2\pi$.

15. Refer to the triangle at the right. Find $\csc \alpha$.
    $\frac{25}{7}$

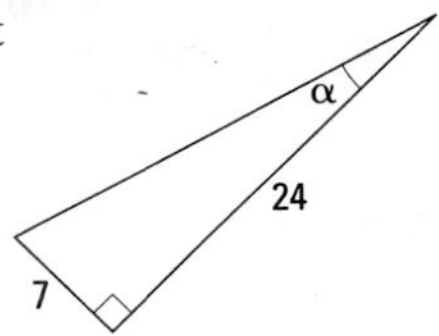

16. Refer to the graph of function h below. Evaluate each of the following.

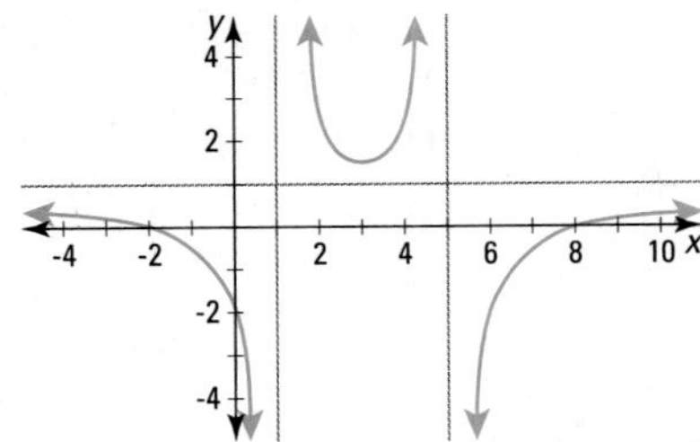

   a. $\lim_{x \to 1^+} h(x)$ ∞ b. $\lim_{x \to 5^+} h(x)$ $-\infty$
   c. $\lim_{x \to -\infty} h(x)$ 1 d. $\lim_{x \to \infty} h(x)$ 1

Progress Self-Test

For the development of mathematical competence, feedback and correction, along with the opportunity to practice, are necessary. The Progress Self-Test provides the opportunity for feedback and correction; the Chapter Review provides additional opportunities and practice. We cannot overemphasize the importance of these end-of-chapter materials. It is at this point that the material "gels" for many students, allowing them to solidify skills and understanding. In general, student performance should be markedly improved after these pages.

Assign the Progress Self-Test as a one-night assignment. Worked-out *solutions* for all questions are in the Selected Answers section of the student book. Encourage students to take the Progress Self-Test honestly, grade themselves, and then be prepared to discuss the test in class.

Advise students to pay special attention to those Chapter Review questions (pages 344–347) that correspond to questions missed on the Progress Self-Test.

Additional Answers

1. a. $\frac{2x(4x+9)}{(x+1)(x+2)(x+3)}$
   b. $x \ne -3$, $x \ne -2$, and $x \ne -1$
2. b. $t \ne \frac{5}{3}$, $t \ne -1$, $t \ne 1$, and $t \ne -4$
5. Assume the negation is true, that $\sqrt{11}$ is rational. By definition, there exist integers a and b, with $b \ne 0$, such that $\sqrt{11} = \frac{a}{b}$, where $\frac{a}{b}$ is in lowest terms. Then, $11 = \frac{a^2}{b^2} \Rightarrow a^2 = 11b^2$. Thus, a^2 has a factor of 11. And a has a factor of 11, because if a is an integer and a^2 is divisible by a prime, then a is divisible by that prime. Therefore, let $a = 11k$ for some integer k. Then $11b^2 = (11k)^2 \Rightarrow b^2 = 11k^2$. So b^2 and b have a common factor of 11. This is a contradiction since $\frac{a}{b}$ is in lowest terms. Hence, the assumption must be false, and so $\sqrt{11}$ is irrational.
6. $\frac{8(10+\sqrt{5})}{95}$
7. a.,b. Irrational. It is impossible to find any polynomial formulas whose quotient equals this.
   c. Rational. The function is the quotient of two polynomials.
   d. $\lim_{x \to +\infty} f(x) = +\infty$; $\lim_{x \to -\infty} f(x) = -\infty$
8. The limit of $f(x)$ as x approaches 2 from the left is infinity.
9, 14. See Additional Answers at the back of this book.

Chapter 5 Review

Resources

From the ***Teacher's Resource File***

- Answer Master for Chapter 5 Review
- Assessment Sourcebook: Chapter 5 Test, Forms A–D Chapter 5 Test, Cumulative Form

Additional Resources

- TestWorks CD-ROM

The main objectives for the chapter are organized in the Chapter Review under the four types of understanding this book promotes—Skills, Properties, Uses, and Representations.

Whereas end-of chapter material may be considered optional in some texts, in UCSMP *Precalculus and Discrete Mathematics* we have selected these objectives and questions with the expectation that they will be covered. Students should be able to answer these questions with about 85% accuracy after studying the chapter.

You may assign these questions over a single night to help students prepare for a test the next day, or you may assign the questions over a two-day period. If you work the questions over two days, then we recommend assigning the *evens* for homework the first night so that students get feedback in class the next day, then assigning the *odds* the night before the test, because answers are provided to the odd-numbered questions.

CHAPTER REVIEW

Questions on SPUR Objectives

SPUR stands for **S**kills, **P**roperties, **U**ses, and **R**epresentations. The Chapter Review questions are grouped according to the SPUR Objectives for this chapter.

SKILLS DEAL WITH THE PROCEDURES USED TO GET ANSWERS.

2–5, 7–28, 30) See margin.

Objective A: *Simplify rational expressions.* *(Lesson 5-2)*

In 1–6, an operation is done with rational expressions.

a. Write as a simple rational expression in lowest terms.

b. State any restrictions on the variables.

1. $\frac{x + 5}{3x - 2} + \frac{4x + 3}{2 - 3x}$ a) -1 b) $x \neq \frac{2}{3}$

2. $\frac{9}{y^2 + 7y + 12} + \frac{4}{y^2 + 8y + 15}$

3. $\frac{z - 3}{2(z + 1)(z - 2)} \cdot \frac{6z - 12}{(z - 3)(z + 4)}$

4. $\frac{2p^2 + p - 1}{p^2 + 6p + 5} \div \frac{6p^2 + p - 2}{p^2 + 11p + 30}$

5. $\frac{t + 2}{t - 5} - \frac{3t + 1}{t + 4}$

6. $\frac{1}{r + 1} - \frac{1}{r - 1}$ a) $\frac{-2}{r^2 - 1}$ b) $r \neq 1$ and $r \neq -1$

In 7 and 8, write the expression in lowest terms.

7. $\frac{6x^2 - 27x - 15}{2x^2 - 11x - 6}$ **8.** $\frac{z^3 - 3z^2 - 4z}{z^4 - z^3 - 12z^2}$

In 9 and 10, write as a simple fraction and state any restrictions on the variables.

9. $\frac{\frac{1}{3} - \frac{3}{a^2}}{\frac{1}{3a} + \frac{1}{a^2}}$ **10.** $\frac{\frac{x^2 + 7x + 12}{x^2 - 25}}{\frac{x^2 - 3x - 18}{x^2 - 3x - 10}}$

In 11–13, show that the first expression simplifies to the second expression, and state any restrictions on the variables.

11. $\frac{z^2 - z - 2}{z^2 - 4z - 5} \cdot \frac{z - 5}{z^2 + z - 6}$, $\frac{1}{z + 3}$

12. $\frac{5}{y^2 - 9} + \frac{7}{y^2 - 2y - 3}$, $\frac{12y + 26}{(y + 1)(y + 3)(y - 3)}$

13. $\frac{\frac{1}{x} + \frac{2}{x^2}}{1 - \frac{4}{x^2}}$, $\frac{1}{x - 2}$

Objective B: *Identify numbers as rational or irrational.* *(Lessons 5-1, 5-6)*

In 14–21, identify each number as rational or irrational. Justify your reasoning.

14. e^5 **15.** -7

16. .01001000100001 . . . (pattern continues)

17. the approximation $\frac{22}{7}$ to π

18. 0 **19.** $9.42\overline{67}$

20. $\sqrt{36} + \frac{8}{3}$ **21.** $\frac{\sqrt{3}}{4}$

Objective C: *Simplify expressions involving radicals.* *(Lesson 5-6)*

In 22–25, rationalize the denominator to simplify the expression.

22. $\frac{5}{3 - \sqrt{5}}$ **23.** $\frac{12}{4 + \sqrt{6}}$

24. $\frac{4\sqrt{3}}{\sqrt{2} + \sqrt{3}}$ **25.** $\frac{-9\sqrt{2}}{\sqrt{5} - \sqrt{2}}$

In 26 and 27, rationalize the numerator.

26. $\frac{3 - \sqrt{2}}{5}$ **27.** $\frac{\sqrt{x + h} - \sqrt{x}}{h}$

Objective D: *Identify rational functions and their domains.* *(Lessons 5-4, 5-7)*

In 28–31, determine if the function defined by the given rule is a rational function. If not, explain why not.

28. $f(x) = \frac{\sqrt{x} - 5}{x + 7}$

29. $f(z) = \frac{z^2 + 7z}{z^3 - z}$ rational

30. $h(\theta) = \frac{\cos \theta}{\sin \theta}$

31. $g(y) = 4y^3 + 3y^2 - 2y + 1$ rational

Additional Answers

2. a. $\frac{13y + 61}{(y + 4)(y + 5)(y + 3)}$
   b. $y \neq -4$, $y \neq -5$, and $y \neq -3$
3. a. $\frac{3}{(z + 1)(z + 4)}$
   b. $z \neq -1$, $z \neq 2$, $z \neq 3$, and $z \neq -4$
4. a. $\frac{p + 6}{3p + 2}$
   b. $p \neq \frac{1}{2}$, $p \neq -\frac{2}{3}$, $p \neq -1$, $p \neq -5$, and $p \neq -6$
5. a. $\frac{-2t^2 + 20t + 13}{(t - 5)(t + 4)}$
   b. $t \neq 5$ and $t \neq -4$
7. $\frac{3(x - 5)}{(x - 6)}$
8. $\frac{z + 1}{z(z + 3)}$
9. $a \neq 3$, $a \neq -3$, and $a \neq 0$
10. $\frac{x^2 + 6x + 8}{x^2 - x - 30}$, $x \neq 6$, $x \neq -3$, $x \neq -2$, and $x \neq -5$
11. a. $\frac{z^2 - z - 2}{z^2 - 4z - 5} \cdot \frac{z - 5}{z^2 + z - 6} = \frac{(z + 1)(z - 2)}{(z + 1)(z - 5)} \cdot \frac{z - 5}{(z - 2)(z + 3)} = \frac{1}{z + 3}$
    b. $z \neq -1$, $z \neq 5$, $z \neq 2$, and $z \neq -3$
12. a. $\frac{5}{y^2 - 9} + \frac{7}{y^2 - 2y - 3} = \frac{5}{(y + 3)(y - 3)} + \frac{7}{(y + 1)(y - 3)} = \frac{5y + 5 + 7y + 21}{(y + 3)(y - 3)(y + 1)} = \frac{12y + 26}{(y + 3)(y - 3)(y + 1)}$
    b. $y \neq -3$, $y \neq -1$, and $y \neq 3$

CHAPTER FIVE

In 32 and 33, determine the values of the independent variable which are excluded from the domain.

32. $f(y) = \frac{(y + 5)(y - 8)}{(y + 2)(y - 3)}$ $y \neq 2$ and $y \neq 3$

33. $h(x) = \frac{x}{x^2 - x}$ $x \neq 0$ and $x \neq 1$

Objective E: *Solve rational equations.* *(Lesson 5-8)*

In 34–38, solve each equation.

34. $1 + \frac{12}{x^2 - 4} = \frac{3}{x - 2}$ $x = 1$

35. $\frac{m}{m - 1} - \frac{2}{m + 3} = \frac{-m + 5}{(m - 1)(m + 3)}$ no solutions

36. $\frac{3}{t} + \frac{2}{t + 1} = 4$ $t = \frac{-3}{4}$ or $t = 1$

37. $\frac{2}{v + 1} - \frac{v - 1}{v} = \frac{1}{v^2 + v}$ $v = 2$

38. $\frac{5}{y + 1} - \frac{7}{y - 2} = 8$ $y = \frac{1}{2}$ or $y = \frac{1}{4}$

39) $\frac{893}{1000}$ 40) $\frac{245}{99}$ 41) $\frac{3583}{9000}$

42) $\frac{-1}{k^2 - k}$, since k is an integer >1, $k(k-1)$ is an integer

PROPERTIES DEAL WITH THE PRINCIPLES BEHIND THE MATHEMATICS.

43–47, 51, 52) See margin.

Objective F: *Prove properties of rational and irrational numbers.* *(Lessons 5-1, 5-6)*

In 39–42, show that each number is a rational number by expressing it as a ratio of integers $\frac{a}{b}$, where $b \neq 0$. See above right.

39. .893

40. $2.\overline{47}$

41. $3.98\overline{1}$

42. $\frac{1}{k} - \frac{1}{k - 1}$, where k is an integer > 1

43. Show that $\sqrt{13}$ is irrational.

In 44–46, *true or false*. Justify your answer.

44. *Every integer is a rational number.*

45. *The product of any two rational numbers is rational.*

46. *The product of any two irrational numbers is irrational.*

47. Prove: *If p is a rational number and q is an irrational number, then p − q is irrational.*

48) d

Objective G: *Use limit notation to describe the behavior of rational functions.* *(Lessons 5-4, 5-5)*

48. *Multiple choice.* The notation $x \to -4^+$ is read
(a) x approaches positive four from the left.
(b) x approaches positive four from the right.
(c) x approaches negative four from the left.
(d) x approaches negative four from the right.

49. Write in words: $\lim_{x \to -\infty} f(x) = 1.3$.
The limit of $f(x)$ as x decreases without bound is 1.3.

50. Consider the function $f: x \to \frac{1}{x + 2}$.
a. What transformation maps $g: x \to \frac{1}{x}$ to function f? $T_{2,0}$
b. Find each.
i. $\lim_{x \to -2^+} f(x)$ ∞ **ii.** $\lim_{x \to -2^-} f(x)$ $-\infty$
iii. $\lim_{x \to -\infty} f(x)$ 0 **iv.** $\lim_{x \to \infty} f(x)$ 0

51. Consider the function h defined by the rule $h(x) = \frac{2x + 5}{x - 6}$.
a. Use limit notation to describe the behavior of the function as $x \to 6^+$.
b. Use limit notation to describe the behavior of the function as $x \to 6^-$.
c. Use limit notation to describe the end behavior of h.

52. Consider the function f defined by $f(t) = \frac{3t^2 - 11}{t^2 - 4}$.
a. Identify the vertical asymptotes.
b. Use limit notation to describe the behavior of f near the value(s) of t indicated in part **a**.
c. Use limit notation to describe the end behavior of f.
d. Sketch a graph of the function.

In 53 and 54, find the oblique asymptote of the graph of the function.

53. $f: x \to \frac{3x^3 + 2x^2 + x}{4x^2 + 2x + 1}$ $y = \frac{3}{4}x + \frac{1}{8}$

54. $g: t \to \frac{18t^2 - 3t + 1}{2t + 5}$ $y = 9t - 24$

It is effective to ask students which questions they still do not understand and use the day or days as a total class discussion of the material which the class finds most difficult.

Assessment

Evaluation The Assessment Sourcebook provides five forms of the Chapter 5 Test. Forms A and B present parallel versions in a short-answer format. Forms C and D offer performance assessment. The fifth test is Chapter 5 Test, Cumulative Form. About 50% of this test covers Chapter 5, 25% of it covers Chapter 4, and 25% of it covers earlier chapters.

For information on grading, see *General Teaching Suggestions: Grading* in the *Professional Sourcebook*, which begins on page T20 in the Teacher's Edition.

26. $\frac{7}{15 + 5\sqrt{2}}$
27. $\frac{1}{\sqrt{x + h} + \sqrt{x}}$
28. Irrational, there are no polynomials whose quotient equals this.
30. Irrational, cos θ and sin θ are not polynomial functions.
43. See Additional Answers at the back of this book.
44. True, every integer a can be expressed as $\frac{a}{1}$.
45. True, if $\frac{a}{b}$ and $\frac{c}{d}$ are two rational numbers, where $b \neq 0$ and $d \neq 0$, then $\frac{a}{b} \cdot \frac{c}{d} = \frac{ac}{bd}$. ac and bd are both integers and $bd \neq 0$ since $b \neq 0$ and $d \neq 0$. Hence, $\frac{ac}{bd}$ is rational.
46. False, counterexample: $\sqrt{2} \cdot \sqrt{2} = 2$
51. a. $\lim_{x \to 6^+} h(x) = +\infty$
b. $\lim_{x \to 6^-} h(x) = -\infty$
c. $\lim_{x \to +\infty} h(x) = 2$; $\lim_{x \to -\infty} h(x) = 2$

47, 52. See Additional Answers at the back of this book.

13. $\frac{\frac{1}{x} + \frac{2}{x^2}}{1 - \frac{4}{x^2}} = \frac{x + 2}{x^2 - 4} = \frac{x + 2}{(x + 2)(x - 2)} = \frac{1}{x - 2}$; $x \neq 0, x \neq -2, x \neq 2$
14. irrational, since e^x is irrational for any nonzero number x
15. rational, because -7 is an integer
16. irrational, the decimal expansion neither terminates or repeats
17. rational, since the decimal expression of $\frac{22}{7}$ repeats, $3.\overline{142857}$.
18. rational, since 0 is an integer
19. rational, equals $\frac{3733}{396}$
20. rational, equals $\frac{26}{3}$
21. irrational, $\sqrt{3}$ is not an integer
22. $\frac{15 + 5\sqrt{5}}{4}$
23. $\frac{24 - 6\sqrt{6}}{5}$
24. $12 - 4\sqrt{6}$
25. $-3\sqrt{10} - 6$

CHAPTER FIVE

Feedback After students have taken the test for Chapter 5 and you have scored the results, return the tests to students for discussion. Class discussion of the questions that caused trouble for the most students can be very effective in identifying and clarifying misunderstandings. You might want to have them write down the items they missed and work, either in groups or at home, to correct them. It is important for students to receive feedback on every chapter test, and we recommend that students see and correct their mistakes before proceeding too far into the next chapter.

Additional Answers

58. True; $\csc y = \frac{1}{\sin y}$, and $\sin y = 0$ for $y = n\pi$, for any integer n

60. $x = (2n + 1)\frac{\pi}{2}$, n an integer

61. Sample: $\frac{x^2 - 16}{x - 4}$

66. a. $v = 3$
    b. $v = 3$: essential
    c. none
    d. x-intercept: $-\sqrt[3]{6} \approx -1.8$; y-intercept: -2
    e. $\lim_{v \to +\infty} f(v) = \infty$; $\lim_{v \to +\infty} f(v) = \infty$
    f.

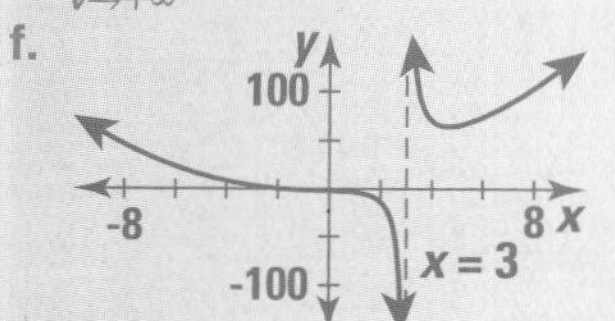

In 55–57, find a constant function, a power function, or a reciprocal of a power function that has the same end behavior as the given function.

55. $h(y) = \frac{7y^4 - 8y^2 - 2y + 1}{3y^2 + 7y + 2}$ $h(y) = \frac{1}{3}y^2$

56. $p(t) = \frac{11t^5 - 5t^4 + 6t^3 + 2t + 1}{9t^5 + 4t^2 - 7t + 2}$ $p(t) = \frac{11}{9}$

57. $q(z) = \frac{z^5 + 4z^2 + 2}{4z^6 + z - 1}$ $q(z) = \frac{1}{4z}$

58, 60, 61) See margin.

Objective H: *Classify discontinuities as essential or removable.* *(Lessons 5-4, 5-7)*

58. *True or false.* The cosecant function has essential discontinuities at $y = n\pi$ $\forall$ integers n.

59. The function $f: x \to \frac{x + 5}{x^2 - 25}$ is undefined at $x = 5$ and at $x = -5$. c) $f(5) = -0.1$
    a. At which of these values is there an essential discontinuity? 5
    b. At which of these values is there a removable discontinuity? -5
    c. Redefine the function at the value in part **b** so that the discontinuity is removed.

60. Consider the tangent function $f: x \to \tan x$. For what values of x does this function have essential discontinuities?

61. Construct a rule for a function which has a removable discontinuity at $x = 4$ and which has no essential discontinuities.

USES DEAL WITH APPLICATIONS OF MATHEMATICS IN REAL SITUATIONS.

Objective I: *Apply rational expressions and rational equations.* *(Lessons 5-1, 5-2, 5-8)*

62. The velocity v of a wave is given by the formula

$$v = \frac{\lambda}{\frac{1}{f}},$$

where λ is the wavelength and f is the frequency of the wave. (λ is the distance between two consecutive points in corresponding positions and f is the number of waves passing a given point per time period.) Find a simple expression for the velocity of the wave. $v = f\lambda$

63. Suppose a person drives 10,000 miles a year and a gallon of gas costs \$1.15 on average. How much would this person save in a year by driving a car that gets 25 $\frac{\text{mi}}{\text{gal}}$ over one that gets 18 $\frac{\text{mi}}{\text{gal}}$? $\approx$ \$179

64. A plane capable of flying at 500 miles per hour makes a 3000 mile trip. Because of a headwind, the return flight takes 1.5 hours longer than the original flight, which had the advantage of a tailwind. Find the speed of the wind. 61.6 mph

65. To score computerized tests, two computers work on the task. Working alone the first computer would take c hours and the second computer would take h hours.
    a. What expression represents the portion of the task done by the first computer each hour? $\frac{1}{c}$
    b. What expression represents the portion of the task done by the second computer each hour? $\frac{1}{h}$
    c. Write a single fraction that represents the portion of the task completed each hour if both computers work together. $\frac{c + h}{ch}$
    d. If c is 4 hours and h is 6 hours, how long does it take the two computers to do the job when working together? 2.4 hr

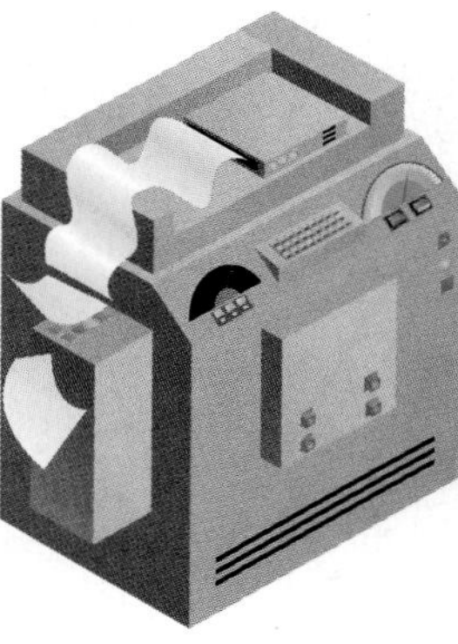

67. a. $x = 1$ and $x = -1$
    b. $x = 1$ and $x = -1$: essential
    c. $y = 2$
    d. x-intercept: none; y-intercept: - 3
    e. $\lim_{x \to +\infty} h(x) = 2$; $\lim_{x \to -\infty} h(x) = 2$
    f. See the graph at the right.

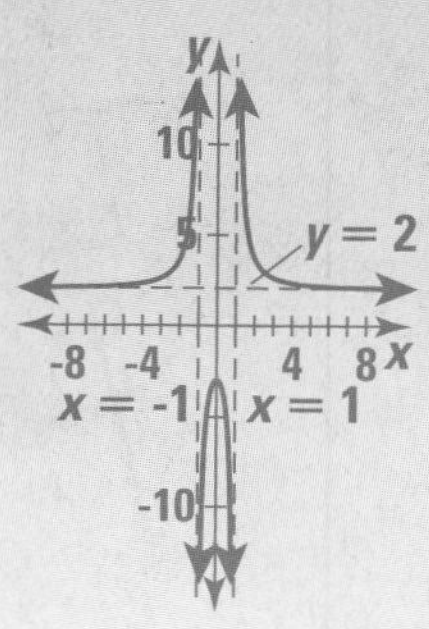

68. a. $x = 0$ and $x = -4$
    b. $x = 0$: essential; $x = -4$: removable
    c. $y = 0$
    d. x-intercept: none; y-intercept: one
    e. $\lim_{x \to +\infty} g(x) = 0$; $\lim_{x \to -\infty} g(x) = 0$
    f. See the graph at the right.

REPRESENTATIONS DEAL WITH PICTURES, GRAPHS, OR OBJECTS THAT ILLUSTRATE CONCEPTS.

Objective J: *Graph rational functions.* *(Lessons 5-3, 5-4, 5-5)*

In 66–68, use the given function. See margin.

a. For what value(s) is the function undefined?

b. Identify any discontinuities as essential or removable.

c. Find an equation for any horizontal asymptotes.

d. Find the x- and y-intercepts.

e. Describe the end behavior.

f. Sketch a graph of the function.

66. $f: v \to \frac{x^3 + 6}{x - 3}$

67. $h: x \to \frac{2x^2 + 3}{x^2 - 1}$

68. $g: x \to \frac{x + 4}{x^2 + 4x}$

Objective K: *Relate the limit of a function to its graph, and find equations for its asymptotes.* *(Lessons 5-3, 5-4, 5-5, 5-7)* See margin.

69. Consider the function f graphed below.

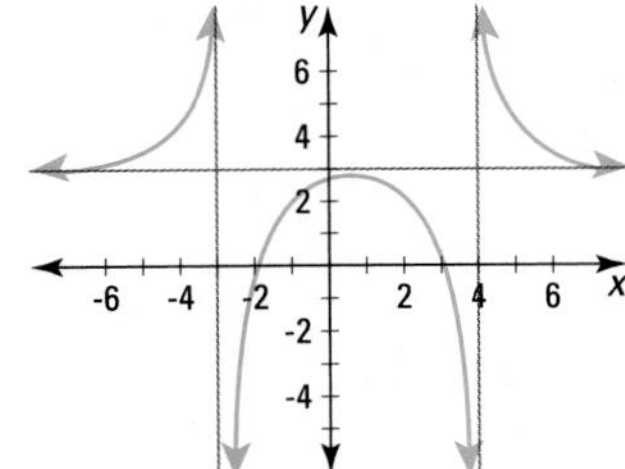

a. Use limit notation to describe the behavior of the function near $x = 4$.

b. Use limit notation to describe the behavior of the function near $x = -3$.

c. Use limit notation to describe the behavior of the function near the horizontal asymptote.

d. Find equations of all asymptotes.

70. Consider a function f with the following properties:

$\lim_{x \to 5^+} f(x) = -\infty$ $\quad \lim_{x \to 5^-} f(x) = -\infty$

$\lim_{x \to \infty} f(x) = -2$ $\quad \lim_{x \to -\infty} f(x) = -2.$

a. Construct a possible graph of function f.

b. Write equations for its horizontal and vertical asymptotes.

71. a. Graph the function $f(x) = \tan x + 3$.

b. Give the asymptotes of $f(x)$.

72. Graph the function f defined by $f(x) = \frac{-1}{(x + 1)^2}$ and write equations for its horizontal and vertical asymptotes.

Objective L: *Use right triangles or graphs to find values of the tangent, cotangent, secant, and cosecant functions.* *(Lesson 5-7)*

In 73 and 74, use the triangle at the right to find the indicated value.

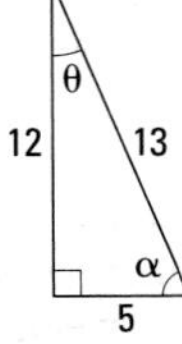

73. $\tan \alpha$ $\frac{12}{5}$

74. $\csc \theta$ $\frac{13}{5}$

75. Use the right triangle shown below to find $\sec \alpha$. $\frac{13}{\sqrt{169 - x^2}}$

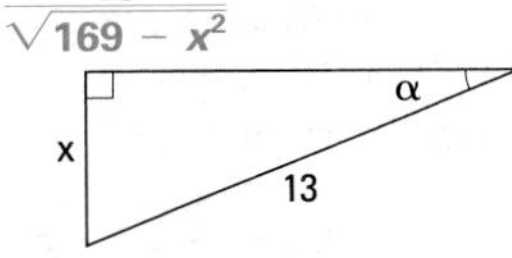

76. Let $\sin x = -.6$ and $\cos x = .8$, and find the value of each. a) $\frac{-3}{4}$ b) $\frac{-4}{3}$ c) $\frac{5}{4}$ d) $\frac{-5}{3}$

a. $\tan x$ **b.** $\cot x$ **c.** $\sec x$ **d.** $\csc x$

77. Suppose $\sin x = \frac{1}{3}$. Find $\csc x$. 3

In 78–80, find the indicated value.

78. $\tan \frac{\pi}{4}$ 1 **79.** $\cot \frac{\pi}{6}$ $\sqrt{3}$ **80.** $\sec \pi$ -1

70. a.

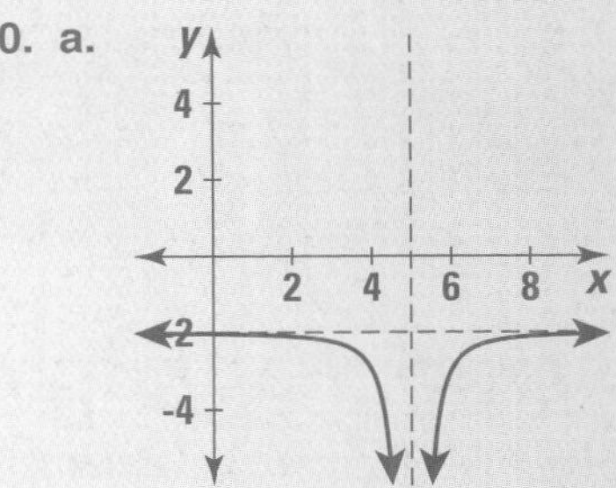

b. $y = -2$, $x = 5$

71. a.

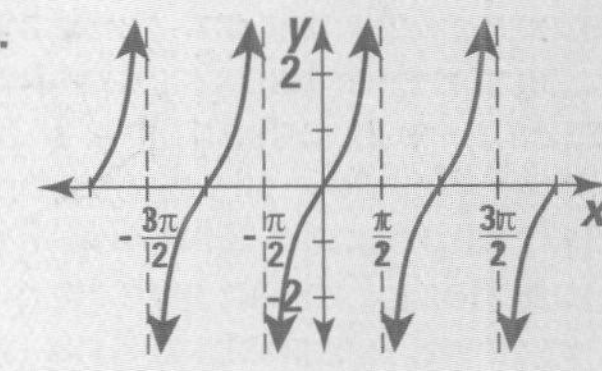

b. $x = (2n + 1)\frac{\pi}{2}$, all integers n

72.

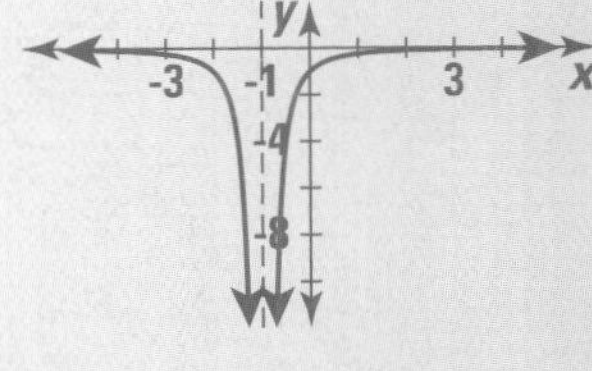

$y = 0$; $x = -1$

68. f.

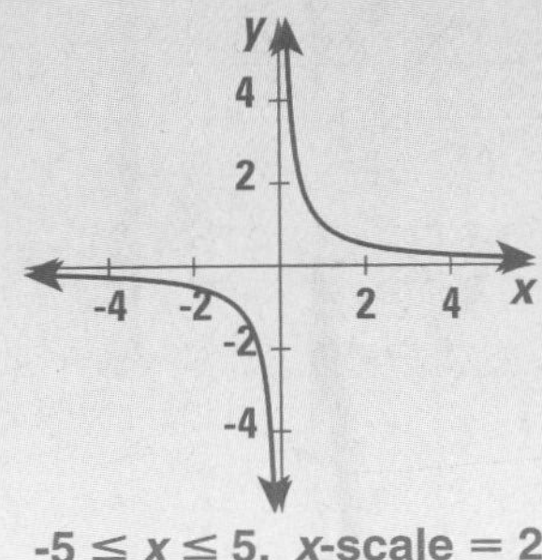

$-5 \le x \le 5$, x-scale = 2
$-5 \le y \le 5$, y-scale = 2

69. a. $\lim_{x \to 4^+} f(x) = \infty$; $\lim_{x \to 4^-} f(x) = -\infty$

b. $\lim_{x \to 3^+} f(x) = -\infty$; $\lim_{x \to 3^-} f(x) = +\infty$

c. $\lim_{x \to \infty} f(x) = 3$; $\lim_{x \to -\infty} f(x) = 3$

d. $x = 4$, $x = -3$, and $y = 3$

Chapter 6 Planner

Chapter 6 Pacing Chart

Day	Full Course	Minimal Course
1	6-1	6-1
2	6-2	6-2
3	6-3	6-3
4	Quiz*; 6-4	Quiz*; begin 6-4.
5	6-5	Finish 6-4.
6	6-6	6-5
7	Quiz*; 6-7	6-6
8	6-8	Quiz*; begin 6-7.
9	Self-Test	Finish 6-7.
10	Review	6-8
11	Test*	Self-Test
12	Comprehensive Test*	Review
13		Review
14		Test*
15		Comprehensive Test*

*in the Teacher's Resource File

Adapting to Individual Needs

The student text is written for the vast majority of students. The chart at the right suggests two pacing plans to accommodate the needs of your students. Students in the Full Course should complete the entire text by the end of the year. Students in the Minimal Course will spend more time when there are quizzes and more time on the Chapter Review. Therefore, these students may not complete all of the chapters in the text.

Options are also presented to meet the needs of a variety of teaching and learning styles. For each lesson, the Teacher's Edition provides a section entitled *Adapting to Individual Needs.* This section regularly includes **Optional Activities, Challenge** problems, **English Language Development** suggestions, and suggestions for providing **Extra Help.** The Teacher's Edition also frequently includes an **Error Alert,** an **Extension,** and an **Assessment** alternative. The options available in Chapter 6 are summarized in the chart below.

In the Teacher's Edition...

Lesson	Optional Activities	Extra Help	Challenge	English Language Development	Error Alert	Extension	Cooperative Learning	Ongoing Assessment
6-1	●	●	●		●	●	●	Oral
6-2	●	●	●		●	●		Written
6-3	●	●	●		●	●		Quiz
6-4	●	●	●		●	●	●	Written
6-5	●	●	●		●	●		Written
6-6	●	●	●		●	●		Quiz
6-7	●	●	●		●	●		Oral
6-8	●	●	●		●	●		Oral

In the Additional Resources...

	In the Teacher's Resource File							
Lesson	Lesson Masters	Teaching Aids*	Answer Masters	Technology Sourcebook	Assessment Sourcebook	Visual Aids**	Technology	Explorations Software
6-1	6-1	53, 57	6-1			53, 57, AM		
6-2	6-2	53	6-2			53, AM		
6-3	6-3	54, 58	6-3	Comp 3	Quiz	54, 58, AM	Graph Explorer	
6-4	6-4	55, 59	6-4			55, 59, AM		
6-5	6-5	55	6-5	Calc 10		55, AM		
6-6	6-6	55, 59	6-6		Quiz	55, 59, AM		6-6
In-class Activity		60	6-7			60, AM		
6-7	6-7	56, 61	6-7			56, 61, AM		6-7
6-8	6-8	56	6-8			56, AM		6-8
End of chapter					Tests			

*Teaching Aids are pictured on pages 348C and 348D.

**Visual Aids provide transparencies for all Teaching Aids and all Answer Masters.

Also available is the Study Skills Handbook which includes study-skill tips related to reading, note-taking, and comprehension.

Integrating Strands and Applications

	6-1	6-2	6-3	6-4	6-5	6-6	6-7	6-8
Mathematical Connections								
Number Sense			●	●	●			
Algebra	●	●	●	●	●	●	●	●
Geometry					●			
Measurement				●	●			●
Logic and Reasoning	●	●	●	●	●	●	●	●
Patterns and Functions	●	●	●	●	●	●	●	●
Discrete Mathematics						●		
Interdisciplinary and Other Connections								
Science		●	●			●	●	●
Social Studies			●		●			●
Multicultural	●	●		●				
Technology	●	●	●	●		●	●	●
Career						●		●
Sports						●		

Teaching and Assessing the Chapter Objectives

Chapter 6 Objectives (Organized into the SPUR catetgories—Skills, Properties, Uses, and Representations)	**Lessons**	**Progress Self-Test Questions**	**Chapter Review Questions**	**In the Teacher's Resource File: Chapter Test, Forms A and B**	**Chapter Test, Forms C**	**Chapter Test, Forms D**
Skills						
A: Without a calculator, use trigonometric identities to express values of trigonometric functions in terms of rational numbers and radicals.	6-4, 6-5, 6-6	1, 5, 6	1-12		2	
B: Evaluate inverse trigonometric functions with or without a calculator.	6-7	3, 4	13-17		3	X
C: Solve trigonometric equations and inequalities algebraically.	6-8	10	18-25		4	
Properties						
D: Prove trigonometric identities and identify their domains.	6-2, 6-4, 6-5, 6-6	2, 8, 9	26-38		1	
Uses						
E: Solve problems using inverse trigonometric functions.	6-7	14	39-41		3	X
F: Use trigonometric equations and inequalities to solve applied problems.	6-8	13	42-44			
Representations						
G: Find an equation for the image of a graph under a transformation.	6-3	11, 12	45-50		5	
H: Use an automatic grapher to test proposed trigonometric identities.	6-1, 6-2	7	51-56			
I: Use graphs to solve trigonometric equations and inequalities.	6-8	15, 16	57-59			

Assessment Sourcebook
Quiz for Lessons 6-1 through 6-3
Quiz for Lessons 6-4 through 6-6
Chapter 6 Test, Forms A–D
Chapter 6 Test, Cumulative Form
Comprehensive Test, Chapters 1–6

TestWorks CD-ROM

Teaching Aids

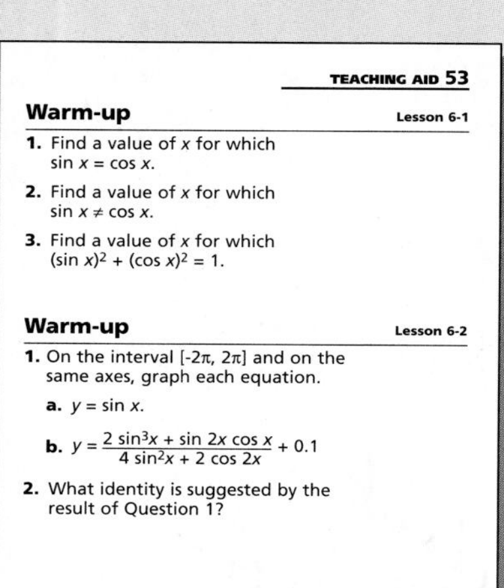

TEACHING AID 53

Warm-up
Lesson 6-1

1. Find a value of x for which $\sin x = \cos x$.
2. Find a value of x for which $\sin x \neq \cos x$.
3. Find a value of x for which $(\sin x)^2 + (\cos x)^2 = 1$.

Warm-up
Lesson 6-2

1. On the interval $[-2\pi, 2\pi]$ and on the same axes, graph each equation.
   a. $y = \sin x$.
   b. $y = \dfrac{2\sin^3 x + \sin 2x \cos x}{4\sin^2 x + 2\cos 2x} + 0.1$
2. What identity is suggested by the result of Question 1?

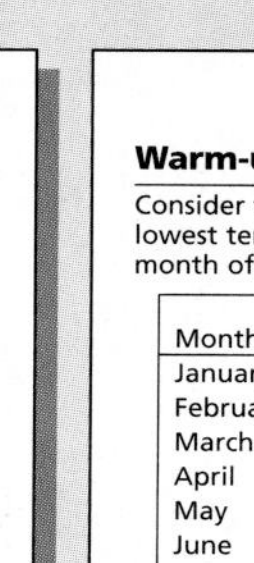

TEACHING AID 54

Warm-up
Lesson 6-3

Consider the following table of highest and lowest temperatures (in °F) on record for each month of the year, for the city of Pittsburgh.

Month	Month Number	Highest	Lowest
January	1	69	-22
February	2	68	-12
March	3	82	-1
April	4	89	14
May	5	91	26
June	6	98	34
July	7	103	42
August	8	100	39
September	9	97	31
October	10	87	16
November	11	82	-1
December	12	74	-12

(Source: Statistical Abstract of the United States 1997)

1. a. Graph the set of ordered pairs (number of month, highest). The pattern will repeat from year to year.
   b. Does it look sinusoidal?
2. a. Graph the set of ordered pairs (number of month, lowest). The pattern will repeat from year to year.
   b. Does it look sinusoidal?
3. a. Graph the set of ordered pairs (highest, lowest) and place the number of the month by each point.
   b. Describe the result.

TEACHING AID 55

Warm-up
Lesson 6-4

1. Find the distance between (cos 150°, sin 150°) and (cos 120°, sin 120°).
2. Find the distance between (cos 30°, sin 30°) and (1, 0°).
3. Generalize the results of Questions 1 and 2.

Warm-up
Lesson 6-5

If $x = \frac{\pi}{2}$ and $y = \frac{\pi}{3}$, find $\sin(x + y)$, $\sin(x - y)$, $\tan(x + y)$, and $\tan(x - y)$.

Warm-up
Lesson 6-6

Without using a calculator, find $\cos 2t$ and $\sin 2t$ for the given value of t. (These answers can be used to verify the identities for $\cos 2x$ and $\sin 2x$ found in the lesson.)

1. $t = \frac{\pi}{8}$
2. $t = -7\pi$
3. $t = -60°$

TEACHING AID 56

Warm-up
Lesson 6-7

Find at least one value of q that satisfies each equation.

1. $\sin q = -1$
2. $\cos q = \frac{\sqrt{3}}{2}$
3. $\tan q = -\sqrt{3}$

Warm-up
Lesson 6-8

Find all real solutions to each equation.

1. $x^2 = 1$
2. $x^3 = 1$
3. $x^4 = 1$
4. $\sqrt{x} = 1$
5. $e^x = 1$
6. $\log x = 1$
7. $\ln x = 1$
8. $|x| = 1$
9. $\lfloor x \rfloor = 1$
10. $\tan x = 1$

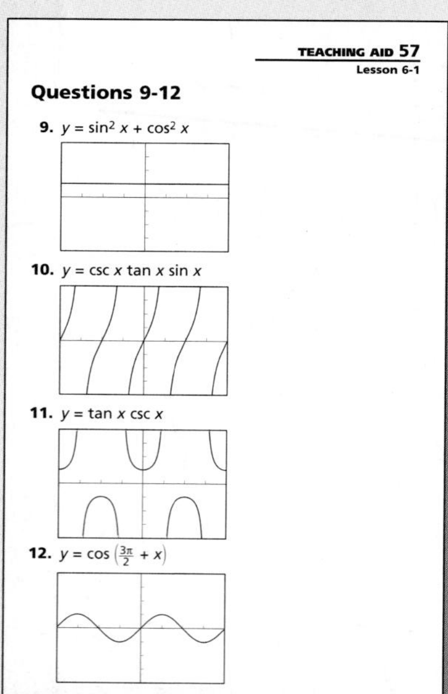

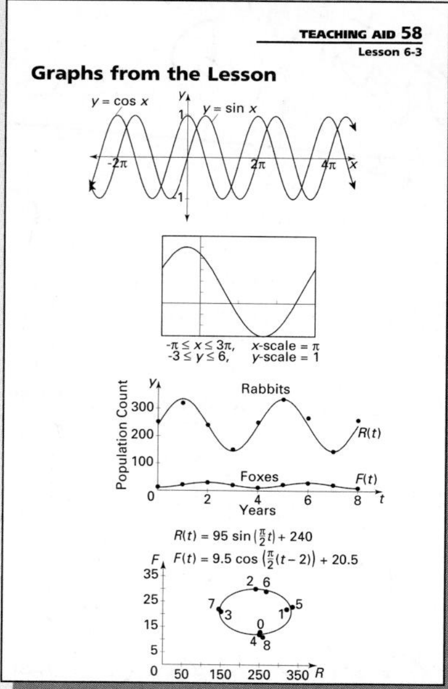

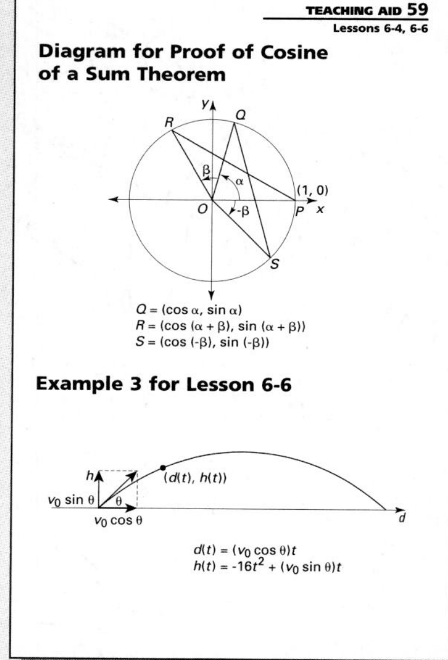

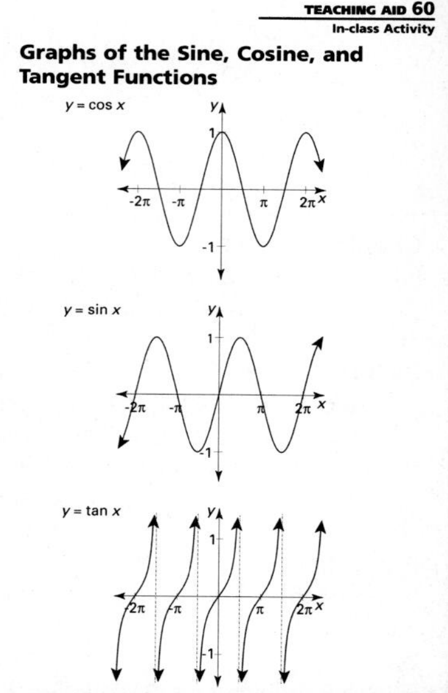

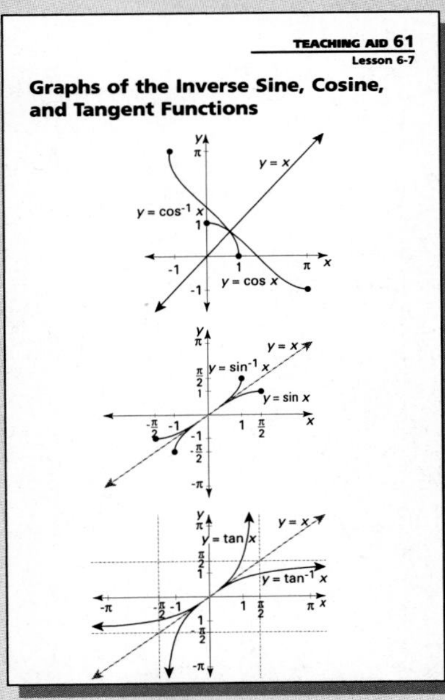
TEACHING AID 61
Lesson 6-7
Graphs of the Inverse Sine, Cosine, and Tangent Functions
y = x
y = cos⁻¹ x
y = cos x
y = sin⁻¹ x
y = sin x
y = tan x
y = tan⁻¹ x

Chapter Opener

Pacing

All lessons in this chapter are designed to be covered in one day. At the end of the chapter, you should plan to spend 1 day to review the Progress Self-Test, 1–2 days for the Chapter Review, and 1 day for a test. You may wish to spend a day on projects, and possibly a day is needed for quizzes and the In-class Activity. This chapter should therefore take 11–14 days. Spending more than 15 days on this chapter is not recommended; there is ample opportunity to review ideas in later chapters.

Using Pages 348–349

It is not well-known today that, before logarithms were invented, trigonometric identities were used for the simplification of computations. The identity $2 \sin x \sin y = \cos(x - y) - \cos(x + y)$ was used for this purpose. You might tell students that they will be able to prove this identity with what they learn in **Question 9** in Lesson 6-4.

You might ask for values of x and y simpler than those on page 349 to check the identity. For instance, if $x = 0$ and $y = \pi$, then the left side equals $2 \sin 0 \sin \pi = 0$, and the right side equals $\cos(-\pi) - \cos \pi = 0$. This confirms the notion that an identity works for all values of the variables in its domain, an idea to be emphasized in the first two lessons of the chapter.

CHAPTER 6

348

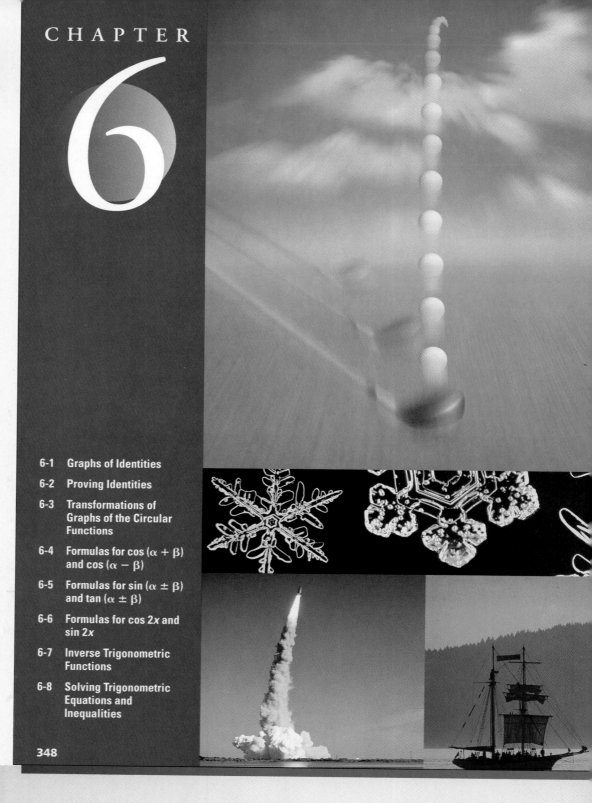

Chapter 6 Overview

This chapter continues the multi-year treatment of trigonometry that is present in UCSMP materials. If students have studied from *Functions, Statistics, and Trigonometry,* they will have seen all this material, but they will not have had as much experience proving identities.

Although the content of this chapter is standard for a precalculus course, the approach taken here is different.

In the first lesson, graphing technology is used to conjecture that an equation might be an identity or to determine a counter-example to invalidate a proposed identity. Proof techniques are introduced in Lesson 6-2 as a means to validate proposed conjectures. Several proof techniques are discussed so that students and teachers can choose the one(s) most appropriate for a situation. Lesson 6-3 applies the ideas from Chapter 3 to graph rubberband transformation images of the parent circular functions sine and cosine.

The next three lessons apply the proof techniques to deduce the familiar formulas for $\cos(\alpha \pm \beta)$ and $\sin(\alpha \pm \beta)$, and then apply these formulas to obtain formulas for $\cos 2x$ and $\sin 2x$. The last of these identities is applied to derive an equation for the range of a projectile.

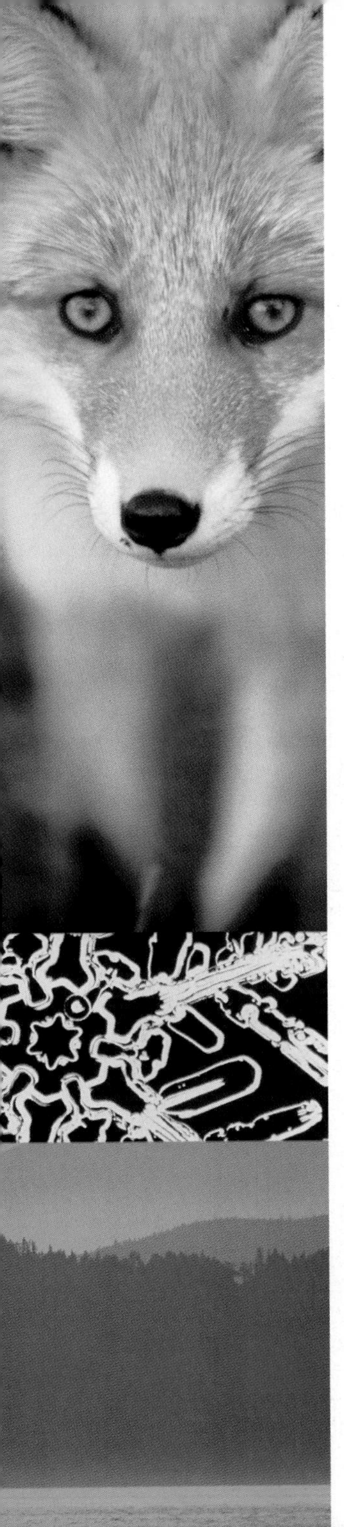

Trigonometric Identities and Equations

How would you proceed if you had to multiply hundreds of pairs of numbers like 5,842,497 and 1,950,903, and give answers accurate to seven significant digits, without a calculator?

That was the problem facing Renaissance astronomers, who had tables of sines and cosines but no calculators, logarithms, or other aids which would simplify the computations resulting from their studies of the planets and stars. Relief came from a surprising area of mathematics: trigonometry. In 1593, the Italian Christopher Clavius applied the *trigonometric identity*

$$2 \sin x \sin y = \cos (x - y) - \cos (x + y)$$

together with tables of trigonometric values to change a multiplication problem into one which used addition and subtraction. For instance, for the numbers at the top of this page, use

$$0.5842497 \approx \sin 35°45'$$

and

$$0.1950903 \approx \sin 11°15'.$$

Now, with $x = 35°45'$ and $y = 11°15'$, the identity yields

$$\begin{aligned} 2 \cdot \sin 35°45' \cdot \sin 11°15' &= \cos (35°45' - 11°15') - \cos (35°45' + 11°15') \\ &= \cos 24°30' - \cos 47° \\ &\approx 0.2279629. \end{aligned}$$

Thus

$$\sin 35°45' \cdot \sin 11°15' = \frac{\cos 24°30' - \cos 47°}{2}.$$

$$0.5842497 \cdot 0.1950903 \approx 0.1139815$$

To multiply the corresponding integers, all that is left is to put the decimal point in the proper place. This is left for you to do.

Clavius credits Nicolaus Raymarus Ursus Dithmarsus with the discovery of the identity. Clavius's proof required heavy use of complicated geometrical arguments. In this chapter you will see many trigonometric identities. From some of these you will be able to prove the identity $2 \sin x \sin y = \cos (x - y) - \cos (x + y)$ as a homework question! We hope you will be as pleased with this material as Clavius was when he wrote "these things are entirely new and full of pleasure and satisfaction."

Photo Connections

The photo collage makes real-world connections to the content of the chapter: trigonometric identities and equations.

Golf Ball: On a golf club, the angle of the club face helps determine the height and distance of a shot—a greater angle gives more height but less distance. In Lesson 6-6, students deal with questions about a projectile (such as a golf ball) launched from ground level.

Fox: The fox preys on small animals that it can easily catch, such as mice, rodents, birds, and insects. In Lesson 6-3, students find that sinusoidal curves are often used to model phenomena that are periodic, such as the interaction of predators and prey.

Snowflakes: At below-freezing temperatures, snow crystals form around tiny particles in clouds. The crystals then cling together to form snowflakes. In the Exploration question in Lesson 6-3, students find that, for most areas, monthly high and low temperatures can be approximated by a sine wave.

Rocket: In **Question 19** on page 390, students express the angle of elevation of a rocket from the tracking station as a function of the altitude of the rocket.

Sailing Ship: Distances on water are often measured in nautical miles, which, because Earth flattens at the poles, vary with latitude. **Question 13** on page 395 deals with latitude and nautical miles.

Chapter 6 Projects

At this time, you might want to have students look over the projects on pages 397–398.

Lesson 6-7 discusses the inverse trigonometric functions in detail and provides a careful treatment of their development. Students are led through a discussion of the need to restrict the trigonometric functions in order for their inverses to be functions and they are provided with the criteria to be used in making those restrictions.

Lesson 6-8 applies the sentence-solving techniques from earlier chapters to equations and inequalities involving trigonometric functions. Students are expected to solve these equations over specific intervals as well as over the set of real numbers. Graphing technology is used here to provide a first stage of analysis for solving inequalities.

Proofs of trigonometric identities are found in all lessons after Lesson 6-2 and students are expected to gain some facility with them. Although this is traditional content, some people have suggested that it is not particularly important. We feel that this amount of emphasis is appropriate, for the following reasons: (1) Proving relationships between values of functions is a broad skill useful in all later mathematics. (2) The key identities have some very nice applications. (3) Some identities are gorgeous and motivate students to want to find others.

Lesson 6-1

Objectives

H Use an automatic grapher to test proposed trigonometric identities.

Resources

From the ***Teacher's Resource File***

- Lesson Master 6-1
- Answer Master 6-1
- Teaching Aids
  53 Warm-up
  57 Questions 9–12

Additional Resources

- Visuals for Teaching Aids 53, 57

Teaching Lesson 6-1

Warm-up

1. Find a value of x for which $\sin x = \cos x$. **Sample:** $\frac{\pi}{4}$
2. Find a value of x for which $\sin x \neq \cos x$. **Sample:** $\frac{\pi}{3}$
3. Find a value of x for which $(\sin x)^2 + (\cos x)^2 = 1$. **Any value will do.**

Notes on Reading

Before beginning this lesson you may want to review the six parent trigonometric functions. Students should be able to provide a rough sketch and be able to identify the domain and range of each function. Facility with the parent functions is essential if students are to formulate conjectures about possible identities. Appendix A can serve as a reference for this review.

LESSON

6-1 *Graphs of Identities*

Consider the equations

$$\text{(a) } \sin^2 x + \cos^2 x = 1 \quad \text{and} \quad \text{(b) } \tan x = \frac{\sin x}{\cos x}.$$

Equation (a) is true for all real numbers x and equation (b) is true for all real numbers x for which $\cos x \neq 0$. Recall from Lesson 5-1 that an *identity* is an equation that is true for all values of the variables for which both sides are defined. The set of all such values is called the **domain of the identity**. Equations (a) and (b) are, therefore, examples of identities.

Identities need not involve the trigonometric functions; $2(x + 3) = 2x + 6$, $\log t^3 = 3 \log t$, and $\frac{1}{N} + \frac{1}{N-2} = \frac{2N-2}{N^2-2N}$ are identities. Also, identities can involve more than one variable; $2(x + y) = 2x + 2y$ is yet another identity.

Discovering Trigonometric Identities

In mathematics, identities are useful for simplifying complicated expressions and for solving equations and inequalities. So it is important to know that an equation is indeed an identity before using it. In the next lesson you will learn to prove identities. In this lesson you will see how to use graphs to discover and conjecture possible identities.

Example 1

Graph the function defined by the equation $y = \cos^2 x - \sin^2 x$ for $-2\pi \leq x \leq 2\pi$. Find another equation that appears to produce the same graph, and conjecture a possible identity.

Solution

It is helpful to use an automatic grapher to graph this function.

$y = \cos^2 x - \sin^2 x$

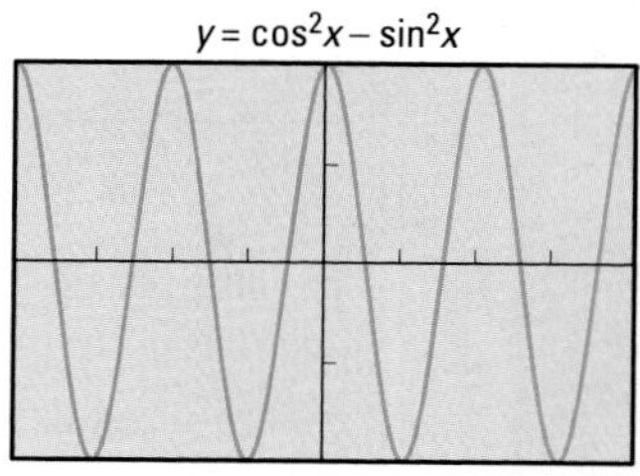

$-2\pi \leq x \leq 2\pi$, x-scale $= \frac{\pi}{2}$
$-1 \leq y \leq 1$, y-scale $= 0.5$

The result looks like a cosine curve with period π. An equation for that curve is $y = \cos 2x$. The graph of $y = \cos 2x$ with the same window is shown on page 351.

350

Lesson 6-1 Overview

Broad Goals The goal of this lesson is to provide students with a visual understanding of the meaning of an identity.

Perspective Students have been introduced to identities in Chapter 5, so the ideas of this lesson are not new. To test whether $f(x) = g(x)$ is true for all x, you can graph $y = f(x)$ and $y = g(x)$ on some appropriate interval and see if the graphs are identical. A key point is that, regardless of how the graphs look, the graphs by themselves do not constitute a proof. However, if the graphs are different, then a value of x can be found for which $f(x) \neq g(x)$. This is a "low-stress" lesson to follow the Chapter 5 test, but it does bring home the difference between identities and other equations, a difference that some students find hard to see.

Technology Students need access to an automatic grapher throughout the lesson and throughout the problem set. If available, use an automatic grapher that allows you to select different colors for graphs. Ask students to use different colored pens or pencils when sketching more than one graph on a single coordinate system.

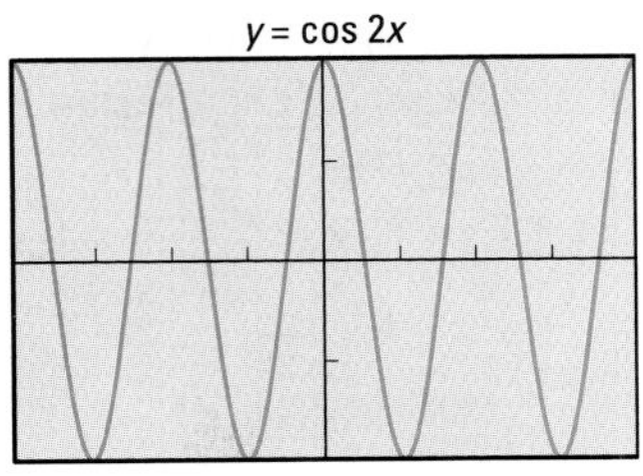

$-2\pi \le x \le 2\pi$, x-scale $= \frac{\pi}{2}$
$-1 \le y \le 1$, y-scale $= 0.5$

The graphs seem to be identical. From this evidence, the equation

$$\cos^2 x - \sin^2 x = \cos 2x$$

seems to hold true for all x in the interval $-2\pi \le x \le 2\pi$. Because the sine and cosine are periodic, it seems reasonable to conjecture that this equation holds for all real numbers x. Thus this equation appears to be an identity.

Be cautious, however, when drawing conclusions from graphs. Even the most powerful computer grapher cannot show the behavior at *every* point on the graph. A graph can only *suggest* identities, not prove them.

Showing that Equations Are Not Identities

A single counterexample shows that a given equation is not an identity; if $f(a) \ne g(a)$ for a single real number a, then the equation $f(x) = g(x)$ is not an identity.

Example 2

Use a graph to help decide whether

$$(\cos x + \sin x)^2 = \cos^2 x + \sin^2 x$$

is an identity. If it is not an identity, find a value for x for which the equation is not true.

Solution

On the same set of axes, graph the functions with equations $y = (\cos x + \sin x)^2$ and $y = \cos^2 x + \sin^2 x$. The first function's graph is shown in blue, the second in orange.

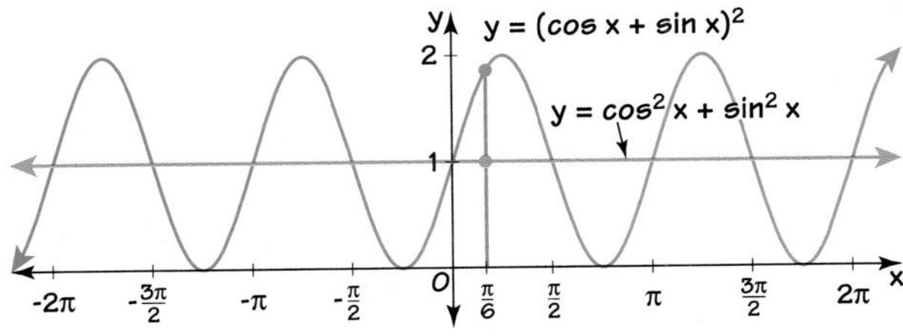

Example 1 uses the graph of $y = \cos 2x$. Students should realize that this graph is the image of the graph of $y = \cos x$ under a horizontal stretch of magnitude $\frac{1}{2}$. That is why the period of $y = \cos 2x$ is $\frac{1}{2}$ the period of $y = \cos x$. These ideas will be used again in Lesson 6-3.

A real number x for which $f(x) \ne g(x)$ is not a counterexample unless x is in the domains of both f and g. For example, -2 is not a counterexample for $\log x^4 = 4 \log x$ since -2 is not in the domain of $\log x$. In the situation of **Example 2,** the domain does not come into play because both sides of the equation are defined for all values of x.

It should be relatively easy for students to see that situations such as those in **Example 2** are not identities because the two graphs do not coincide for many values of the independent variable. If you want graphs that are not identical but are almost identical for part of the domain, you might try $\cos x = 1 - \frac{x^2}{2!} + \frac{x^4}{4!} - \frac{x^6}{6!}$, when $-1 < x < 1$. Such an exercise helps drive home the point that the graph *cannot prove* that a sentence is an identity but can only *suggest* an identity. To show that a sentence is true for all values in its domain, a logical argument is needed. **Question 26** is similar to this.

Ask students if they can explain why $\cos x \tan x = \sin x$ is true for all values of x in the domain of $\tan x$. The proof illustrates that some identities are quite easy to prove. [Begin with the definition of tangent and multiply both sides by $\cos x$.]

Optional Activities

Cooperative Learning After discussing the lesson, you might have students experiment with their knowledge of the six parent trigonometric functions and their automatic graphers to suggest two other identities in the manner of **Questions 9–12.** As a class, you might start a list that students may prove (or disprove!) later on in the chapter. Later attempts to prove any especially challenging possible identities could become extra credit or project work.

[Sample: Some simple identities students might discover are
a) $\cot x \sin x = \cos x$;
b) $\sin\left(x - \frac{\pi}{2}\right) = -\cos x$;
c) $\tan x \csc x = \sec x$]

Additional Examples

1. Find another equation that appears to produce the same graph as $y = 1 - 2\sin^2 x$ for $-2\pi \le x \le 2\pi$, and conjecture a possible identity. $y = \cos 2x$; $1 - 2\sin^2 x = \cos 2x$

2. Does the given equation appear to be an identity? If not, find a value of x for which the equation is not true.
   a. $\sin\left(x + \frac{\pi}{6}\right)\sin\left(x - \frac{\pi}{6}\right) = \sin^2 x - \sin^2 \frac{\pi}{6}$
   It seems to be an identity.
   b. $(\cos x - \sin x)^2 = \cos^2 x - \sin^2 x$
   It is not an identity. Sample: Let $x = \frac{\pi}{6}$. Then the left side has the value $\frac{(\sqrt{3} - 1)^2}{4}$ and the right side equals $\frac{1}{2}$, so the two sides do not have the same value.

3. Use an automatic grapher to help decide whether $\sec x \sin x = \tan x$ seems to be an identity. If so, describe its domain. If not, find a counterexample. This equation seems to be an identity. The domain is the set of all reals x such that $x \neq \frac{k\pi}{2}$ where k is an odd number, that is, the set of all reals x such that $x \not\equiv \frac{\pi}{2} \pmod{\pi}$ or $x \neq \frac{\pi}{2} + k\pi$, where k is an integer.

(Notes on Questions begin on page 354.)

It is apparent that the two graphs are quite different from each other. For instance, the graphs have different values at $\frac{\pi}{6}$. You can check this as follows.

$$\left(\cos\frac{\pi}{6} + \sin\frac{\pi}{6}\right)^2 = \left(\frac{\sqrt{3}}{2} + \frac{1}{2}\right)^2 = \left(\frac{\sqrt{3}+1}{2}\right)^2 = \frac{3 + 2\sqrt{3} + 1}{4} = \frac{4 + 2\sqrt{3}}{4} = 1 + \frac{\sqrt{3}}{2},$$

whereas from the Pythagorean identity,

$$\left(\cos\frac{\pi}{6}\right)^2 + \left(\sin\frac{\pi}{6}\right)^2 = 1.$$

Since $(\cos x + \sin x)^2 = \cos^2 x + \sin^2 x$ is not true when $x = \frac{\pi}{6}$, it is not an identity.

Although the graphs in Example 2 do not suggest an identity, they can be used to help solve the equation $(\cos x + \sin x)^2 = \cos^2 x + \sin^2 x$. The solutions are the x-coordinates of the points of intersection of the graphs. The graphs suggest that the solutions are at $x = \frac{k\pi}{2}$ for all integers k. In Lesson 6-8, the algebraic solution to this equation is discussed.

Watching Out for Domains

One limitation of automatic graphers is that they may not show gaps in the graph of the function at values for which the function is undefined.

Example 3

a. Use an automatic grapher to help decide whether $\cos x \tan x = \sin x$ is an identity.
b. If it seems to be an identity, identify its domain; if it is not an identity, give a counterexample.

Solution

a. Below is the graph of $y = \cos x \tan x$.

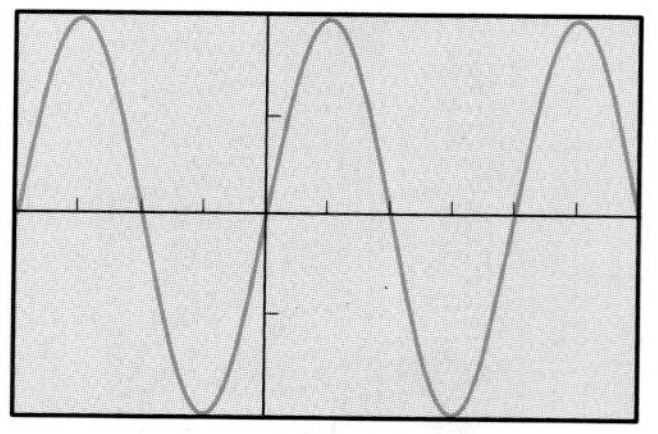

$-2\pi \le x \le 3\pi$, x-scale $= \frac{\pi}{2}$
$-1 \le y \le 1$, y-scale $= 0.5$

Adapting to Individual Needs

Extra Help
Students sometimes have difficulty determining from their automatic graphers whether the graphs of two functions f and g coincide or are just very close to each other. (See the notes on **Question 13.**) They could graph $f - g$, for which $y = (f - g)(x) = 0$ if $f = g$. But since $y = 0$ can also be difficult to discern on an automatic grapher, suggest graphing $f(x) - g(x) + 1$, which yields $y = 1$ if $f = g$.

Challenge
Writing Have students write a report on one of the following topics.
1. Find a table of values of trigonometric functions.
   a. What identities are used to make the table as short as possible? [$\sin(90^\circ - x) = \cos x$]
   b. Try some arithmetic of large numbers using Clavius' method.
   c. How is linear interpolation used to find values in between the table values?
2. John Napier developed the concept of logarithms slightly after, and possibly inspired by, Clavius' work. Write a report on how tables of logarithms were used (until just a few years ago) in the arithmetic of large numbers.

Technique 2

Rewrite each side *independently* until expressions are obtained that are known to be equal.

When using this technique, since you cannot be sure that the proposed identity actually is an identity until you have finished, you should not write an equal sign between the two sides until the very end. We draw a vertical line between the two sides as a reminder of this restriction. A proof will, therefore, have the following form.

$$\begin{array}{r|l} A & B \\ = \ldots & = \ldots \\ = \ldots & = \ldots \\ = E & = E \end{array}$$
$$\therefore \quad A = B$$

The steps of the derivation must show that $A = E$ and that $B = E$. Then $A = B$ follows by the symmetric and transitive properties of equality.

Proof

For all real numbers x for which tan x and sec x are defined,

	$1 + \tan^2 x$	$\sec^2 x$	
definition of tangent	$= 1 + \frac{\sin^2 x}{\cos^2 x}$	$= \frac{1}{\cos^2 x}$	definition of secant
Distributive Property	$= \frac{\cos^2 x + \sin^2 x}{\cos^2 x}$		
Pythagorean Identity	$= \frac{1}{\cos^2 x}$		

$\therefore \quad 1 + \tan^2 x = \sec^2 x$ Transitive Property of Equality

Technique 3

Begin with a known identity and transform it using reversible steps until the desired identity appears.

A natural identity to use is the Pythagorean Identity $\sin^2 x + \cos^2 x = 1$. Because $\tan x = \frac{\sin x}{\cos x}$, the quantity $\tan x$ can be introduced into the Pythagorean Identity by dividing both sides by $\cos^2 x$.

Proof

For all real numbers x,

	$\sin^2 x + \cos^2 x = 1$	Pythagorean Identity
$\Leftrightarrow$	$\frac{\sin^2 x}{\cos^2 x} + \frac{\cos^2 x}{\cos^2 x} = \frac{1}{\cos^2 x}$	$M_{\frac{1}{\cos^2 x}}$, provided $\cos x \neq 0$
$\Leftrightarrow$	$\tan^2 x + 1 = \sec^2 x$	definitions of tangent and secant

This shows that the equation $\tan^2 x + 1 = \sec^2 x$ holds for all x for which $\cos x \neq 0$.

In **Technique 1** we write "left side" and then what it equals. We believe this helps students focus on the idea of beginning with one side of the proposed identity and transforming it until it equals the other side, at which time we write "right side." Point out that the phrases "left side" and "right side" are for recording only and are not part of the proof.

In **Technique 2,** known identities are used to transform both sides simultaneously. However, insist that students draw a vertical line between the two sides until they have shown that the two sides yield the same result. This vertical line should help remind students that they are not permitted to add a quantity to both sides or to multiply both sides by a quantity unless they already know the sides are equal.

Although we present **Technique 3** as an alternative, it is likely that many students will feel uncomfortable with this method, despite the fact that it is quite powerful. To be successful with this technique, students must be able to choose the appropriate identity with which to start the proof. This is difficult for most students because they frequently lack the mathematical sophistication or experience to make the proper choice for the starting identity. With Technique 3, students should not become discouraged if their first choice for a starting identity fails to lead to the desired result. Remind students that mathematicians often try several paths before finding the one that is successful in obtaining new knowledge.

For **Technique 4,** point out to students that the final line of this technique is the beginning line of Technique 3. Mathematicians will sometimes do a proof "backwards." In private they will begin with Technique 4 and apply reversible steps until they achieve an identity. Then, for the written proof, they begin with the identity derived by Technique 4. This should explain how, in Technique 3, $\sin^2 x + \cos^2 x = 1$ was "a natural identity to use."

Optional Activities

Question 22 introduces students to hyperbolic sines and cosines. Depending on your students you might want to discuss these functions further, especially as some scientific calculators contain a "hyp" key that is used in conjunction with the "cos" and "sin" keys to evaluate the hyperbolic functions cosh and sinh. Graphing calculators can also be used to graph these functions.

The definitions also provide a useful vehicle for reviewing the exponential function:

$\cosh x = \frac{e^x + e^{-x}}{2}$

$\sinh x = \frac{e^x - e^{-x}}{2}$.

Technique 4

Transform both sides of the equation to be proved using reversible steps until an equation known to be an identity appears.

When you use this technique, keep the domain of the identity in mind.

Proof

For all real numbers x for which $\cos x \neq 0$,

$$\tan^2 x + 1 = \sec^2 x$$

$$\Leftrightarrow \quad \frac{\sin^2 x}{\cos^2 x} + 1 = \frac{1}{\cos^2 x} \qquad \text{definitions of tangent and secant}$$

$$\Leftrightarrow \quad \cos^2 x\left(\frac{\sin^2 x}{\cos^2 x} + 1\right) = \cos^2 x \cdot \frac{1}{\cos^2 x} \qquad M_{\cos^2 x} \text{ (reversible since } \cos x \neq 0)$$

$$\Leftrightarrow \quad \sin^2 x + \cos^2 x = 1 \qquad \text{Distributive Property}$$

The last line is true $\forall$ x because it is the Pythagorean Identity. Consequently, $\tan^2 x + 1 = \sec^2 x$.

Because $\tan x = \frac{\sin x}{\cos x}$ and $\sec x = \frac{1}{\cos x}$, both $\tan x$ and $\sec x$ are undefined when $\cos x = 0$. It follows that the domain of the identity is the set of all x for which $\cos x \neq 0$. But $\cos x = 0$ for all numbers of the form $\frac{\pi}{2} + n\pi$ where n is an integer. Consequently, the domain is the set of all x such that $x \neq \frac{\pi}{2} + n\pi$ for any integer n; that is, the set of all x such that $x \not\equiv \frac{\pi}{2} \pmod{\pi}$.

When using Technique 4, it is essential that you explicitly indicate the reversible steps. You must take care when multiplying both sides of the equation by an expression containing a variable. Unless the proof excludes those values of the variable that make the expression 0 (as we did by noting $\cos x \neq 0$), the step will not be reversible.

When doing proofs, unless you are asked to use a particular technique, you can use any of these methods.

All the above proofs use the Pythagorean Identity: $\sin^2 x + \cos^2 x = 1$. At this point, you are expected to know that identity, the definitions of the trigonometric functions, and the identities $\sin(-x) = -\sin x$ and $\cos(-x) = \cos x$. In the next two lessons, these properties are employed to deduce some additional very powerful and important identities.

QUESTIONS

Covering the Reading

1. a. Use Technique 1 to prove that $\cot^2 x + 1 = \csc^2 x$ for all real numbers x for which both sides are defined.
   b. What is the domain of the identity in part **a**?
   See margin.
2. Use Technique 2 to prove the identity in Question 1. See margin.

2.

	$\cot^2 x + 1$	$\csc^2 x$	
Def. of cot	$= \frac{\cos^2 x}{\sin^2 x} + \frac{\sin^2 x}{\sin^2 x}$	$= \frac{1}{\sin^2 x}$	Def. of csc
Add of fractions	$= \frac{\cos^2 x + \sin^2 x}{\sin^2 x}$		
Pyth. Identity	$= \frac{1}{\sin^2 x}$		
$\therefore \cot^2 x + 1 = \csc^2 x$			

Additional Examples

Have students use all four techniques on the identity $\sin x \cot x = \cos x$.

Technique 1:
$\sin x \cot x = \sin x \cdot \frac{\cos x}{\sin x} = \cos x$.

Technique 2:

$\sin x \cot x$	$\cos x$
$= \sin x \cdot \frac{\cos x}{\sin x}$	$= \cos x$
$= \cos x$	$= \cos x$

$\therefore \sin x \cot x = \cos x$

Technique 3: From the definition of cotangent, $\cot x = \frac{\cos x}{\sin x}$. Multiply both sides by $\sin x$ (a reversible step since $\sin x \neq 0$) to get the desired identity.

Technique 4: Begin with $\sin x \cot x = \cos x$. Divide both sides by $\sin x$ to obtain $\cot x = \frac{\cos x}{\sin x}$, a known identity.

Additional Answers

1. a. left side: $\cot^2 x + 1$
   $= \frac{\cos^2 x}{\sin^2 x} + \frac{\sin^2 x}{\sin^2 x}$ Def. of cot
   $= \frac{\cos^2 x + \sin^2 x}{\sin^2 x}$ Add. of fractions
   $= \frac{1}{\sin^2 x}$ Pythagorean Identity
   $= \csc^2 x$ Def. of csc
   $=$ right side
   $\therefore \cot^2 x + 1 = \csc^2 x$ for all real numbers x for which both sides are defined.
   b. $\{x: x \neq n\pi, \forall \text{ integers } n\}$

LESSON MASTER 6-2

Questions on SPUR Objectives
See pages 401–403 for objectives.

Properties Objective D

In 1–4, prove the identity and specify its domain. Sample proofs are given.

1. $\sec^2 x + \csc^2 x = \sec^2 x \csc^2 x$
   $\sec^2 x + \csc^2 x = \frac{1}{\cos^2 x} + \frac{1}{\sin^2 x} = \frac{\sin^2 x + \cos^2 x}{\cos^2 x \sin^2 x} = \frac{1}{\cos^2 x \sin^2 x} = \frac{1}{\cos^2 x} \cdot \frac{1}{\sin^2 x} = \sec^2 x \csc^2 x$
   domain: $\{x: x \neq \frac{n\pi}{2}, n \text{ an integer}\}$
2. $\sin^4 x - \cos^4 x = \frac{\tan x - \cot x}{\sec x \csc x}$ domain: $\{x: x \neq \frac{n\pi}{2}, n \text{ an integer}\}$
   $\sin^4 x - \cos^4 x = \frac{\frac{\sin x}{\cos x} - \frac{\cos x}{\sin x}}{\frac{1}{\cos x} \cdot \frac{1}{\sin x}}$
   $= \frac{\sin^2 x - \cos^2 x}{\cos x \sin x} \cdot \frac{\cos x \cdot \sin x}{1} = \sin^2 x - \cos^2 x \cdot 1$
   $= (\sin^2 x - \cos^2 x)(\sin^2 x + \cos^2 x)$
   $= \sin^4 x - \cos^4 x$
3. $\tan\theta + \cot\theta = \sec\theta \csc\theta$
   $\tan\theta + \cot\theta = \frac{\sin\theta}{\cos\theta} + \frac{\cos\theta}{\sin\theta} = \frac{\sin^2\theta + \cos^2\theta}{\cos\theta \sin\theta} = \frac{1}{\cos\theta \sin\theta} = \sec\theta \csc\theta$
   domain: $\{x: x \neq \frac{n\pi}{2}, n \text{ an integer}\}$
4. $\cot 2x \tan 2x = \sin 2x \csc 2x$
   $\cot 2x \tan 2x = \frac{1}{\tan 2x} \cdot \tan 2x = 1 = \sin 2x \cdot \frac{1}{\sin 2x} = \sin 2x \csc 2x$
   domain: $\{x: x \neq \frac{n\pi}{4}, n \text{ an integer}\}$
5. Fill in the blank to make an identity: $\cos x + \sin x \tan x =$ $\sec x$

358

3. Use Technique 3 or 4 to derive the identity of Question 1. (Identify which technique you use.) See margin.

4. Consider the following identity: $\sin x \cot x = \cos x$.
   a. Give the domain of the identity. b. Prove the identity.
See margin.

Applying the Mathematics

In 5–8, prove the identity and give its domain. See margin.

5. $\cos x \tan x = \sin x$

6. $\tan x \cot x = \cos^2 x + \sin^2 x$

7. $\csc^2 x \sin x = \frac{\sec^2 x - \tan^2 x}{\sin x}$

8. $\tan x + \cot x = \sec x \csc x$

9. Use an automatic grapher or calculator to determine whether $\sin^2 x (\cot^2 x + 1) = 1$ might be an identity. If you think it might be, prove it; if you think it is not, give a counterexample. See margin.

10. Suppose x is in the interval $\frac{3\pi}{2} < x < 2\pi$ and $\tan x = -\frac{3}{8}$. Use trigonometric identities to determine each.
   a. $\cot x$ $-\frac{8}{3}$ b. $\sec x$ $\frac{\sqrt{73}}{8}$ c. $\sin x$ $\frac{-3}{\sqrt{73}}$

11. Here is a graph of $y = \tan^2 x$. Use the identity $\tan^2 x + 1 = \sec^2 x$ to sketch a graph of $y = \sec^2 x$. See left.

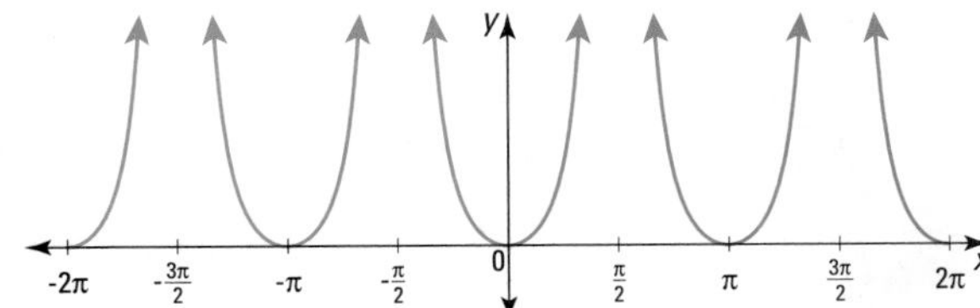

11) [graph: y-axis 2, 4, 6, 8, 10; x-axis $-\frac{3\pi}{2}$, $-\frac{\pi}{2}$, $\frac{\pi}{2}$, $\frac{3\pi}{2}$]

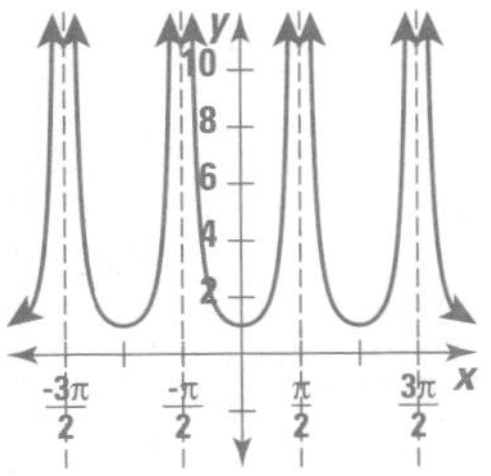

13a) $\sin x$, $\tan x$, $\csc x$, $\cot x$
b) $\cos x$, $\sec x$

14) $\frac{9(x-3)}{x(1-3x)}$, $x \neq 0$, $x \neq \frac{1}{3}$

15a) $\{n: n = 3 + 7q$ for any integer $q\}$
b) The set in part a is the set of all integers with remainder of 3 when divided by 7.

Review

12. Solve $\frac{1}{x} + \frac{4}{x^2} = \frac{x+4}{5x}$. *(Lesson 5-8)* $x = 5$ or $x = -4$

13. Let f be one of the six trigonometric functions sin, cos, tan, cot, sec, csc.
   a. For which of these functions is $f(-x) = -f(x)\ \forall\ x$?
   b. For which of these functions is $f(-x) = f(x)\ \forall\ x$? *(Lessons 2-6, 5-7)*
See left.

14. Simplify and state any restrictions on the variable. *(Lesson 5-2)*
$$\frac{\frac{3}{x} - \frac{9}{x^2}}{\frac{1}{3x} - 1}$$

15. a. Here is a congruence class mod 7: {. . . , 3, 10, 17, 24, 31, . . .}. Describe this congruence class algebraically.
   b. Relate your description in part **a** to the results for division by 7 as expressed in the Quotient-Remainder Theorem. *(Lessons 4-2, 4-5)*

Notes on Questions

Questions 1–3 All the techniques of the lesson are covered here.

Question 4 See *Additional Examples* on page 358.

Question 10 Error Alert For students whose answers have the wrong signs, the following diagram may be helpful. The trigonometric functions whose values are positive within each quadrant are shown.

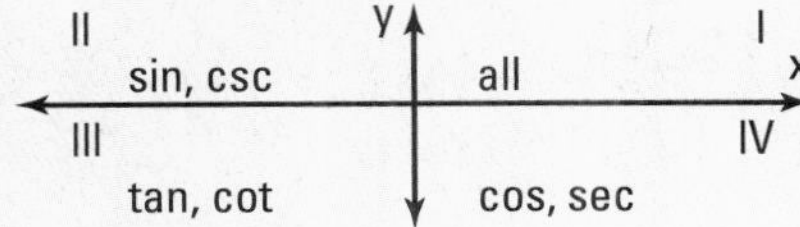

Question 11 Ask students why they should know in advance why the graphs of both equations are never below the x-axis. [Squares of real numbers are nonnegative.]

Question 13 Classifying each trigonometric function as odd or even can be helpful for determining whether a given equation is an identity for all real numbers x. If one side is a formula for an odd function and the other for an even function, they cannot be equal for all x.

Question 15a Another way to describe the set of integers in the congruence class is as the solutions to $x \equiv 3 \pmod 7$.

Additional Answers
3–9. See Additional Answers at the back of this book.

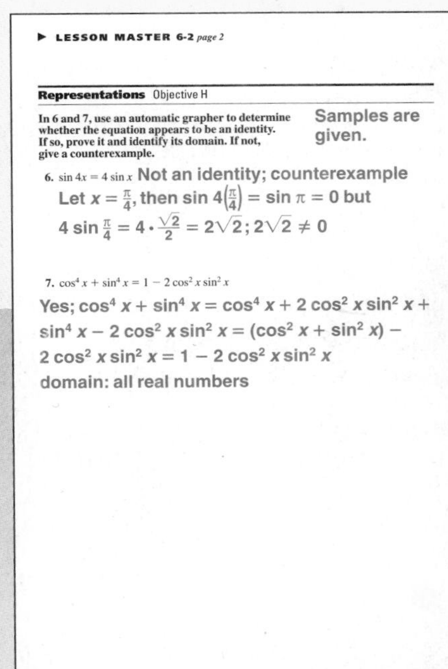
▸ LESSON MASTER 6-2 *page 2*

Representations Objective H

In 6 and 7, use an automatic grapher to determine whether the equation appears to be an identity. If so, prove it and identify its domain. If not, give a counterexample. Samples are given.

6. $\sin 4x = 4 \sin x$ Not an identity; counterexample Let $x = \frac{\pi}{4}$, then $\sin 4\left(\frac{\pi}{4}\right) = \sin \pi = 0$ but $4 \sin \frac{\pi}{4} = 4 \cdot \frac{\sqrt{2}}{2} = 2\sqrt{2}$; $2\sqrt{2} \neq 0$

7. $\cos^4 x + \sin^4 x = 1 - 2\cos^2 x \sin^2 x$
Yes; $\cos^4 x + \sin^4 x = \cos^4 x + 2\cos^2 x \sin^2 x + \sin^4 x - 2\cos^2 x \sin^2 x = (\cos^2 x + \sin^2 x) - 2\cos^2 x \sin^2 x = 1 - 2\cos^2 x \sin^2 x$
domain: all real numbers

Adapting to Individual Needs

Extra Help
You might invite students to begin a notebook of trigonometric identities. Tell them to add new identities as they are proved. Keep a record of how each identity was proved. These identities and techniques of proof should be used in helping prove more identities. Be sure that each identity is accompanied by all restrictions on its domain.

Challenge
Have students simplify each expression as either a constant or as one of the six trigonometric functions.
1. The product of all six trigonometric functions [1]
2. The product of any five of the six trigonometric functions [The reciprocal of the sixth function]
3. $\sec x - \sin^2 x \sec x$ [$\cos x$]
4. $\sin^4 x + 2\cos^2 x - \cos^4 x$ [1]

Notes on Questions

Question 19 Science Connection Students may wonder why the oil company does not drill above the point of the oil-bearing rock near the surface? (Because they would run out of oil more quickly.)

Question 22 This question is extended in the *Optional Activities* on page 357.

Follow-up for Lesson 6-2

Practice

For more questions on SPUR Objectives, use **Lesson Master 6-2** (shown on pages 358–359).

Assessment

Written Communication Have each student select one of **Questions 5–8** and solve it using a technique different from the one they used originally and compare results. [Students use various techniques for proving trigonometric identities.]

Extension

Building off of **Question 10,** ask students to find expressions for the three reciprocal trigonometric functions of θ, given that $\tan\theta = \frac{a}{b}$, $a \neq 0$, $b \neq 0$. Have them justify their work using identities in the lesson. [$\cot\theta = \frac{b}{a}$; $\sec\theta = \frac{\pm\sqrt{a^2+b^2}}{b}$; $\csc\theta = \frac{\pm\sqrt{a^2+b^2}}{a}$] Then have students find expressions for sin θ and cos θ, and explain why the expressions make sense in terms the definitions of sine, cosine, and tangent.

[$\sin\theta = \frac{a}{\sqrt{a^2+b^2}}$; $\cos\theta = \frac{b}{\sqrt{a^2+b^2}}$. $\tan\theta = \frac{y}{x}$, so in this question, $y = a$ and $x = b$. $\sin\theta = \frac{y}{r}$ and $\cos\theta = \frac{x}{r}$, but $r = \sqrt{a^2+b^2}$. Substitution yields the expressions above.]

Project Update Project 2, *"Pseudotrigonometric" Functions,* on page 398, relates to the content of this lesson.

16. **a.** Give an equation for the image of the graph of $y = 2^x$ under the scale change $(x, y) \rightarrow (x, 8y)$. $y = 8(2^x)$
    b. Give an equation for the image of the graph of $y = 2^x$ under the translation T: $(x, y) \rightarrow (x - 3, y)$. $y = 2^{x+3}$
    c. Your answers to parts **a** and **b** should be equivalent equations. Why? *(Lessons 2-7, 3-8)* $2^{x+3} = 2^x \cdot 2^3 = 8(2^x)$

17. Give an equation for the image of the graph of $y = \sin x$ under a translation $\frac{\pi}{2}$ units to the left. *(Lessons 2-6, 3-8)* $y = \sin\left(x + \frac{\pi}{2}\right)$

18. Let (a, b) be the image of $(1, 0)$ under a rotation of θ with center $(0, 0)$. Give the distance between $(1, 0)$ and (a, b). *(Previous course, Lesson 2-6)* $d = \sqrt{(a-1)^2 + b^2}$ or $\sqrt{2 - 2\cos\theta}$

19. Oil company geologists have determined that there is a rich strip of oil-bearing rock starting 30 m underground and descending at 28° to the horizontal, as pictured. To get the optimal amount of crude oil from this source, they decide to build the well 750 m away from the initial spot. How deep do they need to drill? *(Lesson 2-6)* ≈ 429 m

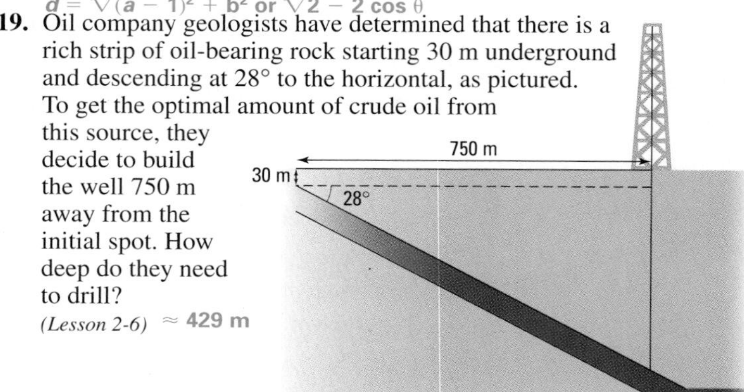

20. Determine whether the following argument is valid or invalid. Justify your reasoning. *(Lessons 1-6, 1-7)* invalid; inverse error

    If the septic tank is cleaned and the electrical wires are repaired, then the Gutierrez family will buy the house.

    The septic tank is not cleaned, or the electrical wires are not repaired.

    Therefore, the Gutierrez family does not buy the house.

21. *Multiple choice.* $\forall x$ and $\forall y$, $x - y =$ _?_. *(Previous course, Lesson 1-1)*
    (a) $y - x$ (b) $-(y - x)$ (c) $-x + y$ (d) $-(x - y)$ (e) $-(x + y)$
    b

Exploration

22. There are functions called the *hyperbolic cosine* and *hyperbolic sine* functions. See margin.
    a. Using other references, find how they are defined.
    b. Find one or more hyperbolic identities analogous to the trigonometric identities mentioned in this lesson.

Additional Answers

22. a. Hyperbolic cosine: $\cosh x = \frac{1}{2}(e^x + e^{-x})$; Hyperbolic sine: $\sinh x = \frac{1}{2}(e^x - e^{-x})$
    b. Samples: $\cosh^2 x - \sinh^2 x = 1$; $\frac{\sinh x}{\cosh x} = \tanh x$; $1 - \tanh^2 x = \text{sech}^2 x$

Setting Up Lesson 6-3

You can use **Question 11** as an introduction to the next lesson, pointing out how nice it is to be able to use equations to see how graphs are related to each other. Also be sure to discuss **Questions 16 and 17.**

LESSON

6-3

Transformations of Graphs of the Circular Functions

red fox (See page 363)

You can discover identities using graphs. For instance, below are graphed $y = \sin x$ (in blue) and $y = \cos x$ (in orange). It certainly looks as if the sine graph is the translation image of the cosine graph $\frac{\pi}{2}$ units to the right. Using the Graph-Translation Theorem from Lesson 3-8, that would mean $y = \sin x$ and $y = \cos\left(x - \frac{\pi}{2}\right)$ have the same graph.

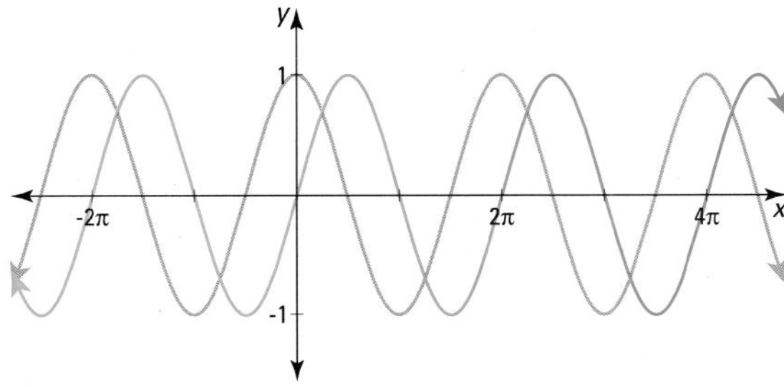

This would signify the identity

$$\sin x = \cos\left(x - \frac{\pi}{2}\right).$$

In the next lesson, this equation will be proved to be an identity.

Rubberband Transformation Images of Circular Functions

Translation and scale-change images of sine and cosine graphs are often found in models of periodic phenomena. The following example explores the effect of a rubberband transformation on the graph of $y = \cos x$.

Lesson 6-3

Objectives

G Find an equation for the image of a graph under a transformation.

Resources

From the ***Teacher's Resource File***

- Lesson Master 6-3
- Answer Master 6-3
- Assessment Sourcebook: Quiz for Lessons 6-1 through 6-3
- Teaching Aids 54 Warm-up 58 Graphs from the Lesson
- Technology Sourcebook Computer Master 3

Additional Resources

- Visuals for Teaching Aids 54, 58
- Graph Explorer or similar software

Teaching Lesson 6-3

Warm-up

Consider the following table of highest and lowest temperatures (in °F) on record for each month of the year, for the city of Pittsburgh.

Month	Month Number	Highest	Lowest
Jan	1	69	-22
Feb	2	68	-12
Mar	3	82	-1
Apr	4	89	14
May	5	91	26
Jun	6	98	34
Jul	7	103	42
Aug	8	100	39
Sep	9	97	31
Oct	10	87	16
Nov	11	82	-1
Dec	12	74	-12

(Source: Statistical Abstract of the United States 1997)

(Warm-up continues on page 362.)

Lesson 6-3 Overview

Broad Goals The major goal of this lesson is the modeling of data using sine waves. To achieve this goal, rubberband transformation images of the graphs of the sine and cosine function are discussed, and the connection with parametric equations is made.

Perspective The Graph-Transformation Theorems deal with the effects on the graph of a sentence in x and y by the replacements $x - h$ and $y - k$ (translation), by the replacements $\frac{x}{a}$ and $\frac{y}{b}$ (scale changes), and by the replacements $\frac{x-h}{a}$ and $\frac{y-k}{b}$ (rubberband transformations). Traditionally, replacements like these were discussed for the sine and cosine functions but not for nontrigonometric functions. Here, because students have already studied these replacements in one or two prior courses,

(Overview continues on page 362.)

1. a. Graph the set of ordered pairs (number of month, highest). The pattern will repeat from year to year.

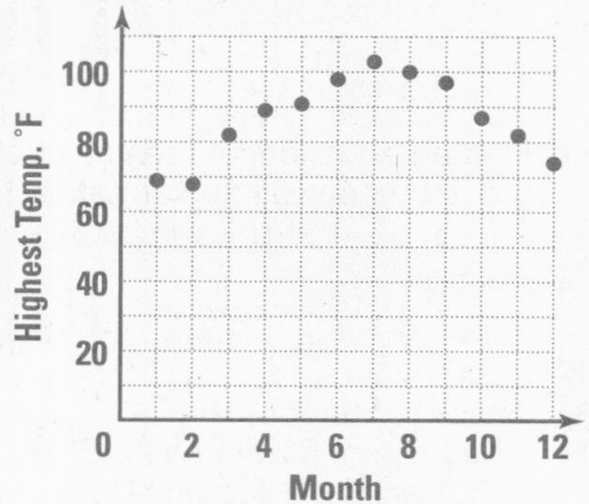

b. Does it look sinusoidal?
Answers will vary.

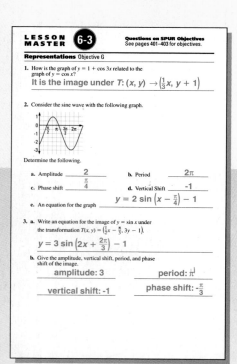

2. a. Graph the set of ordered pairs (number of month, lowest). The pattern will repeat from year to year.

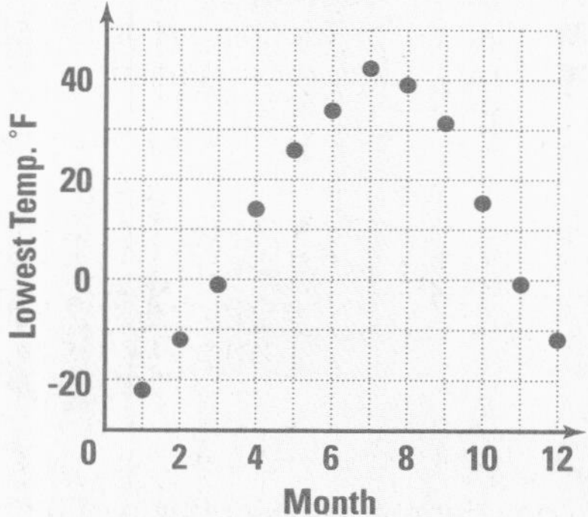

b. Does it look sinusoidal?
Answers will vary.

LESSON MASTER 6-3 **Questions on SPUR Objectives** See pages 401–403 for objectives.

Representations Objective G

1. How is the graph of $y = 1 + \cos 3x$ related to the graph of $y = \cos x$?
It is the image under $T: (x, y) \rightarrow \left(\frac{1}{3}x, y + 1\right)$

2. Consider the sine wave with the following graph.

Determine the following.

a. Amplitude 2   b. Period 2π

c. Phase shift $\frac{\pi}{4}$ d. Vertical Shift -1

e. An equation for the graph $y = 2\sin\left(x - \frac{\pi}{4}\right) - 1$

3. a. Write an equation for the image of $y = \sin x$ under the transformation $T(x, y) = \left(\frac{1}{2}x - \frac{\pi}{3}, 3y - 1\right)$.
$y = 3\sin\left(2x + \frac{2\pi}{3}\right) - 1$

b. Give the amplitude, vertical shift, period, and phase shift of the image.
amplitude: 3   period: π
vertical shift: -1   phase shift: $-\frac{\pi}{3}$

Example

Graph the image of $y = \cos x$ under the rubberband transformation

$$T(x, y) = \left(2x - \frac{\pi}{3}, 4y + 1\right).$$

Solution

Since $x' = 2x - \frac{\pi}{3}$ and $y' = 4y + 1$, $x = \frac{x' + \frac{\pi}{3}}{2}$ and $y = \frac{y' - 1}{4}$. By the Graph-Standardization Theorem, substitute $\frac{x' + \frac{\pi}{3}}{2}$ for x and $\frac{y' - 1}{4}$ for y to obtain an equation for the image. Then remove the "prime" symbols.

$$\frac{y - 1}{4} = \cos\left(\frac{x + \frac{\pi}{3}}{2}\right)$$

To graph this function on an automatic grapher, solve for y in terms of x.

$$y - 1 = 4\cos\left(\frac{1}{2}\left(x + \frac{\pi}{3}\right)\right)$$
$$y = 4\cos\left(\frac{1}{2}\left(x + \frac{\pi}{3}\right)\right) + 1$$

Now enter and plot this function with the window $-\pi \le x \le 3\pi$, $-3 \le y \le 6$ to obtain the graph below.

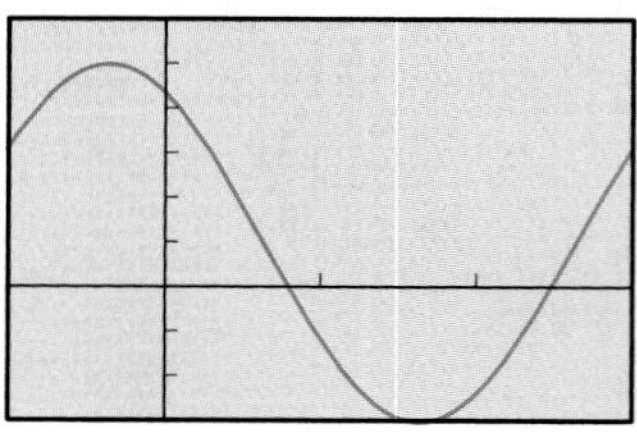

$-\pi \le x \le 3\pi$, x-scale $= \pi$
$-3 \le y \le 6$, y-scale $= 1$

Check

Apply the rubberband transformation to specific points on the graph of $y = \cos x$, such as the maximum at $(0, 1)$ and the minimum at $(\pi, -1)$. Their images should be on the image graph above.

$$T(0, 1) = \left(2 \cdot 0 - \frac{\pi}{3}, 4 \cdot 1 + 1\right) = \left(\frac{-\pi}{3}, 5\right)$$
$$T(\pi, -1) = \left(2 \cdot \pi - \frac{\pi}{3}, 4(-1) + 1\right) = \left(\frac{5\pi}{3}, -3\right)$$

Note from the displayed graph that there appears to be a maximum at $\left(\frac{-\pi}{3}, 5\right)$ and a minimum $\left(\frac{5\pi}{3}, -3\right)$, as expected.

Because the function with equation $\frac{y - k}{b} = \cos\left(\frac{x - h}{a}\right)$ can be obtained from $y = \cos x$ by the rubberband transformation $(x, y) \rightarrow (ax + h, by + k)$, it is easy to find amplitude, period, and shifts from those of $y = \cos x$.

Lesson 6-3 Overview, continued

and earlier in Lesson 3-8, for *all* functions, we need only to apply them to the sine and cosine functions and record what happens. This provides an opportunity to review the amplitude, period, and phase shift of trigonometric functions. This is entirely review for students who have studied from *Functions, Statistics, and Trigonometry.*

The second part of the lesson follows through on the parametric description of the trigonometric functions of Lesson 2-6.

In particular, the populations of rabbits and foxes are each approximately sinusoidal over time (the parameter), so that when the pairs (number of rabbits, number of foxes) are graphed, the points lie nearly on an ellipse.

Theorem

The functions defined by $y = b \sin\left(\frac{x-h}{a}\right) + k$ or $y = b \cos\left(\frac{x-h}{a}\right) + k$ have:

$$\text{amplitude} = |b|$$
$$\text{period} = 2\pi|a|$$
$$\text{phase shift} = h$$
$$\text{vertical shift} = k.$$

Thus, for example, the graph of $y = b \sin\left(\frac{x-h}{a}\right)$ has a maximum of $|b|$, a minimum of $-|b|$, it repeats itself every $2\pi|a|$ units, and it is shifted horizontally from the standard position by $|h|$ units (to the right if $h > 0$ and to the left if $h < 0$). If this curve is shifted vertically by k units (upward if $k > 0$, downward if $k < 0$), the equation of the resulting curve is $y = b \sin\left(\frac{x-h}{a}\right) + k$, and this equation has a maximum value of $|b| + k$ and a minimum value of $-|b| + k$.

Modeling with Sine and Cosine Functions

Year	Rabbits	Foxes
0	252	13
1	320	22
2	240	30
3	151	21
4	250	12
5	335	23
6	267	29
7	145	22
8	259	11

A **sinusoidal curve** is the image of the graph of a sine or cosine function under a rubberband transformation. Sinusoidal curves are often used to model phenomena that are periodic. For example, studies of animal populations show that certain pairings of predators and prey interact in such a way that their respective populations fluctuate in related periodical patterns. One study of a region of a western state showed that the numbers of foxes and rabbits varied from year to year, but over a long period of time showed a related repeating pattern. The data for an eight-year study produced the table at the left.

The scatterplots show that the data follow a sinusoidal pattern. This is shown on the graph below. We have superimposed a sine curve on the rabbit numbers and a cosine curve on the fox numbers in a manner that appears to fit the data reasonably well. The function we use for rabbit counts $R(t)$ in year t is

$$R(t) = 95 \sin\left(\frac{\pi}{2}t\right) + 240.$$

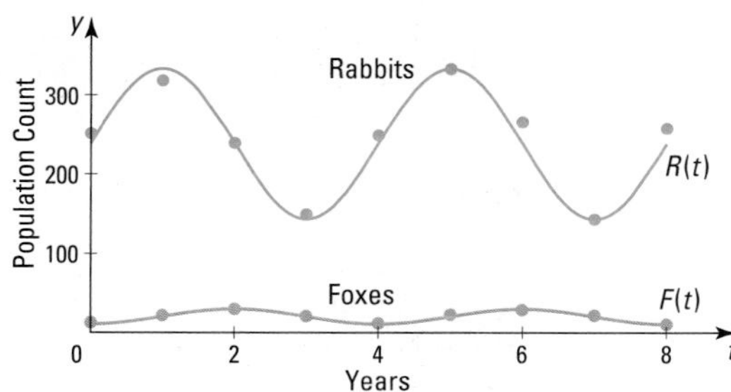

We found this function in the following way. For the rabbit data, we decided to make the curve go through the maximum point (5, 335) (335 rabbits in year 5) and minimum (7, 145) (145 rabbits in year 7).

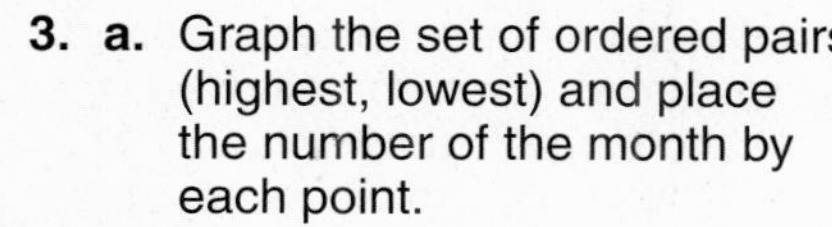

3. a. Graph the set of ordered pairs (highest, lowest) and place the number of the month by each point.

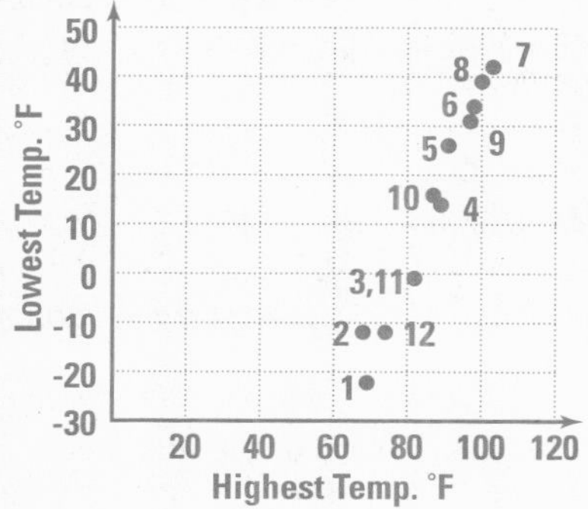

b. Describe the result.
Answers will vary.

Notes on Reading

The ideas in this lesson are as much visual as they are symbolic. **Teaching Aid 58** shows four of the graphs in the lesson: the graph on page 361 of $y = \sin x$ and $y = \cos x$, the graph for the **Example,** and the graphs of the rabbits and foxes on pages 363 and 364.

If your students are having trouble with the first part of the lesson, you may wish to consider simpler transformations. Begin with the graph of the sine function and make certain students know its amplitude (half the distance between its maximum and minimum values) is 1, its period is 2π, and it is not viewed as having any phase shift.

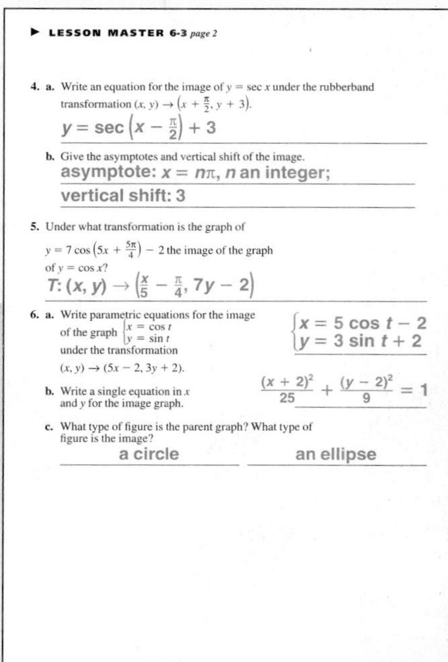

▶ **LESSON MASTER 6-3** *page 2*

4. a. Write an equation for the image of $y = \sec x$ under the rubberband transformation $(x, y) \to \left(x + \frac{\pi}{2}, y + 3\right)$.
$y = \sec\left(x - \frac{\pi}{2}\right) + 3$

b. Give the asymptotes and vertical shift of the image.
asymptote: $x = n\pi$, n an integer;
vertical shift: 3

5. Under what transformation is the graph of $y = 7\cos\left(5x + \frac{5\pi}{4}\right) - 2$ the image of the graph of $y = \cos x$?
$T: (x, y) \to \left(\frac{x}{5} - \frac{\pi}{4}, 7y - 2\right)$

6. a. Write parametric equations for the image of the graph $\begin{cases} x = \cos t \\ y = \sin t \end{cases}$ under the transformation $(x, y) \to (5x - 2, 3y + 2)$.
$\begin{cases} x = 5\cos t - 2 \\ y = 3\sin t + 2 \end{cases}$

b. Write a single equation in x and y for the image graph.
$\frac{(x+2)^2}{25} + \frac{(y-2)^2}{9} = 1$

c. What type of figure is the parent graph? What type of figure is the image?
a circle   an ellipse

Optional Activities

Technology Connection In *Technology Sourcebook, Computer Master 3,* students use Graph Explorer or similar software to explore the relationship between various properties of ellipses and their parametric equations.

Ask: Which of the amplitude, period, and phase shift may be affected by a scale change? [amplitude and period] Now refer to the graph of $y = \cos 2x$ from the previous lesson, and note that its amplitude is the same but its period is half the period of $y = \cos x$. Generalize to the graph of $y = \cos \frac{x}{a}$. (amplitude 1, period $2\pi|a|$). Now consider $y = 4\cos\frac{x}{a}$. (amplitude 4, period $2\pi|a|$). Writing this as $\frac{y}{4} = \cos\frac{x}{a}$ can show the general pattern.

Now ask: Which of the amplitude, period, and phase shift may be affected by a translation? [phase shift] The graph of $y = \cos\left(x - \frac{\pi}{2}\right)$, on page 361, opens the lesson and provides a simple example.

When both scale changes and translations are involved, think of scaling before translating. For instance, to sketch the graph of $y = 3\sin(2x - 10) + 18$ from the graph of $y = \sin x$, first determine the scale and translation factors to be applied to the parent graph. The equation needs to be rewritten so that these factors are obvious: $\frac{y-18}{3} = \sin\frac{x-5}{\frac{1}{2}}$. Now it should be clear that the scale change is $S_{1/2,3}$ and the translation is $T_{5,18}$. Notice that for both the x and y variables, you want to write them in expressions of the form $\frac{x-h}{a}$ and $\frac{y-k}{b}$. Then it is clear that the scale change is $S_{a,b}$ and the translation is $T_{h,k}$.

Students might be encouraged to use colored pencils when sketching the graphs to distinguish the graphs.

Students who have studied from *Functions, Statistics, and Trigonometry* have seen the modeling of periodic data with a sine wave. What is new here is the connection with parametric equations. The general idea is as follows: If $x = f(t)$ and $y = g(t)$ and both f and g are sinusoidal, then the graph of (x, y) will be an ellipse. You can use the Warm-Up as an additional example. Because of the familiarity of the temperature context, students should be able to find other data for which this kind of model is appropriate.

This sinusoidal curve must therefore have amplitude $\frac{335 - 145}{2} = 95$. The vertical shift is the average of maximum and minimum: $\frac{335 + 145}{2} = 240$. The period should be 4 years. Since $2\pi a = 4$, $a = \frac{4}{2\pi} = \frac{2}{\pi}$. By the last theorem,

$$y = 95 \cdot \sin\left(\frac{t}{\frac{2}{\pi}}\right) + 240.$$

That is,

$$y = 95 \cdot \sin\left(\frac{\pi}{2} \cdot t\right) + 240.$$

Graphing the function indicated that no phase shift was needed.

In a similar way we determined a cosine equation to model the fox population. We graphed

$$y = 9.5\cos\left(\frac{\pi}{2} \cdot t\right) + 20.5,$$

but found that the maxima were at years 0 and 4 rather than at years 2 and 6. Therefore, we shifted the graph 2 years to the right.

$$F(t) = 9.5\cos\left(\frac{\pi}{2}(t - 2)\right) + 20.5$$

To model the fox population, we could just as easily have determined a sine function as a cosine function. However, using the cosine function, we can more readily connect the populations to earlier work you have done with graphs of ellipses.

The equations for $R(t)$ and $F(t)$ give the rabbit and fox populations in terms of the time parameter t. They can be used to make a parametric graph with R on the horizontal axis and F on the vertical.

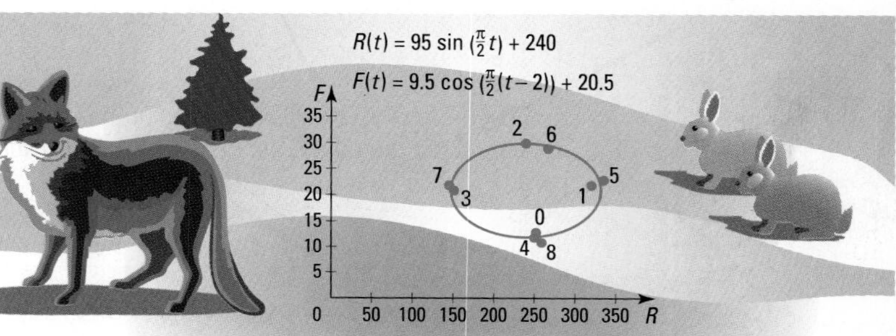

Recall that $\begin{cases} x = \cos t \\ y = \sin t \end{cases}$ are parametric equations for a circle. The equations for $R(t)$ and $F(t)$ describe the image of that circle under a rubberband transformation. The image is an ellipse. The point numbered by year t represents the actual numbers of foxes and rabbits in year t. Trace from year 0 to year 1 to years 2 through year 8. As you move counterclockwise about the ellipse, you can see that even though the populations fluctuate, the two species are in balance over the long term if their population variations continue in the patterns of these data.

Adapting to Individual Needs

Extra Help

While we continue to emphasize that students should think of scaling before translating in rubberband transformations, you may wish to point out that translating and then scaling also results in a rubberband transformation, *but not the same one.*

QUESTIONS

Covering the Reading

In 1–3, give an equation for the image of the graph of $y = \sin x$ under the indicated transformation.

1. $S: (x, y) \to (x + \pi, y)$ $y = \sin(x - \pi)$
2. $T: (a, b) = (3a, 4b)$ $y = 4\sin\left(\frac{x}{3}\right)$
3. $U: (x, y) \to \left(\frac{x + 3\pi}{2}, y - 6\right)$ $y = \sin(2x - 3\pi) - 6$
4. a. Give an equation for the image of $y = \sin x$ under the rubberband transformation $(x, y) \to \left(\frac{1}{3}x + \frac{\pi}{2}, 2y - 5\right)$. $y = 2\sin\left(3x - \frac{3\pi}{2}\right) - 5$
   b. Graph the image. See left.
   c. Give the amplitude, vertical shift, period, and phase shift of the image. See left.
5. Write an equation whose graph is a rubberband transformation image of the graph of $y = \cos x$ and has amplitude = 9, vertical shift = -2, period = 6π, and phase shift = $-\frac{2\pi}{3}$. $y = 9\cos\left(\frac{x + \frac{2\pi}{3}}{3}\right) - 2$
6. Which of the image graphs in Questions 1–4 are sinusoidal curves? All of them.

In 7–9, refer to the example of rabbits and foxes in the lesson.

7. a. According to the formulas for $R(t)$ and $F(t)$, how many rabbits and foxes will there be in year 9? 335 rabbits; 20 foxes
   b. If the point $(R(9), F(9))$ is graphed, to what two points will it be closest? (335, 20) and (335, 21)
8. a. In the equation for $R(t)$, where does the number 240 come from?
   b. In the equation for $R(t)$, where does the number 95 come from? See left.
9. a. In the equation for $F(t)$, where does the number 20.5 come from?
   b. In the equation for $F(t)$, where does the number 9.5 come from?
   c. In the equation for $F(t)$, why has t been replaced by $t - 2$? See margin.

4b)

c) amplitude: 2; period: $\frac{2\pi}{3}$; phase shift: $\frac{\pi}{2}$

8a) The average of the maximum and minimum rabbit populations: $240 = \frac{335 + 145}{2}$

b) Half the difference of the maximum and minimum rabbit populations: $95 = \frac{335 - 145}{2}$

Applying the Mathematics

10. For the sine wave graphed at the left, determine the following.
    a. amplitude 2 b. period 2π
    c. phase shift Sample: π d. a formula Sample: $y = 2\sin(x + \pi)$

11. A function is defined by $y = -5\cos\left(3\left(x + \frac{\pi}{2}\right)\right)$.
    a. Determine the amplitude, period, and phase shift of the function.
    b. Sketch a graph of the function.
    See margin.
12. The graph of $\begin{cases} x = \sin t \\ y = \cos t \end{cases}$ is transformed into the graph of $\left(\frac{x-2}{5}\right)^2 + \left(\frac{y+8}{\frac{1}{3}}\right)^2 = 1$. Give the parametric equations for the image graph.
    See margin.

Additional Examples

The graph of $y = \sin x$ has been transformed to this image graph.

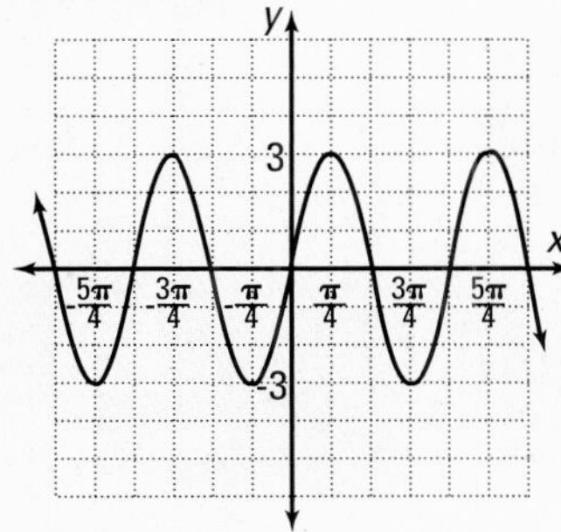

For the image, determine each of the following.

1. The amplitude 3
2. The period π
3. The phase shift 0
4. An equation $y = 3\sin 2x$

Point out to students that the same graph could be the image of the graph of either a sine or a cosine function.

Notes on Questions

Questions 7–9 These are important to check whether students have understood the main idea in the lesson.

Question 10 Ask students to write a family of sine functions, all of which have the given graph. Also challenge them to write a cosine function with the given graph.

Question 11 Error Alert Students who missed this question, might have rewritten the equation

$y = -5\,\frac{\cos x - -\frac{\pi}{2}}{3}$, instead of

$y = -5\,\frac{\cos x - -\frac{\pi}{2}}{\frac{1}{3}}$. These students

need constant reminders that, in general, $kx = \frac{x}{\frac{1}{k}}$.

Question 12 Point out how easy it is to find the parametric equations once the rubberband transformation has been determined.

Additional Answers

9, 11. See Additional Answers at the back of this book.

12. $\begin{cases} x = 5\sin t + 2 \\ y = \frac{1}{3}\cos t - 8 \end{cases}$

Adapting to Individual Needs

Challenge

Have students use a graphing calculator to graph equations shown at the right, using the simultaneous mode, if available. Then have them describe what happens and explain why it happens. [The sinusoidal curve oscillates between $f(x)$ and $-f(x)$, because $\sin nx$ and $\cos nx$ oscillate between -1 and 1.]

1. $y_1 = x^2\sin 3x$; $y_2 = x^2$; $y_3 = -x^2$
2. $y_1 = e^x\sin 4x$; $y_2 = e^x$; $y_3 = -e^x$
3. $y_1 = \ln x\sin 6x$; $y_2 = \ln x$; $y_3 = -\ln x$
4. Other functions of the form $y = f(x) \cdot \sin nx$ or $y = f(x) \cdot \cos nx$

Notes on Questions

Question 14 Science Connection A physics teacher may be able to share the apparatus needed to put this problem into motion.

Questions 20–21 These questions are preparation for Lesson 6-4.

Follow-up for Lesson 6-3

Practice

For more questions on SPUR Objectives, use **Lesson Master 6-3** (shown on pages 362–363).

Assessment

Quiz A quiz covering Lessons 6-1 through 6-3 is provided in the *Assessment Sourcebook.*

Extension

Have students determine a cosine function to model the data for the rabbit population given on page 363. Have students determine a sine function to model the fox population data. They should discuss the similarities and the differences between their functions and the ones given in the text.

[$R(t) = 95 \cos\left(\frac{\pi}{2}(t-1)\right) + 240$;

$F(t) = 9.5 \sin\left(\frac{\pi}{2}(t-1)\right) + 20.5$.

The only difference is the phase shift!] Have students verify on their automatic graphers that either function for R with either function for F produce the same ellipse when the equations are graphed parametrically.

Project Update Project 1, *Mechanical Vibration,* and Project 3, *Modeling Weather,* on pages 397–398, relate to the content of this lesson.

Additional Answers

13. $\begin{cases} x = 3\cos t + 4 \\ y = 4\cos t + 1 \end{cases}$

14. b.

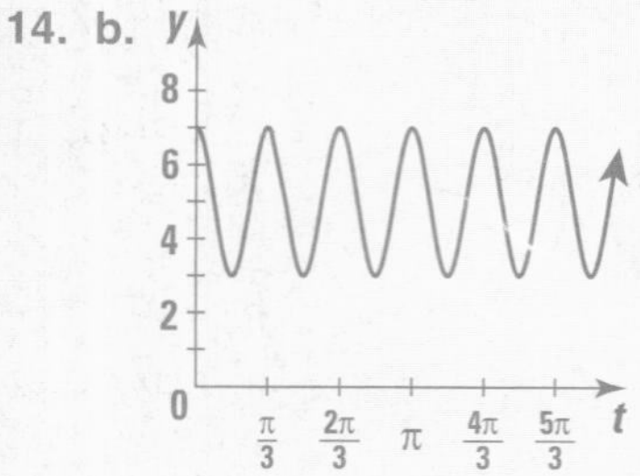

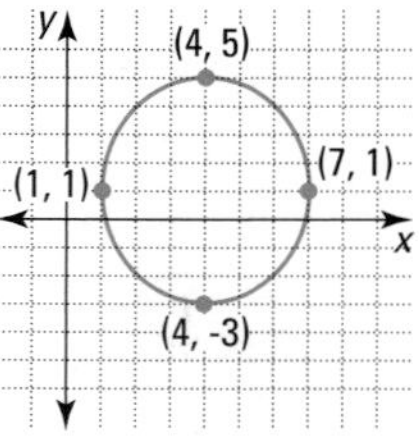

13. Write parametric equations for the ellipse graphed at the left. See margin.

14. At rest, a mass stretches a spring 5 inches. The mass is then pulled so that the spring is stretched 2 more inches. When the mass is released, it will oscillate up and down. The distance from the mass to the fixed support at time t can be described by the equation $y = 5 + 2\cos 6t$.

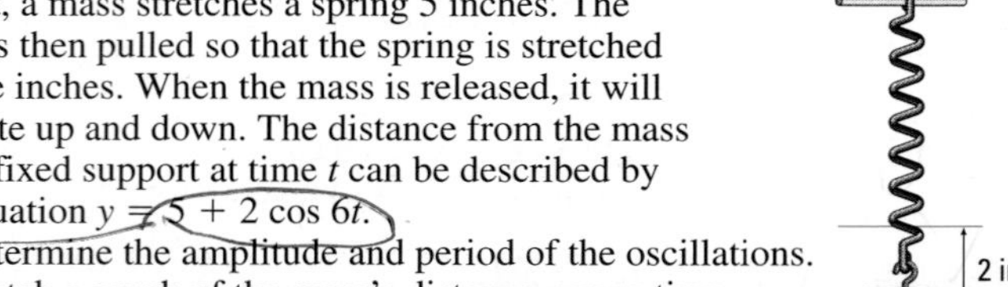

a. Determine the amplitude and period of the oscillations.
b. Sketch a graph of the mass's distance versus time.
c. What is the maximum distance from the mass to the support? 7 in.
d. What is the minimum distance from the mass to the support? 3 in.
a) amplitude: 2; period: $\frac{\pi}{3}$ b) See margin.

Review

15. Use an automatic grapher to guess whether or not the equation below is an identity. If it is, prove it; if not, find a counterexample. See margin.

$$\cos x \cot x = \csc x - \sin x \quad \text{(Lessons 6-1, 6-2)}$$

16. a. Prove the identity: $\frac{1}{1+\sin x} + \frac{1}{1-\sin x} = 2\sec^2 x$. See margin.
b. What is the domain of this identity? *(Lesson 6-2)* See margin.

17. a. Graph $y = 2^x + 2^{-x}$ and $y = x^2 + 2$ on the same axes, for $-1 \le x \le 1$.
b. Is $2^x + 2^{-x} = x^2 + 2$ an identity for $-1 \le x \le 1$? Justify your answer. *(Lesson 6-1)*
See left.

17a)

$y = x^2 + 2$

$y = 2^x + 2^{-x}$

$-1 \le x \le 1$, x-scale = 0.2
$-1 \le y \le 4$, y-scale = 0.5

b) No. Counterexample: For $x = 1$, $2^x + 2^{-x} = 2^1 + 2^{-1} = \frac{5}{2}$, but $x^2 + 2 = 1 + 2 = 3$

18. a. Use division of polynomials to rewrite $h(x) = \frac{4x^2 + 23}{x^2 + 3}$ as the sum of a polynomial and a rational expression.
b. Determine the end behavior of the function h. Write your results using limit notation.
c. Does h have any discontinuities? If so, identify them as essential or removable. If not, explain why not.
d. Use an automatic grapher to graph h. Is the graph consistent with your results in part **b**? *(Lessons 4-3, 5-4, 5-5)*
See margin.

19. Describe the translation transformation that maps the graph of $y = x^2$ onto the graph of $y = x^2 + 12x - 5$. *(Lesson 3-8)* $T(x, y) = (x - 6, y - 41)$

20. What is the image of (1, 0) under the rotation with magnitude θ and center (0, 0)? *(Lesson 2-6)* (cos θ, sin θ)

21. Use the distance formula to find the distance between (cos θ, sin θ) and (2 cos θ, 2 sin θ). *(Lesson 2-6)* 1

Exploration

22. Find the average monthly high temperatures (or low temperatures) for a community near where you live. (The information may be in an almanac or on the Internet.) Graph these. For most communities, these values can be approximated by a sine wave. Find the amplitude and period of the wave. See margin.

15, 16, 18, 22. See Additional Answers at the back of this book.

Setting Up Lesson 6-4

Discuss **Questions 20 and 21** to ensure that students remember the definitions for sine and cosine and the formula for the distance between two points on a coordinate plane.

LESSON

6-4

Formulas for $\cos(\alpha+\beta)$ and $\cos(\alpha-\beta)$

In Lesson 2-6, calculation of the exact values of the sine and cosine functions for the domain values 0, $\frac{\pi}{6}$, $\frac{\pi}{4}$, $\frac{\pi}{3}$ and $\frac{\pi}{2}$ was reviewed. In this lesson, you will see how to compute cosines for sums and differences of these domain values. For example, because

$$\frac{5\pi}{6} = \frac{\pi}{2} + \frac{\pi}{3} \quad \text{and} \quad \frac{\pi}{12} = \frac{\pi}{3} - \frac{\pi}{4},$$

you will be able to compute $\cos \frac{5\pi}{6}$ and $\cos \frac{\pi}{12}$, using formulas for $\cos(\alpha + \beta)$ and $\cos(\alpha - \beta)$. These expressions also arise from translation images of the cosine function, as you saw in the last lesson.

You might hope that $\cos(\alpha + \beta)$ would equal $\cos \alpha + \cos \beta$ for all real numbers α and β, but one counterexample proves that this proposed identity is false. For example, if $\alpha = 0$ and $\beta = \frac{\pi}{3}$,

$$\cos(\alpha + \beta) = \cos\left(0 + \frac{\pi}{3}\right) = \cos \frac{\pi}{3} = \frac{1}{2},$$

but

$$\cos \alpha + \cos \beta = \cos 0 + \cos \frac{\pi}{3} = 1 + \frac{1}{2} = \frac{3}{2}.$$

Therefore $\cos(\alpha + \beta) = \cos \alpha + \cos \beta$ is *not* an identity. The identity is a little more complicated.

An Identity for $\cos(\alpha + \beta)$

❶ **Theorem (Cosine of a Sum)**
For all real numbers α and β,

$$\cos(\alpha + \beta) = \cos \alpha \cos \beta - \sin \alpha \sin \beta.$$

Proof
The proof we give here applies when $\alpha > 0$, $\beta > 0$, and $\alpha + \beta < \pi$. Variations of this proof can be done to prove the identity for other values of α and β. The diagram at the right shows the images Q, R, and S of $P = (1, 0)$ under rotations with center $(0, 0)$ of α, $\alpha + \beta$, and $-\beta$. Notice that the first coordinate of R is $\cos(\alpha + \beta)$, which is the left side of the proposed identity. The aim is to describe this expression in terms of sines and cosines of α and β. This suggests using the coordinates of Q and S.

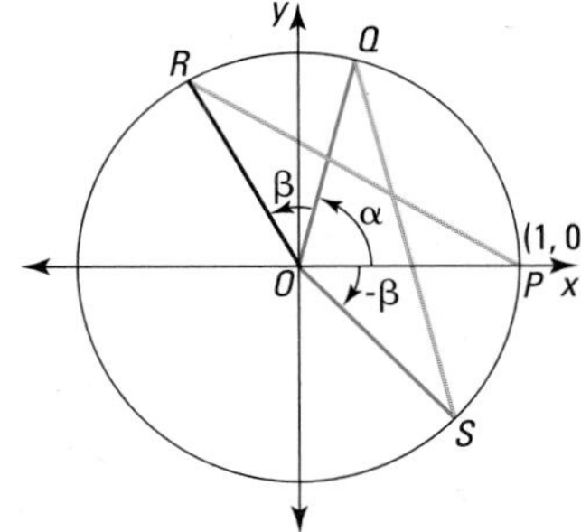

Lesson 6-4

Objectives

A Without a calculator, use trigonometric identities to express values of trigonometric functions in terms of rational numbers and radicals.

D Prove trigonometric identities and identify their domains.

Resources

From the ***Teacher's Resource File***
- Lesson Master 6-4
- Answer Master 6-4
- Teaching Aids
  55 Warm-up
  59 Diagram for Proof of Cosine of a Sum Theorem

Additional Resources
- Visuals for Teaching Aids 55, 59

Teaching Lesson 6-4

Warm-up

1. Find the distance between (cos 150°, sin 150°) and (cos 120°, sin 120°). $\sqrt{2 - \sqrt{3}}$
2. Find the distance between (cos 30°, sin 30°) and (1, 0). $\sqrt{2 - \sqrt{3}}$
3. Generalize the results of Questions 1 and 2. The distance between (cos x, sin x) and (cos y, sin y) equals the distance between (cos $(x - y)$, sin $(x - y)$) and (1, 0).

Notes on Reading

❶ The proof of the identity for $\cos(\alpha + \beta)$ is based on the unit circle and the distance formula. **Teaching Aid 59** shows the diagram for the proof to make it easier for you go through the algebra of the proof. In some books, the identity for $\cos(\alpha - \beta)$ is proved first. We chose our method because the addition identity is more natural to try to prove first.

Lesson 6-4 Overview

Broad Goals This section derives the formulas for $\cos(\alpha + \beta)$ and $\cos(\alpha - \beta)$ and applies them in proofs and in obtaining values of sines and cosines.

Perspective Without the identities in this section, students can easily give exact values of the trigonometric functions only for arguments that are multiples of $\frac{\pi}{6}$, $\frac{\pi}{3}$, and $\frac{\pi}{4}$.

This section gives students the tools they need to find exact values of the trigonometric functions for many other arguments.

Students who have studied from *Functions, Statistics, and Trigonometry* will have seen the formulas for $\cos(\alpha + \beta)$ and $\sin(\alpha + \beta)$ derived simultaneously using matrices for rotations. In this book, a circular function

(Overview continues on page 368.)

❷ In the proof of the Cosine of a Sum Theorem, recognizing that $\cos^2(\alpha + \beta) + \sin^2(\alpha + \beta)$ is a form of $\cos^2 x + \sin^2 x$ allows for a wonderfully simplifying substitution. Students need to be able to recognize identities that are disguised.

The elegant proof of this identity using matrices, which yields the identities for $\cos(\alpha + \beta)$ and $\sin(\alpha + \beta)$ simultaneously, is outlined in **Question 13** of Lesson 6-5. Students who have taken other UCSMP courses should be familiar with matrix operations, and those who have used *Functions, Statistics, and Trigonometry* will have seen the matrix proof before.

Examples 1–2 show two immediate applications of identities in two variables. By substituting numbers for both variables (as in **Example 1**), a value may be obtained that we have not seen before. By substituting a number for just one variable (as in **Example 2**), an identity in one variable may appear.

Now notice that $m\angle ROP = \alpha + \beta$ and $m\angle QOS = \alpha + \beta$. Thus, by the SAS Triangle Congruence Theorem, $RP = QS$. Now translate $RP = QS$ into cosines and sines using the coordinates of these points and the distance formula.

$$\sqrt{(\cos(\alpha + \beta) - 1)^2 + (\sin(\alpha + \beta) - 0)^2} = \sqrt{(\cos\alpha - \cos(-\beta))^2 + (\sin\alpha - \sin(-\beta))^2}$$

On the right side, apply the identities $\cos(-\theta) = \cos(\theta)$ and $\sin(-\theta) = -\sin(\theta)$ for all real numbers θ.

$$\sqrt{(\cos(\alpha + \beta) - 1)^2 + (\sin(\alpha + \beta))^2} = \sqrt{(\cos\alpha - \cos\beta)^2 + (\sin\alpha + \sin\beta)^2}$$

Squaring both sides is a reversible operation since the quantities under the $\sqrt{\ }$ signs are positive.

$$(\cos(\alpha + \beta) - 1)^2 + (\sin(\alpha + \beta))^2 = (\cos\alpha - \cos\beta)^2 + (\sin\alpha + \sin\beta)^2$$

Expand the squared terms.

$$\cos^2(\alpha + \beta) - 2\cos(\alpha + \beta) + 1 + \sin^2(\alpha + \beta) = \cos^2\alpha - 2\cos\alpha\cos\beta + \cos^2\beta + \sin^2\alpha + 2\sin\alpha\sin\beta + \sin^2\beta$$

❷ Rearrange the sums so that squares of cosines and sines are next to each other.

$$(\cos^2(\alpha + \beta) + \sin^2(\alpha + \beta)) - 2\cos(\alpha + \beta) + 1 = (\cos^2\alpha + \sin^2\alpha) + (\cos^2\beta + \sin^2\beta) - 2\cos\alpha\cos\beta + 2\sin\alpha\sin\beta$$

Apply the Pythagorean Identity $\sin^2 x + \cos^2 x = 1$.

$$1 - 2\cos(\alpha + \beta) + 1 = 1 + 1 - 2\cos\alpha\cos\beta + 2\sin\alpha\sin\beta$$

Solve for $\cos(\alpha + \beta)$.

$$-2\cos(\alpha + \beta) = -2\cos\alpha\cos\beta + 2\sin\alpha\sin\beta \quad A_{-2}$$
$$\cos(\alpha + \beta) = \cos\alpha\cos\beta - \sin\alpha\sin\beta \quad M_{-\frac{1}{2}}$$

Using the Cosine of a Sum to Find Exact Values

In Example 1, the formula for the cosine of a sum is used to determine a value of the cosine function.

Example 1

Express $\cos\frac{7\pi}{12}$ in terms of rational numbers and radicals.

Solution

Write $\frac{7\pi}{12}$ as a sum of two numbers for which you know exact values of the sine and cosine.

$$\frac{7\pi}{12} = \frac{\pi}{4} + \frac{\pi}{3}$$

Lesson 6-4 Overview, continued

proof of the formula for $\cos(\alpha + \beta)$ is given. Then, in a process that is repeated in later lessons with other identities, the identity for $\cos(\alpha + \beta)$ is used to obtain an exact cosine value for an argument that is not a multiple of $\frac{\pi}{4}$ or $\frac{\pi}{6}$, but a sum of a combination of both. Also from the identity is derived a formula for $\cos(\alpha - \beta)$, and then the identity $\cos\left(\frac{\pi}{2} - x\right) = \sin x$.

Then apply the identity $\cos(\alpha + \beta) = \cos\alpha\cos\beta - \sin\alpha\sin\beta$ with $\alpha = \frac{\pi}{4}$ and $\beta = \frac{\pi}{3}$.

$$\begin{aligned}\cos\frac{7\pi}{12} &= \cos\left(\frac{\pi}{4} + \frac{\pi}{3}\right)\\ &= \cos\frac{\pi}{4}\cos\frac{\pi}{3} - \sin\frac{\pi}{4}\sin\frac{\pi}{3}\\ &= \frac{\sqrt{2}}{2}\cdot\frac{1}{2} - \frac{\sqrt{2}}{2}\cdot\frac{\sqrt{3}}{2}\\ &= \frac{\sqrt{2} - \sqrt{6}}{4}\end{aligned}$$

Check

With a calculator, $\cos\frac{7\pi}{12} \approx -.259$ and $\frac{\sqrt{2} - \sqrt{6}}{4} \approx -.259$.

Because $\frac{7\pi}{12} = 75°$, Example 1 also shows that $\cos 75° = \frac{\sqrt{2} - \sqrt{6}}{4}$.

An Identity for cos (α − β)

A formula for $\cos(\alpha - \beta)$ can be obtained easily from the formula for $\cos(\alpha + \beta)$ as follows. For all real numbers α and β,

$$\begin{aligned}\cos(\alpha - \beta) &= \cos(\alpha + (-\beta))\\ &= \cos\alpha\cos(-\beta) - \sin\alpha\sin(-\beta) && \text{Replace } \beta \text{ by } -\beta \text{ in the identity for } \cos(\alpha + \beta).\\ &= \cos\alpha\cos\beta - \sin\alpha(-\sin\beta) && \forall\ \theta, \cos(-\theta) = \cos\theta \text{ and } \sin(-\theta) = -\sin\theta.\\ &= \cos\alpha\cos\beta + \sin\alpha\sin\beta.\end{aligned}$$

This proves the following theorem.

Theorem (Cosine of a Difference)
For all real numbers α and β,

$$\cos(\alpha - \beta) = \cos\alpha\cos\beta + \sin\alpha\sin\beta.$$

The Complement's Sine

Sines and cosines are related in many ways. In a right triangle ABC with right angle at C, $\angle A$ and $\angle B$ are complements because their measures add to 90°. From the right triangle definitions of sine and cosine, $\cos A = \sin B$. That is, the cosine of an angle equals its complement's sine. More generally, if x and y are real numbers with $x + y = \frac{\pi}{2}$, then $y = \frac{\pi}{2} - x$, and from the formula for $\cos(\alpha - \beta)$ it can be proved that $\cos y = \sin x$.

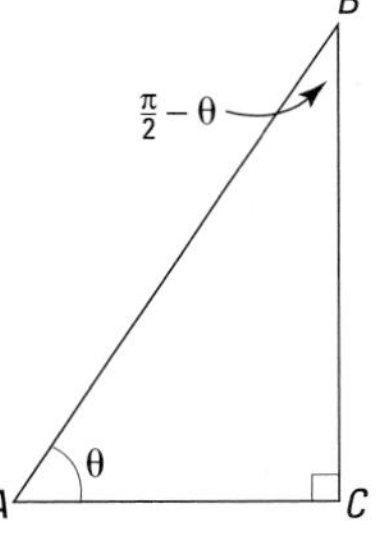

Error Alert In finding $\cos\frac{7\pi}{12}$ using known values, many students have trouble determining a useful sum equal to $\frac{7\pi}{12}$. They will write $\frac{7\pi}{12} = \frac{\pi}{12} + \frac{6\pi}{12}$ or $\frac{7\pi}{12} = \frac{2\pi}{12} + \frac{5\pi}{12}$ and quickly become frustrated. Here are two suggestions.

1. Ask students to write $\frac{7\pi}{12}$ as the sum of two fractions, both of which reduce. Thus, possible numerators must be nontrivial factors of 12 (2, 3, 4, 6). Ask which pair(s) also add to 7.
2. Write $\frac{\pi}{6} = \frac{2\pi}{12}, \frac{\pi}{4} = \frac{3\pi}{12}, \frac{\pi}{3} = \frac{4\pi}{12}$, and $\frac{\pi}{2} = \frac{6\pi}{12}$ on the board and ask which pair adds to $\frac{7\pi}{12}$.

We use α and β when there are two variables to make it easier to substitute for them when there will be one variable. For instance, with $\cos(\alpha + \beta) = \cos\alpha\cos\beta - \sin\alpha\sin\beta$, replace α by π and replace β by x. Then $\cos(\pi + x) = \cos\pi\cos x - \sin\pi\sin x$. Inform students that many people remember the formulas using x and y where we have α and β; students should be flexible enough to deal with either form.

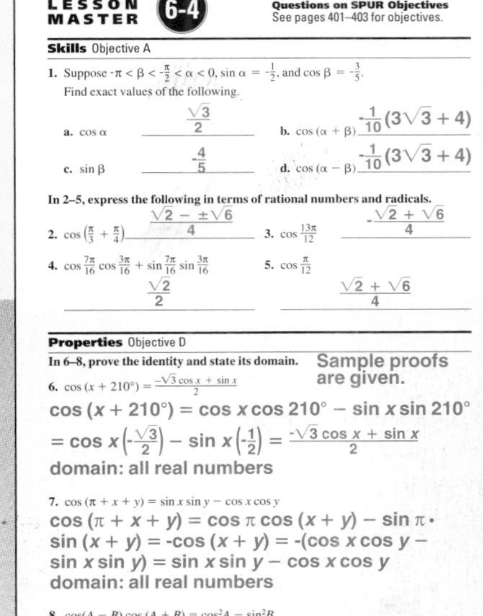

LESSON MASTER 6-4

Questions on SPUR Objectives
See pages 401–403 for objectives.

Skills Objective A

1. Suppose $-\pi < \beta < -\frac{\pi}{2} < \alpha < 0$, $\sin\alpha = -\frac{1}{2}$, and $\cos\beta = -\frac{3}{5}$. Find exact values of the following.
   a. $\cos\alpha$ $\frac{\sqrt{3}}{2}$
   b. $\cos(\alpha + \beta)$ $-\frac{1}{10}(3\sqrt{3} + 4)$
   c. $\sin\beta$ $-\frac{4}{5}$
   d. $\cos(\alpha - \beta)$ $-\frac{1}{10}(3\sqrt{3} + 4)$

In 2–5, express the following in terms of rational numbers and radicals.

2. $\cos\left(\frac{\pi}{3} + \frac{\pi}{4}\right)$ $\frac{\sqrt{2} - \pm\sqrt{6}}{4}$
3. $\cos\frac{13\pi}{12}$ $-\frac{\sqrt{2} + \sqrt{6}}{4}$
4. $\cos\frac{7\pi}{16}\cos\frac{3\pi}{16} + \sin\frac{7\pi}{16}\sin\frac{3\pi}{16}$ $\frac{\sqrt{2}}{2}$
5. $\cos\frac{\pi}{12}$ $\frac{\sqrt{2} + \sqrt{6}}{4}$

Properties Objective D

In 6–8, prove the identity and state its domain. Sample proofs are given.

6. $\cos(x + 210°) = \frac{-\sqrt{3}\cos x + \sin x}{2}$
   $\cos(x + 210°) = \cos x\cos 210° - \sin x\sin 210° = \cos x\left(-\frac{\sqrt{3}}{2}\right) - \sin x\left(-\frac{1}{2}\right) = \frac{-\sqrt{3}\cos x + \sin x}{2}$
   domain: all real numbers
7. $\cos(\pi + x + y) = \sin x\sin y - \cos x\cos y$
   $\cos(\pi + x + y) = \cos\pi\cos(x + y) - \sin\pi\cdot\sin(x + y) = -\cos(x + y) = -(\cos x\cos y - \sin x\sin y) = \sin x\sin y - \cos x\cos y$
   domain: all real numbers
8. $\cos(A - B)\cos(A + B) = \cos^2 A - \sin^2 B$
   $(\cos A\cos B + \sin A\sin B)(\cos A\cos B - \sin A\sin B) = (\cos A\cos B)^2 - (\sin A\sin B)^2 = \cos^2 A(1 - \sin^2 B) - (1 - \cos^2 A)\sin^2 B = \cos^2 A - \cos^2 A\sin^2 B - \sin^2 B + \cos^2 A\sin^2 B = \cos^2 A - \sin^2 B$ domain: all real numbers

Optional Activities

Cooperative Learning As a class, have students brainstorm a list of the numbers between 0 and 2π whose cosine values they can now find exactly, using the Cosine of a Sum and Cosine of a Difference identities. Have them include what sum or difference of numbers they could use in the formulas. [They can now find the exact cosines of the $\frac{\pi}{12}$ "family" of numbers. Sample, between 0 and π: $\frac{\pi}{12} = \frac{\pi}{4} - \frac{\pi}{6}$; $\frac{5\pi}{12} = \frac{\pi}{4} + \frac{\pi}{6}$; $\frac{7\pi}{12} = \frac{\pi}{3} + \frac{\pi}{4}$; $\frac{11\pi}{12} = \frac{7\pi}{6} - \frac{\pi}{4}$; etc. Be sure to point out to students that sometimes there are several sums or differences of this type that will produce a given angle.]

Additional Examples

1. Express $\cos \frac{5\pi}{12}$ in terms of rational numbers and radicals.
   $\cos \frac{5\pi}{12} = \cos\left(\frac{2\pi}{12} + \frac{3\pi}{12}\right) =$
   $\cos\left(\frac{\pi}{6} + \frac{\pi}{4}\right) = \frac{\sqrt{6} - \sqrt{2}}{4}$
2. Prove the following identity:
   $\cos\left(x - \frac{\pi}{2}\right) = \sin x.$
   $\cos\left(x - \frac{\pi}{2}\right) = \cos\left[-\left(-x + \frac{\pi}{2}\right)\right] =$
   $\cos\left(-x + \frac{\pi}{2}\right) = \cos\left(\frac{\pi}{2} - x\right) = \sin x.$
   Another method is to use the identity for $\cos(\alpha - \beta)$.

Notes on Questions

Question 3 Ask if a difference other than $15 = 45 - 30$ could have been used. [Yes, $15 = 60 - 45$]

Question 4 Students are expected to translate the identity $\cos\left(\frac{\pi}{2} - x\right) = \sin x$ into degrees. Alternatively, they could use the right triangle definition of sine and cosine, or the unit circle definition and symmetry.

Question 9 Suggest using Technique 1 of Lesson 6-2. Work on the right side of the identity.

Question 10 This leads to the formula for $\cos 2\alpha$ that will be discussed in Lesson 6-6.

Question 13 Since $\frac{17\pi}{12} = \frac{\pi}{6} + \frac{5\pi}{4} = \frac{\pi}{4} + \frac{7\pi}{6} = \frac{2\pi}{3} + \frac{3\pi}{4}$, there is more than one way to determine the answer. You might find out which pair was the most used by students and why.

Question 19d When $x = \frac{\theta}{2}$, this identity becomes a "half-angle" formula: $\cos \frac{\theta}{2} = \pm\sqrt{\frac{1 + \cos\theta}{2}}$.

Example 2

Prove the following identity: $\forall$ real numbers x, $\cos\left(\frac{\pi}{2} - x\right) = \sin x$.

Solution

Transform the left side using the formula for $\cos(\alpha - \beta)$ with $\alpha = \frac{\pi}{2}$ and $\beta = x$. Then use the exact values of $\cos \frac{\pi}{2}$ and $\sin \frac{\pi}{2}$.

(left side)

$\cos\left(\frac{\pi}{2} - x\right) = \cos \frac{\pi}{2} \cos x + \sin \frac{\pi}{2} \sin x$ — Cosine of a Difference Theorem

$= 0 \cdot \cos x + 1 \cdot \sin x$ — $\cos \frac{\pi}{2} = 0$, $\sin \frac{\pi}{2} = 1$

$= \sin x$ (right side)

Notice that since $\cos(-\theta) = \cos\theta\ \forall\ \theta$, $\cos\left(\frac{\pi}{2} - x\right) = \cos\left(x - \frac{\pi}{2}\right)$. Thus from Example 2, we can show $\cos\left(x - \frac{\pi}{2}\right) = \sin x$, the identity mentioned at the start of Lesson 6-3.

The identity in Example 2 is called a **cofunction identity**. In the next lesson, it is applied to derive a formula for $\sin(\alpha + \beta)$.

Do You Have to Memorize All the Identities?

In this and the next few lessons, many identities will be proved. You do not need to memorize all of them. If you memorize the key identities, you can quickly derive the others. The one key identity you should memorize from this lesson is the formula for the cosine of a sum, $\cos(\alpha + \beta) = \cos\alpha\cos\beta - \sin\alpha\sin\beta$, because its derivation is so lengthy.

QUESTIONS

Covering the Reading

1. Explain why $RP = QS$ in the beginning of the proof of the identity for $\cos(\alpha + \beta)$. See margin.
2. Give formulas for $\cos(x + y)$ and $\cos(x - y)$. See left.
3. Express $\cos 15°$ in terms of rational numbers and radicals. (Hint: $15 = 45 - 30$.) See left.
4. If $0° < x < 90°$ and $\sin x = \cos 15°$, what is x? 75°
5. Prove directly that $\cos\left(x - \frac{\pi}{2}\right) = \sin x$. See left.
6. Interpret the result of Question 5 in terms of graphs of functions.
7. Verify the identity for $\cos(\alpha + \beta)$ when $\alpha = \frac{\pi}{4}$ and $\beta = \frac{\pi}{4}$. See margin.
8. Prove: $\forall$ *real numbers x*, $\cos\left(\frac{3\pi}{2} + x\right) = \sin x$. See margin.

2) $\cos(x + y) = \cos x \cdot \cos y - \sin x \sin y$; $\cos(x - y) = \cos x \cdot \cos y + \sin x \sin y$

3) $\frac{\sqrt{6} + \sqrt{2}}{4}$

5) $\cos\left(x - \frac{\pi}{2}\right) = \cos x \cdot \cos \frac{\pi}{2} + \sin x \sin \frac{\pi}{2} = 0 + \sin x = \sin x$

6) The graph of $y = \sin x$ is identical to the graph of $y = \cos x$ phase shifted by $\frac{\pi}{2}$.

Adapting to Individual Needs

Extra Help

If you did not discuss cofunctions in Chapter 5, this is a good time to do so. If $x + y = \frac{\pi}{2}$, then we may think of x and y as measures of two complementary angles. If $f(x) = g(y)$, then we say that f and g are cofunctions because f(one angle) = g(its complement). Using complete names of the trigonometric functions, ask students to write the pairs of cofunctions.

Challenge

Have students use identities from this lesson to derive identities for each of the following.

1. $\cos x \cos y$ $\left[\frac{1}{2}(\cos(x + y) + \cos(x - y))\right]$
2. $\cos x + \cos y$ $\left[2\cos\frac{x + y}{2}\cos\frac{x - y}{2}\right]$
3. $\cos x - \cos y$ $\left[\left(-2\sin\frac{x + y}{2}\sin\frac{x - y}{2}\right)\right]$
4. $\cos(x + y)\cos(x - y)$ $[\cos^2 x + \cos^2 y - 1$, or $\cos^2 y - \sin^2 x$, or $\cos^2 x\cos^2 y - \sin^2 x\sin^2 y$, or $\cos^2 x - \sin^2 y]$

Applying the Mathematics

Christopher Clavius, 1537–1612

9. Prove Christopher Clavius's identity shown on page 349. See margin.

10. What happens in the formula for $\cos(\alpha - \beta)$ when $\alpha = \beta$? The formula becomes $\cos 0 = \cos^2 \alpha + \sin^2 \alpha = 1$

11. Consider the cofunction identity in Example 2. Substitute $\frac{\pi}{2} - x$ for x on each side of the equation and simplify the result to obtain a new identity. See below.

12. a. Use an automatic grapher to graph the function f defined by $f(x) = \frac{\sqrt{3}}{2}\cos x + \frac{1}{2}\sin x$.
    b. Based on the graph, conjecture a formula for f of the form $f(x) = \cos(x \pm k)$.
    c. Prove your conjecture.
    See margin.

13. Express $\cos\frac{17\pi}{12}$ in terms of rational numbers and radicals. $\frac{\sqrt{2} - \sqrt{6}}{4}$

11) $\sin\left(\frac{\pi}{2} - x\right) = \cos x$

Review

14. a. Give the amplitude, period, and phase shift of the function $f: \theta \to \frac{1}{2}\sin 5\theta$. amplitude: $\frac{1}{2}$; period $\frac{2\pi}{5}$; phase shift: 0
    b. Identify all zeros of this function such that $0 \le \theta \le 2\pi$. *(Lesson 6-3)* See left.

15. a. Graph the curve defined by the parametric equations
$$\begin{cases} x = 3\cos t + 5 \\ y = 4\sin t - 2. \end{cases}$$
    b. Give an equation in x and y for this curve. *(Lessons 2-5, 6-3)* See left.

16. Suppose α is in the interval $\pi < \alpha < \frac{3\pi}{2}$ and $\cot \alpha = 0.6$. Find $\sec \alpha$. *(Lesson 6-2)* $-\frac{\sqrt{34}}{3}$

17. Prove the identity $\frac{\csc x}{\sec x} = \cot x$ and give its domain. *(Lesson 6-2)* See left.

18. Evaluate without using a calculator. *(Lessons 2-6, 5-7)*
    a. $\cos \pi$ −1
    b. $\sin \pi$ 0
    c. $\tan \pi$ 0
    d. $\cot \pi$ undefined
    e. $\sec \pi$ −1
    f. $\csc \pi$ undefined

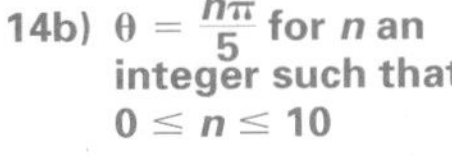

14b) $\theta = \frac{n\pi}{5}$ for n an integer such that $0 \le n \le 10$

15a)

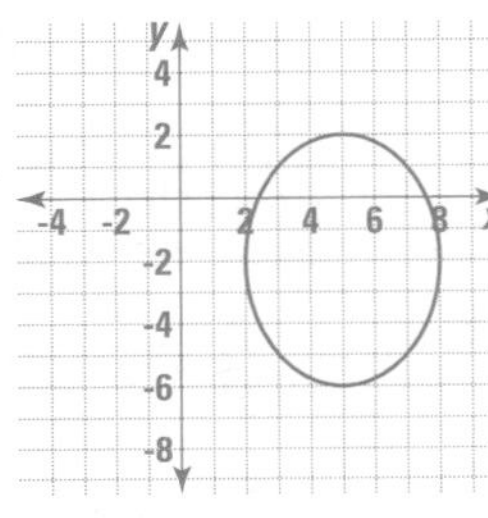

b) $\frac{(x-5)^2}{9} + \frac{(y+2)^2}{16} = 1$

17) $\frac{\csc x}{\sec x} = \frac{\frac{1}{\sin x}}{\frac{1}{\cos x}} = \frac{\cos x}{\sin x} = \cot x$

domain: $\{x: x \ne \frac{n\pi}{2}, \forall$ integers $n\}$

Exploration

19. Consider the equation $\sqrt{\frac{1 + \cos 2x}{2}} = \cos x$. See margin.
    a. Use an automatic grapher to graph each side as a function of x for $-\pi \le x \le \pi$.
    b. For what values of x in the interval $-\pi \le x \le \pi$ does the equation seem to be true?
    c. Check your answer to part **b** by evaluating both sides of the equation for the following values of x.
       i. $x = \frac{\pi}{4}$
       ii. $x = \frac{3\pi}{4}$
    d. Modify the equation to make it an identity.

Follow-up for Lesson 6-4

Practice

For more questions on SPUR Objectives, use **Lesson Master 6-4** (shown on page 369).

Assessment

Written Communication Have students use the technique of **Example 1** to find the exact value of $\cos\theta$ where θ is $\frac{13\pi}{12}$, $\frac{19\pi}{12}$, and $\frac{23\pi}{12}$. [Students use trigonometric identities to give exact values of the cosine function.]

Extension

Ask students to test whether the Cosine of a Sum formula holds true for sine. That is, have them investigate whether $\sin(\alpha + \beta) = \sin\alpha\sin\beta - \cos\alpha\cos\beta$. They can choose several values for β and graph on an automatic grapher. Have them conjecture what seems to be true about the statement. [The graphs don't match by a phase shift of $\frac{\pi}{2}$.] As a challenge, ask them to conjecture how they might use the identities in this lesson to come up with a sum formula for sine. [This prodding anticipates the next lesson and may motivate students to learn the material and understand it!]

Project Update Project 2, *"Pseudo-trigonometric" Functions,* and Project 4, *Rational and Radical Expressions for Sines and Cosines,* on page 398, relate to the content of this lesson.

Additional Answers

1. OP, OQ, OR, and OS are all radii of circle O, so they are all equal. $m\angle POR = \alpha + \beta = m\angle QOS$. So, $\triangle ROP \cong \triangle QOS$ (Side-Angle-Side Congruence). Hence $RP = QS$.

7. $\cos\left(\frac{\pi}{4} + \frac{\pi}{4}\right) = \cos\frac{\pi}{2} = 0$;
$\cos\frac{\pi}{4}\cos\frac{\pi}{4} - \sin\frac{\pi}{4}\sin\frac{\pi}{4} = \frac{\sqrt{2}}{2} \cdot \frac{\sqrt{2}}{2} - \frac{\sqrt{2}}{2} \cdot \frac{\sqrt{2}}{2} = \frac{1}{2} - \frac{1}{2} = 0$

12. a.

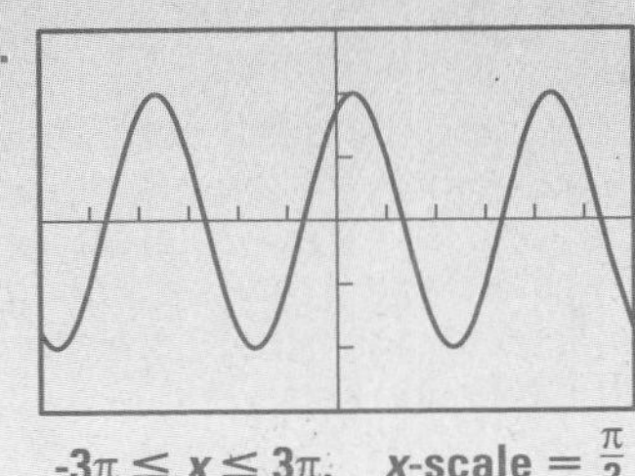

$-3\pi \le x \le 3\pi$, x-scale $= \frac{\pi}{2}$
$-1.5 \le y \le 1.5$, y-scale $= .5$

b. $f(x) = \cos\left(x - \frac{\pi}{6}\right)$

c. $\cos\left(x - \frac{\pi}{6}\right) = \cos x \cos\frac{\pi}{6} + \sin x \sin\frac{\pi}{6} = \frac{\sqrt{3}}{2}\cos x + \frac{1}{2}\sin x$

8, 9, 19. See Additional Answers at the back of this book.

Lesson 6-5

Objectives

A Without a calculator, use trigonometric identities to express values of trigonometric functions in terms of rational numbers and radicals.

D Prove trigonometric identities and identify their domains.

Resources

From the ***Teacher's Resource File***

- Lesson Master 6-5
- Answer Master 6-5
- Teaching Aid 55: Warm-up
- Technology Sourcebook Calculator Master 10

Additional Resources

- Visual for Teaching Aid 55

Teaching Lesson 6-5

Warm-up

If $x = \frac{\pi}{2}$ and $y = \frac{\pi}{3}$, find $\sin(x + y)$, $\sin(x - y)$, $\tan(x + y)$, and $\tan(x - y)$. **0.5, 0.5, $-\frac{1}{\sqrt{3}}$, $\frac{1}{\sqrt{3}}$**

Notes on Reading

❶ **Reading Mathematics** The last sentence of this paragraph can be hard reading. Replacing x by $\frac{\pi}{2} - x$ in $\sin x = \cos\left(\frac{\pi}{2} - x\right)$ to obtain $\sin\left(\frac{\pi}{2} - x\right) = \cos\left(\frac{\pi}{2} - \left(\frac{\pi}{2} - x\right)\right)$ confuses many students. You might begin with $\sin \alpha = \cos\left(\frac{\pi}{2} - \alpha\right)$ and then replace α by $\frac{\pi}{2} - x$.

❷ Point out the two applications of cofunctions in proving the Sine of a Sum Theorem. The first is quite clever and the second requires recognizing one side of an identity in a larger context. Some students will need help in going from the second to the third line of the proof. Write $\cos(x - y) = \cos x \cos y + \sin x \sin y$ and tell them to replace x by $\frac{\pi}{2} - \alpha$ and y by β. Then simplify the resulting expression.

LESSON 6-5

Formulas for $\sin(\alpha \pm \beta)$ and $\tan(\alpha \pm \beta)$

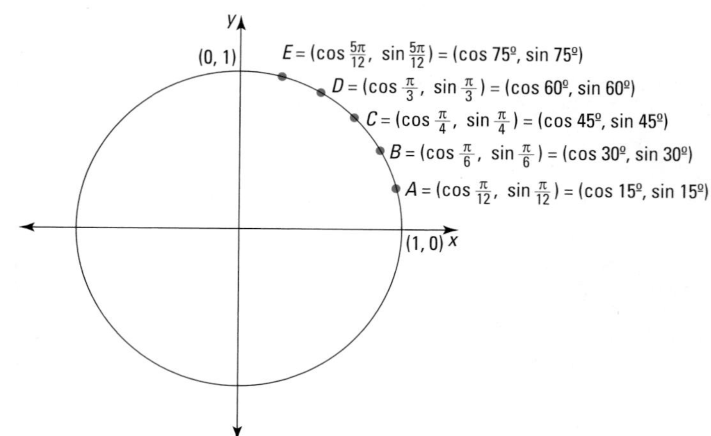

In the unit circle shown here, points *A, B, C, D,* and *E* are equally spaced at intervals of $\frac{\pi}{12}$ or 15° between (1, 0) and (0, 1). From properties of 30-60-90 and 45-45-90 right triangles, the coordinates of *B, C,* and *D* can be deduced, giving the cosines of 30°, 45°, and 60°. The identities for $\cos(\alpha + \beta)$ and $\cos(\alpha - \beta)$ enable the first coordinates of *A* and *E* to be found.

An Identity for $\sin(\alpha + \beta)$

❶ Because of the cofunction identity $\sin x = \cos\left(\frac{\pi}{2} - x\right)$, the second coordinates of *A* and *E* can be found. To find $\sin x$, just find the cosine of the complement of *x*. Also, replacing *x* by $\frac{\pi}{2} - x$ on each side, as you were asked to do in Question 11 of Lesson 6-4,

$$\sin\left(\frac{\pi}{2} - x\right) = \cos\left(\frac{\pi}{2} - \left(\frac{\pi}{2} - x\right)\right) = \cos x.$$

These two uses of the cofunction identity help in deducing an identity for $\sin(\alpha + \beta)$.

Theorem (Sine of a Sum)
For all real numbers α and β,

$$\sin(\alpha + \beta) = \sin\alpha\cos\beta + \cos\alpha\sin\beta.$$

❷ **Proof**

$\sin(\alpha + \beta) = \cos\left(\frac{\pi}{2} - (\alpha + \beta)\right)$	Cofunction Identity
$= \cos\left(\left(\frac{\pi}{2} - \alpha\right) - \beta\right)$	Associative Property of Addition
$= \cos\left(\frac{\pi}{2} - \alpha\right)\cos\beta + \sin\left(\frac{\pi}{2} - \alpha\right)\sin\beta$	Cosine of a Difference Theorem
$= \sin\alpha\cos\beta + \cos\alpha\sin\beta.$	Cofunction Identities

You should memorize this identity for $\sin(\alpha + \beta)$.

Lesson 6-5 Overview

Broad Goals The motivation for this lesson might be said to be the desire of the human spirit for closure, to finish the task. Since we have identities for $\cos(\alpha + \beta)$ and $\cos(\alpha - \beta)$, it is natural to want to find similar identities for the other common trigonometric functions.

Perspective This lesson follows naturally from the last. Using the identities for $\cos\left(\frac{\pi}{2} - x\right)$ and $\cos(\alpha - \beta)$, an identity for $\sin(\alpha + \beta)$ is deduced. This leads to identities for $\sin(\alpha - \beta)$ and $\sin(\pi - x)$. By dividing the formulas for the sine by the corresponding formulas for the cosine, the corresponding identities for the tangent function are then derived.

An Identity for sin (α − β)

The theorem below is a corresponding identity for sin (α − β). It can be proved by replacing β in sin (α + β) by -β. You are asked to write this proof in the Questions.

❸ **Theorem (Sine of a Difference)**
For all real numbers α and β,

$$\sin(\alpha - \beta) = \sin\alpha\cos\beta - \cos\alpha\sin\beta.$$

Example 1

Prove the identity $\sin(\pi - x) = \sin x$.

Solution

Use the formula for the sine of a difference, with $\alpha = \pi$ and $\beta = x$.

$$\begin{aligned}\sin(\pi - x) &= \sin\pi\cos x - \cos\pi\sin x\\ &= 0\cdot\cos x - (-1)\sin x\\ &= \sin x\end{aligned}$$

The identity in Example 1 has geometric significance. When $0 < x < \pi$, x and $\pi - x$ are measures of supplementary angles, and so the sines of supplements are equal. Graphically, the identity shows that for all x, $(x, \sin x)$ and $(x, \sin(\pi - x))$ lie on the same horizontal line.

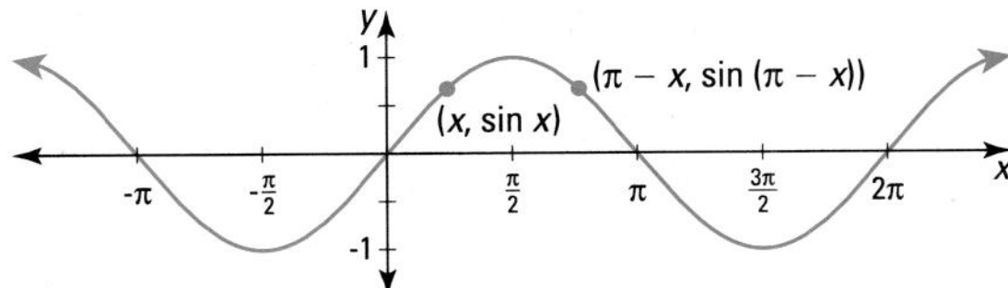

Identities for tan (α + β) and tan (α − β)

Identities for the tangent of a sum and the tangent of a difference can be derived from the corresponding identities for the sine and cosine.

❹ **Theorem (Tangent of a Sum and Tangent of a Difference)**
For all real numbers α and β such that tan α, tan β, and tan (α + β) are defined,

$$\tan(\alpha + \beta) = \frac{\tan\alpha + \tan\beta}{1 - \tan\alpha\tan\beta}$$
$$\tan(\alpha - \beta) = \frac{\tan\alpha - \tan\beta}{1 + \tan\alpha\tan\beta}.$$

❸ The proof of the identity for sin (α − β) is easy for most students. From that **Example 1** is also not a difficult application. Still, you might use a unit circle to provide another proof and a visual picture of the identity of **Example 1.**

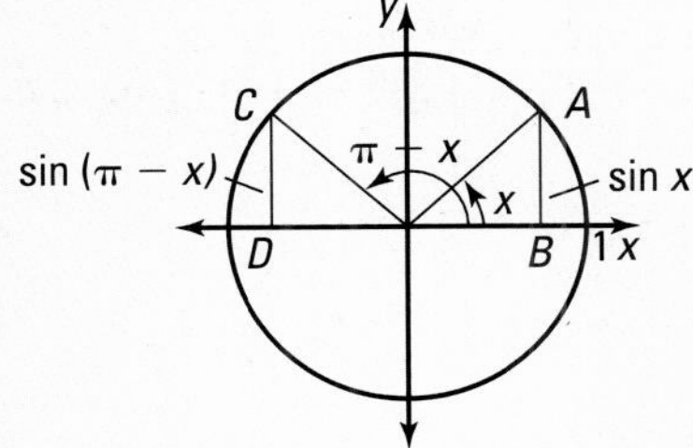

Since C is the reflection image of A over the y-axis, A and C have the same second coordinates. Thus $\sin x = \sin(\pi - x)$.

❹ In the proof of $\tan(\alpha + \beta) = \frac{\tan\alpha + \tan\beta}{1 - \tan\alpha\tan\beta}$, many students do not understand how (or even why)

(1) $\frac{\sin\alpha\cos\beta + \cos\alpha\sin\beta}{\cos\alpha\cos\beta - \sin\alpha\sin\beta}$ was divided by $\cos\alpha\cos\beta$. Encourage them to look at (1) with an eye to the goal of seeing only tangents in the final result. Because $\tan x = \frac{\sin x}{\cos x}$, we need to create fractions with only sines in numerators and corresponding cosines in denominators. Because the $\cos\alpha\cos\beta$ term in the lower left of (1) lacks any sines, it cannot be transformed into tangents and must therefore be "eliminated" by dividing by $\cos\alpha\cos\beta$. A wonderful bonus is that all the remaining terms are transformed into tangents. Our identity is proved!

Error Alert In **Example 2** on page 374, some students might not follow the simplification of the compound fraction. You might want to go over this in more detail, showing explicitly that first the numerator and the denominator are each rewritten as a single fraction:

$$\frac{\frac{-3 + \sqrt{3}}{3}}{\frac{3 + \sqrt{3}}{3}}.$$

Don't overlook the last paragraph of this lesson. The finding or creation of functions L that would satisfy $L(ab) = L(a) + L(b)$ greatly facilitated astronomers in their search for heavenly truths. For 350 years, tables of logarithms were the most widely available hand-held calculators! Developing identities is part of the process of creating new knowledge in mathematics.

Optional Activities

Activity 1 Writing For these identities: Cosine of a Sum, Cosine of a Difference; Sine of a Sum, Sine of a Difference; Tangent of a Sum, Tangent of a Difference, you might have students describe how they can remember each formula. [Sample: The cosine formulas start out with "cos cos" and the sign in the formula is opposite the sign in the desired argument. (That is, for a sum, the sign in the formula will be minus; for a difference, the sign will be plus.) The sine formulas start out "sin cos" and then switch to "cos sin," keeping α and β in the same order. The signs in these formulas match the desired argument. For the tangent formulas, the sign in the numerator of the formula matches the desired argument, while the sign in the denominator is opposite. The pattern is the same for both: the numerator is always a sum or difference of tangents, while the denominator is 1 ± "tan tan."]

Additional Examples

1. Prove the identity $\sin\left(\frac{3\pi}{2} + x\right) = -\cos x$. $\sin\left(\frac{3\pi}{2} + x\right) = \sin\frac{3\pi}{2}\cos x + \cos\frac{3\pi}{2}\sin x = (-1)\cos x + 0(\sin x) = -\cos x$
2. Express $\tan\frac{7\pi}{12}$ in terms of rational numbers and radicals.
   Solution 1:
   $\tan\frac{7\pi}{12} = \tan\left(\frac{3\pi}{12} + \frac{4\pi}{12}\right) = \tan\left(\frac{\pi}{4} + \frac{\pi}{3}\right) = \frac{1 + \sqrt{3}}{1 - \sqrt{3}}$
   Solution 2:
   $\tan\frac{7\pi}{12} = \tan\left(\frac{9\pi}{12} - \frac{2\pi}{12}\right) = \tan\left(\frac{3\pi}{4} - \frac{\pi}{6}\right) = \frac{-3 - \sqrt{3}}{3 - \sqrt{3}}$
   Students should multiply both numerator and denominator of the first solution by $-\sqrt{3}$ to show that the two solutions are equal.

Notes on Questions

Question 2 Students will need to remember that $\sin(-x) = -\sin x$ and $\cos(-x) = \cos x$.

Proof
Suppose that α and β are real numbers such that $\cos(\alpha + \beta)$, $\cos\alpha$, and $\cos\beta$ are nonzero. Then

$\tan(\alpha + \beta) = \frac{\sin(\alpha + \beta)}{\cos(\alpha + \beta)}$ — ? Definition of tangent

$= \frac{\sin\alpha\cos\beta + \cos\alpha\sin\beta}{\cos\alpha\cos\beta - \sin\alpha\sin\beta}$ — ? Identifies for $\sin(\alpha + \beta)$ and $\cos(\alpha + \beta)$

$= \dfrac{\frac{\sin\alpha\cos\beta}{\cos\alpha\cos\beta} + \frac{\cos\alpha\sin\beta}{\cos\alpha\cos\beta}}{\frac{\cos\alpha\cos\beta}{\cos\alpha\cos\beta} - \frac{\sin\alpha\sin\beta}{\cos\alpha\cos\beta}}$ — Divide numerator and denominator by $\cos\alpha\cos\beta$.

$= \frac{\tan\alpha + \tan\beta}{1 - \tan\alpha\tan\beta}$ — ? Simplify; Definition of tangent

You are asked to prove the identity for $\tan(\alpha - \beta)$ in the Questions.

Activity

Supply the missing reasons for each step in the above proof. See above.

Example 2

Express $\tan\frac{11\pi}{12}$ in terms of rational numbers and radicals.

Solution

First rewrite $\frac{11\pi}{12}$ as a sum of two numbers whose tangents you know.

$$\frac{11\pi}{12} = \frac{3\pi}{4} + \frac{\pi}{6}$$

Then $\tan\left(\frac{11\pi}{12}\right) = \tan\left(\frac{3\pi}{4} + \frac{\pi}{6}\right)$

$= \dfrac{\tan\frac{3\pi}{4} + \tan\frac{\pi}{6}}{1 - \tan\frac{3\pi}{4}\cdot\tan\frac{\pi}{6}}$ — Tangent of a Sum Theorem

$= \dfrac{-1 + \frac{\sqrt{3}}{3}}{1 - (-1)\left(\frac{\sqrt{3}}{3}\right)}$ — substituting for $\tan\frac{3\pi}{4}$, and $\tan\frac{\pi}{6}$

$= \frac{-3 + \sqrt{3}}{3 + \sqrt{3}}$ — simplifying complex fraction

$= \frac{-3 + \sqrt{3}}{3 + \sqrt{3}}\cdot\frac{3 - \sqrt{3}}{3 - \sqrt{3}}$ — rationalizing the denominator

$= \frac{-12 + 6\sqrt{3}}{6}$ — multiplying fractions

$= -2 + \sqrt{3}$ — putting in lowest terms

The sum and difference formulas for the sine, cosine, and tangent lead to many marvelous identities involving these functions. Some of these are in the Questions, some are in the next lesson, and still more are to be found in Chapter 8. For instance, from the formula for $\tan(\alpha + \beta)$, you can prove that for all x, $\tan(x + \pi) = \tan x$. This is left to you as a Question.

Optional Activities

Activity 2 Technology Connection
You might wish to assign *Technology Sourcebook, Calculator Master 10.* In this activity, students propose trigonometric identities and then use a graphics calculator to test their conjectures. Students are then asked to prove three of the identities they create.

Adapting to Individual Needs

Extra Help
If you have not already done so, you might want to have students begin a list of the trigonometric identities covered in this and previous lessons. While students are not expected to memorize all of them, it is often helpful to be able to refer to a summary of these identities when applying them or using them to prove new identities. After you cover the next lesson, have students add those new identities to the list.

Additional Answers

9. a. $\tan(x + \pi) = \frac{\tan x + \tan\pi}{1 - \tan x\tan\pi} = \frac{\tan x + 0}{1 - (\tan x)\cdot 0)} = \tan x$
   b. The period is no larger than π.
10. $\tan(\alpha - \beta) = \tan(\alpha + (-\beta)) = \frac{\tan\alpha + \tan(-\beta)}{1 - \tan\alpha\tan(-\beta)} = \frac{\tan\alpha - \tan\beta}{1 + \tan\alpha\tan\beta}$
11. The identity becomes $\tan 2\beta = \frac{2\tan\beta}{1 - \tan^2\beta}$.

Relationships among the values of a function, or among the values of different functions, tell you how the function behaves. For instance, the identity $\tan(x + \pi) = \tan x$ indicates that the tangent function is periodic. The identity $\log(xy) = \log x + \log y$ for $x > 0$ and $y > 0$ indicates that the log function converts a multiplication into an addition. The real number property $a^{x+y} = a^x \cdot a^y$ can be thought of as an identity involving the values of the exponential function $f: x \to a^x$, and shows how powers with the same base can be multiplied.

QUESTIONS

Covering the Reading

1. Write formulas for $\sin(x + y)$ and $\sin(x - y)$. See left.
2. Substitute $-\beta$ for β in the identity for $\sin(\alpha + \beta)$ to derive the identity for $\sin(\alpha - \beta)$. See left.

In 3 and 4, refer to the unit circle at the beginning of the lesson.

3. Write the coordinates of points A and B in terms of radicals and rational numbers. See left.
4. Write the coordinates of points C, D, and E in terms of radicals and rational numbers. See left.
5. Prove: $\forall$ *real numbers x*, $\sin\left(\frac{\pi}{2} + x\right) = \cos x$. See left.
6. Show your work from the Activity in this Lesson. See page 374.

In 7 and 8, find the value in terms of rational numbers and radicals.

7. $\tan \frac{7\pi}{12}$ $\frac{1 + \sqrt{3}}{1 - \sqrt{3}}$
8. $\sin 105°$ $\frac{\sqrt{6} + \sqrt{2}}{4}$

9. a. Prove: $\forall$ *real numbers x*, $\tan(x + \pi) = \tan x$.
   b. What does the theorem in part **a** indicate about the period of the tangent function?

See margin.

Applying the Mathematics

10. Prove the identity for $\tan(\alpha - \beta)$. See margin.
11. In the identity for $\tan(\alpha - \beta)$, let $\alpha = \beta$. What happens? See margin.
12. Suppose a ramp has a slope of 15°. Then for every meter of horizontal distance, how much of an increase in height is there? Answer to the nearest millimeter. 268 mm

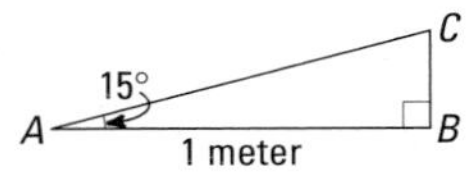

1) $\sin(x + y) = \sin x \cos y + \cos x \sin y$; $\sin(x - y) = \sin x \cos y - \cos x \sin y$

2) $\sin(\alpha + (-\beta)) = \sin\alpha \cos(-\beta) + \cos\alpha \sin(-\beta) = \sin\alpha\cos\beta - \cos\alpha\sin\beta$

3) $A = \left(\frac{\sqrt{2} + \sqrt{6}}{4}, \frac{\sqrt{6} - \sqrt{2}}{4}\right)$ $B = \left(\frac{\sqrt{3}}{2}, \frac{1}{2}\right)$

4) $C = \left(\frac{\sqrt{2}}{2}, \frac{\sqrt{2}}{2}\right)$ $D = \left(\frac{1}{2}, \frac{\sqrt{3}}{2}\right)$ $E = \left(\frac{\sqrt{6} - \sqrt{2}}{4}, \frac{\sqrt{6} + \sqrt{2}}{4}\right)$

5) $\sin\left(\frac{\pi}{2} + x\right) = \sin\frac{\pi}{2} \cos x + \cos\frac{\pi}{2} \sin x = 1 \cdot \cos x + 0 \cdot \sin x = \cos x$

Question 10 Students should be able to do this in two ways: (1) $\tan(\alpha - \beta) = \frac{\sin(\alpha - \beta)}{\cos(\alpha - \beta)} = \ldots$ as in the proof for $\tan(\alpha + \beta)$ in the lesson; (2) $\tan(\alpha - \beta) = \tan(\alpha + (-\beta))$ and then apply the $\tan(x + y)$ identity.

(Notes on Questions continue on page 376.)

Follow-up for Lesson 6-5

Practice

For more questions on SPUR Objectives, use **Lesson Master 6-5** (shown below).

Assessment

Written Communication Have students work with a partner to find exact values for the coordinates of points A, B, C, D, and E on the unit circle at the beginning of the lesson. Have them check their answers using a calculator, as shown in the check for **Example 1** in Lesson 6-4. [Students use trigonometric identities to give exact values of the trigonometric functions.]

(Follow-up continues on page 376.)

Adapting to Individual Needs

Challenge

Have students answer the following questions.

1. From the identities in this lesson, derive identities for:
   a. $\sin x \cos y$ $\left[\frac{1}{2}(\sin(x + y) + \sin(x - y))\right]$
   b. $\cos x \sin y$ $\left[\frac{1}{2}(\sin(x + y) - \sin(x - y))\right]$
   c. $\sin x + \sin y$ $\left[2 \sin\frac{x + y}{2} \cos\frac{x - y}{2}\right]$
   d. $\sin x - \sin y$ $\left[2 \cos\frac{x + y}{2} \sin\frac{x - y}{2}\right]$
   e. $\tan(x + y + z)$ $\left[\frac{\tan x + \tan y + \tan z - \tan x \tan y \tan z}{1 - \tan y \tan z - \tan x \tan y - \tan x \tan z}\right]$
2. If $x + y + z = 180°$, show that $\tan x + \tan y + \tan z = \tan x \tan y \tan z$. [Use identity 1e above, where $\tan(x + y + z) = \tan 180° = 0$. This forces the numerator to be 0, which gives the required result.]

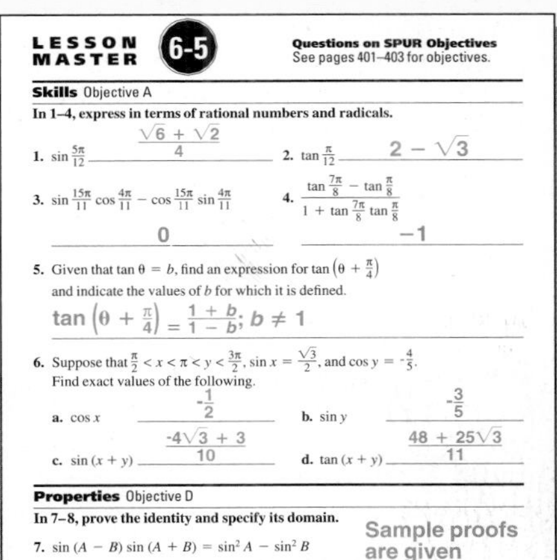
LESSON MASTER 6-5 **Questions on SPUR Objectives** See pages 401–403 for objectives.

Skills Objective A

In 1–4, express in terms of rational numbers and radicals.

1. $\sin\frac{5\pi}{12}$ $\frac{\sqrt{6} + \sqrt{2}}{4}$
2. $\tan\frac{\pi}{12}$ $2 - \sqrt{3}$
3. $\sin\frac{15\pi}{11}\cos\frac{4\pi}{11} - \cos\frac{15\pi}{11}\sin\frac{4\pi}{11}$ 0
4. $\frac{\tan\frac{7\pi}{8} - \tan\frac{\pi}{8}}{1 + \tan\frac{7\pi}{8}\tan\frac{\pi}{8}}$ -1
5. Given that $\tan\theta = b$, find an expression for $\tan\left(\theta + \frac{\pi}{4}\right)$ and indicate the values of b for which it is defined.
   $\tan\left(\theta + \frac{\pi}{4}\right) = \frac{1 + b}{1 - b}; b \neq 1$
6. Suppose that $\frac{\pi}{2} < x < \pi < y < \frac{3\pi}{2}$, $\sin x = \frac{\sqrt{3}}{2}$, and $\cos y = -\frac{4}{5}$. Find exact values of the following.
   a. $\cos x$ $-\frac{1}{2}$
   b. $\sin y$ $-\frac{3}{5}$
   c. $\sin(x + y)$ $\frac{-4\sqrt{3} + 3}{10}$
   d. $\tan(x + y)$ $\frac{48 + 25\sqrt{3}}{11}$

Properties Objective D

In 7–8, prove the identity and specify its domain. Sample proofs are given

7. $\sin(A - B)\sin(A + B) = \sin^2 A - \sin^2 B$
   $\sin(A - B)\sin(A + B) = (\sin A\cos B - \cos A\sin B)\cdot(\sin A\cos B + \cos A\sin B) = \sin^2 A\cos^2 B - \cos^2 A\sin^2 B = \sin^2 A(1 - \sin^2 B) - (1 - \sin^2 A)\sin^2 B = \sin^2 A - \sin^2 A\sin^2 B - \sin^2 B + \sin^2 A\sin^2 B = \sin^2 A - \sin^2 B$ domain: set of real numbers
8. $\tan(45° - x)\tan(135° - x) = -1$ $\tan(45° - x)\tan(135° - x) = \frac{\tan 45° - \tan x}{1 + \tan 45°\tan x}\cdot\frac{\tan 135° - \tan x}{1 + \tan 135°\tan x} = \frac{1 - \tan x}{1 + \tan x}\cdot\frac{-1 - \tan x}{1 - \tan x} = 1(1 - 1) = -1$
   domain: $\{x: x \neq (2n + 1)\frac{\pi}{4}$, n an integer

Extension

Technology Connection Use an automatic 3-D grapher to examine identities that involve two variables. For example, to verify $\sin(x + y) = \sin x \cos y + \cos x \sin y$, graph $z_1 = \sin(x + y)$ and $z_2 = \sin x \cos y + \cos x \sin y$. You may even graph $z_3 = z_1 - z_2$. *Mathematica, Derive,* and *Theorist* are software packages that do 3-D graphics.

Project Update Project 2, *"Pseudotrigonometric" Functions,* Project 4, *Rational and Radical Expressions for Sines and Cosines,* and Project 5, *Gravity,* on page 398, relate to the content of this lesson.

Notes on Questions

Question 13 Students who used *Functions, Statistics, and Trigonometry* will have seen this gorgeous proof.

Question 14 In expanding $\cos\left(x + \frac{\pi}{2}\right)$ using the Cosine of a Sum theorem, students will be proving the identity as they find it.

Question 15 This question sends an important message: there are identities that do not involve the trigonometric functions. Students may be surprised at the number of simple relationships among squares that can be obtained by picking different values of k.

Question 18 The simpler task of factoring $(3x - 4)(x - 3) - (3x - 4)^2$ was on the 1993 Brevet exam in the Caen region of France, taken after 9th grade by most students. (Source: *What Students Abroad Are Expected To Know About Mathematics*, American Federation of Teachers and National Center for Improving Science Education, 1997)

Question 19 Geography Connection The longest road tunnel connects Göschenen and Airolo, Switzerland; it is just over 10 miles long.

13. An elegant alternate proof of two of the identities of this and the previous lesson is possible using matrices. For any real number θ,

$$\begin{bmatrix} \cos\theta & -\sin\theta \\ \sin\theta & \cos\theta \end{bmatrix}$$

is the matrix for R_θ, where R_θ is the rotation of θ about the origin. Translate the transformation identity $R_{\theta+\phi} = R_\theta \cdot R_\phi$ into matrices and then multiply the matrices. Which two identities result? See margin.

Review

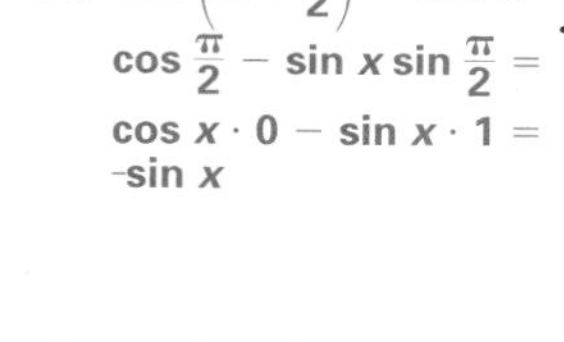
14) $\cos\left(x + \frac{\pi}{2}\right) = \cos x \cos\frac{\pi}{2} - \sin x \sin\frac{\pi}{2} = \cos x \cdot 0 - \sin x \cdot 1 = -\sin x$

14. Find and prove an identity involving $\cos\left(x + \frac{\pi}{2}\right)$. *(Lesson 6-4)* See left.

15. a. Prove: If $a + b = c + d$, then $a^2 + b^2 + (c + k)^2 + (d + k)^2 = c^2 + d^2 + (a + k)^2 + (b + k)^2$. (Hint: Use Technique 1 of Lesson 6-2.) See margin.

b. Suppose $a = 1$, $b = 4$, $c = 2$, and $d = 3$. Pick integer values for k and show what identities arise. *(Previous course, Lesson 6-2)* See margin.

How Wheat It Is. *This large, 30-foot-wide combine is harvesting hard red spring wheat.*

16. A small grain combine can harvest 100 acres in 24 hours, a medium combine can do the same job in 18 hours, and a large combine can do the job in 12 hours. If all three combines are used at the same time, how long will it take to harvest 800 acres? *(Lesson 5-8)* ≈ 44.3 hours

17. Tell whether each number is rational or irrational. *(Lessons 5-1, 5-6)*

a. $.8\overline{7}$ rational　**b.** $\sqrt{15}$ irrational　**c.** $\frac{\sqrt{36}}{9}$ rational

18. Express in factored form: $(8x + 3)^2(5x - 7)^3 + (8x + 3)(5x - 7)^2$. *(Lesson 4-7)* See below.

19. A semicircular tunnel through a mountain has a radius of 15 feet. A truck with a height of 12 feet needs to pass through the tunnel. If the truck straddles the center line of the road when passing through the tunnel, what is the maximum allowable width for the truck? *(Previous course)* 18 ft

18) $(8x + 3)(5x - 7)^2((8x + 3)(5x - 7) + 1)$

Exploration

20. a. Find an identity for $\sin(\alpha + \beta + \gamma)$ in terms of $\sin\alpha$, $\sin\beta$, $\sin\gamma$, $\cos\alpha$, $\cos\beta$, and $\cos\gamma$.

b. Use this identity to predict a similar identity for $\cos(\alpha + \beta + \gamma)$.

c. Determine whether your prediction is true. See margin.

a) $\sin(\alpha + \beta + \gamma) = \sin\alpha\cos\beta\cos\gamma + \cos\alpha\sin\beta\cos\gamma + \cos\alpha\cos\beta\sin\gamma - \sin\alpha\sin\beta\sin\gamma$

b) $\cos(\alpha + \beta + \gamma) = \cos\alpha\cos\beta\cos\gamma - \sin\alpha\sin\beta\cos\gamma - \sin\alpha\cos\beta\sin\gamma - \cos\alpha\sin\beta\sin\gamma$

Additional Answers
13, 15, 20c. See Additional Answers at the back of this book.

Setting Up Lesson 6-6

Discuss **Question 11,** which provides a bridge to the next lesson.

376

LESSON

6-6

Formulas for cos 2x and sin 2x

Keep Your Eye on the Ball. *Time-lapse photos of a golf ball in flight show the first part of its path, a parabola. See Example 3.*

Identities for cos 2x

In Example 1 of Lesson 6-1 you saw that the graph of $y = \cos^2 x - \sin^2 x$ looks like the graph of $y = \cos 2x$.

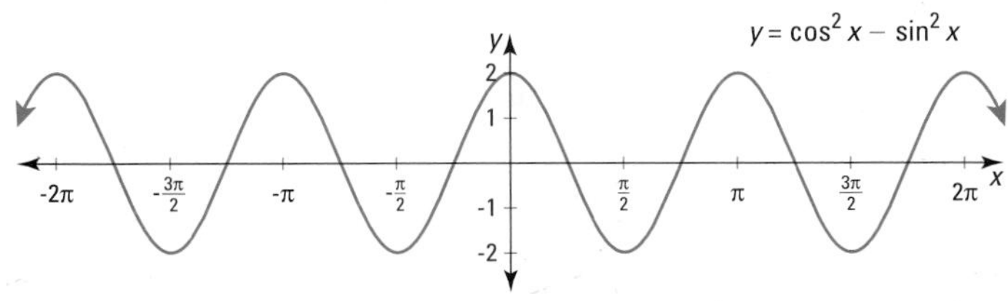

In other words, the equation $\cos^2 x - \sin^2 x = \cos 2x$ appears to be an identity. From the identities for $\cos(\alpha + \beta)$ and $\sin(\alpha + \beta)$ you can prove this identity as well as some others.

Theorem (Identities for cos 2x)
For all real numbers x:

(1) $\cos 2x = \cos^2 x - \sin^2 x$
(2) $\cos 2x = 2\cos^2 x - 1$
(3) $\cos 2x = 1 - 2\sin^2 x$.

Proof
(1) This identity is a special case of the identity for $\cos(\alpha + \beta)$. For all real numbers α and β,

$$\cos(\alpha + \beta) = \cos\alpha\cos\beta - \sin\alpha\sin\beta.$$

Now let $\alpha = x$ and $\beta = x$. Then

$$\cos(x + x) = \cos x\cos x - \sin x\sin x.$$

That is, $$\cos 2x = \cos^2 x - \sin^2 x.$$

Lesson 6-6

Objectives

A Without a calculator, use trigonometric identities to express values of trigonometric functions in terms of rational numbers and radicals.

D Prove trigonometric identities and identify their domains.

Resources

From the ***Teacher's Resource File***
- Lesson Master 6-6
- Answer Master 6-6
- Assessment Sourcebook: Quiz for Lessons 6-4 through 6-6
- Teaching Aids
  55 Warm-up
  59 Example 3 Drawing

Additional Resources
- Visuals for Teaching Aids 55, 59
- Exploration 6-6

Teaching Lesson 6-6

Warm-up

Without using a calculator, find cos 2*t* and sin 2*t* for the given value of *t*. (These answers can be used to verify the identities for cos 2*x* and sin 2*x* found in the lesson.)

1. $t = \frac{\pi}{8}$ $\frac{\sqrt{2}}{2}, \frac{\sqrt{2}}{2}$
2. $t = -7\pi$ 1, 0
3. $t = -60°$ $-0.5, -\frac{\sqrt{3}}{2}$

Lesson 6-6 Overview

Broad Goals This lesson uses the formulas for $\cos(\alpha + \beta)$ and $\sin(\alpha + \beta)$ to deduce formulas for cos 2*x* and sin 2*x*.

Perspective It is natural to let $\alpha = \beta = x$ in the formulas for $\cos(\alpha + \beta)$ and $\sin(\alpha + \beta)$ and thus derive formulas for cos 2*x* and sin 2*x*.

In the previous lessons, two reasons for having identities are shown: to prove other identities and to find exact values of circular functions for new arguments. In **Example 3b** of this lesson, an additional reason is exemplified: to simplify a formula.

Optional Activities

Activity 1 Technology Connection
Materials: Explorations software

Students may use *Exploration 6-6, Finding the Projectile Range,* as an alternative to **Example 3.** Students can input an initial velocity, launch angle, and time. The range of the projectile is shown algebraically and graphically. Students can locate a specific point on the graph or see an animation of the projectile's path.

(2) This identity follows from (1) using the Pythagorean Identity $\cos^2 x + \sin^2 x = 1$, from which it follows that $\sin^2 x = 1 - \cos^2 x$.

(left side) $\cos 2x$	
$= \cos^2 x - \sin^2 x$	from (1)
$= \cos^2 x - (1 - \cos^2 x)$	$\sin^2 x = 1 - \cos^2 x$
$= \cos^2 x - 1 + \cos^2 x$	Distributive Property
$= 2\cos^2 x - 1$ (right side)	adding like terms

The proof of (3) is left for you to do.

Example 1

If $\cos x = -\frac{3}{5}$ and $\frac{\pi}{2} < x < \pi$, find $\cos 2x$.

Solution

You could solve this problem using either (1), (2), or (3), but by choosing (2), you can avoid computing $\sin x$.

$$\cos 2x = 2\cos^2 x - 1 = 2\left(-\frac{3}{5}\right)^2 - 1 = 2 \cdot \frac{9}{25} - 1 = \frac{18}{25} - 1 = -\frac{7}{25}$$

An Identity for sin 2x

A special case of the formula for $\sin(\alpha + \beta)$ leads to the next theorem. Its proof is like proof (1) of the previous theorem and is left for you to do.

Theorem (Identity for sin 2x)
For all real numbers x,

$$\sin 2x = 2\sin x \cos x.$$

Example 2

If $\cos x = -\frac{3}{5}$ and $\frac{\pi}{2} < x < \pi$, find $\sin 2x$.

Solution 1

Since you already know the value of $\cos 2x$ from Example 1, you can use the Pythagorean Identity to find $\sin 2x$.

$$\cos^2 2x + \sin^2 2x = 1$$
$$\left(-\frac{7}{25}\right)^2 + \sin^2 2x = 1$$
$$\sin^2 2x = \frac{576}{625}$$
$$\sin 2x = \pm\sqrt{\frac{576}{625}}$$

Notes on Reading

Stress that since the double angle identities $\cos 2x = \cos^2 x - \sin^2 x$ and $\sin 2x = 2\sin x \cos x$ come so quickly from the formulas $\cos(x + y)$ and $\sin(x + y)$, they need not be memorized. They can be derived each time. Still, most good students memorize them. Also, show how the $\cos 2x$ identities (2) and (3) follow from (1).

Example 2 utilizes two ideas from earlier lessons. First is the Pythagorean Identity. Second is the double inequality $\frac{\pi}{2} < x < \pi$ that needs to be transformed to $\pi < 2x < 2\pi$ in order to analyze the sign of $\sin 2x$.

Science Connection Teaching Aid 59 shows the drawing for **Example 3.** This example derives a formula that physics students either have seen or will see. The horizontal and vertical components of the velocity should be reasonable to students if you picture a right triangle whose hypotenuse is v_0. Students should recognize that the formula for the height is the standard quadratic equation for the motion of a projectile thrown into the air:
$h = -\frac{1}{2}gt^2 + v_0 t + h_0$, where
g is the acceleration due to gravity, v_0 is the initial velocity in the vertical direction, and h_0 is the initial height from which the object is thrown. This is a formula that should be very familiar to students who have studied from prior UCSMP books. Make sure

LESSON MASTER 6-6
Questions on SPUR Objectives
See pages 401–403 for objectives.

Skills Objective A

1. Given that $\cos\theta = \frac{12}{13}$ and $\sin\theta = -\frac{5}{13}$, find exact values of $\cos 2\theta$, $\cos\frac{\theta}{2}$, $\sin 2\theta$, and $\sin\frac{\theta}{2}$.
   $\cos 2\theta = \frac{119}{169}$ $\sin 2\theta = \frac{-120}{169}$
   $\cos\frac{\theta}{2} = \frac{-5\sqrt{26}}{26}$ $\sin\frac{\theta}{2} = \frac{\sqrt{26}}{26}$

In 2 and 3, express the following in terms of rational numbers and radicals.

2. $\sin\frac{\pi}{8}$ $\frac{1}{2}\sqrt{2 - \sqrt{2}}$
3. $\cos 15°$ $\frac{1}{2}\sqrt{2 + \sqrt{3}}$
4. a. Use the identity for $\sin(\alpha + \beta)$ to find $\sin\frac{5\pi}{12}$. $\frac{1}{4}(\sqrt{6} + \sqrt{2})$
   b. Use the identity $\cos 2\alpha = 1 - 2\sin^2\alpha$ to find $\sin\frac{5\pi}{12}$. $\frac{1}{2}(\sqrt{2 + \sqrt{3}})$
   c. Show that your answers to parts a and b are equal.
   $\left(\frac{\sqrt{6} + \sqrt{2}}{4}\right)^2 = \frac{6 + 2 + 4\sqrt{3}}{16} = \frac{2 + \sqrt{3}}{4}$; $\left(\frac{\sqrt{2 + \sqrt{3}}}{2}\right)^2 = \frac{2 + \sqrt{3}}{4}$; Thus, $\frac{\sqrt{6} + \sqrt{2}}{4} = \frac{\sqrt{2 + \sqrt{3}}}{4}$.

Properties Objective D

5. Prove that $\sin 3x = 3\sin x - 4\sin^3 x$. (Hint: Express $\sin 3x$ in the form $\sin(2x + x)$ and expand.)
   $\sin 3x$
   $= \sin(2x + x) = \sin 2x \cos x + \cos 2x \sin x$
   $= 2\sin x \cos x \cdot \cos x + (\cos^2 x - \sin^2 x)\sin x$
   $= 2\sin x \cos^2 x + \cos^2 x \sin x - \sin^3 x$
   $= 3\sin x \cos^2 x - \sin^3 x$
   $= 3\sin x(1 - \sin^2 x) - \sin^3 x$
   $= 3\sin x - 3\sin^3 x - \sin^3 x$
   $= 3\sin x - 4\sin^3 x$

Optional Activities

Activity 2 Ask students to find the maximum height of the projectile in **Question 6.** To consider this question, first prompt them to find the x-coordinate of the maximum height. [It is half of the range, as long as the initial height is zero.] Then ask if they can determine the time of maximum height. [Yes, solve for t in the formula for $d(t)$.] Finally, they should be able to find the maximum height. [Substitute this t value into $h(t)$.] As a challenge, ask them to find formulas for the x-coordinate of maximum height, time of maximum height, and maximum height in terms of v_0 and θ. [The vertex of the throw of the projectile will be $\left(\frac{v_0^2 \sin 2\theta}{64}, \frac{v_0^2 \sin^2\theta}{64}\right)$ and the time of max. ht. = $\frac{v_0 \sin\theta}{32}$. For **Question 6,** the vertex ≈ (126.6', 63.3') with $t \approx 2.0$ seconds.]

So $\sin 2x = \frac{24}{25}$ or $\sin 2x = -\frac{24}{25}$. To determine which value of $\sin 2x$ satisfies the conditions of the problem, you need to determine the quadrant in which $2x$ lies. Since $\frac{\pi}{2} < x < \pi$, multiplying by 2 gives $\pi < 2x < 2\pi$. Thus $2x$ is in quadrant 3 or 4. The sine is negative in both of these quadrants. Therefore,

$$\sin 2x = -\frac{24}{25}.$$

Solution 2

The formula $\sin 2x = 2 \sin x \cos x$ can be used, but you need to know $\sin x$. If $\cos x = -\frac{3}{5}$ and $\frac{\pi}{2} < x < \pi$, x is in the 2nd quadrant, so $\sin x$ is positive. Now $\sin^2 x + \cos^2 x = 1$, so $\sin^2 x + \left(-\frac{3}{5}\right)^2 = 1$, and thus $\sin^2 x = \frac{16}{25}$, from which $\sin x = \frac{4}{5}$. Thus $\sin 2x = 2 \cdot -\frac{3}{5} \cdot \frac{4}{5} = -\frac{24}{25}$.

One of the main reasons for proving identities is to simplify formulas, as Example 3 illustrates.

A kicked soccer ball follows the laws of any other projectile.

Example 3

A projectile is launched from ground level with an initial speed of v_0 feet per second at an angle θ above the horizontal. The following is a drawing of this situation showing the components of the initial velocity vector.

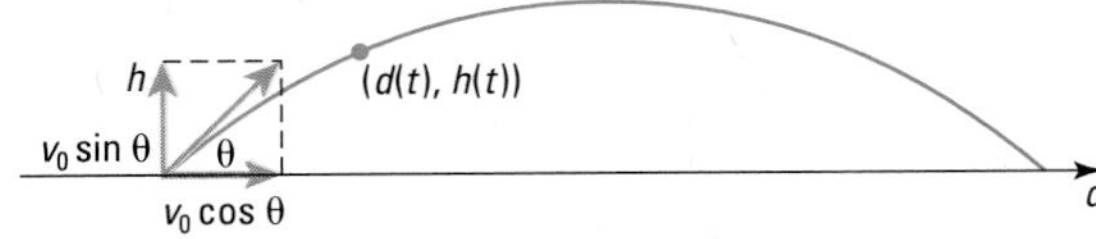

Let $h(t)$ be the height in feet of the projectile t seconds after it is launched, and let $d(t)$ be the horizontal distance of the projectile from the launch site. If only the force of gravity on the projectile is considered and other forces such as air resistance are ignored, then

$$d(t) = (v_0 \cos \theta)t$$

and

$$h(t) = -16t^2 + (v_0 \sin \theta)t.$$

a. How long will the projectile remain airborne?

b. The range R is the horizontal distance traveled by the projectile. Find a formula for R in terms of v_0 and θ.

c. What is the range when the projectile is launched at 120 ft/sec at an angle of 30°?

Solution

a. The length of time the projectile is airborne is the positive value of t for which $h(t) = 0$. Thus, substituting for $h(t)$,

$$-16t^2 + (v_0 \sin \theta)t = 0$$

$$(-16t + v_0 \sin \theta)t = 0 \qquad \text{factoring}$$

$$-16t + v_0 \sin \theta = 0 \quad \text{or} \quad t = 0 \qquad \text{Zero-Product Property}$$

$$t = \frac{v_0 \sin \theta}{16} \quad \text{or} \quad t = 0.$$

that students are comfortable with the formulas for height and range from this example as they will be used in **Lesson 6-7.**

Review **Example 4.** Students find it unusual to use a "double angle" formula to determine a "half angle." Tell them why $\cos 2x = 2\cos^2 x - 1$ was chosen to help calculate $\cos \frac{a}{2}$. Some students will need to see the following steps explicitly.

$\cos 2x = 2\cos^2 x - 1$

Let $2x = \alpha$, so $x = \frac{\alpha}{2}$

$\cos 2\left(\frac{\alpha}{2}\right) = 2\cos^2\left(\frac{\alpha}{2}\right) - 1$

$\cos \alpha = 2\cos^2\left(\frac{\alpha}{2}\right) - 1$, and so on.

Students may be uncomfortable with the two possible answers to **Example 4.** Here is an argument.

$\cos \alpha = \frac{3}{5} \Rightarrow \cos \alpha > 0$

$\Rightarrow 0 < \alpha < \frac{\pi}{2}$ or $\frac{3\pi}{2} < \alpha < 2\pi$.

But we want $\frac{\alpha}{2}$, so divide each of these double inequalities by 2.

$\Rightarrow 0 < \frac{\alpha}{2} < \frac{\pi}{4}$ or $\frac{3\pi}{4} < \frac{\alpha}{2} < \pi$

$\Rightarrow \cos \frac{\alpha}{2} > 0$ or $\cos \frac{\alpha}{2} < 0$

For this reason, the sign of $\cos \frac{\alpha}{2}$ is not uniquely determined.

Have students check results to problems such as those of **Example 5.** A scientific calculator can be used to approximate the value of $\sin \frac{\pi}{8}$. Students can then approximate their exact value on the calculator to see if the results appear to be equal, within

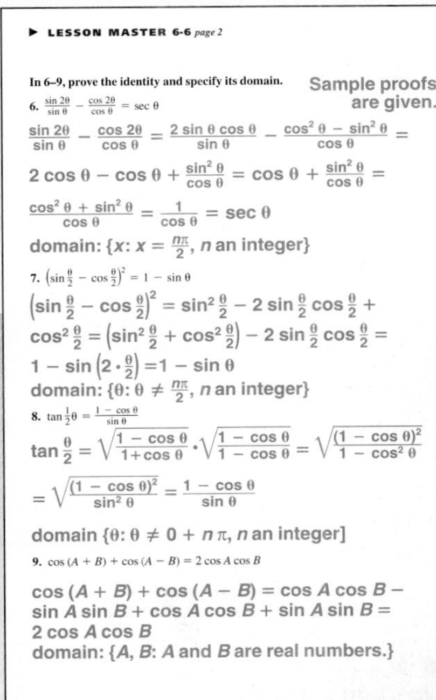

▶ **LESSON MASTER 6-6** *page 2*

In 6–9, prove the identity and specify its domain. Sample proofs are given.

6. $\frac{\sin 2\theta}{\sin \theta} - \frac{\cos 2\theta}{\cos \theta} = \sec \theta$

$\frac{\sin 2\theta}{\sin \theta} - \frac{\cos 2\theta}{\cos \theta} = \frac{2 \sin \theta \cos \theta}{\sin \theta} - \frac{\cos^2 \theta - \sin^2 \theta}{\cos \theta} =$

$2\cos \theta - \cos \theta + \frac{\sin^2 \theta}{\cos \theta} = \cos \theta + \frac{\sin^2 \theta}{\cos \theta} =$

$\frac{\cos^2 \theta + \sin^2 \theta}{\cos \theta} = \frac{1}{\cos \theta} = \sec \theta$

domain: $\{x: x = \frac{n\pi}{2}$, n an integer$\}$

7. $\left(\sin \frac{\theta}{2} - \cos \frac{\theta}{2}\right)^2 = 1 - \sin \theta$

$\left(\sin \frac{\theta}{2} - \cos \frac{\theta}{2}\right)^2 = \sin^2 \frac{\theta}{2} - 2 \sin \frac{\theta}{2} \cos \frac{\theta}{2} +$

$\cos^2 \frac{\theta}{2} = \left(\sin^2 \frac{\theta}{2} + \cos^2 \frac{\theta}{2}\right) - 2 \sin \frac{\theta}{2} \cos \frac{\theta}{2} =$

$1 - \sin\left(2 \cdot \frac{\theta}{2}\right) = 1 - \sin \theta$

domain: $\{\theta: \theta \neq \frac{n\pi}{2}$, n an integer$\}$

8. $\tan \frac{1}{2}\theta = \frac{1 - \cos \theta}{\sin \theta}$

$\tan \frac{\theta}{2} = \sqrt{\frac{1 - \cos \theta}{1 + \cos \theta}} \cdot \sqrt{\frac{1 - \cos \theta}{1 - \cos \theta}} = \sqrt{\frac{(1 - \cos \theta)^2}{1 - \cos^2 \theta}}$

$= \sqrt{\frac{(1 - \cos \theta)^2}{\sin^2 \theta}} = \frac{1 - \cos \theta}{\sin \theta}$

domain $\{\theta: \theta \neq 0 + n\pi$, n an integer$]$

9. $\cos(A + B) + \cos(A - B) = 2 \cos A \cos B$

$\cos(A + B) + \cos(A - B) = \cos A \cos B -$
$\sin A \sin B + \cos A \cos B + \sin A \sin B =$
$2 \cos A \cos B$

domain: $\{A, B$: A and B are real numbers.$\}$

Adapting to Individual Needs

Extra Help

Point out that some computations give only one possibility for the sign of the answer, as in **Example 1.** In this case, one need not analyze which quadrant $2x$ is in. Other times, the computation involves taking a square root, as in **Examples 2** and **4.** Then the sign of the answer could be either positive or negative. Then one must go back to the given information to see if the quadrant for $2x$, and hence the sign of the answer, can be determined. In **Example 2** there is enough given information to determine the sign while in **Example 4** there is not.

normal round-off error. Such a check should determine incorrect signs as well as major computational errors introduced while using the identities.

For **Example 5,** students may need additional explanation why $\cos 2x = 1 - 2\sin^2 x$ was chosen to find $\sin \frac{\pi}{8}$. Some students prefer this beginning: $\frac{\pi}{8} = \frac{1}{2} \cdot \frac{\pi}{4}$. Let $x = \frac{\pi}{8}$. Then $\cos 2x = 1 - 2\sin^2 x$ becomes $\cos 2\left(\frac{\pi}{8}\right) = 1 - 2\sin^2 \frac{\pi}{8}$ and so on.

If you have time, invite students to use $\cos 2x = 2\cos^2 x - 1$ and chunking $\left(\text{let } x = \frac{\theta}{2}\right)$ to derive $\cos \frac{\theta}{2} = \pm\sqrt{\frac{1 + \cos\theta}{2}}$. Many texts call this a *half-angle formula.*

Similarly, you can use $\cos 2x = 1 - 2\sin^2 x$ to develop $\sin \frac{\theta}{2} = \pm\sqrt{\frac{1 - \cos\theta}{2}}$.

The projectile is on the ground at 0 seconds and $\frac{v_0 \sin\theta}{16}$ seconds, so it remains airborne for $\frac{v_0 \sin\theta}{16}$ seconds.

b. The range R is simply the value of $d(t)$ when $t = \frac{v_0 \sin\theta}{16}$. In other words,

$$R = (v_0 \cos\theta)t$$
$$= (v_0 \cos\theta)\left(\frac{v_0 \sin\theta}{16}\right)$$
$$= \frac{\cos\theta \sin\theta\, v_0^2}{16} \text{ feet.}$$

This formula can be simplified using the identity $\sin 2\theta = 2\cos\theta\sin\theta$.

$$R = \frac{2\cos\theta\sin\theta\, v_0^2}{32}$$
$$= \frac{v_0^2 \sin 2\theta}{32} \text{ feet}$$

c. Here $v_0 = 120$ ft/sec and $\theta = 30°$. So

$$R = \frac{(120)^2 \sin(2 \cdot 30°)}{32}$$
$$\approx 390 \text{ feet.}$$

Finding $\cos \frac{x}{2}$ and $\sin \frac{x}{2}$

The formulas for $\cos 2x$ and $\sin 2x$ are sometimes called **double-angle identities**. From the formulas for $\cos 2x$, **half-angle identities** for $\cos \frac{x}{2}$ and $\sin \frac{x}{2}$ can be deduced. Examples 4 and 5 show how this can be done.

Example 4

If $\cos\alpha = \frac{3}{5}$, find $\cos\frac{\alpha}{2}$.

Solution

Begin with the identity

$\cos 2x = 2\cos^2 x - 1.$

Let $\alpha = 2x$, so $\frac{\alpha}{2} = x$.

$\cos\alpha = 2\cos^2\frac{\alpha}{2} - 1$ — substitution ($\frac{\alpha}{2}$ for x)

Since $\cos\alpha = \frac{3}{5}$,

$\frac{3}{5} = 2\cos^2\frac{\alpha}{2} - 1.$ — substitution ($\frac{3}{5}$ for $\cos x$)

Now solve for $\cos\frac{\alpha}{2}$. (Think of $\cos\frac{\alpha}{2}$ as a chunk.)

$\frac{8}{5} = 2\cos^2\frac{\alpha}{2}$ — A_1

$\frac{4}{5} = \cos^2\frac{\alpha}{2}$ — $M_{\frac{1}{2}}$

$\cos\frac{\alpha}{2} = \frac{2}{\sqrt{5}}$ or $\cos\frac{\alpha}{2} = -\frac{2}{\sqrt{5}}$ — Apply $h(x) = \sqrt{x}$ and $h(x) = -\sqrt{x}$ to both sides.

Adapting to Individual Needs

Challenge

Have students answer the following questions.

1. Derive identities for:
   a. $\tan 2x$ $\left[\frac{2\tan x}{1 - \tan^2 x}\right]$
   b. $\tan\frac{x}{2}$ $\left[\frac{\sin x}{1 + \cos x} \text{ or } \frac{1 - \cos x}{\sin x}\right]$
2. Simplify each expression as either one of the six trig functions of x or as a constant.
   a. $(1 - \cos x)\left(\cot\frac{x}{2}\right)$ [$\sin x$]
   b. $\frac{1}{2}\sin x \tan\frac{x}{2}\csc^2\frac{x}{2}$ [1]
   c. $\tan x \sin 2x + \cos 2x$ [1]

Example 4 indicates that when $\cos \alpha$ is known, there are two choices for $\cos \frac{\alpha}{2}$: $\frac{2}{\sqrt{5}}$ or $-\frac{2}{\sqrt{5}}$. To determine the particular value of $\cos \frac{\alpha}{2}$, you need to know which quadrant $\frac{\alpha}{2}$ is in. In Example 4, you do not know which quadrant α is in so you cannot determine which quadrant $\frac{\alpha}{2}$ is in.

Example 5

Write the value of $\sin \frac{\pi}{8}$ in terms of rational numbers and radicals.

Solution

First note that $2 \cdot \frac{\pi}{8} = \frac{\pi}{4}$, and the cosine and sine of $\frac{\pi}{4}$ are known. This suggests using the formula

$$\cos 2x = 1 - 2\sin^2 x, \text{ with } \tfrac{\pi}{8} \text{ in place of } x.$$

$$\cos 2 \cdot \frac{\pi}{8} = 1 - 2\sin^2 \frac{\pi}{8} \quad \text{identity for } \cos 2x$$

$$\cos \frac{\pi}{4} = 1 - 2\sin^2 \frac{\pi}{8}$$

$$\frac{\sqrt{2}}{2} = 1 - 2\sin^2 \frac{\pi}{8}$$

Now the problem is reduced to solving an equation for $\sin \frac{\pi}{8}$.

$$\frac{\sqrt{2}}{2} - 1 = -2\sin^2 \frac{\pi}{8} \quad A_{-1}$$

$$-\frac{\sqrt{2}}{4} + \frac{1}{2} = \sin^2 \frac{\pi}{8} \quad M_{-\frac{1}{2}}$$

$$\frac{2 - \sqrt{2}}{4} = \sin^2 \frac{\pi}{8} \quad \text{Use common denominator.}$$

$$\sin \frac{\pi}{8} = \pm\sqrt{\frac{2 - \sqrt{2}}{4}} \quad \text{Apply both } h(x) = -\sqrt{x} \text{ and } h(x) = \sqrt{x} \text{ to both sides.}$$

As in Example 4, there are two solutions. But $\frac{\pi}{8}$ is in the first quadrant, so $\sin \frac{\pi}{8}$ is positive. Therefore, $\sin \frac{\pi}{8} = \pm\sqrt{\frac{2 - \sqrt{2}}{4}} = \frac{\sqrt{2 - \sqrt{2}}}{2}$.

Check

A calculator indicates that both $\frac{\sqrt{2 - \sqrt{2}}}{2}$ and $\sin \frac{\pi}{8}$ are approximately equal to .38268.

QUESTIONS

Covering the Reading

1. Prove identity (3) for $\cos 2x$. See left.

2. Prove the identity $\sin 2x = 2 \sin x \cos x$. See left.

3. a. Use the identities in this lesson to find $\cos\left(2 \cdot \frac{\pi}{6}\right)$ and $\sin\left(2 \cdot \frac{\pi}{6}\right)$.
   b. Check that your answers agree with the known values for $\cos \frac{\pi}{3}$ and $\sin \frac{\pi}{3}$.

See margin.

1) $\cos 2x = \cos^2 x - \sin^2 x = (1 - \sin^2 x) - \sin^2 x = 1 - 2\sin^2 x$

2) $\sin 2x = \sin(x + x) = \sin x \cos x + \cos x \cdot \sin x = 2 \sin x \cos x$

Additional Examples

1. If $\sin x = \frac{12}{13}$, determine $\cos 2x$. $-\frac{119}{169} \approx -0.70414$
2. If $\sin x = \frac{12}{13}$ and $\frac{\pi}{2} < x < \pi$, determine $\sin 2x$. $-\frac{120}{169}$ (This result can be found either by finding $\sin x$ and then using the formula for $\sin 2x$, or by using the result of Additional Example 1 and the Pythagorean Identity.)
3. Harry the Human Cannonball is shot from a cannon with an initial velocity of 50 ft/sec. The cannon barrel makes an angle of 30° with the ground. (Ignore air resistance.)
   a. How long will Harry remain in the air? $\frac{50(\sin 30°)}{16} = 1.56$ sec
   b. What is the maximum height that he attains in flight? ≈ 9.77 ft
   c. What horizontal distance does he travel? ≈ 67.7 ft
4. If $\cos \theta = \frac{5}{13}$ and $0 < \theta < \frac{\pi}{2}$, determine $\cos \frac{\theta}{2}$. $\frac{3}{\sqrt{13}}$
5. Write $\sin \frac{\pi}{12}$ in terms of rational numbers and radicals.
   Solution 1: $\sin \frac{\pi}{12} = \sin\left(\frac{1}{2} \cdot \frac{\pi}{6}\right) = \sqrt{\frac{1 - \cos \frac{\pi}{6}}{2}} = \frac{\sqrt{2 - \sqrt{3}}}{2}$
   Solution 2: $\sin \frac{\pi}{12} = \sin\left(\frac{\pi}{4} - \frac{\pi}{6}\right) = \frac{\sqrt{6} - \sqrt{2}}{4}$.
   From (1) and (2), we may conclude that $\frac{\sqrt{2 - \sqrt{3}}}{2} = \frac{\sqrt{6} - \sqrt{2}}{4}$. A calculator verifies both $\approx .2588190451$; the result can be proved analytically by squaring both sides and noting that both sides are positive numbers with the same square.

Additional Answers

3. a. $\cos\left(2 \cdot \frac{\pi}{6}\right) = \cos^2\left(\frac{\pi}{6}\right) - \sin^2\left(\frac{\pi}{6}\right) = \frac{3}{4} - \frac{1}{4} = \frac{1}{2}$,
   $\sin\left(2 \cdot \frac{\pi}{6}\right) = 2 \sin\left(\frac{\pi}{6}\right) \cos\left(\frac{\pi}{6}\right) = 2 \cdot \frac{1}{2} \cdot \frac{\sqrt{3}}{2} = \frac{\sqrt{3}}{2}$
   b. $\cos\left(2 \cdot \frac{\pi}{6}\right) = \cos \frac{\pi}{3} = \frac{1}{2}$;
   $\sin\left(2 \cdot \frac{\pi}{6}\right) = \sin \frac{\pi}{3} = \frac{\sqrt{3}}{2}$

Notes on Questions

Question 7 Some students prefer $\cos\left(\frac{1}{2}y\right)$ to $\cos\left(\frac{y}{2}\right)$. To determine the sign of $\cos \frac{y}{2}$, note that $\frac{\pi}{2} < \frac{y}{2} < \frac{3\pi}{4}$, so $\frac{y}{2}$ is in quadrant 2. Therefore $\cos \frac{y}{2}$ is negative.

Question 11 Invite students to derive identities for $\sin 4x$ in three ways:
(1) $\sin 4x = \sin(3x + x) = \dots$
(2) $\sin 4x = \sin 2(2x) = \dots$
(3) $\sin 4x = \sin(2x + 2x) = \dots$

Question 12 Another way to show that these expressions are equal is to square both sides. Since they are positive numbers with the same square, they must be equal.

Question 13 Error Alert If students have difficulty with this problem, point out that they need to do **parts a and b** before they do **parts c and d.**

Question 21 Just as there are three identities for $\cos 2x$ in terms of $\cos x$ or $\sin x$, there are many identities for $\cos 3x$ and $\cos 4x$. You may wish to make the restriction that these identities be in terms of $\cos x$. Then the answer is a unique polynomial in $\cos x$.

9)

$-2\pi \le x \le 2\pi$, x-scale $= \frac{\pi}{2}$
$-2 \le y \le 2$, y-scale $= 0.5$

Both f and g are the function $x \to \cos 2x$

12a) $\frac{\sqrt{6}+\sqrt{2}}{4}$
b) $\frac{\sqrt{2+\sqrt{3}}}{4}$
c) since the answers to parts a and b both represent $\cos \frac{\pi}{12}$, they are equal.

4. Suppose $\sin x = \frac{5}{13}$ and $0 < x < \frac{\pi}{2}$.
a. Find $\cos 2x$. $\frac{119}{169}$ **b.** Find $\sin 2x$. $\frac{120}{169}$

5. Suppose $\cos x = \frac{1}{4}$ and $\frac{3\pi}{2} < x < 2\pi$.
a. Find $\cos 2x$. $\frac{-7}{8}$ **b.** Find $\sin 2x$. $\frac{-\sqrt{15}}{6}$

6. Refer to Example 3.
a. What is the range of a projectile launched with an initial speed of 90 ft/sec at an angle 45° above the horizontal? ≈ 253 ft
b. How long will it be in the air? ≈ 4 sec

7. If $\cos y = -\frac{12}{13}$ and $\pi < y < \frac{3\pi}{2}$, find $\cos \frac{y}{2}$. $-\frac{1}{\sqrt{26}}$

8. Express $\sin \frac{3\pi}{8}$ in terms of rational numbers and radicals. $\frac{\sqrt{2+\sqrt{2}}}{2}$

Applying the Mathematics

9. Graph $f: x \to 2\cos^2 x - 1$ and $g: x \to 1 - 2\sin^2 x$ on the same axes. Explain the results you get. See left.

10. Refer to Example 3. a) $\frac{\pi}{4}$
a. If the velocity v_0 is fixed, find the angle θ which maximizes the range.
b. What is the maximum range when $v_0 = 30 \frac{\text{m}}{\text{sec}}$? 450 ft
c. When $v_0 = 30 \frac{\text{m}}{\text{sec}}$ and θ is chosen to maximize the range, what is the greatest height attained by the projectile? 112.5 ft

11. Prove the identity $\sin 3x = 3\sin x - 4\sin^3 x$. See margin. (Hint: Express $3x$ as $2x + x$.)

12. Prove that $\sqrt{\frac{\sqrt{3}+2}{4}} = \frac{\sqrt{2}+\sqrt{6}}{4}$ in the following way. See left.
a. Find a value for $\cos \frac{\pi}{12}$ by thinking of $\frac{\pi}{12}$ as $\frac{\pi}{3} - \frac{\pi}{4}$ and using the identity for $\cos(\alpha - \beta)$.
b. Find a value for $\cos \frac{\pi}{12}$ by thinking of $\frac{\pi}{6}$ as twice $\frac{\pi}{12}$ and using an identity for $\cos 2x$.
c. Why do parts **a** and **b** prove the desired result?

Review

13. Suppose $\pi < x < \frac{3\pi}{2}$, $\frac{\pi}{2} < y < \pi$, $\sin x = -\frac{4}{5}$, and $\cos y = -\frac{1}{3}$.
a. Find $\cos x$. **b.** Find $\sin y$.
c. Find $\cos(x + y)$. **d.** Find $\sin(x + y)$.
e. Check your answers to parts **c** and **d** using the Pythagorean Identity. *(Lessons 2-6, 6-4, 6-5)* See margin.

14. Prove the identity $\tan^2\theta(\cot^2\theta + \cot^4\theta) = \csc^2\theta$ and specify its domain. *(Lesson 6-2)* See margin.

Additional Answers

11. left side $= \sin 3x = \sin(2x + x)$
$= \sin 2x \cos x + \cos 2x \sin x$ — Sine of a Sum Theorem
$= (2\sin x \cos x)\cos x + (\cos^2 x - \sin^2 x)\sin x$ — Double-angle Identities
$= 2\sin x \cos^2 x + \cos^2 x \sin x - \sin^3 x$ — Multiplication
$= 3\sin x \cos^2 x - \sin^3 x$ — Addition
$= 3\sin x(1 - \sin^2 x) - \sin^3 x$ — Pythagorean Identity
$= 3\sin x - 3\sin^3 x - \sin^3 x$ — Multiplication
$= 3\sin x - 4\sin^3 x$ — Addition
= right side

15. If $x - 5$ is a factor of a polynomial $p(x)$ then $p(5) =$ __?__. *(Lesson 4-4)* 0

16. Solve: $t^4 - 13t^2 + 36 = 0$. *(Lesson 3-6)* $t = \pm 3, \pm 2$

17. A function f is defined by the formula $y = f(x) = 3x + 2$. What is a formula for f^{-1}? *(Lesson 3-2)* $f^{-1}(x) = \frac{x-2}{3}$

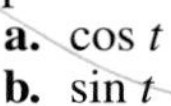

18. In a circle of radius 5, the point (5, 0) is rotated t radians counterclockwise to the point $P = (-3, 4)$. Find each.
   a. $\cos t$
   b. $\sin t$
   c. $\tan t$
   d. t *(Lesson 2-6)*

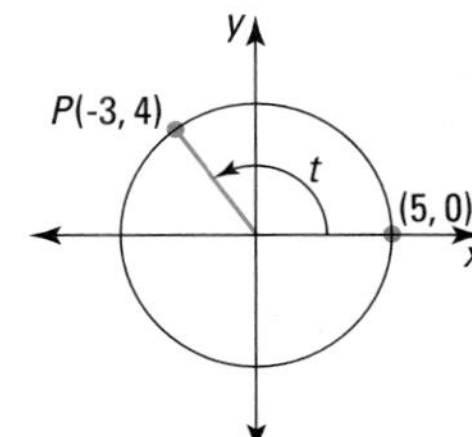

a) $-\frac{3}{5}$ b) $\frac{4}{5}$ c) $-\frac{4}{3}$ d) ≈ 2.214

The seeds of the berries on this Arabica coffee bush can be roasted and then ground for coffee.

19. Determine whether the following argument is valid or invalid. Justify your reasoning. Invalid; converse error

   If this coffee is a mild blend, then it is from Colombia.
   If this coffee is popular in the United States, then it is a mild blend.
   This coffee is from Colombia.
   ∴ This coffee is a mild blend.
   (Lessons 1-6, 1-7)

20. **a.** Write the negation of
   ∀ real numbers x, $\sqrt{x-2}$ *is a real number.*
   ∃ a real number x such that $\sqrt{x-2}$ is not real

   b. Which is true, the statement or its negation? *(Lessons 1-1, 1-2)* the negation

Exploration

21. **a.** Find identities for $\cos 3x$ and for $\cos 4x$.
   b. Is there a pattern in the identities for $\cos 2x$, $\cos 3x$, and $\cos 4x$? If so, describe the pattern.
   a) $\cos 3x = 4\cos^3 x - 3\cos x$; $\cos 4x = 8\cos^4 x - 8\cos^2 x + 1$
   b) Sample: For $\cos(nx)$, the leading terms are always $2^{n-1}\cos^n x$.

Follow-up for Lesson 6-6

Practice

For more questions on SPUR Objectives, use **Lesson Master 6-6** (shown on pages 378–379).

Assessment

Quiz A quiz covering Lessons 6-4 through 6-6 is provided in the *Assessment Sourcebook*.

Extension

You might encourage a group of students to develop identities for $\tan(nx)$ for $n = 2, 3, 4, \ldots$. The generalization for $\tan nx$ in terms of $\tan x$ involves binomial coefficients and is quite beautiful.

You might invite students to use the method of **Examples 4 and 5** to find values for the following in terms of rational numbers and radicals:
$\sin\frac{\pi}{4}, \sin\frac{\pi}{8}, \sin\frac{\pi}{16}, \sin\frac{\pi}{32}, \ldots$ and $\cos\frac{\pi}{4}, \cos\frac{\pi}{8}, \cos\frac{\pi}{16}, \cos\frac{\pi}{32}, \ldots$.

Look for patterns and predictability. The nested radicals can be a real turn-on. This beauty is lost to those who would use a calculator for these problems! Also, this process involves recursion, a very powerful concept that is studied in Chapter 7.

Project Update Project 1, *Mechanical Vibration,* and Project 4, *Rational and Radical Expressions for Sines and Cosines,* on pages 397–398, relate to the content of this lesson.

Additional Answers

13. a. $-\frac{3}{5}$ b. $\frac{2\sqrt{2}}{3}$
   c. $\frac{3+8\sqrt{2}}{15}$ d. $\frac{4-6\sqrt{2}}{15}$
   e. Does $\sin^2(x+y) + \cos^2(x+y) = 1$?
   Does $\left(\frac{3+8\sqrt{2}}{15}\right)^2 + \left(\frac{4-6\sqrt{2}}{15}\right)^2 = 1$?
   Does $\frac{137+48\sqrt{2}}{225} + \frac{88-48\sqrt{2}}{225} = 1$?
   Does $\frac{225}{225} = 1$? Yes

14.

	$\tan^2\theta(\cot^2\theta + \cot^4\theta)$	$\csc^2\theta$	
Def. of tan and cot	$= \frac{\sin^2\theta}{\cos^2\theta}\left(\frac{\cos^2\theta}{\sin^2\theta} + \frac{\cos^4\theta}{\sin^4\theta}\right)$	$= \frac{1}{\sin^2\theta}$	def. of csc
Simplifying	$= 1 + \frac{\cos^2\theta}{\sin^2\theta}$		
Add. of fractions	$= \frac{\sin^2\theta + \cos^2\theta}{\sin^2\theta}$		
Pythagorean Identity	$= \frac{1}{\sin^2\theta}$		

$\therefore \tan^2\theta(\cot^2\theta + \cot^4\theta) = \csc^2\theta$

Domain: $\theta \neq \frac{n\pi}{2}$, ∀ integers n

In-class Activity

Resources

From the ***Teacher's Resource File***
- Teaching Aid 60: Graphs of the Sine, Cosine, and Tangent Functions
- Answer Master 6-7

Additional Resources
- Visual for Teaching Aid 60

Every function has an inverse. The question is whether that inverse is a function. The trigonometric functions obviously do not have inverses over their whole domain, so the question is to find a part of the domain on which they could have an inverse. The purpose of this activity is to state the three criteria which together determine what domain is usually taken for the trigonometric function so that its inverse is a function. (This domain becomes the range of the inverse function.)

For the sine and cosine, criteria (b) and (c) force the domain to be a half-cycle of the function; that is, an interval of the function with length π. For the tangent, criteria (b) and (c) force the domain to be an interval between two undefined values of the function. Then, including criterion (a) forces the domains which appear at the beginning of Lesson 6-7.

Teaching Aid 60 contains graphs of the sine, cosine, and tangent functions.

Introducing Lesson 6-7

Inverse Trigonometric Functions

IN-CLASS

ACTIVITY

Read the next five paragraphs together with another person; then answer the questions that follow.

Because a function $f\colon x \rightarrow y$ cannot map a particular value of x onto more than one value of y, the graph of a real function cannot intersect any vertical line more than once. This is the Vertical Line Test for a function. In Lesson 3-2, it was shown that if a real function f has an inverse f^{-1}, then the graph of $y = f^{-1}(x)$ is the reflection image, over the line $y = x$, of the graph of $y = f(x)$.

When a vertical line is reflected over the line $y = x$, the image is a horizontal line. It follows that if a real function f has an inverse f^{-1} that is a function, f must pass the Horizontal Line Test: that is, the graph of f cannot intersect any horizontal line more than once.

Now recall the graphs of the cosine, sine, and tangent functions.

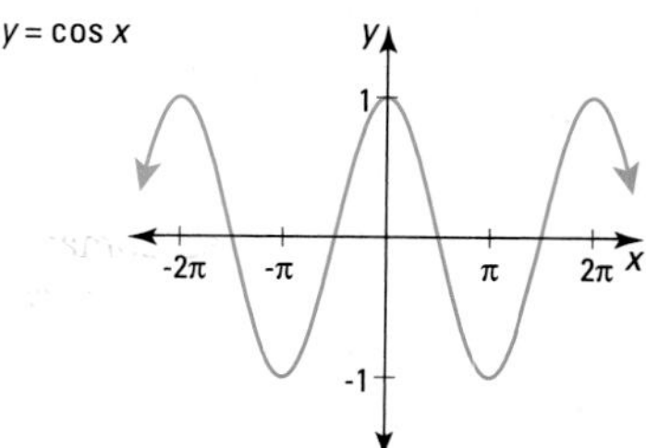

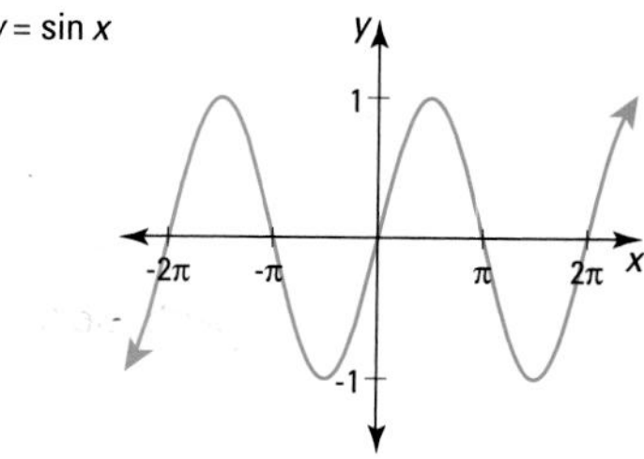

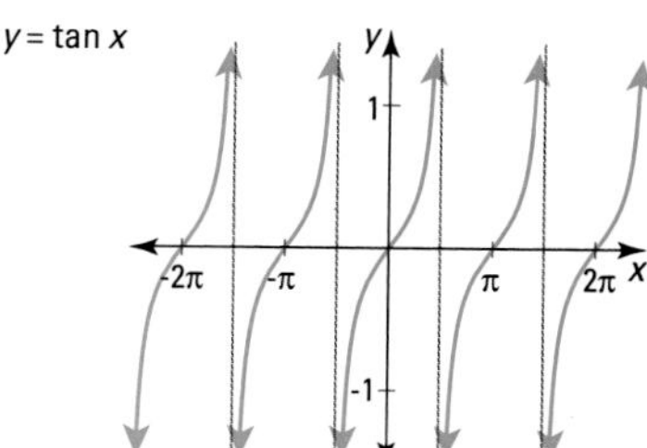

Notice that all three functions fail the Horizontal Line Test miserably! There are horizontal lines that intersect each graph at infinitely many points. For instance, if $y = \frac{1}{2}$, there are many values of x for which $\sin x = \frac{1}{2}$.

In order that the inverse of any of these functions be a function, the domain must be restricted so that for each y there is only one x with $f(x) = y$. But how should the domain be restricted? The following criteria for the choice of the restricted domains have become generally accepted:

(a) The domain should include the angles between 0 and $\frac{\pi}{2}$ because these are the measures of the acute angles in a right triangle.
(b) On the restricted domain, the function should take on all values in the range exactly once.
(c) If possible, the function should be continuous on the restricted domain.

1 **a.** What restricted domain of the cosine function meets the above criteria? **$0 < \theta < \pi$** **b–e) See margin.**
b. Sketch a graph of $y = \cos x$ with this restricted domain.
c. Reflect this graph over the line $y = x$ to obtain a graph of $y = \cos^{-1} x$.
d. Give the coordinates of four points on the graph of $y = \cos^{-1} x$.
e. Graph $y = \cos^{-1} x$ with an automatic grapher. Compare this graph with the graph you drew in part **c**. Explain any differences.

2 Repeat part 1 with the sine function.
a) $-\frac{\pi}{2} \le \theta \le \frac{\pi}{2}$ **b–e) See margin.**

3 Repeat part 1 with the tangent function.
a) $-\frac{\pi}{2} \le \theta \le \frac{\pi}{2}$ **b–e) See margin.**

Reading Mathematics You may wish to read this activity as a class instead of in pairs. But with pairs of students, the activity provides an opportunity to read mathematics for understanding.

Students who have studied from *Functions, Statistics, and Trigonometry* will have seen this content before, but most students need the review.

Additional Answers

1. b, c.

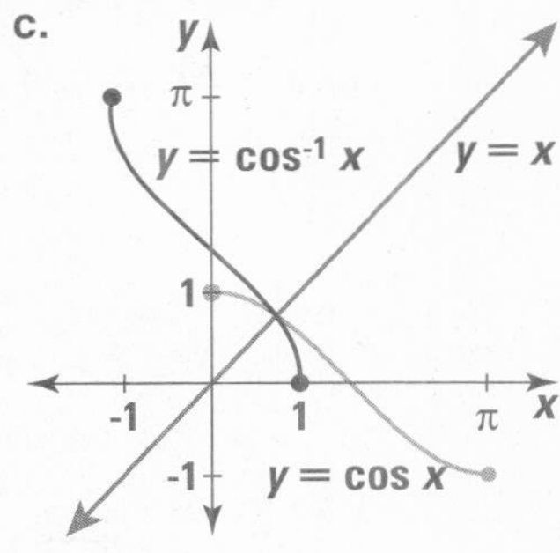

d. $(1, 0)$ $\left(0, \frac{\pi}{2}\right)$ $\left(\frac{\sqrt{2}}{2}, \frac{\pi}{4}\right)$ $(-1, \pi)$
e. Answers may vary, but graphs should be similar.

2. b, c.

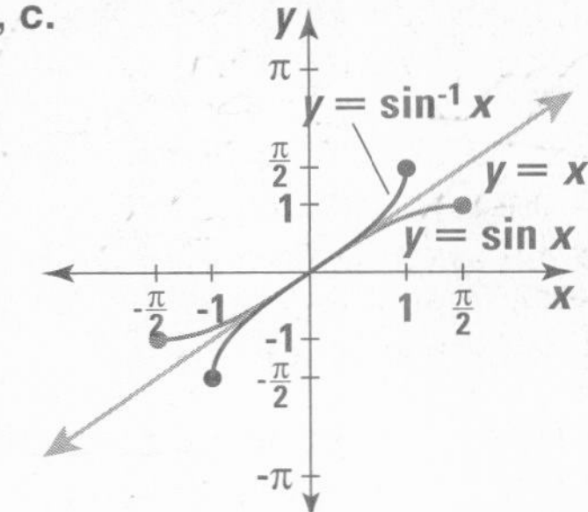

d. $(0, 0)$ $\left(\frac{\sqrt{2}}{2}, \frac{\pi}{4}\right)$ $\left(1, \frac{\pi}{2}\right)$ $\left(-1, -\frac{\pi}{2}\right)$
e. Answers may vary, but graphs should be similar.

3. b, c.

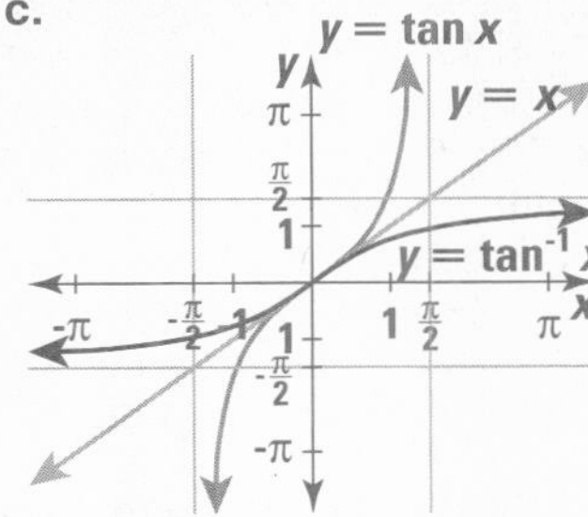

d. $(0, 0)$ $\left(1, \frac{\pi}{4}\right)$ $\left(-1, -\frac{\pi}{4}\right)$ $\left(\sqrt{3}, \frac{\pi}{3}\right)$
e. Answers may vary, but graphs should be similar.

Lesson 6-7

Objectives

B Evaluate inverse trigonometric functions with or without a calculator.

E Solve problems using inverse trigonometric functions.

Resources

From the ***Teacher's Resource File***
- Lesson Master 6-7
- Answer Master 6-7
- Teaching Aids
  56 Warm-up
  61 Graphs of the Inverse Sine, Cosine, and Tangent Functions

Additional Resources
- Visuals for Teaching Aids 56, 61
- Exploration 6-7

Teaching Lesson 6-7

Warm-up

Find at least one value of θ that satisfies each equation. Sample answers are given.

1. $\sin\theta = -1$ $\quad \frac{3\pi}{2}$
2. $\cos\theta = \frac{\sqrt{3}}{2}$ $\quad \frac{\pi}{6}$
3. $\tan\theta = -\sqrt{3}$ $\quad -\frac{\pi}{3}$

Notes on Reading

The criteria on page 385 of the In-class Activity provide the basis for choosing the domain over which to restrict the trigonometric functions so that their inverses are also functions. Students should understand these criteria and how they are put into practice in the actual definitions at the beginning of the lesson.

In discussing the criteria on restricting domains, emphasize that these criteria are applied to original functions to create new restricted functions. These restricted functions are then the source for the inverse functions. A restriction on the *domain* of the original function becomes a restriction on the *range* of the inverse.

LESSON 6-7

Inverse Trigonometric Functions

Definitions of the Inverse Cosine, Inverse Sine, and Inverse Tangent Functions

In the In-class Activity on pages 384–385, you were asked to determine restrictions on the cosine, sine, and tangent functions so that their inverses would be functions. These inverses are denoted by $\cos^{-1}$, $\sin^{-1}$, and $\tan^{-1}$, and are defined as follows:

Definition

$\forall$ *x* in the interval $-1 \le x \le 1$, the **inverse cosine of *x*, $\cos^{-1} x$,** is the unique number θ in the interval

$$0 \le \theta \le \pi \text{ such that } \cos\theta = x.$$

1 $\forall$ *x* in the interval $-1 \le x \le 1$, the **inverse sine of *x*, $\sin^{-1} x$,** is the unique number θ in the interval

$$-\frac{\pi}{2} \le \theta \le \frac{\pi}{2} \text{ such that } \sin\theta = x.$$

$\forall$ *x*, the **inverse tangent of *x*, $\tan^{-1} x$,** is the unique number θ in the interval

$$-\frac{\pi}{2} < \theta < \frac{\pi}{2} \text{ such that } \tan\theta = x.$$

From the definition,

$$y = \cos^{-1} x \Leftrightarrow \cos y = x \text{ and } 0 \le y \le \pi.$$

We therefore read $\cos^{-1} x$ as the number from 0 to π whose cosine is *x*. For instance, $\cos^{-1}\frac{1}{2} = \frac{\pi}{3}$ because $0 \le \frac{\pi}{3} \le \pi$ and $\cos\frac{\pi}{3} = \frac{1}{2}$. In degrees, $\cos^{-1}\frac{1}{2} = 60°$ because $0 \le 60° \le 180°$ and $\cos 60° = \frac{1}{2}$.

Activity

Write similar statements for $\sin^{-1}$ and $\tan^{-1}$. See Question 1 on page 389.

Example 1

A rectangular picture 4 feet high is hung on a wall so that the bottom edge is at your eye level. Your view of this picture is determined by the angle θ formed by the lines of sight from your eye to the top and bottom edges of the picture.

a. How does the angle θ depend on the distance *d* between you and the wall?

b. Find θ when *d* = 8 ft.

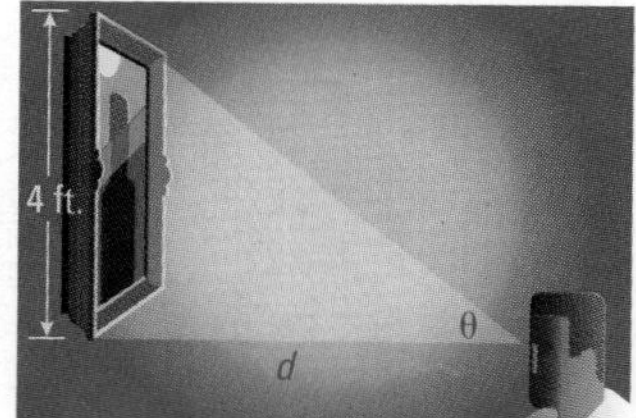

Lesson 6-7 Overview

Broad Goals In preparation for the solving of equations, this lesson studies the inverses of the sine, cosine, and tangent functions in detail.

Perspective In order to have inverse functions, the domains of the trigonometric functions have to be restricted. Criteria for the domains of the trigonometric functions are given which force a particular choice of domain for each function: $-\frac{\pi}{2} \le x \le \frac{\pi}{2}$ for the sine, $0 \le x \le \pi$ for the cosine, and $-\frac{\pi}{2} < x < \frac{\pi}{2}$ for the tangent. This is done in the In-class Activity on page 385. In the lesson, graphs of the inverse functions are shown to confirm these domains. A major objective is to be able to evaluate the inverse functions, that is, to obtain exact values or approximations to $\sin^{-1}x$, $\cos^{-1}x$, and $\tan^{-1}x$ for any *x* in their domains.

Solution

a. From the given information, $\tan\theta = \frac{4}{d}$. Using the definition of $\tan^{-1}$,

$$\theta = \tan^{-1}\frac{4}{d}.$$

b. Substitute 8 for d in the answer to part **a**.

$$\theta = \tan^{-1}\frac{4}{8} = \tan^{-1} .5$$
$$\approx 26.6^\circ \text{ or } .46 \text{ radians}$$

Example 2

a. Find the domain and range of $\cos^{-1}$.
b. Is $\cos^{-1}$ increasing or decreasing?

Solution

Graph the restricted cosine function and its inverse $\cos^{-1}$.

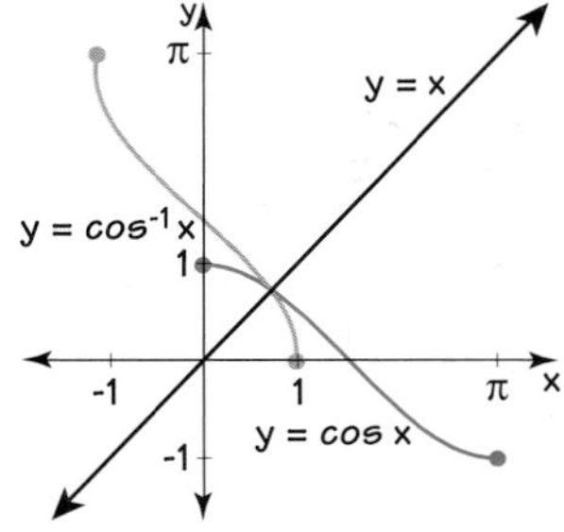

a. The domain of $\cos^{-1}$ is the range of the restricted cosine function. Therefore, **the domain of $\cos^{-1}$ is $-1 \le x \le 1$. By definition of $\cos^{-1}$, its range is $0 \le y \le \pi$.**
b. As x increases from 0 to π, as you move from left to right along the curve $y = \cos^{-1} x$, the y-values decrease. Thus, **the inverse cosine function is a decreasing function.** Another argument: Since the cosine function is decreasing on this interval, so is its inverse, because the inverse of any decreasing function is decreasing.

You can answer similar questions for $\sin^{-1}$ and $\tan^{-1}$ in a similar way. Their graphs are shown below.

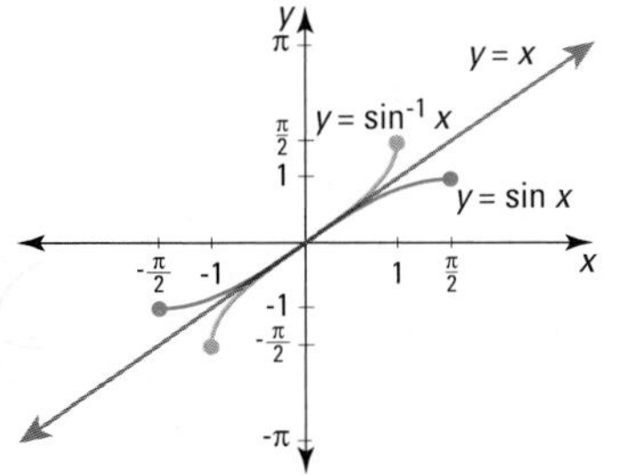

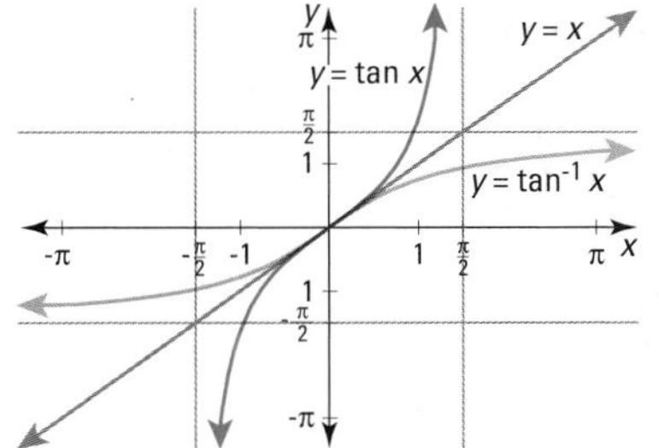

Concerning the criteria used to determine the restricted domains, discuss the following: Criterion (a) does not limit the domain to angles between 0 and $\frac{\pi}{2}$. Some students assume this. Criterion (b) is needed so that the function f passes the horizontal line test and so has an inverse function. Criterion (c) implies that the domain of the inverse function must be continuous.

Students may wonder why the restricted interval for the sine is from $-\frac{\pi}{2}$ to $\frac{\pi}{2}$ rather than from 0 to $\frac{\pi}{2}$ and then from $\frac{3\pi}{2}$ to 2π. By using the interval from $-\frac{\pi}{2}$ to $\frac{\pi}{2}$ the domain is continuous.

❶ Note that the range for the inverse tangent is the open interval $-\frac{\pi}{2} < \theta < \frac{\pi}{2}$, whereas the range for the inverse sine is the closed interval with the same endpoints. You might ask students why there is this difference. [The tangent is undefined at both $-\frac{\pi}{2}$ and at $\frac{\pi}{2}$.]

Error Alert You may need to remind students once again that $\sin^{-1} x$ means "the inverse of the sine function" and not $\frac{1}{\sin x}$. You might mention that some books use arcsin x or Arcsin x where we use $\sin^{-1} x$ to avoid this confusion, but $\sin^{-1} x$ is now more popular, as students can see from their calculators. Some books use arcsin to denote the *relation* that is the inverse of the sine function and Arcsin to denote the *function* that is the inverse of the restricted sine function. Then Arcsin = $\sin^{-1}$, Arccos = $\cos^{-1}$, and Arctan = $\tan^{-1}$.

See Activity 2 in *Optional Activities* below for an alternate approach to the text's method of determining the range of the inverse trigonometric functions.

We do not encourage students to memorize the graphs of $y = \cos^{-1} x$, $y = \sin^{-1} x$, or $y = \tan^{-1} x$. Rather, students should use the fact that these graphs can be obtained by reflecting the restricted portion of the trigonometric function over the line $y = x$. **Teaching Aid 61** shows the graphs of the inverse sine, cosine, and tangent functions.

Optional Activities

Activity 1 Technology Connection
Materials: Explorations software

You may use Exploration 6-7, *Inverse Functions for Sine, Cosine, and Tangent,* to introduce Lesson 6-7. You can choose either the sine, cosine or tangent function to graph. Students can then see how the inverse function is drawn as a reflection of the original function over the line $y = x$.

Activity 2 Alternate Approach We found the range of inverse trigonometric functions by focusing on the original functions. Change that focus to the inverse. Begin with a graph of $y = \sin x$ for $-2\pi \le x \le 2\pi$ and reflect it over the line $y = x$. Ask students how to restrict the range of the image to make the image a function. [The range of the image is the domain of the original function; applying criteria similar to that in the text, the same results follow.]

We also have deliberately avoided discussion of $y = \sec^{-1}x$, $y = \csc^{-1}x$, or $y = \cot^{-1}x$. In practice, these three functions are seldom used.

Discuss **Example 3** carefully. The notation $\cos\left(\tan^{-1}\frac{b}{a}\right)$ is confusing to some students. Translating the problem into a triangle with appropriately labeled sides is a new strategy for the students. Mention that calling $\tan^{-1}\frac{b}{a}$ "θ" was arbitrary—we could have called it α or β or anything else. Some students may try to do this problem algebraically. Knowing $1 + \tan^2\theta = \sec^2\theta$, they replace $\tan\theta$ by $\frac{b}{a}$ and solve for $\sec\theta$. Because $0 < \theta < \frac{\pi}{2}$, $\sec\theta > 0$. Then they use $\cos\theta = \frac{1}{\sec\theta}$ to get the final result.

Additional Examples

1. a. Every morning at scout camp Benny plays the bugle while the flag is being raised. He loves to follow Old Glory with his eyes as the flag is being pulled skyward. If the flagpole is 32 feet tall, Benny's eyes are 4 feet above the ground, and he is standing d feet from the flagpole, at what angle θ with the horizontal is Benny's head tilted when the flag reaches the top of the pole?
   $\theta = \tan^{-1}\left(\frac{28}{d}\right)$
   b. If $d = 100$ feet, what is θ?
   $\theta \approx .273$ radians $\approx 15.64°$
2. The graph below shows $y = \cos x$ over the restricted domain $-\pi \le x \le 0$. Why was this restricted domain not chosen to be the restricted cosine function from which $\cos^{-1}x$ would be defined?

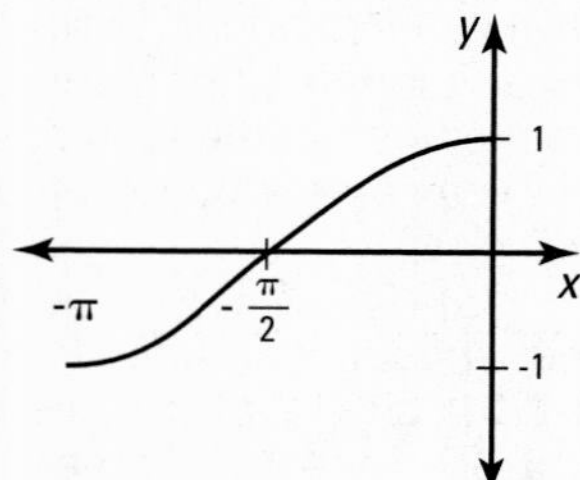

It excludes the right triangle values $0 \le x \le \frac{\pi}{2}$ from its domain.

Composing Trigonometric and Inverse Trigonometric Functions

Inverse trigonometric functions, like other functions, can be added, subtracted, multiplied, divided, or composed with other functions. For instance, the expression $\cos\left(\sin^{-1}\frac{1}{2}\right)$, read "the cosine of the number whose sine is $\frac{1}{2}$," is obtained by composing the cosine and inverse sine functions. $\cos\left(\sin^{-1}\frac{1}{2}\right) = \frac{\sqrt{3}}{2}$, as shown here.

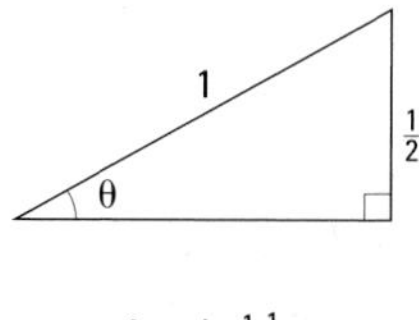

$\theta = \sin^{-1}\frac{1}{2}$

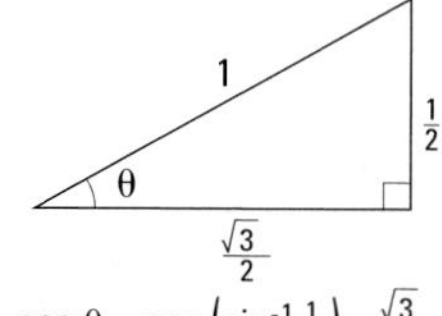

$\cos\theta = \cos\left(\sin^{-1}\frac{1}{2}\right) = \frac{\sqrt{3}}{2}$

Example 3

If $a > 0$ and $b > 0$, write $\cos\left(\tan^{-1}\frac{b}{a}\right)$ in terms of a and b.

Solution

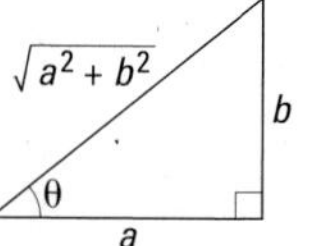

By definition of cosine and $\tan^{-1}$, $\cos\left(\tan^{-1}\frac{b}{a}\right)$ is the cosine of the number θ whose tangent is $\frac{b}{a}$. Also, θ has to be in the interval $-\frac{\pi}{2} < \theta < \frac{\pi}{2}$. Because a and b are positive, θ, a, and b can be pictured as in the triangle at the right, with $\tan\theta = \frac{b}{a}$. The hypotenuse of this triangle is $\sqrt{a^2 + b^2}$.

You can see from the diagram that

$$\cos\left(\tan^{-1}\left(\frac{b}{a}\right)\right) = \cos\theta = \frac{\text{side adjacent to }\theta}{\text{hypotenuse}} = \frac{a}{\sqrt{a^2 + b^2}}.$$

Check

Pick values for a and b, say $a = 3$ and $b = 2$. Then

$$\tan^{-1}\frac{b}{a} = \tan^{-1}\frac{2}{3} \approx .588.$$

Then $\cos\left(\tan^{-1}\frac{2}{3}\right) \approx \cos .588 \approx .832$.

Now substitute 3 for a and 2 for b in the answer.

$$\cos\left(\tan^{-1}\left(\frac{b}{a}\right)\right) = \frac{3}{\sqrt{2^2 + 3^2}} \approx \frac{3}{\sqrt{13}} \approx .832. \qquad \text{It checks.}$$

Adapting to Individual Needs

Extra Help

Since the domain and range of the sine and cosine functions are the same, students may incorrectly assume that the domain and range of the inverse functions are the same. Be sure to stress that this is not the case, referring back to the In-class Activity on pages 384–385 to provide justification.

Challenge

Have students answer the following questions.

1. Write the equation of an equivalent function on an appropriate domain.
   a. $y = \sin(\sin^{-1} x)$ [$y = x$ on [-1, 1]]
   b. $y = \sin(\tan^{-1} x)$.
   $\left[y = \frac{x}{\sqrt{1 + x^2}} \text{ for all } x\right]$
   c. $y = \cos(\sin^{-1} x)$
   $\left[y = \sqrt{1 - x^2} \text{ on } [-1, 1]\right]$

QUESTIONS

Covering the Reading

1. Refer to the statement about $\cos^{-1}$ immediately following the definitions of the inverse cosine, sine, and tangent functions. Fill in the blanks.
   a. $y = \sin^{-1} x \Leftrightarrow$ _?_ and _?_. $x = \sin y$ and $-\frac{\pi}{2} \le y \le \frac{\pi}{2}$
   b. $y = \tan^{-1} x \Leftrightarrow$ _?_ and _?_. $x = \tan y$ and $-\frac{\pi}{2} < y < \frac{\pi}{2}$

2. Refer to Example 1. Let h be the height of the bottom of the picture. Suppose an individual stands 6 feet away from the wall.
   a. Write an equation which describes how θ depends on h.
   b. Find the viewing angle if the picture is 8 ft from top to bottom.
   See margin.

3. a. Copy and complete the table of values below. See margin.

points on $y = \sin x$	$(-\frac{\pi}{2}, ?)$	$(-\frac{\pi}{3}, ?)$	$(-\frac{\pi}{4}, ?)$	$(-\frac{\pi}{6}, ?)$	$(0, ?)$	$(\frac{\pi}{6}, ?)$	$(\frac{\pi}{4}, ?)$	$(\frac{\pi}{3}, ?)$	$(\frac{\pi}{2}, ?)$
corresponding points on $y = \sin^{-1} x$									

   b. Give the domain and range of $\sin^{-1}$. Domain: $-1 \le x \le 1$; Range: $-\frac{\pi}{2} \le y \le \frac{\pi}{2}$
   c. Is $\sin^{-1}$ increasing or decreasing? increasing

4. Refer to the graph of $y = \tan^{-1} x$.
   a. Find the domain of $\tan^{-1}$. all real numbers
   b. Find the range of $\tan^{-1}$. $-\frac{\pi}{2} < y < \frac{\pi}{2}$
   c. Is $\tan^{-1}$ increasing or decreasing? increasing
   d. What are $\lim_{x \to \infty} \tan^{-1} x$ and $\lim_{x \to -\infty} \tan^{-1} x$? $\frac{\pi}{2}$; $-\frac{\pi}{2}$

In 5–7, use your knowledge of the values of the trigonometric functions for integer multiples of $\frac{\pi}{6} = 30°$ and $\frac{\pi}{4} = 45°$ to find the value in radians and in degrees.

5. $\sin^{-1}\left(-\frac{\sqrt{2}}{2}\right)$ $-\frac{\pi}{4}$; $-45°$
6. $\cos^{-1} 0$ $\frac{\pi}{2}$; $90°$
7. $\tan^{-1}(-\sqrt{3})$ $-\frac{\pi}{3}$; $-60°$

In 8–10, use your calculator to compute the value (in radians).

8. $\cos^{-1}\left(\frac{\sqrt{3}}{3}\right)$ 0.955
9. $\sin^{-1}(-.9)$ -1.120
10. $\tan^{-1} 2$ 1.107

11. a. How is the expression $\sin\left(\cos^{-1} \frac{3}{5}\right)$ read? the sine of the number whose cosine is $\frac{3}{5}$
    b. Evaluate $\sin\left(\cos^{-1} \frac{3}{5}\right)$. $\frac{4}{5}$

12. Evaluate $\cos(\tan^{-1}(-1))$. $\frac{\sqrt{2}}{2} \approx .707$

In 13 and 14, draw an appropriate triangle to help evaluate the expression.

13. $\sin\left(\tan^{-1} \frac{b}{a}\right)$ See left.
14. $\sin\left(\cos^{-1} \frac{x}{3}\right)$ $x > 0$ See left.

Frida Kahlo's Self Portrait

2a) $\theta = \tan^{-1}\left(\frac{h}{6}\right)$
b) $\approx 53°$

13)

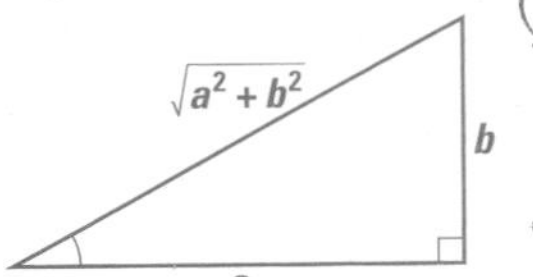

14)

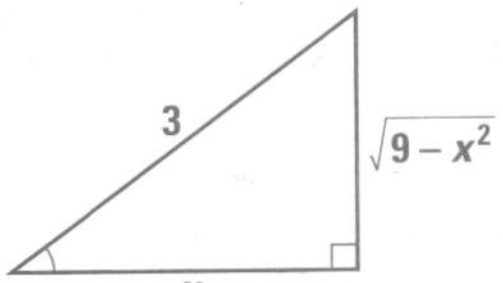

3. a. Find the domain and range of $\sin^{-1} x$.
   domain = $\{x: -1 \le x \le 1\}$;
   range = $\{y: -\frac{\pi}{2} \le y \le \frac{\pi}{2}\}$
   b. Is $\sin^{-1} x$ increasing or decreasing? increasing

4. If $a > 0$ and $b > 0$, write $\csc\left(\tan^{-1} \frac{b}{a}\right)$ in terms of a and b.
   $\csc\left(\tan^{-1} \frac{b}{a}\right) = \frac{\sqrt{a^2 + b^2}}{b}$

(Notes on Questions begin on page 390.)

Follow-up for Lesson 6-7

Practice

For more questions on SPUR Objectives, use **Lesson Master 6-7** (shown below).

Assessment

Oral Assessment Have students state the restrictions on the sine, cosine, and tangent functions and explain how and why these restrictions were determined. [Students demonstrate understanding of the restricted domains of trigonometric functions.]

(Follow-up continues on page 390.)

Additional Answers
3a. See Additional Answers at the back of this book.

LESSON MASTER 6-7
Questions on SPUR Objectives
See pages 401–403 for objectives.

Skills Objective B

In 1 and 2, *true or false*.

1. $\forall x$ in the interval $-1 \le x \le 1$, $\cos(\sin^{-1} x) \ge 0$. True
2. $\forall x$, $\sin(\tan^{-1} x) \ge 0$. False

In 3–6, give exact values.

3. $\cos^{-1}\left(-\frac{\sqrt{2}}{2}\right)$ $\frac{3\pi}{4}$
4. $\sec\left(\sin^{-1}\left(-\frac{\sqrt{3}}{2}\right)\right)$ 2
5. $\sin^{-1}\left(\sin \frac{5\pi}{4}\right)$ $-\frac{\pi}{4}$
6. $\tan\left(\cos^{-1}\left(\sin\left(-\frac{\pi}{6}\right)\right)\right)$ $-\sqrt{3}$

7. Use $\triangle PQR$ to evaluate each expression.
   a. $\tan^{-1}\left(\frac{r}{p}\right)$ α
   b. $\csc\left(\cos^{-1}\left(\frac{r}{q}\right)\right)$ $\frac{q}{p}$

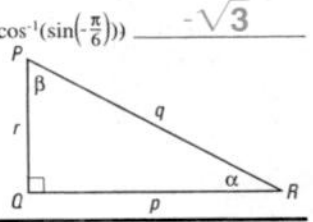

Uses Objective E

8. A 24-foot ladder is used to reach the top of an 18-foot wall. If the ladder extends 2 feet beyond the top of the wall, what angle does it make with the horizontal? $\approx 55°$

9. An aircraft is flying eastward at an altitude of 2 miles and a speed of 240 miles per hour. An observer standing directly under the flight path of the aircraft initially spots it overhead and watches it until it is 12 miles east of his position.
   a. Express the angle of elevation of the line of sight from the observer to the aircraft as a function of the time in minutes after he initially spots the aircraft. (Assume the observer is at the origin and that east is the positive direction along the horizontal axis.) $\theta = \tan^{-1}\left(\frac{1}{2t}\right)$
   b. What is the angle of elevation at time $t = 0.5$ minute? $\frac{\pi}{4} = 45°$

d. $y = \tan^{-1} x + \tan^{-1} \frac{1}{x}$
   $[y = \frac{\pi}{2}$ for all $x \ne 0]$
e. $y = \cos(\cos^{-1} x)$
   $[y = x$ on $[-1, 1]]$

2. Describe the graphs of $y = \sin^{-1}(\sin x)$ and $y = \cos^{-1}(\cos x)$. [Sawtooth graphs that agree with $y = x$ on the appropriate intervals]

3. Graph the function $y = \tan^{-1} x$ along with each of the following: $y = x - \frac{x^3}{3}$; $y = x - \frac{x^3}{3} + \frac{x^5}{5}$; $y = x - \frac{x^3}{3} + \frac{x^5}{5} - \frac{x^7}{7}$. How does the graph of $y = \tan^{-1} x$ compare with the graph of $y = x - \frac{x^3}{3} + \frac{x^5}{5} - \frac{x^7}{7} + \ldots + \frac{(-1)^n x^{2n+1}}{2n+1}$ for n an integer and $n \ge 0$? [With more terms, each polynomial becomes a closer approximation of $y = \tan^{-1} x$ on an interval including 0.]

Extension

Students often think of the inverse of a function as a function that "undoes" an operation; for example, if $f(x) = x^3$ and $g(x) = \sqrt[3]{x}$, $g(x)$ "undoes" $f(x)$, and $f(g(x)) = g(f(x)) = x$. To test this idea out on trigonometric functions, ask students whether the following are true or false for all x. If false, ask them to give a counterexample.

1. $\sin(\sin^{-1}(x)) = x$ [True]
2. $\sin^{-1}(\sin(x)) = x$
   [False; $\sin^{-1}\left(\sin\left(\frac{3\pi}{4}\right)\right) = \left(\frac{\pi}{4}\right)$]
3. $\cos(\cos^{-1}(x)) = x$ [True]
4. $\cos^{-1}(\cos(x)) = x$
   [False; $\cos^{-1}\left(\cos\left(\frac{7\pi}{6}\right)\right) = \frac{5\pi}{6}$]

Notes on Questions

Questions 15–16 These questions relate back to Lesson 3-2 on function composition. Students should recall that if f and f^{-1} are inverses, then $f(f^{-1}(x)) = x$ for all x in the domain of f^{-1} and $f^{-1}(f(x)) = x$ for all x in the domain of f. These questions relate to the first of these relationships. Discuss with students why $\sin^{-1}(\sin x) = x$ is not true for all real numbers. (There are values of x in the domain of the sine function that are not in the range of the $\sin^{-1}$ function.) Invite students to use an automatic grapher to graph $y = \sin(\sin^{-1}x)$ and $y = \sin^{-1}(\sin x)$ for $-2\pi \le x \le 2\pi$, $-2\pi \le y \le 2\pi$. Relate the graphs to the above discussion. (The graph of the first is part of the line $y = x$; the graph of the second is a zigzag.)

Question 23a Remind students that only one value of x is needed. One way to find such a value is to graph $y = \sin x$ and $y = \sin\left(x + \frac{\pi}{4}\right) + \sin\left(x - \frac{\pi}{4}\right)$ on the same pair of axes.

Question 23b Ask students to generalize the given identity, replacing $\frac{\pi}{3}$ by β. [$\sin(\alpha + \beta) + \sin(\alpha - \beta) = 2\sin\alpha\cos\beta$; in this question $\cos\beta = \frac{1}{2}$.]

Question 25b This question prepares students for the descriptions of solutions to trigonometric equations that they will see in Lesson 6-8.

Additional Answers
23, 25. See Additional Answers at the back of this book.

Applying the Mathematics

In 15 and 16, compute without using a calculator.

15. $\sin\left(\sin^{-1}\left(-\frac{\sqrt{2}}{2}\right)\right)$ $-\frac{\sqrt{2}}{2}$

16. $\tan(\tan^{-1}(1.2))$ 1.2

17. Use the Pythagorean Identity to determine $\cos(\sin^{-1} .6)$ without using a calculator. .8

18. Use the Law of Sines to approximate the value of θ, in degrees, for the triangle pictured at the left. $\approx 74°$

1 rad. 6 θ 5.25

19. A radar tracking station is located 16 kilometers from a rocket launching pad. If a rocket is launched straight upward, express the angle of elevation of the rocket from the tracking station as a function of the altitude (in kilometers) of the rocket.

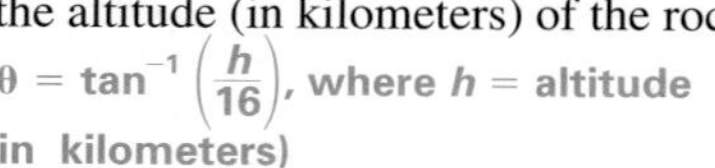

$\theta = \tan^{-1}\left(\frac{h}{16}\right)$, where h = altitude (in kilometers)

Review

20. Express $\sin\frac{5\pi}{8}$ in terms of rational numbers and radicals. *(Lesson 6-6)* $\frac{\sqrt{2+\sqrt{2}}}{2}$

21. Suppose that $\sin x = \frac{2}{3}$ and $\frac{\pi}{2} < x < \pi$. Find $\sin 2x$ and $\cos 2x$. *(Lesson 6-6)* $\sin 2x = -\frac{4\sqrt{5}}{9}$, $\cos 2x = \frac{1}{9}$

22. Prove: $\forall\ \alpha$, *such that* $\cos\alpha \ne 0$, $\frac{\sin 2\alpha}{\cos\alpha} = 2\sin\alpha$. *(Lesson 6-6)* See left.

22) $\frac{\sin 2\alpha}{\cos\alpha} = \frac{2\sin\alpha\cos\alpha}{\cos\alpha} = 2\sin\alpha$

23. a. Prove: $\exists\ x$, *such that* $\sin\left(x + \frac{\pi}{4}\right) + \sin\left(x - \frac{\pi}{4}\right) = \sin x$.

b. Prove: $\forall\ x$, $\sin\left(x + \frac{\pi}{3}\right) + \sin\left(x - \frac{\pi}{3}\right) = \sin x$. *(Lessons 6-2, 6-5)*

See margin.

24. Graph $y = \sin x$, $y = \sin\left(x + \frac{\pi}{3}\right)$, and $y = \sin\left(x - \frac{\pi}{3}\right)$ on the same pair of axes. Pick a value of x and show that the identity in Question 23b is true for that value of x. *(Lessons 3-1, 6-3)* See margin.

25. a. Find ten positive integers satisfying $y \equiv 4 \pmod{11}$.

b. Use the definition of *modulus* to find five numbers satisfying $z \equiv \frac{\pi}{2} \pmod{2\pi}$. *(Lesson 4-5)* See margin.

Exploration

26. a. Use an automatic grapher to guess the values of x for which $\sin(\cos^{-1}x) = \cos(\sin^{-1}x)$. $-1 \le x \le 1$

b. Prove your conjecture in part **a** by finding an expression which contains no trigonometric functions and is equal to both sides of the equation for the values of x you specified. See left.

c. Find and prove another identity (valid only on an interval you specify) which contains one trigonometric and one inverse trigonometric function on each side of the equation. See left.

26b) $\sin(\cos^{-1}x) = \sqrt{1 - x^2} = \cos(\sin^{-1}x)$

c) Sample: $\tan(\cot^{-1}x) = \cot(\tan^{-1}x)$ for $x > 0$

390

24. The graphs of $\sin\left(x + \frac{\pi}{3}\right)$, $\sin\left(x - \frac{\pi}{3}\right)$, and $y = \sin x$ are identical. Sample: Let $x = \frac{\pi}{2}$; $\sin\left(\frac{\pi}{2} + \frac{\pi}{3}\right) + \sin\left(\frac{\pi}{2} - \frac{\pi}{3}\right) =$ $\sin\frac{\pi}{2}\cos\frac{\pi}{3} + \cos\frac{\pi}{2}\sin\frac{\pi}{3} +$ $\sin\frac{\pi}{2}\cos\frac{\pi}{3} - \cos\frac{\pi}{2}\sin\frac{\pi}{3} =$ $1\left(\frac{1}{2}\right) + 0\left(\frac{\sqrt{3}}{2}\right) + 1\left(\frac{1}{2}\right) - 0\left(\frac{\sqrt{3}}{2}\right) =$ $\frac{1}{2} + \frac{1}{2} = 1 = \sin\frac{\pi}{2}$

Setting Up Lesson 6-8

Discuss **Question 25b.**

Solving Trigonometric Equations and Inequalities

Don't Try This at Home. *This human cannonball relies on his safety net being in the correct place to catch him. See Example 5 for the computations necessary to assure this.*

In this lesson algebraic and graphical methods for solving equations and inequalities are applied to trigonometric equations and inequalities.

Solving Trigonometric Equations

The first example illustrates how you can compute and describe the numbers that give rise to a particular value of a trigonometric function.

Example 1

Find and describe all real numbers x such that $\sin x = \frac{3}{4}$.

Solution

One solution of this equation is $x = \sin^{-1}\frac{3}{4}$.

You can use a calculator to find that $x \approx .84806$ radians $\approx 48.59°$. By the definition of the inverse sine function, this is the only solution of the given equation in the interval $-\frac{\pi}{2} \le x \le \frac{\pi}{2}$. However, because $\sin(\pi - x) = \sin x$ for all real numbers x, another solution to the equation is

$$\pi - x \approx (\pi - .84806) \text{ radians} \approx 2.29353 \text{ radians} \approx 131.41°.$$

This second solution lies in the interval from $\frac{\pi}{2}$ to π.

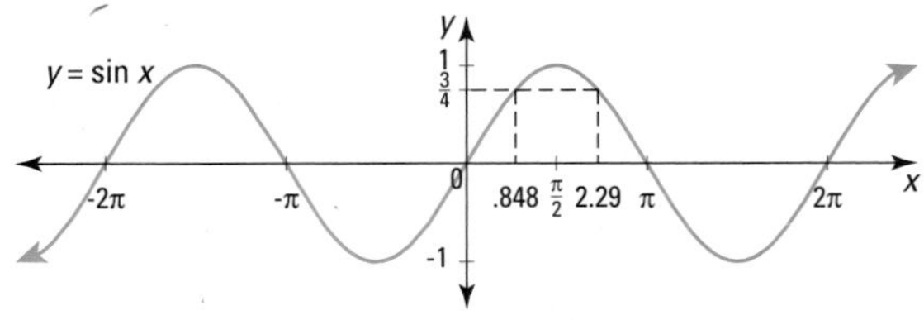

Lesson 6-8

Objectives

C Solve trigonometric equations and inequalities algebraically.

F Use trigonometric equations and inequalities to solve applied problems.

I Use graphs to solve trigonometric equations and inequalities.

Resources

From the ***Teacher's Resource File***

- Lesson Master 6-8
- Answer Master 6-8
- Teaching Aid 56: Warm-up

Additional Resources

- Visual for Teaching Aid 56
- Exploration 6-8

Teaching Lesson 6-8

Warm-up

Find all real solutions to each equation.

1. $x^2 = 1$ — 1 or -1
2. $x^3 = 1$ — 1
3. $x^4 = 1$ — 1 or -1
4. $\sqrt{x} = 1$ — 1
5. $e^x = 1$ — 0
6. $\log x = 1$ — 10
7. $\ln x = 1$ — e
8. $|x| = 1$ — 1 or -1
9. $\lfloor x \rfloor = 1$ — the interval [1,2)
10. $\tan x = 1$ — $\frac{\pi}{4} + n\pi$ for all integers n

Notes on Reading

The use of an automatic grapher can enhance the discussion of this lesson. You might consider spending one day just having students solve equations and inequalities graphically. This visual understanding of the meaning of a solution should prove helpful when shifting the focus to algebraic techniques. It should also help students realize that, when solved over the reals, trigonometric equations frequently have infinitely many solutions.

Lesson 6-8 Overview

Broad Goals This lesson discusses the solving of trigonometric equations over various intervals.

Perspective Students may have solved simple trigonometric equations before, particularly with the help of a calculator, but now the solving is couched in the language of inverse functions and inequalities are also considered. To solve an equation such as $\sin x = k$, first the single value $\sin^{-1}k$ is found, and then identities are used to find other solutions. The solutions to $\sin x = k$ are combined with graphical techniques to solve sentences like $\sin x < k$. The other trigonometric functions are treated similarly.

There is a jump in complexity of problems from **Example 1** to **Example 2.** You may wish to move gradually, as suggested in Activity 2 in *Optional Activities* on page 393.

Error Alert Students often do not know how many solutions to expect in the $0 \le x \le 2\pi$ interval. Using an automatic grapher will help. For **Example 2,** suggest graphing on the same coordinate system $y = 2\cos^2 x + \cos x$ and $y = 1$ for $-2\pi \le x \le 2\pi$ and $-3 \le y \le 3$. Students will see that the period of the first function is 2π and that there are three solutions over the desired interval.

Chunking ideas reviewed throughout this chapter are used in this lesson to help factor trigonometric equations. Furthermore, students see in **Example 3** that identities must often be used before attempting a solution. Remind students that dividing by a variable or by an expression containing a variable will not necessarily give an equivalent equation when the expression has value 0. There is the possibility that solutions might be lost.

In **Examples 1–4,** all of the quadratic equations are factorable and all equations come out with familiar standard solutions $\left(0, \frac{\pi}{6}, \frac{\pi}{4}, \frac{\pi}{3}, \text{etc.}\right)$. We have done this to make the examples easier, but there is the danger that students will think that all trigonometric equations have these kinds of solutions. Here is one that does not: $10\sin^2 x + 2\sin x - 1 = 0$. The quadratic formula is needed and leads to the following solutions (to nearest .001 radians) in the interval $0 \le x \le 2\pi$: .234, 2.908, 3.588, and 5.837.

You can see from the graph that these are the only two solutions of the given equation in the interval $0 \le x \le 2\pi$. Because the sine function is periodic with period 2π, the solutions to the given equation are numbers of the form

$$x = .84806 + 2n\pi \quad \text{or} \quad x = 2.29353 + 2n\pi, \quad \text{for all integers } n.$$

Another way of writing this is with modular arithmetic.

$$x \equiv .84806 \pmod{2\pi} \quad \text{or} \quad x \equiv 2.29353 \pmod{2\pi}$$

The next example involves the solving of a quadratic equation in $\cos x$.

Example 2

Solve $2\cos^2 x + \cos x = 1$ in the given domain for x.

a. the interval $0 \le x \le 2\pi$

b. the set of all real numbers

Solution

a. Rewrite the equation as $2\cos^2 x + \cos x - 1 = 0$. If you think of "$\cos x$" as a chunk, then the left side has the form $2q^2 + q - 1$ which equals $(2q - 1)(q + 1)$. Thus the given equation can be written as

$(2\cos x - 1)(\cos x + 1) = 0.$		factoring
$2\cos x - 1 = 0$ or $\cos x + 1 = 0$		Zero-Product Property
$\cos x = \frac{1}{2}$ or $\cos x = -1$		A_1 and $M_{\frac{1}{2}}$, and A_{-1}

Now find the solutions in the interval $0 \le x \le 2\pi$, which contains one cycle of the cosine function.

$$x = \frac{\pi}{3} \quad \text{or} \quad x = \frac{5\pi}{3} \quad \text{or} \quad x = \pi$$

b. Use the result of part **a**, together with the fact that the cosine function has period 2π, to conclude that the solutions are all x of the form

$$x = \frac{\pi}{3} + 2\pi n \quad \text{or} \quad x = \frac{5\pi}{3} + 2\pi n \quad \text{or} \quad x = \pi + 2\pi n = (2n + 1)\pi$$

for all integers n. You could also write

$$x \equiv \frac{\pi}{3} \pmod{2\pi} \quad \text{or} \quad x \equiv \frac{5\pi}{3} \pmod{2\pi} \quad \text{or} \quad x \equiv \pi \pmod{2\pi}.$$

Examples 1 and 2 illustrate a general two-step strategy for finding all real-number solutions of a trigonometric equation.

Step 1: Solve the given equation over a restricted domain equal to the period of the given trigonometric functions.

Step 2: Use periodicity properties of the trigonometric functions, together with the solutions from Step 1, to find all solutions.

At times you may need to use an identity to rewrite one side of the equation in a form which can be factored.

Optional Activities

Activity 1 Technology Connection
Materials: Explorations software

Students may use Exploration 6-8, *Solving Trigonometric Equations,* as an alternative to **Example 1** in Lesson 6-8. Students explore the graphical and algebraic solutions to trigonometric equations. They can see that the intersection of a horizontal line and the graph of the trigonometric function represents a possible solution to the equation.

Activity 2 Alternate Approach There is a jump in complexity of problems from **Example 1** to **Example 2.** You may wish to increase the complexity of the problems more gradually, by having students use the domain $0 \le x \le 2\pi$, and solve each of the following.

a. $\sin x = 1$ $\left[x = \frac{\pi}{2}\right]$

b. $\sin x = \frac{1}{2}$ $\left[x = \frac{\pi}{6} \text{ or } x = \frac{5\pi}{6}\right]$

c. $\sin x - 1 = 0$ [Same as a]

d. $2\sin x - 1 = 0$ [Same as b]

e. $(\sin x - 1)(2\sin x - 1) = 0$ [Solutions to a or b]

f. $2\sin^2 x - 3\sin x + 1 = 0$ [Same as e]

Note that solving quadratic trigonometric equations often involves going from **step f** to **steps a and b.** A goal in problem-solving is to simplify; another is to transform the unfamiliar into the familiar.

Example 3

Find the solution set for the equation $\tan x + \sec^2 x - 1 = 0$.

Solution

Use the identity $1 + \tan^2 x = \sec^2 x$ to substitute for $\sec^2 x$. The resulting equation is quadratic in $\tan x$ and can be solved over the restricted domain $-\frac{\pi}{2} < x < \frac{\pi}{2}$.

$$\tan x + (1 + \tan^2 x) - 1 = 0$$
$$\tan^2 x + \tan x = 0$$
$$\tan x (1 + \tan x) = 0$$
$$\tan x = 0 \quad \text{or} \quad 1 + \tan x = 0$$
$$\tan x = -1$$
$$x = 0 \quad \text{or} \quad x = -\frac{\pi}{4}$$

Because $\tan x$ has period π, it follows that the exact solution set is the set of all real numbers of the form

$$x = 0 + n\pi = n\pi \quad \text{or} \quad x = -\frac{\pi}{4} + n\pi$$

for all integers n. That is,

$$x \equiv 0 \pmod{\pi} \quad \text{or} \quad x \equiv -\frac{\pi}{4} \pmod{\pi}.$$

Solving Trigonometric Inequalities

Graphing can help solve trigonometric inequalities.

Example 4

a. Use an automatic grapher to approximate the solutions to $2 \sin^2 x + \sin x - 1 \geq 0$ in the interval $0 \leq x \leq 2\pi$.

b. Find the exact solutions to the inequality.

Solution

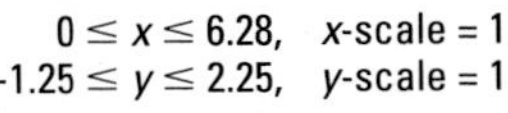

$0 \leq x \leq 6.28$, x-scale = 1
$-1.25 \leq y \leq 2.25$, y-scale = 1

a. Use an automatic grapher to plot the function $f(x) = 2 \sin^2 x + \sin x - 1$ on the interval $0 \leq x \leq 2\pi$. Then use the trace function on the grapher to estimate the solution set for the inequality. **A reasonable estimate is that x can be any value in the interval $.52 \leq x \leq 2.62$, or may be the single value 4.71, or in a small interval around 4.71.**

b. To determine the exact solution set of the inequality, first solve the equation $2 \sin^2 x + \sin x - 1 = 0$ by noting that the left side has the form $2q^2 + q - 1 = 0$ which can be factored.

	$(2 \sin x - 1)(\sin x + 1) = 0$	
$\Leftrightarrow$	$2 \sin x - 1 = 0$ or $\sin x + 1 = 0$	Zero-Product Property
$\Leftrightarrow$	$\sin x = \frac{1}{2}$ or $\sin x = -1$	A_1 and $M_{\frac{1}{2}}$, and A_{-1}
$\Leftrightarrow$	$x = \frac{\pi}{6}$ or $x = \frac{5\pi}{6}$ or $x = \frac{3\pi}{2}$	Apply $\sin^{-1}$ and identity $\sin(\pi - x) = \sin x$.

Many students are intimidated by problems like **Example 4.** The combination of quadratics, trigonometric functions, and inequalities can be overwhelming. Note that the first thing done is to consider the related equation. This equation is easier than the one in **Example 3.** If need be, substitute t for $\sin x$ and solve $2t^2 + t - 1 = 0$. For some (but not all) students, this may be clearer.

Example 5 on page 394 utilizes the formula for the range of a projectile that was developed in **Lesson 6-6.** The graph relates horizontal distance to the angle the cannon makes with the horizontal.

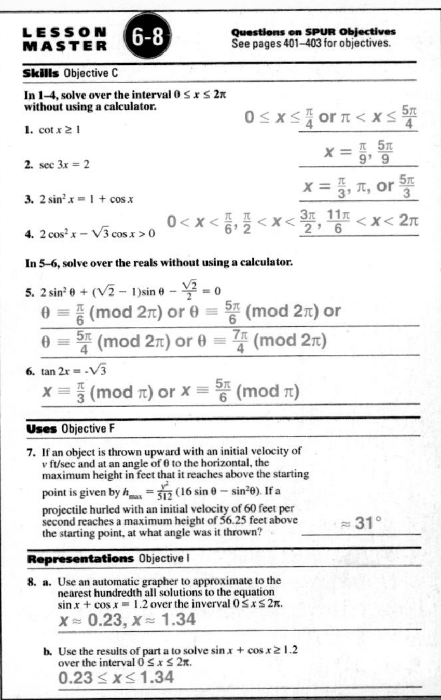

LESSON MASTER 6-8

Questions on SPUR Objectives
See pages 401–403 for objectives.

Skills Objective C

In 1–4, solve over the interval $0 \leq x \leq 2\pi$ without using a calculator.

1. $\cot x \geq 1$ — $0 \leq x \leq \frac{\pi}{4}$ or $\pi < x \leq \frac{5\pi}{4}$
2. $\sec 3x = 2$ — $x = \frac{\pi}{9}, \frac{5\pi}{9}$
3. $2 \sin^2 x = 1 + \cos x$ — $x = \frac{\pi}{3}, \pi$, or $\frac{5\pi}{3}$
4. $2 \cos^2 x - \sqrt{3} \cos x > 0$ — $0 < x < \frac{\pi}{6}, \frac{\pi}{2} < x < \frac{3\pi}{2}, \frac{11\pi}{6} < x < 2\pi$

In 5–6, solve over the reals without using a calculator.

5. $2 \sin^2 \theta + (\sqrt{2} - 1)\sin \theta - \frac{\sqrt{2}}{2} = 0$
$\theta \equiv \frac{\pi}{6} \pmod{2\pi}$ or $\theta \equiv \frac{5\pi}{6} \pmod{2\pi}$ or
$\theta \equiv \frac{5\pi}{4} \pmod{2\pi}$ or $\theta \equiv \frac{7\pi}{4} \pmod{2\pi}$

6. $\tan 2x = -\sqrt{3}$
$x \equiv \frac{\pi}{3} \pmod{\pi}$ or $x \equiv \frac{5\pi}{6} \pmod{\pi}$

Uses Objective F

7. If an object is thrown upward with an initial velocity of v ft/sec and at an angle of θ to the horizontal, the maximum height in feet that it reaches above the starting point is given by $h_{max} = \frac{v^2}{512}(16 \sin \theta - \sin^2 \theta)$. If a projectile hurled with an initial velocity of 60 feet per second reaches a maximum height of 56.25 feet above the starting point, at what angle was it thrown? — $\approx 31°$

Representations Objective I

8. **a.** Use an automatic grapher to approximate to the nearest hundredth all solutions to the equation $\sin x + \cos x = 1.2$ over the inverval $0 \leq x \leq 2\pi$.
$x \approx 0.23, x \approx 1.34$

b. Use the results of part a to solve $\sin x + \cos x \geq 1.2$ over the interval $0 \leq x \leq 2\pi$.
$0.23 \leq x \leq 1.34$

Additional Examples

1. Find and describe all real numbers x such that:
   a. $\cos x = \frac{1}{2}$ $x = \frac{\pi}{3} + 2n\pi$ or $x = \frac{5\pi}{3} + 2n\pi$
   b. $\cos x = \frac{3}{4}$ $x \approx .7227342478 + 2n\pi$ or $x \approx 5.560451059 + 2n\pi$
2. Solve $4 \sin^2 x - 1 = 0$:
   a. over the interval $0 \leq x \leq 2\pi$ $x = \frac{\pi}{6}, \frac{5\pi}{6}, \frac{7\pi}{6}, \frac{11\pi}{6}$
   b. over the set of all real numbers $x = \frac{\pi}{6} + n\pi$ or $x = \frac{11\pi}{6} + n\pi$
3. Find all solutions to the equation $\cot x + \csc^2 x = 1$. $x = \frac{3\pi}{4} + n\pi$ or $x = \frac{\pi}{2} + n\pi$
4. a. Approximate the solutions to $4 \cos^2 x - 1 \geq 0$ on the interval $0 \leq x \leq 2\pi$. $0 \leq x \leq 1.05$ or $2.09 \leq x \leq 4.19$ or $5.24 \leq x \leq 6.28$
   b. Find the exact solutions to the inequality. $0 \leq x \leq \frac{\pi}{3}$ or $\frac{2\pi}{3} \leq x \leq \frac{4\pi}{3}$ or $\frac{5\pi}{3} \leq x \leq 2\pi$
5. The formula $H = \frac{v_0^2 \sin^2\theta}{64}$ estimates the maximum height achieved by the person launched by the Rocket Launcher in flight. Given that the person's initial velocity is 50 ft/sec and that the person wishes to clear a banner which is 20 ft above the ground and go below a supportive beam (just above the banner) of the circus tent which is only 30 feet above the ground, find the values of θ ($0° < \theta < 90°$) for a safe flight. $45.69° < \theta < 61.21°$
6. A Ferris wheel has a 40-foot diameter and rotates counterclockwise at a rate of 2 revolutions per minute. Take the center of the wheel to be the center of a coordinate system. Since there are 2π radians in each revolution and there are 2 revolutions per minute, the wheel covers 4π radians each minute and $4\pi t$ radians in t minutes. So, if a person has boarded at $t = 0$ and the wheel begins to rotate immediately, the coordinates of the rider's position after t minutes, relative to the center of the wheel, are given by $x = 20 \cos(4\pi t)$ and $y = 20 \sin(4\pi t)$. At what times in the first two minutes after boarding is a rider 10 feet to the right of the center of the wheel?

The function f is continuous, so the Test-Point Method can be used. With this method, you should find that $2 \sin^2 x + \sin x - 1 \geq 0$ *when x is in the interval* $\frac{\pi}{6} \leq x \leq \frac{5\pi}{6}$ *and when* $x = \frac{3\pi}{2}$.

Check

Since $\frac{\pi}{6} \approx .52$, $\frac{5\pi}{6} \approx 2.62$, and $\frac{3\pi}{2} \approx 4.71$, these values agree with the estimates found from graphing.

The following example uses the results on projectile motion developed in Example 3 of Lesson 6-6.

Example 5

In recent years, the Ringling Brothers Circus featured an act called the Rocket Launcher. A person is launched like a rocket with an initial velocity of 64 ft/sec. The formula

$$R = \frac{v_0^2}{32} \sin 2\theta$$

estimates the horizontal distance R (in feet) traveled when the person is launched at an angle of θ with an initial speed of v_0 ft/sec. Find the values of θ so that the "human rocket" will travel a horizontal distance greater than 100 ft, the distance to the nearest part of the safety net.

Solution

Given $v_0 = 64$ *ft/sec, the solution set consists of all values of* θ *such that*

$$100 < \frac{(64)^2}{32} \sin 2\theta$$

or, equivalently,

$$100 < 128 \sin 2\theta.$$

The situation requires that θ lie in the interval $0° < \theta < 90°$. The orange part of the graph at the right indicates those points on the graph of $y = 128 \sin 2\theta$ whose y-coordinates are greater than $y = 100$. To find the corresponding x-coordinates, solve the equation

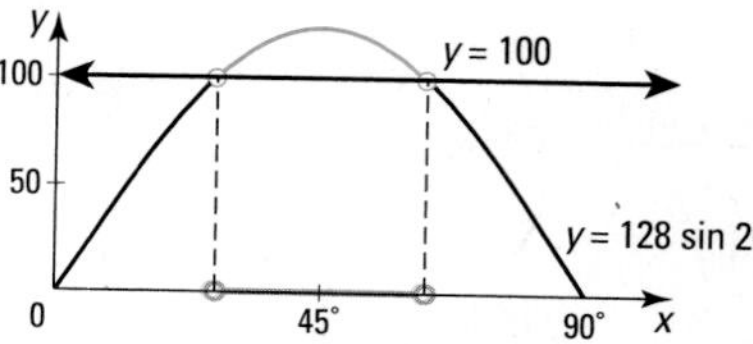

$$100 = 128 \sin 2\theta$$

or $\quad .78125 = \sin 2\theta.$

A calculator shows $\quad 2\theta \approx 51.38°$, making $\theta \approx 25.69°$.

But since $\quad \sin x = \sin(\pi - x) = \sin(180° - x)$,

the other solution is $\quad 2\theta \approx 128.62°$.

Thus the solutions to the equation are

$$\theta \approx 25.69° \quad \text{or} \quad \theta \approx 64.31°.$$

Thus the human rocket will travel greater than 100 feet when shot at an angle between 25.69° and 64.31°.

Adapting to Individual Needs

Extra Help

As an aid in finding all values in $0 \leq x \leq 2\pi$ that have given sine, cosine or tangent, as in **Example 1** show students the following:

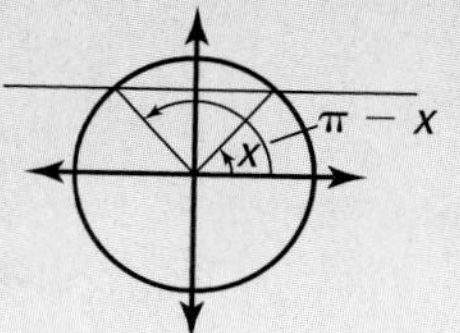

Two numbers with same sine are x and $\pi - x$.

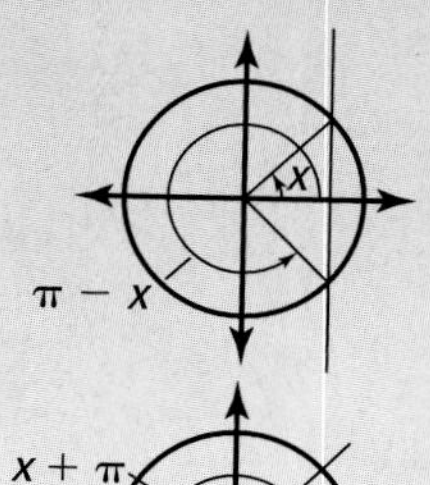

Two numbers with same cosine are x and $2\pi - x$.

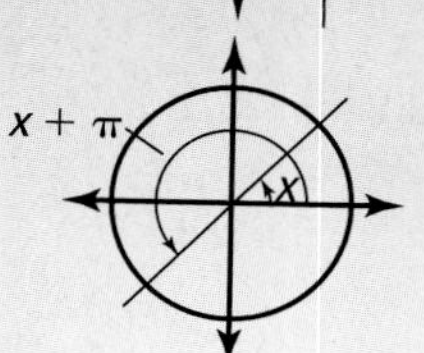

Two numbers with same tangent are x and $\pi + x$.

QUESTIONS

Covering the Reading

1) $x = \frac{\pi}{2} + 2\pi n$, n an integer, or equivalently $x \equiv \frac{\pi}{2} \pmod{2\pi}$

2) $y = \frac{\pi}{3} + \pi n$, n an integer or $y = \frac{5\pi}{3} + \pi n$, n an integer or equivalently $y \equiv \frac{\pi}{3} \pmod{\pi}$ or $y \equiv \frac{5\pi}{3} \pmod{\pi}$

3) $x = \frac{\pi}{4} + \pi n$, n an integer or equivalently $x \equiv \frac{\pi}{4} \pmod{\pi}$

In 1–3, describe all real numbers satisfying the equation. See left.

1. $\sin x = 1$ **2.** $\cos y = \frac{1}{2}$ **3.** $\tan z = 1$

4. Describe all solutions (to the nearest thousandth) to $\cos x = \frac{2}{3}$ over the indicated domain. b) $\pm 0.841 + 2\pi n$, n an integer
- **a.** the interval $0 \le x \le 2\pi$ 0.841 and 5.442
- **b.** the set of real numbers

5. Solve the equation $2 \sin^2 \theta - 5 \sin \theta - 3 = 0$ when θ has the given domain. See margin.
- **a.** the interval $[0, 2\pi]$
- **b.** the set of real numbers

6. Use an appropriate trigonometric identity to help find all real numbers x such that $\cos^2 x - \sin x + 1 = 0$. $\frac{\pi}{2} + 2\pi n$, n an integer

7. Use the result of Example 1 to find an approximate solution set for the inequality $\sin x \le \frac{3}{4}$ over the interval $0 \le x \le 2\pi$. $0 \le x \le .848$ or $2.29 \le x \le 2\pi$

In 8 and 9, find the exact solutions to the inequality over the interval $0 \le x \le 2\pi$. (Hint: Refer to Example 2.)

8. $\tan x \ge \sqrt{3}$ $\frac{\pi}{3} \le x < \frac{\pi}{2}, \frac{4\pi}{3} \le x < \frac{3\pi}{2}$

9. $2\cos^2 x + \cos x - 1 \le 0$ $\frac{\pi}{3} \le x \le \frac{5\pi}{3}$

10. Refer to Example 5. Find all angle values so that the person will travel a horizontal distance greater than 30 feet. $6.78° < \theta < 83.22°$

Applying the Mathematics

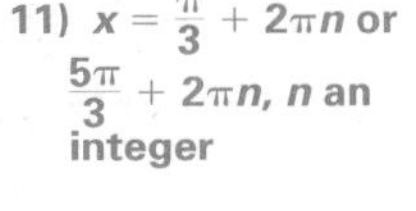
11) $x = \frac{\pi}{3} + 2\pi n$ or $\frac{5\pi}{3} + 2\pi n$, n an integer

11. Find exact values of all real solutions of $\sin x \tan x + \cos x = 2$. See left.

12. To solve the inequality $\sin x + \cos x \ge 0$ over the interval $0 \le x \le 2\pi$, a student divided by $\cos x$ to obtain $\tan x + 1 \ge 0$.
- **a.** Is this a reversible step? No
- **b.** Solve the original inequality. $0 \le x \le \frac{3\pi}{4}, \frac{7\pi}{4} \le x \le 2\pi$

13. A nautical mile was originally defined as the length of a minute of arc $\left(\frac{1}{60}\text{ of degree}\right)$ of a meridian. Because Earth flattens at the poles, the number of feet in this nautical mile varies with latitude. Let y be the number of feet in the original nautical mile at latitude θ degrees. Then y and θ are approximately related by the equation $y = 6077 + 31 \cos 2\theta$.
- **a.** At what latitude is the original nautical mile equal to 6080 feet, called an Admiralty mile? $\approx 42.22°$
- **b.** At what latitude is a nautical mile equal to 6076.115 feet (1852 meters), the nautical mile now used officially throughout the world? $\approx 41.40°$

Clipper ship from the 1700s

A person is 10 feet to the right of the wheel's center when $10 = 20 \cos (4\pi t)$, that is, when $\cos 4\pi t = .5$. Solutions to this equation for $4\pi t < 2\pi$ are $t = \frac{\frac{\pi}{3}}{4\pi}$ and $t = \frac{\frac{5\pi}{3}}{4\pi}$, that is, when $t = \frac{1}{12}$ or $t = \frac{5}{12}$ minutes, or 5 seconds and 25 seconds. Since a revolution takes 30 seconds, the person is 10 feet to the right of center after 5, 25, 35, 55, 65, 85, 95 and 115 seconds.]

Notes on Questions

Question 1 In this and other questions in which the domain is the set of real numbers, allow solutions to be presented in a variety of manners. Some students may prefer modular arithmetic; others may prefer adding $\pm 2\pi n$ or some other indication of period to a basic solution; still others may wish to combine the algebra to obtain $x = \left(2n + \frac{1}{2}\right)\pi$; and others may prefer set notation $\left\{x\colon x = \frac{\pi}{2} + 2\pi n\right\}$. The important criteria are clarity and completeness. All solutions should be indicated clearly.

Question 6 Students should use the strategy of rewriting the equation so that it contains only one type of trigonometric function, so as to facilitate factoring. Ask if it is simpler to rewrite $\cos^2 x$ in terms of $\sin x$ or to rewrite $\sin x$ in terms of $\cos x$. [The former is easier because no square root is involved.]

Adapting to Individual Needs

Challenge

Have students do the following.

1. Give the exact value of the solution to $\cos^{-1} x = \tan^{-1} x$. $\left[\sqrt{\frac{-1 + \sqrt{5}}{2}}\right]$
2. Give the exact value of the point(s) of intersection for $y = \cos^{-1} x$ and $y = \sin^{-1} x$. $\left[\left(\frac{\sqrt{2}}{2}, \frac{\pi}{4}\right)\right.$ How does this compare with the point(s) of intersection for $y = \cos x$ and $y = \sin x$? [The coordinates are reversed and the second pair has an infinite number of points of intersection of the form $\left(\frac{\pi}{4} + 2\pi n, \frac{\sqrt{2}}{2}\right)$ and $\left.\left(\frac{5\pi}{4} + 2\pi n, -\frac{\sqrt{2}}{2}\right)\right]$
3. Refer to the hyperbolic functions in the Exploration of Lesson 6-2. Use a graphing calculator to find the point of intersection for $y = \tan^{-1}(\sinh x)$ and $y = \sin^{-1}(\tanh x)$. [The functions are identical for all x.]

Additional Answers

5. a. $\frac{7\pi}{6}, \frac{11\pi}{6}$

b. $x = \frac{7\pi}{6} + 2n\pi$ or $x = \frac{11\pi}{6} + 2n\pi$, where n is any integer, or equivalently $x \equiv \frac{7\pi}{6} \pmod{2\pi}$ or $x \equiv \frac{11\pi}{6} \pmod{2\pi}$.

Follow-up for Lesson 6-8

Practice

For more questions on SPUR Objectives, use **Lesson Master 6-8** (shown on page 393).

Assessment

Oral Communication Have students discuss their solution to one of **Questions 4–9** and show how to use an automatic grapher to check the solution. [Students solve trigonometric equations algebraically and graphically.]

Extension

Ask students to consider the solutions to $\sin 2x = \frac{1}{2}$ on the interval $0 < x < 2\pi$. They may not realize at first that there are *four* solutions. Ask them to explain why and to generalize their findings. That is, for $\sin nx = \frac{a}{b}$, with n a positive integer, $a \neq b$, $b \neq 0$, how many solutions will there be on the interval $0 \leq x < 2\pi$? [There are four solutions to the equation $\sin 2x = \frac{1}{2}$ because the period of $y = \sin 2x$ is π, (the function moves through TWO full cycles on the interval $0 < x < 2\pi$, yielding $x = \frac{\pi}{12}, \frac{5\pi}{12}, \frac{13\pi}{12}, \frac{17\pi}{12}$. For $\sin nx = \frac{a}{b}$, there are $2n$ solutions. A strategy for finding the solutions algebraically is to search for all solutions in the domain $0 \leq nx < 2n\pi$.]

Project Update Project 5, *Gravity*, on page 398, relates to the content of this lesson.

18)

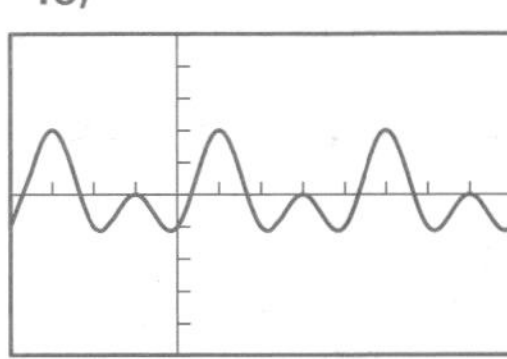

$-2\pi \leq x \leq 4\pi$, x-scale $= \frac{\pi}{2}$
$-5 \leq y \leq 5$, y-scale = 1

b) Values of the function repeat every interval of length 2π; that is $f(x + 2\pi) = f(x)\ \forall$ real numbers

19e)

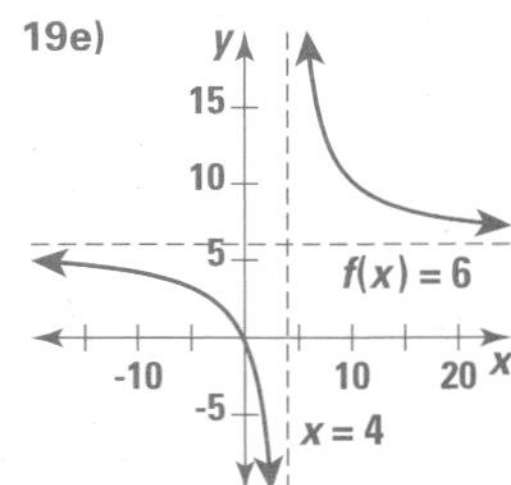

Review

14. Suppose $\theta = \sin^{-1} \frac{2}{\sqrt{5}}$.
   a. Approximate θ to the nearest hundredth of a degree. $\theta \approx 63.43°$
   b. Find the exact value of $\cos \theta$. *(Lesson 6-7)* $\cos \theta = \frac{1}{\sqrt{5}}$

15. Evaluate without a calculator. *(Lesson 6-7)*
   a. $\sin^{-1}\left(-\frac{\sqrt{2}}{2}\right)$ $-\frac{\pi}{4}$ **b.** $\tan^{-1}\sqrt{3}$ $\frac{\pi}{3}$ **c.** $\cos^{-1}\left(\frac{1}{2}\right)$ $\frac{2\pi}{3}$

16. Prove the identity $\sin x = \frac{2 \sin^3 x + \sin 2x \cos x}{4 \sin^2 x + 2 \cos 2x}$ mentioned at the beginning of Lesson 6-2. *(Lessons 6-2, 6-6)* See margin.

17. Use the values of cos 45°, sin 45°, cos 60°, and sin 60° to find radicals or rational expressions for each value.
   a. cos 105° $\frac{\sqrt{2} - \sqrt{6}}{4}$ **b.** sin 105° $\frac{\sqrt{6} + \sqrt{2}}{4}$ **c.** tan 105° $\frac{\sqrt{6} + \sqrt{2}}{\sqrt{2} - \sqrt{6}}$
   (Lessons 6-4, 6-5)

18. Plot the function f from Example 4 over a longer interval than $0 \leq x \leq 2\pi$. See left.
   a. What is the period of f? 2π
   b. Explain why f has this period. *(Lesson 6-3)* See left.

19. Let the function f be defined by $f(x) = \frac{6x + 1}{x - 4}$.
   a. *True or false.* f is a rational function. True
   b. Find all zeros of f. $x = -\frac{1}{6}$
   c. Determine the equations of all vertical asymptotes of the graph of f. $x = 4$
   d. Find $\lim_{x \to \infty} f(x)$. 6
   e. Use parts **b–d** to sketch a graph of the function. *(Lessons 5-4, 5-5)* See left.

20. Find the base 10 representation of 11101_2. *(Lesson 4-6)* 29

21. Solve $|2t - 5| > 3$. *(Lesson 3-9)* $t < 1$ or $t > 4$

22. a. Rewrite the following statement in if-then form: *Having one right angle is a sufficient condition for a parallelogram to be a rectangle.*
   b. Is the conditional *true* or *false*? *(Previous course, Lesson 1-5)* True
   a) *If a parallelogram has one right angle, then it is a rectangle.*

Exploration

23. a. Use the result of Question 5 to find all real solutions of the following.
   i. $2 \sin^2 3x - 5 \sin 3x - 3 = 0$
   ii. $2 \sin^2 (x + \pi) - 5 \sin (x + \pi) - 3 = 0$
   iii. $2 \sin^2 \frac{1}{x} - 5 \sin \frac{1}{x} - 3 = 0$
   b. If f is a function, how are the solutions of $2 \sin^2 x - 5 \sin x - 3 = 0$ related to those of $2 \sin^2 [f(x)] - 5 \sin [f(x)] - 3 = 0$?
See margin.

Additional Answers

16. right side

$= \frac{2 \sin^3 x + \sin 2x \cos x}{4 \sin^2 x + 2 \cos 2x}$

$= \frac{2 \sin^3 x + 2 \sin x \cos x \cos x}{4 \sin^2 x + 2(1 - 2 \sin^2 x)}$ Formulas for sin 2x and cos 2x

$= \frac{2 \sin^3 x + 2 \sin x \cos x \cos x}{4 \sin^2 x + 2 - 4 \sin^2 x}$ Distributive properties

$= \frac{2 \sin x}{2} = \sin x$ Pythagorean Identity

= left side

$\therefore \frac{2 \sin^3 x + \sin 2x \cos x}{4 \sin^2 x + 2 \cos 2x} = \sin x$

23. a. i. $\frac{7\pi}{18} + \frac{2\pi n}{3}, \frac{11}{18} + \frac{2\pi n}{3}$

ii. $\frac{\pi}{6} + 2\pi n, \frac{5\pi}{6} + 2\pi n$

iii. $\left(\frac{1}{\frac{7\pi}{6} + 2\pi n}\right), \left(\frac{1}{\frac{11\pi}{6} + 2\pi n}\right)$

b. The solutions of $2 \sin^2[f(x)] - 5 \sin [f(x)] - 3 = 0$ are all numbers x such that $f(x)$ is equal to the solutions of $2 \sin^2 x - 5 \sin x - 3 = 0$.

A project presents an opportunity for you to extend your knowledge of a topic related to the material of this chapter. You should allow more time for a project than you do for a typical homework question.

1 Mechanical Vibration

The pleasant sounds produced by many musical instruments result from the vibrations of tightly stretched strings or wooden reeds. The collapse of the Tacoma Narrows Bridge in 1940 and the failure of aircraft components due to metal fatigue are also examples of effects of mechanical vibrations.

Mathematicians, engineers, and scientists use a simple physical model to study mechanical vibration. It consists of a weight w hanging from the lower end of a spring whose upper end is attached to a support.

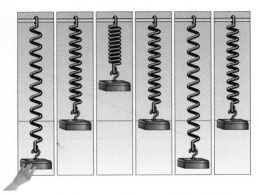

Let $f(t)$ represents the distance of the weight above or below its equilibrium or rest position (blue line) t seconds after the weight was disturbed.

If the spring is assumed to be perfectly elastic and only the forces of gravity and of the spring are considered, then f can be described by the equation

$$f(t) = a \cos ct + b \sin ct$$

where a, b, and c are constants, $c \neq 0$, and at least one of a or b is nonzero. The values of a, b, and c are determined by the spring, weight, and initial disturbance.

For instance, the motion of a spring-weight system could be modeled by

$$f(t) = 3 \cos 2t + 4 \sin 2t$$

where $f(t)$ is measured in inches.

a. Graph $y = f(t)$.

b. The graph of $y = f(t)$ has the general shape of a graph of a sine or cosine function. Show that the graph of $y = f(t)$ is just a translation image of the graph of $y = 5 \cos 2t$.

c. Give the amplitude and period of the graph of $y = f(t)$ and estimate its phase shift from $y = 5 \cos 2t$.

d. With real springs frictional forces resist the motion of the weight and cause the spring to eventually stop moving. If these are taken into account, then the resulting mathematical model is

$$f(t) = e^{-kt}(a \cos ct + b \sin ct)$$

where a, b, c, and k are constants such that $k > 0$, $c \neq 0$, and at least one of a or b is nonzero. For example, after an initial disturbance, the spring-weight system might oscillate according to the formula

$$h(t) = e^{-\frac{1}{8}t}(-3 \cos 2t + 4 \sin 2t)$$

where $h(t)$ is the distance in inches of the weight from its equilibrium position t seconds after the weight is initially disturbed. Graph the function h on the interval $0 \leq t \leq 10$.

e. Give the distance between successive relative maxima of the graph.

f. If h represents a sound wave over time t, explain what has happened to the sound.

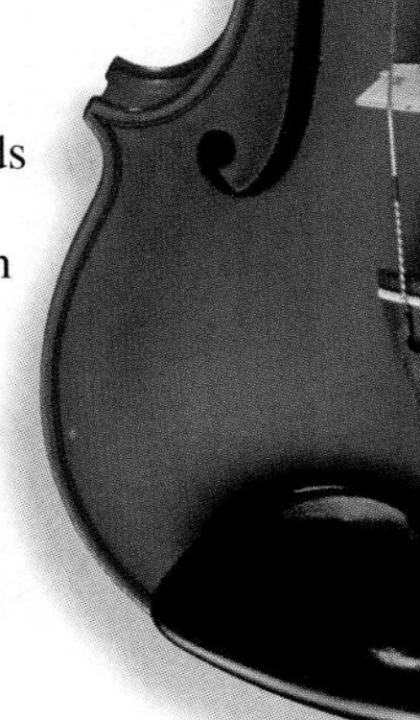

Chapter 6 Projects

The projects relate chiefly to the content of the lessons of this chapter as follows:

Project	Lesson(s)
1	6-3, 6-6
2	6-2, 6-4, 6-5
3	6-3
4	6-4, 6-5, 6-6
5	6-5, 6-8

1 Mechanical Vibration Some encyclopedias contain material on the Tacoma Narrows Bridge disaster. Students may have seen the news clip showing this bridge swaying uncontrollably; it seems as if it is science fiction or special effects, but it was not!

2 "Pseudotrigonometric" Functions This project may be too easy if students explored the hyperbolic functions in Lesson 6-2. These functions are like hyperbolic functions, but with e replaced by 2.

3 Modeling Weather Students who have studied from *Functions, Statistics, and Trigonometry* may have seen projects like this one before. The data for this project are available from local weather bureaus or the Internet.

1. d. continued

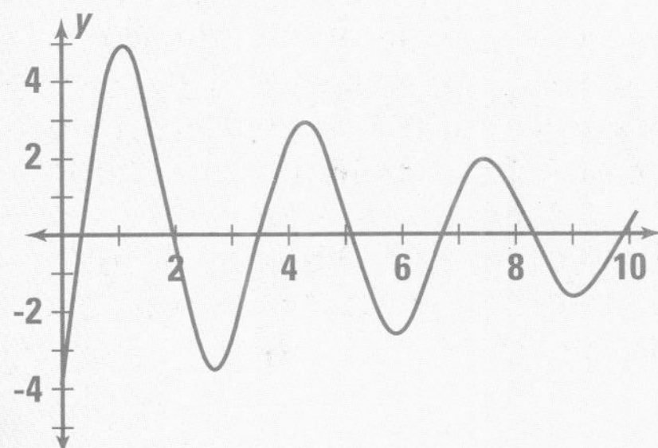

e. π

f. If a sound wave is produced by striking a tuning fork, for example, the amplitude of the sound wave diminishes over time, because air resistance dampens the tuning fork vibrations.

(Responses continue on page 398.)

Possible Responses

1. a.

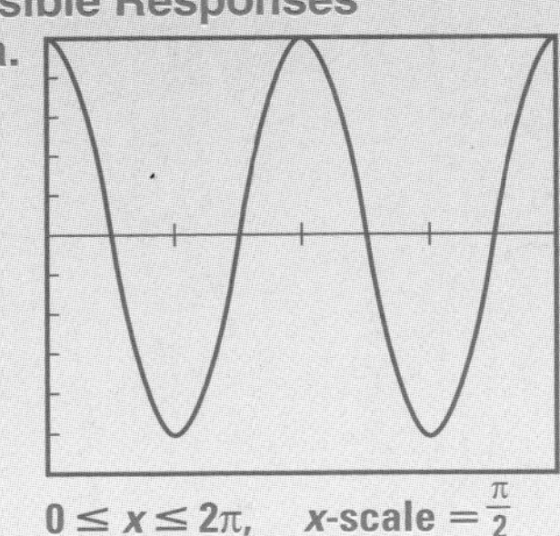

$0 \leq x \leq 2\pi$, x-scale $= \frac{\pi}{2}$
$-6 \leq y \leq 5$, y-scale $= 1$

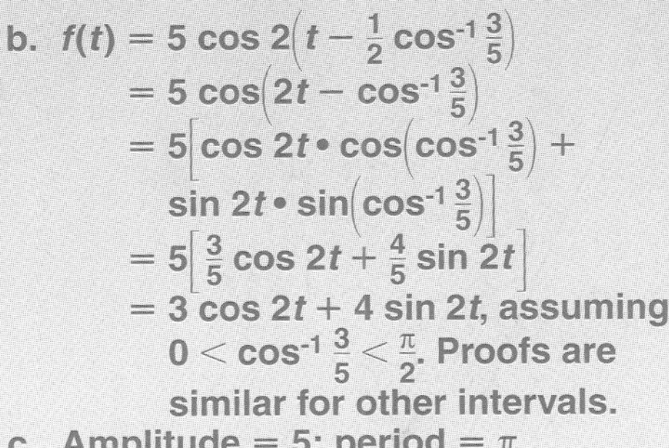

b. $f(t) = 5 \cos 2\left(t - \frac{1}{2}\cos^{-1}\frac{3}{5}\right)$
$= 5 \cos\left(2t - \cos^{-1}\frac{3}{5}\right)$
$= 5\left[\cos 2t \cdot \cos\left(\cos^{-1}\frac{3}{5}\right) + \sin 2t \cdot \sin\left(\cos^{-1}\frac{3}{5}\right)\right]$
$= 5\left[\frac{3}{5}\cos 2t + \frac{4}{5}\sin 2t\right]$
$= 3 \cos 2t + 4 \sin 2t$, assuming $0 < \cos^{-1}\frac{3}{5} < \frac{\pi}{2}$. Proofs are similar for other intervals.

c. Amplitude $= 5$; period $= \pi$
Phase shift $= \frac{1}{2}\cos^{-1}\left(\frac{3}{5}\right) \approx .46$

4 Rational and Radical Expressions for Sines and Cosines As a hint, you might inform students that x can be any integer multiple of 3.

5 Gravity Parts a to c are straightforward. **Part d** will require some searching. Physics books, books on geodesy, or encyclopedias may help.

Additional Responses, page 398

2. See below
3. Answers will vary.
4. Samples:

$\sin 18° = \sqrt{\frac{1 - \cos 36°}{2}}$

$= \sqrt{\frac{1 - \frac{\sqrt{5}+1}{4}}{2}} = \frac{1}{2}\sqrt{\frac{3 - \sqrt{5}}{2}}$

$\sin 36° = \sqrt{1 - \cos^2 36°}$

$= \sqrt{1 - (\frac{\sqrt{5}+1}{4})^2}$

$= \frac{\sqrt{16 - (6 + 2\sqrt{5})}}{4} = \frac{\sqrt{10 - 2\sqrt{5}}}{4}$

$\sin 54° = \sin(90° - 36°)$
$= \sin 90° \cos 36° -$
$\cos 90° \sin 36°$
$= 1 \bullet \cos 36° - 0 \bullet \sin 36°$
$= \frac{\sqrt{5}+1}{4}$

$\sin 72° = 2 \sin 36° \cos 36°$

$= 2\left(\frac{\sqrt{10 - 2\sqrt{5}}}{4}\right)\left(\frac{\sqrt{5}+1}{4}\right)$

$= \frac{\sqrt{(10 - 2\sqrt{5})5} + \sqrt{10 - 2\sqrt{5}}}{8}$

$= \frac{\sqrt{50 - 10\sqrt{5}} + \sqrt{10 - 2\sqrt{5}}}{8}$

5. a–c. Answers will vary.
   d. To find g at any altitude, $g = \frac{4 \times 10^4}{(6.38 \times 10^6 + h)^2}$ m/sec^2, where h is the distance above sea level.

(continued)

2 "Pseudotrigonometric" Functions

Define the functions psin, pcos, ptan, and psec for all real numbers x as follows.

$\text{psin}\, x = 2^{x-1} - 2^{-x-1}$ $\quad \text{pcos}\, x = 2^{x-1} + 2^{-x-1}$

$\text{ptan}\, x = \frac{2^{2x} - 1}{2^{2x} + 1}$ $\quad \text{psec}\, x = \frac{2^{x+1}}{2^{2x} + 1}$

a. Prove the following identities:
  i. "Pseudo-Pythagorean identity".
  $\text{pcos}^2 x - \text{psin}^2 x = 1$
  ii. Quotient identity: $\frac{\text{psin}\, x}{\text{pcos}\, x} = \text{ptan}\, x$
  iii. Reciprocal identity: $\frac{1}{\text{pcos}\, x} = \text{psec}\, x$

b. Define pcot and pcsc, and prove some identities which involve them and are similar to those in part **a**.

c. Prove the addition identities.
  i. $\text{psin}\,(x + y) = \text{psin}\, x \,\text{pcos}\, y + \text{pcos}\, x \,\text{psin}\, y$
  ii. $\text{pcos}\,(x + y) = \text{pcos}\, x \,\text{pcos}\, y + \text{psin}\, x \,\text{psin}\, y$
  iii. $\text{ptan}\,(x + y) = \frac{\text{ptan}\, x + \text{ptan}\, y}{1 + \text{ptan}\, x \,\text{ptan}\, y}$

d. Prove other pseudotrigonometric identities that are analogous to trigonometric identities you have seen in the chapter.

3 Modeling Weather

Many weather conditions, such as temperature, vary throughout the year in a way that can be modeled by a sine function.

a. Use your library or the weather bureau to get information on average monthly high and low temperatures for your area. Graph the yearly cycle of these averages.

b. Find equations for sine functions h and ℓ that approximate each graph.

c. To show how well your function h models the temperatures in your area, compare the real data with the approximate values. Graph the absolute and actual errors for each month. Are there any general trends?

4 Rational and Radical Expressions for Sines and Cosines

In this chapter, the sines and cosines of several acute angles were expressed in terms of rational numbers and radicals. It also happens that $\cos 36° = \frac{\sqrt{5}+1}{4}$. With this additional information, use the sum and difference formulas, as well as the formulas for $\sin 2x$ and $\cos 2x$, to express $\sin x°$, where x is an integer between 0 and 90, in terms of rational numbers and radicals for as many values of x as possible.

5 Gravity

Refer to Question 44 in the Chapter Review on page 402.

a. Determine the acceleration due to gravity at your latitude.

b. Using an identity for $\sin 2\theta$, rewrite this expression as a polynomial in terms of $\sin \theta$.

c. Using the Quadratic Formula, find the latitude at which $g = 9.8$ m/s^2. How well does your answer agree with that found in part **a** of Question 44?

d. Through other sources, find out what further modifications may be necessary to determine g at high altitudes and at very low altitudes.

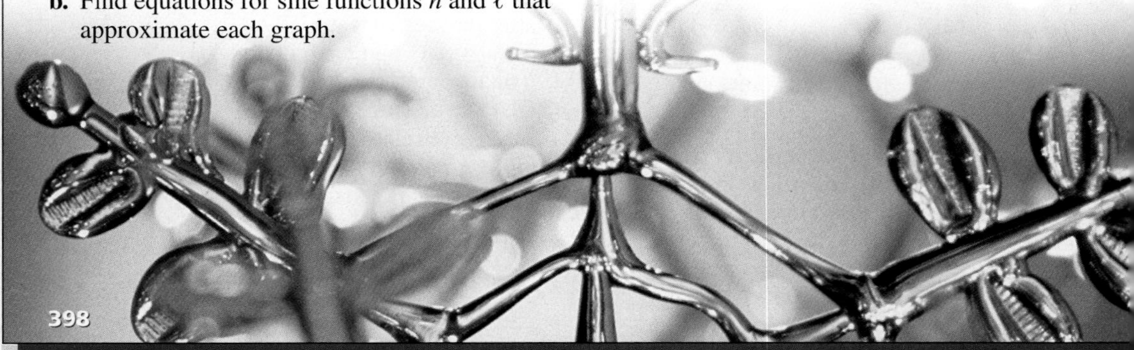

2. a.
  i. $\text{pcos}^2 x - \text{psin}^2 x = (2^{x-1} + 2^{-x-1})^2 - (2^{x-1} - 2^{-x-1})^2 = 2^{2x-2} + 2^{-1} + 2^{-2x-2} - 2^{2x-2} + 2^{-1} - 2^{-2x-2} = 2(2^{-1}) = 1$

  ii. $\frac{\text{psin}\, x}{\text{pcos}\, x} = \frac{2^{x-1} - 2^{-x-1}}{2^{-x-1} + 2^{-x-1}} = \frac{\frac{2^{x-1}}{2^{-x-1}} - \frac{2^{-x-1}}{2^{-x-1}}}{\frac{2^{x-1}}{2^{-x-1}} + \frac{2^{-x-1}}{2^{-x-1}}} = \frac{2^{2x} - 1}{2^{2x} + 1} = \text{ptan}\, x$

  iii. $\frac{1}{\text{pcos}\, x} = \frac{1}{2^{x-1} + 2^{-x-1}} = \frac{\frac{1}{2^{-x-1}}}{\frac{2^{x-1}}{2^{-x-1}} + \frac{2^{-x-1}}{2^{-x-1}}} = \frac{2^{x+1}}{2^{2x} + 1} = \text{psec}\, x$

SUMMARY

The emphasis of this chapter is on proving or disproving trigonometric identities. A graph cannot prove that an equation is an identity, but it can indicate when an equation is not an identity. When a graph suggests that a proposed identity is valid, other techniques are needed to provide an algebraic proof. These techniques include transforming one side of the identity to obtain the other, transforming each side of the identity separately to obtain identical expressions, using a previously known identity to obtain the desired identity, and working with reversible steps from the identity to be proved to a known identity.

Several important identities were proved in this chapter. These form the basis for proofs of many other identities. You should memorize the following identities if you have not already done so.

$$\cos(\alpha + \beta) = \cos\alpha\cos\beta - \sin\alpha\sin\beta$$
$$\sin(\alpha + \beta) = \sin\alpha\cos\beta + \cos\alpha\sin\beta$$

The following identities are used frequently. You should either learn them by heart or be able to derive them quickly when you need them.

$$\cos 2\alpha = \cos^2\alpha - \sin^2\alpha$$
$$\sin 2\alpha = 2\sin\alpha\cos\alpha$$
$$\tan(\alpha + \beta) = \frac{\tan\alpha + \tan\beta}{1 - \tan\alpha\tan\beta}$$

By replacing β by $-\beta$, you can obtain formulas for $\cos(\alpha - \beta)$, $\sin(\alpha - \beta)$, and $\tan(\alpha - \beta)$. These identities can be used to express values of trigonometric functions in terms of rational numbers and radicals. They also explain why certain graphs are sinusoidal. The functions defined by

$$y = b\sin\left(\frac{x - h}{a}\right) + k \text{ or } y = b\cos\left(\frac{x - h}{a}\right) + k$$

are rubberband transformation images of $y = \sin x$ or $y = \cos x$ and have amplitude $|b|$, period $2\pi|a|$, phase shift h, and vertical shift k.

By restricting the domains of the trigonometric functions, it is possible to define their inverses in such a way that the inverses are also functions. In particular,

$\cos^{-1} x$ is the unique number θ in the interval $0 \le \theta \le \pi$ whose cosine is x,

$\sin^{-1} x$ is the unique number θ in the interval $-\frac{\pi}{2} \le \theta \le \frac{\pi}{2}$ whose sine is x,

$\tan^{-1} x$ is the unique number θ in the interval $-\frac{\pi}{2} < \theta < \frac{\pi}{2}$ whose tangent is x.

The graphs of the inverse trigonometric functions are obtained by reflecting the graphs of the restricted trigonometric functions over the line $y = x$.

Trigonometric equations and inequalities can be solved using identities and algebraic techniques with which you are already familiar. They can then be applied to solve a wide variety of problems.

VOCABULARY

Below are the most important terms and phrases for this chapter. You should be able to give a general description and a specific example of each and a precise definition for those marked with an asterisk (*).

Lesson 6-1
*identity
domain of an identity

Lesson 6-3
sinusoidal curve

Lesson 6-4
*identity for $\cos(\alpha + \beta)$
identity for $\cos(\alpha - \beta)$
cofunction identity

Lesson 6-5
*identity for $\sin(\alpha + \beta)$
identity for $\sin(\alpha - \beta)$
identity for $\tan(\alpha + \beta)$
identity for $\tan(\alpha - \beta)$

Lesson 6-6
identities for $\cos 2x$
identity for $\sin 2x$
double-angle identities
half-angle identities

Lesson 6-7
*inverse cosine of x, $\cos^{-1} x$
*inverse sine of x, $\sin^{-1} x$
*inverse tangent of x, $\tan^{-1} x$

Summary

The Summary gives an overview of the entire chapter and provides an opportunity for students to consider the material as a whole. Thus, the Summary can be used to help students relate and unify the concepts presented in the chapter.

Vocabulary

Terms, symbols, and properties are listed by lesson to provide a checklist of concepts a student must know. Emphasize to students that they should read the vocabulary list carefully before starting the Progress Self-Test. If students do not understand the meaning of a term, they should refer back to the indicated lesson.

2. b. $\text{pcot } x = \frac{\text{pcos } x}{\text{psin } x} = \frac{2^{x-1} + 2^{-x-1}}{2^{x-1} - 2^{-x-1}} = \frac{2^{2x}+1}{2^{2x}-1}$, and $\text{pcsc } x = \frac{1}{\text{psin } x} = \frac{1}{2^{x-1} - 2^{-x-1}} = \frac{2^{x+1}}{2^{2x}-1}$.
Sample identity: $\text{pcot}^2 x - 1 = \text{pcsc}^2 x$.
$\text{pcot}^2 x - 1 = \left(\frac{2^{2x}+1}{2^{2x}-1}\right)^2 - 1 = \frac{2^{4x} + 2^{2x+1} + 1 - 2^{4x} + 2^{2x+1} - 1}{(2^{2x}-1)^2} = \frac{2^{2(x+1)}}{(2^{2x}-1)^2} = \left(\frac{2^{x+1}}{2^{2x}-1}\right)^2 = \text{pcsc}^2 x$

2. c. i. $\text{psin } x \text{ pcos } y + \text{pcos } x \text{ psin } y = (2^{x-1} - 2^{-x-1})(2^{y-1} + 2^{-y-1}) + (2^{x-1} + 2^{-x-1}) \cdot (2^{y-1} - 2^{-y-1})$
$= 2^{x+y-2} + 2^{x-y-2} - 2^{-x+y-2} - 2^{-x-y-2} + 2^{x+y-2} - 2^{x-y-2} + 2^{-x+y-2} - 2^{-x-y-2}$
$= 2^{x+y-2} - 2^{-x-y-2} + 2^{x+y-2} - 2^{-x-y-2} = 2^{(x+y)-1} - 2^{-(x+y)-1} = \text{psin}(x+y)$

ii. $\text{pcos } x \text{ pcos } y + \text{psin } x \text{ psin } y$
$= (2^{x-1} + 2^{-x-1})(2^{y-1} + 2^{-y-1}) + (2^{x-1} - 2^{-x-1}) \cdot (2^{y-1} - 2^{-y-1})$
$= 2^{x+y-2} + 2^{x-y-2} + 2^{-x+y-2} + 2^{-x-y-2} + 2^{x+y-2} - 2^{x-y-2} - 2^{-x+y-2} + 2^{-x-y-2}$
$= 2^{x+y-2} + 2^{-x-y-2} + 2^{x+y-2} + 2^{-x-y-2} = 2^{(x+y)-1} + 2^{-(x+y)-1} = \text{pcos}(x+y)$

2c–2d. See Additional Answers at the back of this book.

Progress Self-Test

For the development of mathematical competence, feedback and correction, along with the opportunity to practice, are necessary. The Progress Self-Test provides the opportunity for feedback and correction; the Chapter Review provides additional opportunities and practice. We cannot overemphasize the importance of these end-of-chapter materials. It is at this point that the material "gels" for many students, allowing them to solidify skills and understanding. In general, student performance should be markedly improved after these pages.

Assign the Progress Self-Test as a one-night assignment. Worked-out *solutions* for all questions are in the Selected Answers section of the student book. Encourage students to take the Progress Self-Test honestly, grade themselves, and then be prepared to discuss the test in class.

Advise students to pay special attention to those Chapter Review questions (pages 401–403) that correspond to questions missed on the Progress Self-Test.

Additional Answers

1. $-\sqrt{1-\left(\frac{x}{3}\right)^2}$ or $-\frac{1}{3}\sqrt{9-x^2}$

7.

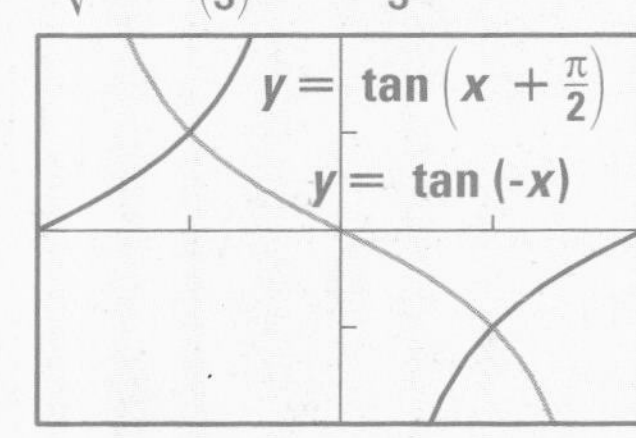

$-\frac{\pi}{2} \le x \le \frac{\pi}{2}$, x-scale $= \frac{\pi}{4}$
$-2 \le y \le 2$, y-scale $= 1$

not an identity; Counterexample: Let $x = -\frac{\pi}{6}$. Then $\tan\left(-\frac{\pi}{6} + \frac{\pi}{2}\right) = \sqrt{3}$, but $\tan\left(-\frac{\pi}{6}\right) = -\frac{1}{\sqrt{3}}$.

PROGRESS SELF-TEST

Take this test as you would take a test in class. Then check the test yourself using the solutions at the back of the book.

1, 7–11, 16) See margin.

For Questions 1–6, do not use a calculator.

1. Suppose $\pi < \alpha < \frac{3\pi}{2}$ and $\cos \alpha = \frac{x}{3}$. Find $\sin \alpha$.
2. *Multiple choice.* b
   $\cos \frac{x}{3} \cos \frac{\pi}{6} + \sin \frac{x}{3} \sin \frac{\pi}{6} =$ ___?___
   (a) $\cos\left(\frac{\pi}{3} + \frac{\pi}{6}\right)$ (b) $\cos\left(\frac{\pi}{3} - \frac{\pi}{6}\right)$
   (c) $\sin\left(\frac{\pi}{3} + \frac{\pi}{6}\right)$ (d) $\sin\left(\frac{\pi}{3} - \frac{\pi}{6}\right)$
3. Evaluate $\sin\left(\cos^{-1} \frac{1}{2}\right)$. $\frac{\sqrt{3}}{2}$
4. Determine $\cos\left(\tan^{-1} \frac{2}{3}\right)$. $\frac{3}{\sqrt{13}}$

In 5 and 6, use an appropriate trigonometric identity to express the following in terms of rational numbers and radicals.

5. $\cos \frac{7\pi}{12}$ $\frac{\sqrt{2}-\sqrt{6}}{4}$
6. $\sin 15°$ $\frac{\sqrt{6}-\sqrt{2}}{4}$
7. Use an automatic grapher to determine whether $\tan\left(x + \frac{\pi}{2}\right) = \tan(-x)$ appears to be an identity. If it does, prove that it is indeed an identity. If not, find a counterexample.

In 8 and 9, prove the identity and determine its domain.

8. $\cos x + \tan x \sin x = \sec x$
9. $\frac{\sin(\alpha + \beta)}{\cos \alpha \cos \beta} = \tan \alpha + \tan \beta$
10. Solve $2 \sin^2 x - \sin x - 1 = 0$ over the given domain for x.
    a. $0 \le x \le 2\pi$ **b.** the set of real numbers
11. The sinusoidal curve graphed below is the image of a rubberband transformation of the graph of $y = \sin x$.
    a. Find the transformation.
    b. Find an equation for the graph.

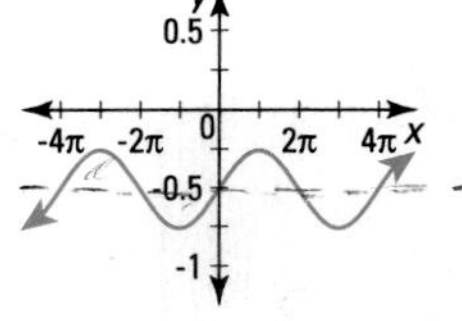

12. Give the parametric equations for the ellipse graphed at the right.
    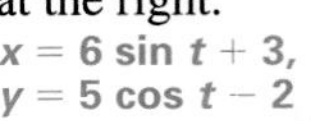
    $x = 6 \sin t + 3$,
    $y = 5 \cos t - 2$

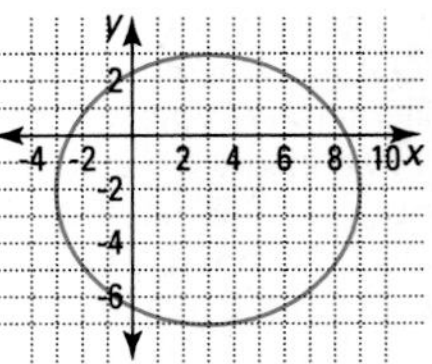

13. When light travels from one medium to another, the angle that the light ray makes with the vertical changes. This bending of light where the two mediums intersect is called *refraction* and is governed by Snell's law:
    $$n_1 \sin \theta_1 = n_2 \sin \theta_2,$$
    where n_1 and n_2 are the *indices of refraction* in the two mediums. Suppose light in air ($n = 1.0$) traveling at an angle of 20° from the vertical hits water ($n = 1.33$). In the water, the light ray will make what angle with the vertical? ≈ 14.9°

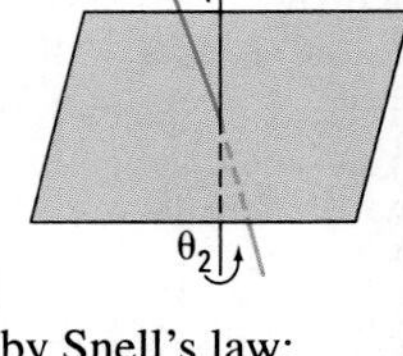

14. A 150-ft radio tower is held in place by two guy wires. Find a formula for the angle θ the guy wire makes with the ground in terms of its distance d from the base of the tower. $\theta = \tan^{-1}\left(\frac{150}{d}\right)$

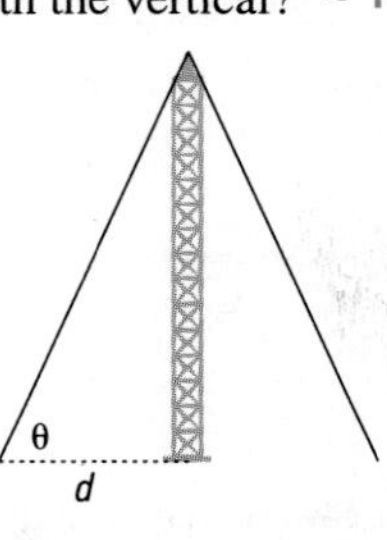

In 15 and 16, refer to the graph below.

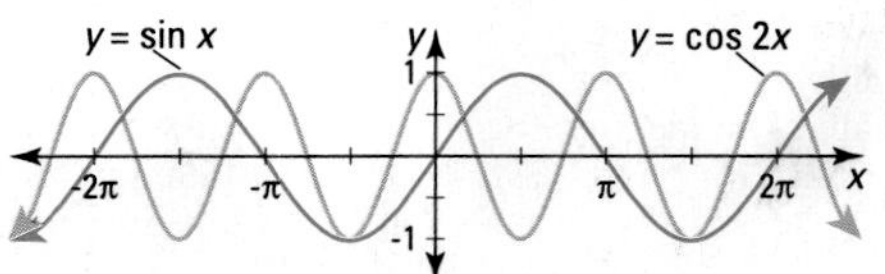

15. In the interval $0 \le x \le \frac{\pi}{2}$, determine exactly where $\cos 2x = \sin x$. $x = \frac{\pi}{6}$
16. On the interval $-2\pi \le x \le 0$, determine where $\sin x \le \cos 2x$.

8.

	$\cos x + \tan x \sin x$	$\sec x$	
Def. of tan	$= \cos x + \frac{\sin^2 x}{\cos x}$	$= \frac{1}{\cos x}$	def. of sec
Add fractions	$= \frac{\cos^2 x + \sin^2 x}{\cos x}$		
Pyth. Identity	$= \frac{1}{\cos x}$		

$\therefore \cos x + \tan x \sin x = \sec x$

Domain: $x \ne (2n + 1)\frac{\pi}{2}$, n an integer

9. See Additional Answers at the back of this book.

10. a. $x = \frac{7\pi}{6}, \frac{11\pi}{6}$, or $\frac{\pi}{2}$
    b. $x = \frac{7\pi}{6} + 2\pi n, \frac{11\pi}{6} + 2\pi n, \frac{\pi}{2} + 2\pi n$, n an integer
11. a. $T_{2,-1/2}$
    b. $y = \sin\left(\frac{1}{2}x\right) - \frac{1}{2}$
16. $-\frac{7\pi}{6} \le x \le 0$ or $-2\pi \le x \le -\frac{11\pi}{6}$

CHAPTER REVIEW

Questions on SPUR Objectives

SPUR stands for **S**kills, **P**roperties, **U**ses, and **R**epresentations. The Chapter Review questions are grouped according to the SPUR Objectives for this chapter.

SKILLS DEAL WITH THE PROCEDURES USED TO GET ANSWERS.

4–6, 8–12, 17, 21–24) See margin.

Objective A: *Without a calculator, use trigonometric identities to express values of trigonometric functions in terms of rational numbers and radicals.* *(Lessons 6-4, 6-5, 6-6)*

In 1–3, suppose x is in the interval $\pi < x < \frac{3\pi}{2}$ and $\sin x = \frac{-3}{8}$. Use trigonometric identities to find each value.

1. $\cos x$ $-\frac{\sqrt{55}}{8}$ **2.** $\tan x$ $\frac{3}{\sqrt{55}}$ **3.** $\csc x$ $-\frac{8}{3}$

In 4–6, use appropriate identities to express the following in terms of rational numbers and radicals.

4. $\sin \frac{3\pi}{8}$ **5.** $\cos \frac{\pi}{8}$ **6.** $\tan \frac{\pi}{12}$

7. *Multiple choice.* b

$\cos \frac{\pi}{4} \cos \frac{\pi}{6} - \sin \frac{\pi}{4} \sin \frac{\pi}{6} =$ _?_

(a) $\sin\left(\frac{\pi}{4} + \frac{\pi}{6}\right)$ (b) $\cos\left(\frac{\pi}{4} + \frac{\pi}{6}\right)$

(c) $\sin\left(\frac{\pi}{4} - \frac{\pi}{6}\right)$ (d) $\cos\left(\frac{\pi}{4} - \frac{\pi}{6}\right)$

In 8–11, suppose x is in the interval $\frac{\pi}{2} < x < \pi$ with $\cos x = -\frac{1}{3}$ and y is in the interval $0 < y < \frac{\pi}{2}$ with $\sin y = \frac{2}{5}$. Use this information to find each value.

8. $\cos(x + y)$

9. $\sin(x - y)$

10. $\sin 2x$

11. $\sin \frac{x}{2}$

12. a. Use the identity for $\sin(x - y)$ to find $\sin \frac{5\pi}{12}$.

b. Use the identity $\cos 2x = 1 - 2\sin^2 x$ to find $\sin \frac{5\pi}{12}$.

c. Show that your answers to parts **a** and **b** are equal.

Objective B: *Evaluate inverse trigonometric functions with or without a calculator.* *(Lesson 6-7)*

In 13–16, find the exact value without using a calculator.

13. $\sin^{-1}\left(\frac{-\sqrt{2}}{2}\right)$ $-\frac{\pi}{4}$ **14.** $\cos^{-1} 1$ 0

15. $\sin(\tan^{-1} 1)$ $\frac{\sqrt{2}}{2}$ **16.** $\sin\left(\sin^{-1} \frac{-1}{2}\right)$ $-\frac{1}{2}$

17. Draw an appropriate triangle to determine $\sin\left(\cos^{-1} \frac{2}{5}\right)$.

Objective C: Solve trigonometric equations and inequalities algebraically. *(Lesson 6-8)*

In 18–20, solve over the interval $0 \le x \le 2\pi$.

18. $\cos x = \frac{1}{2}$ $x = \frac{\pi}{3}, \frac{5\pi}{3}$

19. $\tan x = -1$ $x = \frac{3\pi}{4}, \frac{7\pi}{4}$

20. $\sin x = \frac{-\sqrt{3}}{2}$ $x = \frac{4\pi}{3}, \frac{5\pi}{3}$

21. Solve over the set of real numbers: $(\sin x + 1)(\tan x - 1) = 0$.

22. Solve $2\sin^2 x - \cos x - 1 = 0$ over the indicated domain.

a. $0 \le x \le 2\pi$

b. the set of real numbers

23. Use an automatic grapher to determine the values of x in the interval $0 \le x \le 2\pi$ that satisfy $.8 \le \cos x$.

24. Find the exact solutions of the inequality $\cos x(\cos x - 2) < 0$ in the interval $0 \le x \le 2\pi$.

25. Solve $\cos 2x + 7\sin x - 4 > 0$ given that $0 \le x \le 2\pi$. $\frac{\pi}{6} < x < \frac{5\pi}{6}$

Chapter 6 Review

Resources

From the ***Teacher's Resource File***

- Answer Master for Chapter 6 Review
- Assessment Sourcebook: Chapter 6 Test, Forms A–D; Chapter 6 Test, Cumulative Form; Comprehensive Test, Chapter 1–6

Additional Resources

- TestWorks CD-ROM

The main objectives for the chapter are organized in the Chapter Review under the four types of understanding this book promotes—Skills, Properties, Uses, and Representations.

Whereas end-of-chapter material may be considered optional in some texts, in UCSMP *Precalculus and Discrete Mathematics* we have selected these objectives and questions with the expectation that they will be covered. Students should be able to answer these questions with about 85% accuracy after studying the chapter.

You may assign these questions over a single night to help students prepare for a test the next day, or you may assign the questions over a two-day period. If you work the questions over two days, then we recommend assigning the *evens* for homework the first night so that students get feedback in class the next day, then assigning the *odds* the night before the test, because answers are provided to the odd-numbered questions.

Additional Answers

4. $\frac{\sqrt{2 + \sqrt{2}}}{2}$ 5. $\frac{\sqrt{2 + \sqrt{2}}}{2}$

6. $2 - \sqrt{3}$ 8. $-\frac{4\sqrt{2} + \sqrt{21}}{15}$

9. $\frac{2\sqrt{42} + \sqrt{2}}{15}$ 10. $-\frac{4\sqrt{2}}{9}$ 11. $\frac{\sqrt{6}}{3}$

12. a. $x = \frac{2}{3}\pi$, $y = \frac{\pi}{4}$, $\sin \frac{5\pi}{12} = \frac{\sqrt{6} + \sqrt{2}}{4}$

b. $x = \frac{\sqrt{\sqrt{3} + 2}}{2}$

c. Does $\left(\frac{\sqrt{\sqrt{3} + 2}}{2}\right)^2 = \left(\frac{\sqrt{6} + \sqrt{2}}{4}\right)^2$?

Does $\frac{\sqrt{3} + 2}{4} = \frac{8 + 4\sqrt{3}}{16}$?

Does $\frac{\sqrt{3} + 2}{4} = \frac{2 + \sqrt{3}}{4}$? Yes

17. $\frac{\sqrt{21}}{5}$

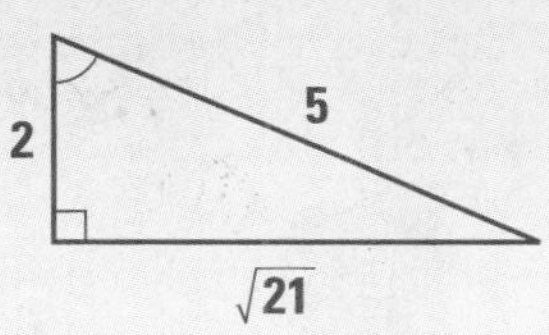

21. $x = -\frac{\pi}{2} + 2\pi n, \frac{\pi}{4} + \pi n$, n an integer

22. a. $x = \frac{\pi}{3}, \pi, \frac{5\pi}{3}$

b. $x = \frac{\pi}{3} + 2\pi n, (2n + 1)\pi$, or $\frac{5\pi}{3} + 2\pi n$, n an integer

23. $0 \le x \le 0.644$ or $5.640 \le x \le 2\pi$, approximately

24. $0 \le x < \frac{\pi}{2}, \frac{3\pi}{2} < x \le 2\pi$

 CHAPTER SIX

It is effective to ask students which questions they still do not understand and use the day or days as a total class discussion of the material which the class finds most difficult.

Assessment

Evaluation The Assessment Sourcebook provides six forms of the Chapter 6 Test. Forms A and B present parallel versions in a short-answer format. Forms C and D offer performance assessment. The fifth test is Chapter 6 Test, Cumulative Form. About 50% of this test covers Chapter 6, 25% of it covers Chapter 5, and 25% of it covers earlier chapters. In addition to these tests, Comprehensive Test Chapters 1–6 gives roughly equal attention to all chapters covered thus far.

For information on grading, see *General Teaching Suggestions: Grading* in the *Professional Sourcebook,* which begins on page T20 in this Teacher's Edition.

Feedback After students have taken the test for Chapter 6 and you have scored the results, return the tests to students for discussion. Class discussion of the questions that caused trouble for the most students can be very effective in identifying and clarifying misunderstandings. You might want to have them write down the items they missed and work, either in groups or at home, to correct them. It is important for students to receive feedback on every chapter test, and we recommend that students see and correct their mistakes before proceeding too far into the next chapter.

PROPERTIES DEAL WITH THE PRINCIPLES BEHIND THE MATHEMATICS.

31–44) See margin.

Objective D: *Prove trigonometric identities and identify their domains.* *(Lessons 6-2, 6-4, 6-5, 6-6)*

In 26–30, complete each blank so that the resulting equation is an identity.

26. $\cos^2 x + \sin^2 x =$ __?__ 1

27. $\cos x \sin y - \sin x \cos y =$ __?__ $\sin(y - x)$

28. $\sin 2x =$ __?__ $2 \sin x \cos x$

29. $\cos^2 x - 1 =$ __?__ $-\sin^2 x$

30. $\sin(x + y) =$ __?__ $\sin x \cos y + \cos x \sin y$

In 31–38, prove the identity and identify its domain.

31. $\cos\left(\frac{3\pi}{2} + x\right) = \sin x$

32. $\sec x \cot x = \csc x$

33. $\sin\left(\frac{\pi}{2} + x\right) = \cos x$

34. $\frac{1}{1 + \cos\alpha} + \frac{1}{1 - \cos\alpha} = 2\csc^2\alpha$

35. $\cos(\alpha - \beta) - \cos(\alpha + \beta) = 2 \sin\alpha \sin\beta$

36. $\sec x + \cot x \csc x = \sec x \csc^2 x$

37. $\cos 4x = \cos^4 x - 6\cos^2 x \sin^2 x + \sin^4 x$

38. $\tan^2 x = \frac{1 - \cos 2x}{1 + \cos 2x}$

USES DEAL WITH APPLICATIONS OF MATHEMATICS IN REAL SITUATIONS.

Objective E: *Solve problems using inverse trigonometric functions.* *(Lesson 6-7)*

39. A child, holding the spool of string 3 feet above ground, flies a kite on a 200-foot string. Find a formula for the angle θ that the string makes with the horizontal in terms of the height of the kite above the ground.

dragonfly kite

40. A ship travels on a bearing of θ degrees, where θ is measured clockwise from due north. When the ship has traveled 100 km north of its original position, describe how its bearing depends on its easterly position.

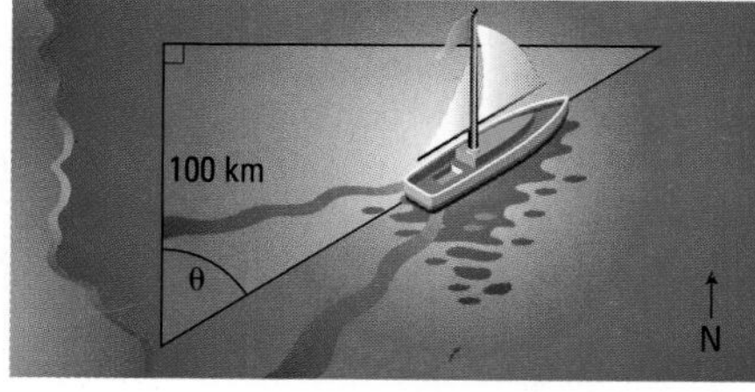

41. A weight is placed at the end of a spring so that, at rest, the weight is 15 cm from the top of its stand. It is then shoved upward so that the spring is compressed 7 cm. When released, the weight oscillates up and down with a displacement of ±7 cm from its equilibrium position. If the time for one complete oscillation is .4 sec, then the equation $d = 7 \cos 5\pi t$ gives the distance, in centimeters, of the spring from its equilibrium position. Solve this equation for t.

Objective F: *Use trigonometric equations and inequalities to solve applied problems.* *(Lesson 6-8)*

In 42 and 43, a quarterback throws a football during a game with an initial velocity of 64 ft/sec. The range is approximated by the equation from Lesson 6-6: $R = \frac{v_0^2}{32} \sin 2\theta$.

42. If the quarterback wants to make a 40-yard pass (120 ft), at approximately what angle should the football be thrown?

43. For what angle values is the range more than 30 yards (90 ft)?

44. In many situations, the value 9.8 m/sec^2 is used for acceleration due to gravity. Actually, the equation $g = 9.78049(1 + 0.005288 \sin^2\theta - 0.000006 \sin^2 2\theta)$ estimates the acceleration g due to gravity (in m/sec^2) at sea level as a function of the latitude θ in degrees.

a. Use an automatic grapher to estimate the latitude(s) at which g is 9.8 m/sec^2.

b. For what latitudes is the acceleration due to gravity greater than 9.81 m/sec^2.

Additional Answers

31. left side $= \cos\left(\frac{3\pi}{2} + x\right)$
$= \cos\frac{3\pi}{2}\cos x - \sin\frac{3\pi}{2}\sin x$ Identity for the Cosine of a sum
$= 0 - (-\sin x)$ Evaluating trig. functions
$= \sin x$ Multiplication
= right side
$\therefore \cos\left(\frac{3\pi}{2} + x\right) = \sin x$
Domain: all real numbers

32. left side
$= \sec x \cot x$
$= \frac{1}{\cos x} \cdot \frac{\cos x}{\sin x}$ Def. of secant and cotangent
$= \frac{1}{\sin x}$ Multiplication of fractions
$= \csc x$ Def. of cosecant
= right side
$\therefore \sec x \cot x = \csc x$
Domain: $x \neq \frac{n\pi}{2}$, n an integer

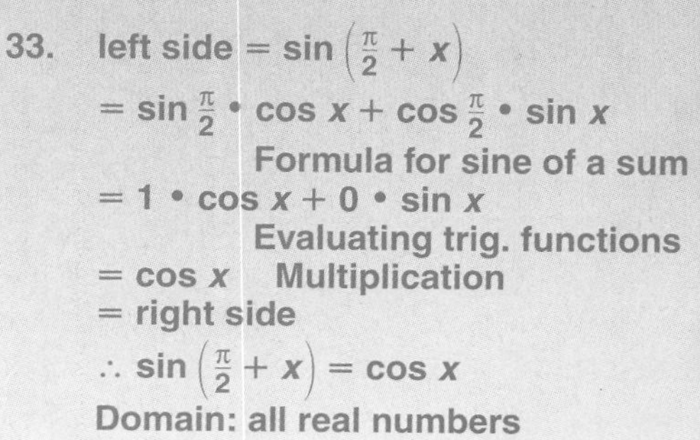

33. left side $= \sin\left(\frac{\pi}{2} + x\right)$
$= \sin\frac{\pi}{2} \cdot \cos x + \cos\frac{\pi}{2} \cdot \sin x$ Formula for sine of a sum
$= 1 \cdot \cos x + 0 \cdot \sin x$ Evaluating trig. functions
$= \cos x$ Multiplication
= right side
$\therefore \sin\left(\frac{\pi}{2} + x\right) = \cos x$
Domain: all real numbers

CHAPTER SIX

REPRESENTATIONS DEAL WITH PICTURES, GRAPHS, OR OBJECTS THAT ILLUSTRATE CONCEPTS.

45–49, 51–57, 58a) See margin.

Objective G: *Find an equation for the image of a graph under a transformation.* *(Lesson 6-3)*

In 45 and 46, find an equation for the graph at the right as an image of the given equation.

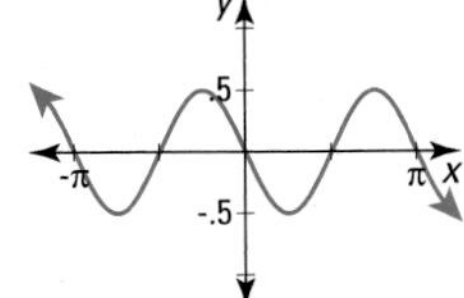

45. $y = \sin x$

46. $y = \cos x$

47. Consider the image of $y = \sin x$ under the rubberband transformation $T(x, y) = \left(\frac{x}{\pi} + \frac{1}{4}, 2y - 1\right)$.

a. Find an equation for the image.

b. Graph the image.

c. State the amplitude, period, phase shift, and vertical shift of the image.

48. The function f defined by $f(x) = \sin 4x$ is transformed so that the amplitude is 3 times that of f and the period is half the period of f.

a. Write the equation of the new function g.

b. Graph the new function.

49. The graph of $\begin{cases} x = \sin t \\ y = \cos t \end{cases}$ is transformed into the graph of $\left(\frac{x+7}{9}\right)^2 + \left(\frac{y-4}{6}\right)^2 = 1$. Give the parametric equations for the image graph.

50. Write parametric equations for the ellipse graphed at the right.

$x = 5 \sin t + 4$,
$y = 2 \cos t - 1$

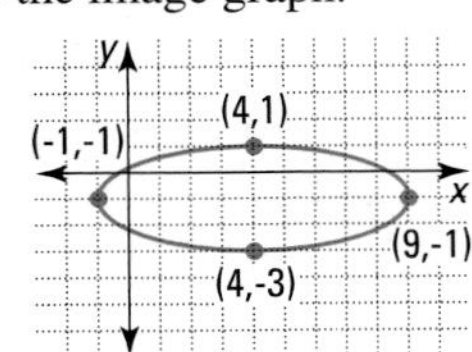

Objective H: *Use an automatic grapher to test proposed trigonometric identities.* *(Lessons 6-1, 6-2)*

In 51–53, use an automatic grapher to determine whether the proposed identity appears to be an identity. If it does, prove it algebraically. If not, give a counterexample.

51. $1 + \cot^2 x = \csc^2 x$

52. $\cos 2x = 2 \cos x$

53. $\tan(\pi + \gamma) = \tan \gamma$

54. Use an automatic grapher to determine over what domain $\cos x$, with x in radians, can be approximated by $f(x) = 1 - \frac{x^2}{2!} + \frac{x^4}{4!} + \frac{x^6}{6!}$ to within .01.

55. How can you use a graph to determine whether the proposed identity

$\sin(\alpha + \beta) = \sin \alpha \cos \beta - \cos \alpha \sin \beta$

is true? (Do not actually use the graph, just describe the procedure.)

56. a. Graph the function f with $f(x) = \sin x \sec x$.

b. What single trigonometric function has a similar graph?

c. What identity is suggested?

Objective I: *Use graphs to solve trigonometric equations and inequalities.* *(Lesson 6-8)*

57. a. Use an automatic grapher to find all solutions to $\sin x - \cos x = \frac{1}{2}$ (to the nearest tenth) over the interval $0 \le x \le 2\pi$.

b. Use your answer to part **a** to solve $\sin x - \cos x < \frac{1}{2}$.

58. Refer to the graph below of $y = 1.5$ and $y = \cos^2 x + 1$.

a. Solve $\cos^2 x + 1 = 1.5$ over the interval from -2π to 2π.

b. Solve the inequality $\cos^2 x + 1 < 1.5$ over the interval $0 < x < \pi$. $\frac{\pi}{4} < x < \frac{3\pi}{4}$

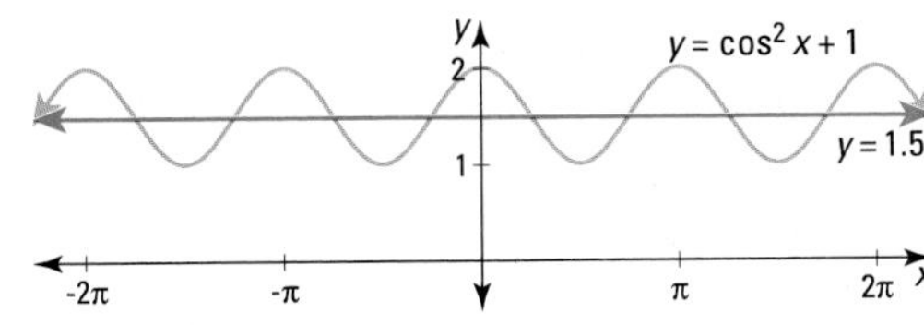

59. Solve $\tan x \le 0.8$ over the interval $0 \le x < \frac{\pi}{2}$. $0 \le x \le 0.675$

39. $\theta = \sin^{-1}\left(\frac{h-3}{200}\right)$, where h = height of the kite above the ground in feet.
40. $\theta = \tan^{-1}\left(\frac{x}{100}\right)$
41. $t = \frac{1}{5\pi}\cos^{-1}\left(\frac{d}{3}\right)$
42. $\approx 34.8°$ or $55.2°$
43. $22.3° \le \theta \le 67.7°$, approximately
44. a. $\theta = \pm 38.0°$
    b. $\theta < -49.1°$ or $\theta > 49.1°$, approximately
45. $y = -\frac{1}{2}\sin(2x)$
46. $y = -\frac{1}{2}\cos\left(2x - \frac{\pi}{2}\right)$
47. a. $y = 2\sin\left(\pi x - \frac{\pi}{4}\right) - 1$
    b.

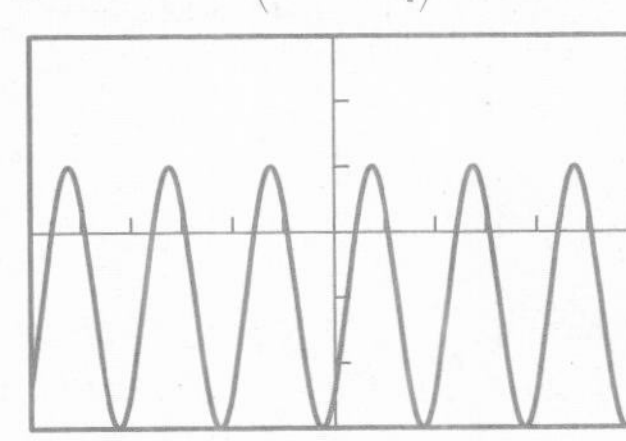

$-6 \le x \le 6$, x-scale = 1
$-3 \le y \le 3$, y-scale = 1

c. amplitude = 2, period = 2, phase shift = $\frac{\pi}{4}$

48. a. $3 \sin(8x)$
    b.

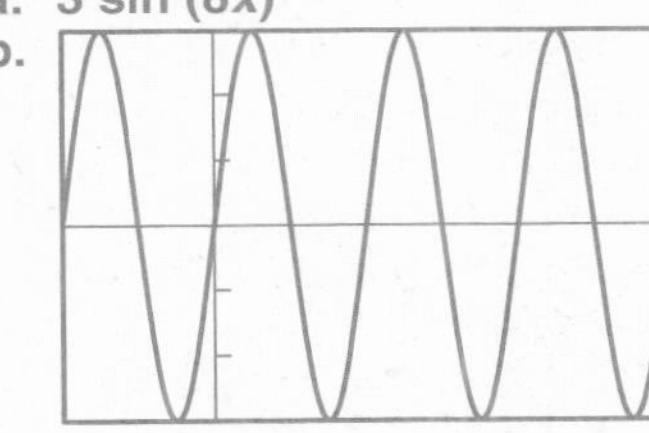

$-\frac{\pi}{4} \le x \le \frac{3\pi}{4}$, x-scale = $\frac{\pi}{4}$
$-3 \le y \le 3$, y-scale = 1

49. $x = 9 \sin t - 7$, $y = 6 \cos t + 4$
52. not an identity; Counterexample: Let $x = 0$. Then $\cos(2 \cdot 0) = 1$, but $2\cos(0) = 2$.

34. left side

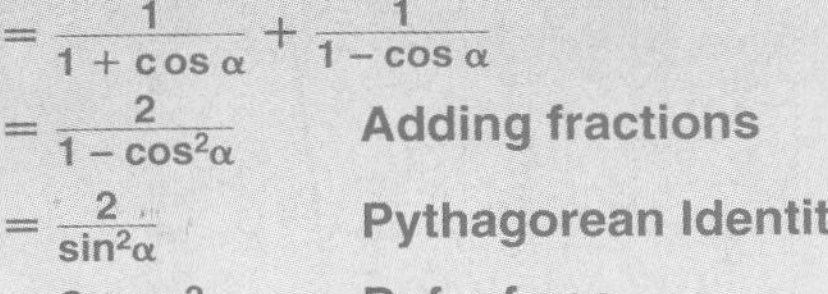

$= \frac{1}{1 + \cos\alpha} + \frac{1}{1 - \cos\alpha}$

$= \frac{2}{1 - \cos^2\alpha}$ Adding fractions

$= \frac{2}{\sin^2\alpha}$ Pythagorean Identity

$= 2\csc^2\alpha$ Def. of csc

= right side

$\therefore \frac{1}{1 + \cos\alpha} + \frac{1}{1 - \cos\alpha} = 2\csc^2\alpha$

Domain: $\alpha \ne n\pi$, n an integer

35. left side

$= \cos(\alpha - \beta) - \cos(\alpha + \beta)$

$= \cos\alpha\cos\beta + \sin\alpha\sin\beta - \cos\alpha\cos\beta + \sin\alpha\sin\beta$ Sum and difference identities

$= 2\sin\alpha\sin\beta$ Addition

= right side

$\therefore \cos(\alpha - \beta) - \cos(\alpha + \beta) = 2\sin\alpha\sin\beta$

38. right side $= \frac{1 - \cos 2x}{1 + \cos 2x}$

$= \frac{1 - (1 - 2\sin^2 x)}{1 + (2\cos^2 x - 1)}$ Identities for cos 2x

$= \frac{2\sin^2 x}{2\cos^2 x}$ Simplification

$= \tan^2 x$ Simplification; def. of tan

= left side $\therefore \frac{1 - \cos 2x}{1 + \cos 2x} = \tan^2 x$

Domain: $x \ne \frac{\pi}{2} + n\pi$, n an integer

36, 37, 51, 53–58a. See Additional Answers at the back of this book.

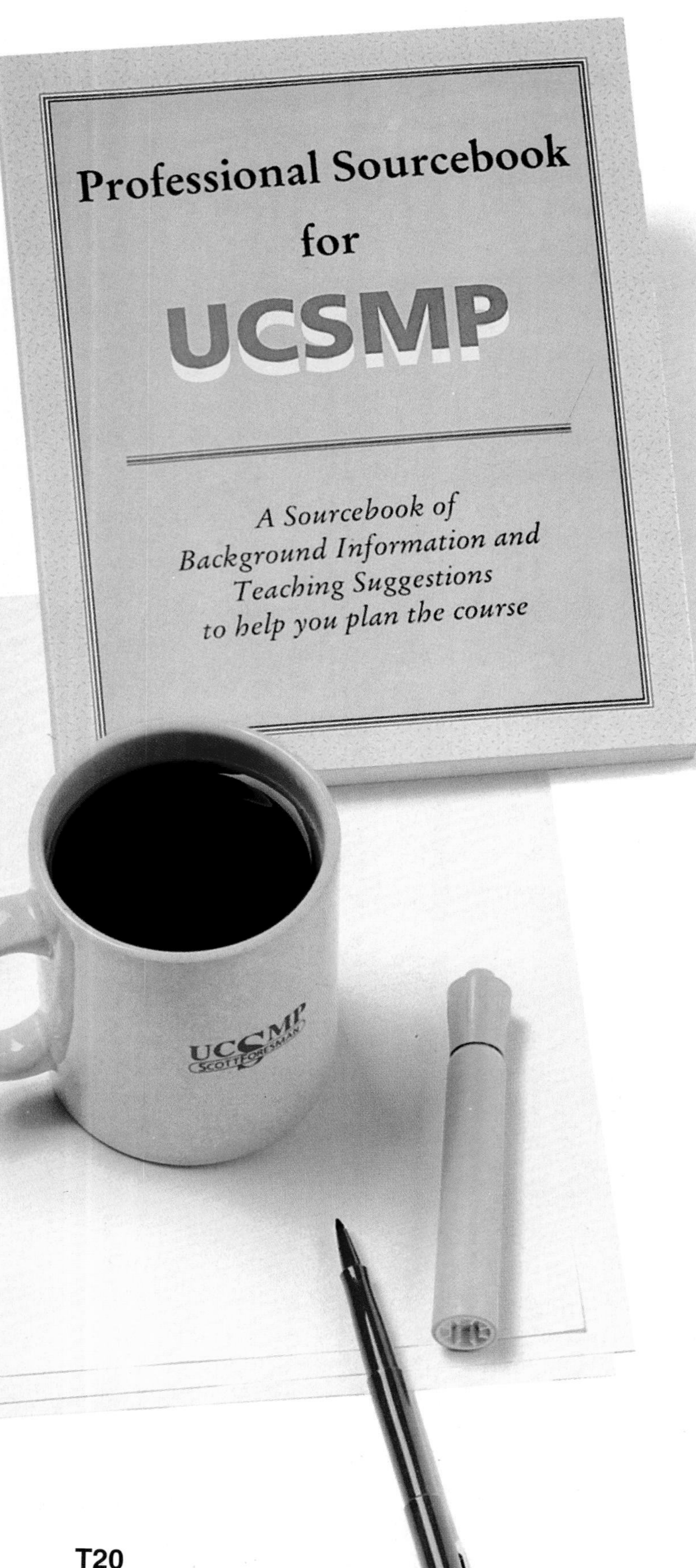

Table of Contents

Professional Sourcebook: SECTION **1** OVERVIEW OF UCSMP

The Reasons for UCSMP

Recommendations for Change

The mathematics curriculum has undergone changes in every country of the world throughout this century. This is as a result of an increasing number of students staying in school longer, the need for a greater number of technically competent workers and citizens, and major advances in mathematics itself. In the last twenty years, these developments have accelerated due to the widespread appearance of computers with their unprecedented abilities to handle and display information.

In the last 100 years, national groups have examined the curriculum periodically in light of these changes in society. A study of reports before 1970 can be found in *A History of Mathematics Education in the United States and Canada,* the 30th Yearbook of the National Council of Teachers of Mathematics, 1970. A summary of reports from 1970 to 1984 can be found in Z. Usiskin, "We Need Another Revolution in Secondary School Mathematics," in *The Secondary School Mathematics Curriculum,* the 1985 Yearbook of NCTM.

The most recent era of reports can be said to have begun in the years 1975–1980, with the publication of reports by various national mathematics organizations calling attention to serious problems in the education of our youth. These reports from inside mathematics education were joined by governmental and private reports through the 1980s and into the 1990s decrying the state of American education and providing broad recommendations for school practice. Two of the most notable of these reports for their specific remarks about mathematics education appeared in 1983, the year that the University of Chicago School Mathematics Project (UCSMP) began.

1983: National Commission on Excellence in Education. *A Nation At Risk.*

> The teaching of mathematics in high school should equip graduates to: (a) understand geometric and algebraic concepts; (b) understand elementary probability and statistics; (c) apply mathematics in everyday situations; and (d) estimate, approximate, measure, and test the accuracy of their calculations.
>
> In addition to the traditional sequence of studies available for college-bound students, new, equally demanding mathematics curricula need to be developed for those who do not plan to continue their formal education immediately. (p. 25)

1983: College Board (Project EQuality). *Academic Preparation for College: What Students Need to Know and Be Able to Do.*

> All students (college-bound or not) should have:
>
> The ability to apply mathematical techniques in the solution of real-life problems and to recognize when to apply those techniques.
>
> Familiarity with the language, notation, and deductive nature of mathematics and the ability to express quantitative ideas with precision.
>
> The ability to use computers and calculators.
>
> Familiarity with the basic concepts of statistics and statistical reasoning.
>
> Knowledge in considerable depth and detail of algebra, geometry, and functions. (p. 20)

The specific remarks about school mathematics in these documents for the most part mirror what appeared in the earlier reports. Thus, given what seemed to be a broad consensus on the problems and desirable changes in pre-college mathematics instruction, it was decided, at the outset of UCSMP, that UCSMP would not attempt to form its own set of recommendations, but undertake the task of translating the existing recommendations into the reality of classrooms and schools. It was also decided that UCSMP would look at the best that other countries had to offer, and so in 1983 UCSMP began to translate materials from Japan and some countries of Eastern Europe known for excellence in mathematics education.

Universities for many years have recognized that mathematics encompasses far more than algebra, geometry, and analysis. The term *mathematical sciences* is an umbrella designation which includes traditional mathematics as well as a number of other disciplines. The largest of these other disciplines today are statistics, computer science, and applied mathematics, not coincidentally the areas in which recent reports have recommended greater emphasis. In 1983, the Conference Board of the Mathematical Sciences produced a report, *The Mathematical Sciences Curriculum: What Is Still Fundamental and What Is Not.* The UCSMP Grades 7–12 curriculum is the first mathematical sciences curriculum for average students in the United States.

In the middle 1980s, as the first edition of UCSMP secondary textbooks were being developed and tested, the Second International Mathematics Study (SIMS) verified our conception that we were quite a bit behind some other foreign countries in performance. SIMS was conducted in 1981–1982 and involved 23 populations in 21 countries. At the eighth-grade level, virtually all students attend school in all those countries, and our students scored at or below the international average on all five subtests: arithmetic, measurement, algebra, geometry, and statistics. The median Japanese 7th-grader performed at the 95th percentile of the United States 8th-graders (McKnight et al., *The Underachieving Curriculum,* 1987).

These SIMS results have been confirmed in other studies comparing students at the eighth-grade levels. In a study conducted by the Educational Testing Service in 1988–89, U.S. eighth-grade students were last in average mathematics proficiency compared with students in Ireland, South Korea, Spain, the United Kingdom, and Canada (Center for the Assessment of Educational Progress, *A World of Differences,* 1989).

Why do we perform so poorly? National Assessment results have shown that emphasizing algebra and geometry leads to higher test scores for eighth graders (U.S. Department of Education, National Center for Education Statistics, *The State of Mathematics Achievement: NAEP's 1990 Assessment of the Nation and the Trial Assessment of the States,* 1992). Historically, schools in the United States have delayed concentrated study of algebra and geometry longer than schools in other countries of the world.

SIMS recommended steps to renew school mathematics in the United States.

1987: Second International Mathematics Study (SIMS). *The Underachieving Curriculum.*

> A fundamental revision of the U.S. school mathematics curriculum, in both form and substance, is needed. This activity should begin at the early grades of the elementary school.
>
> With respect to form, the excessive repetition of topics from year to year should be eliminated. A more focused organization of the subject matter, with a more intense treatment of topics, should be considered.
>
> Concerning substance, the continued dominating role of arithmetic in the junior high school curriculum results in students entering high school with very limited mathematical backgrounds. The curriculum for all students should be broadened and enriched by the inclusion of appropriate topics in geometry, probability and statistics, as well as algebra. (*The Underachieving Curriculum,* p. xii)

UCSMP took these recommendations to heart and instituted a strengthened curriculum in 7th and 8th grades which includes all these areas and encouraged more students to take algebra before 9th grade.

The first results of the Third International Mathematics and Science Study (TIMSS) were announced for 8th grade in 1996. Over forty countries participated at this level. The results confirm that at the 8th grade level we have made some gains. Students in the U.S. were now equal to the international average in arithmetic, algebra, and statistics, but remained behind in geometry and measurement, and the total U.S. average is still behind the international average. Also, our algebra students perform well in comparison to other countries, and the percent of students in algebra has almost doubled since 1981–82 (Beaton et al., *Mathematics Achievement in the Middle School Years: IEA's Third International Mathematics and Science Study (TIMSS),* November 1996.

A consortium of suburban Chicago school districts in which over 50% of students enroll in 8th-grade algebra was allowed to participate in TIMSS as a country. Eighth-grade students in this consortium scored at a level equal to the second-highest in the world (Kroeze and Johnson, *Achieving Excellence,* 1997). This indicates that students in the United States can score as well as any other country if the curriculum, schools, and community provide appropriate support.

Turning to the 12th grade, at this level in 1981–82, about 13% of our population was enrolled in precalculus or calculus; the mean among developed countries is about 16%. Thus, the U.S. no longer kept more students in mathematics than other developed countries, yet our advanced placement students did not perform well when compared to their peers in other countries.

SIMS found:

> In the U.S., the achievement of the Calculus classes, the nation's best mathematics students, was at or near the average achievement of the advanced secondary school mathematics students in other countries. (In most countries, all advanced mathematics students take calculus. In the U.S., only about one-fifth do.) The achievement of the U.S. Precalculus students (the majority of twelfth grade college-preparatory students) was substantially below the international average. In some cases the U.S. ranked with the lower one-fourth of all countries in the Study, and was the lowest of the advanced industrialized countries. (*The Underachieving Curriculum,* p. vii)

The situation has been even worse for those who do not take precalculus mathematics in high school. Such students either have performed poorly in their last mathematics course, a situation which has caused them not to go on in mathematics, or they were performing poorly in junior high school and had to take remedial mathematics as 9th-graders. If these students go to college, they invariably take remedial mathematics, which is taught at a faster pace than in high school, and the failure rates in such courses often exceed 40%. If they do not go to college but join the job market, they lack the mathematics needed to understand today's technology. It is no understatement to say that **UCSMP received its funding from business and industry because those who leave schooling to join the work force have been woefully weak in the mathematics they will need.**

The TIMSS results for 12th grade, released in early 1998, confirm the results of fifteen years ago. The United States was again last of the developed countries. However, no country had a mean score significantly higher than the mean scores of students from the schools in the suburban Chicago consortium. This suggests that while overall the U.S. performance is nowhere near where we want it to be, in selected areas we are doing quite well.

In 1986, the National Council of Teachers of Mathematics began an ambitious effort to detail the curriculum it would like to see in schools. The "NCTM Standards," as they have come to be called, involve both content and methodology. The long Curriculum and Evaluation Standards document is divided into four sections, K–4, 5–8, 9–12, and Evaluation. Space limits our discussion here to just a few quotes from the 9–12 standards.

1989: National Council of Teachers of Mathematics. *Curriculum and Evaluation of Standards for School Mathematics.*

> The standards for grades 9–12 are based on the following assumptions:
>
> Students entering grade 9 will have experienced mathematics in the context of the broad, rich curriculum outlined in the K–8 standards.
>
> The level of computational proficiency suggested in the K–8 standards will be expected of all students; however, no student will be denied access to the study of mathematics in grades 9–12 because of a lack of computational facility.
>
> Although arithmetic computation will not be a direct object of study in grades 9–12, conceptual and procedural understandings of number, numeration, and operations, and the ability to make estimations and approximations and to judge the reasonableness of results will be strengthened in the context of applications and problem solving, including those situations dealing with issues of scientific computation.
>
> Scientific calculators with graphing capabilities will be available to all students at all times.
>
> A computer will be available at all times in every classroom for demonstration purposes, and all students will have access to computers for individual and group work.

> At least three years of mathematical study will be required of all secondary school students.
>
> These three years of mathematical study will revolve around a core curriculum differentiated by the depth and breadth of the treatment of topics and by the nature of applications.
>
> Four years of mathematical study will be required of all college-intending students.
>
> These four years of mathematical study will revolve around a broadened curriculum that includes extensions of the core topics and for which calculus is no longer viewed as the capstone experience.
>
> All students will study appropriate mathematics during their senior year. (pp. 124–125)

In 1991, NCTM came out with a second Standards document, concerned with the development of teachers and classroom teaching processes. Space limits our discussion to just a few quotes from the Standards for Teaching Mathematics section of this document.

1991: National Council of Teachers of Mathematics. *Professional Standards for Teaching Mathematics*.

> The standards for teaching are based on four assumptions about the practice of mathematics teaching:
>
> 1. The goal of teaching mathematics is to help all students develop mathematical power . . .
>
> 2. What students learn is fundamentally connected with How they learn.
>
> 3. All students can learn to think mathematically.
>
> 4. Teaching is a complex practice and hence not reducible to recipes or prescriptions. (pp. 21–22)
>
> The teacher of mathematics should pose tasks that are based on—
>
> sound and significant mathematics;
>
> knowledge of students' understandings, interests, and experiences;
>
> knowledge of the range of ways that diverse students learn mathematics;
>
> and that
>
> engage students' intellect;
>
> develop students' mathematical understandings and skills;
>
> stimulate students to make connections and develop a coherent framework for mathematical ideas;
>
> call for problem formulation, problem solving, and mathematical reasoning;
>
> promote communication about mathematics;
>
> represent mathematics as an ongoing human activity;
>
> display sensitivity to, and draw on, students' diverse background experiences and dispositions;
>
> promote the development of all students' dispositions to do mathematics. (p. 25)

The UCSMP secondary curriculum is the first full mathematics curriculum that is consistent with the recommendations of the NCTM standards.

In 1989, the Mathematical Sciences Education Board (MSEB), a committee of the National Research Council that coordinates efforts for improvement of mathematics education in the United States, came out with the report *Everybody Counts*, emphasizing the need for the mathematics curriculum to be appropriate for as many students as possible. This thrust reflects the UCSMP position that as many students as possible be accommodated with the curriculum taken by those who go to college. It represents a change in thinking from the two-tiered system recommended in *A Nation at Risk*.

Following up and elaborating on the NCTM Evaluation Standards, many national reports have dealt with issues related to assessment. Among these are three MSEB reports: *For Good Measure* (1991), *Measuring Up* (1993), and *Measuring What Counts* (1993); and the NCTM *Assessment Standards for School Mathematics* (1995). The themes of these reports are that we need to change assessment instruments to be aligned with new curricula, to incorporate a variety of ways in which students can demonstrate their knowledge of mathematics, and to ensure that assessments are used in positive ways to enhance learning and teaching rather than in negative ways to keep students from having future opportunities to learn. (For further discussion of assessment, see pages T52–T55.)

Some changes have already occurred in assessment. The ACT exams, the SAT I and SAT II and Advanced Placement calculus exams of the College

Board now allow any calculator without a QWERTY keyboard. Some states have altered their testing to focus on applying mathematics and higher-order thinking rather than on skills out of context.

Many of the ideas of recent reports are summarized in a 1991 MSEB report, *Reshaping School Mathematics: A Philosophy and Framework for Curriculum*. Six changes are identified there as affecting the context of mathematics education:

- Changes in the need for mathematics.
- Changes in mathematics and how it is used.
- Changes in the role of technology.
- Changes in American society.
- Changes in understanding of how students learn.
- Changes in international competitiveness.

In the UCSMP secondary curriculum we have attempted to respond to each of these changes.

Recognizing the Problems and Accomplishing the Goals

Three general problems in mathematics education in the United States lead to three major goals of the UCSMP secondary mathematics curriculum.

General Problem 1: Students do not learn enough mathematics by the time they leave school.

Specifically:

(A) Many students lack the mathematics background necessary to succeed in college, on the job, or in daily affairs.

(B) Even those students who possess mathematical skills are not introduced to enough applications of the mathematics they know.

(C) Students do not get enough experience with problems and questions that require some thought before answering.

(D) Many students terminate their study of mathematics too soon, not realizing the importance mathematics has in later schooling and in the marketplace.

(E) Students do not read mathematics books and, as a result, do not learn to become independent learners capable of acquiring mathematics outside of school when the need arises.

Goal 1: Upgrade students' achievement.

General Problem 2: The school mathematics curriculum has not kept up with changes in mathematics and the ways in which mathematics is used.

Specifically:

(A) Many mathematics curricula have not taken into account today's calculator and computer technology.

(B) Students who do succeed in secondary school mathematics generally are prepared for calculus, but generally are not equipped for the other mathematics they will encounter in college.

(C) Statistical ideas are found everywhere, from newspapers to research studies, but are not found in most secondary school mathematics curricula.

(D) The emergence of computer science has increased the importance of a background in discrete mathematics.

(E) Mathematics is not applied to areas outside the realm of the physical sciences, as much as within the field itself, but these applications are rarely taught and even more rarely tested.

(F) Estimation and approximation techniques are important in all of mathematics, from arithmetic on.

Goal 2: Update the mathematics curriculum.

General Problem 3: Too many students have been sorted out of the mathematics needed for employment and further schooling.

Specifically:

(A) Tracks make it easy to go down levels but almost impossible to go up.

(B) Remedial programs tend to put students further behind instead of catching them up.

(C) Enrichment classes often cover many topics, such as probability, statistics, discrete mathematics, and applications, and with activities of broader scope that are appropriate and important for all students.

(D) Courses for better students are often taught following the belief that the difficulty of a course is more important than its content, and with the view that if all survive, then the course was not a good one.

(E) Relative standards and preset numbers of students who go into special classes are incorrectly used as absolute indicators of ability to perform.

Goal 3: Increase the number of students who take mathematics beyond algebra and geometry.

We at UCSMP believe that these goals can be accomplished, and they already have been realized in some school districts using UCSMP materials. But substantial reworking of the curriculum has to be involved. It is not enough simply to insert applications, a bit of statistics, and take students a few times a year to a computer. Currently the greatest amount of time in arithmetic is spent on calculation, in algebra on manipulating polynomials and rational expressions, in geometry on proof, in advanced algebra and later courses on functions. These topics are the most affected by technology.

It is also not enough to raise graduation requirements, although that is the simplest action to take. Increases in requirements often lead to one of two situations. If the courses are kept the same, the result is typically a greater number of failures and an even greater number of dropouts. If the courses are eased, the result is lower performance for many students as they are brought through a weakened curriculum.

The fundamental problem, as the studies mentioned above noted, is the curriculum, and the fundamental problem in the curriculum is time. There is not enough time in the current 4-year algebra-geometry-algebra-precalculus curriculum to prepare students for calculus. The data reported by Bert Waits and Frank Demana in the *Mathematics Teacher* (January, 1988) are typical. Of students entering Ohio State University with exactly four years of college preparatory high-school mathematics, only 8% placed into calculus on the Ohio State mathematics placement test. The majority placed into precalculus, with 31% requiring one semester and 42% requiring two semesters of work. The remaining 19% placed into remedial courses below precalculus. Thus, even with the current curriculum, four years are not enough to take a typical student from algebra to calculus.

Today even most students who take four years of college preparatory mathematics successfully in high schools do not begin college with calculus. Given that the latest recommendations ask for students to learn more mathematics, *we believe five years of college preparatory mathematics beginning with algebra are necessary to provide the time for students to learn the mathematics they need for college.* Thus we do not believe the current NCTM Curriculum Standards for grades 9–12 can be accomplished in four years.

The time can be found by starting reform in grades 6–8. Examining textbooks of the early 1980s, James Flanders found that over half the pages in grades 6–8 are totally review ("How Much of the Content in Mathematics Textbook is New?" *Arithmetic Teacher*, September, 1987). This result, too, has been confirmed by TIMSS studies of curriculum (Schmidt et al., *Characterizing Pedagogical Flow: An Investigation of Mathematics and Science Teaching in Six Countries,* 1996). This amount of review, coupled with the magnitude of review in previous years, effectively decelerates students at least 1–2 years compared to students in other countries. It explains why almost all industrialized countries of the world, except the U.S. and Canada (and some French-speaking countries who do geometry before algebra), can begin concentrated study of algebra and geometry in the 7th or 8th grade.

In stark contrast to the review in grades 6–8, Flanders found that almost 90% of the pages of first-year algebra texts have content new to the student. This finding indicates why so many students in the U.S. have difficulty in first-year algebra. The student, having sat for years in mathematics classes where little was new, is overwhelmed. Some people interpret the overwhelming as the student "not being ready" for algebra, but we interpret it as the student being swamped by the pace. When you have been in a classroom in which at most only 1 of 3 days is devoted to anything new, you are not ready for a new idea every day. Thus we believe that algebra should be taught one year earlier to most students than is currently the case (Z. Usiskin, "Why Elementary Algebra Can, Should, and Must Be an Eighth-Grade Course for Average Students," *Mathematics Teacher,* September 1987).

Some school districts are attempting to do away with tracking by placing all students in the same classes, and with very similar expectations. We believe this is too simplistic a solution. Almost all of the many schools that have implemented the UCSMP secondary curriculum with all their students at the same time have found that student differences in interests, cultural background, and learning style can be handled by their teachers who take advantage of the richness of the UCSMP textbooks and the wealth of teaching suggestions and ancillary materials that accompany them. Even so, they have almost all had to create slower-paced sections for students who enter with the least knowledge or who are unwilling to do homework. And they almost all realize that many students could have begun the curriculum a year earlier than the other students.

The most successful school districts realize that complex problems seldom have simple solutions. We believe strongly that the UCSMP curriculum is appropriate for virtually all students, but not at the same time. No student should be deprived of the opportunity to be successful in any of the courses, but no child who is ready should have to wait a year or two to begin the curriculum. Our evidence is strong that the national percentiles that we show on page T29 are good predictors of readiness for UCSMP courses. We recommend that school districts follow these percentiles by strongly recommending that students who fit them take our courses. Additionally, students who miss these percentiles by small amounts or who very much wish to take our courses should be allowed to take them. We strongly urge school districts to emphasize the importance of entering knowledge by strengthening their curricula in the preceding years, and stress that students must do homework every day when studying from UCSMP materials.

Finally, because UCSMP materials are not like traditional materials, we urge that school districts provide sufficient in-service training on the newer ideas incorporated in them. Teachers differ in ability, entering knowledge, preferred teaching style, and cultural background almost as much as students differ. Some love cooperative learning; others have never used it. Some are computer experts; others are neophytes. Some enjoy using manipulative materials; others avoid them. Some have had courses in statistics and discrete mathematics; others have not. Some are already trying writing and alternate assessment in their classrooms; others have not heard of these things. No single in-service can handle such variety. We encourage school districts to send teachers to professional conferences where teachers have choices on what to attend. In particular, districts should take advantage of in-service opportunities offered by UCSMP and Scott Foresman Addison Wesley. It is also beneficial to hold periodic meetings on site to discuss local issues.

The UCSMP Secondary Curriculum

The Six UCSMP Courses

Each UCSMP course is designed for the equivalent of a school year of at least 170 days in which mathematics is taught for at least 45 minutes (preferably 50 minutes or more) each day.

Many teachers in block-scheduling situations maintain that, due to the richness of the content and the number of activities, UCSMP courses are particularly well-designed for use in block scheduling. In block scheduling situations, our testing indicates that teachers whose mathematics classes meet every other day for twice the amount of time should expect to cover about 10% less material. We believe those teachers whose mathematics classes meet every day for twice the amount of time, but only for half the year, will cover even less material, but we have no studies to support this belief.

All UCSMP courses have the following general features: wider scope of content; continual emphasis on applications to the real world and to problem solving; up-to-date use of calculators and computers; a multi-dimensional (SPUR) approach to understanding; and review and mastery strategies for enhancing performance. These are described below and on pages iv–v of the Student Edition.

***Transition Mathematics* (*TM*)** weaves three themes—applied arithmetic, pre-algebra and pre-geometry—by focusing on arithmetic operations in mathematics and the real world. Variables are used as pattern generalizers, abbreviations in formulas, and unknowns in problems, and are represented on the number line and graphed in the coordinate plane. Basic arithmetic and algebraic skills are connected to corresponding geometry topics.

Algebra has a scope far wider than most other algebra texts. Applications motivate all topics. Exponential growth and compound interest are covered. Statistics and geometry are settings for work with linear expressions and sentences. Probability provides a context for algebraic fractions, functions, and set ideas. Graphing technology is highly recommended.

Geometry integrates coordinates and transformations throughout, and gives strong attention to measurement formulas and three-dimensional figures in the first two-thirds of the book. Work with proof-writing follows a carefully sequenced development of the logical and conceptual precursors to proof. Geometry drawing technology is highly recommended.

Advanced Algebra emphasizes facility with algebraic expressions and forms, especially linear and quadratic forms, powers and roots, and functions based on these concepts. Students study logarithmic, trigonometric, polynomial, and other special functions both for their abstract properties and as tools for modeling real-world situations. A geometry course or its equivalent is a prerequisite, for geometric ideas are utilized throughout. Graphing technology is assumed to be available for students.

***Functions, Statistics, and Trigonometry* (*FST*)** integrates statistical and algebraic concepts, and previews calculus in work with functions and intuitive notions of limits. Enough trigonometry is available to constitute a standard precalculus course in trigonometry and circular functions. Technology is assumed available for student use in graphing, analyzing data, and simulating experiments.

***Precalculus and Discrete Mathematics* (*PDM*)** integrates the background students must have to be successful in calculus (advanced work with functions and trigonometry, an introduction to limits and other calculus ideas), with the discrete mathematics (number systems, combinatorics, recursion, graphs) helpful in computer science. Mathematical thinking, including specific attention to formal logic and proof, is a theme throughout. Graphing technology is assumed available for students.

Target Populations

We believe that all high-school graduates should take courses through *Advanced Algebra,* that all students planning to go to college should take courses through *Functions, Statistics, and Trigonometry,* and that students planning majors in technical areas should take all six UCSMP courses or their equivalents.

The critical juncture is when first-year algebra is completed. All qualified students should be afforded the possibility of taking *Transition Mathematics* in 6th grade to maximize the potential for them to complete *Algebra* in 7th grade and thus take calculus in high school without any acceleration. As many students as possible should be given the opportunity to finish a year's course in algebra or its equivalent before the end of 8th grade. In cases where there is some question about a student's readiness to go on to *Geometry,* we believe the student should be given the benefit of the doubt. Special summer review sessions of one or two weeks length may help in preparing borderline students for the next mathematics course.

The fundamental principle in placing students into courses is that entry should not be based on age, but on mathematical knowledge. Our studies indicate that with a standard curriculum, about 10% of students nationally are ready for *Transition Mathematics* at 6th grade, about another 40% at 7th grade, another 20% at 8th grade, and another 10–15% at 9th grade. We caution that these percentages are national, not local percentages, and the variability in our nation is enormous. We have tested the materials in school districts where few students are at grade level, where *Transition Mathematics* is appropriate for no more than the upper half of 8th-graders. We have tested also in school districts where as many as 90% of the students have successfully used *Transition Mathematics* in 7th grade. School districts have increased the percentages at the 6th and 7th grade by strengthening the mathematics curriculum in grades K–5 or K–6.

We also caution that the percentages are not automatic. Students who do not reach 7th-grade competence until the 9th-grade level often do not possess the study habits necessary for successful completion of these courses. At the 9th-grade level, *Transition Mathematics* has been substituted successfully either for a traditional pre-algebra course or for the first year of an algebra course spread out over two years. It often does not work as a substitute for a general mathematics course in which there is no expectation that students will take algebra the following year.

In the next column is a chart identifying the courses and the populations for which they are intended. The percentiles are national percentiles on a 7th-grade standardized mathematics test using 7th-grade norms, and apply to potential *Transition Mathematics* students. Page T30 also provides advice for starting in the middle of the series.

Each course is meant to stand alone. However, to take best advantage of these materials, and have them appropriate for the greatest number of students, it is preferable to use them in sequence. Although it is

Grade	**The top 10% of Students** are ready for *Transition Mathematics* in 6th grade. These students can proceed through the entire curriculum by 11th grade and take calculus in the 12th grade.	**Students in the 50th–90th percentile** on a 7th-grade standardized mathematics test should be ready to take *Transition Mathematics* in 7th grade.	Students who do not reach the 7th-grade level in mathematics until the 8th grade **(in the 30th–70th percentile)** begin *Transition Mathematics* in 8th grade.	Students who don't reach the 7th-grade level in Mathematics until the 9th grade **(in the 15th–50th percentile)** begin *Transition Mathematics* in the 9th grade.
6	Transition Mathematics			
7	Algebra	Transition Mathematics		
8	Geometry	Algebra	Transition Mathematics	
9	Advanced Algebra	Geometry	Algebra	Transition Mathematics
10	Functions, Statistics, and Trigonometry	Advanced Algebra	Geometry	Algebra
11	Precalculus and Discrete Mathematics	Functions, Statistics, and Trigonometry	Advanced Algebra	Geometry
12	Calculus (Not available through UCSMP)	Precalculus and Discrete Mathematics	Functions, Statistics, and Trigonometry	Advanced Algebra

suggested that students begin with *Transition Mathematics,* students may enter the UCSMP curriculum at any point. Below is a brief description of the UCSMP curriculum and the populations for which it is intended.

Left column: These students are often more interested in school, and they should be offered the Challenges suggested in the Teacher's Edition. Teachers may also wish to enrich courses for these students further with problems from mathematics contests.

2nd column: These students should be expected to take mathematics at least through the 11th grade, by which time they will have the mathematics needed for all college majors except those in the hard sciences and engineering. For that they will have the opportunity to take 12th-grade mathematics.

3rd column: Students in the 30th–70th percentile can complete *Advanced Algebra* by taking three years of high school mathematics. Currently over half of these students go to college. By completing *FST,* they will have studied the kind of mathematics needed for most majors.

Right column: Students in the 15th–50th percentile should not be tracked into courses that put them further behind. Rather they should be put into this curriculum and counseled on study skills. The logic is simple: Students who are behind in mathematical knowledge need to work harder at it, not less, in order to catch up.

Starting in the Middle of the Series

Every UCSMP course has been designed so that it could be used independently of other UCSMP courses. Accordingly, about half of the testing of UCSMP courses after *Transition Mathematics* has been with students who have not had any previous UCSMP courses. We have verified that any of the UCSMP courses can be taken successfully following the typical prerequisite courses in the standard curriculum.

Starting with UCSMP *Algebra* No additional prerequisites other than those needed for success in any algebra course are needed for success in UCSMP *Algebra*.

Students who have studied *Transition Mathematics* tend to cover more of UCSMP *Algebra* than other students because they have been introduced to more of the applications of algebra.

UCSMP *Algebra* prepares students for any standard geometry course.

Starting with UCSMP *Geometry* No additional prerequisites other than those needed for success in any geometry course are needed for success in UCSMP *Geometry*.

UCSMP *Geometry* can be used with faster, average, and slower students who have these prerequisites. Prior study of *Transition Mathematics* and UCSMP *Algebra* ensures this background, but this content is also found in virtually all existing middle school or junior high school texts. Classes of students who have studied UCSMP *Algebra* tend to cover more UCSMP *Geometry* than other classes because they know more geometry—e.g., they are familiar with geometric transformations—and are better at the algebra used in geometry. Students who have studied UCSMP *Geometry* are ready for any second-year algebra text.

Starting with UCSMP *Advanced Algebra* UCSMP *Advanced Algebra* can be used following any standard geometry text.

Students who have had UCSMP *Geometry* before UCSMP *Advanced Algebra* tend to be better prepared in the transformations and coordinate geometry they will need in this course, and geometry courses using other books should be careful to cover this content.

Students who have studied from UCSMP *Algebra* tend to be better prepared for the graphing and applications found in this course.

Students who have studied UCSMP *Advanced Algebra* are prepared for courses commonly found at the senior level, including trigonometry or precalculus courses.

Starting with *Functions, Statistics, and Trigonometry (FST)* *FST* assumes that students have completed a second-year algebra course. Students who have studied some trigonometry, like that found in UCSMP *Advanced Algebra,* will be at an advantage. No additional prerequisites other than those found in any second-year algebra text are needed for success in *FST*.

FST provides sufficient background for success in a non-proof-oriented calculus, such as is often taken by business or social studies majors in college, and for many of the reform calculus courses that emphasize applications and technology.

Starting with *Precalculus and Discrete Mathematics (PDM)* *PDM* can be taken successfully by students who have had *FST,* by students who have had typical senior level courses that include study of trigonometry and functions, and by top students who have successfully completed full advanced algebra and trigonometry courses.

PDM provides the background necessary for any typical calculus course, either at the high school or college level, including those that place a heavy emphasis on proof, and including advanced placement calculus courses at either the AB or BC level.

Professional Sourcebook: SECTION **2** **ABOUT UCSMP *PRECALCULUS AND DISCRETE MATHEMATICS***

Goals of UCSMP *Precalculus and Discrete Mathematics*

The material in UCSMP *Precalculus and Discrete Mathematics* constitutes a course that did not exist prior to UCSMP. As a new course, there was some latitude in selecting and organizing the content of this book. Guiding principles for including a topic in the curriculum were:

(1) it contributes to a balanced preparation for college mathematics courses in calculus and discrete mathematics;

(2) it is important for daily living, career development, or future study of mathematics;

(3) it is at a suitable level of difficulty for average 12th-grade students with the appropriate prerequisites (see page T28–30) and is accessible to them with current technology;

(4) it can be done by all students who have successfully completed UCSMP *Functions, Statistics, and Trigonometry* or its equivalent.

In this course, visual information derived from the use of an automatic grapher is employed to obtain conjectures about functions, equations, and inequalities, which are then verified through algebraic means. Technology also allows students to explore and apply calculus concepts. In this way students cover all the dimensions of the understanding of functions: the skills, properties, uses, and representations. For each, we want to update the curriculum and upgrade students' achievement. Specifically, we want students to be better able to work with linear, quadratic, exponential, logarithmic, trigonometric, and rational expressions, sentences, and functions. With technology students are able to do this work in ways that were inaccessible a generation ago.

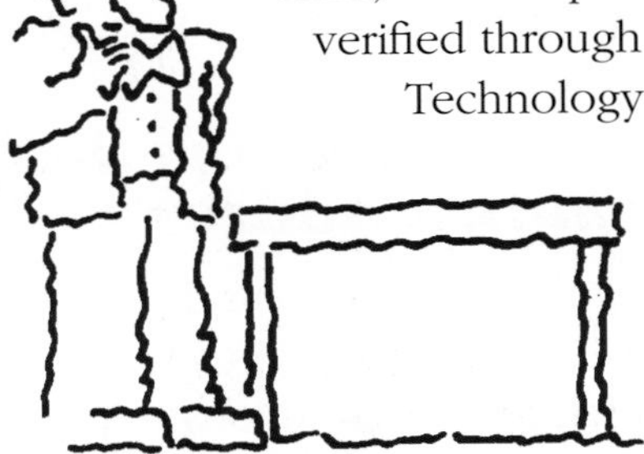

The discrete mathematics in this book plays a number of roles. Some of it, such as the work with algorithms, combinatorics, and graphs and circuits, is studied primarily for its own sake. Some topics, such as recursion and integers, are important not only for their own sake but also for the insight they provide into other mathematics at this level. For example, we often study continuous functions by examining their values at a set of discrete points. The transition from the discrete to the continuous is a natural way to approach ideas from calculus. As another example, we find similarities in the algebraic properties of integers (a discrete topic) and polynomials (a topic that is not discrete).

Mathematical thinking is a theme throughout this course, and as such, we expect students to gain competence with algebraic proofs. The subject matter of logic and proof encompasses all the content of the book. The logic is connected with everyday thinking and the ways computers operate. Logic provides a higher-level look at the solving of equations and inequalities, and provides the basis for the direct proofs, indirect proofs, and proofs by induction that students are expected to handle in this course.

Overall, we want students to learn how to study mathematics. To accomplish this goal we want students to learn to take advantage of many resources. They should try to learn from the reading of the lesson, as well as from their teacher and from their fellow classmates.

We have other, more lofty goals. We want students to view their study of mathematics as worthwhile, as full of interesting and entertaining information, as related to almost every endeavor. We want them to realize that mathematics is still growing and is changing fast. We want them to look for and recognize mathematics in places they haven't before, to use the library and the Internet, to search through newspapers or almanacs, to get excited by knowledge.

We want to convey to the student, through historical references and references to recent mathematical work that mathematics was developed by people and continues to develop. WE WANT STUDENTS TO VIEW THEIR STUDY OF MATHEMATICS AS WORTHWHILE, AS FULL OF INTERESTING AND ENTERTAINING INFORMATION, AS RELATED TO ALMOST EVERY ENDEAVOR. Through explorations and projects, we want students to look for and recognize mathematics in places they haven't before, to use the library, to search through newspapers or almanacs, to get excited by knowledge.

In summary, we would like to help students develop what the NCTM Standards call mathematical power, that is, the ability to explore, conjecture, and reason logically; to solve non-routine problems; to communicate about and through mathematics; and to connect ideas within mathematics and between mathematics and other disciplines. We also want students to develop personal self-confidence, positive attitudes, and effective study skills in mathematics.

Who Should Take UCSMP *Precalculus and Discrete Mathematics*?

Virtually all students who expect to go to college and major in the sciences, engineering, or other areas that require trigonometry and calculus should learn the content of this course, for this course provides the beginning of strong precalculus training. This course also provides a strong introduction to discrete mathematics for those who are going to major in computer science, economics, business, and many other areas that make use of finite mathematics.

The prerequisite for *Precalculus and Discrete Mathematics* is UCSMP *Functions, Statistics, and Trigonometry* or the equivalent of two years of algebra, one year of geometry, and a course in trigonometry. In particular, students should have a strong background in algebra, functions, and trigonometry. They should be adept at solving linear and quadratic equations and linear systems. They should be able to make and read coordinate graphs of linear, quadratic, power functions (i.e. functions of the type $f(x) = x^n$, for n a positive integer), exponential, and logarithmic functions. They should have studied the trigonometric functions from two standpoints—right triangle ratios and circular functions, and should be able to solve triangles and be able to graph the circular functions. Also, the book assumes that the student has previously studied geometric transformations (reflections, rotations, translations, and size changes) and permutations, combinations, and probability.

Students who do not have all the prerequisite skills can still be successful in this course. However, you may need to spend more time on certain chapters. We have made comments in the lessons on topics where teachers using the first edition of the book had to slow down because their students had little or no previous background. For example, if your students have not studied functions in some depth, Chapter 2 will take longer than the recommended pace. If they have not studied polynomial functions in detail, Chapter 4 will take more time. If students are not familiar enough with trigonometric functions, then Chapter 6 will take longer. Chapter 8's pace assumes that students have seen various counting problems, including permutations and combinations.

We know of a few schools that have used UCSMP *Precalculus and Discrete Mathematics* after UCSMP *Advanced Algebra*. We do not recommend this unless the students are exceptional. For almost all students, UCSMP *Functions Statistics, and Trigonometry* is the appropriate course to follow a second course in algebra—even if it contains some trigonometry.

Problems UCSMP *Precalculus and Discrete Mathematics* Addresses

UCSMP received its funding because the funders agreed with us that there are major problems with school mathematics and felt that the solutions require a significant departure from school practice. This book is meant to follow UCSMP *Functions Statistics, and Trigonometry* or an equivalent study of two years of algebra and one year of geometry, a half-year of trigonometry, and an in-depth study of functions.

But it is quite different from most precalculus or high school analysis courses. The differences are due to its attempt to respond to eight serious problems in mathematics education that cannot be treated by small differences in content or approach. Here are the problems that this book addresses and the UCSMP response to each.

Problem 1: *The traditional sequence of four years of high school mathematics does not prepare most students for a successful study of calculus.*

As we pointed out on page T26, data from studies of mathematics placement testing show that only a small minority—less than 10% in one study—of the students who take the traditional four years of college preparatory mathematics (algebra I, geometry, algebra II, precalculus) in the United States place into calculus in college (Waits & Demana, 1988). Most students who have taken mathematics through precalculus in high school need to take one or two *college* courses (typically called College Algebra and Trigonometry) in order to qualify for college calculus. Furthermore, international comparisons show that the mean performance of U.S. precalculus students on tests of algebra, geometry, and functions ranks among the lowest of industrialized nations, even though almost all of these nations now retain as large a percentage of students in school and in mathematics as we do (McKnight et al., 1987; Beaton et al., 1998).

The UCSMP response to this problem is to provide an extra year of mathematics for students. We offer a more challenging, less repetitive program (*Transition Mathematics*) for average students in grade 7 and recommend starting the study of *Algebra* in grade 8 even for average college-intending students. This leaves the average student an additional year to prepare for college mathematics, and so UCSMP has created two courses to replace the traditional year of precalculus mathematics. In the first of these courses, *Functions, Statistics, and Trigonometry,* students study the various manifestations of function (set of ordered pairs, mapping, equation, graph), and they study polynomial, exponential, logarithmic, and trigonometric functions in depth. They also extend the work begun in UCSMP *Advanced Algebra* with quadratic relations, and the concepts of inverse and composition of functions. In this course, *Precalculus and Discrete Mathematics,* students continue the study of functions, trigonometry, sequences, limits, and continuity and study other precalculus topics such as rational functions, operations with functions (e.g., addition and multiplication), vectors, parametric equations. Students are also introduced to the derivative and the integral and the graphical representation of functions is reviewed and extended. Specific attention is given to the concepts and symbolism of calculus. The mechanics of algebraic manipulation is integrated throughout the book.

Our evidence is that UCSMP students who complete both courses perform as well as on precalculus content as other students who have had calculus. That is, we believe we have closed the international performance gap even while teaching a greater variety of content.

Problem 2: *Even when students are prepared for calculus, they are often not prepared for the other mathematics they will encounter in college. In particular, the traditional curriculum ignores fundamental ideas of discrete mathematics.*

The term "discrete" is usually used to contrast with the word "continuous." A "discrete set" is a set that can be put in one-to-one correspondence with the set of integers or a subset thereof. The real line is considered continuous, but the set of integers on that line is discrete. "Discrete mathematics" refers to that mathematics that deals with or relies on the integers or other discrete sets (sequences, mathematical induction, the steps in algorithms or proofs, networks, counting problems). Discrete sets are critical to computer programming and computer science.

Discrete mathematics has only become important in the last 35 years or so. In 1965, computer science was unknown as a college major, and a business major needed no more than second-year algebra to succeed. But by the early 1980s, there were many times more computer science majors than mathematics majors, and even students not majoring in mathematics or the physical sciences were required to take statistics, computer science, and linear algebra in addition to calculus.

The emergence of computer science as a field of study has increased the importance of a background in topics from discrete mathematics. Some of these topics, such as the counting principles found in *Transition Mathematics* and UCSMP *Algebra,* are traditional content that we introduce earlier. Other topics, such as the networks studied in UCSMP *Geometry,* are newer topics.

In *Precalculus and Discrete Mathematics,* students study properties of iteration and recursion, and extend their study of probability, counting, sequences, and series. The logic and axiomatic nature of mathematics is employed to provide justification for some procedures students have used for some time, and to introduce new procedures. Students are expected to follow and write simple direct proofs, proof by contradiction (indirect proofs), and proofs involving mathematical induction. They are also expected to recognize fallacious reasoning.

Problem 3: *Many students do not realize the importance mathematics has in later schooling, on the job, or in daily affairs.*

Perhaps one of the most telling indicators of the lack of connection between the mathematics studied in traditional courses and the mathematics found outside of school is that at the end of a course students are less likely to see the value in what they took than before they studied the course. Many teachers tell students that the reason for studying a course beyond second year algebra in high school is to be successful in college mathematics but do not tell the students why they are required to study mathematics in college.

Fundamentally, when calculus and computer science are required or recommended in a college major, it is not because they are beautiful subjects (even though they are), but because they have many important applications.

As in all UCSMP texts, in *Precalculus and Discrete Mathematics* applications are used to motivate the study of skills and concepts. Students use mathmatics to investigate facts about themselves and their environment, both in and out of school. We make aserious effort to connect the world of the classroom with the so-called "real world." Although it is often necessary because of time constraints to have problems which are contrived to fit the needs of the mathematics being studied, we have attempted to pick contexts which are relevant to young adults thinking about college, careers, and their responsibilities in a complicated society. When possible, we use actual data and ask the kinds of questions that workers, concerned citizens, or curious observers would ask. Teachers who have used earlier versions of this and other UCSMP texts frequently remark that students no longer ask "Why are we studying this?" We believe this approach provides a deeper appreciation for the value of mathematics and enhances the performance of students.

Problem 4: *Despite the nearly universal availability of calculators and widespread availability of computers, most contemporary textbooks ignore the existence of this technology.*

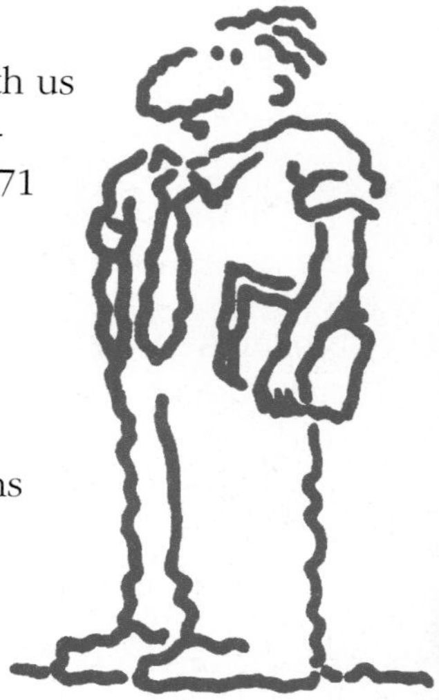

This problem has not been with us for a long time. Four-function hand-held calculators first appeared in 1971 and even by 1976 cost more than $50, equivalent to well over $150 today. The first personal computer appeared in 1977 with a storage of 16K. The first easy-to-use calculator with the capability to graph functions appeared in 1985. Only in recent years has there been effective, easy-to-use computer software for graphing and for statistics. Thus the reason that many books do not accommodate contemporary technology is that the technology was not available when the book was written.

From its inception, UCSMP has had a policy of using the latest in technology, provided that technology is produced by more than one manufacturer, that it is user-friendly, and that its cost is not prohibitive. Scott Foresman - Addison Wesley has enhanced this policy by developing software to insure that appropriate calculator and computer technology is available with each of the UCSMP texts.

Scientific calculators and computers allow students to work with realistic numbers, to practice estimation skills, to avoid tedious or repetitive calculations, and to solve problems that would not be solvable otherwise. For these reasons all UCSMP secondary courses refer to calculators and computers in the lessons, and assume that students have access to calculators for every lesson and on all tests.

Continual access to an *automatic grapher* (a graphing calculator or function-graphing software) is required for this course. Such technology promotes students' ability to visualize functions, to explore relations between equations and their graphs, to approximate relative and zeros of virtually any function, to generate or analyze data, and to develop the concept of limit. It also enables students to conjecture identities. To say that such technology enhances student understanding of these ideas is obvious to anyone who has ever taught with it.

Access to a *symbol manipulator* is not required for all students at all times, but should be available. A symbol manipulator can help to verify patterns, to check work, to perform difficult algebraic manipulations, and to save you and your students a great deal of time.

This course is not geared to a particular brand of technology. For many years, computers with symbol manipulating software such as *Maple, Derive,* and *Mathematica,* have been available. At the time this second edition is appearing, calculators with symbol manipulating capability are available from Hewlett Packard, Texas Instruments, and Casio, and their cost is decreasing while their power is increasing. For graphing, any graphing calculator or computer with graphics capabilities can be used. Other necessary software for the calculator or computer is a programming language.

More detailed information about technology is included on pages T42–T44.

***Problem 5:** Students do not read mathematics textbooks.*

Students tell us that they do not read because (1) the text is uninteresting, and (2) they do not need to read—their teacher explains it for them. But students *must* learn to read for future success in mathematics. Our response to (1) is to include informative and interesting reading in every lesson. The text of the lesson develops concepts and principles, provides examples and non-examples, and shows relations between important ideas. Many of the questions themselves require reading to set the context of a problem. Also, the last lesson of some chapters is a "reading lesson", and simulates the reading a student might do in non-mathematics courses where mathematics is used. Reading lessons cover a wide range of applications, theoretical discussions, and historical themes.

Our response to (2) above is to encourage teachers not to explain everything *in advance* to students. Because students can read and understand the text, the teacher has the freedom to teach in a variety of ways and it is not necessary for the teacher to explain every day what the text says. The teacher can concentrate on helping students with difficult new symbols or vocabulary, and on developing further examples and explanations specifically tailored to his or her class.

"Not explaining everything" is not the same as "explaining nothing." Every good teacher needs to and should explain some things almost every day to students. Teachers should point out what is important and how things are connected, they should respond to questions and help students to correct their errors and they should customize a class to their own interests and the concerns of the school and community. Many ideas for explanations and other enhancements of the reading are found in the extensive teacher notes with each lesson.

More detailed information about reading and reading lessons can be found on pages T49–T50.

Problem 6: *Students do not get enough experience with problems and questions which require some thought before answering.*

In general, the evidence is that students are rather skillful at simple routine problems, but have a great deal of difficulty with complicated numbers, different wordings, or new contexts. Throughout this book, Applying the Mathematics questions are given with all sorts of numbers, a variety of wordings, and the many different contexts which arise naturally from applications. Exploration questions confront students with open-ended problems, problems requiring more sophisticated generalization, or with problems requiring the use of outside references.

In preparation for the more sophisticated analysis and synthesis expected in college, the end of each chapter contains a set of Projects. The Projects require more elaborate data collection or more extensive analyses and provide a wonderful opportunity for students to develop reasoning and communication skills. Many teachers have found it useful to have students present their projects orally. (See page T44 for more detail.)

Problem 7: *Students do not understand how, when, or why mathematicians do proofs.*

Rigorous deductive thinking is how mathematicians determine whether statements are true relative to a set of postulates; it is the way in which new mathematics is established. Without such thinking, mathematics would only be a collection of assorted principles whose connection with each other would not have been established and whose truth with respect to each other is subject to question.

Despite the importance of proof in mathematics, most students are expected to do proofs only in connection with their study of geometry. They associate proofs, therefore, with geometry and not with mathematics as a whole, and they are not very good at doing them.

Imagine if students only solved equations in one course. They would not be very good at it. In all UCSMP courses after UCSMP *Geometry,* we do some proofs. But in *Precalculus and Discrete Mathematics,* we give strong attention to proof for a second time, in a manner that takes advantage of students' greater mathematical knowledge, technical skill, and prior experience. Even so, we proceed carefully through the course so that students have time to incorporate these ideas.

Problem 8: *Students do not get enough experience in the people skills needed in the workforce when problems are being solved.*

Mathematics has traditionally been done by students exclusively as a solitary activity. Talking among students in a class was discouraged if not prohibited. Joint efforts at solving a problem were viewed as cheating and as deleterious to self-improvement and personal understanding. Mathematics has also been viewed as *the* subject in which a single answer suffices.

Yet, as computers have come to perform the routine tasks of jobs, what is left are tasks that require human judgment and group problem solving. These requirements in turn require that workers be able to work with others to identify problems, to weigh various alternative solutions, and to communicate their conclusions to others.

Throughout the second editions of all UCSMP courses, we have increased our emphasis on these aspects of problem solving. In-class Activities in the student text are usually meant to be done in pairs or larger groups. Suggestions for group work and cooperation are found in almost all lessons. And many of the end-of-chapter Projects lend themselves to group work.

What's New in the Second Edition

Writing of the first draft of UCSMP *Precalculus and Discrete Mathematics* began in 1986 and the first edition appeared in its commercial form in 1992. National reports issued since the testing of the first project version of the book have stressed the importance of many of the innovations present in UCSMP texts and have suggested enhancement of certain features of the text. The Second Edition of UCSMP *Precalculus and Discrete Mathematics* has also benefited from user reports and surveys of users from all regions throughout the United States.

A person familiar with the First Edition of UCSMP *Precalculus and Discrete Mathematics* will note a large number of small changes in each lesson, and the following more major changes in the development of the content:

- Parametric equations are introduced in Chapter 2 and used in later chapters.
- Some of the work on trigonometric functions formerly in Chapter 2 has been moved to Chapter 6.
- Symbol manipulators are discussed in many places.
- A number of reading lessons have been deleted to make room for this new content and to enable more classes to give more depth to existing content.

There are also major new features in the approach.

- Colored headers appear in the lessons to help outline the reading.
- Full-page In-class Activities and shorter Activities (within lessons) are included to provide students with more hands-on experiences. Many of the In-class Activities are especially suitable for small-group work.
- Solutions to Examples are printed in a special font to help model what students should write when they do the Questions.
- A global, multicultural view of mathematics is enhanced with new photos from around the world. Informative captions are now included.

There are also new materials available for teaching.

- An enhanced Teacher's Edition now provides daily suggestions for adapting to individual needs, optional activities, and assessment alternatives.
- An augmented ancillary package offers new Lesson Masters, performance tests and forms for authentic assessment, and an expanded Technology Sourcebook.
- New Explorations software provides 40 interactive demonstrations and activities tied to specific lessons in the textbook. (Windows/Macintosh)
- A new TestWorks CD-ROM provides an editable database of questions for each objective, along with numerous prepared tests and quizzes for each chapter. (Windows/Macintosh)

Professional Sourcebook: SECTION 3 GENERAL TEACHING SUGGESTIONS FOR UCSMP *PRECALCULUS AND DISCRETE MATHEMATICS*

UCSMP *Precalculus and Discrete Mathematics* is a textbook which assists students in learning mathematics. It is not meant to substitute for a teacher, nor does it attempt to prescribe rigidly how to teach mathematics. We have seen the First Edition of this text used effectively with a variety of models of teaching—from direct instruction through cooperative learning, and we expect the Second Edition to be at least as flexible.

We feel a need to restate one of the assumptions of the *Professional Standards for Teaching Mathematics* (NCTM, 1991), that "teaching is a complex practice and hence not reducible to recipes or prescriptions." The suggestions which follow should not be construed as rigid: students, teachers, classes, and schools vary greatly. But the suggestions should not be ignored. They come from extensive discussions with teachers of earlier versions of these materials, written comments from experienced users of the First Edition, and from test results. We encourage you to read them, and to try as many of them as you can in your classroom.

Planning

It hardly needs to be said that good teaching begins with careful planning. In this section we concentrate on features that may be different from other books from which you have taught.

First Steps

1. Find out more about these materials. If you have not already done so, skim Section 1 and read Section 2 of this Professional Sourcebook. These sections will inform you if your students are among the typical UCSMP *Precalculus and Discrete Mathematics* students, and they give the motivation for many of the features you will find. Also read pages iv–v of the Student Edition for additional information on UCSMP in general and UCSMP *Precalculus and Discrete Mathematics* in particular.

2. Make certain that you have all the materials you need. A list of components that are available with the Second Edition of UCSMP *Precalculus and Discrete Mathematics* is on page T00 of this book. If you do not have all the materials, contact your local Scott Foresman Addison Wesley representative or call the national office at 1-800-554-4411.

Before the school year starts you should assemble some resources for your teaching. Some materials you will want to have in your classroom throughout the year are: a dictionary, an atlas, an almanac, and either a globe or a large world map for the wall. It is also important to know the technology that you can have available for display; an overhead projector with a display panel connected to a calculator or computer is recommended at all times. A calculator that can do symbol manipulation or a computer with symbol manipulation software should be available at all times.

3. Check that your students will have all the materials they need. In addition to pencils and various types of paper (lined, unlined, and graph), all students are expected to have a graphing calculator and a ruler. A list of calculator specifications is given in the "To the Student" section on pages 1–3. Be certain to cover this section with your students.

4. Familiarize yourself with the general layout of the two-part Teacher's Edition (Part I and Part II). Part 1 of the Teacher's Edition contains Chapters 1– 6. Part 2 contains Chapters 7–13. At the beginning of each chapter are four extra pages (tinted) that display pacing schedules, objectives, available materials, and overall notes for the chapter. Following Chapter 6 in Part 1 are the Selected Answers (for Chapters 1–6) and the Glossary and the Index for both Parts I and II. In Part 2, Chapter 13 is followed by the Selected Answers (for Chapters 7–13), and again the Glossary and Index.

5. Familiarize yourself with the features of the Student Edition. There are 13 chapters, with 6–10 lessons each. Each chapter begins with a 2-page chapter opener that serves as an introduction and is meant to be read. Then come the lessons, each with reading followed by four types of questions: Covering the Reading, Applying the Mathematics, Review, and Exploration. Following the lessons are Projects. (See page T44.) Each chapter ends with a Summary and list of new Vocabulary for the chapter, a Progress Self-Test, and a Chapter Review. The Progress Self-Test and Chapter Review are not optional; they are designed to focus students' attention to the important material and objectives of the chapter. (See pages T41–T42.) The Selected Answers section, beginning on page 852 in the Student Edition, provides answers to odd-numbered Applying the Mathematics and Review Questions.

6. Consider sending information about UCSMP *Precalculus and Discrete Mathematics* home with your students. A letter or flyer to parents conveys your and your school district's concern for each child and at the same time can let parents know your expectations regarding materials and homework. Suggestions concerning what form a letter or flyer can take, and what to put in it are provided below. These suggestions come to us from UCSMP users.

Sample Letter to Parents

Because the adoption of books is generally done by a school or school district, it may be best if the letter comes from the mathematics department, the mathematics department chair or supervisor, or the principal. (If your school district has used UCSMP materials for some time, a personal letter may be more fitting.) The letter should be on school or school district stationery. Here are the kinds of information schools have conveyed:

UCSMP beliefs/philosophy Mathematics is valuable to the average citizen, and all students can learn a significant amount of mathematics. We can learn from other countries. A major cause of our problems lies in the curriculum. The mathematics curriculum can make better use of time by spending less time on review (from previous years) and outmoded content and skills. Calculators and computers render some content obsolete, make other content more important, and change the ways we should view still other content. The scope of mathematics should expand at all levels and include statistics and the mathematics used in programming computers. The classroom should draw examples from the real world. To make significant changes in any school, teachers, administrators, and parents must work together.

Features of UCSMP texts that parents will notice Students are expected to read. They are expected to use calculators. There are a variety of problems in each question set rather than a single type of problem repeated a large number of times. It is best if each feature is followed by a sentence or two with a rationale for that feature. Such information may be found throughout this Sourcebook.

Materials students need This can be similar to the list found in the "To The Student" section of the student book (pages 1–3). It should include a list of the features of the calculators students should have, and information on how students can obtain such calculators (whether from the school or from a local store). If possible, include prices.

How parents can help It is wise to include statements that describe the roles of parents in their child's education, particularly because at this level, parents are sometimes given the feeling that they no longer are integral. Here are some suggestions: Encourage your child to read the textbook. Check with your children to see that they have the supplies they need. See that your children are doing homework every night. Encourage determination and perseverance; if your child is having a problem, ask your child to tell you what he or she knows about the idea. Monitor your child's absences (perhaps include the school's absence policy). Contact the teacher as soon as a problem arises; do not wait. Encourage your child to seek help whenever necessary (give places to get help).

With this letter, some teachers include their mathematics course sequence. Some indicate their grading policies. Whatever you include, you should expect responses from parents who seek clarification. *Welcome* each response as a sign of an interested parent and because the responses will help you in drafting what you send next year.

Planning for Teaching

Planning for teaching with UCSMP *Precalculus and Discrete Mathematics* is similar to the planning you might do for any mathematics class.

Global planning can be done by looking over the Table of Contents and setting goals for each grading period. The chapters in this book are meant to be covered in order, at a pace of about one lesson per day, and we suggest that first-time users adhere to this pattern. This means that most teachers should plan to cover 11–12 chapters. This amounts to approximately two chapters each marking period if you give grades every six weeks, or three chapters per marking period if you give grades every nine or ten weeks. In block scheduling situations in which classes meet every day, each chapter should take no more than two weeks. Teachers of very well-prepared students in schools which do not lose much instructional time to other matters are likely to be able to cover more, and those who are teaching under prepared students in classes with numerous interruptions may cover less.

To get an overview of the content in each chapter, read the Chapter Overview on the pages in this Teacher's Edition corresponding to the first two pages of the chapter; read the lesson titles shown there; and scan the Summary and Vocabulary, Progress Self-Test, and Chapter Review at the end of the chapter. Collectively these will give you a good idea of what the chapter is about, and how much of the content will be new to you or your students. Make a tentative schedule for working through the chapter. Be sure to leave 2 or 3 days for review before the chapter test (See Strategies for Mastery on page T41.)

Read each lesson in the Student Edition. Then read the Overview, the Notes on Reading, the Notes on the Questions, and other side and bottom notes in the Teacher's Edition. They indicate the Resources you may need for the lesson. They also provide ideas for various ways of approaching the lesson. They will help you decide what instructional modes (whole-class discussion, small-group work, demonstration, lecture, etc.) you might use, how you might go over the assignment from the previous day, how you could sequence the class activities from opening to closing, and what assignment you can make for the next class.

Do all of the questions before assigning them. Note any questions with directions which might need clarification to your students, or any questions which you think are particularly important or exceptionally difficult.

Pace

There is a natural tendency, when using a new book, to go more slowly, to play it safe should you forget something. Teachers using these materials for the first time have almost invariably said that they would move more quickly the next year. Do not be afraid to move quickly. As in all UCSMP texts, virtually all lessons in UCSMP *Precalculus and Discrete Mathematics* are intended to be read and discussed in one day.

Students adjust to the pace set by the teacher. It is especially important that Chapter 1 be taught at a one-day-per-lesson pace. At the end of the chapter, spend a few days on the Progress Self-Test and Chapter Review to cinch the major skills. We know from our studies that this pace produces the highest performance levels. Students need to be exposed to content in order to learn it.

Some classes in our studies of this book went very slowly; their teachers seemed reluctant to move to any new content. Where this happens, the students get into a rut. Better students are bored because they know the material. Slower students are frustrated because they are being asked to spend more time on the stuff they don't know. They all get discouraged and perform far lower than any other comparable students at the end of the year. We can state this rather strongly: If you want to guarantee poor performance, go slowly through a book. If you feel you are going too quickly, then spend an extra day reviewing for a chapter test after you have done the reviews. It is frustrating to everyone to go back to a chapter after the test has been given.

There are times when it will be difficult to maintain this pace. But be advised: a slow pace can make it too easy to lose perspective and difficult to relate ideas. You need to get to later content to realize why you were asked to learn earlier content! If you spend too much time in the lessons, you may find that your slowest students may have learned more by having gone through content slowly, but all the other students will have learned less. The wise teacher strikes a balance, goes quickly enough to keep things interesting but slowly enough to have time for explanations. David R. Johnson's booklets *Every Minute Counts* and *Making Minutes Count Even More* give excellent practical suggestions on making use of class time.

Average students should be able to complete 11 chapters of UCSMP *Precalculus and Discrete Mathematics*. If you find in spring that you have been going through the chapters more slowly than recommended, rather than omitting entire chapters, we suggest omitting certain lessons. However, please be aware that these lessons are reviewed later. You will need to adjust your homework assignments accordingly.

Assignments

We recommend that a typical homework assignment be one of the following:

1. read Lesson n; write answers to all Questions in Lesson n;

   or

2. read Lesson n; write answers to Questions Covering the Reading in Lesson n, and Applying the Mathematics, Review, and Exploration in Lesson $n - 1$.

Thus virtually every day students should be expected to do either the equivalent of a complete set of questions from a lesson, or nearly so. You may wish to reserve certain questions as groupwork in class or for a class activity and not assign them. At times you will want to preview the reading, but for typical classes this should not be a regular part of the plan. (See Using the Reading, pages T49–T50.)

The Questions in each lesson have been designed to cover the key skills, properties, uses, and representations in the lesson. Questions were not written with an odd-even assignment plan in mind. Skipping too many questions may lead to gaps in student understanding. The Exploration questions may be assigned for all to do, or left as optional work for extra credit. For extra practice, you should use the Lesson Masters. These have been written to complement the questions in each lesson.

We recommend that assignments be given on the days following chapter tests. If this is not done, then there will be up to 12 days without homework, the equivalent of a complete chapter's work.

Taking Review Into Account

Every lesson includes a set of Review questions. These questions serve a variety of purposes. First, they develop competence in a topic. Because we do not expect students to master a topic on the day they are introduced to it, these questions, coming on the days after introduction, help to solidify the ideas. Second, they maintain competence from preceding chapters. This review is particularly effective with topics that have not been studied for some time.

Third, at times we are able to give harder questions in reviews than we could expect students to be able to do on the day they were introduced to the topic. Thus the reviews sometimes serve as questions which integrate ideas from previous lessons.

Fourth, we occasionally review an idea that has not been discussed for some time, just before it is to surface again in a lesson. The Notes on Questions usually alert you to this circumstance.

Teachers of classes that perform the best assign all the Review questions, give students the answers each day, and discuss them when needed. Those who do not assign all reviews tend to get poorer performance; their students never get enough practice to solidify and master the ideas and, even when mastered, the ideas are forgotten. The Review questions must be assigned to ensure optimum performance.

Strategies for Mastery

Some students master the content of one lesson in one day; but many do not. Why then do we suggest that you spend only one day per lesson? We do so because the combination of Review questions in each lesson and the end-of-chapter material has proved to be a powerful vehicle for achieving mastery, while allowing teachers and students to cover a substantial amount of material.

The mastery strategy used at the end of each chapter of UCSMP *Precalculus and Discrete Mathematics* is one that has been validated by a great deal of research. Its components are a Progress Self-Test (the "formative test" in the parlance of some mastery learning literature), solutions to that test in the student's textbook (the "feedback"), review questions tied to the same objectives used to make up the self-test (the "correctives"), and finally a chapter test covering the same objectives.

Following the strategy means assigning the Progress Self-Test as a homework assignment to be done under simulated test conditions. The next day should be devoted to answering student questions about the problems and doing some problems from the Chapter Review.

For most classes, as a second night's assignment, we suggest the even-numbered questions from the Chapter Review. Neither solutions nor answers to the even-numbered questions are in the student text, so students will have to work on their own without these aids. The next day, discuss these questions in class.

Give the test on the third day. The odd-numbered Chapter Review questions, for which answers are given in the student text, can be useful for studying for that test. In some classes, a third day before the test may be needed. If so, either the odd-numbered Chapter Review questions, selected Lesson

Masters, or questions generated by the TestWorks CD-ROM can be used as sources of problems. The test should be returned to students so that they can see how they did and learn from their errors. You may wish to give students some credit for correcting errors on their tests.

We strongly recommend that, except for classes of exceptionally talented students (where less review may be needed), teachers follow this strategy. The evidence is substantial that it promotes higher levels of performance.

Using Technology

We use calculators and computers in UCSMP because they are tools important to most users of mathematics today, whether on the job or in one's personal life. They are popular because they make important mathematical ideas accessible to students at an early age and to people who might otherwise find mathematics difficult; they relieve the drudgery of calculation, particularly with numbers and equations encountered in realistic contexts; they enable quick picturing of mathematical ideas; and they facilitate exploration and open-ended problem solving by making multiple instances easy to examine. Furthermore, our use of technology has resulted in no loss of paper-and-pencil skill in arithmetic, and has freed up time in the curriculum to spend on other topics that lead to overall better performance by UCSMP students.

Calculators Hand-held calculators first appeared in 1971. Not until 1976 did the price for a four-function calculator come below \$50 (equivalent to well over \$150 today). Still, in 1975, a national commission recommended that hand calculators be used on all mathematics tests starting in eighth grade, and in 1980 the National Council of Teachers of Mathematics recommended that calculators be used in all grades of school from kindergarten on. The ACTs and the SAT I, SAT II, and Advanced Placement tests of the College Board already allow all standard scientific and graphing calculators. Several standardized test batteries are being developed with calculators. And slowly but surely calculators are being expected on more and more licensing exams outside of school.

The business and mathematics education communities generally believe that paper-and-pencil algorithms are becoming obsolete. Do not be surprised. The long division algorithm we use was born only in the late 1400s; it can have a death as well. Increasingly, businesses do not want their employees to use paper-and-pencil algorithms to get answers to arithmetic problems. Banks require that their tellers do all arithmetic using a calculator.

It is wonderful to live in the age when calculators have been developed that quickly and efficiently do arithmetic. This frees us to use arithmetic more and allows students to spend more time on mental arithmetic, estimation, and problem solving. It is inevitable that calculators will be considered as natural as pencils for doing mathematics. A century from now people will be amazed when they learn that some students as recently as the 1990s went to schools where calculators were not used. Students of the future will no doubt consider it cruel and unusual punishment.

In the early 1970s, computer programs appeared that could do algebra and calculus and differential equations and linear algebra symbolically. In the early 1990s, the first easy-to-use calculators with this capability appeared, but they were too expensive to expect student purchase. Recently the prices of these calculators has started to decrease, and you should not find it unusual if some of your students have such calculators.

Students *will* overuse calculators. Part of learning to use any machine is to make mistakes: using it when you shouldn't, not using it when you should. Anyone who has a word processor has used it for short memos that could much more easily have been handwritten. Anyone who has a microwave has used it for food that could have been cooked either in a conventional oven or on top of the stove.

The overuse dies down, but it takes some months. In the meantime, stress this important idea. There are three ways to get answers to problems: by paper and pencil, mentally, or by using some automatic means (a table, a calculator, a trusty friend, etc.). Some problems require more than one of these means, but the wise user of mathematics knows when to use each of these ways.

Generally this means that good mathematicians do a lot of calculations mentally, either because they are basic facts (e.g., 3×5) or because they follow simple rules (e.g., $2/3 \times 4/5$ or 100×4.72). They picture graphs of functions without writing them down. They may not use a calculator in these situations because the likelihood of making an error entering or reading is greater than the likelihood of making a mental error. As a rule, we seldom say, "Do not use calculators here." We want students to learn for themselves when calculator use is appropriate and when it is not. However, you may feel the need to prod some students to avoid the calculator. An answer of 2.9999999 instead of $\sqrt{9}$ should be strongly discouraged. Similarly, students should not use a calculator if they need only to graph a linear function. However, they may wish to use calculators to do simple calculations or draw simple graphs if that is only one part of a more difficult or complicated problem.

Graphing calculators In this book we often refer to an *automatic grapher.* By this we mean a graphing calculator or a computer with a function grapher. For this course, we assume that students have graphing calculators like those of the TI-80s family, Casio fx-7700G, or Sharp EL 9300C. A good graphing calculator should display as many as four graphs simultaneously, allow the window to be changed with ease, and in general be easy to use. Graphing calculators can perform all the operations we expect in a scientific calculator. Though their order of operations is often different from that found in scientific calculators, and key sequences for scientific calculators will often not work with them, their key sequences more closely parallel what is written on a page.

If students do not have access to an automatic grapher, do not have high expectations of student success. It takes time to do a good graph, and many questions require rather complicated graphs.

The reasons for a graphing calculator go beyond the fact that they can display the graph of any function students will encounter in this course. They have the advantage of displaying numbers in computations, allowing students to more easily see patterns and detect errors in their work. Many of them have the ability to perform statistical operations such as finding a line of best fit. Recent models can generate tables, which enables them to simulate spreadsheet operations. A nice summary of research on graphing calculators is available (Dunham and Dick, 1994).

There is also available today calculator-size technology from Texas Instruments, Casio, and Hewlett-Packard that can do all algebraic manipulation, and we encourage their use. Your classroom should certainly have such a calculator for checking work, if for no other reason. When we were planning the second edition of this text, our teachers were nearly unanimous in feeling that these calculators are too expensive to require their purchase by students. However, cheaper models are now beginning to appear.

Computers The computer is a powerful tool for you to use in your classroom to demonstrate the relationships, patterns, properties, and algorithms of mathematics (see, e.g., Heid and Baylor, 1993). From the very first chapter of this book, questions appear in which a computer could be helpful, either for displaying or analyzing data or graphing a function or simulating an experiment. Do not ignore these questions even if you do not have computers available. The goal is not to teach computer programming, but to use the computer as a tool. Students are not surprised that the computer can do difficult tasks, but many students are surprised that a computer can do easy things, for instance, act as a calculator.

Some questions ask students to use a computer. If students do not have access to a computer, exercise caution in your assigning of such questions. As mathematical tools, a desirable computer has the ability to deal with a good amount of data and to display graphs with accuracy and precision. *GraphExplorer* and *StatExplorer* software, published by Scott Foresman Addison Wesley for IBM (or IBM compatibles) and Macintosh computers, is designed for this course.

Computers also enable links to the Internet, which is of particular advantage to classes using *Precalculus and Discrete Mathematics* because the

Internet makes accessible a large amount of information. In the References (page T64) we have indicated some of the particular Internet locations that were found to be most useful in writing the Second Edition.

Programming Many graphing calculators are programmable. At times in UCSMP *Precalculus and Discrete Mathematics* we give programs in a calculator programming language. We have chosen the TI-82 language because this is the most commonly found calculators in UCSMP classes, and because the syntax of the programs closely parallels that of the BASIC language.

The BASIC computer language is used in this book because it is available for the computers which are most popular in American schools and because it is easy to understand and translate into other languages. Programs have been kept short so that students can type them relatively quickly. It is not necessary for every student to type and run a program. Most programs can be used as classroom demonstrations.

Computer educators have recommended that students be required to provide a block structure to programs; document their programs with abundant remarks; and declare variables. Since this is a mathematics course, not a programming course, you should emphasize the computational steps of a program. Can the students follow the steps of a program and tell what the output will be? Can the student modify a given program to solve an exercise with different values?

Whether you are a novice or expert in programming, we encourage you to try the programs we provide on your own system. Each version of BASIC and each calculator has slightly different characteristics, and our generic programs may need to be modified slightly for your system.

Projects

The very positive responses from teachers and students of the First Edition of both *Functions, Statistics, and Trigonometry* and *Precalculus and Discrete Mathematics* to the projects in those books led us to develop projects for each chapter of the Second Edition of other UCSMP texts. Each project is an extended activity, often open-ended, meant to take the student several hours to complete. Some projects provide

an opportunity to engage in library research; others require that students draw or build something; some require the student to collect data through surveys or measurements; others involve independent work with computers. The Projects are designed for the wide range of interests and abilities one might find in a class of average students.

The projects serve many purposes.

(a) Students experience using real data in a mode comparable to that actually used by people in business, science, and many other careers.

(b) Students understand that a higher level of persistence than normal is expected. Too often in mathematics the greatest demand we make of students is to apply 5–10 minutes of effort on a single task. Longer-term projects demand more persistence and stretch a student's personal level of expectation.

(c) Projects, with some allowances for student choice, provide a sense of ownership of a task.

(d) Projects provide a chance for students to share their learning publicly in a visual or oral presentation.

(e) Projects provide an opportunity for students to apply graphic, writing, and oral talents in mathematical situations.

(f) Projects provide an alternative way to assess students' achievement.

(g) Projects provide an opportunity for students to work together.

The Projects appear immediately after the last lesson in the chapter, but we do not recommend that they be done immediately after the last lesson has been completed. Typically this would interrupt the flow of the chapter. You can schedule work on them in a number of ways. Here are two suggestions: (1) Assign one project when you reach the middle of a chapter, due in the middle of the next chapter. (2) Assign one project per grading period from any of the chapters covered in that period. Some teachers are more comfortable limiting the students' choice of projects at the beginning (e.g., do any one of Projects 2 or 5); other teachers want to give students free choice at all times. Do whatever makes sense for you and your class.

All students need guidance on projects, even if they have done projects in previous UCSMP courses. Be very specific and clear on what you expect (e.g. length of paper, format of poster, number of minutes of oral presentation, etc.). If possible, show sample student work. Tell students how you will grade their work. You may want to use the first project as a trial run, with somewhat relaxed grading standards. Then you can show (without mentioning names) work you consider exemplary, and work which is good but not exemplary, in preparation for the second project. English, social studies or art teachers, or the school librarian can often assist with advice on how to structure assigning or grading projects.

Here are two suggested ways to grade projects: (1) Give a certain number of points for various parts of the project, e.g., 20 points for completing all required work, 20 points for the mathematical content, 5 points for neatness and organization, and 5 points for mechanics of the paper (spelling, grammar, etc.); then convert the total number of points (in the previous case as a percent of 50) to the grading scale you use on other assignments. Teachers using this type of grading scheme often give a small number of bonus points for creativity. (2) Use a holistic approach. Develop a set of general criteria (often called a rubric), and sort the papers into categories based on your criteria. This is the way many English and social studies teachers grade papers. See Stenmark (1989, 1991) for descriptions of rubrics with four and seven categories developed in California for use in that state's mathematics assessment program.

We recommend that however you use the projects, please do not avoid them. They often have impact far beyond the mathematics classroom. Teachers from one school remarked that by the end of the year graphs like those that had been made for projects were appearing in the school yearbook! In fact, you may find students to be encouraged if they are given time to put together a first-rate presentation to be displayed on a bulletin board or a school display case, or to be entered in a mathematics fair.

Teaching

Teaching Models and Strategies

Traditionally teachers have relied heavily on lecture, supervised practice, and recitation of answers as their dominant modes of instruction. When these dominate instruction, the mathematics studied is often limited to simple algorithms which can be easily mimicked, and students learn to depend almost exclusively on the teacher as the sole source of their information.

In recent years the importance of communication skills in all school subjects has been noted. To achieve these skills students must read, write, and speak to each other in class. These skills are in line with the broader curricular and process goals of UCSMP *Precalculus and Discrete Mathematics* and are more easily developed in classrooms which are dominated less by the teacher, that is, in classrooms in which students are actively engaged throughout the period.

Thus, in effective UCSMP classrooms, one sees smaller amounts of lecture, recitation, and individual seatwork than in comparison classes, and more discussions in small groups or with the whole class, individual or group work with calculators, computers, or other physical materials, and opportunities for students to do extended projects outside of class. Also, students read more of the book outside of class because they realize that this reading enables more to go on inside class.

The notes with each lesson in this Teacher's Edition provide a variety of teaching ideas, grouped under the following categories: Warm-up, Notes on Reading, Additional Examples, Optional Activities, Notes on Questions, Adapting to Individual Needs, Assessment, and Extension. All lessons contain more ideas than can be used in one period. None of the lists is exhaustive; there are innumerable ways to teach any lesson.

You should use your professional judgment to select and sequence the activities you think are appropriate for the length of your class period and your students' needs. This selection needs to be made before you enter class. We note that teachers who have never used group work, manipulatives, or technology often assume that they are very time-consuming. Our experience is that, when well-planned ahead of time, many such activities can be done in relatively short periods of time, and we encourage you to try them. Also, you should understand that when a particular type of activity is done for the first time, it always takes longer because students need more guidance. The second time to the computer lab, or using group work, or presenting projects, or bringing out some manipulatives should go more easily than the first.

A variety of teaching models and strategies have been effectively used in the classroom by UCSMP teachers. Some teachers have students read each lesson and do all the questions before class. Then the teacher and students (sometimes in small groups, sometimes as the entire class) discuss the lesson and engage in various activities related to it during the next period. Some teachers preview the next day's lesson with some guidance as to the key points they think their students will need in reading or doing the questions. Some teachers begin the reading of the next lesson in class.

With less-prepared students, teachers need to adjust strategies. Most teachers do more back-and-forth explaining, engage in more manipulative activities, and use more Lesson Masters. Group work is often more important in these classes. Some teachers prefer these kinds of behaviors with all their classes.

To give you a better picture of the variety of instructional techniques employed in classes using UCSMP materials, we have included reprints of the articles, "A 'Typical Day' in a UCSMP Classroom," and "Using Cooperative Reading Strategies," both written by experienced UCSMP teachers.

A "TYPICAL DAY" IN A UCSMP CLASSROOM

by Sharon Mallo, Lake Park High School, Roselle, IL

No matter how much our textbooks may or may not change over the years, one fact remains: students have different learning styles, and teachers need to address each of them. Therefore, there's really no "typical day" in the classroom. In my classroom, means of presentation vary from lesson to lesson, with common threads woven in for continuity and class management. The threads that tie my teaching strategies together are those that reinforce good mathematics study skills and those that help students "learn how to learn."

The UCSMP program gives me an easy-to-use, flexible tool through which to accomplish these goals. I'd like to show you some of the ways I use the supplementary materials and options in the program for presenting lessons—particularly the UCSMP Lesson Masters, Technology Masters, Teaching Aids, and Activity Sourcebook. Each class begins with a warm-up activity, followed by coverage of the previous day's homework. These two activities take up no more than half of the class period. Next, there is an introduction to the new lesson, followed by a related activity.

Warm-up Activity

The warm-up activity usually consists of the Lesson Master from the previous day's lesson being handed out as students arrive. I ask students to work out some or all of the questions, depending on the length of the master. This allows me to identify students who are having difficulty. I give individual help, reteach, and/or ask students to help each other as I circulate. For example, on the day I will be teaching Lesson 4-2, I will use Lesson Master 4-1 as the warm-up.

The warm-up can also be cooperative. Each student does the warm-up, and then students exchange papers and solve the problems.

The warm-up can also be a lead-in for today's lesson or a problem-solving activity that will later tie into today's lesson. This kind of warm-up is often found in this Teacher's Edition.

▶

Going Over Homework

One of my most important requirements is that students correct each answer on their homework and write out the steps for answers they've gotten wrong. Using the answers found at the back of the book to correct their work is part of the assignment. Students have already marked problems they need help with before coming to class. After we've done the warm-up activity, I'll put answers on the overhead projector. Then we discuss problems I've chosen as the most important or students have identified as stumbling blocks. Three or four times during the chapter, I have students discuss their questions within their cooperative groups, (Groups have one high, two middle, and one low student, and they change after every two chapter tests.)

Students need a reason to be concerned about whether or not their homework answers are correct and, more importantly, how to get the correct answer. I give an unannounced Homework Quiz once or twice a week. Students use their own notebooks of homework assignments and a clean sheet of paper—no textbook. They divide their papers into four or six sections. I do the same on a transparency to show them which questions I want. Students are to copy the correct answer for each question from their notebooks. If they've made the corrections in their notebooks, each student should have a perfect paper. It takes five to ten minutes to correct a set of these quizzes. Scores are low at the beginning of the school year but they steadily get better.

Presenting a Lesson

The method I choose to present a lesson depends on the difficulty of the content and the applications. With a lesson that is difficult, we may review it together and I stop students at each Example.

If the students are able to read a lesson on their own, either in school or at home, I focus their reading. Vocabulary words (not their definitions) are pointed out. Sometimes I write an Additional Example from the margin of the Teacher's Edition and tell students that they should have an idea of how to solve it once they've read the lesson. Now they have a purpose for reading.

When students have read a difficult lesson in class, I put one of the Additional Examples on the overhead. (Some are already on transparencies in the Teaching Aids.) Then I ask students to find the parallel Example in the reading. This is one of the hardest things for them to do when they get stuck on a problem at home, so we practice it in class.

I do lectures and give notes on a lesson about 10–15 percent of the time. This is usually after students have read the lesson and done the Covering the Reading questions. The most common assignment I give is to complete the Applying the Mathematics, Review, and Exploration questions of a given lesson and then to read or re-read the following lesson and do Covering the Reading. Occasionally, they read a lesson and do all the questions, and once in a while I develop an assignment from outside the book.

As you can see, there is no "typical day" in my classroom. With UCSMP, my students are not afraid to tackle problems, and they're learning how to learn.

Lesson 4-2	
#8	#12
#18	#22

Lesson 5-6	Lesson 5-7
#14	#18
Lesson 5-8	**Lesson 5-8**
#14	#30
Lesson 5-9	**Lesson 5-9**
#18	#24

Sharon Mallo has been teaching UCSMP courses in the Chicago area since 1984. She is an author on the Second Edition of UCSMP Transition Mathematics.

USING COOPERATIVE READING STRATEGIES:

Students helping each other understand their textbook

by Tom Stone, Sheldon High School, Eugene, OR

There are many ways in which cooperative learning strategies can be used effectively in the mathematics classroom. Because of the important role reading plays in determining students' success in the UCSMP program, I would like to focus on this application of these strategies and to share some ways that the use of cooperative learning groups can help students learn good reading habits.

First, let me briefly explain my classroom organization. My students are familiar with two seating arrangements: 1) individual seating in six rows of desks, and 2) group seating with each set of four desks formed into a tight square. Each student in the group is assigned a number, 1 through 4. I do this for management purposes which should become clear later. The following scenarios illustrate how I use small-group instruction to help my students with their reading.

Scenario 1 (Key Ideas)
Students are seated individually. After identifying a few vocabulary words they will encounter, I assign the reading of Section 1-3 in the textbook. Students read the material individually and take notes as they go along. When they have had time to finish, they move into their groups. Using his/her notes, Student 1 in each group selects a major idea from the reading and shares it with the group. After several minutes, Student 2 in each group discusses another idea found in the reading. This is continued until all four students in each group have had an opportunity to share. In this way, students receive important practice identifying the key ideas from a given section of their book.

Scenario 2 (Share the Pain)
Say the reading of a lesson is to be done outside of class as part of the homework assignment and includes two examples that I expect will be difficult for my students to read. Therefore, I have them encounter the challenging part of the reading in class in teams before they try to handle it on their own outside of class. I assign the reading of the first example to Students 1 and 2 in each group and the second example to Students 3 and 4. After students have completed the reading, they move into their groups. Students 1 and 2 discuss their understanding of the first example while Students 3 and 4 do the same with the second example. Now all students should be able to comprehend the reading of the section on their own.

Scenario 3 (Experts)
Sometimes I break a lesson into four parts. Student 1 is assigned to read the first ideas, Student 2 the second, and so on. Upon finishing the reading, students move into their groups and each student takes a turn presenting to the rest of the group. Then students begin working on the problem set for the section. Each student acts as the "expert" for questions related to the idea for which he/she was responsible.

Scenario 4 (The Set-up)
Let's suppose my class is going to learn about a new idea tomorrow. Today, I have students move into their groups and I give each team a worksheet to do together. Tonight, the students will be well prepared to read about the new idea.

The above scenarios are only a few examples of how small-group instruction and cooperative-learning strategies can be used to help students develop the skill needed for reading mathematics. Equally important, they provide variety in lesson structure. I hope that the ideas presented here are helpful and can serve as catalysts for generating more ideas that can be put to effective use in the classroom.

Tom Stone has taught UCSMP Transition Mathematics, Algebra, Geometry, *and* Advanced Algebra. *He was chosen as the 1991 Oregon Secondary Mathematics Teacher of the Year by the American Electronic Association.*

Using the Reading

In order to become an independent learner of mathematics, a student must learn to learn mathematics from reading. You should expect students to read all lessons. At the beginning of the course, this may require time in class. Do not expect overnight changes in behavior from students who have never read their math book before except to find questions to solve.

A student in UCSMP *Precalculus and Discrete Mathematics* who has studied from previous UCSMP texts will generally be accustomed to reading mathematics. But students new to UCSMP texts may require some period of adjustment to a new style of text and to new types of questions. Such students may never have been asked to read mathematics. As a result, it is common for students to ask why they have to read.

We tell them: You must read because you must learn to read for success in all future courses that use mathematics, not just in mathematics; because you must learn to read for success in life outside of school and on any job; because the reading will help you understand the uses of mathematics; because the reading contains interesting information; because the reading tells you how the material from one lesson is related to other material in the book; because there is not enough time in class to spend doing something that you can do in a study period or at home. Of course, in college students will normally be expected to read from a textbook or other printed material and learn from that reading.

Students often do not know how to read a mathematics text. They read too quickly and they gloss over little words ("if," "but," "not," and so on) that may be very important to the meaning of a statement. Students may not be able to read $\log_3 5$ (the logarithm of 5 to the base 3) or 8! (8 factorial) or $\sqrt[4]{x} + 5 < 9$ (the fourth root of x plus 5 is less than 9). They may not realize that text and graphics are often related and they should move back and forth from one to the other. Thus on occasion it is important to have students read out loud.

To teach (or remind) your students how to read mathematics, we suggest that at the beginning of the school year some class time be spent reading a lesson in class. You can have students read out loud, and give them feedback on their ability to read technical words and symbols correctly. (In general, it is not a good idea to call on students in any particular obvious order. That just gets some students nervous that their turn is coming up, and encourages others not to pay attention, because they are likely not to be called on.) Be sure to point out how the colored headers in the lessons help outline the important concepts and provide an overview (advance organizer) of what they are about to read.

You might have students answer the Covering the Reading questions orally, and point out how these questions are meant to test comprehension of the material in the text. The answers for these questions can be found literally in the reading or by mimicking worked examples. The questions can be used as oral exercises during or after oral reading of the text, or as part of a written assignment. Once students are comfortable with the format of the lessons, we suggest you begin to expect that reading be done outside of class on a regular basis.

Some days you may want to ask some questions that set up the reading of the lesson. Other days you might give a brief summary of the key ideas in the reading, have students read silently in class, and then ask them to identify where in the exposition those main ideas are covered. Once students have become somewhat comfortable with reading on their own, you can rely more and more on them to summarize or probe key ideas without your assistance.

To help stress the importance of reading as a tool for learning mathematics, some teachers give brief (2–5 minute) "reading quizzes" at the beginning of class. These may consist of a request for a summary of the key ideas in the text, or the answers to several even-numbered questions from the homework. Doing so for 3 or 4 consecutive days early in the year lets students know you are serious about their attempts to do the reading and to answer the questions. Allowing students to use their notes, but not their book, encourages students to take good notes, and to organize their solutions to homework problems.

Although we believe that reading their text is an important strategy by which students learn mathematics, we know that it is not the only way they learn. In particular, if you want to give a brief overview of the new lesson before students read it, please do. We do, however, wish to discourage the practice of *always* explaining how to do questions before the students have had the opportunity to learn on their own. Particularly counterproductive is to tell students that certain problems do not have to be tried "because we have not yet done them in class." This only teaches students that they cannot learn on their own and to be dependent on you.

Students learn enormous amounts from discussing alternate strategies to problems with you and their classmates, from engaging in well-constructed activities, and from doing open-ended explorations and projects. By teaching students to read outside of class, you are free to use class time more creatively and effectively than if you were compelled to develop all major ideas yourself in class.

Going Over Homework Questions

Feedback to student work is very important, and to reinforce the positive aspects of doing homework it is important to go over questions. We are frequently asked how we want the teacher to go over the questions. Our response is that there are multiple ways to do so. We recommend that each teacher use a couple of methods regularly so students can get used to a routine, and use a couple of others occasionally for variety.

Below are some of the more commonly used techniques which we support:

1. Show answers (using the Answer Masters provided) on an overhead projector at beginning of period; have students correct their own papers (you can use time to take roll); have whole class discussion on questions that were particularly troublesome.
2. Same as (1) above; but after students have checked their own papers, have them form groups of 2 to 4 to discuss what they missed; after a few minutes have a whole class discussion only on questions the groups could not resolve.
3. Have students form small groups; provide one copy of answers on paper to each group; have groups discuss what they missed; after a few minutes have a whole class discussion only on questions the groups could not resolve.
4. Read all answers out loud; have students correct their own papers; when done reading answers, have whole class discussion to explain questions that were particularly troublesome.
5. Have students write the numbers of the questions they could not answer on the board as they come into class; have them put tick marks after numbers to indicate how many students want to discuss that one; have student volunteers do those problems on the board, and explain their work; explain how to do the ones no student could solve.
6. Preselect questions which you feel are particularly important or may be particularly troublesome; have a whole class discussion about those.

It is important to remember that "going over the homework" should be more than providing correct answers. It is a wonderful opportunity to consider alternate solution strategies, to address any misconceptions that are uncovered, to relate ideas in one question to ideas in another, and to extend ideas in the questions via "what if" questions. In short, it is an opportunity to have the kind of rich classroom discourse described in the NCTM's *Professional Teaching Standards*. Many ideas are given in the Notes on Questions for each lesson. Do not ignore these notes; they indicate which questions are important to discuss so that students will be better-prepared for the next lesson. Virtually all of these notes were written either by authors of the text and indicate why the question is there, or by teachers suggesting ideas they had while reviewing the questions.

Writing in Mathematics

The NCTM *Curriculum and Evaluation Standards* stress the importance of students' ability to communicate mathematics. Through writing, communication opens up in the classroom on a variety of levels. As they write, students apply concepts to their own experience; construct meaning for mathematical symbols, procedures, and concepts; and internalize meaning as they explore and examine mathematical ideas in words.

At times, writing may consist simply of the steps in answering a question, but to be most effective it should be more than that. It can include comments about what was being done, why a particular strategy was chosen, and how the student felt about the question. The careful examination of thought that writing requires may lead students to see the process of thinking as more important than the ability to quote rules; consequently, mathematics becomes a richer pastime. Furthermore, students will be developing a skill that many of them will need throughout their lives, the ability to explain what they are thinking to others.

In UCSMP *Precalculus and Discrete Mathematics* we often ask students to write explanations of what they are doing. Do not be surprised if at first students' explanations are vague, imprecise, or too brief. Writing good explanations takes time, experience, and guidance, and students may have never been asked to write in their previous mathematics classes. You can encourage greater thoroughness and effectiveness by discussing good explanations in the text with your students. The solutions of the examples in each lesson are meant to serve as models. The portions of the solutions that you may expect students to write are printed in a special font.

To be considered important by students, writing must be discussed in class. Reading good student efforts aloud in class can encourage good writing. Having students read their own efforts in small groups or to the entire class can inform them about whether others understood what they wrote. Writing and talking are part of the communication that is necessary to learn the language of mathematics.

There are different forms which writing may take. *Chatter* refers to writing explanations of procedures a student used to solve a problem. It can communicate a student's thought process, and can therefore alert you (and the student!) to hidden misconceptions and incomplete understandings as well as to wonderful insights. Arthur Powell of Rutgers University suggests that chatter be written in a separate column of the page from the actual solution of the problem.

Journal writing is believed by some people to be one of the most effective methods of writing to learn mathematics; however, informal explorative writing in class and on homework (not necessarily in a bound or spiral notebook) achieves similar results. Journals and *informal explorative writing* allow students to put concepts in their own words, to speculate on extensions to problems, and to relate material they are learning to what they already know. This kind of writing allows students to write freely without worrying excessively over mechanics. It also can focus students' minds. Writing at the beginning of a period can interest and involve students in a topic; writing at the end of a period can help them to summarize and organize what happened that day.

Here is some general advice: If you use journals, you may wish to keep the journals in the classroom; asking students to bring yet another item to class may prove difficult for them and frustrating to you. For this reason, informal explorative writing on ideas and on homework may prove to be a better option.

In general, undirected journal writing does not provoke as much focus or response from students as carefully and thoughtfully worded questions, sometimes called *prompts*. The more concise the prompt, the better. Longer, more complex prompts that are intended to yield more writing often do not.

Collect and examine journals regularly to communicate to students that they are important. You do not have to examine all journals at the same time. (Reading students' writing is often not as time-consuming as you might think, and it can be very interesting.) Give credit for journals, but don't grade them. When giving credit, look for frequency and length of entries and for self-initiated topics. Give feedback on the writing to students; comments indicate that you care. Do not emphasize mechanics or grammar. Above all, be patient and flexible.

Do not penalize students when they don't write. When students have difficulty writing, claiming they do not know what to say, you might try freewriting, an activity where the goal is simply to empty thoughts on the page without censoring. Write yourself and share what you wrote with your students.

It is appropriate to keep examples of student writing of mathematics in a portfolio along with other examples of student work.

Dealing with Individual Differences

Every student differs from all others in many ways. Differences in ability, entering knowledge, willingness to work, interest, learning style, and cultural background are the most commonly referred to by teachers and researchers.

In Section 1 of this Professional Sourcebook, we point out that not enough is known about individual differences in ability to make judgments based on them. Individual differences in entering knowledge are far better predictors. These differences are great enough to warrant differences in what is offered to students at a particular grade level, and based on them we suggest that students take UCSMP courses at different ages. However, a wide range of entering knowledge exists within every class and needs to be considered when teaching.

For all students, we have included an enormous variety of activities, questions, and contexts to bring out the brilliance, surprise, applicability, and structure of mathematics, and to appeal to students with the panoply of cultural backgrounds found in the United States. These are found in the student book and in this Teacher's Edition as well. You should take these into account, because familiar contexts are critical to the understanding of mathematics, the contributions of various cultures are important in conveying the universality of mathematical ideas, and because it helps students to develop a sense of ownership of these ideas. Differences in interest can be handled by giving students choice of the end-of-chapter Projects, by asking students to elaborate on questions and or ideas they particularly liked, and by other optional activities.

For better-prepared students, or students with more willingness to work, you may wish to offer, assign, and discuss:

- Challenge and Extension problems and activities contained in the Teacher's Notes;
- Technology activities from the Technology Sourcebook;
- Contest problems from such sources as the American High School Mathematics Examination (AHSME)

For students needing more preparation or with limited language development, consider using:

- Suggestions for additional practice contained in these Teacher's Notes;
- Manipulative activities from the Activity Sourcebook;
- English Language Development and Extra Help activities provided in these Teacher's Notes.

We must stress that *many of these ideas should be used with all your students.* In particular, manipulative, technology, and other activities are appropriate for all students, and *all* students need some practice in order to develop high levels of competence.

Assessment

The NCTM Evaluation Standards provide some sensible guidelines for student assessment. The first is Alignment. Simply put, this standard suggests that you assess what you teach. In particular, because the UCSMP *Precalculus and Discrete Mathematics* course has much broader goals than most other courses at this level, many tests, quizzes, final exams, and other forms of assessment you have used in the past will not be appropriate for this course.

The second Evaluation Standard is Multiple Forms of Assessment. This standard reminds us that no single instrument is perfect. Each test, quiz, or homework assignment provides a small picture of what each student knows. A teacher who wants to develop mathematical power must use instruments which reflect the broad range of goals of the curriculum. In particular, using the Projects to assess understanding will give you insights into student thinking that you cannot get from tests and quizzes.

The third Evaluation Standard is Purposes of Assessment. This standard reminds the reader that instruments developed for one purpose usually are not appropriate for another purpose. Specifically, traditional standardized tests are usually not appropriate for evaluating students at the end of any single mathematics course because they are usually not well-aligned with the objectives of the course. The best measure of success of a student is the extent to which the student has accomplished the goals and objectives of the individual course.

Assessment Options

To help you accomplish the above goals, the Assessment Sourcebook (in the Teacher's Resource File) provides a wide variety of assessment instruments. These include Quizzes, Chapter Tests, Cumulative Tests (by chapter), Comprehensive Tests, and several types of alternative assessment. The Chapter Tests include parallel traditional Forms A and B, in which most questions are short-answer, and Forms C and D, which provide more open-ended performance assessment. We encourage you to examine all the available forms for a test and select the one you believe to be most appropriate for your students. The TestWorks CD-ROM enables you to produce a virtually unlimited number of versions for a quiz or chapter test. The notes in the Teacher's Edition provide additional assessment suggestions for every lesson.

Tests, quizzes, or homework assignments provide only a small picture of what each student knows. In order to help you develop your students' abilities to do open-ended questions or longer more elaborate tasks, you should consider the Exploration questions at the end of each lesson and the Projects at the end of each chapter as part of your assessment tool kit. (The grading of Projects is discussed on page T49.)

Understanding—The SPUR Approach

"Understanding" is an easy goal to have, for who can be against it? Yet understanding means different things to different people. In UCSMP texts an approach to the development of mathematical power is taken that we call the SPUR approach. The SPUR approach involves four different aspects, or dimensions, of understanding.

Skills: For many people, understanding mathematics means simply knowing how to get an answer to a problem with no help from any outside source. But in classrooms, when we speak of understanding how to use a calculator or a computer, we mean using the technology to do something for us. In UCSMP texts, these are both aspects of the same kind of understanding, the understanding of algorithms (procedures) for getting answers. This is the S of SPUR, the Skills dimension, and it ranges from the rote memorization of basic facts to the development of new algorithms for solving problems. These include doing things "in your head," with paper and pencil, or with technology.

Properties: During the 1960s, understanding why became at least as important as understanding how. Mathematicians often view this kind of understanding as the ultimate goal. For instance, mathematics courses for prospective elementary school teachers assume these college students can do arithmetic and instead teach the properties and principles behind that arithmetic. This is the P of SPUR, the Properties dimension, and it ranges from the rote identification of properties to the discovery of new proofs. UCSMP *Precalculus and Discrete Mathematics* is notable for its attention to this dimension of understanding.

Uses: To the person who applies mathematics, neither knowing how to get an answer nor knowing the mathematical reasons behind the process is as important as being able to use the answer. For example, a person does not possess full understanding of linear equations until that person can apply them appropriately in real situations. This dimension ranges from the rote application of ideas (for instance, when you encounter a direct-variation situation, form a proportion) to the discovery of new applications or models for mathematical ideas.

Representations: To some people, even having all three dimensions of understanding given above does not comprise full understanding. They require that students represent a concept and deal with the concept in that representation in some way. Ability to use concrete materials and models, or graphs and other pictorial representations demonstrates this dimension of understanding. This is the R of SPUR, the Representations dimension, and it ranges from the rote manipulation of objects to the invention of new representations of concepts. This dimension, too, is emphasized in UCSMP *Precalculus and Discrete Mathematics*.

There are continual arguments among educators as to which dimension should come first and which should be emphasized. For each there are people for whom that type of understanding is preeminent, and who believe that the other types do not convey the real understanding of mathematics.

Each dimension has aspects that can be memorized, and each has the potential for the highest level of creative thinking. Also, each dimension has its easy aspects and its difficult ones. Some skills (for example, long division) take at least as long to learn as geometry proofs; some uses are as easy as putting together beads. Furthermore, some students prefer applications, some would rather do manipulative skills, some most want to know the theory, and still others like the models and representations best. Thus we believe that the most effective teaching allows students opportunities in all these dimensions.

For a specific example of what understanding signifies in these four dimensions, consider the idea of standard deviation and what would constitute evidence of a simple form of that understanding in each dimension.

Some students prefere one of these dimensions over the others as a stepping point for learning mathematics. Some students prefer to begin with applications, some would rather use graphs, some work best from the theory, and still others like working through the skills. Most students need to work with several dimensions of understanding before a concept makes sense to them. One might say that a concept is not realized unless more than one of these dimensions are involved. Thus the most effective teaching allows students opportunities in all these dimensions.

In this book, you see the SPUR categorization at the end of each chapter with the Chapter Review questions. The Progress Self-Test for each chapter and the Lesson Masters (in the Teacher's Resource File) are also keyed to these objectives. We never ask students (or teachers) to categorize tasks into the various kinds of understanding; that is not a suitable goal. The categorization is meant to be a convenient and efficient way to ensure that the book provides the opportunity for teachers to teach and for students to gain a broader and deeper understanding of mathematics than is normally the case.

Skills understanding means knowing a way to obtain a solution. (Determine the end behavior of the function *f*, where $f(x) = \frac{150 \cdot 4000}{(4000 + x)^2}$.)

Properties understanding means knowing properties which you can apply. (Prove that the end behavior found is correct.)

Uses understanding means knowing situations in which you could apply the solving of this equation. (Know that *f* gives the approximate weight of an object *x* miles above Earth if the object weighs 150 lb at Earth's surface, and thus that its behavior as $x \to \infty$ should be 0, signifying a weightless object.)

Representations understanding means having a representation of the solving process or a graphical way of interpreting the solution. (The *x*-axis is an asymptote to the graph of the function *f*.)

Grading

No problem seems more difficult than the question of grading. If a teacher has students who perform so well that they all deserve As and the teacher gives them As a result, the teacher will probably not be given plaudits for being successful but will be accused of being too easy. This suggests that the grading scale ought to be based on a fixed level of performance, which is what we recommend. We recommend this because the performance that gives an A in one school or with one teacher may only rate a C in another, and we think it unfair.

Seldom in this book are there ten similar questions in a row. To teach students to be flexible, questions in UCSMP texts and on UCSMP tests have all sorts of wordings. The problems are varied because that's the way problems come in later courses and in life outside of school. We believe a student should be able to do each set of objectives at about the 85% mastery level. An 85% score on a test deserves no less than a high B, and probably an A. In the past, our tests have often led us to the following curve: 85–100 = A, 72–84 = B, 60–71 = C, 50–59 = D, 0–49 = F. Such a low curve alarms some teachers, but students in UCSMP courses generally learn more mathematics overall than students in comparison classes. We believe that the above grading policy rewards students fairly for work well done.

Some teachers have said our suggested grading scale is too easy. Maybe they have better students. They simply raise our scale. Why? Must every class have D students? Wouldn't it be nice if all students got As?

One January a teacher of *Transition Mathematics* presented us with a problem. She had to make out grades for the fall semester. Her quandary was as follows: "I've never had a class that learned so much, but my grades are lower." Later she said, "I have students who are failing. But I can't switch them to another class [using another book at the same level] because they know too much." Her problem was that she was using a 93–100 scale for A, 85–92 for B, 77–84 for C, and 70–76 for D. No wonder she had so many failures! Low percentages on tough tests are not unusual: scores on tests of higher-order thinking are generally lower than scores on tests of routine skills. To encourage students, we often make a basketball analogy. In a traditional course, all the shots students ever have are lay-ups (exercises) and an occasional free throw (easy problems). They shoot these over and over again, from the same spot ("Do the odds from 1–49."). In UCSMP *Precalculus and Discrete Mathematics,* almost every question is a different shot (a problem)—some close in, some from middle distance, and a few from half-court. To expect percentages of correct shots to be the same is unrealistic.

We have found that a word to your students about why your grading scale is "different" is helpful. They may be so accustomed to another grading scale that they feel they are doing poorly, while you think they are doing well.

Some teachers have found that because of the way that the Review questions maintain and improve performance, cumulative tests at the end of each marking period give students an opportunity to do well. The *Assessment Sourcebook* has Cumulative Tests for each chapter beginning with Chapter 2. When you want to practice one specific shot to make it automatic, we suggest focusing in on a few topics for quizzes.

Two final points: First, let students know what they need to know in order to get good grades. All research on the subject indicates that telling students what they are supposed to learn increases the amount of material covered and tends to increase performance. Second, have confidence in your students. Do not arbitrarily consign some of them to low grades. Let them know that it is possible for all of them to get As if they learn the material. If students perform well on tests, it has a real effect on interest and motivation. As the newer evaluation documents stress, you should endeavor to use grading as a vehicle for breeding success as well as for evaluating students.

RESEARCH AND DEVELOPMENT OF UCSMP *PRECALCULUS AND DISCRETE MATHEMATICS*

Planning and Selection of Authors

From its inception, UCSMP believed that students who finished the UCSMP secondary curriculum should be prepared for *all* the mathematics they would encounter in college, including statistics, discrete mathematics, linear algebra, and applied mathematics—in addition to a thorough grounding for calculus. In the early days of UCSMP, the last two courses in the secondary curriculum were entitled simply "Pre-College Mathematics 1" and "Pre-College Mathematics 2." After some discussions with the advisory board to the project, it was decided that, because of their importance to all college-bound students regardless of major, functions and statistics should be the two major themes of the first course. (See the corresponding material in the Professional Sourcebook for the course *Functions, Statistics, and Trigonometry* for details on the development of that course.)

The second course was planned to be for college-bound students who would major in technical subjects, including those who might major in mathematics, engineering, computer science, or physical sciences, or other areas that required a strong background in mathematics. The precalculus theme was seen as a natural continuation of the functions theme of the previous course, providing a two-year background for calculus where one year was the norm. A background in discrete mathematics was seen as appropriate not only for those who wished to major in computer science, but also for any other technical subjects. Two major themes for the second course, precalculus and discrete mathematics, were thus determined. Linear algebra, through work with transformations and matrices, was considered to have been covered rather well in previous courses, but it was felt that vectors should be discussed in this course. Applied mathematics is a theme of all UCSMP courses, and this theme was to be continued here. Lastly, it was considered critical that this book provide a smooth transition to the discourse of college mathematics, and thus also include work both with mathematical reasoning and proof and with the manipulative algebra required in some calculus courses.

It was natural, consequently, that both high school and college mathematics faculty were sought as members of the writing team. The two college members of the first writing team had important qualifications for such a task. Anthony Peressini, Professor of Mathematics at the University of Illinois at Urbana-Champaign, had been in charge of the university-wide placement examinations in mathematics and thus was acutely aware of the needs and possible shortcomings of entering college students with regard to preparation for calculus. Susanna Epp, Associate Professor of Mathematics at DePaul University, had been involved in a conference on reform of the collegiate curriculum and was in the process of completing a textbook on discrete mathematics. The two high school teachers, Kathleen Hollowell, who taught at Newton North H.S., Newton, MA, and Jack Sorteberg of Burnsville H.S., Burnsville, MN, had both taught many advanced high school courses, including advanced placement calculus, and were familiar with the use of technology in the classroom.

First Pilot Study

Writing began in the summer of 1987 and continued during the 1987–88 school year. The manuscript was edited at UCSMP by Denisse Thompson and Dora Aksoy, each of whom had experience with teaching this kind of content. Overall direction for UCSMP was given by Zalman Usiskin. Two of the authors of this manuscript and an author of another UCSMP book used the materials. The materials, entitled *Pre-College Mathematics,* were loose-leaf and sent to schools one chapter at a time. No formal testing was done at this stage, but the teachers commented on each lesson and twice were brought to the University of Chicago for full-day meetings.

Several themes emerged from the first draft and the first pilot. One was that discrete mathematics provided a wonderful setting for work with proof and allowed the theme of mathematical thinking to be sustained through the course. The second was that discussion of the precalculus ideas was quite affected by the existence of technology which gave the student the ability to graph functions, and though computers might not be required in such a course, graphing calculators should be recommended. (This theme seems obvious now, but remember that graphing calculators only first appeared in 1985, and were not as friendly as today's graphing calculators.) The third was that the manipulative algebra in this first pilot (work with the kinds of complex rational expressions one sometimes sees in calculus) was hard for the students. This was true even though the students tended to be stronger students who had taken two years of algebra from *non*-UCSMP texts and the teachers devoted a great deal of time to such manipulation. It became clear that, even at this level, manipulative algebra could not be successfully taught for its own sake; for maximum performance, it had to be in context.

Second Pilot Study

A major revision was made of the materials during the summer and fall of 1988. Greg McRill and Jeff Birky joined the editorial team during this year. In addition to the considerations given to the difficulty of lessons, to the clarity of the expositions, and to the value of the questions throughout the book, the second pilot also reflected the continuing increase in the use of graphing technology. Access to an automatic grapher was at first strongly recommended, and then became required. In this pilot, three schools in three states used the materials, none of them a school of an author. The materials were again loose-leaf, sent to schools one chapter at a time. The current title, *Precalculus and Discrete Mathematics,* reflecting the two major themes of the course, was used for the first time.

As in all other UCSMP evaluations, the teachers were asked to keep detailed records on each lesson. These were sent back to the project as the year progressed. Again, all teachers were invited to visit the University of Chicago during the year for full-day meetings to discuss all aspects of teaching and learning from the materials. There were three of these meetings.

Continuing a pattern found in earlier UCSMP courses, the use of technology seemed to make it possible for the materials to work well with a wide variety of students, from slow students at this level to the best-prepared. Teachers enjoyed the variety of content that the two themes engendered and particularly liked the work with proof. Some commented that, for the first time, their students were feeling successful with proof. Length of the manuscript, however, was seen as a problem.

Formative Evaluation and Test Results

In the summer of 1989, the materials were again revised into what was termed the Field Trial Edition. Because of the need to have more materials ready by the beginning of the school year, two experienced UCSMP authors, John McConnell and Susan Brown, were asked to join the writing team. Wade Ellis, Jr., of West Valley College, in Saratoga, California, an expert on the use of computers to teach mathematics, and an experienced teacher of students at the community college level, joined the team because of the increasing need to incorporate technology. The materials were printed in three spiral-bound parts with students and teachers receiving the course one part at a time.

The formative evaluation of *Precalculus and Discrete Mathematics (PDM)* is detailed in the doctoral dissertation of Denisse Thompson (Thompson, 1992). As a doctoral dissertation, it had the benefit of guidance from several University of Chicago faculty members from its design to its writing. Some results of the study can be found in journal articles (Thompson, Senk, and Viktora 1991; Thompson and Senk, 1993; Thompson 1996).

Many studies of implementation of materials look only at students. From previous UCSMP studies, we have learned that teachers utilize materials with such diversity that, for many questions, the teacher or the school is the appropriate level of study. Nine schools in eight states participated in this evaluation. These schools responded to a call for participants and were selected merely because they were the first to inform the project that they planned to use the materials in class-size quantities. Three schools are private, and six are public schools. Of the six public schools, two are in large cities (one being a magnet school), two are in mid-sized cities, one is in a small city, and one is in an affluent suburban area. At five of these schools, *PDM* was intended as a fifth-year course (with algebra considered as the first year) for students unprepared or unwilling to take calculus. At one site, calculus was not offered, and *PDM* replaced a fifth-year honors precalculus course. At three sites, *PDM* was a fourth-year course taken mostly by sophomore and junior students after an enriched second-year algebra/trigonometry course.

One teacher participated from each school. Four of the nine teachers had previously taught from UCSMP texts, but only one from a previous version of *PDM*. One was a first-year teacher. No special training was given the teachers. During the school year, all nine teachers met in Chicago in November and May to discuss how things were going in their classrooms and how they felt about the materials. Their classes were observed and some students were interviewed by Denisse Thompson.

A total of 180 students participated in the study, 53% male and 47% female. Most (70%) were seniors, 27% were juniors, and 3% were sophomores. The racial/ethnic background of the students was 73% white, 13% black, 9% Asian or Pacific Islander, 4% Hispanic or Latino, and 1% not known. Of the 175 students who responded to the question, all but one indicated definite plans to go to college. Almost all (96%) had used a scientific calculator before, and 15% had used a graphing calculator. A large percentage (69%) had computers at home. Of the 178 students who completed a form detailing their mathematics backgrounds, 29 (16%) had completed one previous UCSMP course—27 had *Functions, Statistics and Trigonometry* and 2 had *Advanced Algebra*—and 14 (8%) had both these courses.

No comparison classes were involved in this study, for it was impossible to give a test whose content was fair to both UCSMP and comparison classes.

During the first week of school, one of two forms of a 29-item pretest was given to all students. The pretest was designed to measure prerequisite skills and also to provide a base to see if student performance improved during the year. Different items on functions and algebraic skills were in the forms, and common to both forms were items on logic, proof, discrete mathematics, trigonometry, and calculus. The range of school means was wide, from 10.1 to 20.1. The three schools in which *PDM* was a fourth-year course ranked 2nd, 8th, and 9th among the nine schools on the pretest. In the lower scoring schools on the pretest, the students typically did not have the opportunity to master some of the function and trigonometry topics that are expected to have been mastered by entering *PDM* students. Thus the sample of students is perhaps less well prepared than a typical class of students that would take *PDM* today.

All of the classes utilized technology for graphing, finding zeros, and comparing functions. In seven of the nine schools, graphing calculators were used for these purposes; in six schools computers were used (four schools used both). In general, teachers and students who had graphing calculators used them several days per week, compared to an average of once a week for those who had computers.

Assessment of achievement occurred through the use of a mid-course proof test and a two-part posttest. The mid-course proof test consisted of two non-overlapping forms and was administered at the completion of Chapter 6 of the text. At this point, all forms of proof, except proof by mathematical induction, would have been covered. Each form contained 12 items, including number theory divisibility proofs, indirect proofs in the context of rational number properties, trigonometric identities, and the use of technology to test the truth of a statement.

The posttest consisted of two parts, a 32-question multiple-choice part that was the same for all students, and an open-ended part that had two forms each taken by half the students. Each open-ended test contained five items, including one proof of a trigonometric identity, one other proof, two questions about functions that required graphing technology, and a question applying the mathematics.

Students were quite successful on the trigonometric identity proofs on both the mid-course proof assessment and the open-ended posttest. On the mid-course proof test, when expected to "prove or disprove a given statement," the percentage successful ranged from 44% to 61%. When expected to "prove" a given statement, 87% of the students were successful in a fill-in-the-blank format and 75% were successful in completing the identity in its entirety. On the open-ended posttest, 83% were successful on an easy identity and 71% were successful on a more difficult identity.

On the mid-course proof test, about half of the students were successful on a number theory divisibility proof in a fill-in-the-blank format and about a third were successful when completing such a proof entirely on their own. On a similar item on the open-ended posttest, about a third of the students were successful. These proofs are items typically found only in college-level courses. About 43% of the students could explain how to use an automatic grapher to test the truth of a statement involving rational functions and about 83% could complete the same task in a trigonometric setting. Students developed the ability to use graphing technology for a wide variety of tasks.

Proof by contradiction and proof by mathematical induction were both difficult topics for students. About 37% of the students could explain the process of proof by contradiction, about 17% could write and prove their own statement using proof by contradiction, and about 3 to 4% could use proof by contradiction to prove a property of rational and irrational numbers. In retrospect, the context for these proofs was exceedingly difficult. Likewise, proof by mathematical induction was difficult for most students, with only 12% successful on the given proof item.

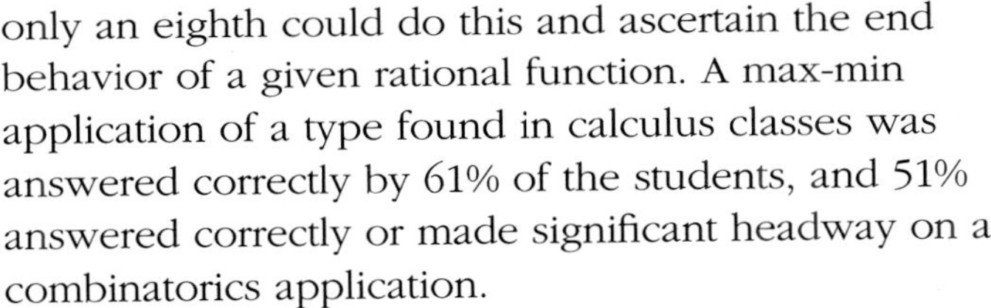

Almost all of the students (95%) used graphing technology on the open-ended test. Half of the students were able to graph complicated polynomial functions and could use the graph to determine zeros or relative extrema. Half could graph another rather complicated function, but only a third could find zeros of such a function, and only an eighth could do this and ascertain the end behavior of a given rational function. A max-min application of a type found in calculus classes was answered correctly by 61% of the students, and 51% answered correctly or made significant headway on a combinatorics application.

On the multiple-choice posttest, 17 items were repeated from one or both forms of the pretest. These items covered a variety of precalculus and discrete mathematics topics. The mean percent correct on these

Percent of teachers giving favorable ratings about textbooks

Item	UCSMP ($n = 9$)	Weiss ($n = 517$)
explains concepts clearly	89	73
develops problem-solving skills	89	68
good suggestions for computers	89	31
good suggestions for calculators*	89	27
good suggestions for activities/assignments	78	55
appropriate reading level	67	87
interesting to students	33	43
high quality supplements	33	33

(*The Weiss item was modified for this study to read "good suggestions for automatic graphers.")

items was 34% on the pretest and 65% on the posttest; the gains on items ranged from 5% to 58%. In general, the gains were about equal on discrete mathematics and precalculus topics. It is clear that students learned quite a bit in this course.

Because there had not been any comparison classes, a decision was made to use some items on the posttest that had been used in the Second International Mathematics Study (SIMS). Eleven items from SIMS were administered to the *PDM* students. On all eleven items, the percent of *PDM* students successful on the item was higher than the percent of SIMS students successful on the item. The difference in percents ranged from 6%, on an item dealing with identifying trigonometric properties, to 42% on an item dealing with finding the intersection of a polynomial function and the *x*-axis. Four of the six-items with the greatest differences deal with functions.

Teacher attitudes towards the book were compared with attitudes of teachers in a study by Iris Weiss of the Research Triangle Institute for the 1985–86 National Survey of Science and Mathematics Education. (The Weiss study deals with mathematics texts in all the grades 10–12, not merely texts at this level.)

The teachers were also asked to compare *PDM* in general to other texts at this level. Seven of nine responded, as follows: much better (4), slightly better (1), about the same (2), slightly worse (0), much worse (0).

Changes Made for the First Edition

The study of *Precalculus and Discrete Mathematics* convinced us that the approach we took is fundamentally sound. And, as was desired and is to be expected, the study suggested ways to improve the course. The first edition differed from the edition used in the formative evaluation in many ways. Many lessons and a few chapters were reworked to simplify the exposition and clarify connections between ideas. One chapter was deleted—some of its content was integrated with other chapters—in order to shorten the overall length of the text. The increasing use of graphing technology was accommodated throughout the book.

The ScottForesman first edition of *Precalculus and Discrete Mathematics* also included four colors, attractive pictures, an expanded Teacher's Edition, and many more supplementary materials for teachers and students, such as Lesson Masters for teachers who wish more questions on a particular lesson, Teaching Aids to help in explanations, and extra quizzes and tests.

Second Edition Study

To help in preparation for the second edition, towards the end of the 1995–96 school year we invited teachers who had attended UCSMP inservice sessions and taught *Precalculus and Discrete Mathematics* for at least one full year to evaluate each lesson of the text and each project, and to provide feedback on other aspects of the course, such as the use of technology. Seventeen teachers returned the long survey form. On the average, these teachers had taught *Precalculus and Discrete Mathematics* for 2.7 years, and 13 of them had also taught UCSMP *Functions, Statistics, and Trigonometry.*

In the average of the classes, 1% were sophomores, 27% were juniors, and 72% were seniors. About 80% of the sophomores and juniors were expecting to take AP calculus the next year, about 11% a non-AP calculus, and most of the rest a calculus class at a local college.

All of the classes used Texas Instruments calculators, most commonly the TI-82, but often the TI-85, and two used the TI-92. Only two of the teachers also used computers throughout the course. The teachers taught an average of 10 chapters of the book, omitting many of the reading lessons. Chapters 12, 11, and 13 were the most commonly deleted, in that order.

The ratings of lessons showed quite a bit of variation among the teachers, as one might expect. On a scale from -1 to 1, where -1 means make major changes, 0 means make minor changes, and 1 means keep as is, the average score of the 108 lessons was 0.67. This compares favorably with the corresponding statistic 0.53 for *Functions, Statistics, and Trigonometry.* No lesson was rated by more teachers in need of major change than to be kept as is. Lessons 1-1, 8-1,

8-5, 11-5, and 11-6 were rated by all teachers as keep as is, and many other lessons came close. By chapters, Chapter 3 was felt to need the most work and Chapters 9 and 11–13 the least. Lesson 7-8 was skipped by more teachers than any other non-reading lesson, but those who taught it rated it highly. The global results directed the authors to examine all lessons, but particularly a few lessons in which the teacher ratings were under 0.5. They also caused the removal of some of the reading lessons either because of low ratings or because of low usage.

Teachers were asked how the second edition of *PDM* should treat symbol manipulator technology. Two teachers felt such technology should be required; 11 felt it should be strongly recommended but their use made optional; 3 felt such technology should not be used. Many teachers who wished it should be used remarked that the present cost prevents requiring these sorts of calculators.

Half of the teachers (8 of 17) used the projects. These teachers were asked to suggest projects for deletion or for continued use. Teachers were also asked if they supplement the book; 11 of the 17 reported using additional materials, but aside from the technology masters available with the first edition, no more than two teachers supplemented in the same way.

Over the years 1992–96, UCSMP had also kept notes on comments made by many users of *Precalculus and Discrete Mathematics.* Scott Foresman editors, too, had kept notes on the lessons, both from their editing and from communications that had come directly to the publisher. The teachers in the second edition study described above were also asked to indicate errors they had found. Some of the second edition authors are experienced teachers of *Precalculus and Discrete Mathematics* who had made presentations about the book to school districts. Thus they had both first-hand experience and many discussions about the materials with other teachers. All of these comments were assembled and made available to the writing team. Writing by the second edition authors took place in the summer of 1996 and editing took place through the 1996–1997 school year.

Continuing Research and Development

Each August since 1989, UCSMP has sponsored an in-service on its texts open to all those who will be using the materials the next school year. We encourage users to attend these conferences.

Each November since 1985, UCSMP has sponsored an annual conference at the University of Chicago at which users *and* prospective users of its materials can meet with each other and with authors. This conference also provides UCSMP authors and staff with a valuable opportunity for reports on UCSMP materials from those not involved in formal studies.

Both Scott Foresman Addison Wesley, and UCSMP welcome comments on our books, and desire to know of any studies school districts conduct using these materials. Please address comments either to Mathematics Product Manager, Scott Foresman Addison Wesley, 1900 East Lake Avenue, Glenview, IL 60025, or to Zalman Usiskin, Director, UCSMP, 5835 S. Kimbark Avenue, Chicago, IL 60637.

Professional Sourcebook: SECTION  BIBLIOGRAPHY

References for Sections 1–4 of Professional Sourcebook

Beaton, Albert, et al., *Mathematics Achievement in the Middle School Years: IEA's Third International Mathematics and Science Study (TIMSS).* Boston: Boston College, 1996.

Center for the Assessment of Educational Progress. *A World of Differences.* Princeton, NJ: Educational Testing Service, 1989.

College Board. *Academic Preparation for College: What Students Need To Know and Be Able To Do.* New York: College Board, 1983.

Dunham, Penelope H., and Thomas P. Dick. "Research on Graphing Calculators." *The Mathematics Teacher,* September 1994, pp. 440–445.

Flanders, James. "How Much of the Content in Mathematics Textbooks Is New?" *Arithmetic Teacher,* September 1987: 18–23.

Heid, M. Kathleen and Terry Baylor. "Computing Technology." In *Research Ideas for the Classroom: High School Mathematics,* edited by Patricia S. Wilson. New York: Macmillan, 1993.

Johnson, David R. *Every Minute Counts.* Palo Alto, CA: Dale Seymour Publications, 1982.

Johnson, David R. *Making Minutes Count Even More.* Palo Alto, CA: Dale Seymour Publications, 1986.

Jones, Philip and Coxford, Arthur F. *A History of Mathematics Education in the United States and Canada.* 30th Yearbook of the National Council of Teachers of Mathematics. Reston, VA: National Council of Teachers of Mathematics, 1970.

Kroeze, David J., and Daniel P. Johnson. *Achieving Excellence: A Report of Initial Findings of Eighth Grade Performance from the Third International Mathematics and Science Study.* Northbrook, IL: First in the World Consortium, 1997.

McKnight, Curtis, et al. *The Underachieving Curriculum: Assessing U.S. School Mathematics from an International Perspective.* Champaign, IL: Stipes Publishing Company, 1987.

National Commission on Excellence in Education. *A Nation at Risk: The Imperative for Educational Reform.* Washington, DC: U.S. Department of Education, 1983.

National Council of Teachers of Mathematics. *Curriculum and Evaluation Standards for School Mathematics.* Reston, VA: National Council of Teachers of Mathematics, 1989.

National Council of Teachers of Mathematics. *Professional Standards for Teaching Mathematics.* Reston, VA: National Council of Teachers of Mathematics, 1991.

National Council of Teachers of Mathematics. *Assessment Standards for School Mathematics.* Reston, VA: National Council of Teachers of Mathematics, 1995.

National Research Council. *Everybody Counts.* Washington, DC: National Academy Press, 1989.

National Research Council. *For Good Measure.* Washington, DC: National Academy Press, 1991.

National Research Council. *Measuring Up: Prototypes for Mathematics Assessment.* Washington, DC: National Academy Press, 1993.

National Research Council. *Measuring What Counts.* Washington, DC: National Academy Press, 1993.

National Research Council. *Reshaping School Mathematics: A Philosophy and Framework for Curriculum.* Washington, DC: National Academy Press, 1991.

Schmidt, William H., et al. *Characterizing Pedagogical Flow: An Investigation of Mathematics and Science Teaching in Six Countries.* Norwell, MA: Kluwer Academic Publishers, 1996.

Steen, Lynn, editor. *On the Shoulders of Giants.* Washington, DC: National Academy Press, 1991.

Stenmark, Jean Kerr. Assessment Alternatives in Mathematics. Berkeley, CA: EQUALS, 1989.

Stenmark, Jean Kerr, editor. *Mathematics Assessment: Myths, Models, Good Questions, and Practical Suggestions.* Reston, VA: National Council of Teachers of Mathematics, 1991.

Thompson, Denisse Rubilee. "An Evaluation of a New Course in Precalculus and Discrete Mathematics." Ph.D. diss., University of Chicago, 1992.

Thompson, Denisse R. "Learning and Teaching Indirect Proof" *The Mathematics Teacher,* 89 (September 1996): 474–482.

Thompson, Denisse R. and Senk, Sharon L. "Assessing Reasoning and Proof in High School." In Norman L. Webb & Arthur F. Coxford (Eds.) *Assessment in the Mathematics Classroom,* pp. 167–176. Reston, VA: National Council of Teachers of Mathematics, 1993.

Thompson, Denisse R., Senk, Sharon L., & Viktora, Steven S. "Matrices at the Secondary School Level." In Margaret J. Kenney and Christian R. Hirsch (Eds.) *Discrete Mathematics Across the Curriculum, K-12,* pp. 104–116. Reston, VA: National Council of Teachers of Mathematics, 1991.

Usiskin, Zalman. "Conceptions of School Algebra and Uses of Variables." In *The Ideas of Algebra, K–12,* 1988 Yearbook of the National Council of Teachers of Mathematics, edited by Arthur F. Coxford and Albert P. Shulte, pp. 8–19. Reston, VA: NCTM, 1988.

Usiskin, Zalman. "We Need Another Revolution in Secondary School Mathematics." In *The Secondary School Mathematics Curriculum,* 1985 Yearbook of the National Council of Teachers of Mathematics, edited by Christian R. Hirsch and Marilyn J. Zweng, pp. 1–21. Reston, VA: NCTM, 1985.

Usiskin, Zalman. "Why Elementary Algebra Can, Should, and Must Be an Eighth-Grade Course for Average Students." *Mathematics Teacher,* September 1987: 428–438.

Waits, Bert, and Demana, Franklin. "Is Three Years Enough?" *Mathematics Teacher,* January 1988: 11–15.

Additional References

Fey, James T. and Hirsch, Christian R., editors. *Calculators in Mathematics Education.* Reston, VA: National Council of Teachers of Mathematics, 1992.

Hirsch, Christian R., and Laing, Robert, editors. *Activities for Active Learning and Teaching: Selections from the Mathematics Teacher.* Reston, VA: NCTM, 1993.

Joseph, George Gheverghese. *The Crest of the Peacock: Non-European Roots of Mathematics.* New York, NY: Penguin Books USA, 1991.

Katz, Victor J. *A History of Mathematics.* New York, NY: HarperCollins, 1993.

Mathematics Teacher. National Council of Teachers of Mathematics. 1906 Association Drive, Reston, VA.

Silver, Edward A., Kilpatrick, Jeremy, and Schlesinger, Beth. *Thinking through Mathematics: Fostering Inquiry and Communication in Mathematics Classrooms.* New York: College Entrance Examination Board, 1990.

Whitmer, John C. *Spreadsheets in Mathematics and Science Teaching.* Bowling Green, OH: School, Science and Mathematics Association, 1992.

Additional References on Discrete Mathematics

Dossey, John. *Discrete Mathematics.* Glenview, IL: Scott Foresman, 1987.

Epp, Susanna S. *Discrete Mathematics with Applications.* Second Edition. Belmont, CA: Wadsworth, 1995.

Hirschfelder, R., and Hirschfelder, J. *Introduction to Discrete Mathematics.* Pacific Grove, CA: Brooks-Cole, 1991.

Johnsonbaugh, Richard. *Discrete Mathematics.* Second edition. New York: Macmillan, 1990.

Leffton, Phyllis. "Number Theory and Public Key Cryptography." *The Mathematics Teacher,* January 1991, pp. 54-62.

Maurer, Stephen B., and Ralston, Anthony. *Discrete Algorithmic Mathematics.* Menlo Park, CA: Addison-Wesley, 1991.

Oystein Ore. *Graphs and Their Uses.* Washington: The Mathematical Association of America, 1990.

Ross, Kenneth A., and Wright, Charles R.B. *Discrete Mathematics.* Second edition. Englewood Cliffs, NJ: Prentice-Hall, 1988.

Print Sources for Data or Additional Problems

Austin, Joe Dan, editor. *Applications of Secondary School Mathematics: Readings from the Mathematics Teacher.* Reston, VA: NCTM, 1991.

Brunner, Borgna, editor. *The World Almanac and Book of Facts.* Mahwah, NJ: World Almanac Books, yearly.

Conway, H. McKinley, Jr., editor. *The Weather Handbook.* Atlanta: Conway Publications, 1963.

Eves, Howard. *An Introduction to the History of Mathematics.* 5th ed. Philadelphia. Saunders College Publishing, 1983.

Garfunkel, Solomon and Steen, Lynn A., editors. *For All Practical Purposes: An Introduction to Contemporary Mathematics.* New York: W.H. Freeman, 1988.

Hoffman, Mark, editor. *The World Almanac and Book of Facts.* New York: World Almanac, yearly.

Johnson, Otto, executive editor. *Information Please Almanac.* Boston: Houghton Mifflin Company, yearly.

Joint Committee of the Mathematical Association of America and the National Council of Teachers of Mathematics. *A Sourcebook of Applications of School Mathematics.* Reston, VA: National Council of Teachers of Mathematics, 1980.

Joint Committee of the Mathematical Association of America and the National Council of Teachers of Mathematics. *A Sourcebook of Applications of School Mathematics.* Reston, VA: NCTM, 1980.

Kastner, Bernice. *Space Mathematics.* Washington, D.C.: U.S. Government Printing Office, 1985.

Progression of World Best Performances and Official IAAF World Records. Monaco: International Athletic Foundation, 1987.

U.S. Bureau of the Census. *Historical Statistics of the United States.* Washington D.C., 1975.

U.S. Bureau of the Census. *Statistical Abstract of the United States.* Washington D.C., annual.

UMAP Journal, Consortium for Mathematics and Its Applications Project, Inc. 271 Lincoln Street, Suite Number 4, Lexington, MA.

On-Line Sources of Data

Journal of Statistics Education Data Archive
http://www2.ncsu.edu/ncsu/pams/stat/info/jse/datasets.index.html

FedStats
Provides links to the homepages of federal agencies who collect statistical data, as well as direct links to those pages containing the data.
http://www.fedstats.gov/index20.html

Statistical Abstract of the United States
The complete Statistical Abstract is now on-line in Adobe Acrobat's Portable Document Format (PDF).
http://www.census.gov:80/stat_abstract/

International Data Base (IDB)
The International Data Base (IDB) is a computerized data bank containing statistical tables of demographic, and socio-economic data for all countries of the world.
http://www.census.gov/ipc/www/idbacc.html

United States Interactive Climate Pages
Provides lots of climatological data.
http://www.cdc.noaa.gov/USclimate/

Software

Abrams, Joshua. *GraphExplorer.* Scott Foresman Addison Wesley, 1900 East Lake Avenue, Glenview, IL 60025. (Macintosh, DOS)

Derive. Soft Warehouse Inc., 3660 Waialae Ave., #304, Honolulu, HI 96816-3259. (DOS, Windows)

Microsoft Excel. Microsoft Corporation, One Microsoft Way, Redmond, WA 98052-6399 (Windows, Macintosh)

Maple. V.® Waterloo Maple, 450 Phillip Street, Waterloo, Ontario, Canada N2L512 (Macintosh, Windows)

Mathematica. Wolfram Research Inc., 100 Trade Centre Drive, Champaign, IL 61820-7237 (Macintosh, Windows)

Schwartz, Judah. *The Function Analyzer.* Sunburst Communications, Pleasantville, NY 10570. (DOS)

Theorems and Properties

Chapter 1

Law of Substitution: If a universal statement is true for all elements of a given set, then it is true for each element of that set. *(Lesson 1-1, p. 7)*

The Negation of a Universal Statement Theorem: Let S be a set and $p(x)$ be a property that may or may not be true for elements x in S. The negation of $\forall x$ *in S, p(x).* is $\exists x$ *in S such that not p(x).* *(Lesson 1-2, p. 15)*

The Negation of an Existential Statement Theorem: Let S be a set and $p(x)$ be a property that may or may not be true for elements x in S. The negation of $\exists$ *x in S such that p(x).* is $\forall x$ *in S, not p(x).* *(Lesson 1-2, p. 16)*

De Morgan's Laws Theorem: For all statements p and q:

1. $\sim(p \text{ and } q) \equiv (\sim p) \text{ or } (\sim q)$
2. $\sim(p \text{ or } q) \equiv (\sim p) \text{ and } (\sim q)$ *(Lesson 1-3, p. 23)*

Negation of a Simple Conditional Theorem: The negation of the conditional statement *If p then q.* is *p and (not q).* *(Lesson 1-5, p. 37)*

Negation of a Universal Conditional Theorem: Let S be a set and let $p(x)$ and $q(x)$ be statements that may or may not hold for elements x in S. The negation of $\forall x$ *in S, if p(x) then q(x).* is $\exists$ *x in S such that p(x) and not q(x).* *(Lesson 1-5, p. 38)*

Contrapositive Theorem: A conditional and its contrapositive are logically equivalent. That is, they always have the same truth values. *(Lesson 1-5, p. 39)*

Law of Detachment (*Modus Ponens*) Theorem: The following are valid forms of argument:

Simple form	Universal form
If p then q.	$\forall x$, *if p(x) then q(x).*
p	*p(c), for a particular c.*
$\therefore$ *q.*	$\therefore$ *q(c).*

(Lesson 1-6, p. 46)

The Law of Transitivity Theorem: The following are valid forms of argument:

Simple form	Universal form
If p then q.	$\forall x$, *if p(x), then q(x).*
If q then r.	$\forall x$, *if q(x), then r(x).*
$\therefore$ *If p then r.*	$\therefore$ $\forall x$, *if p(x), then r(x).*

(Lesson 1-6, p. 47)

Law of Indirect Reasoning (*Modus Tollens*) Theorem: The following are valid forms of argument:

Simple form	Universal form
If p then q.	$\forall x$, *if p(x) then q(x).*
not q	*not q(c) for a particular c.*
$\therefore$ *not p.*	$\therefore$ *not p(c).*

(Lesson 1-6, p. 48)

Chapter 2

Theorem: The logarithm function $\log x$ is increasing on its domain $(0, \infty)$. *(Lesson 2-3, p. 94)*

Pythagorean Identity Theorem: For all θ, $\sin^2 \theta + \cos^2 \theta = 1$. *(Lesson 2-6, p. 113)*

Theorem: For any real numbers a and b with $a > 0$ and $b > 1$, the exponential function f with $f(x) = ab^x$ is increasing on the set $(-\infty, \infty)$ of all real numbers. *(Lesson 2-7, p. 118)*

Theorems: $\forall$ real numbers r and s and $\forall$ positive real numbers b, u, and v with $b \neq 1$,

Law of Exponents	Law of Logarithms
$b^r \cdot b^s = b^{r+s}$	$\log_b (u \cdot v) = \log_b u + \log_b v$ (Logarithm of a Product)
$\frac{b^r}{b^s} = b^{r-s}$	$\log_b \left(\frac{u}{v}\right) = \log_b u - \log_b v$ (Logarithm of a Quotient)
$(b^r)^s = b^{rs}$	$\log_b (u^s) = s \log_b u$ (Logarithm of a Power)

(Lesson 2-9, p. 132)

Change of Base Theorem: Let a and b be positive real numbers both unequal to 1, then for all $x > 0$, $\log_b x = \log_b a \cdot \log_a x$. *(Lesson 2-9, p. 133)*

Chapter 3

Theorem: A function has an inverse function if and only if it is a 1-1 function. *(Lesson 3-2, p. 157)*

Zero-Product Property: Let f, g, and h be functions. If there exists c such that $h(c) = 0$ and $h = f \cdot g$, then either $f(c) = 0$ or $g(c) = 0$. *(Lesson 3-3, p. 161)*

Addition Property of Equality: For any real expressions $f(x)$ and $g(x)$: if $f(x) = g(x)$, then $f(x) + c = g(x) + c$. *(Lesson 3-3, p. 161)*

Multiplication Property of Equality: For any real expressions $f(x)$ and $g(x)$: if $f(x) = g(x)$, then $f(x) \cdot c = g(x) \cdot c$. *(Lesson 3-3, p. 161)*

Function Composition and Equality Property: For any real functions f, g, and h, and values of x for which f, g, $h \circ f$, and $h \circ g$ are defined: if $f(x) = g(x)$, then $h(f(x)) = h(g(x))$. *(Lesson 3-3, p. 164)*

Reversible Steps Theorem: Let $f(x)$ and $g(x)$ be any real expressions. Then for all real expressions c and real functions h: (1) $f(x) = g(x) \Leftrightarrow f(x) + c = g(x) + c$. (2) $f(x) = g(x) \Leftrightarrow f(x) \cdot c = g(x) \cdot c$, provided $c \neq 0$. (3) $f(x) = g(x) \Leftrightarrow h(f(x)) = h(g(x))$, provided h^{-1} exists. *(Lesson 3-3, p. 165)*

The Intermediate Value Theorem: Suppose that f is a continuous function on the interval $[a, b]$. Then for every real number y_0 between $f(a)$ and $f(b)$, there is at least one real number x_0 between a and b such that $f(x_0) = y_0$. *(Lesson 3-4, p. 170)*

Addition Property of Inequality: For any real expressions $f(x)$ and $g(x)$: if $f(x) < g(x)$, then $f(x) + c < g(x) + c$. *(Lesson 3-5, p. 175)*

Multiplication Properties of Inequality: For any real expressions $f(x)$ and $g(x)$, where $f(x) < g(x)$: $f(x) \cdot c < g(x) \cdot c$, if $c > 0$; and $f(x) \cdot c > g(x) \cdot c$, if $c < 0$. *(Lesson 3-5, p. 175)*

Theorem: Suppose that f is a real function. If f is increasing throughout its domain, or if f is decreasing throughout its domain, then f is a 1-1 function. *(Lesson 3-5, p. 176)*

Corollary: If f is an increasing function throughout its domain, or if f is a decreasing function throughout its domain, then the inverse of f is a function. *(Lesson 3-5, p. 176)*

Theorem: Let f be a real function. (1) If f is increasing on its entire domain, then f^{-1} is increasing on its entire domain. (2) If f is decreasing on its entire domain, then f^{-1} is decreasing on its entire domain. *(Lesson 3-5, p. 177)*

Function Composition and Inequality Properties: or any real expressions $f(x)$, $g(x)$ and real function h, (1) $f(x) < g(x) \geq h(f(x)) < h(g(x))$, if h is an increasing function, and (2) $f(x) < g(x) \Leftrightarrow h(f(x)) > h(g(x))$, if h is a decreasing function. *(Lesson 3-5, p. 178)*

Reversible Steps Theorem for Inequalities: Let $f(x)$ and $g(x)$ be any real expressions. Then for all real expressions c and real functions h:
(1) $f(x) < g(x) \Leftrightarrow f(x) + c < g(x) + c$.
(2) $f(x) < g(x) \Leftrightarrow f(x) \cdot c < g(x) \cdot c$, if $c > 0$.
$f(x) < g(x) \Leftrightarrow f(x) \cdot c > g(x) \cdot c$, if $c < 0$.
(3) $f(x) < g(x) \Leftrightarrow h(f(x)) < h(g(x))$, if h is increasing.
$f(x) < g(x) \Leftrightarrow h(f(x)) > h(g(x))$, if h is decreasing.
(Lesson 3-5, p. 179)

Function Inequality Theorem: Suppose that f is a continuous real function. If f has zeros a and b and no zeros between a and b, then either $f(x) > 0$ for all x between a and b or $f(x) < 0$ for all x between a and b. *(Lesson 3-7, p. 190)*

Graph-Translation Theorem: In a relation described by a sentence in x and y, the following two processes yield the same graph: (1) replacing x by $x - h$, and y by $y - k$; (2) applying the translation $T_{h,k}$: $(x, y) \rightarrow (x + h, y + k)$ to the graph of the original relation. *(Lesson 3-8, p. 195)*

Graph Scale-Change Theorem: In a relation described by a sentence in x and y, the following two processes yield the same graph: (1) replacing x by $\frac{x}{a}$, and y by $\frac{y}{b}$; (2) applying the scale change $S_{a,b}$: $(x, y) \rightarrow (ax, by)$ to the graph of the original relation. *(Lesson 3-8, p. 196)*

Graph-Standardization Theorem: Suppose that G is the graph of a relation in x and y. Let h and k be any real numbers and let a and b be nonzero real numbers. Let G' be the image of G under the rubberband transformation $T: (x, y) \rightarrow (ax + h, by + k)$.

x-y form: If G is described by a rule relating x and y, then a rule for G' is found by replacing x by $\frac{x-h}{a}$ and y by $\frac{y-k}{b}$.

parametric form: If G is described by $\begin{cases} x = f(t) \\ y = g(t), \end{cases}$ then G' is described by $\begin{cases} x = af(t) + h \\ y = bg(t) + k. \end{cases}$
(Lesson 3-8, p. 198)

Theorem: For all real numbers x and a with $a > 0$, $|x| < a$ if and only if $-a < x < a$; that is, the solution set of $|x| < a$ is the interval $(-a, a)$ of real numbers. *(Lesson 3-9, p. 202)*

Theorem: For all real numbers x and a, $|x| > a$ if and only if $x < -a$ or $x > a$. *(Lesson 3-9, p. 205)*

Chapter 4

Transitive Property of Integer Factors Theorem: For all integers a, b, and c, if a is a factor of b and b is a factor of c, then a is a factor of c. *(Lesson 4-1, p. 226)*

Factor of an Integer Sum Theorem: For all integers a, b, and c, if a is a factor of b and a is a factor of c, then a is a factor of $b + c$. *(Lesson 4-1, p. 226)*

Theorems: For all polynomials $a(x)$, $b(x)$, and $c(x)$:

Transitive Property of Polynomial Factors: If $a(x)$ is a factor of $b(x)$ and $b(x)$ is a factor of $c(x)$, then $a(x)$ is a factor of $c(x)$.

Factor of a Polynomial Sum Theorem: If $a(x)$ is a factor of $b(x)$ and $a(x)$ is a factor of $c(x)$, then $a(x)$ is a factor of $b(x) + c(x)$. *(Lesson 4-1, p. 227)*

Factor of an Integer Product Theorem: For all integers m, n, and p, if m is a factor of n, then m is a factor of $n \cdot p$. *(Lesson 4-1, p. 229)*

Quotient-Remainder Theorem for Integers: If n is an integer and d is a positive integer, then there exist unique integers q (the **integer quotient**) and r (the **integer remainder**) such that $n = q \cdot d + r$ and $0 \le r < d$. *(Lesson 4-2, p. 232)*

Quotient-Remainder Theorem for Polynomials: If $p(x)$ is a polynomial and $d(x)$ is a nonzero polynomial, then there exist unique polynomials $q(x)$ (the **quotient**) and $r(x)$ (the **remainder**) such that $p(x) = q(x) \cdot d(x) + r(x)$ and either degree of $r(x) <$ degree of $d(x)$ or $r(x)$ is the zero polynomial. *(Lesson 4-2, p. 234)*

The Remainder Theorem: If a polynomial $p(x)$ of degree $n \ge 1$ is divided by $x - c$, then the remainder is the constant $p(c)$. That is, $p(x) = q(x)(x - c) + p(c)$. *(Lesson 4-3, p. 240)*

The Factor Theorem: For all polynomials $p(x)$, $x - c$ is a factor of $p(x)$ if and only if $p(c) = 0$, that is, if and only if c is a zero of $p(x)$. *(Lesson 4-4, p. 244)*

Theorem: If c_1 is a zero of a polynomial $p(x)$ and if c_2 is a zero of the quotient polynomial $q(x)$ obtained when $p(x)$ is divided by $x - c_1$, then c_2 is a zero of $p(x)$. *(Lesson 4-4, p. 245)*

Number of Zeros of a Polynomial Theorem: A polynomial of degree n has at most n zeros. *(Lesson 4-4, p. 246)*

Theorem: Let $p(x)$ be a polynomial of degree $n \ge 1$ with real coefficients. The graph of $y = p(x)$ can cross any horizontal line $y = k$ *at most* n times. *(Lesson 4-4, p. 246)*

Congruence Theorem: $\forall$ integers a and b and positive integers m, $a \equiv b \pmod{m}$ if and only if m is a factor of $a - b$. *(Lesson 4-5, p. 253)*

Properties of Congruence Theorem: Let a, b, c, and d be any integers and let m be a positive integer. If $a \equiv b \pmod{m}$ and $c \equiv d \pmod{m}$, then

Addition Property of Congruence

$$a + c \equiv b + d \pmod{m}$$

Subtraction Property of Congruence

$$a - c \equiv b - d \pmod{m}$$

Multiplication Property of Congruence

$$ac \equiv bd \pmod{m}.$$

(Lesson 4-5, p. 254)

Prime Factor Theorem: Every integer greater than 1 is either prime or has a prime factor. *(Lesson 4-7, p. 266)*

Validity of Proof by Contradiction Theorem: The following form of argument is valid.

If not s then (p and (not p)).

∴ s. (Lesson 4-7, p. 266)

Infinitude of Primes Theorem: There are infinitely many prime numbers. *(Lesson 4-7, p. 267)*

Factor Search Theorem: If an integer n has no prime factors between 1 and $\sqrt{n}$ inclusive, then n is prime. *(Lesson 4-7, p. 267)*

Fundamental Theorem of Arithmetic: Suppose that n is an integer and that $n > 1$. Then either n is a prime number or n has a prime factorization which is unique except for the order of the factors. *(Lesson 4-7, p. 268)*

Unique Factorization Theorem for Polynomials: Suppose that $p(x)$ is a polynomial with integer coefficients. Then either $p(x)$ is prime over the real numbers or $p(x)$ has a factorization into polynomials prime over the reals which is unique except for the order of the factors or multiplications by real constants. *(Lesson 4-7, p. 269)*

Chapter 5

Discontinuity Theorem: Given a rational function f with $f(x) = \frac{p(x)}{q(x)}$, where $p(x)$ and $q(x)$ are polynomials over the reals: If $\exists$ a real number c such that $q(c) = 0$ but $p(c) \neq 0$, then f has an essential discontinuity when $x = c$ and the line $x = c$ is a vertical asymptote to the graph of f. *(Lesson 5-4, p. 304)*

End Behavior of Rational Functions Theorem: Suppose $f(x) = \frac{a_m x^m + \ldots + a_1 x + a_0}{b_n x^n + \ldots + b_1 x + b_0}$ $\forall$ real numbers x for which the denominator is nonzero, where the a_i and b_i are real numbers $\forall$ i, $a_m \neq 0$, and $b_n \neq 0$. Then the end behavior of f is the same as the end behavior of the function g defined $\forall$ x by $g(x) = \frac{a_m}{b_n} x^{m-n}$. *(Lesson 5-5, p. 311)*

The Irrationality of $\sqrt{2}$ Theorem: $\sqrt{2}$ is irrational. *(Lesson 5-6, p. 316)*

Theorem: If a real number x can be written as a terminating or infinite repeating decimal, then x is a rational number. *(Lesson 5-6, p. 317)*

Rational Zero Theorem: Suppose that p is a polynomial function with integer coefficients: $p(x) = a_n x^n + a_{n-1} x^{n-1} + \ldots + a_1 x + a_0$, with $a_n \neq 0$. If $r = \frac{m}{k}$ is a rational number in lowest terms that is a zero of p, then m is a factor of the constant coefficient a_0 and k is a factor of the leading coefficient a_n. *(Chapter 5 Projects, p. 340)*

Chapter 6

Theorem: The functions defined by $y = b \sin\left(\frac{x-h}{a}\right) + k$ or $y = b \cos\left(\frac{x-h}{a}\right) + k$ have: amplitude $= |b|$, period $= 2\pi |a|$, phase shift $= h$, and vertical shift $= k$. *(Lesson 6-3, p. 363)*

Cosine of a Sum Theorem: For all real numbers α and β, $\cos(\alpha + \beta) = \cos\alpha \cos\beta - \sin\alpha \sin\beta$. *(Lesson 6-4, p. 367)*

Cosine of a Difference Theorem: For all real numbers α and β, $\cos(\alpha - \beta) = \cos\alpha \cos\beta + \sin\alpha \sin\beta$. *(Lesson 6-4, p. 369)*

Sine of a Sum Theorem: For all real numbers α and β, $\sin(\alpha + \beta) = \sin\alpha \cos\beta + \cos\alpha \sin\beta$. *(Lesson 6-5, p. 372)*

Sine of a Difference Theorem: For all real numbers α and β, $\sin(\alpha - \beta) = \sin\alpha \cos\beta - \cos\alpha \sin\beta$. *(Lesson 6-5, p. 373)*

Tangent of a Sum and Tangent of a Difference Theorem: For all real numbers α and β such that $\tan\alpha$, $\tan\beta$, and $\tan(\alpha + \beta)$ are defined, $\tan(\alpha + \beta) = \frac{\tan\alpha + \tan\beta}{1 - \tan\alpha \tan\beta}$, and $\tan(\alpha - \beta) = \frac{\tan\alpha + \tan\beta}{1 + \tan\alpha \tan\beta}$. *(Lesson 6-5, p. 373)*

Identities for cos 2x Theorem: For all real numbers x: $\cos 2x = \cos^2 x - \sin^2 x = 2\cos^2 x - 1 = 1 - 2\sin^2 x$. *(Lesson 6-6, p. 377)*

Identity for sin 2x Theorem: For all real numbers x, $\sin 2x = 2 \sin x \cos x$. *(Lesson 6-6, p. 378)*

Chapter 7

Recursion Principle: Suppose that a recurrence relation defines x_{n+1} in terms of x_n and n for each integer $n \geq 1$. Then there is exactly one sequence X defined by this recurrence relation and the initial condition $x_1 = a$. *(Lesson 7-1, p. 406)*

Principle of Mathematical Induction: Let $S(n)$ be a sentence in n. If (1) $S(1)$ is true (the **basis step**), and (2) for all integers $k \geq 1$, the assumption that $S(k)$ is true implies that $S(k+1)$ is true (the **inductive step**), then $S(n)$ is true for all positive integers n. *(Lesson 7-3, p. 418)*

Sum of the First *n* Powers Theorem: If $r \neq 1$, then $1 + r + r^2 + \ldots + r^{n-1} = \frac{1 - r^n}{1 - r}$ $\forall$ integers $n \geq 1$. *(Lesson 7-6, p. 435)*

Evaluation of a Finite Geometric Series Theorem: If a is any real number and r is any real number other than 1, then for all integers $n \geq 1$, $a + ar + ar^2 + \ldots + ar^{n-1} = a\left(\frac{1 - r^n}{1 - r}\right)$. *(Lesson 7-6, p. 436)*

Evaluation of an Infinite Geometric Series Theorem: If a is any real number and r is a real number with $0 < |r| < 1$, then $\sum_{k=0}^{\infty} ar^k = \frac{a}{1 - r}$. *(Lesson 7-6, p. 438)*

Principle of Mathematical Induction (Strong Form): Suppose that for each positive integer n, $S(n)$ is a sentence in n. If

(1) $S(1)$ is true, and

(2) for all integers, $k \geq 1$, the assumption that $S(1)$, $S(2)$, . . . , $S(k-1)$, $S(k)$ are all true implies that $S(k+1)$ is also true, then $S(n)$ is true for all integers $n \geq 1$. *(Lesson 7-7, p. 442)*

Theorem: Every positive integer $n \geq 2$ is either a prime or a product of primes. *(Lesson 7-7, p. 446)*

Quicksort Theorem: For each integer $n \geq 0$, the Quicksort algorithm arranges any list of n distinct real numbers in increasing order. *(Lesson 7-8, p. 454)*

Chapter 8

Theorem: For any particular values of r and θ, the following polar coordinate representations name the same point.

a. $[r, \theta]$

b. $[r, \theta + 2\pi n]$, $\forall$ integers n

c. $[-r, \theta + (2n + 1)\pi]$, $\forall$ integers n *(Lesson 8-2, p. 481)*

Polar-Rectangular Conversion Theorem: If $[r, \theta]$ is a polar coordinate representation of a point P, then the rectangular coordinates (x, y) of P are given by $x = r\cos\theta$ and $y = r\sin\theta$. *(Lesson 8-2, p. 483)*

Geometric Addition Theorem: Let $z = a + bi$ and $w = c + di$ be two complex numbers that are not collinear with (0, 0). Then the point representing $z + w$ is the fourth vertex of a parallelogram with consecutive vertices $z = a + bi$, 0, and $w = c + di$. *(Lesson 8-3, p. 488)*

Geometric Multiplication Theorem: Let z and w be complex numbers. If $z = [r, \theta]$ and $w = [s, \phi]$, then $zw = [rs, \theta + \phi]$. That is, multiplying a complex number z by w applies to z the composite of a size change of magnitude s and a rotation of ϕ about the origin. *(Lesson 8-3, p. 490)*

DeMoivre's Theorem:

(Polar Form) For all positive integers n, if $z = [r, \theta]$, then $z^n = [r^n, n\theta]$.

(Trigonometric Form) For all positive integers n, if $z = r(\cos\theta + i\sin\theta)$, then $z^n = r^n(\cos n\theta + i\sin n\theta)$. *(Lesson 8-6, p. 508)*

Complex *n*th Roots Theorem:

(Polar Form) The n nth roots of $[r, \theta]$ are $\left[\sqrt[n]{r}, \frac{\theta}{n} + k \cdot \frac{2\pi}{n}\right]$, where $k = 0, 1, 2, \ldots, n - 1$.

(Trigonometric Form) The n nth roots of $r(\cos\theta + i\sin\theta)$ are $\sqrt[n]{r}\left(\cos\left(\frac{\theta}{n} + k \cdot \frac{2\pi}{n}\right) + i\sin\left(\frac{\theta}{n} + k \cdot \frac{2\pi}{n}\right)\right)$, where $k = 0, 1, 2, \ldots, n - 1$. *(Lesson 8-7, p. 515)*

Geometric *n*th Roots Theorem: When graphed in the complex plane, the n nth roots of any nonzero complex number z are the vertices of a regular n-gon whose center is at (0, 0). *(Lesson 8-7, p. 516)*

Theorem: Every polynomial of odd degree with real coefficients has at least one real zero. *(Lesson 8-8, p. 520)*

Fundamental Theorem of Algebra: If $p(x)$ is any polynomial of degree $n \geq 1$, with real or complex coefficients, then $p(x)$ has at least one complex zero. *(Lesson 8-8, p. 521)*

Theorem: If $p(x)$ is any polynomial of degree n with real or complex coefficients, then $p(x)$ has exactly n real or complex zeros provided that each zero of multiplicity m is counted m times. *(Lesson 8-8, p. 522)*

Conjugate Zeros Theorem: Let $p(x)$ be a polynomial with real coefficients. If $z = a + bi$ is a zero of $p(x)$, then its complex conjugate $\bar{z} = a - bi$ is also a zero of $p(x)$. *(Lesson 8-9, p. 526)*

Chapter 9

Derivative of a Quadratic Function Theorem: If $f(x) = ax^2 + bx + c$, where a, b, and c are real numbers and $a \neq 0$, then $f'(x) = 2ax + b$ for all real numbers x. *(Lesson 9-3, p. 572)*

Theorems: (Derivative of a Linear Function) If $f(x) = mx + b$, then $f'(x) = m$.
(Derivative of a Constant Function) If $\forall x, f(x) = k$, then $f'(x) = 0$. *(Lesson 9-3, p. 572)*

Theorem: Suppose f is a function whose derivative function f' exists for all x in the interval $a < x < b$.

(1) If $f'(x) > 0$ $\forall x$ in the interval $a < x < b$, then f is increasing on the interval.

(2) If $f'(x) < 0$ $\forall x$ *in the interval* $a < x < b$, then f is decreasing on the interval. *(Lesson 9-5, p. 581)*

Vertex of a Parabola Theorem: Let a, b, and c be real numbers with $a \neq 0$. Then the parabola that is the graph of $f(x) = ax^2 + bx + c$ has its vertex at the point where $x = -\frac{b}{2a}$. *(Lesson 9-5, p. 582)*

Chapter 10

The Multiplication Counting Principle: Suppose that strings result from a procedure which consists of k successive steps and that:

the 1st step can be done in n_1 ways,

the 2nd step can be done in n_2 ways,

⋮

and the kth step can be done in n_k ways.

Then the number of strings is $n_1 n_2 \cdot \ldots \cdot n_k$. *(Lesson 10-2, p. 609)*

Theorem: If repetition is allowed, the number of r-symbol strings that can be made from a set of n symbols is n^r. *(Lesson 10-2, p. 610)*

Permutation Theorem: There are $n!$ permutations of n different elements. *(Lesson 10-3, p. 616)*

***P*(*n*, *r*) Calculation Theorem:** The number $P(n, r)$ of permutations of n elements taken r at a time is given by $P(n, r) = \frac{n!}{(n-r)!}$. *(Lesson 10-3, p. 618)*

***C*(*n*, *r*) Calculation Theorem:** The number $C(n, r)$ of combinations of n elements taken r at a time is given by $C(n, r) = \frac{n!}{r!(n-r)!}$. *(Lesson 10-4, p. 623)*

Basic Properties of Combinations Theorem: For all n and r for which $C(n, r)$ is defined:

a. $C(n, r) = C(n, n-r)$, $\binom{n}{r} = \binom{n}{n-r}$;

b. $C(n, n) = C(n, 0) = 1$, $\binom{n}{n} = \binom{n}{0} = 1$.

(Lesson 10-4, p. 624)

The Binomial Theorem:

For all positive integers n and numbers x and y,

$$(x+y)^n = \binom{n}{0}x^n + \binom{n}{1}x^{n-1}y + \binom{n}{2}x^{n-2}y^2 + \ldots + \binom{n}{k}x^{n-k}y^k + \ldots + \binom{n}{n-1}xy^{n-1} + \binom{n}{n}y^n = \sum_{k=0}^{n}\binom{n}{k}x^{n-k}y^k.$$ *(Lesson 10-5, p. 630)*

Sum of Binomial Coefficients Theorem: $\forall$ integers $n \geq 0$,

$$\binom{n}{0} + \binom{n}{1} + \binom{n}{2} + \ldots + \binom{n}{k} + \ldots + \binom{n}{n} = \sum_{k=0}^{n}\binom{n}{k} = 2^n.$$ *(Lesson 10-6, p. 633)*

Theorem: Suppose that n and r are positive integers. The number of r-element collections that can be constructed from a set with n elements with repetitions allowed is given by $\binom{r + (n-1)}{r}$. *(Lesson 10-7, p. 642)*

Theorem: Let k and n be positive integers. In the expansion of $(x_1 + x_2 + \ldots + x_k)^n$, the coefficient of $x_1{}^{a_1}x_2{}^{a_2} \ldots x_k{}^{a_k}$ is $\frac{n!}{a_1!a_2!\ldots a_k!}$. *(Lesson 10-8, p. 645)*

Chapter 11

Total Degree of a Graph Theorem: The total degree of any graph equals twice the number of edges in the graph. *(Lesson 11-3, p. 674)*

Corollaries:

1. Total Degree is Even: The total degree of any graph is an even positive integer.
2. Number of Odd Vertices is Even: Every graph has an even number of vertices of odd degree. *(Lesson 11-3, p. 675)*

Euler Circuit Theorem: If a graph has an Euler circuit, then every vertex of the graph has even degree. *(Lesson 11-4, p. 680)*

Sufficient Condition for an Euler Circuit Theorem: If a graph G is connected and every vertex of G has even degree, then G has an Euler circuit. *(Lesson 11-4, p. 682)*

Circuits and Connectedness Theorem: If a connected graph contains a circuit and an edge is removed from the circuit, then the resulting graph is also connected. *(Lesson 11-4, p. 683)*

Theorem: Let G be a graph with vertices $v_1, v_2, \ldots, v_m$, and let n be a positive integer. Let A be the adjacency matrix for G. Then the element a_{ij} in A^n is the number of walks of length n from v_i to v_j. *(Lesson 11-5, p. 689)*

Convergence of Powers Theorem: Let T be an $n \times n$ stochastic matrix with no zero entries. Then $\lim_{k\to\infty} T^k$ is a stochastic matrix with n identical rows. *(Lesson 11-6, p. 695)*

Theorem: Let G be a connected graph with no crossings, and let V, E, and F be the number of vertices, edges, and faces of G. The following alterations to G do not change the value of $V - E + F$:

(1) removing a vertex of degree 1 along with its adjacent edge, and

(2) removing an edge that is part of a circuit. *(Lesson 11-7, p. 702)*

Theorem: Let G be a graph with at least one edge. If G has no circuits, then G has a vertex of degree 1. *(Lesson 11-7, p. 703)*

Euler's Formula: Let G be a connected graph with no crossings, and let V, E, and F be the number of vertices, edges, and faces of G. Then $V - E + F = 2$. *(Lesson 11-7, p. 703)*

Chapter 12

Theorem: If $\vec{u} = (u_1, u_2)$, then $|\vec{u}| = \sqrt{u_1{}^2 + u_2{}^2}$. *(Lesson 12-1, p. 724)*

Theorem: For all vectors $\vec{u}$, $[|\vec{u}|, \theta] = (|\vec{u}| \cos \theta, |\vec{u}| \sin \theta)$. *(Lesson 12-1, p. 724)*

Theorem:

a. If $\vec{v}$ is a vector with polar representation $[r, \theta°]$, then $-\vec{v} = [r, 180° + \theta°]$.

b. If $\vec{v}$ has component representation (v_1, v_2), then $-\vec{v} = (-v_1, -v_2)$. *(Lesson 12-2, p. 729)*

Theorem: Nonzero vectors $\vec{u}$ and $\vec{v}$ are parallel if and only if one of the vectors is a nonzero scalar multiple of the other. *(Lesson 12-3, p. 733)*

Theorem: A point $Q = (x, y)$ is on the line through $P = (x_0, y_0)$ parallel to the vector $\vec{v} = (v_1, v_2)$ if and only if there is a real number t with $\overrightarrow{PQ} = t\vec{v}$, or $(x - x_0, y - y_0) = t(v_1, v_2)$. *(Lesson 12-3, p. 734)*

Theorem: The line through (x_0, y_0) that is parallel to the vector $\vec{v} = (v_1, v_2)$ has parametric equations $\begin{cases} x = x_0 + tv_1 \\ y = y_0 + tv_2 \end{cases}$ where t may be any real number. *(Lesson 12-3, p. 734)*

Theorem: The dot product of a vector with itself equals the square of its length: For all vectors $\vec{w}$, $\vec{w} \cdot \vec{w} = |\vec{w}|^2$. *(Lesson 12-4, p. 740)*

Angle Between Vectors Theorem: Suppose that θ is the measure of the angle between two nonzero vectors $\vec{u}$ and $\vec{v}$ and $0 \le \theta \le \pi$. Then $\cos\theta = \frac{\vec{u} \cdot \vec{v}}{|\vec{u}|\,|\vec{v}|}$. *(Lesson 12-4, p. 741)*

Theorem: Two nonzero vectors $\vec{u}$ and $\vec{v}$ are perpendicular if and only if their dot product is zero. *(Lesson 12-4, p. 742)*

Theorem: The distance of the point (x, y, z) from the origin is $\sqrt{x^2 + y^2 + z^2}$. *(Lesson 12-5, p. 748)*

Distance in Space Theorem: The distance between $P = (x_1, y_1, z_1)$ and $Q = (x_2, y_2, z_2)$ is given by $PQ = \sqrt{(x_2 - x_1)^2 + (y_2 - y_1)^2 + (z_2 - z_1)^2}$. *(Lesson 12-5, p. 748)*

Equation of a Sphere Theorem: The sphere with center (a, b, c) and radius r has equation $r^2 = (x - a)^2 + (y - b)^2 + (z - c)^2$. *(Lesson 12-5, p. 749)*

Theorem: Let $\vec{u}$ and $\vec{v}$ be any three dimensional vectors and let θ be the measure of the angle between them. Then (1) $\cos\theta = \frac{\vec{u} \cdot \vec{v}}{|\vec{u}|\,|\vec{v}|}$, and (2) $\vec{u}$ and $\vec{v}$ are orthogonal $\Leftrightarrow \vec{u} \cdot \vec{v} = 0$. *(Lesson 12-6, p. 753)*

Equations for a Line in 3-Space Theorem: A point $Q = (x, y, z)$ is on the line ℓ through $P = (x_0, y_0, z_0)$ parallel to $\vec{v} = (v_1, v_2, v_3)$ if and only if there is a real number t such that

a. $\overrightarrow{PQ} = t\vec{v}$, or equivalently $(x - x_0, y - y_0, z - z_0) = t(v_1, v_2, v_3)$ (vector equation for ℓ) or

b. $\begin{cases} x = x_0 + tv_1 \\ y = y_0 + tv_2 \\ z = z_0 + tv_3 \end{cases}$

(parametric equations for ℓ). *(Lesson 12-7, p. 760)*

Equation for a Plane Theorem: The set of points $\{(x, y, z)\colon ax + by + cz = d\}$, where at least one of the coefficients a, b, or c is nonzero, is a plane perpendicular to the vector $\vec{v} = (a, b, c)$. *(Lesson 12-7, p. 762)*

Chapter 13

Theorem: If f is a continuous function on the interval $[a, c]$, and $a < b < c$, then $\int_a^b f(x)\,dx + \int_b^c f(x)\,dx = \int_a^c f(x)\,dx$. *(Lesson 13-4, p. 805)*

Theorem: If f is a continuous function on the interval $0 \le x \le b$, and $0 < a < b$, then $\int_a^b f(x)\,dx = \int_0^b f(x)\,dx - \int_0^a f(x)\,dx$. *(Lesson 13-4, p. 806)*

Sum Property of Integrals Theorem: If f and g are continuous functions on the interval from a to b, then $\int_a^b (f(x) + g(x))\,dx = \int_a^b f(x)\,dx + \int_a^b g(x)\,dx$. *(Lesson 13-4, p. 808)*

Constant Multiple Property of Integrals Theorem: If f is a continuous function on the interval from a to b, and c is a real number, then $\int_a^b c\,f(x)\,dx = c\int_a^b f(x)\,dx$. *(Lesson 13-4, p. 808)*

Theorem: If $a > 0$, $\int_0^a x^2\,dx = \frac{a^3}{3}$. *(Lesson 13-5, p. 814)*

Integral of a Quadratic Function Theorem: If $a > 0$, $\int_0^a (c_2x^2 + c_1x + c_0)\,dx = c_2\frac{a^3}{3} + c_1\frac{a^2}{3} + c_0a$. *(Lesson 13-5, p. 815)*

Theorem: The volume of a sphere of radius r is $\frac{4}{3}\pi r^3$. *(Lesson 13-6, p. 822)*

Fundamental Theorem of Calculus: Let f be a continuous function on the interval from a to b.

1. If g is a function whose derivative is f, then $\int_a^b f(x)\,dx = g(b) - g(a)$.
2. If $g(x) = \int_a^x f(t)\,dt$ for all x from a to b, then $g'(x) = f(x)$ for all such x. *(Lesson 13-7, p. 827)*

 APPENDIX B

Parent Functions and Their Graphs

Type of Function	Parent Function, f *	Graph of f	Inverse Function, f^{-1} †	Graph of f^{-1}
polynomial–constant	$f(x) = k$ domain: R range: $\{k\}$	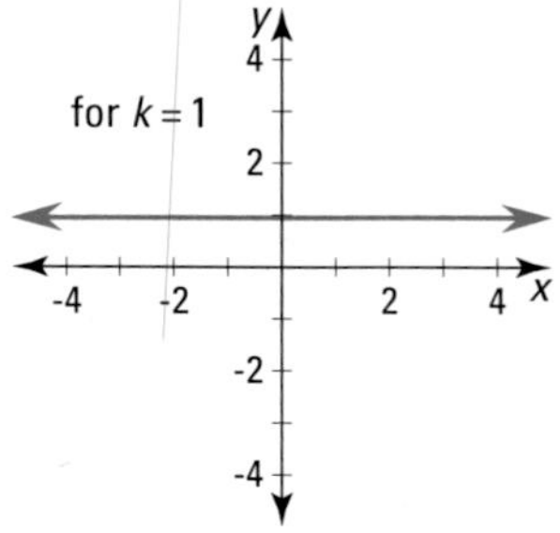	none	
polynomial–linear	$f(x) = x$ domain: R range: R	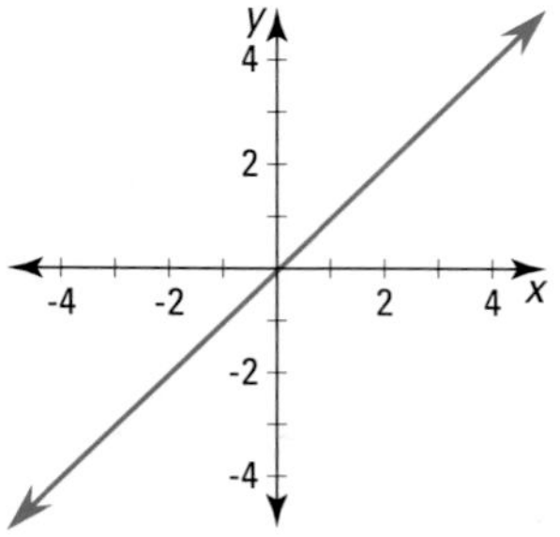	$f^{-1}(x) = x$	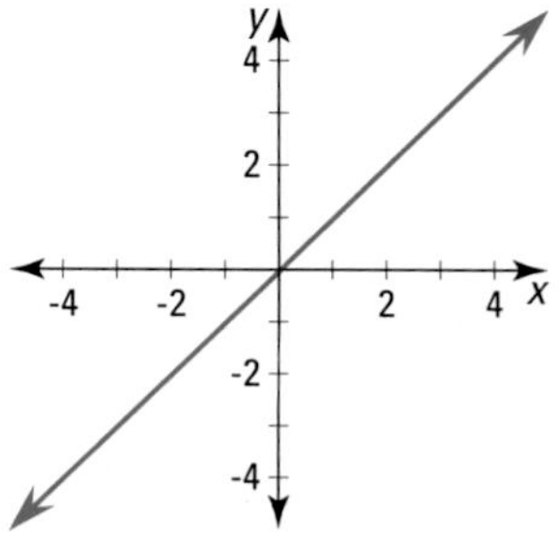
absolute value	$f(x) = \|x\|$ domain: R range: $R^+ \cup \{0\}$	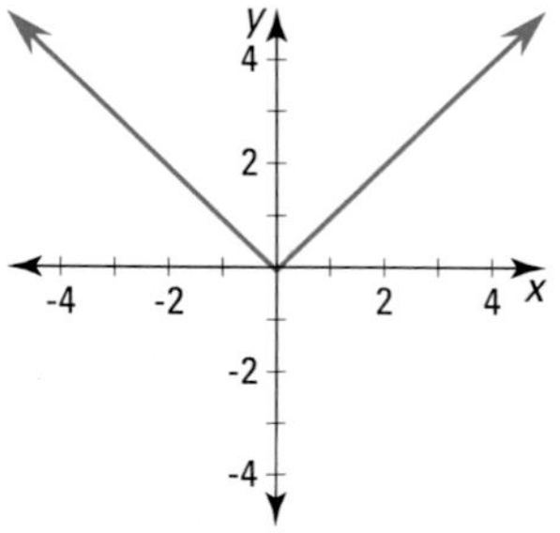	none	
greatest integer	$f(x) = \lfloor x \rfloor$ domain: R range: set of integers	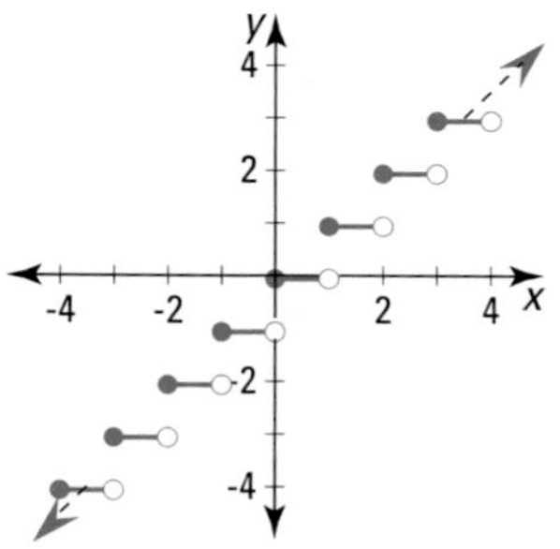	none	

* R = set of real numbers, R^+ = set of positive real numbers.

† The domain and range of f^{-1} are the reverse of those for f except where indicated.

Type of Function	Parent Function, f *	Graph of f	Inverse Function, f^{-1} †	Graph of f^{-1}
polynomial–quadratic	$f(x) = x^2$ domain: R range: $R^+ \cup \{0\}$	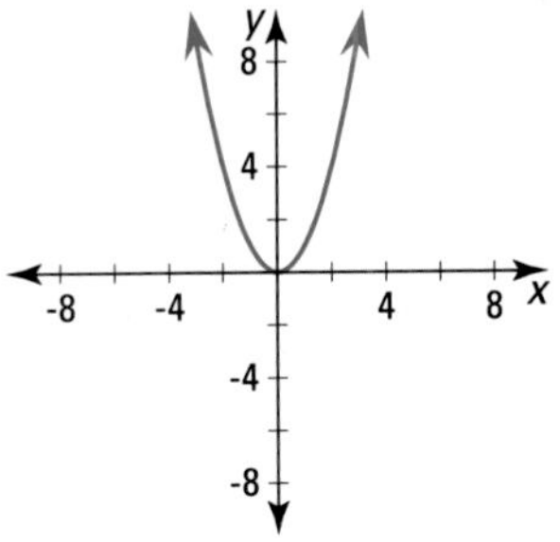	$f^{-1}(x) = \sqrt{x}$ domain: $R^+ \cup \{0\}$ range: $R^+ \cup \{0\}$	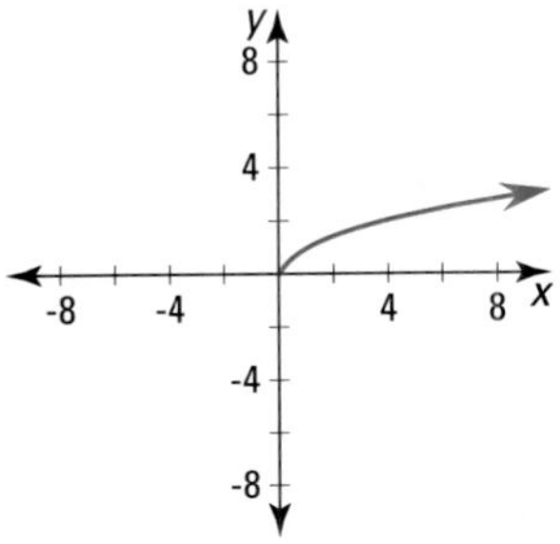
polynomial–cubic	$f(x) = x^3$ domain: R range: R	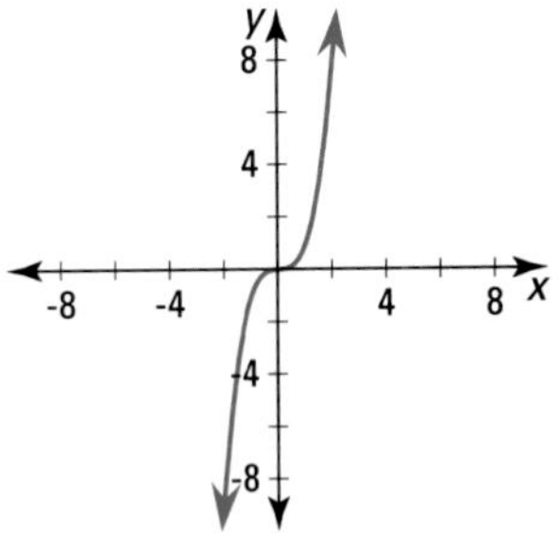	$f^{-1}(x) = \sqrt[3]{x}$	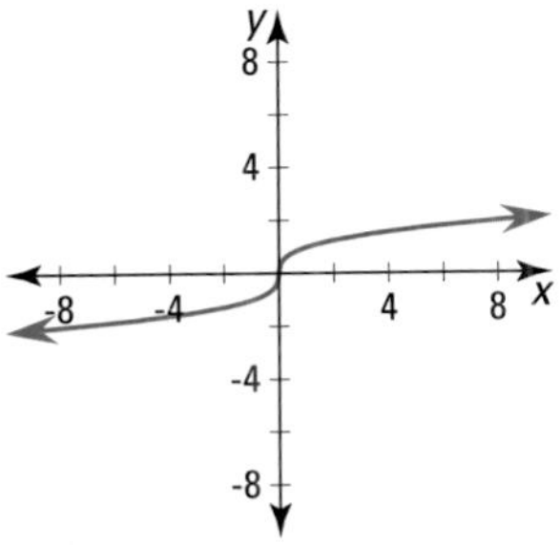
polynomial of higher degree	$f(x) = x^n$ n an odd integer domain: R range: R	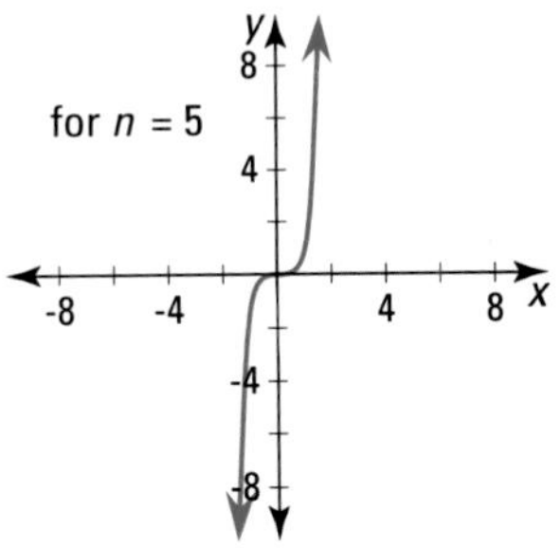 for $n = 5$	$f^{-1}(x) = \sqrt[n]{x}$	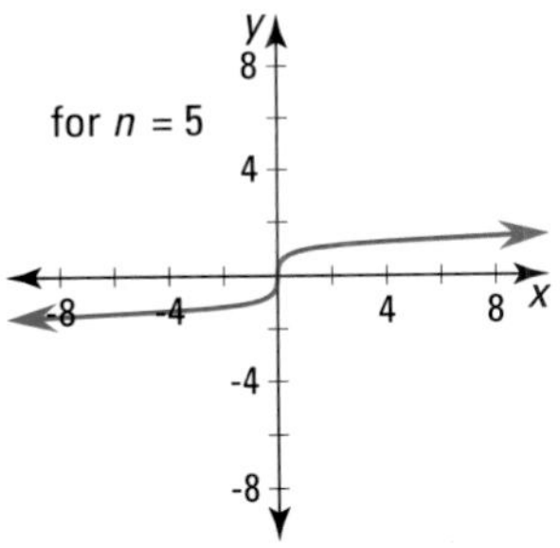 for $n = 5$
	$f(x) = x^n$ n an even integer domain: R range: $R^+ \cup \{0\}$	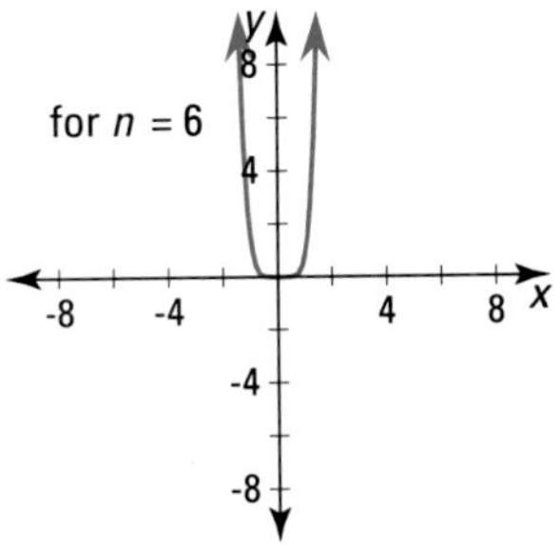 for $n = 6$	$f^{-1}(x) = \sqrt[n]{x}$ domain: $R^+ \cup \{0\}$ range: $R^+ \cup \{0\}$	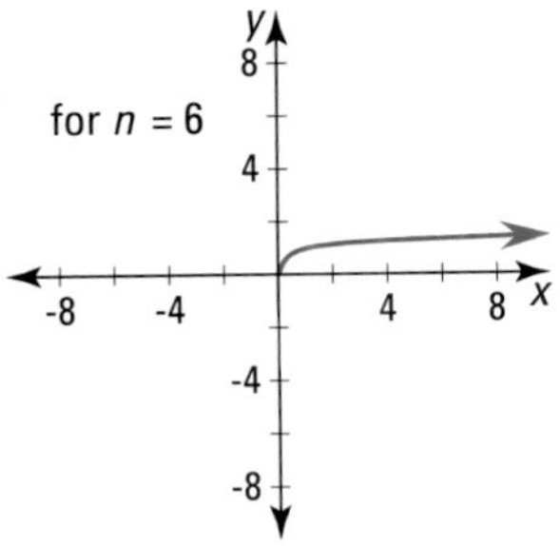 for $n = 6$

Type of Function	Parent Function, f *	Graph of f	Inverse Function, f^{-1} †	Graph of f^{-1}
hyperbola	$f(x) = \frac{1}{x}$ domain: set of nonzero reals range: set of nonzero reals	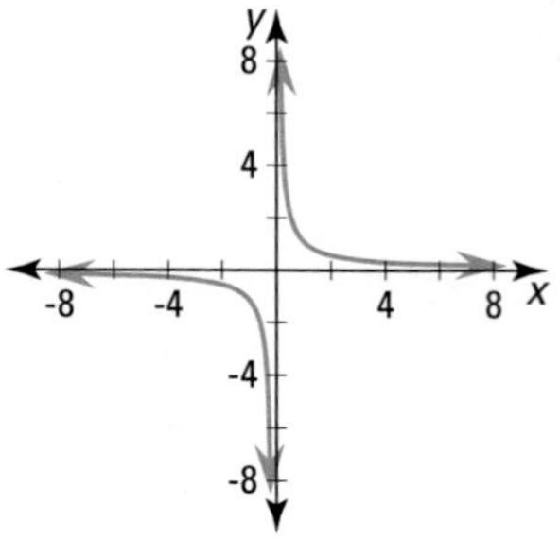	$f^{-1}(x) = \frac{1}{x}$	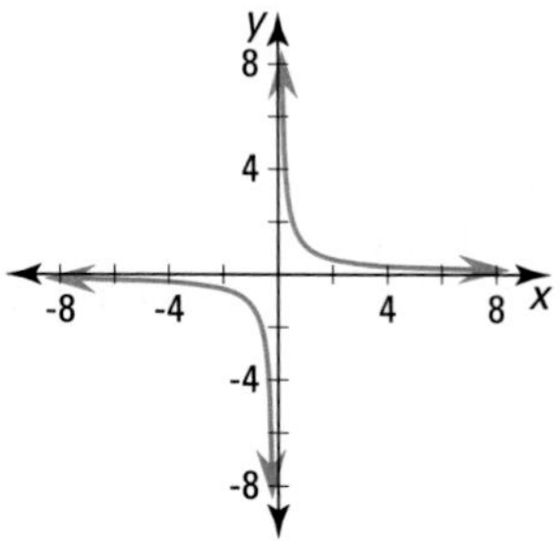
inverse-square	$f(x) = \frac{1}{x^2}$ domain: set of nonzero reals range: R^+	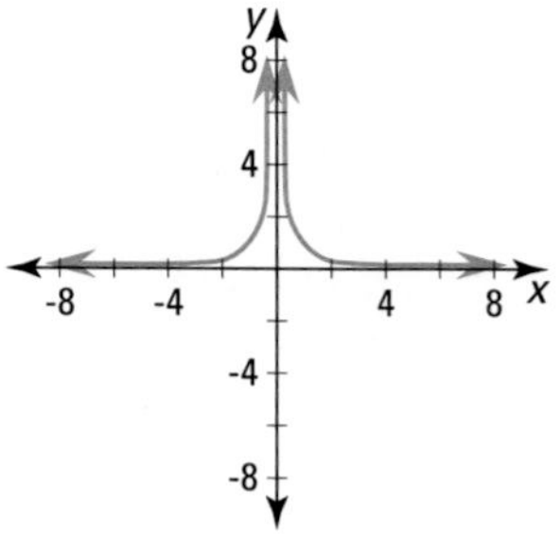	$f^{-1}(x) = \sqrt{\frac{1}{x}}$ domain: R^+ range: R^+	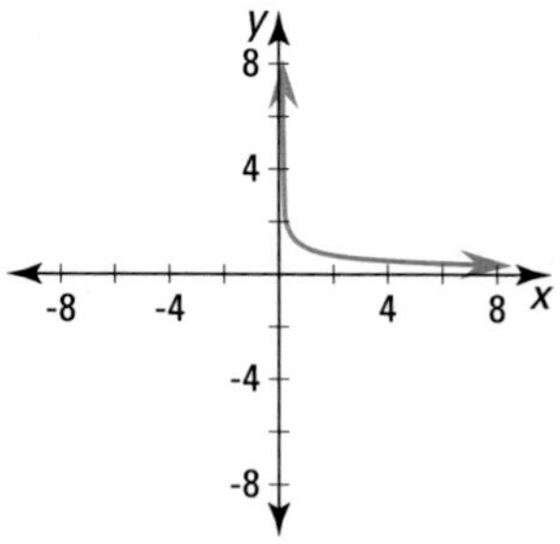
exponential any base	$f(x) = b^x$ $b > 1$ domain: R range: R^+	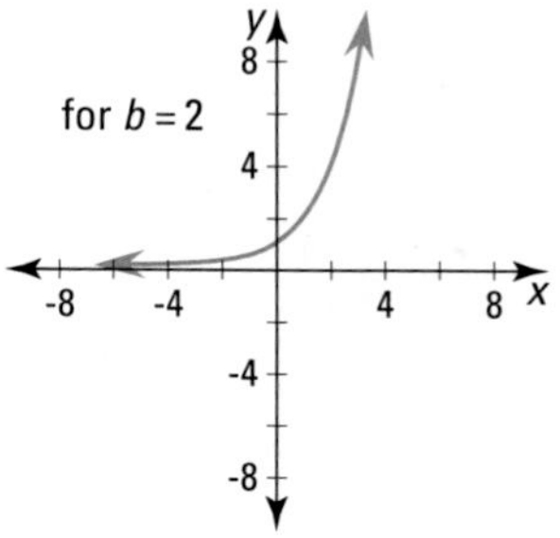 for $b = 2$	$f^{-1}(x) = \log_b x$	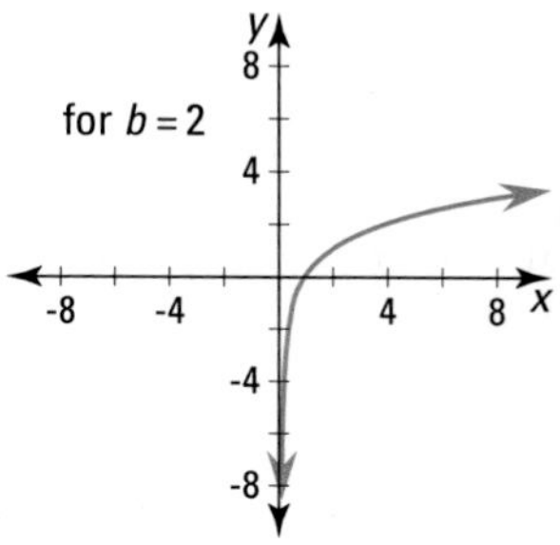 for $b = 2$
	$f(x) = b^x$ $0 < b < 1$ domain: R range: R^+	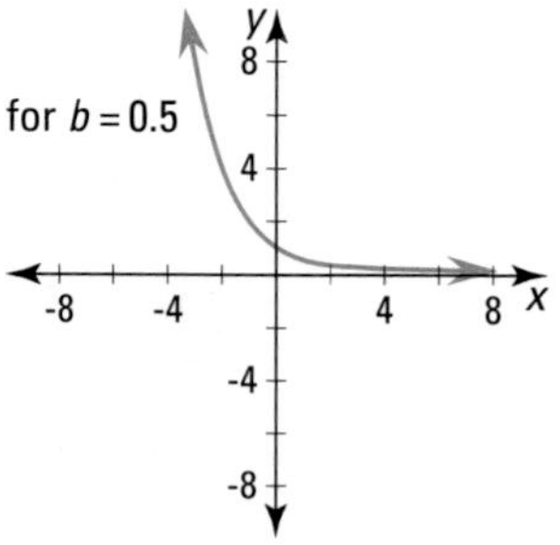 for $b = 0.5$	$f^{-1}(x) = \log_b x$	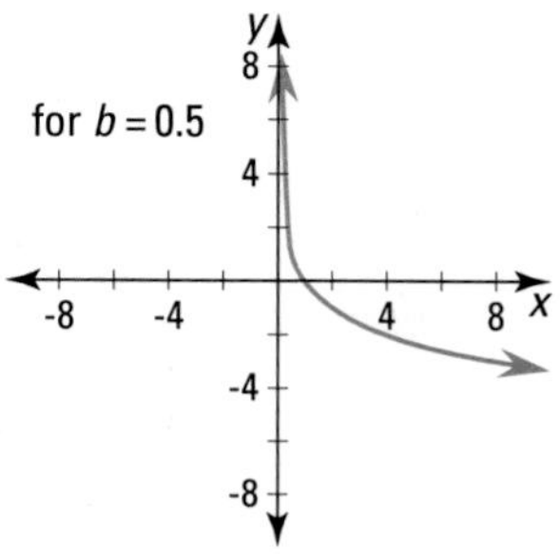 for $b = 0.5$

Type of Function	Parent Function, f *	Graph of f	Inverse Function, f^{-1} †	Graph of f^{-1}
exponential base e	$f(x) = e^x$ domain: R range: R^+	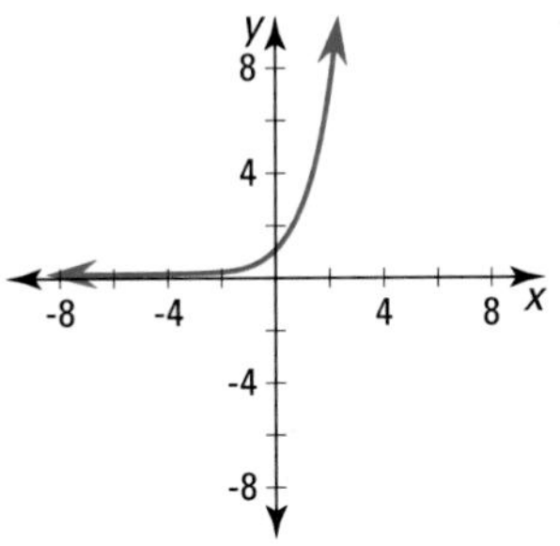	$f^{-1}(x) = \ln x$	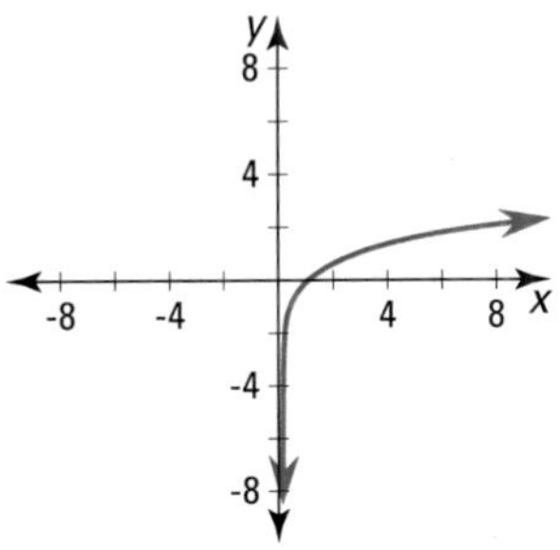
circular–sine	$f(x) = \sin x$ domain: R range: $\{y: -1 \leq y \leq 1\}$	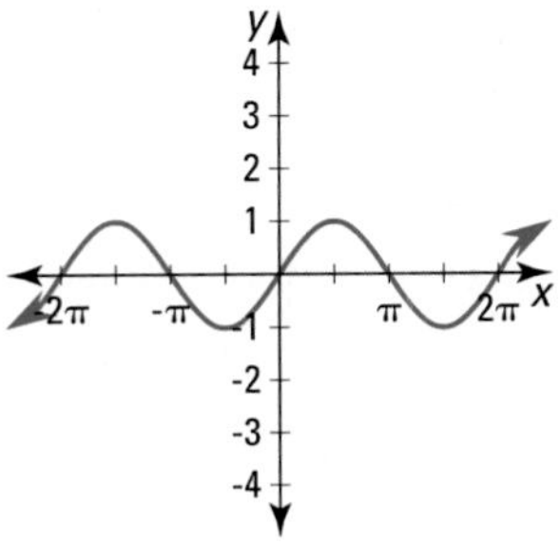	$f^{-1}(x) = \sin^{-1} x$ domain: $\{x: -1 \leq x \leq 1\}$ range: $\{y: \frac{\pi}{2} \leq y \leq \frac{\pi}{2}\}$	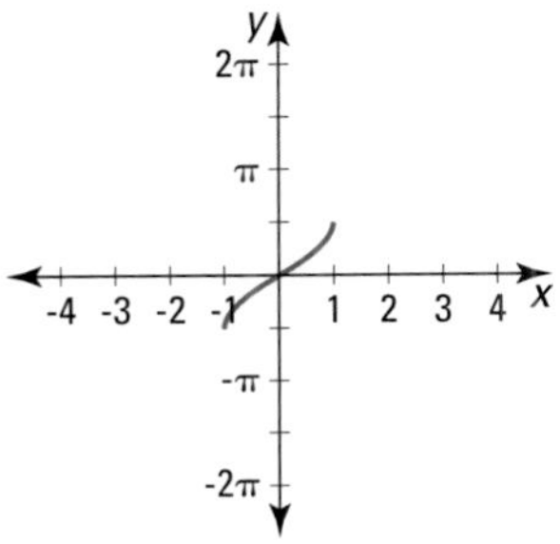
circular–cosine	$f(x) = \cos x$ domain: R range: $\{y: -1 \leq y \leq 1\}$	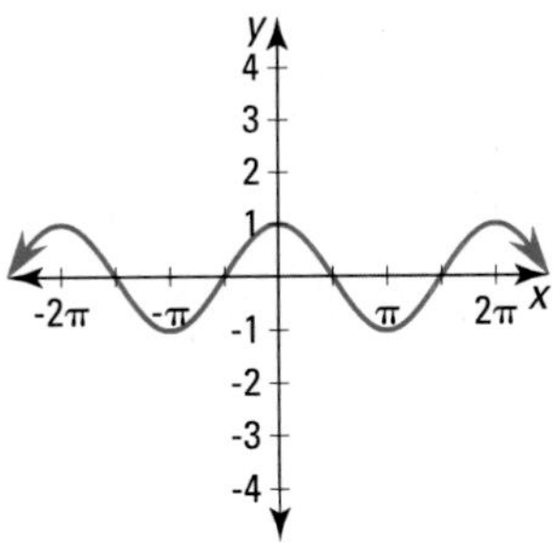	$f^{-1}(x) = \cos^{-1} x$ domain: $\{x: -1 \leq x \leq 1\}$ range: $\{y: 0 \leq y \leq \pi\}$	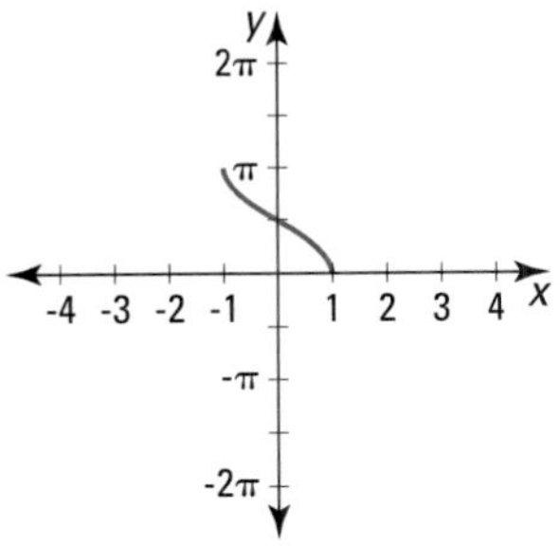
circular–tangent	$f(x) = \tan x$ domain: R except $\frac{\pi}{2} + n\pi$, n an integer range: R	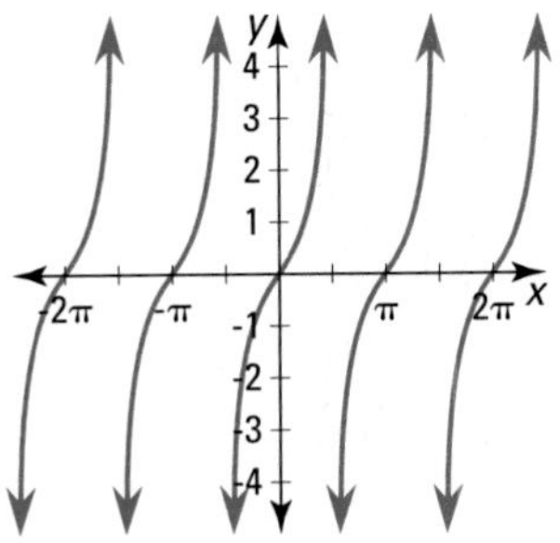	$f^{-1}(x) = \tan^{-1} x$ domain: R range: $\{y: -\frac{\pi}{2} < y < \frac{\pi}{2}\}$	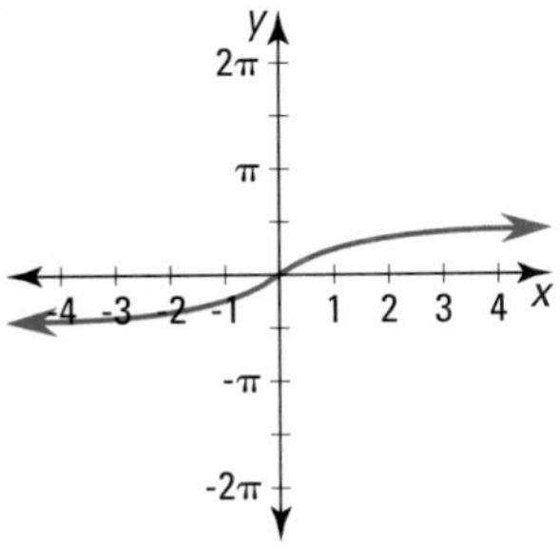

Type of Function	Parent Function, f	Graph of f
reciprocal circular–cosecant	$f(x) = \csc x = \frac{1}{\sin x}$ domain: set of reals except $n\pi$, where n is an integer range: $\{y: y \geq 1 \text{ or } y \leq -1\}$	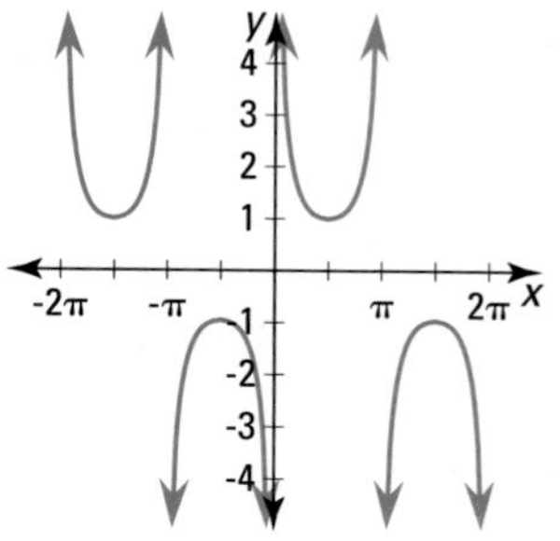
reciprocal circular–secant	$f(x) = \sec x = \frac{1}{\cos x}$ domain: set of reals except $\frac{\pi}{2} + n\pi$, where n is an integer range: $\{y: y \geq 1 \text{ or } y \leq -1\}$	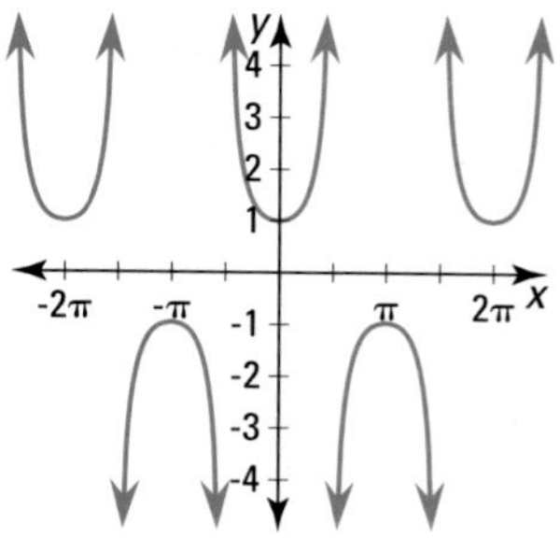
reciprocal circular–cotangent	$f(x) = \cot x = \frac{1}{\tan x}$ domain: set of reals except $n\pi$, where n is an integer range: R	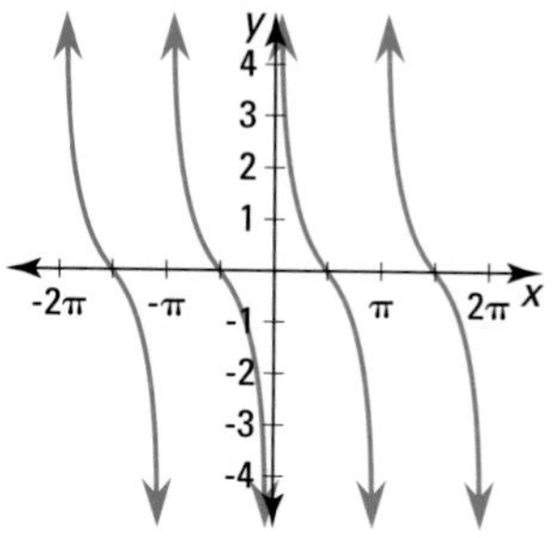
normal	$f(x) = e^{-x^2}$ domain: R range: $\{y: 0 < y \leq 1\}$	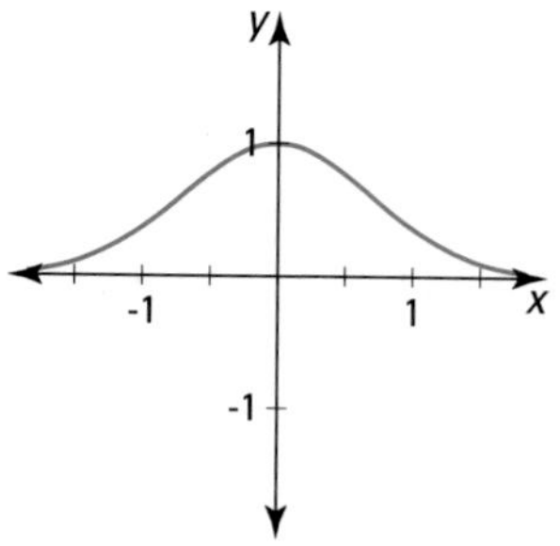

LESSON 1-1 (pp. 6–13)

15. a. yes **b.** no **c.** for 0, 1 and all integers greater than or equal to 5 **17.** Sample: There exists a student in my math class who owns a car. **19.** False, e.g., $\log\left(\frac{1}{10}\right) = -1$ and $\frac{1}{10} > 0$. **21.** Sample: Let $x = 0$; $\forall$ real numbers y, $0 \cdot y = 0 \neq 1$. **23.** $\forall$ circles x, x is not a parabola. **25. a.** 3 **b.** $c^2 - c + 1$ **c.** $a^2 - 2ab + b^2 - a + b + 1$

LESSON 1-2 (pp. 14–20)

13. a. *There is a man who is not mortal.* **b.** the given statement **15. a.** *$\exists$ n in S such that $n \geq 11$.* **b.** the negation; 11 is in S and $11 = 11$. **17. a.** *$\exists$ a real number x such that $\forall$ real numbers y, $\tan x \neq y$.* **b.** the negation. For $x = \frac{\pi}{2}$, $\tan \frac{\pi}{2}$ is undefined so *$\forall$ real numbers y, $\tan \frac{\pi}{2} \neq y$.* **19.** The flaw occurs after the fourth line. Since $x - y = 0$, one cannot divide both sides of the equation by $x - y$. **21.** e **23.** Sample: $\sqrt{(-1)^2} = 1 \neq -1$ **25. a.** 4 **b.** -3 **c.** 0

LESSON 1-3 (pp. 21–26)

13. $5 < x \leq 11$ **15.** exclusive

17. a.

p	q	p or q
T	T	F
T	F	T
F	T	T
F	F	F

b.

p	q	p or q	not p	not q	(not p) and q	p and (not q)	((not p) and q) or (p and (not q))
T	T	F	F	F	F	F	F
T	F	T	F	T	F	T	T
F	T	T	T	F	T	F	T
F	F	F	T	T	F	F	F

same truth values (columns "p or q" and "((not p) and q) or (p and (not q))")

19. a. *$\forall$ real numbers $x > 0$, $\log_{10} x \neq 0$.* **b.** The statement is true.

21. $\sin\left(\frac{7\pi}{12}\right) = \sin\left(\frac{\pi}{3} + \frac{\pi}{4}\right) = \sin\frac{\pi}{3} \cdot \cos\frac{\pi}{4} + \cos\frac{\pi}{3} \cdot \sin\frac{\pi}{4} = \frac{\sqrt{3}}{2} \cdot \frac{\sqrt{2}}{2} + \frac{1}{2} \cdot \frac{\sqrt{2}}{2} = \frac{\sqrt{6} + \sqrt{2}}{4}$ **23.** **See below.**

23.

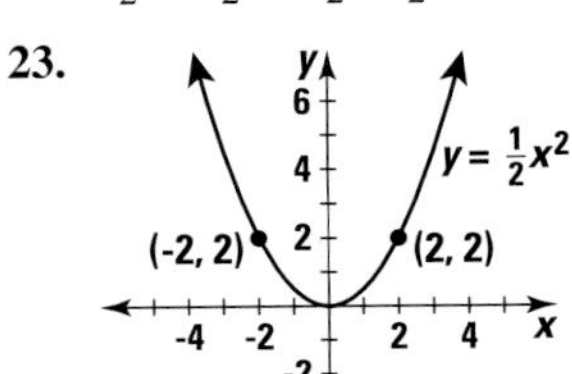

LESSON 1-4 (pp. 27–34)

5. *((not p) or q) and not((not q) and r)* **7. a.** 11¢ **b.** 7¢ **c.** the network in question 6

9.

p	q	~q	(p and ~q)
T	T	F	F
T	F	T	T
F	T	F	F
F	F	T	F

11. *There is a symphony orchestra with a full-time banjo player.* **13.** False; counterexample: Let n be 3.

15. See below. x-intercepts: 2 and 5; y-intercept: 10; the axis of symmetry: $x = 3.5$; vertex: (3.5, -2.25)

15.

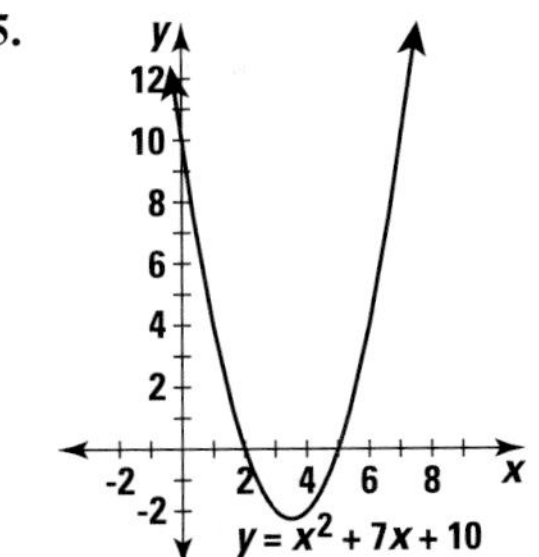

LESSON 1-5 (pp. 35–43)

13. a. False **b.** False **15.** *If one has been convicted of a felony, then that person is not allowed to vote.* **17. a.** *If Jon wasn't at the scene of the crime, then Jon didn't commit the crime.* **b.** If one has a true alibi, then one is innocent. **19.** If a satellite can stay in orbit, then it is at a height of at least 200 miles above the earth. **21.** If one is elected to the honor society, then one's GPA is at least 3.5.

23.

p	q	p AND q	NOT q	(NOT q) OR (p AND q)
1	1	1	0	1
1	0	0	1	1
0	1	0	0	0
0	0	0	1	1

25. a. and **b.** $-5 \geq x$ or $x > 2$. **c. See below.**

25. c. (number line: closed dot at -5, open dot at 2; labels -5, 0, 2, x)

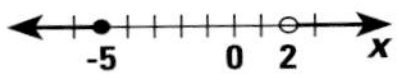

LESSON 1-6 (pp. 44–52)

11. a. If p, then q
If q, then r
$\therefore$ If p, then r

b. Yes, it follows from the Law of Transitivity.

13. *The diagonals of ABCD bisect each other.* **15.** -3 and -1 are not positive real numbers, so the universal statement does not apply. **17.** c **19.** yes **21.** True **23. a.** center (3, -5); radius 7; **b. See below.**

23. b.

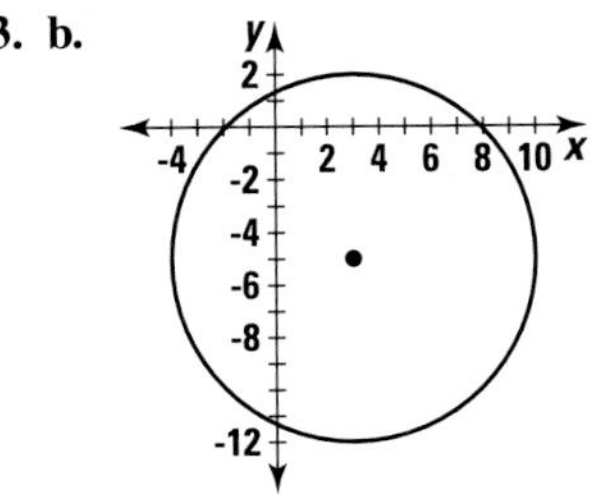

LESSON 1-7 (pp. 53–60)

11. a. p: *Peter is not at home.*
q: *The answering machine is on.*
$p \Rightarrow q$
q
$\therefore$ p

b. invalid, converse error

13. a. $p(x)$: *x is President of the United States.*
$q(x)$: *x is at least 35 years old.*
Let c be *Queen Elizabeth.*
$\forall x, p(x) \Rightarrow q(x)$
$q(c)$
$\therefore \quad p(c)$
b. yes; no
c. invalid; converse error

15. $p(x)$: *x is a real number.*
$q(x)$: $x^2 \geq 0$
$r(x)$: *x is a pure imaginary number.*
Let $c = 2i$
$\forall x, p(x) \Rightarrow q(x)$
$\forall x, r(x) \Rightarrow \sim q(x)$
$r(c)$
$\therefore \quad \sim p(c)$
Valid; $r(c) \Rightarrow \sim q(c)$ by the Law of Detachment, and $\sim q(c) \Rightarrow \sim p(c)$ by the Law of Indirect Reasoning.

17. a.

p	q	$p \Rightarrow q$	$\sim p$	$(p \Rightarrow q)$ and $\sim p$	$\sim q$	$((p \Rightarrow q)$ and $\sim p) \Rightarrow \sim q$
T	T	T	F	F	F	T
T	F	F	F	F	T	T
F	T	T	T	T	F	F
F	F	T	T	T	T	T

b. inverse error

19. a. Let p: *Devin is a boy.*
Let q: *Devin plays baseball.*
Let r: *Devin is a pitcher.*
$p \Rightarrow q$
$q \Rightarrow r$
$\sim r$
$\therefore \quad \sim p$

b. The argument correctly uses the Law of Indirect Reasoning and the Law of Transitivity.

21. $p \Rightarrow q$ (4)
$q \Rightarrow r$ (2)
$r \Rightarrow s$ contrapositive of (5)
$s \Rightarrow t$ contrapositive of (3)
$\therefore \quad p \Rightarrow t$ Law of Transitivity
p (1)
$\therefore \quad t$ Law of Detachment

23. $\forall$ *integers a and b, if* $\frac{a}{b} = \sqrt{2}$ then $\frac{a^2}{b^2} = 2$. **25. a.** $\forall$ real numbers x and a, $x^2 - a^2 = (x - a)(x + a)$. **b.** i. Let $a = 4$. By substitution, $x^2 - 16 = (x - 4)(x + 4)$. **c.** -400 ii. Let $x = 3y^2$ and $a = z$. By substitution, $9y^4 - z^2 = (3y^2 - z)(3y^2 + z)$.

LESSON 1-8 (pp. 61–66)

9. $y < 90$;

Conclusions	Justifications
$\frac{1}{2}y - 5 < \frac{1}{3}y + 10$	Given
$\frac{1}{6}y < 15$	Addition Property of Inequality
$y < 90$	Multiplication Property of Inequality

11. converse error **13.** invalid; inverse error **15.** False. x could be -3. **17. a.** HELLO **b.** IF (A ≠ 7) or (B ≤ 4) THEN PRINT "HELLO" ELSE PRINT "GOODBYE" **c.** (A = 7 and B > 4)

19.

p	q	p AND q	NOT q	(NOT q) OR (p AND q)
1	1	1	0	1
1	0	0	1	1
0	1	0	0	0
0	0	0	1	1

21. $\forall$ *real numbers x and y, xy ≠ 0.*
23. a. -84 **b.** $-4h^2 - 19h - 21$ **c.** $-4t^2 - 11t - 6$

CHAPTER 1 PROGRESS SELF-TEST (pp. 69–70)

1. c **2.** d **3.** True **4.** d, e **5.** True **6.** $\exists$ a real number y, such that $0 + y \neq y$. **7.** $\sqrt{(-7c)^2} = |-7c| = |7c|$ **8.** ($x > -8$ or $x = -8$) and ($x < 12$). **9.** *The bald eagle is not our national bird or "The Star-Spangled Banner" is not our national anthem.* **10.** SELECT IF NOT (LOCATION = 2) AND NOT (LOCATION = 3) **11.** *If a person can be admitted to an R-rated movie, then the person is at least 17 years old.* **12.** $s \leq -4$ **13.** c **14.** b **15.** *If two lines are parallel, then when cut by a transversal, corresponding angles have the same measure. If two lines cut by a transversal have corresponding angles with the same measure, then the lines are parallel.* **16.** b, valid **17.** e, invalid **18.** Valid; using the Law of Detachment followed by the Law of Indirect Reasoning.
19. -1; 11
Proof: It is given that
$$2(x + 5)^2 = 40x + 72.$$
Expanding the left side, yields
$$2x^2 + 20x + 50 = 40x + 72.$$
Adding $-40x - 72$ to both sides results in
$$2x^2 - 20x + 22 = 0.$$
Factoring the left side yields
$$2(x + 1)(x - 11) = 0.$$
By the Zero Product Theorem,
$$x + 1 = 0 \text{ or } x - 11 = 0.$$
Therefore, $x = -1$ or $x = 11$.

20. $p(x)$ is called the "given." **21.** *(p or q) and (not q)*
22.

p	q	p OR q	NOT q	output
1	1	1	0	0
1	0	1	1	1
0	1	1	0	0
0	0	0	1	0

23.

p	q	p or q	not (p or q)
T	T	T	F
T	F	T	F
F	T	T	F
F	F	F	T

24. False; counterexample:
Let $x = 1$ and $y = 1$.
$\sqrt{1 + 1} = \sqrt{2}, \sqrt{1} + \sqrt{1} = 2$
But $\sqrt{2} \neq 2$. So
$\sqrt{1 + 1} \neq \sqrt{1} + \sqrt{1}$.

The chart below keys the questions on the **Progress Self-Test** to the objectives in the **Chapter Review** on pages 71–75 or to the **Vocabulary** (Voc.) on page 68. This will enable you to locate those **Chapter Review** questions that correspond to questions you missed on the **Progress Self-Test.** The lesson where the material is covered is also indicated on the chart.

Question	**1**	**2**	**3**	**4**	**5**	**6**	**7**
Objective	A, E	A	I	B	D	C	F
Lesson	1-1	1-1	1-1, 1-2	1-1, 1-3, 1-5	1-1	1-2	1-1
Question	**8**	**9**	**10**	**11**	**12**	**13**	**14**
Objective	B	C	B	B	E	E	A
Lesson	1-3	1-2, 1-3	1-3, 1-5	1-5	1-1, 1-2, 1-5	1-1, 1-2, 1-5	1-5
Question	**15**	**16**	**17**	**18**	**19**	**20**	**21**
Objective	B	G	G	J	H	H	K
Lesson	1-1, 1-5	1-6, 1-7	1-6, 1-7	1-6, 1-7, 1-8	1-8	1-1, 1-8	1-4
Question	**22**	**23**	**24**				
Objective	K	L	H, F				
Lesson	1-4	1-3	1-8				

CHAPTER 1 REVIEW (pp. 71–75)

1. universal **3.** existential **5.** *∀ countries c, c has not landed people on Mars.* **7.** *∀ composite numbers n, ∃ a positive integer y, such that y ≠ n, y ≠ 1, and y is a factor of n.* **9.** b, c **11.** *If one passes a state's bar exam, then one can practice law in the state. If one can practice law in a state, then one has passed the state's bar exam.* **13.** *If $x > 1$, then $\log x > 0$.* **15.** *Some British bobby carries a gun.* **17.** *A person wants to travel from the U.S. to Europe and doesn't travel by plane or by ship.* **19.** *Excessive bail shall be required, or excessive fines shall be imposed, or cruel and unusual punishments shall be inflicted.* **21.** *p and (not q)* **23.** False **25.** True **27.** Yes **29.** False **31.** False **33.** $(3x + 4)^3 = 27x^3 + 108x^2 + 144x + 64$ **35.** invalid by IV **37.** valid by III **39. a.** yes **b.** no **41.** c **43.** $|\pi + -13| \le |\pi| + |-13| = \pi + 13$, by the Law of Substitution. **45.** $\frac{-b + \sqrt{b^2 - 4ac}}{2a} \cdot \frac{-b - \sqrt{b^2 - 4ac}}{2a} = \frac{b^2 - (b^2 - 4ac)}{4a^2} = \frac{4ac}{4a^2} = \frac{c}{a}$ **47.** True; all campers participate in a sports activity. **49.** False; no camper participates in all sports activities **51.** False; Oscar participates in nature identification, but he does not participate in arts & crafts. **53.** False; no camper participates in both jewelery design and in swimming **55.** valid by I **57.** valid by II and III **59. a.** *(p and q) or (q and r)* **b.** 0

61.

p	q	p or q
T	T	T
T	F	T
F	T	T
F	F	F

63.

p	q	r	$p \Rightarrow q$	$(p \Rightarrow q) \Rightarrow r$
T	T	T	T	T
T	T	F	T	F
T	F	T	F	T
T	F	F	F	T
F	T	T	T	T
F	T	F	T	F
F	F	T	T	T
F	F	F	T	F

65.

p	q	p and q	not(p and q)	not p	not q	(not p) or (not q)
T	T	T	F	F	F	F
T	F	F	T	F	T	T
F	T	F	T	T	F	T
F	F	F	T	T	T	T

same truth values (not(p and q) and (not p) or (not q))

LESSON 2-1 (pp. 78–84)

11. a. 3 **b.** {0, 1, 3, 5, 7, 9, 11, 13, 15} **c.** Its domain is a finite set which is discrete. **13.** [-2, 2] **15.** (-∞, -2), (-2, 1), (1, ∞) **17.** $8a + 23$ **19. a.** $h = \frac{V}{\pi r^2}$ **b.** The height will be $\frac{1}{4}$ of its original value. **21.** F'(2, -1), I'(1, 0), R'(1, 1), E'(2, 0) **See right.**

21.

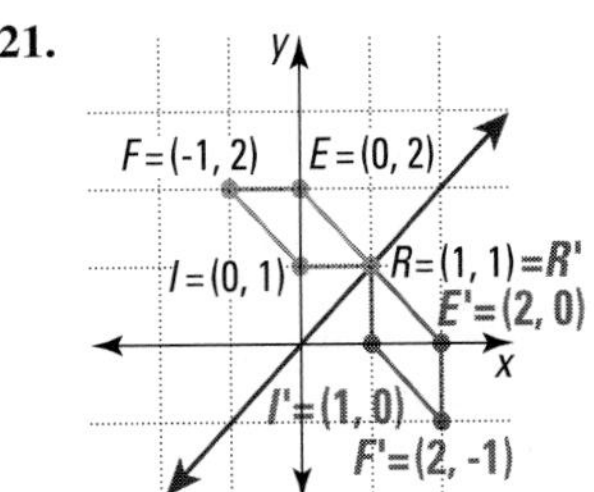

LESSON 2-2 (pp. 86–90)

7. Estimated range: [-0.1, 4] **See page 855.** **9. a.** $\ell = \frac{20000}{w}$ **b.** $P = \frac{40000}{w} + 2w$ **c.** $P(130) \approx 567.7$; $P(140) \approx 565.7$; $P(150) \approx 566.7$ **d.** (141.4, 565.7) **See page 855.** **e.** 565.7 m **11. a.** minimum: -3; maximum: 3 **b.** domain: [-5, 6] range: [-3, 3] **c.** $x = 0$ and $x = 3$ **d.** [-5, -4) and (-1, 4) **13. a.** Yes, because each element in R corresponds to exactly one element in P. **b.** No, because each element in P corresponds to more than one element in R. **c.** i. 8 ii. not possible iii. 15

15. a.

Switch 1	Switch 2	Light
1	1	1
1	0	0
0	1	0
0	0	1

A "1" in the first or second column means that the indicated switch is up, and a "0" means that it is down.

b.

p	q	$p \Leftrightarrow q$
T	T	T
T	F	F
F	T	F
F	F	F

If 1 corresponds to T and 0 to F, it is apparent that the two truth tables are equivalent. Hence, the stairway light situation is a physical representation of $p \Leftrightarrow q$.

7.

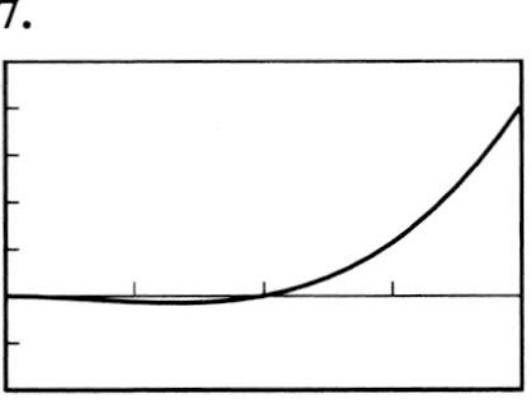

$0 \le x \le 2$, x-scale $= \frac{1}{2}$
$-2 \le y \le 5$, y-scale $= 1$

9. d.

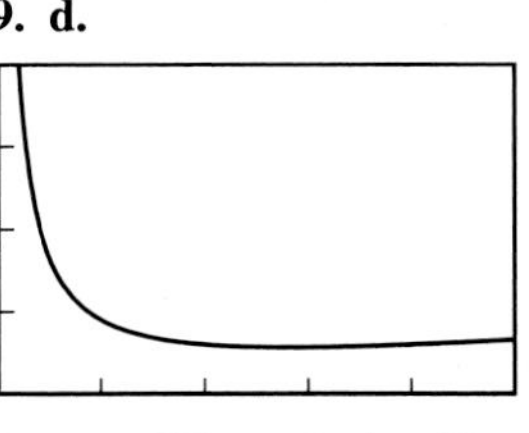

$0 \le x \le 250$, x-scale $= 50$
$0 \le y \le 4000$, y-scale $= 1000$

LESSON 2-3 (pp. 91–96)

9. a. $\frac{1}{x_1} > \frac{1}{x_2}$ **b.** positive real numbers; $x_1 \cdot \frac{1}{x_1x_2} < x_2 \cdot \frac{1}{x_1x_2}$; $>$ **11. a.** $t \ge 1.2775$ sec **b.** At $t = 1.2755$ seconds, the object reaches maximum height and starts to descend. **13.** Its domain is a discrete set, {integers x: $1954 \le x \le 1995$}. **15.** 2^{105} **17.** 1.2

LESSON 2-4 (pp. 97–101)

11. a. **See below.** **b.** 5 **c.** $y = 5$ **d.** Sample: $x > 10$
13. a. $\lim_{x\to\infty} h(x) = -3$ **b.** Sample: **See below.** **15. a.** (-3, 0), (4, 5] **b.** relative maximum: -3, occurs at $x = -5$; 2.5, occurs at $x = 0$; 0, occurs at $x = 5$; relative minimum: -3 occurs at $x = -2$; -2 occurs in the interval (2, 3); -3 occurs at $x = 4$ **c.** [-3, 3] **d.** -3.1; -1; 1.5; 4.8 **e.** $-3 < x < -1$, and $32 \le x \le 4.8$ **17.** domain = $(-\infty, -3), (-3, 2), (2, \infty)$; range = $(-\infty, -1.12], (0, \infty)$ **19.** $\frac{x^{\frac{7}{6}}}{y}$ **21.** $n \ge 5$; Law of Indirect Reasoning

11. a.

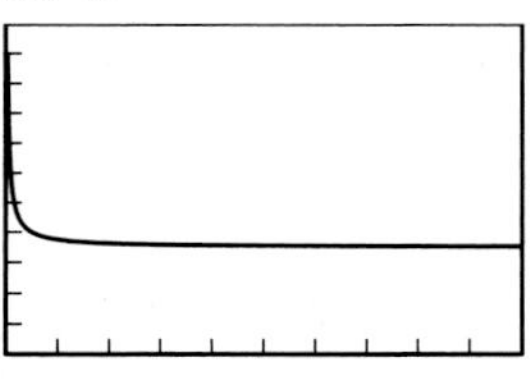

$0 \le x \le 20$, x-scale $= 2$
$-2 \le y \le 20$, y-scale $= 2$

13. b.

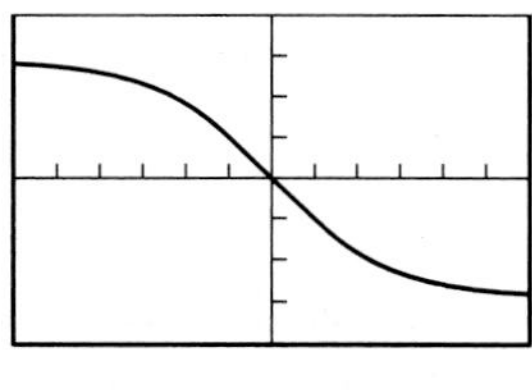

$-6 \le x \le 6$, x-scale $= 1$
$-4 \le y \le 4$, y-scale $= 1$

LESSON 2-5 (pp. 102–108)

9. From $x = 3t - 7$, $t = \frac{x + 7}{3}$; therefore, $y = 6 \cdot \frac{x + 7}{3} + 5 = 2x + 19$. This means that the parametric equations are equivalent to the equation $y = 2x + 19$. **11.** Sample: $v_x = 18.5 \frac{\text{m}}{\text{sec}}$, $v_y = 14.7 \frac{\text{m}}{\text{sec}}$,

13. Sample:
$x(t) = \frac{1}{2}(1 + t)(1 - t^2)$,
$y(t) = \frac{1}{2}(1 - t)(1 - t^2)$, $-1 \le t \le 1$ The graph of the above parametric equations is the image of the graph in Example 2 under the size change with center (0,0) and magnitude $\frac{1}{2}$ (a contraction).
15. a. **See below.** **b.** $(0, 2), (2, \infty)$ **c.** $(2, \infty)$
17. $\frac{x^3}{y^2}$ **19.** $1 + 4x^2$ **21. a.** $\frac{1}{2}$ **b.** $\frac{\sqrt{3}}{2}$ **c.** $\frac{\sqrt{2}}{2}$

15. a.

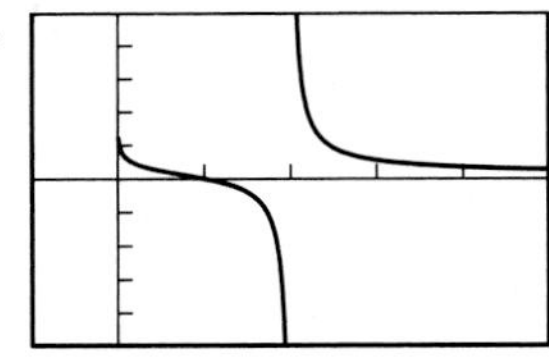

$-1 \le x \le 5$, x-scale $= 1$
$-5 \le y \le 5$, y-scale $= 1$

LESSON 2-6 (pp. 109–116)

15. Because (cos θ, sin θ) is the image of (1, 0) under a counterclockwise rotation of θ about the origin and [cos (-θ), sin (-θ)] can be considered as the image of (1, 0) under a clockwise rotation of θ about the origin.
cos (-θ) = cos θ
sin (-θ) = - sin θ
See below.
17. a. Sample: $0 \le x \le \pi$; $-7 \le y \le 23$ **b.** $\frac{\pi}{2}$ **c.** maximum: 23; minimum: -7 **19.** d **21.** $(x + y)^2$ **23.** cannot be simplified

15.

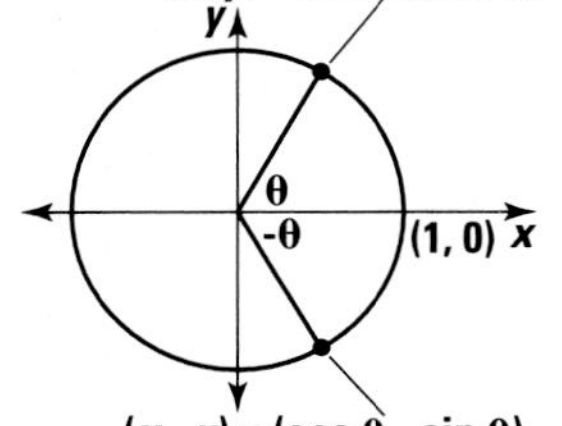

LESSON 2-7 (pp. 117–123)

9. a. $P(t) = (3.93)(e^{(.029655)t})$ **b.** 1990.6 million **c.** i. 23.29 million ii. 102.59 million iii. 451.89 million The formula is a reasonable accurate predictor of the population for the period from 1790 to 1850.
11. ≈ 32% of the original amount **13. a.** $\frac{1}{2}$ **b.** $\frac{-\sqrt{3}}{2}$ **c.** $\frac{\sqrt{2}}{2}$ **d.** -1
15. 1 **17.** 12, 16, 20, 24, 28

LESSON 2-8 (pp. 124–129)

11. difference equation: $a_{n+1} = a_n + d$
explicit formula: $a_n = b + (n - 1)d$
13. a. 0, 0, 0, 0, 0; lim = 0 **b.** 1, 0, $-\frac{1}{3}$, 0, ; lim = 0
15. An ellipse with center (5, -4), minor axis with vertices (3, -4) and (7, -4), and major axis with vertices (5, -1) and (5, -7).
17. a. 4 **b.** 2

LESSON 2-9 (pp. 130–136)

13. $\log_b 5 + 2 \log_b n - \log_b w$ **15.** about 23.9 years **17.** $x = 20$
19. recursive: $a_{n+1} = a_n - 4$, $a_1 = 100$; explicit: $a_n = 104 - 4n$
21. a. $h_n = \frac{n + 1}{2n}$ **b.** .55, .505, .5005 **c.** 0.5
23. slope; $\ell = \left(\frac{b - d}{a - c}\right)$, $\ell' = \frac{a - c}{b - d} = \left(\frac{b - d}{a - c}\right)^{-1} = l^{-1}$

CHAPTER 2 PROGRESS SELF TEST (p. 141)

1. a. w **b.** z **c.** $z + 5 > 0 \Leftrightarrow z > -5$, so the domain = $\{z: z > -5\}$. **2.** The x-coordinate of the vertex of a parabola occurs at $\frac{-b}{2a}$, so $x = \frac{-4}{4} = -1$. The minimum value is $f(-1) = 2(-1)^2 + 4(-1) + 3 = 1$. So the range = $\{y: y \geq 1\}$
3. a. increasing over $[-\infty, -1]$, $[1, \infty]$; decreasing over $[-1, 1]$
b. relative max. = 1; relative min. = -1 **c.** ∞ **d.** $(-\infty, -2] \cup [0, 2]$
4. Sample: $[\pi, 2\pi]$ **5. a. See right. b.** increasing **c.** 0
6. a. $\ell \cdot w = 300 \Leftrightarrow \ell = \frac{300}{w}$ **b.** $f(w) = \ell + 2w = \frac{300}{w} + 2w$
c. See right. d. f has a relative minimum value at $w \approx 12.25$ ft. So $\ell \approx \frac{300}{12.25} \approx 24.49$ ft **7.** $\log_a \frac{N^2}{P} = \frac{\log_{10} \frac{N^2}{P}}{\log_{10} a} = \frac{1}{\log_{10} a}(2 \log_{10} N - \log_{10} P)$
8. a. $x = 70t$, $y = -16t^2 + 30t$ **b.** The ball lands about 131 ft from home plate; it will not clear the right field wall. **See right.**
9. domain: real numbers; range: $-2 \leq y \leq 2$
relative max = 2 occurs at $x = \frac{3\pi}{2} + 2\pi n$, $\forall$ integers n
relative min = -2 occurs at $x = \frac{\pi}{2} + 2\pi n$, $\forall$ integers n
increasing: $\left[\frac{\pi}{2} + 2n\pi, \frac{3\pi}{2} + 2n\pi\right]$, $\forall$ integers n; decreasing: $\left[-\frac{\pi}{2} + 2n\pi, \frac{\pi}{2} + 2n\pi\right]$, $\forall$ integers n limits undefined
model: phenomena based on rotations, sound waves
special properties: period = 2π, odd function

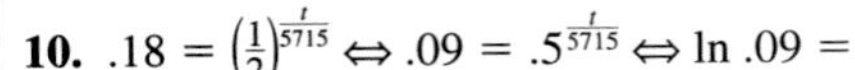

10. $.18 = \left(\frac{1}{2}\right)^{\frac{t}{5715}} \Leftrightarrow .09 = .5^{\frac{t}{5715}} \Leftrightarrow \ln .09 = \frac{t}{5715} \cdot \ln .5 \Leftrightarrow 5715 \cdot \frac{\ln .09}{\ln .5} = t$; $t \approx 19{,}854$ years
11. Let $G_0 = 14.7$, then $G_{n+1} = G_n + 2.5$ (in millions of dollars) $G_n = 14.7 + 2.5n$ (in millions of dollars)

5. a.

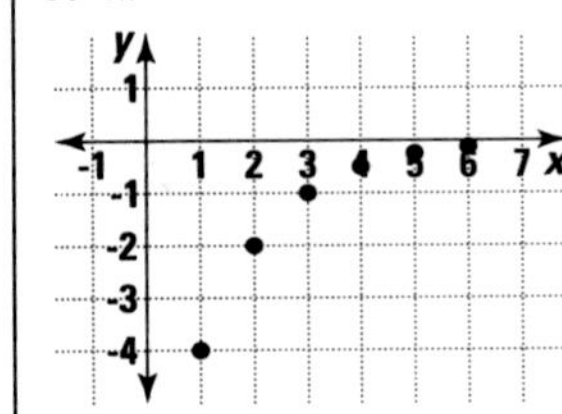

6. c.

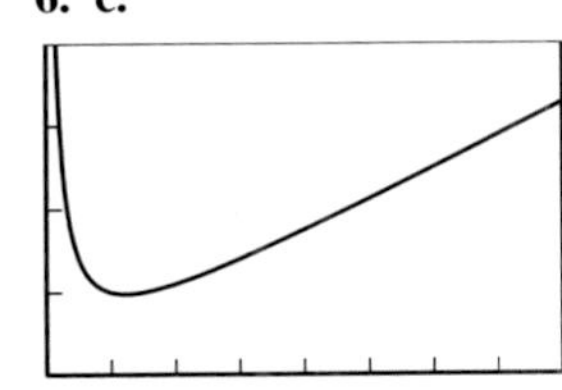

$0 \leq x \leq 80$, x-scale = 10
$0 \leq y \leq 200$, y-scale = 50

8. b.

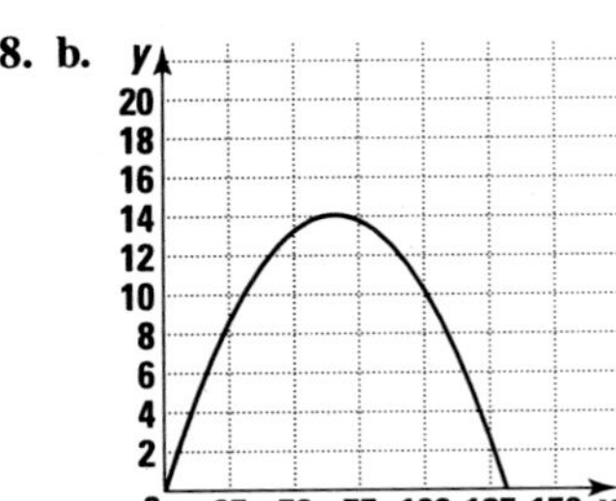

The chart below keys the questions on the **Progress Self-Test** to the objectives in the **Chapter Review** on pages 142–145 or to the **Vocabulary** (Voc.) on page 140. This will enable you to locate those **Chapter Review** questions that correspond to questions you missed on the **Progress Self-Test**. The lesson where the material is covered is also indicated on the chart.

Question	**1**	**2**	**3**	**4**	**5**	**6**	**7**	**8**	**9**
Objective	C	C	G	A	A, D	F	B	H	G
Lesson	2-1	2-2	2-2, 2-3	2-3	2-3, 2-4, 2-8	2-2	2-9	2-5	2-6

Question	**10**	**11**
Objective	E	E
Lesson	2-7	2-8

CHAPTER 2 REVIEW (pp. 142–145)

1. a. increasing on [1900, 1930] and [1950, 1970]; decreasing on [1930, 1950] and [1970, 1990] **b.** No; 1930 < 1940 but 25,678 > 25,111 **3. a.** increasing on $\left(-\infty, \frac{2}{3}\right]$; decreasing on $\left[\frac{2}{3}, \infty\right)$ **b.** relative maximum: $\frac{2}{3}$ **5. a.** arithmetic **b.** decreasing **7. a.** neither **b.** decreasing **9.** $2^x = 8$; $x = 3$ **11.** $b^2 = 9$; $b = 3$ **13.** $3^{-2} = \frac{2z}{5}$; $z = \frac{5}{18}$ **15.** $2 \log N + 3 \log M - \log P$ **17.** No, each element in S corresponds to more than one element in R. **19. a.** Yes, it is a function. It is not discrete since L can take any real values between 0 and 320. **b.** L, length of skid marks **c.** speed of the car, S **d.** $\{L: 0 \leq L \leq 320\}$ **e.** $\{s: 0 \leq s \leq 80\}$ **21.** the set of real numbers except $r \neq 5$, $r \neq -4$ **23.** minimum: -11; maximum: 19; y: {-11, -3, -1, 9, 19} **25.** range: (∞, ∞); no maximum or minimum **27.** [126, 1001] **29.** $\lim\limits_{x \to \infty} \cos x$ = undefined, $\lim\limits_{x \to -\infty} \cos x$ = undefined **31.** no limit exists **33. a.** 1 **b.** $|x| \geq 13$ **c.** 1 **d.** $y = 1$ **35. a.** $\lim\limits_{y \to \infty} g(y) = -\infty$, $\lim\limits_{y \to -\infty} g(y) = -\infty$ **b.** none

37. a. $\lim\limits_{x \to \infty} b^x = 0$, $\lim\limits_{x \to -\infty} b^x = \infty$ **b.** $\lim\limits_{x \to \infty} b^x = \lim\limits_{x \to -\infty} b^x = 1$ **c.** $\lim\limits_{x \to \infty} b^x = \infty$, $\lim\limits_{x \to -\infty} b^x = 0$ **39. a.** $\approx 10.22\%$ **b.** $\approx 13.33\%$ **41.** 20 **43. a.** $P_{n+1} = (1.25)P_n$ **b.** $P_{n+1} = (1.25)P_n + 500$ **c.** $P_{n+1} = (1.25)P_n - \frac{.25P_n^2}{15000}$ **45. a.** $p - 5$ **b.** $-10p^2 + 150p - 500$ **c.** price = \$7.50 profit = \$62.50 **47. a.** increasing over: [-4, 0]; decreasing over: [0, 4] **b.** relative maxima at (0, 4) **c.** even **49. a.** $x = \{-6, -3, -1, 2, 4\}$ **b.** in the intervals (-6, -3), (-1, 2), $(4, \infty)$ **c.** in the intervals $(\infty, -6)$, (-3, -1), (2, 4) **d.** $x = -1.5$, $x = -2.5$, $x = -7$ **e.** x in the intervals $(-\infty, -7)$, (-2.5, -1.5) **51. a.** $\{x: -6 < x < 6\}$ **b.** {0, 1, 2, 3, 4, 5} **c.** False **d.** True **53. a.** decreasing over: $(-\infty, 2.1]$; increasing over: $[2.1, \infty)$ **b.** relative minimum: $y = -4$ **c.** $\lim\limits_{y \to -\infty} f(x) = \infty$, $\lim\limits_{x \to \infty} f(x) = \infty$ **d.** $\{y: y \geq -4\}$ **e.** neither **55. a.** i. Domain: the set of real numbers ii. range: $\{y: y \geq 0\}$ iii. increasing over: $[0, \infty)$; decreasing over: $(-\infty, 0]$

SELECTED ANSWERS

iv. no maximum value; minimum = 0; v. $\lim_{x\to\pm\infty} f(x) = \infty$
vi. models: optics, acoustics (subject to restrictions on domain)
vii. properties: even **b.** i. Domain: the set of real numbers
ii. range: $\{y: y \le 0\}$ iii. increasing over: $(-\infty, 0]$; decreasing over: $[0, \infty)$ iv. maximum = 0; no minimum value
v. $\lim_{x\to\pm\infty} f(x) = -\infty$ vi. model: projectile motion (subject to restrictions on domain) vii. properties: even, a reflection image of $y = |a|x^2$ over the x-axis
57. **See right.** **59.** **a.** $x = 20t$, $y = -4.9t^2 + 25t + 15$
b. Answers will vary. It will depend on the width of the neighboring building. **See right.**

57. a.

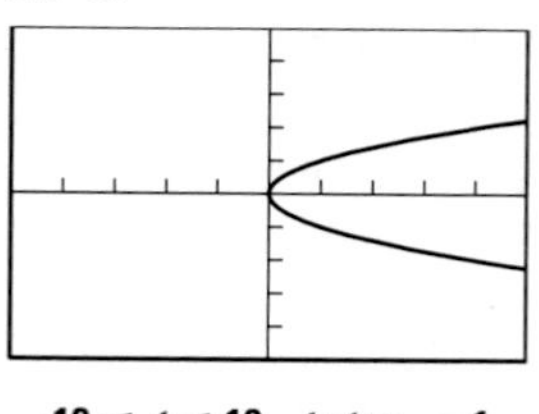

$-10 \le t \le 10$, t-step = 1
$-5 \le x \le 5$, x-scale = 1
$-5 \le y \le 5$, y-scale = 1

59. b.

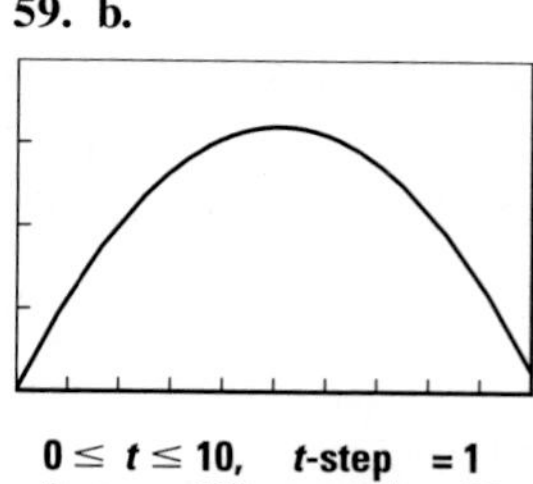

$0 \le t \le 10$, t-step = 1
$0 \le x \le 100$, x-scale = 10
$0 \le y \le 40$, y-scale = 10

LESSON 3-1 (pp. 148–153)

11. **a.** **See below.** **b.** range: $\{y: -0.5 \le y \le 0.5\}$; amplitude: 0.5; period: π **13.** $\left\{\frac{1}{2}, 1, \frac{9}{8}, 1, \frac{25}{32}, \frac{9}{16}, \frac{49}{128}, \frac{16}{63}\right\}$. As $n \to \infty$, $\frac{a_n}{b_n} \to 0$.
15. **a.** As $x \to \infty$, $\frac{u}{v} \to 3$. **See below.**

b. $(u+v)_n = \frac{3n^2+n}{n^2-1} \cdot \frac{\frac{1}{n^2}}{\frac{1}{n^2}} = \frac{\frac{3n^2}{n^2} + \frac{n}{n^2}}{\frac{n^2}{n^2} - \frac{1}{n^2}} = \frac{3 + \frac{1}{n}}{1 - \frac{1}{n^2}}$ **c.** $\lim_{n\to\infty} \frac{3 + \frac{1}{n}}{1 - \frac{1}{n^2}}$

17. the line through P tangent to the circle **19.** **a.** 22 **b.** 485
21. $c = \frac{9}{4}$

11. a.

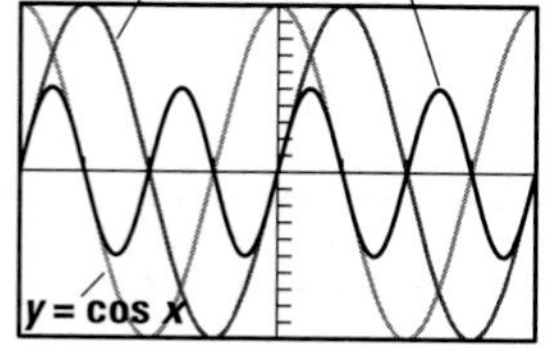

$-2\pi \le x \le 2\pi$, x-scale =
$-1 \le y \le 1$, y-scale = 0.1

15. a.

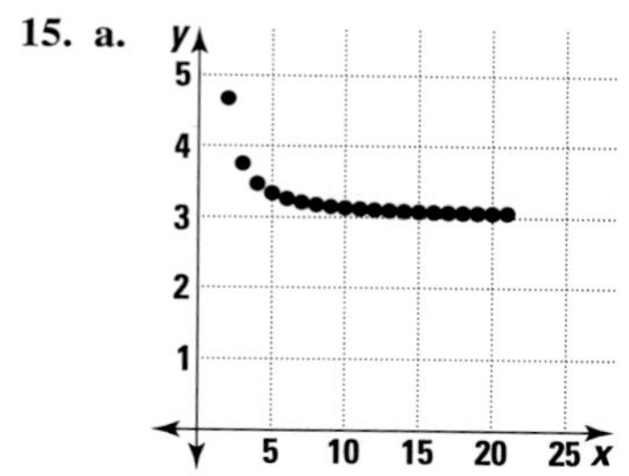

LESSON 3-2 (pp. 154–160)

13. k is a 1-1 function. **See above right.** **15.** x^3 **17.** **a.** Yes, 5^x is 1-1 for all real numbers, therefore its inverse, $\log_5 x$ is 1-1 over the positive real numbers. **b.** $x = 1$ **19.** **a.** $\{x: x$ is real and $x \ne 4\}$ **b.** x-intercept $= \left(\frac{7}{2}, 0\right)$, y-intercept $= \left(0, \frac{7}{4}\right)$
c. $\lim_{x\to\infty} f(x) = 2$, $\lim_{x\to-\infty} f(x) = 2$ **21.** Let n be odd. Then for some integer m, $n = 2m + 1$. Therefore $n^2 + 1 = (2m+1)^2 + 1 = 4m^2 + 4m + 2 = 2 \cdot (2m^2 + 2m + 1)$. Because the integers are closed under addition and multiplication, $(2m^2 + 2m + 1)$ is an integer. Therefore, $n^2 + 1 = 2 \cdot p$, where p is an integer. Therefore $n^2 + 1$ is even.

13.

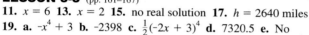

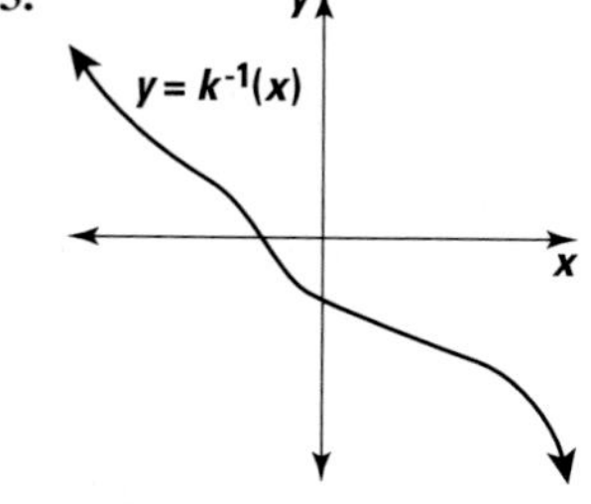

LESSON 3-3 (pp. 161–167)

11. $x = 6$ **13.** $x = 2$ **15.** no real solution **17.** $h = 2640$ miles
19. **a.** $-x^4 + 3$ **b.** -2398 **c.** $\frac{1}{2}(-2x + 3)^4$ **d.** 7320.5 **e.** No
21. **a.** $\frac{1}{100}$ **b.** -2 **c.** They are mutual inverses. **See below.**
23. **a** **See below.** **b.** $x = 0$ and $x = 4$ are zeroes. zeros of $f(x)$ and $g(x)$ are zeros of $h(x)$ **25.** **a.** $\frac{\pi}{6}, \frac{5\pi}{6}$ **b.** $\frac{\pi}{6}, \frac{5\pi}{6}, \frac{7\pi}{6}, \frac{11\pi}{6}$

21. c.

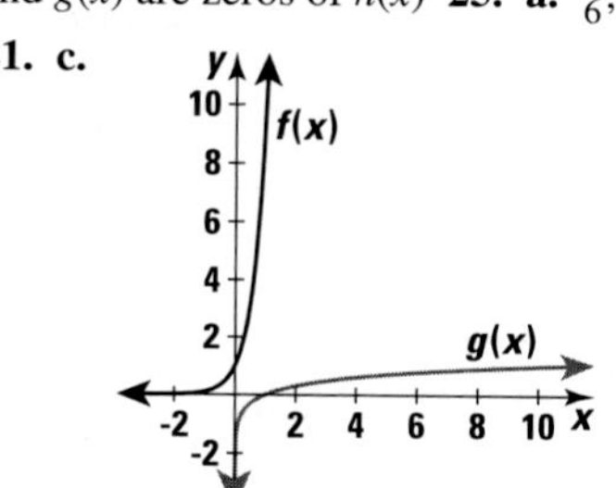

23. a.

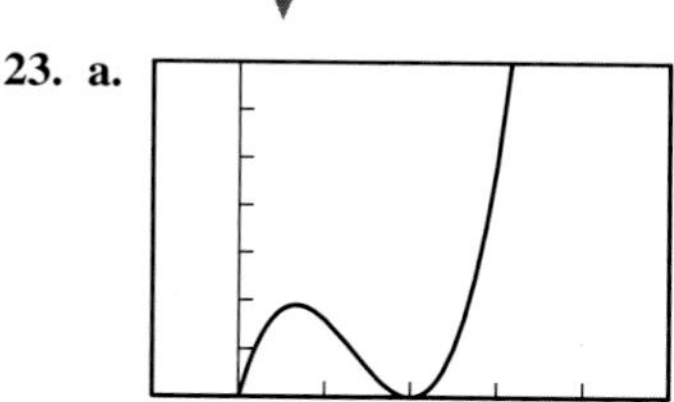

$-2 \le x \le 10$, x-scale = 2
$0 \le y \le 35$, y-scale = 5

LESSON 3-4 (pp. 168–174)

9. **a.** [1, 2] **b.** [1.5, 1.6] **11.** **a.** Yes **b.** No. g is discontinuous at $x = 0$. **13.** after ≈ 1.9 minutes **15.** $e^{\left(\frac{1}{4+x^2}\right)}$; domain: all reals **17.** **a.** Yes **b.** $n = -5$ (middle C) **c.** ≈ 554.4 hertz **19.** b

LESSON 3-5 (pp. 175–181)

11. $t > \frac{40}{3}$ or $0 < t < 5$ **13.** $g(2) = -\ln 2 < 0$ and $g(3) = 5 - \ln 3 > 0$. Thus, by the Intermediate Value Theorem, g must have a zero between 2 and 3. **15. a.** No **b.** Yes **c.** 3.00002 **17.** b **19.** c

LESSON 3-6 (pp. 182–187)

11. 99°C **13.** $x = \left\{\pm\frac{1}{\sqrt{2}}\right\}$ **15.** $n = \left\{\frac{3}{4}, \frac{7}{8}\right\}$ **17. a.** $-\ln 2 \approx -0.693$ **b.** $(-0.693, 2)$ **19. a.** $(-2, -1)$ and $(-1, 0)$ **b.** ≈ -1.3 **21. a.** $\frac{2x - 1}{-4x + 2} = -\frac{1}{2}$ **b.** domain: $x \neq \frac{1}{2}$

LESSON 3-7 (pp. 188-193)

11. Yes, this is true for values on the interval $(-1, 0)$. **13.** $x < -1.9$ or $0 < x < 1.9$ radians **15.** between ≈ 4.21 and ≈ 14.5 seconds **17.** $x = \left\{-1, \frac{44}{5}^{1/3} \approx .928\right\}$ **19. a.** 3 **b.** $[-2, -1)$ and $(0, 1)$ **c.** $(0.7, 0.8)$

LESSON 3-8 (pp. 194-201)

9. a. $\frac{1}{8}$ **b.** $-\frac{7}{8}$ **c.** $-\frac{1}{2}$ **11.** Apply the scale change $(x, y) \rightarrow \left(\frac{1}{\sqrt{2}}x, \frac{1}{\sqrt{2\pi}}y\right)$ **13.** 19,683 **15.** Let $f(x) = mx + b$ and $g(x) = nx + c$. By definition, $f \circ g = (m(nx + c) + b) = mnx + (mc + b)$. This is a line for all values of m and n. Therefore, $f \circ g$ is always a line. **17.** amplitude $= 1$; period $= 2\pi$; phase shift $= 0$ **19. a.** True **b.** False **c.** True **d.** True

LESSON 3-9 (pp. 202-207)

11. a. $m = \frac{2}{3}$ **b.** $(-3, -4.2)$ **13.** $|x - 57| > 2$

15. a. $-4 \le x \le 2, -12 \le x \le -6$ **b. See above right.**

17. $|x| < a$ if and only if $-a < x$ and $x < a$ — 1st theorem of the lesson

$\sim(|x| < a)$ if and only if $\sim(-a < x$ and $x < a)$

$|x| \ge a$ if and only if $\sim(-a < x)$ or $\sim(x < a)$ — De Morgan's Law

$|x| \ge a$ if and only if $x \le -a$ or $x \ge a$

Considering only the case when $|x > a$,

$|x| > a$ if and only if $x < -a$ or $x > a$

19. a. $\frac{1}{2}, \frac{5}{2}$ **b.** The solution set of $|x| < 4$ is $-4 < x < 4$. Scaling this by $\frac{1}{2}$ changes the solution set to $-2 < x < 2$. Translating this by $\frac{5}{2}$ gives $\frac{1}{2} < x < \frac{9}{2}$ which is the solution set of $\frac{|x - \frac{5}{2}|}{\frac{1}{2}} < 4$. **21. a. See below. b.** No. There is a discontinuity at each integral value. **23.** Let m and n be even integers and p be an odd integer. Then, by definition, $m = 2r$ and $n = 2s$ for some integers r and s. Likewise, by definition, $p = 2q + 1$ for some integer q. Then $mn - p = (2r)(2s) - (2q + 1) = 2(2rs - q - 1) + 1$. Since the integers are closed under both multiplication and addition, $2rs - q - 1$ is an integer, making $2(2rs - q - 1) + 1$ an odd integer. Therefore, $mn - p$ is an odd integer.

15. b.

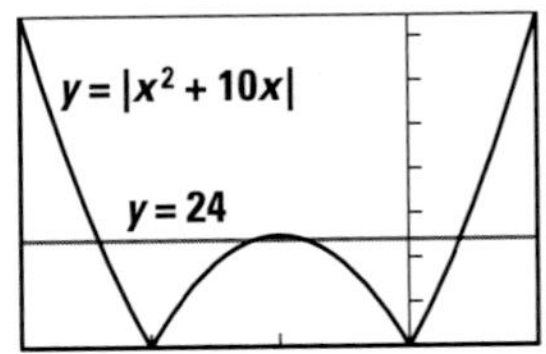

$-15 \le x \le 5$, x-scale = 5
$0 \le y \le 75$, y-scale = 10

21. a.

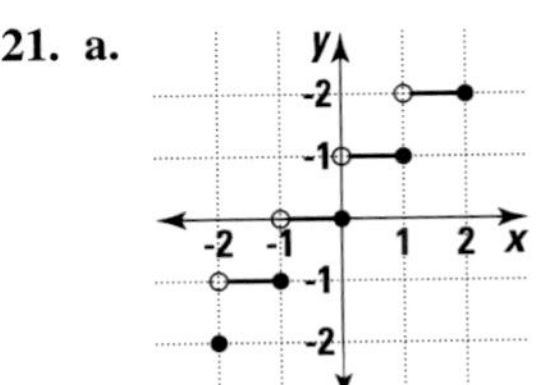

LESSON 3-10: (pp. 208–212)

15. $|T - M| \le 0.001$ **17. a.** 2.5 **b.** -7.5 **c.** 316.2 **19.** $0 < x < 1, 2 < x < 5$ **21.** Sample: **See below.**

21.

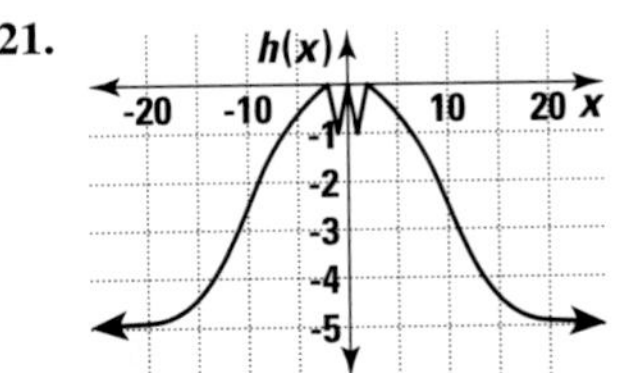

CHAPTER 3 PROGRESS SELF-TEST (p. 217)

1. $\sqrt{8x + 12} = x - 1 \Rightarrow 8x + 12 = (x - 1)^2 \Leftrightarrow 8x + 12 = x^2 - 2x + 1 \Leftrightarrow x^2 - 10x - 11 = 0 \Leftrightarrow (x + 1)(x - 11) = 0 \Leftrightarrow x = 11$ or $x = -1$. -1 is not a solution, so the only solution is $x = 11$. **2.** $2 \log x = \log(6x - 8) \Leftrightarrow x^2 = 6x - 8 \Leftrightarrow x^2 - 6x + 8 = 0 \Leftrightarrow (x - 2)(x - 4) = 0 \Leftrightarrow x = 2$ or $x = 4$ **3.** $|4z - 3| \le 7 \Leftrightarrow -7 \le 4z - 3 \le 7 \Leftrightarrow -4 \le 4z \le 10 \Leftrightarrow -1 \le z \le \frac{5}{2}$ **4.** c; $f: x \rightarrow x^6$ is not 1-1.

5. See page 859.

6. $(a \cdot b)(x) = (5x + 4)(3x^2 + 9) = 15x^3 + 12x^2 + 45x + 36$ **7.** $(f \circ g)(x) = f(g(x)) = (\sqrt{x})^2 = x$, domain all real numbers $x \ge 0$, $(g \circ f)(x) = g(f(x)) = \sqrt{x^2} = x$, domain all real numbers **8. a.** the height of a person in inches **b.** the quarts of water in the body of a person as a function of their height in inches **9.** c; $f(-1) = -18, f(0) = -7, f(1) = -10, f(2) = -15, f(3) = -10, f(4) = 17, f(5) = 78$. The only interval that must contain a zero is $[3, 4]$. **10.** Let $y = \sqrt[3]{x}$, then $y^2 + 2y = 3 \Leftrightarrow y^2 + 2y - 3 = 0 \Leftrightarrow (y + 3)(y - 1) = 0 \Leftrightarrow y = -3$ or $y = 1$. Then either $\sqrt[3]{x} = -3 \Leftrightarrow$

$x = -27$ or $\sqrt[3]{x} = 1 \Leftrightarrow x = 1$. **11.** True **12.** $|x^2 - 8| > 1 \Leftrightarrow$ $x^2 - 8 < -1$ or $x^2 - 8 > 1 \Leftrightarrow x^2 < 7$ or $x^2 > 9 \Leftrightarrow -\sqrt{7} < x < \sqrt{7}$ or $x > 3$ or $x < -3$ **13.** $2x(x - 1)(x + 3)^2 = 0 \Leftrightarrow$ $x = 0$ or $x = 1$ or $x = -3$ **14.** No. The given graph of the function is not "unbroken."

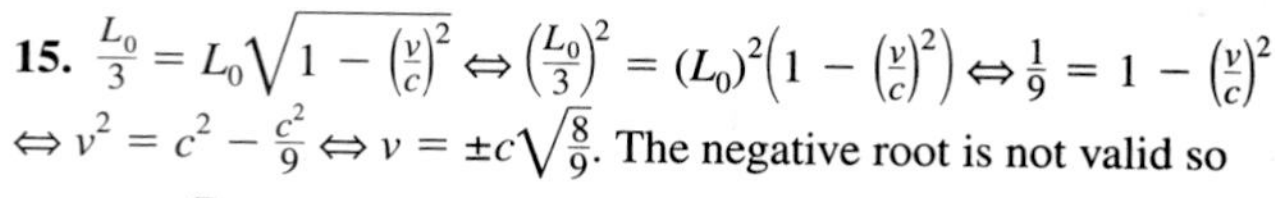

15. $\frac{L_0}{3} = L_0\sqrt{1 - \left(\frac{v}{c}\right)^2} \Leftrightarrow \left(\frac{L_0}{3}\right)^2 = (L_0)^2\left(1 - \left(\frac{v}{c}\right)^2\right) \Leftrightarrow \frac{1}{9} = 1 - \left(\frac{v}{c}\right)^2$ $\Leftrightarrow v^2 = c^2 - \frac{c^2}{9} \Leftrightarrow v = \pm c\sqrt{\frac{8}{9}}$. The negative root is not valid so $v = c\frac{2\sqrt{2}}{3}$. **16.** amplitude = 4; period = π, phase shift = $\frac{\pi}{4}$ **17.** Using an automatic grapher, the zero is found to be at about 0.3. **18.** $0.3A_0 > A_0 e^{-0.00012t} \Leftrightarrow 0.3 > e^{-0.00012t} \Leftrightarrow \ln 0.3 > -0.00012t \Leftrightarrow$ $t > \frac{\ln 0.3}{-0.00012} \approx 10{,}033$ years old.

5. $(f + g)(x)$

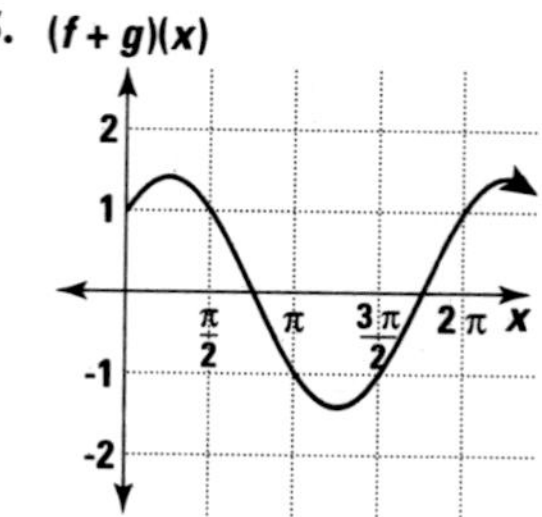

The chart below keys the questions on the **Progress Self-Test** to the objectives in the **Chapter Review** on pages 218–221 or to the **Vocabulary** (Voc.) on page 216. This will enable you to locate those **Chapter Review** questions that correspond to questions you missed on the **Progress Self-Test**. The lesson where the material is covered is also indicated on the chart.

Question	**1**	**2**	**3**	**4**	**5**	**6**	**7**	**8**	**9**	**10**
Objective	A	A	D	E	K	B	B	I	G	C
Lesson	3-3	3-3	3-9	3-3	3-1	3-1	3-2	3-1, 3-2	3-4	3-6
Question	**11**	**12**	**13**	**14**	**15**	**16**	**17**	**18**		
Objective	F	D	C	G	H	L	M	J		
Lesson	3-2	3-9	3-6	3-4	3-3	3-8	3-4	3-5		

CHAPTER 3 REVIEW (pp. 218–221)

1. $x = 5$ **3.** $t = 1$ **5.** $x = -1, x = 2$ **7.** $v = \frac{2}{9}$ **9.** $z = 10$ **11.** $y = -1, y = 7$ **13.** $s = 1$ **15.** $f \cdot g: x \to (-x^3)(\ln x)$; domain: $\{x: x > 0\}$; $\frac{f}{g}: x \to -\frac{\ln x}{x^3}$; domain: $\{x: x > 0\}$; $f \circ g: x \to \ln(-x^3)$; domain: $\{x: x < 0\}$; $g \circ f: x \to -(\ln x)^3$; domain: $\{x: x > 0\}$ **17.** $\frac{x^2 + 6}{\sqrt{x}}$ **19.** $x^3 - x^2 - 6$ **21.** $y = \{-2, -1, 3\}$ **23.** $x = \left\{0, \frac{\pi}{2}, \frac{3\pi}{2}, 2\pi\right\}$ **25.** $x \approx 0.896$ **27.** $-5 \le w \le 1$ **29.** $-7 < x < 5$ **See right.** **31.** $t > -1$ **33. a.** The second step, where both sides of the equation were divided by x^3, is incorrect. This step is valid only if $x \ne 0$ and $x = 0$ is a solution to this equation. **b.** $x = \{-1, 0, 2\}$ **35. a.** $\Rightarrow$ **b.** $\Leftrightarrow$ **c.** $\Leftrightarrow$ **d.** $\Leftrightarrow$ **e.** $\Leftrightarrow$ **f.** $\Leftrightarrow$ **37.** $(f \circ g)(x) = (z^{5/3})^{3/5} = z$; $(g \circ f)(x) = (z^{3/5})^{5/3} = z$. Since $f \circ g = g \circ f = I$, f and g are inverse functions. **39.** By definition, a decreasing function f is such that for all $x_1 < x_2$, $f(x_1) > f(x_2)$. Hence, for $x_1 \ne x_2$, $f(x_1) \ne f(x_2)$. Therefore, f is 1-1 and has an inverse. **41. a.** No **b.** No **c.** Yes **43. a. See right. b.** $[-1, 0]$ and $[0, 1]$ **45.** $v = \frac{c\sqrt{3}}{2}$ **47.** $t \approx 1.369$ sec **49. a.** i. $C: x \to 10000 + 55x$ ii. $S: x \to 150 - 0.06x$ iii. $R: x \to S(x) \cdot x = 150x - 0.06x^2$ iv. $P: x \to R - C = -0.06x^2 + 95x - 10000$ **b. See page 860. c. See page 860.** **51.** $0 \le t \le 3.56$ **53.** possible **See page 860. 55. a. See page 860. b. See page 860. c.** Because the range of $\sin x$ is $[-1, 1]$, $x + \sin x$ is bounded by the lines $y = x + 1$ and $y = x - 1$. Similarly, $x \sin x$ is bounded by the lines $y = x$, $y = -x$. **57. See page 860. 59. a.** $\frac{x^2}{9} + 9y^2 = 1$ **b.** $\frac{(x - 2)^2}{9} + 9(y + 5)^2 = 1$ **61.** -5, 9 **63.** Sample: $.975 \le x \le 1.025$

29.

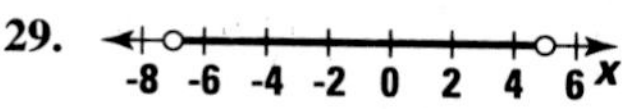

43. a.

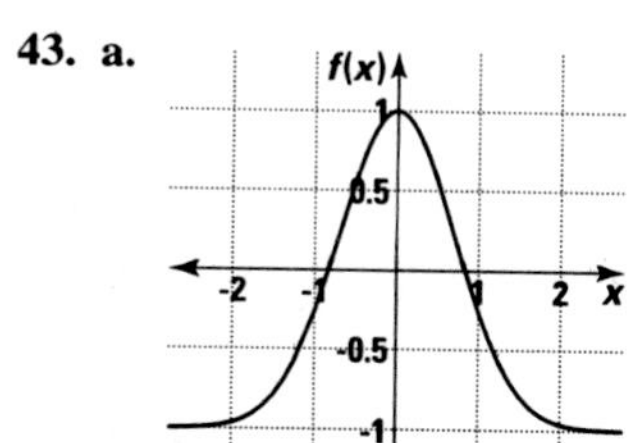

49. b.

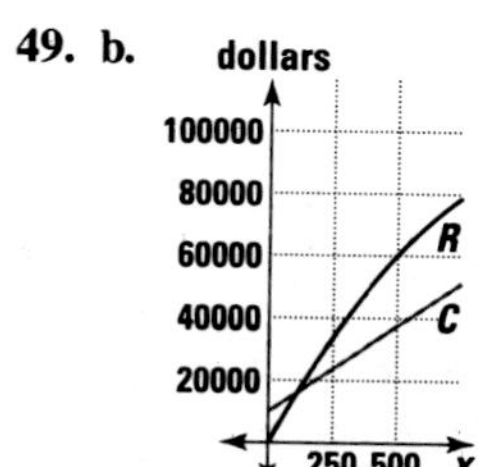

49. c.

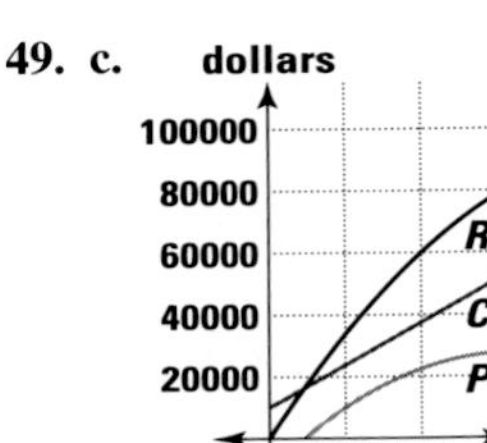

53.

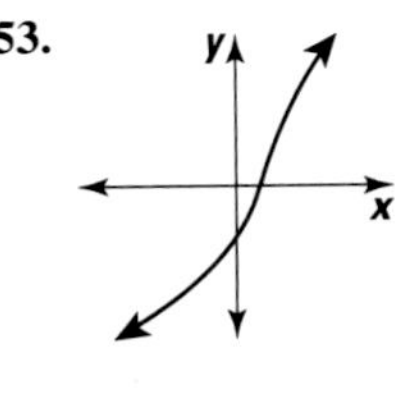

57.

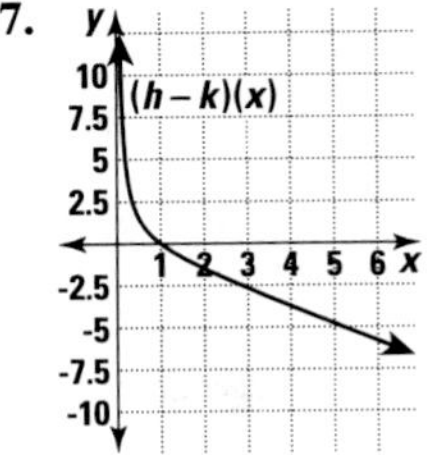

55. a.

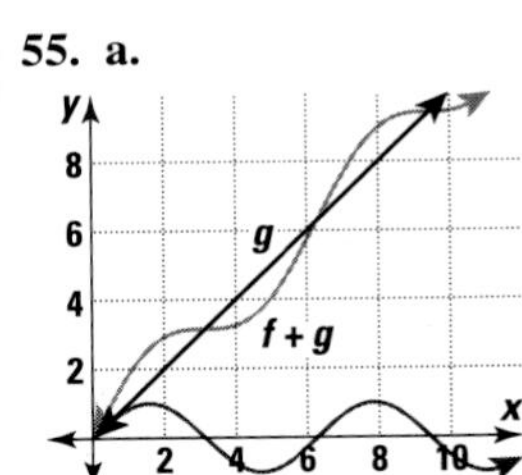

55. b.

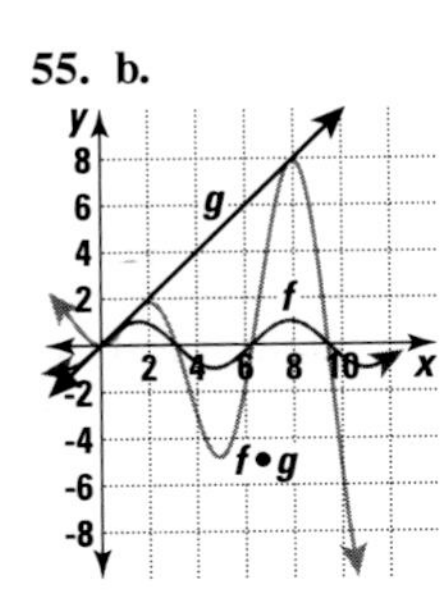

LESSON 4-1 (pp. 224–230)

11. a. Sample: $a = 2, b = -2$ **b.** $\exists$ integers a and b such that a is divisible by b and b is divisible by a and $a \neq b$.
13. a. $s(x) \cdot t(x)$ has degree 6; $s(x) + t(x)$ has degree 4.
b. The degree of the product of two polynomials is equal to the sum of the degrees of the individual polynomials. The degree of the sum of two polynomials is less than or equal to the maximum of the degrees of the individual polynomials. **c.** The conjecture does not need to be modified. **d.** The degree of a polynomial is determined by its term of greatest degree. The product of a polynomial of degree n and a polynomial of degree m will have a term of greatest degree of the form $(a_n \cdot b_m) \cdot x^{n+m}$ so the product has degree $n + m$. If the individual polynomials are both of degree n, their sum will have a term of greatest degree of the form $(a_n + b_n) \cdot x^n$ making the sum a degree n polynomial – unless $a_n = -b_n$ in which case the degree will be less than n. If the individual polynomials are not of the same degree, the larger degree being n, then the term of the greatest degree of the sum will be $a_n \cdot x^n$ making the sum of degree n.
15. Yes, $m! = m \cdot (m - 1) \cdot (m - 2) \cdot \ldots \cdot 4 \cdot 3 \cdot 2 \cdot 1$. Because the integers are closed under multiplication, $n = m \cdot (m - 1) \cdot (m - 2) \cdot \ldots \cdot 4 \cdot 2 \cdot 1$ is an integer. Substituting, we have $m! = n \cdot 3$. Thus, by the definition of factor, $m!$ is divisible by 3. **17. a.** $(8x - 1)(4x + 3)(x + 5)$ **b.** $32x^3 + 180x^2 + 97x - 15$ **19. a.** domain: all real numbers, range: $\{y: y \geq 3\}$ **b.** $\{x: x \geq 2\}$ **c.** neither **d.** $T_{2,3}$ **21.** b is not divisible by a and c is not divisible by a.

LESSON 4-2 (pp. 231–237)

13. integer **15.** integer **17. a.** 8 points **b.** $2150
c. $22150 = 8 \cdot 2500 + 2150$; the quotient is 8, the remainder is 2150. **19.** False. $x^3 + x^2 + x + 1 = x \cdot (x^2 + x + 1) + 1$.
21. $3x^5 + 4x^4 - 8x^3 - 3x^2 - 4x + 8$ **23.** $3y^2 + \frac{1}{4}$
25. a. The vessel that spotted the boat at an angle of 42°.
b. ≈ 0.4 mi **27.** If the citrus crop is not ruined, the temperature did not stay below 28°.

LESSON 4-3 (pp. 238–243)

7. $r(x) = p(-2) = -73$ **9. a.** 2355 **b.** $p(13)$
11. $f(x) = (x + 7); x \neq -3$ **13.** As $x \to \pm\infty$, the values of $f(x)$ become closer and closer to those of the function $q(x) = 3x^3 - 2x^2 + x - \frac{1}{2}$. **15.** $(x^2 - x - 1)(x^2 + x + 1) = x^4 - x^2 - 2x - 1$. Both $(x^2 - x - 1)$ and $(x^2 + x + 1)$ are factors of $x^4 - x^2 - 2x - 1$. **17.** True, this is a statement of the quotient-remainder theorem for $d = 5$. **19.** $t \geq 9, t \leq \frac{-13}{3}$ **21. a.** $h = \frac{540}{s^2}$
b. $A(s) = \frac{2160}{s} + 2s^2$ **c.** The minimum is at $s \approx 8.14$, $h \approx 8.14$ **See below. d.** $\lim_{s \to 0^+} A(s) = \infty$; $\lim_{s \to \infty} A(s) = \infty$

21. c.

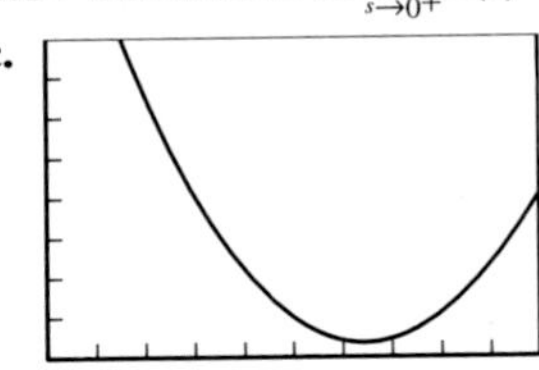

$7.5 \leq x \leq 8.5$, x-scale = 0.1
$397.8 \leq y \leq 399.4$, y-scale = 0.2

LESSON 4-4 (pp. 244–249)

9. $x = -\frac{7}{4}, x = -15, x = 1$ **11. a.** $p(x)$ intersects the line $y = x$ whenever $p(x) = x$ or $p(x) - x = 0$. Since $p(x)$ is a third degree polynomial, the polynomial $p_1(x) = p(x) - x$ is also a third degree polynomial and thus has, at most, three zeros. Therefore, $p(x)$ intersects $y = x$ in, at most, three points. **b.** A polynomial of degree $n \geq 2$ will intersect the line $y = x$ in, at most, n points.
13. $15x^4 + 47x^3 - 50x^2 + 8x + 0$
15. $q(x) = x^3 + 4x^2 - 12x + 34$, $r(x) = -101$
17. $S_{1,\frac{1}{4}}$ followed by $T_{-6,-2}$ **19.** $-2 < x < -1$
21. a. $\forall x, \log_2 x \geq 0$ **b.** the statement

LESSON 4-5 (pp. 251–257)

15. Sample: $x + 360 \equiv x(\text{mod } 360)$
17. By the Quotient-Remainder Theorem, for any integer n there exist unique integers q and r such that $n = q \cdot 3 + r$ where $0 \leq r < 3$. If $r = 0$, then, by definition, n is divisible by 3. If $r \neq 0$, either $r = 1$ so $n + 2 = q \cdot 3 + r + 2 = q \cdot 3 + 3$ or $r = 2$ so $n + 1 = q \cdot 3 + r + 1 = q \cdot 3 + 3$. So one of the three consecutive integers, n, $n + 1$, or $n + 2$ is divisible by 3.
19. a. See below. **b.** 3 **21.** $v = -\frac{1}{2}$, $v = -1 + i$, $v = -1 - i$
23. a. $60a^2 + 150a$ **b.** $30a(2a + 5)$ **c.** $a = 0$, $a = -5/2$
25. a. See below. **b.** $x \leq -3$, $x \geq 1/2$ **27. a.** $3x^2$ **b.** $2y^4$ **c.** $10z^2$

19. a.

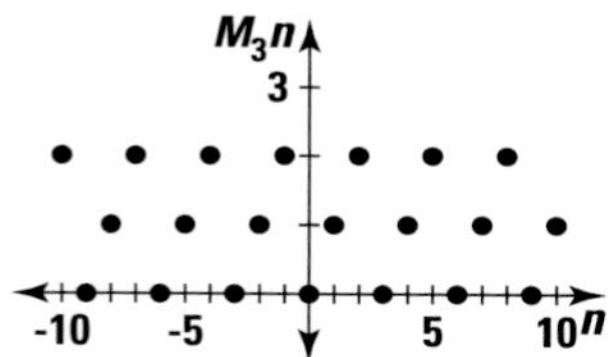

25. a.

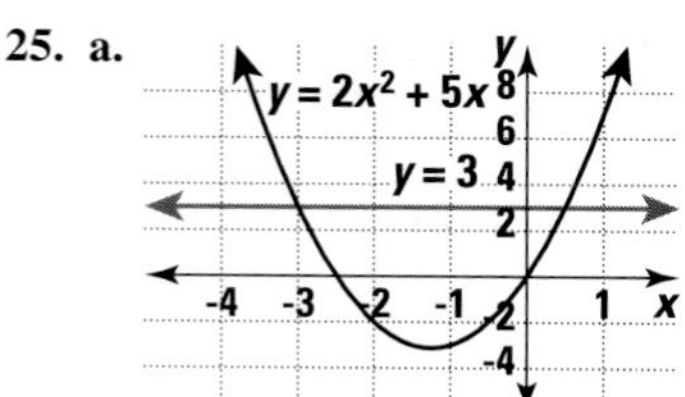

LESSON 4-6 (pp. 258–264)

15. e **17.** 43
19. Addition (Base 8)

+	0	1	2	3	4	5	6	7
0	0	1	2	3	4	5	6	7
1	1	2	3	4	5	6	7	10
2	2	3	4	5	6	7	10	11
3	3	4	5	6	7	10	11	12
4	4	5	6	7	10	11	12	13
5	5	6	7	10	11	12	13	14
6	6	7	10	11	12	13	14	15
7	7	10	11	12	13	14	15	16

Multiplication (Base 8)

·	0	1	2	3	4	5	6	7
0	0	0	0	0	0	0	0	0
1	0	1	2	3	4	5	6	7
2	0	2	4	6	10	12	14	16
3	0	3	6	11	14	17	22	25
4	0	4	10	14	20	24	30	34
5	0	5	12	17	24	31	36	43
6	0	6	14	22	30	36	44	52
7	0	7	16	25	34	43	52	61

21. a. $x = 12$ **b.** $y = 4$
23. $(5x^3 + 22x^2 + 53x + 18) = (x^2 + 4x + 9) \cdot (5x + 2)$
25. Suppose m is any integer. When m is divided by 4, the possible remainders are 0, 1, 2, 3. By the Quotient-Remainder Theorem, there exists an integer k such that $m = 4k$, or $m = 4k + 1$, or $m = 4k + 2$, or $m = 4k + 3$.
27. a. a **b.** d **c.** c **d.** b **29.** False; $|-1| \neq -1$.

LESSON 4-7 (pp. 265–272)

13. True **15.** Assume there exists a number n which is the largest multiple of 5. Then, by the definition of multiple, $n = 5m$, where m is an integer. Because the integers are closed under addition, $m + 1$ is an integer. Because the integers are closed under multiplication, $5(m + 1)$ is an integer which, by the definition of multiple, is a multiple of 5. By the distributive law, $5(m + 1) = 5m + 5$ which is an integer larger than $5m = n$. This contradicts the assumption that n is the largest multiple of 5. Therefore, this assumption is false, so there is no largest multiple of 5.
17. $(x + 2)(x - 2)(x + 3)(x - 3)$ **19. a.** $x^2 + 2x - 35$ **b.** $(x - 2)(x - 5)(x + 7)$ **c.** $x = 2$, $x = 5$, $x = -7$ **21.** 44
23. a. $xy \equiv 12 \text{ (mod 6)} \equiv 0 \text{ (mod 6)}$
b. $10 \cdot 9 = 90 \equiv 0 \text{ (mod 6)}$; $16 \cdot 15 = 240 \equiv 0 \text{ (mod 6)}$
25. a. sine function **b.** period $= \frac{1}{60}$ seconds, amplitude $=$ 15 amperes **c.** $c(t) = 15 \sin(120\pi\, t)$ **d.** 0 amperes **27.** odd
29. Assume n is an even integer. Then, by the definition of even, $n = 2 \cdot m$ for some integer m. Therefore $n^2 = (2m)^2 = 2m \cdot 2m = 2(2m^2)$ because integer multiplication is associative. Therefore, by the definition of an even number, if n is an even number then n^2 is an even number. Consequently, by the Law of the Contrapositive, if n^2 is not an even number then n is not an even number.

CHAPTER 4 PROGRESS SELF-TEST (p. 277)

1. a. $\text{floor}\left(\frac{145230}{8}\right) = 18153$ **b.** $145230 - 18153 \cdot 8 = 6$
c. $145230 = 18153 \cdot 8 + 6$. The quotient is 18153. The remainder is 6.

2. Let n, p, and m be integers such that n is a factor m. If n is a factor of m, then, by the definition of factor, $m = kn$ for some integer k. This means that $pm = p(kn) = (pk)n$ by the associative property. Since p and k are integers and the integers are closed under multiplication, pk is an integer. Therefore, by definition, n is a factor of pm.

3.

$$\begin{array}{r} 3x^2 - 7x + 8 \\ x^2 - 4x\overline{)\,3x^4 - 19x^3 + 36x^2 - 32x + 15} \\ \underline{3x^4 - 12x^3 } \\ -7x^3 + 36x^2 \\ \underline{-7x^3 + 28x^2 } \\ 8x^2 - 32x \\ \underline{8x^2 - 32x } \\ + 15 \end{array}$$

$q(x) = 3x^2 - 7x + 8,\ r(x) = 15$
4. False; $p(4) = 2(4)^3 - 3(4)^2 - 10(4) + 6 = 46 \neq 0$. **5.** 4
6. $p(x) = (x - 1)(4x + 2)(3x + 10)$. The roots are $\left\{1, -\frac{1}{2}, -\frac{10}{3}\right\}$
7. $2^{25} = 33{,}554{,}432 \equiv 4432 \pmod{10{,}000}$
$2^{25} \cdot 2^{25} \equiv 4432 \cdot 4432 \pmod{10{,}000}$
$2^{50} \equiv 19{,}642{,}624 \equiv 2624 \pmod{10{,}000}$
The last four digits are 2624.
8. $151 = 13 \cdot 11 + 8$. Therefore, $(151 - 8)$ is divisible by 11. Therefore, $151 \equiv 8 \pmod{11}$. **9.** n is a factor of $(a - 5)$.

10. Recall that an integer is divisible by three if the sum of its digits is divisible by 3. $819 = 3 \cdot 273 = 3^2 \cdot 91 = 3^2 \cdot 7 \cdot 13$
11. False, 9 is not divisible by any primes less than $\sqrt{9} = 3$ and 9 is not prime. **12.** $7x^4 - 3x^3 - 4x^2 = x^2(7x^2 - 3x - 4) = x^2(7x + 4)(x - 1)$
13. $33 = 32 + 1 = 2^5 + 2^0 = 100001_2$
14. $101_2 + 110_2 = (2^2 + 2^0) + (2^2 + 2^1) = 2^3 + 2^1 + 2^0 = 1011_2$
15. $312_5 = 3 \cdot 5^2 + 1 \cdot 5^1 + 2 \cdot 5^0 = 82$ **16.** Counterexample: Let $a = 5$, $b = 12$. $a^2 - 1 = 24$ and 12 is a factor of 24. However, 12 is not a factor of either $(a - 1) = 4$ or $(a + 1) = 6$.
17. Assume n is largest even integer. Since n is even, $n = 2m$ for some integer m. Since m is an integer, $m + 1$ is an integer because the integers are closed under addition. Since the integers are also closed under multiplication, $2(m + 1)$ is also an integer. Since $(m + 1)$ is an integer, by the definition of factor, $2(m + 1)$ is divisible by 2 and, so, is even. By the distributive property $2(m + 1) = 2m + 2 > 2m = n$, contradicting the initial assumption that n is the largest even integer. Therefore, there is no largest even integer.

SELECTED ANSWERS

The chart below keys the questions on the **Progress Self-Test** to the objectives in the **Chapter Review** on pages 278-281 or to the **Vocabulary** (Voc.) on page 276 . This will enable you to locate those **Chapter Review** questions that correspond to questions you missed on the **Progress Self-Test.** The lesson where the material is covered is also indicated on the chart.

Question	**1**	**2**	**3**	**4**	**5**	**6**	**7**	**8**	**9**	**10**
Objective	A, K	F	B	H	H	E	L	C	G	J
Lesson	4-2	4-1	4-3	4-3	4-4	4-4	4-5	4-5	4-5	4-7
Question	**11**	**12**	**13**	**14**	**15**	**16**	**17**			
Objective	J	D	M	M	M	F	I			
Lesson	4-7	4-4, 4-7	4-6	4-6	4-6	4-1	4-7			

CHAPTER 4 REVIEW (pp. 278–281)

1. $q = 5, r = 6$ **3.** $q = 83, r = 63$ **5.** 66 **7.** $a = -5$
9. $q(x) = 7x - 8, r(x) = 21x + 7$
11. $q(x) = 2x - 5, r(x) = x + 1$
13. $q(x) = 5x^2 + 30x + 181, r(x) = 1082$
15. 4 **17.** 10 **19.** R2 **21.** $5(x - y)(x + y)$ **23.** $x(3x - 5)(x + 2)$
25. $2(3v^2 + 5)^2$ **27.** $(2x + 1)(2x^2 - 4x - 9)$
29. $3, \frac{1}{14}\left(-3 + \sqrt{37}\right), \frac{1}{14}\left(-3 - \sqrt{37}\right)$ **31.** $-\frac{3}{7}, \frac{5}{2}$
33. Because $x^3 - x^2 - x - 2 = (x - 2)(x^2 + x + 1)$ and $x^2 + x + 1$ has no real zeros, 2 is the only real number with this property.
35. True; $90 = 5 \cdot 18$.
37. True; if a and b are even, then $a = 2m$, $b = 2n$ for some integers n, m. Then $2a + 2b = 4m + 4n = 4(m + n)$ by the distributive property. Because the integers are closed under addition, $m + n$ is an integer. Therefore, by the definition of factor, $2a + 2b$ is divisible by 4. **39.** b, c, and e **41.** This is false. For example, $3^3 - 1$ is not divisible by 4. **43.** 11 is a factor of $x - y$
45. If $\sin(x) = -\frac{1}{2}$, then $x \equiv \frac{7\pi}{6} \pmod{2\pi}$ or $x \equiv \frac{11\pi}{6} \pmod{2\pi}$
47. $cd \equiv 2 \pmod{11}$ **49.** Either $r(x)$ is the zero polynomial or the degree of $r(x)$ is less than the degree of $d(x)$.

51.

$$\begin{array}{r} x^2 + 2x - 7 \\ x^4 + 3\overline{)\,x^6 + 2x^5 - 7x^4 - 3x^2 - 6x + 21} \\ \underline{x^6 - 3x^2 } \\ 2x^5 - 7x^4 - 6x + 21 \\ \underline{2x^5 - 6x } \\ -7x^4 + 21 \\ \underline{-7x^4 + 21} \\ 0 \end{array}$$

53. $(x - 7)$ **55.** Assume there exists a smallest integer.
57. Assume that n is the smallest integer. Because the integers are closed under addition, $n - 1$ is also an integer. Since $n - 1 < n$, n cannot be the smallest integer. This is a contradiction. Therefore, there is no smallest integer. **59.** 2311 **61.** six (2, 3, 5, 7, 11, 13)
63. a **65.** Prime **67.** $2 \cdot 3 \cdot 5 \cdot 281$ **69.** 22 laps, 49.5 m left
71. 73 months of 5 days or 5 months of 73 days, 365 months of 1 day, or 1 month of 365 days **73.** 143 **75.** 5 **77.** 10100101_2
79. 42 **81.** 111110_2, $31 + 31 = 62$
83. In base 2, a number divisible by 16 ends in 0000.

LESSON 5-1 (pp. 284–288)

19. Since the average of two rational numbers is rational, between any two numbers there exist a rational number. If r and s are both rational numbers where $r = \frac{a}{b}$ and $s = \frac{c}{d}$ with $b \neq 0$ and $d \neq 0$, then their average is $\frac{ad + bc}{2bd}$. If $r < s$, then $\frac{a}{b} < \frac{ad + bc}{2bd} < \frac{c}{d}$.

21. $\frac{x^2}{x + h^2}$, $x \neq -h^2$ and $x \neq 0$

23. $$\frac{K}{K+1} = 1 - \frac{1}{K+1} = \frac{K+1}{K+1} - \frac{1}{K+1} = \frac{K}{K+1}$$

Yes, both sides are equal for all values where both sides are defined.

25. $\frac{K}{K+4}$; Check: Let $K = 5$, then $\frac{K}{K+1} \cdot \frac{K+1}{K+2} \cdot \frac{K+2}{K+3} \cdot \frac{K+3}{K+4} = \frac{5}{6} \cdot \frac{6}{7} \cdot \frac{7}{8} \cdot \frac{8}{9} = \frac{5}{9}$ and $\frac{K}{K+4} = \frac{5}{9}$

27. a. If n is not an even integer, then n^2 is not an even integer. **b.** Suppose n is any odd integer. By definition, there exists an integer r such that $n = 2r + 1$. Then $n^2 = (2r + 1)^2 = 4r^2 + 4r + 1 = 2(2r^2 + 2r) + 1$. Since $2r^2 + 2r$ is an integer by closure properties, n^2 is not an even integer. **c.** Yes

29. a. 1 **b.** A line with slope = 1 will be 45° from the x-axis.

LESSON 5-2 (pp. 289–294)

19. Suppose that r is any rational number. Then there exist integers a and b with $a \neq 0$ and $b \neq 0$ so that $r = \frac{a}{b}$.

$$r = \frac{a}{b}$$
$$\frac{1}{r} = \frac{1}{\frac{a}{b}}$$
$$\frac{1}{r} = \frac{b}{a}$$

$\frac{b}{a}$ must be a rational number since it is the ratio of two integers.

21. $\frac{x - 3}{2x + 1}$ **23.** 36 **25. a.** $\frac{400}{N}$ **b.** $\frac{400}{N} - \frac{400}{N + 2} = \frac{800}{N^2 + 2N}$

27. $(7\sqrt{2})^2 = 49(2) = 98$

LESSON 5-3 (pp. 295–299)

9. The sun's brightness seen from Earth is 2.25 times the brightness seen from Mars. **11. a.** $\frac{4}{x - 3}$ **b.** $x \neq 3$ **13. a.** $-x$ **b.** $x \neq 0$ **15. a.** $2^{\left(\frac{x^2+2}{2x}\right)}$ **b.** $x \neq 0$ **17. a.** $f \circ g = t^2 - 2t$ **b.** domain: the set of real numbers

LESSON 5-4 (pp. 300–306)

9. a. $\left\{y: y \neq -\frac{5}{3}\right\}$ **b.** essential **c.** $y = -\frac{5}{3}$ **d. See above right.**

11. a. the set of real numbers **b.** none **c.** none **d. See above right.** **13.** $g(x)$ is a function with a removable discontinuity at $x = 1$. Since $\lim_{x\to1} g(x) = \lim_{x\to\infty} (x + 5) = 6$, redefining $g(1) = 6$ makes $g(x)$ continuous for all x. **15. a.** domain: $\{x: x \neq 0\}$; range: $\{y: y > 0\}$ **b.** $\lim_{x\to0^+} h(x) = +\infty$; $\lim_{x\to0^-} h(x) = +\infty$ **c.** $\lim_{x\to\infty} h(x) = 0$; $\lim_{x\to-\infty} h(x) = 0$. **d.** $\forall\, x$, $h(-x) = \frac{5}{(-x)^4} = \frac{5}{x^4} = h(x)$

e. See above right. **17. a.** $\left(1 + \frac{1}{1000}\right)^{1000} = \frac{(1001)^{1000}}{(1000)^{1000}}$, rational **b.** irrational **19.** $q(x) = x^3 + 3x^2 + 2x - 2$; $r(x) = 2x - 8$

21. a. Let $d(x) = \cos x - 0.2x^2$. Since $d(1) > 0$, $d(1.5) < 0$, and $d(x)$ is continuous, the Intermediate Value Theorem ensures that there exists a zero of $d(x)$ in the interval from 1 to 1.5. Where $d(x) = 0$, $\cos x - 0.2x^2 = 0$, so $\cos x = 0.2x^2$, and hence there is a solution to the equation $\cos x = 0.2x^2$ in the interval from 1 to 1.5. **b.** $1.25 \leq x \leq 1.26$

9. d.

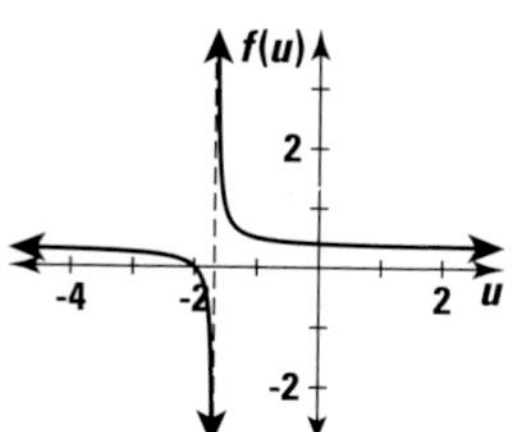

11. d.

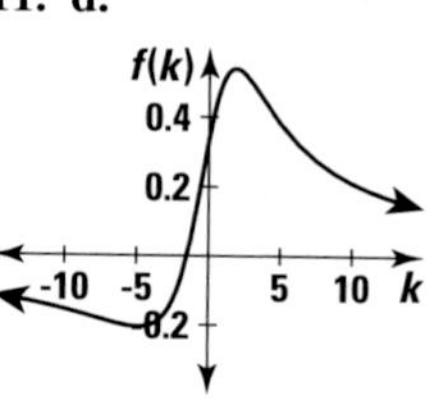

15. e.

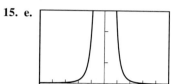

$-5 \leq x \leq 5$, x-scale = 1
$-1 \leq y \leq 7$, y-scale = 3

LESSON 5-5 (pp. 307–314)

9. See below. **11. a. See below.** **b.** As the number of total points increases, Viola's grade approaches 100%. **13. a.** $z = 3$ **b.** $t(z) = \frac{z^2 - z - 6}{z^2 + z - 12} = \frac{(z - 3)(z + 2)}{(z - 3)(z + 4)} = \frac{z + 2}{z + 4}$ $\therefore$ $t(z)$ is always undefined at $z = -4$. **15.** $\frac{-4}{x(x + h)}$, $x \neq 0$, $h \neq 0$, and $x \neq -h$

17. $(3t - 7y)^3(8t + 5y)^3(-8t^2 + 3t - 7y - 13ty - 5y^2)$

19. a. $\frac{\sqrt{2}}{2}$ **b.** $-\frac{1}{2}$ **c.** -1 **d.** $-\frac{\sqrt{3}}{2}$

9.

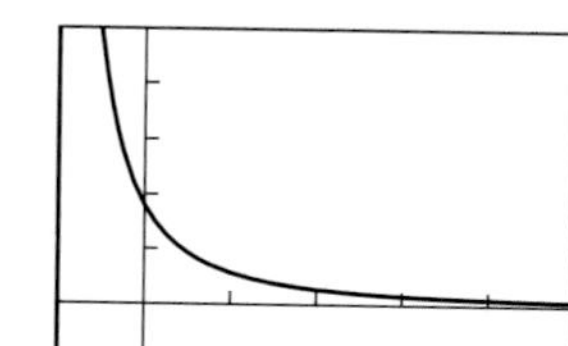

$-2500 \leq x \leq 12500$, x-scale = 2500
$-25 \leq y \leq 125$, y-scale = 25

11. a.

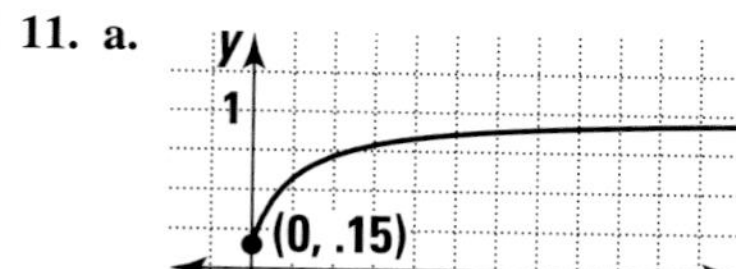

LESSON 5-6 (pp. 315–321)

15. False; counterexample: π and $3 - \pi$ sum to 3, which is rational. **17. a.** when $b^2 - 4ac$ is zero or a perfect square **b.** when $b^2 - 4ac > 0$ and not a perfect square **19.** $\frac{6}{11z}$ **21.** $\frac{3(x^2 + x - 4)}{x(x - 4)}$; $x \neq 0, x \neq 4$ **23.** $\frac{n\pi}{2}$; where n is an odd integer

LESSON 5-7 (pp. 322–326)

9. d **11. a.** The area of the triangle ABO is $\frac{1}{2}(AB)h$. So, the area of the regular n-gon is the sum of the areas of n congruent triangles, $n\frac{1}{2}(AB)h$. $m\angle AOB = \frac{2\pi}{n}$. The altitude h splits $\angle AOB$ into two smaller angles measuring $\frac{\pi}{n} \cdot \tan\left(\frac{\pi}{n}\right) = \frac{\frac{1}{2}AB}{h}$. So, $AB = 2h \tan\frac{\pi}{n}$. Hence, the area of the n-gon is $n\frac{1}{2}\left(2h\tan\frac{\pi}{n}\right)h = nh^2\tan\frac{\pi}{n}$. **b.** Let the radius, r, be 6 and $n = 4$. Then $AB = 6\sqrt{2}$, and $h = 3\sqrt{2}$ by the Pythagorean Theorem. Using the formula from part **a**, the area is $4(3\sqrt{2})^2 \tan\frac{\pi}{4} = 72$. The area of the square is $(AB)^2 = (6\sqrt{2})^2 = 72$ and so the formula checks. **13.** $\frac{-2\sqrt{10} + 10}{5}$ **15. a. See below.** **b.** $\lim_{x\to 2^+} f(x) = +\infty$; $\lim_{x\to 2^-} f(x) = -\infty$ **c.** $\lim_{x\to +\infty} 5x + 10 = +\infty$; $\lim_{x\to -\infty} 5x + 10 = -\infty$
17. $x = \ln 3$ or $x = 0$
19. See above right.

$$\frac{b}{\sin 32°} = \frac{10}{\sin 123°} \qquad \frac{a}{\sin 25°} = \frac{10}{\sin 123°}$$
$$b = \frac{10 \sin 32°}{\sin 123°} \qquad a = \frac{10 \sin 25°}{\sin 123°}$$
$$\approx \frac{(10)(.5299)}{.8387} \qquad \approx \frac{(10)(.4226)}{.8387}$$
$$\approx 6.32 \qquad \approx 5.04$$

The hiker is $\approx$ 6.32 miles from the first and $\approx$ 5.04 miles from the second.

15. a.

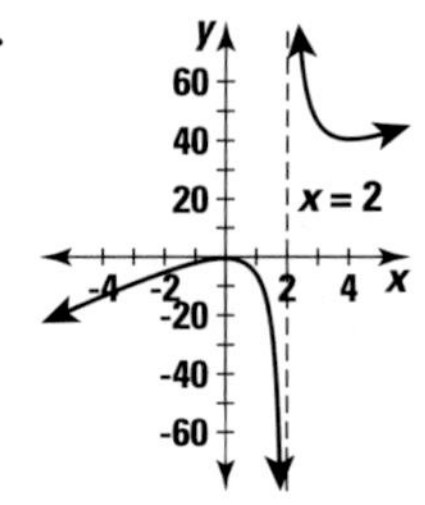

19.

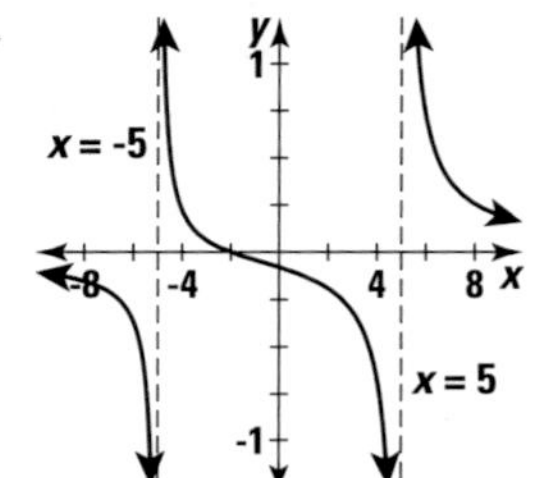

LESSON 5-8 (pp. 328–333)

13. Your average speed returning is 0 mph. **15.** Your return rate does not depend on the distance traveled. **17.** $BC = \sqrt{2} + 1$; $AB = \sqrt{2} + 2$ **19.** $\frac{3(r^3 - 16r)}{3r^2 - 2r - 8}$ **21.** $\sec x = -1.15$; $\csc x = 2$ **23.** $\frac{3\sqrt{10}}{5}$ **25. a.** $\lim_{x\to 0^+} f(x) = +\infty$; $\lim_{x\to 0^-} f(x) = -\infty$ **b.** $\lim_{x\to +\infty} f(x) = 0$; $\lim_{x\to -\infty} f(x) = 0$ **27.** 7.0%

LESSON 5-9 (pp. 334–339)

11. 2.744 cm $< x <$ 2.85 cm **13.** $\tan\frac{5\pi}{3} = -\sqrt{3}$; $\cot\frac{5\pi}{3} = \frac{-\sqrt{3}}{3}$; $\sec\frac{5\pi}{3} = 2$; $\csc\frac{5\pi}{3} = \frac{-2\sqrt{3}}{3}$ **15. a.** $\{x: x \neq 5 \text{ and } x \neq -5\}$ **b.** near $x = 5$: $\lim_{x\to 5^-} h(x) = -\infty$; $\lim_{x\to 5^+} h(x) = +\infty$ near $x = -5$, $\lim_{x\to -5^-} h(x) = -\infty$; $\lim_{x\to -5^+} h(x) = +\infty$ **c.** $\lim_{x\to -\infty} h(x) = 0$; $\lim_{x\to +\infty} h(x) = 0$ **d.** x-intercept: (-2, 0); y-intercept: $(0, \frac{-2}{25})$ **e. See below.** **17.** $2^2 \cdot 1097$

15. e.

x = -5
y
1
-8
-4
4
8
x
x = 5
-1

CHAPTER 5 PROGRESS SELF-TEST (p. 343)

1. a. $\frac{6x}{(x+3)(x+1)} + \frac{2x}{(x+2)(x+1)} = \frac{6x(x+2) + 2x(x+3)}{(x+1)(x+2)(x+3)} = \frac{6x^2 + 12x + 2x^2 + 6x}{(x+1)(x+2)(x+3)} = \frac{8x^2 + 18x}{(x+1)(x+2)(x+3)} = \frac{2x(4x+9)}{(x+1)(x+2)(x+3)}$
b. $x \neq -3$, $x \neq -2$, and $x \neq -1$
2. a. $\frac{2t^2 - t - 1}{3t^2 - 2t - 5} \cdot \frac{3t^2 + 7t - 20}{t^2 + 3t - 4} = \frac{(2t+1)(t-1)}{(3t-5)(t+1)} \cdot \frac{(3t-5)(t+4)}{(t-1)(t+4)} = \frac{2t+1}{t+1}$
b. $t \neq \frac{5}{3}$, $t \neq -1$, $t \neq 1$, and $t \neq -4$

3. $f = \frac{1}{\frac{1}{p} + \frac{1}{q}} \cdot \frac{pq}{pq} = \frac{pq}{\frac{pq}{p} + \frac{pq}{q}} = \frac{pq}{p + q}$
4. a. R (standard rational form) **b.** I (because 24 is not a perfect square) **c.** R $(\sqrt{49} = 7)$ **d.** R (repeating decimal) **e.** I (nonterminating, nonrepeating decimal) **5.** Assume the negation is true, that $\sqrt{11}$ is rational. By definition, there exist integers a and b, with $b \neq 0$, such that $\sqrt{11} = \frac{a}{b}$, where $\frac{a}{b}$ is in lowest terms. Then, $11 = \frac{a^2}{b^2} \Rightarrow a^2 = 11b^2$. Thus, a^2 has a factor of 11. And a has a factor of 11, because if a is an integer and a^2 is divisible by a prime, then a is divisible by that prime. Therefore, let $a = 11k$ for some integer k. Then $11b^2 = (11k)^2 \Rightarrow b^2 = 11k^2$.

So b^2 and b have a common factor of 11. This is a contradiction since $\frac{a}{b}$ is in lowest terms. Hence, the assumption must be false, and so $\sqrt{11}$ is irrational.

6. $\frac{8}{10-\sqrt{5}} = \frac{8}{10-\sqrt{5}} \cdot \frac{10+\sqrt{5}}{10+\sqrt{5}} = \frac{8(10+\sqrt{5})}{100-5} = \frac{8(10+\sqrt{5})}{95}$

7. a.,b. Irrational. It is impossible to find any polynomial formulas whose quotient equals this. **c.** Rational. The function is the quotient of two polynomials. **d.** $\lim_{x\to+\infty} f(x) = +\infty$; $\lim_{x\to-\infty} f(x) = -\infty$

8. The limit of $f(x)$ as x approaches 2 from the left is infinity.

9. a. $\lim_{x\to2^+} g(x) = +\infty$ **b.** $\lim_{x\to2^-} g(x) = -\infty$ **c.** $\lim_{x\to+\infty} g(x) = 3$; $\lim_{x\to-\infty} g(x) = 3$

d. See right. **10.** essential discontinuity

11. $\left(\frac{2}{y-1} + \frac{3y}{y+4}\right)(y-1)(y+4) = 3(y-1)(y+4)$

$2(y+4) + 3y(y-1) = 3(y^2 + 3y - 4)$

$2y + 8 + 3y^2 - 3y = 3y^2 + 9y - 12$

$20 = 10y$

$2 = y$

Check: for $y = 2$ does $\frac{2}{2-1} + \frac{3(2)}{2+4} = 3$? Yes

12. $\tan\frac{2\pi}{3} = \frac{\sin\frac{2\pi}{3}}{\cos\frac{2\pi}{3}} = \frac{\frac{\sqrt{3}}{2}}{-\frac{1}{2}} = -\sqrt{3}$

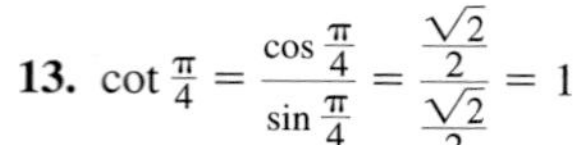

13. $\cot\frac{\pi}{4} = \frac{\cos\frac{\pi}{4}}{\sin\frac{\pi}{4}} = \frac{\frac{\sqrt{2}}{2}}{\frac{\sqrt{2}}{2}} = 1$

14. See below. **15.** $\csc\alpha = \frac{25}{7}$ **16. a.** $+\infty$ **b.** $-\infty$ **c.** 1 **d.** 1

9. d.

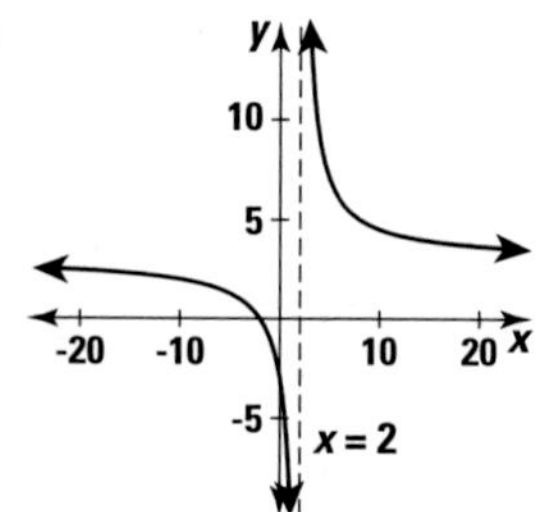

14.

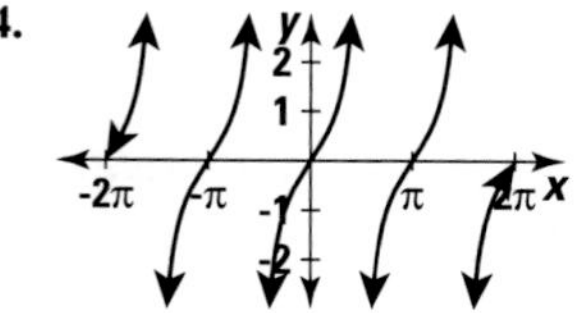

The chart below keys the questions on the **Progress Self-Test** to the objectives in the **Chapter Review** on pages 344–347 or to the **Vocabulary** (Voc.) on page 342. This will enable you to locate those **Chapter Review** questions that correspond to questions you missed on the **Progress Self-Test.** The lesson where the material is covered is also indicated on the chart.

Question	**1**	**2**	**3**	**4**	**5**	**6**	**7**	**8**	**9**	**10**
Objective	A	A	I	B	F	C	D	G	G, J	H
Lesson	5-2	5-2	5-8	5-1, 5-6	5-6	5-6	5-4	5-4	5-4, 5-5	5-4
Question	**11**	**12**	**13**	**14**	**15**	**16**				
Objective	E	L	L	L	L	K				
Lesson	5-8	5-7	5-7	5-7	5-7	5-4, 5-5				

CHAPTER 5 REVIEW (pp. 344-347)

1. a. -1 **b.** $x \neq \frac{2}{3}$ **3. a.** $\frac{3}{(z+1)(z+4)}$ **b.** $z \neq -1, z \neq 2, z \neq 3$, and $z \neq -4$ **5. a.** $\frac{-2t^2+20t+13}{(t-5)(t+4)}$ **b.** $t \neq 5$ and $t \neq -4$

7. $\frac{3(x-5)}{(x-6)}$ **9.** $a - 3$, $a \neq -3$, and $a \neq 0$

11. a. $\frac{z^2-z-2}{z^2-4z-5} \cdot \frac{z-5}{z^2+z-6} = \frac{(z+1)(z-2)}{(z+1)(z-5)} \cdot \frac{z-5}{(z-2)(z+3)} = \frac{1}{z+3}$

b. $z \neq -1, z \neq 5, z \neq 2$, and $z \neq -3$

13. $\frac{\frac{1}{x}+\frac{2}{x^2}}{1-\frac{4}{x^2}} = \frac{x+2}{x^2-4} = \frac{x+2}{(x+2)(x-2)} = \frac{1}{x-2}$; $x \neq 0, x \neq -2, x \neq 2$

15. rational, because -7 is an integer **17.** rational, since the decimal expression of $\frac{22}{7}$ repeats, $3.\overline{142857}$. **19.** rational, equals $\frac{3733}{396}$

21. irrational, $\sqrt{3}$ is not an integer **23.** $\frac{24-6\sqrt{6}}{5}$ **25.** $-3\sqrt{10} - 6$

27. $\frac{1}{\sqrt{x+h}+\sqrt{x}}$ **29.** Rational **31.** Rational **33.** $x \neq 0$ and $x \neq 1$

35. no solutions **37.** $v = 2$ **39.** $\frac{893}{1000}$ **41.** $\frac{3583}{9000}$ **43.** Assume the negation is true, that $\sqrt{13}$ is rational. By definition, there exist integers a and b, with $b \neq 0$ such that $\sqrt{13} = \frac{a}{b}$, where $\frac{a}{b}$ is in lowest terms. Then, $13 = \frac{a^2}{b^2} \Rightarrow a^2 = 13b^2$. Thus, a^2 has a factor of 13, because if a is an integer and a^2 is divisible by a prime, then a is divisible by that prime. Therefore, let $a = 13k$ for some integer k. Then, $13b^2 = (13k)^2 \Rightarrow b^2 = 13k^2$. So b^2 and b have a factor of 13 by similar argument. Thus, a and b have a common factor of 13. This is a contradiction since $\frac{a}{b}$ is in lowest terms. Hence, the assumption must be false, and so $\sqrt{13}$ is irrational.

45. True, if $\frac{a}{b}$ and $\frac{c}{d}$ are two rational numbers, where $b \neq 0$ and $d \neq 0$, then $\frac{a}{b} \cdot \frac{c}{d} = \frac{ac}{bd}$. ac and bd are both integers and $bd \neq 0$ since $b \neq 0$ and $d \neq 0$. Hence, $\frac{ac}{bd}$ is rational.

47. Assume the negation is true. Thus, the difference of a rational number p and an irrational number q is a rational number r. Then $p - q = r$. So $p - r = q$. However, by the closure property of rational numbers the difference between two rational numbers is another rational number. Hence, there is a contradiction, and so the assumption is false, which proves the original statement. **49.** The limit of $f(x)$ as x decreases without bound is 1.3. **51. a.** $\lim_{x \to 6^+} h(x) = +\infty$ **b.** $\lim_{x \to 6^-} h(x) = -\infty$ **c.** $\lim_{x \to +\infty} h(x) = 2$; $\lim_{x \to -\infty} h(x) = 2$ **53.** $y = \frac{3}{4}x + \frac{1}{8}$ **55.** $h(y) = \frac{7}{3}y^2$ **57.** $q(z) = \frac{1}{4z}$ **59. a.** 5 **b.** -5 **c.** $f(5) = -0.1$ **61.** Sample: $\frac{x^2 - 16}{x - 4}$ **63.** $\approx$ \$179 **65. a.** $\frac{1}{c}$ **b.** $\frac{1}{h}$ **c.** $\frac{c + h}{ch}$ **d.** 2.4 hr **67. a.** $x = 1$ and $x = -1$ **b.** $x = 1$ and $x = -1$: essential **c.** $y = 2$ **d.** x-intercept: none; y-intercept: -3 **e.** $\lim_{x \to +\infty} h(x) = 2$; $\lim_{x \to -\infty} h(x) = 2$ **f.** See right. **69. a.** $\lim_{x \to 4^+} f(x) = +\infty$; $\lim_{x \to 4^-} f(x) = -\infty$ **b.** $\lim_{x \to 3^+} f(x) = -\infty$; $\lim_{x \to -3^-} f(x) = +\infty$ **c.** $\lim_{x \to +\infty} f(x) = 3$; $\lim_{x \to -\infty} f(x) = 3$ **d.** $x = 4$, $x = -3$, and $y = 3$ **71. a.** See right. **b.** $x = \frac{-3\pi}{2}, \frac{-\pi}{2}, \frac{\pi}{2}, \frac{3\pi}{2}$ **73.** $\frac{12}{5}$ **75.** $\frac{13}{\sqrt{169 - x^2}}$ **77.** $\csc x = 3$ **79.** $\cot \frac{\pi}{6} = \sqrt{3}$

67. f.

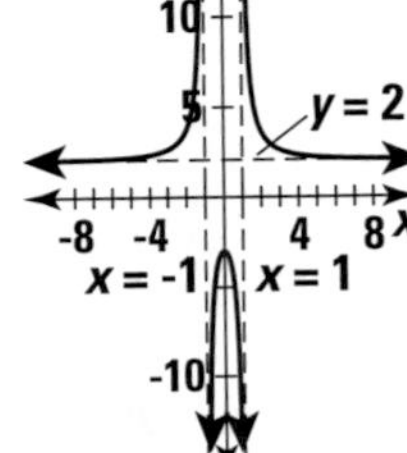

71. a.

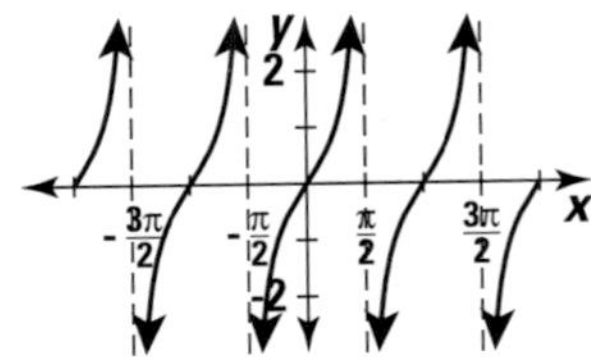

LESSON 6-1 (pp. 350–355)

13. a. This is not an identity. **b.** Sample counterexample: For $x = 0.2$, $\sin(0.2\pi) \approx 0.588$, but $4 \cdot 0.2 \cdot (1 - 0.2) = 0.64$. **15. a.–b.** See below. **c.** See right. **d.** Yes **17.** $-\frac{\sqrt{3}}{2}$ **19.** $\{x: x \not\equiv 0 \pmod{\pi}\}$ **21.** c **23.** $(f + g)(t) = e^t + e^{-t}, \forall\, t$; $(f - g)(t) = e^t + e^{-t}, \forall\, t$; $(f \cdot g)(t) = 1, \forall\, t$; $\left(\frac{f}{g}\right)(t) = e^{2t}, \forall\, t$ **25.** angles in Quadrant 2: $\frac{\pi}{2} < \theta < \pi$; angles in Quadrant 3: $\pi < \theta < \frac{3\pi}{2}$; angles in Quadrant 4: $\frac{3\pi}{2} < \theta < 2\pi$

15. a.

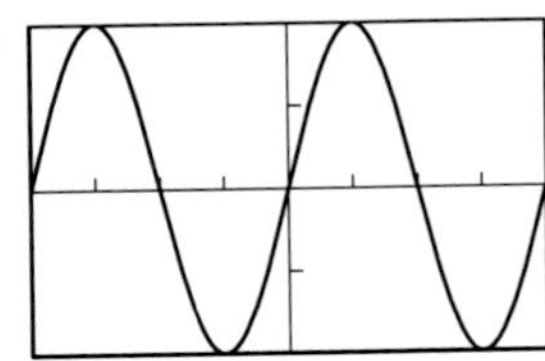

$-2\pi \le x \le 2\pi$, x-scale $= \frac{\pi}{2}$
$-2 \le y \le 2$, y-scale $= 1$

15 b.

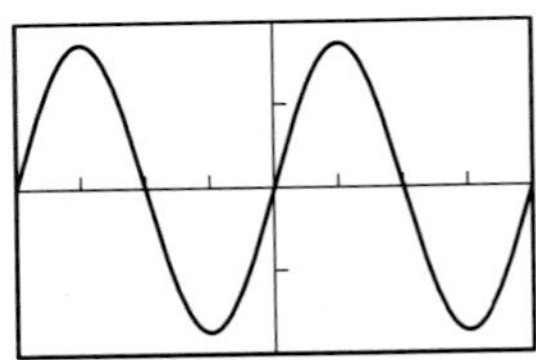

$-2\pi \le x \le 2\pi$, x-scale $= \frac{\pi}{2}$
$-2 \le y \le 2$, y-scale $= 1$

15 c.

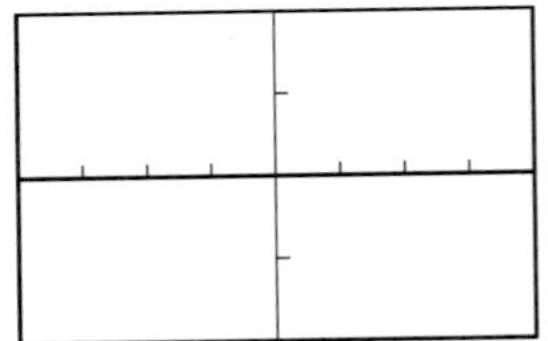

$-2\pi \le x \le 2\pi$, x-scale $= \frac{\pi}{2}$
$-2 \le y \le 2$, y-scale $= 1$

LESSON 6-2 (pp. 356–360)

5.

	$\cos x \tan x$	$\sin x$
definition of tan	$= \cos x \cdot \frac{\sin x}{\cos x}$	
simplification	$= \sin x$	

$\therefore \cos x \tan x = \sin x$

domain: $\left\{x: x \ne \frac{(2n + 1)}{2}\pi, \forall \text{ integers } n\right\}$

7.

	$\csc^2 x \sin x$	$\frac{\sec^2 x - \tan^2 x}{\sin x}$	
definition of csc	$= \frac{1}{\sin^2 x} \cdot \sin x$	$= \frac{\frac{1}{\cos^2 x} - \frac{\sin^2 x}{\cos^2 x}}{\sin x}$	definitions of sec and tan
simplification	$= \frac{1}{\sin x}$	$= \frac{1 - \sin^2 x}{\sin x \cos^2 x}$	
		$= \frac{\cos^2 x}{\sin x \cos^2 x}$	Pythagorean Identity
		$= \frac{1}{\sin x}$	simplification

$\therefore \csc^2 x \sin x = \frac{\sec^2 x - \tan^2 x}{\sin x}$

domain: $\left\{x: x \ne \frac{n\pi}{2}, \forall \text{ integers } n\right\}$

9. an identity:
(left side)

$$\sin^2 x\,(\cot^2 x + 1) = \sin^2 x\left(\frac{\cos^2 x}{\sin^2 x} + 1\right) \quad \text{definition of cot}$$
$$= \frac{\sin^2 x \cos^2 x}{\sin^2 x} + \sin^2 x \quad \text{Distributive Property}$$
$$= \cos^2 x + \sin^2 x \quad \text{simplification}$$
$$= 1 \quad \text{Pythgorean Identity}$$

(right side)

11. See below. **13. a.** $\sin x$, $\tan x$, $\csc x$, $\cot x$ **b.** $\cos x$, $\sec x$ **15. a.** $\{n: n = 3 + 7q$ for any integer $q\}$ **b.** The set in part **a** is the set of all integers with remainder of 3 when divided by 7. **17.** $y = \sin\left(x + \frac{\pi}{2}\right)$ **19.** ≈ 429 m **21.** b

11.

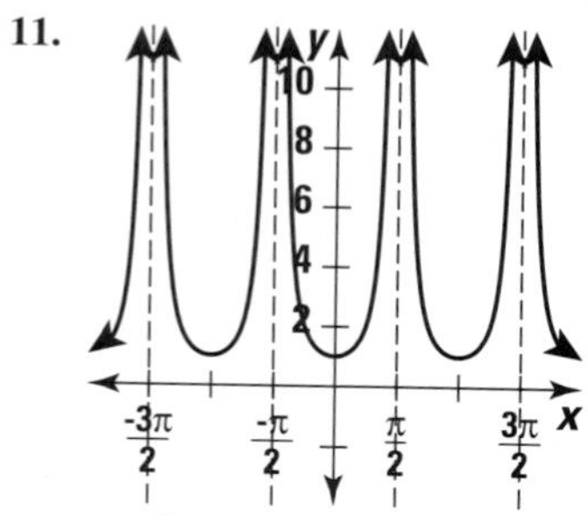

LESSON 6-3 (pp. 361–366)

11. a. amplitude: 5; period: $\frac{2\pi}{3}$; phase shift: $-\frac{\pi}{2}$ **b.** See below.

13. $\begin{cases} x = 3\cos t + 4 \\ y = 4\sin t + 1 \end{cases}$

15. It is an identity. Proof:

	$\cos x \cot x$	$\csc x - \sin x$	
definition of cot	$\cos x \frac{\cos x}{\sin x}$	$\frac{1}{\sin x} - \sin x$	definition of csc
simplification	$\frac{\cos^2 x}{\sin x}$	$\frac{1 - \sin^2 x}{\sin x}$	simplification
		$\frac{\cos^2 x}{\sin x}$	Pythagorean Identity

$\therefore \cos x \cot x = \csc x - \sin x$

17. a. See below.
b. No. Counterexample: For $x = 1$, $2^x + 2^{-x} = 2^1 + 2^{-1} = \frac{5}{2}$, but $x^2 + 2 = 1 + 2 = 3$ Yes. The graph asymptotically approaches $y = 4$ as $x \to \infty$ and $x \to -\infty$. **19.** $T(x, y) = (x - 6, y - 41)$ **21.** 1

11. b.

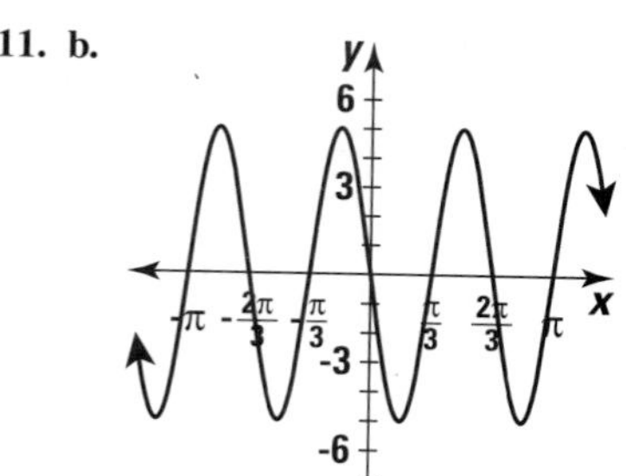

17. a.

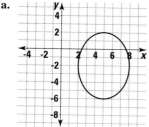

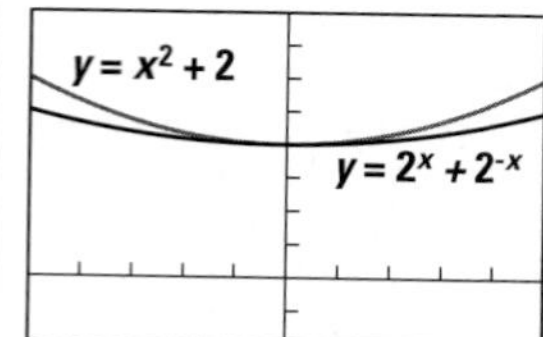

$-1 \le x \le 1$, x-scale = 0.2
$-1 \le y \le 4$, y-scale = 0.5

LESSON 6-4 (pp. 367–371)

9. $\cos(x - y) - \cos(x + y) = \cos x \cos y + \sin x \sin y - (\cos x \cos y - \sin x \sin y) = 2\sin x \sin y$
11. $\sin\left(\frac{\pi}{2} - x\right) = \cos x$ **13.** $\frac{\sqrt{2} - \sqrt{6}}{4}$
15. a. See below **b.** $\frac{(x - 5)^2}{9} + \frac{(y + 2)^2}{16} = 1$
17. $\frac{\csc x}{\sec x} = \frac{\frac{1}{\sin x}}{\frac{1}{\cos x}} = \frac{\cos x}{\sin x} = \cot x$

domain: $\left\{x: x \ne \frac{n\pi}{2}, \forall \text{ integers } n\right\}$

15. a.

LESSON 6-5 (pp. 372–376)

11. The identity becomes $\tan 2\beta = \frac{2\tan\beta}{1 - \tan^2\beta}$.

13. $R_{\theta+\phi} = \begin{bmatrix} \cos(\theta + \phi) & -\sin(\theta + \phi) \\ \sin(\theta + \phi) & \cos(\theta + \phi) \end{bmatrix}$;

$$R_\theta \cdot R_\phi = \begin{bmatrix} \cos\theta & -\sin\theta \\ \sin\theta & \cos\theta \end{bmatrix}\begin{bmatrix} \cos\phi & -\sin\phi \\ \sin\phi & \cos\phi \end{bmatrix}$$
$$= \begin{bmatrix} \cos\theta\cos\phi - \sin\theta\sin\phi & -\cos\theta\sin\phi - \sin\theta\cos\phi \\ \sin\theta\cos\phi + \cos\theta\sin\phi & -\sin\theta\sin\phi + \cos\theta\cos\phi \end{bmatrix}$$

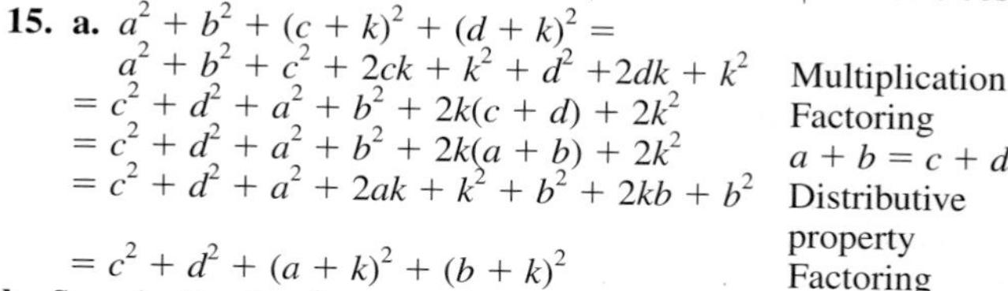

15. a. $a^2 + b^2 + (c + k)^2 + (d + k)^2 =$
$a^2 + b^2 + c^2 + 2ck + k^2 + d^2 + 2dk + k^2$ Multiplication
$= c^2 + d^2 + a^2 + b^2 + 2k(c + d) + 2k^2$ Factoring
$= c^2 + d^2 + a^2 + b^2 + 2k(a + b) + 2k^2$ $a + b = c + d$
$= c^2 + d^2 + a^2 + 2ak + k^2 + b^2 + 2kb + b^2$ Distributive property
$= c^2 + d^2 + (a + k)^2 + (b + k)^2$ Factoring

b. Sample: For $k > 0$, sums of squares are equal to the sums of different squares. If $k = 2$, $1^2 + 4^2 + 4^2 + 5^2 = 2^2 + 3^2 + 3^2 + 6^2 = 58$
17. a. rational **b.** irrational **c.** rational **19.** 18 ft

LESSON 6-6 (pp. 377–383)

9. Both f and g are the function $x \to \cos 2x$ **See below.**

11. Left side $= \sin 3x = \sin(2x + x)$

$= \sin 2x \cos x + \cos 2x \sin x$	Sine of a sum identity
$= (2 \sin x \cos x) \cos x + (\cos^2 x - \sin^2 x) \sin x$	Double angle identities
$= 2 \sin x \cos^2 x + \cos^2 x \sin x - \sin^3 x$	Multiplication
$= 3 \sin x \cos^2 x - \sin^3 x$	Addition
$= 3 \sin x(1 - \sin^2 x) - \sin^3 x$	Pythagorean Identity
$= 3 \sin x - 3 \sin^3 x - \sin^3 x$	Multiplication
$= 3 \sin x - 4 \sin^3 x$	Addition
$=$ Right side	

c. Since the answers to parts **a** and **b** both represent $\cos \frac{\pi}{12}$, they are equal. **13. a.** $-\frac{3}{5}$ **b.** $\frac{2\sqrt{2}}{3}$ **c.** $\frac{3 + 8\sqrt{2}}{15}$ **d.** $\frac{4 - 6\sqrt{2}}{15}$

e. Does $\sin^2(x + y) + \cos^2(x + y) = 1$?

Does $\left(\frac{3 + 8\sqrt{2}}{15}\right)^2 + \left(\frac{4 - 6\sqrt{2}}{15}\right)^2 = 1$?

Does $\frac{137 + 48\sqrt{2}}{225} + \frac{88 - 48\sqrt{2}}{225} = 1$? Does $\frac{225}{225} = 1$? Yes

15. 0 **17.** $f^{-1}(x) = \frac{x - 2}{3}$ **19.** invalid, converse error

9.

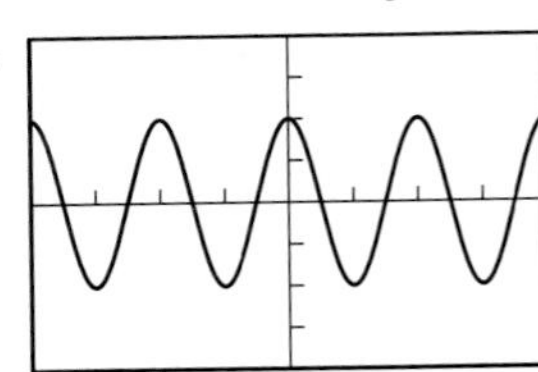

$-2\pi \le x \le 2\pi$, x-scale $= \frac{\pi}{2}$
$-2 \le y \le 2$, y-scale $= 0.5$

LESSON 6-7 (pp. 386–390)

15. $-\frac{\sqrt{2}}{2}$ **17.** .8 **19.** $\theta = \tan^{-1}\left(\frac{h}{16}\right)$, where h = altitude (in kilometers)

21. $\sin 2x = -\frac{4\sqrt{5}}{9}$, $\cos 2x = \frac{1}{9}$ **23. a.** Sample: Let $x = 0$. Then $\sin\left(0 + \frac{\pi}{4}\right) + \sin\left(0 - \frac{\pi}{4}\right) = \sin 0 \cos \frac{\pi}{4} + \cos 0 \sin \frac{\pi}{4} + \sin 0 \cos \frac{\pi}{4} - \cos 0 \sin \frac{\pi}{4} = 0 + \frac{\sqrt{2}}{2} + 0 - \frac{\sqrt{2}}{2} = 0 = \sin 0$

b. $\sin\left(x + \frac{\pi}{3}\right) + \sin\left(x - \frac{\pi}{3}\right) = \sin x \cos \frac{\pi}{3} + \sin \frac{\pi}{3} \cos x + \sin x \cos \frac{\pi}{3} - \sin \frac{\pi}{3} \cos x = 2 \cdot \sin x \cdot \frac{1}{2} = \sin x$

25. a. Sample: 15, 26, 37, 48, 59, 70, 81, 92, 103, 114

LESSON 6-8 (pps. 391–396)

11. $x = \frac{\pi}{3} + 2\pi n$ or $x = \frac{5\pi}{3} + 2\pi n$, n an integer **13. a.** $\approx 42.22°$ **b.** $\approx 41.40°$ **15. a.** $-\frac{\pi}{4}$ **b.** $\frac{\pi}{3}$ **c.** $\frac{2\pi}{3}$ **17. a.** $\frac{\sqrt{2} - \sqrt{6}}{4}$ **b.** $\frac{\sqrt{6} + \sqrt{2}}{4}$ **c.** $\frac{\sqrt{6} + \sqrt{2}}{\sqrt{2} - \sqrt{6}}$ **19. a.** True **b.** $x = -\frac{1}{6}$ **c.** $x = 4$ **d.** 6 **e.** **See below.** **21.** $t < 1$ or $t > 4$

19. e.

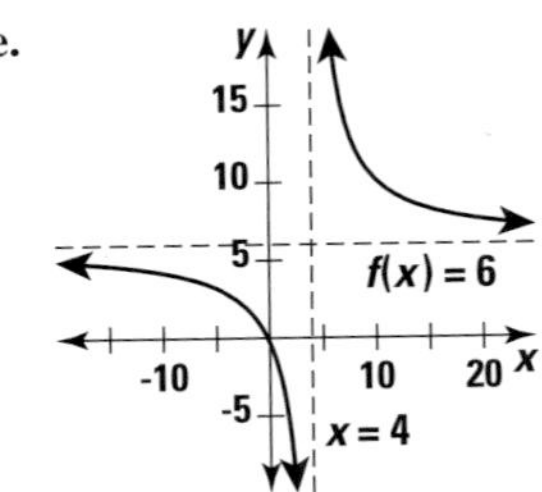

CHAPTER 6 PROGRESS SELF-TEST (p. 400)

1. $-\sqrt{1 - \left(\frac{x}{3}\right)^2}$ or $-\frac{1}{3}\sqrt{9 - x^2}$ **2.** b **3.** $\frac{\sqrt{3}}{2}$ **4.** $\frac{3}{\sqrt{13}}$

5. $\frac{\sqrt{2} - \sqrt{6}}{4}$ **6.** $\frac{\sqrt{6} - \sqrt{2}}{4}$ **7. See right.**

Not an identity; Counterexample: Let $x = -\frac{\pi}{6}$. Then $\tan\left(-\frac{\pi}{6} + \frac{\pi}{2}\right) = \sqrt{3}$, but $\tan\left(-\frac{\pi}{6}\right) = \frac{-1}{\sqrt{3}}$.

8.

	$\cos x + \tan x \sin x$	$\sec x$	
Def. of tan	$= \cos x + \frac{\sin^2 x}{\cos x}$	$= \frac{1}{\cos x}$	Def. of sec
Adding fractions	$= \frac{\cos^2 x + \sin^2 x}{\cos x}$		
Pythagorean Identity	$= \frac{1}{\cos x}$		

$\therefore \cos x + \tan x \sin x = \sec x$
domain: $x \ne (2n + 1)\frac{\pi}{2}$, n an integer

9.

	$\frac{\sin(\alpha + \beta)}{\cos \alpha \cos \beta}$	$\tan \alpha + \tan \beta$
Identity for $\sin(\alpha + \beta)$	$= \frac{\sin \alpha \cos \beta + \cos \alpha \sin \beta}{\cos \alpha \cos \beta}$	$= \frac{\sin \alpha}{\cos \alpha} + \frac{\sin \beta}{\cos \beta}$
Simplifying	$= \frac{\sin \alpha}{\cos \alpha} + \frac{\sin \beta}{\cos \beta}$	

$\therefore \frac{\sin(\alpha + \beta)}{\cos \alpha \cos \beta} = \tan \alpha + \tan \beta$
domain: $\alpha \ne (2n + 1)\frac{\pi}{2}$, $\beta \ne (2n + 1)\frac{\pi}{2}$, n an integer

10. a. $x = \frac{7\pi}{6}, \frac{11\pi}{6}$, or $\frac{\pi}{2}$ **b.** $x = \frac{7\pi}{6} + 2\pi n, \frac{11\pi}{6} + 2\pi n, \frac{\pi}{2} + 2\pi n$, n an integer **11. a.** $T_{2,-1/2}$ **b.** $y = \sin\left(\frac{1}{2}x\right) - \frac{1}{2}$

12. $x = 6 \sin t + 3$, $y = 5 \cos t - 2$ **13.** $\approx 14.9°$

14. $\theta = \tan^{-1}\left(\frac{150}{d}\right)$ **15.** $x = \frac{\pi}{6}$

16. $-\frac{7\pi}{6} \le x \le 0$ or $-2\pi \le x \le -\frac{11\pi}{6}$

7.

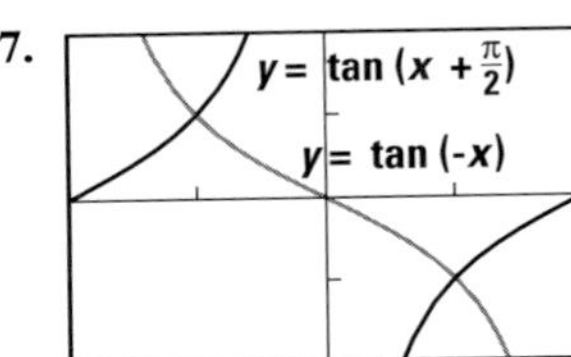

$-\frac{\pi}{2} \le x \le \frac{\pi}{2}$, x-scale $= \frac{\pi}{4}$
$-2 \le y \le 2$, y-scale $= 1$

The chart below keys the questions on the **Progress Self-Test** to the objectives in the **Chapter Review** on pages 401–403 or to the **Vocabulary** (Voc.) on page 399. This will enable you to locate those **Chapter Review** questions that correspond to questions you missed on the **Progress Self-Test.** The lesson where the material is covered is also indicated on the chart.

Question	**1**	**2**	**3**	**4**	**5**	**6**	**7**	**8**	**9**	**10**
Objective	A	D	B	B	A	A	H	D	D	C
Lesson	6-5	6-4	6-7	6-7	6-4	6-5	6-1, 6-2	6-2	6-2, 6-5	6-8
Question	**11**	**12**	**13**	**14**	**15**	**16**				
Objective	G	G	F	E	I	I				
Lesson	6-3	6-3	6-8	6-7	6-8	6-8				

CHAPTER 6 REVIEW (pp. 401–403)

1. $-\frac{\sqrt{55}}{8}$ **3.** $-\frac{8}{3}$ **5.** $\frac{\sqrt{2+\sqrt{2}}}{2}$ **7.** b **9.** $\frac{2\sqrt{42}+\sqrt{2}}{15}$ **11.** $\frac{\sqrt{6}}{3}$ **13.** $-\frac{\pi}{4}$ **15.** $\frac{\sqrt{2}}{2}$ **17.** $\frac{\sqrt{21}}{5}$ **19.** $x = \frac{3\pi}{4}, \frac{7\pi}{4}$ **21.** $x = -\frac{\pi}{2} + 2\pi n, \frac{\pi}{4} + \pi n$, n an integer **23.** $0 \le x \le 0.644$ or $5.640 \le x \le 2\pi$, approximately **25.** $\frac{\pi}{6} < x < \frac{5\pi}{6}$ **27.** $\sin(y - x)$ **29.** $-\sin^2 x$

31. Left side $= \cos\left(\frac{3\pi}{2} + x\right)$

$= \cos\frac{3\pi}{2}\cos x - \sin\frac{3\pi}{2}\sin x$ — Identity for the cosine of a sum

$= 0 - (-\sin x)$ — Evaluating trigonometric functions

$= \sin x$ — Multiplication

$=$ Right side

$\therefore \cos\left(\frac{3\pi}{2} + x\right) = \sin x$

domain: all real numbers

33. Left side $= \sin\left(\frac{\pi}{2} + x\right)$

$= \sin\frac{\pi}{2}\cdot\cos x + \cos\frac{\pi}{2}\cdot\sin x$ — Formula for sine of a sum

$= 1\cdot\cos x + 0\cdot\sin x$ — Evaluating trigonometric functions

$= \cos x$ — Multiplication

$=$ Right side

$\therefore \sin\left(\frac{\pi}{2} + x\right) = \cos x$

domain: all real numbers

35. Left side $= \cos(\alpha - \beta) - \cos(\alpha + \beta)$

$= \cos\alpha\cos\beta + \sin\alpha\sin\beta - \cos\alpha\cos\beta + \sin\alpha\sin\beta$ — Sum and difference identities

$= 2\sin\alpha\sin\beta$ — Addition

$=$ Right side

$\therefore \cos(\alpha - \beta) - \cos(\alpha + \beta) = 2\sin\alpha\sin\beta$

37. Left side $= \cos 4x$

$= \cos^2 2x - \sin^2 2x$ — Identity for cos $2x$

$= (\cos^2 x - \sin^2 x)^2 - (2\sin x\cos x)^2$ — Identities for cos $2x$ and sin $2x$

$= \cos^4 x - 2\sin^2 x\cos^2 x + \sin^4 x - 4\sin^2 x\cos^2 x$ — Multiplication

$= \cos^4 x - 6\sin^2\text{-}x\cos^2 x + \sin^4 x$ — Addition

$=$ Right side

$\therefore \cos 4x = \cos^4 x - 6\sin^2 x\cos^4 x + \sin^4 x$

domain: all real numbers

39. $\theta = \sin^{-1}\left(\frac{h-3}{200}\right)$, where h = height of the kite above the ground in feet. **41.** $t = \frac{1}{5\pi}\cos^{-1}\left(\frac{d}{3}\right)$ **43.** $22.3° \le \theta \le 67.7°$, approximately **45.** $y = -\frac{1}{2}\sin(2x)$ **47. a.** $y = 2\sin\left(\pi x - \frac{\pi}{4}\right) - 1$ **b. See below.**
c. amplitude = 2, period = 2, phase shift = $\frac{\pi}{4}$

49. $x = 9\sin t - 7$, $y = 6\cos t + 4$

51. an identity;

	$1 + \cot^2 x$	$\csc^2 x$	
Def. of cot	$= 1 + \frac{\cos^2 x}{\sin^2 x}$	$= \frac{1}{\sin^2 x}$	Def. of cos
Addition	$= \frac{\sin^2 x + \cos^2 x}{\sin^2 x}$		
Pythagorean Identity	$= \frac{1}{\sin^2 x}$		

$\therefore 1 + \cot^2 x = \csc^2 x$, $x \ne n\pi$, n an integer

53. an identity;

Left side $= \tan(\pi + \gamma)$

$= \frac{\sin(\pi+\gamma)}{\cos(\pi+\gamma)}$ — Def. of tan

$= \frac{\sin\pi\cos\gamma + \sin\gamma\cos\pi}{\cos\pi\cos\gamma - \sin\pi\sin\gamma}$ — Identities for sine and cosine of a sum

$= \frac{-\sin\gamma}{-\cos\gamma}$ — Evaluating specific values of trignometric functions

$= \tan\gamma$ — Def. of tan

$=$ Right side

$\therefore \tan\gamma = \tan(\pi + \gamma)$

55. You can check various different cases by holding α constant and graphing the resulting functions in β. For example, when $\alpha = \frac{\pi}{3}$, you could graph $y = \sin\left(\frac{\pi}{3} + \beta\right)$ and $y = \sin\frac{\pi}{3}\cos\beta - \cos\frac{\pi}{3}\sin\beta$.

57. a. $x \approx 1.1$ or $x \approx 3.6$ **b.** $0 \le x < 1.1$, $3.6 < x < 2\pi$

59. $0 \le x \le 0.675$

47. b.

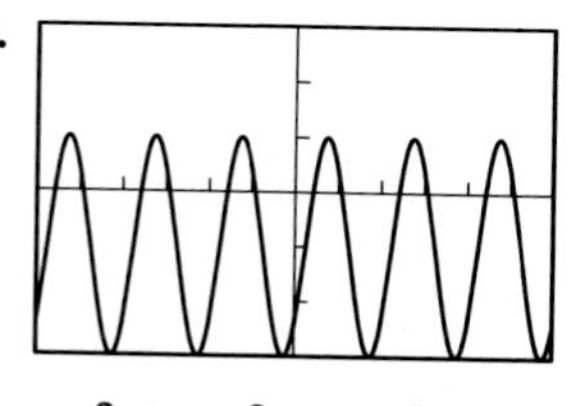

$-6 \le x \le 6$, x-scale = 1
$-3 \le y \le 3$, y-scale = 1

absolute error For an observed value o and an expected value e, $|o - e|$. (202)

absolute value, $|x|$ If $x \geq 0$, then $|x| = x$; if $x < 0$, then $|x| = -x$. Equivalently, $|x| = \sqrt{x^2}$. (202)

absolute value of a complex number, $|z|$ The distance from z to the origin or pole. Also called *modulus*. (489)

acceleration The rate of change of a rate of change. (576)

Addition Property of Equality For any real expressions $f(x)$ and $g(x)$, if $f(x) = g(x)$, then $f(x) + c = g(x) + c$. (161)

Addition Property of Inequality For any real expressions $f(x)$ and $g(x)$, if $f(x) < g(x)$, then $f(x) + c < g(x) + c$. (175)

adjacency matrix For a graph with vertices $v_1, v_2, \ldots, v_n$, the $n \times n$ matrix in which, $\forall$ i, j, the element in the ith row and jth column is the number of edges from vertex v_i to vertex v_j. (669)

adjacent edges Two edges of a graph with a common endpoint. (666)

adjacent vertices Two vertices of a graph connected by an edge. (666)

amplitude One-half the difference between the maximum and minimum values of a sine wave. (Previous course)

AND gate An input-output device for which the output signal is 1 if and only if the two input signals are 1. Otherwise, the output signal is 0. Schematically, the AND gate is represented by [AND]. (28)

Angle Between Vectors Theorem Suppose that θ is the measure of the angle between two nonzero vectors $\vec{u}$ and $\vec{v}$ and $0 \leq \theta \leq \pi$. Then $\cos\theta = \frac{\vec{u} \cdot \vec{v}}{|\vec{u}|\,|\vec{v}|}$. (742)

antecedent p, in the conditional $p \Rightarrow q$. Also called *hypothesis*. (35)

antiderivative of f A function whose derivative is f. (828)

Arccos function See *inverse cosine function*.

Arcsin function See *inverse sine function*.

Arctan function See *inverse tangent function*.

argument A sequence of statements in which the final statement (the **conclusion**) is asserted to follow from preceding statements (the **premises**). (45)

argument of a complex number For the complex number $[r, \theta]$, θ. (489)

arithmetic sequence A sequence in which $\forall\, n > 1$, $a_n = a_{n-1} + d$, where d is a constant. That is, each term beyond the first is d (the **constant difference**) greater than the preceding one. (123)

average rate of change For a function over the interval from x_1 to x_2, the slope of the line through $(x_1, f(x_1))$ and $(x_2, f(x_2))$. (553)

average speed Total distance divided by total time. (327)

average velocity The average rate of change of an object's directed distance from a fixed point (or the position of an object on a line) over a time interval. (554)

base 2 A representation of a number in which the digits are either a 0 or 1 and the place values are consecutive integral powers of 2. Also called *binary*. (258)

base 8 A representation of a number in which the digits can be any of the integers 0–7 and the place values are consecutive integral powers of 8. Also called *octal*. (258)

base 16 A representation of a number in which the digits can be any of the integers 0–9 or any of the letters A–F (representing the values 10–15) and the place values are consecutive integral powers of 16. Also called *hexadecimal*. (258)

base b notation The representation of a number as $d_n d_{n-1} \ldots d_1 d_0$, where each digit d_i is a particular integer from 0 through $b - 1$, and the value of the number is $d_n \cdot b^n + d_{n-1} \cdot b^{n-1} + \ldots + d_1 \cdot b^1 + d_0 \cdot b^0$. (260)

Basic Properties of Combinations Theorem For all n and r for which $C(n, r)$ is defined:

a. $C(n, r) = C(n, n - r)$, $\binom{n}{r} = \binom{n}{n-r}$;

b. $C(n, n) = C(n, 0) = 1$, $\binom{n}{n} = \binom{n}{0} = 1$. (624)

basis step See *Principle of Mathematical Induction*.

biconditional An *if and only if* statement. (40)

binary See *base 2*.

binary digit A single digit (0 or 1) in a base 2 representation of a number. Also called *bit*. (258)

binomial coefficients The coefficients in the series expansion of $(x + y)^n$; the combinations ${}_nC_k$. (628)

binomial probability The probability of k successes in n independent trials of a two-outcome experiment; given by the formula $\binom{n}{k} p^k q^{n-k}$, where p is the probability of success and $q = 1 - p$ is the probability of failure. (635)

Binomial Theorem For all positive integers n and numbers x and y,
$$(x + y)^n = \binom{n}{0} x^n + \binom{n}{1} x^{n-1} y + \binom{n}{2} x^{n-2} y^2 + \ldots + \binom{n}{k} x^{n-k} y^k + \ldots + \binom{n}{n-1} x y^{n-1} + \binom{n}{n} y^n = \sum_{k=0}^{n} \binom{n}{k} x^{n-k} y^k.$$ (630)

Bisection Method A method for obtaining zeros of a continuous function by splitting into successive intervals an interval which has the property that its endpoints produce function values with opposite signs. A zero will be between two such endpoints. At each step, the subinterval with this same property is split in half. By continuing to subdivide, the zero can be estimated to any degree of accuracy desired. (214)

bit See *binary digit*.

Boolean algebra An algebraic system in which the operations act similar to the logical operations of *and*, *or*, and *not* on statements. (31)

GLOSSARY

branch point A node of a tree corresponding to a step in which several choices or results are possible. (608)

Bubblesort A particular iterative sorting algorithm whereby terms are compared with neighboring terms and "bubble up" to the beginning of the list. (450)

byte A group of 8 bits. (260)

$C(n, r)$, $\binom{n}{r}$, $_nC_r$ The number of combinations of n elements taken r at a time. (622)

$C(n, r)$ Calculation Theorem $C(n, r) = \frac{n!}{r!(n-r)!}$. (623)

cardioid The polar graph of any equation of the form $r = a \pm \cos\theta$ or $r = a \pm \sin\theta$. (498)

Change of Base Theorem Let a and b be positive real numbers both unequal to 1; then for all $x > 0$, $\log_b x = \log_b a \cdot \log_a x$. (133)

chaos A property of a system in which small differences in the initial conditions for the system can lead to radically different results. (538)

chunking Treating an expression as if it were a single variable. (182)

circuit A path in a graph that starts and ends at the same vertex. (679)

Circuits and Connectedness Theorem If a connected graph contains a circuit and an edge is removed from the circuit, then the resulting graph is also connected. (683)

circuits connected in series Circuits connected in such a way that current flows through one circuit and then through the other. (476)

closed infinite interval, $[a, \infty)$ or $(-\infty, b]$ The set of numbers greater than or equal to a given number (a), or the set of numbers less than or equal to a given number (b); $\{x\colon a \le x\}$ or $\{x\colon x \le b\}$. (81)

closed interval, $[a, b]$ The set of numbers greater than or equal to one number (a) and less than or equal to a second larger number (b); $\{x\colon a \le x \le b\}$. (81)

closed with respect to an operation The property of a set S and an operation such that when the operation is applied to any element(s) of the set, the result is an element of the set. (284)

cofunction identity $\cos\left(\frac{\pi}{2} - x\right) = \sin x$ or $\sin\left(\frac{\pi}{2} - x\right) = \cos x$. (370)

collection A combination of items in which repetition is allowed and order makes no difference. (640)

combination of the n elements of the set S taken r at a time An r-element subset of a set S with n elements. (622)

combinatorics The science of counting. (601)

common logarithm, log A logarithm with base 10. (133)

complement of a subset A of a set S The elements of S that are not in A. (611)

complete graph A graph in which every pair of vertices is joined by exactly one edge. (673)

complex conjugates The complex numbers $a + bi$ and $a - bi$, where a and b are real numbers. (475)

complex fraction A fraction whose numerator or denominator contains a fraction. (286)

Complex nth Roots Theorem

Polar Form: The n nth roots of $[r, \theta]$ are $\left[\sqrt[n]{r}, \frac{\theta}{n} + k\cdot\frac{2\pi}{n}\right]$, where $k = 0, 1, 2, \ldots,$ and $n - 1$.

Trigonometric Form: The n nth roots of $r(\cos\theta + i\sin\theta)$ are $\sqrt[n]{r}\cdot\left(\cos\left(\frac{\theta}{n} + k\cdot\frac{2\pi}{n}\right) + i\sin\left(\frac{\theta}{n} + k\cdot\frac{2\pi}{n}\right)\right)$, where $k = 0, 1, 2, \ldots,$ and $n - 1$. (515)

complex number A number that can be written in the form $a + bi$ where a and b are real numbers and $i^2 = -1$. The **real part** of $a + bi$ is a and the **imaginary part** is b. (473)

complex number addition Let a, b, c, and d be real numbers and let $z = a + bi$ and $w = c + di$. Then $z + w = (a + c) + (b + d)i$. (474)

complex number multiplication Let a, b, c, and d be real numbers and let $z = a + bi$ and $w = c + di$. Then $zw = (ac - bd) + (ad + bc)i$. (474)

complex plane A coordinate plane for representing complex numbers. The horizontal axis of the complex plane is the **real axis** and the vertical axis is the **imaginary axis**. (476)

component representation For a vector $\vec{u}$, the ordered pair (u_1, u_2), the rectangular coordinates of the point at the tip of the standard position arrow for a vector. The numbers u_1 and u_2 are the ***x*-component** and ***y*-component** of $\vec{u}$, respectively, or the **horizontal** and **vertical components** of $\vec{u}$. (722)

composite, $f \circ g$ The function with the rule $(f \circ g)(x) = f(g(x))$, whose domain is the set of values of x in the domain of g for which $g(x)$ is in the domain of f. (154)

composition of functions The operation of first applying one function, then another. Denoted by the symbol $\circ$. (154)

conclusion q, in the conditional $p \Rightarrow q$. Also called *consequent.* (35)

conclusion of an argument See *argument.* (45)

conditional statement, $p \Rightarrow q$ A statement of the form *If p, then q.* Also read *p implies q.* $p \Rightarrow q$ is true except when p is true and q is false. (35)

congruence class For a given modulus, the set of numbers congruent to each other. (252)

Congruence Theorem $\forall$ integers a and b and positive integers m, $a \equiv b \pmod{m}$ if and only if m is a factor of $a - b$. (253)

congruent modulo m, $a \equiv b \pmod{m}$ a is congruent to b modulo m, denoted by $a \equiv b \pmod{m}$, if and only if a and b have the same integer remainder when they are divided by m (the **modulus** or **mod**). (252)

conjecture A statement believed to be true but not proved. (56)

Conjugate Zeros Theorem Let $p(x)$ be a polynomial with real coefficients. If $z = a + bi$ is a zero of $p(x)$, then its complex conjugate $\bar{z} = a - bi$ is also a zero of $p(x)$. (526)

connected graph A graph G such that $\forall$ vertices v and w in G, $\exists$ a walk from v to w. (681)

connected vertices Two vertices of a graph for which there is a walk from one to the other. (681)

consequent q, in the conditional $p \Rightarrow q$. Also called *conclusion*. (35)

constant difference See *arithmetic sequence*.

Constant Multiple Property of Integrals Theorem If f is a continuous function on the interval from a to b, and c is a real number, then $\int_a^b c\, f(x)\, dx = c \int_a^b f(x)\, dx$. (808)

constant polynomial A polynomial of degree 0, which has the form $p(x) = k \neq 0\ \forall\ x$. (225)

constant ratio See *geometric sequence*.

Continuous Change Model If a quantity grows or decays continuously at a periodic rate r, the amount $A(t)$ after t periods is given by $A(t) = Be^{rt}$ where $B = A(0)$. (120)

continuous function on an interval A function f on an interval $[a, b]$ such that the graph of $y = f(x)$ is an unbroken curve for values of x between a and b. (169)

contrapositive of $p \Rightarrow q$ $(\sim q) \Rightarrow (\sim p)$. (39)

Contrapositive Theorem A conditional and its contrapositive are logically equivalent. (39)

Convergence of Powers Theorem Let T be an $n \times n$ stochastic matrix with no zero entries. Then $\lim_{k\to\infty} T^k$ is a stochastic matrix with n identical rows. (695)

convergent series An infinite series whose sequence of partial sums has a finite limit. (439)

converse error An invalid argument of either of the following forms: (54)

Simple form	Universal form
If p then q.	*$\forall x$, if $p(x)$ then $q(x)$.*
q	*$q(c)$, for a particular c.*
$\therefore$ *p.*	$\therefore$ *$p(c)$.*

converse of $p \Rightarrow q$ $q \Rightarrow p$. (40)

convex polyhedron A polyhedron having the property that all points on the segment connecting any two points on the polyhedron lie on or in the interior of the polyhedron. (701)

cosecant of a real number x, csc x $\frac{1}{\sin x}$, $\forall\ x$ such that $\sin x \neq 0$. (322)

Cosine of a Difference Theorem For all real numbers α and β, $\cos(\alpha - \beta) = \cos\alpha\cos\beta + \sin\alpha\sin\beta$. (369)

cosine of a real number x, cos x The first coordinate of the image of (1, 0) under a rotation of magnitude x about the origin. (110)

Cosine of a Sum Theorem For all real numbers α and β, $\cos(\alpha + \beta) = \cos\alpha\cos\beta - \sin\alpha\sin\beta$. (367)

cotangent of a real number x, cot x $\frac{\cos x}{\sin x}$, $\forall\ x$ such that $\sin x \neq 0$. (322)

counterexample Given a universal statement $\forall$ *x in S, p(x)*, a value of x in S for which $p(x)$ is false. (9)

critical point A point at which the graph of a function changes from that of an increasing function to that of a decreasing function, or vice versa. (247)

cross product of three-dimensional vectors $\vec{u} = (u_1, u_2, u_3)$ and $\vec{v} = (v_1, v_2, v_3)$, $\vec{u} \times \vec{v}$ The vector $\vec{u} \times \vec{v} = (u_2v_3 - u_3v_2, u_3v_1 - u_1v_3, u_1v_2 - u_2v_1)$. (756)

crossing A place in a picture of a graph in which two edges seem to intersect not at their endpoints. (668)

current The rate of flow of electric charge through a circuit (measured in amps). (476)

deceleration Negative acceleration. (577)

decreasing function A function f such that $\forall\ x_1$ and x_2 in its domain, if $x_1 < x_2$ then $f(x_1) > f(x_2)$. (92)

definite integral of f from a to b The limit of upper and lower Riemann sums as the number of subintervals increases; denoted by $\int_a^b f(x)\, dx$. (800)

degree, ° A unit of measure of the magnitude of a rotation. 360 degrees is equivalent to one complete revolution. (109)

degree of a vertex, deg(v) The number of edges that have the vertex as an endpoint, with each edge that is a loop counted twice. (674)

DeMoivre's Theorem
Polar Form: For all positive integers n, if $z = [r, \theta]$, then $z^n = [r^n, n\theta]$.
Trigonometric Form: For all positive integers n, if $z = r(\cos\theta + i\sin\theta)$, then $z^n = r^n(\cos n\theta + i\sin n\theta)$. (508)

DeMorgan's Laws For all statements p and q,
1. $\sim(p \text{ and } q) \equiv (\sim p) \text{ or } (\sim q)$
2. $\sim(p \text{ or } q) \equiv (\sim p) \text{ and } (\sim q)$. (23)

dense One set is dense in another if there is an element of the first set as close as one wishes to every element of the second set. (538)

dependent variable The variable representing range values of a function. (78)

derivative function of f The function with the domain of f whose value at each point is the value of the derivative of f at that point. Denoted by f'. Also called *first derivative*. (570)

Derivative of a Constant Function Theorem If $\forall\ x, f(x) = k$, then $f'(x) = 0\ \forall\ x$. (572)

Derivative of a Linear Function Theorem If $f(x) = mx + b$, then $f'(x) = m$. (572)

Derivative of a Quadratic Function Theorem If $f(x) = ax^2 + bx + c$, where a, b, and c are real numbers and $a \neq 0$, then $f'(x) = 2ax + b$ for all real numbers x. (572)

derivative of a real function f at x Denoted by $f'(x)$ and given by $f'(x) = \lim_{\Delta x\to 0} \frac{f(x_1 + \Delta x) - f(x_1)}{\Delta x}$, provided this limit exists and is finite. (563)

difference equation For a sequence, an equation giving a general relation between the difference between one term of the sequence and the previous term. (124)

difference of two functions For two real-valued functions f and g with domain S, the function $f - g$ defined $\forall\ x$ in S by $(f - g)(x) = f(x) - g(x)$. (149)

GLOSSARY

difference of vectors, $\vec{u} - \vec{v}$ If $\vec{u} = (u_1, u_2)$ and $\vec{v} = (v_1, v_2)$, then $\vec{u} - \vec{v}$ is the vector $\vec{u} + (-\vec{v})$. (729)

difference quotient $\frac{f(x_1 + \Delta x) - f(x_1)}{\Delta x}$. (555)

differential calculus The study of rates of change in continuous functions. (551)

differential equation An equation involving functions and their derivatives. (589)

differentiation The process of finding derivatives of functions. (589)

digraph See *directed graph.*

direct proof A proof that proceeds directly from the antecedent (given) to the conclusion. (63)

directed graph A graph in which each edge has a direction. Also called *digraph.* (662)

direction of a vector The number θ in the polar representation $[r, \theta]$ of a vector. (721)

Discontinuity Theorem Given a rational function f with $f(x) = \frac{p(x)}{q(x)}$, where $p(x)$ and $q(x)$ are polynomials over the reals: if $\exists$ a real number c such that $q(c) = 0$ but $p(c) \neq 0$, then f has an essential discontinuity at $x = c$ and the line $x = c$ is a vertical asymptote to the graph of f. (304)

discrete dynamical system A set D together with a function f from D into itself that is repeatedly applied. (535)

discrete function A function whose domain is a discrete set. (82)

discrete set A set that can be put into 1-1 correspondence with a subset of the set of integers. (81)

Distance in Space Theorem The distance between $P = (x_1, y_1, z_1)$ and $Q = (x_2, y_2, z_2)$ is given by $PQ = \sqrt{(x_2 - x_1)^2 + (y_2 - y_1)^2 + (z_2 - z_1)^2}$. (749)

divergent series An infinite series whose sequence of partial sums does not have a finite limit. (439)

divisor See *factor.*

domain See *function.*

domain of an identity The set of all values of the variables for which both sides in an identity are defined. (285)

dot product of three-dimensional vectors $\vec{u} = (u_1, u_2, u_3)$ and $\vec{v} = (v_1, v_2, v_3)$, $\vec{u} \cdot \vec{v}$ The real number $\vec{u} \cdot \vec{v} = u_1v_1 + u_2v_2 + u_3v_3$. (753)

dot product of $\vec{u} = (u_1, u_2)$ and $\vec{v} = (v_1, v_2)$, $\vec{u} \cdot \vec{v}$ The real number $u_1v_1 + u_2v_2$. (741)

double-angle identities See *Identities for cos 2x Theorem* and *Identity for sin 2x Theorem.*

e The irrational number equal to $\lim_{x \to \infty} (1 + \frac{1}{x})^x$, which is approximately 2.71828 . . . . (119)

edge An arc on a graph. (658)

edge-endpoint function See *graph.*

efficiency of an algorithm The maximum number $E(n)$ of significant operations necessary for the algorithm to solve the given problem if it is of size n. (457)

elementary functions The basic functions from which more complicated functions may be defined, including polynomial, exponential, trigonometric, and logarithmic functions. (77)

end behavior A description of what happens to the values $f(x)$ of a function f as $x \to \infty$ and as $x \to -\infty$. (97)

End Behavior of Rational Functions Theorem Suppose $f(x) = \frac{a_m x^m + \cdots + a_1 x + a_0}{b_n x^n + \ldots + b_1 x + b_0}$ $\forall$ real numbers x for which the denominator is nonzero, where the a_i and b_i are real numbers $\forall$ i, $a_m \neq 0$, and $b_n \neq 0$. Then the end behavior of f is the same as the end behavior of the function g defined $\forall$ x by $g(x) = \frac{a_m}{b_n} x^{m-n}$. (311)

endpoint See *graph* and *interval.*

equality of complex numbers $a + bi = c + di$ if and only if $a = c$ and $b = d$. (474)

Equation for a Plane Theorem The set of points $\{(x, y, z): ax + by + cz = d\}$, where at least one of the coefficients a, b, or c is nonzero, is a plane perpendicular to the vector $\vec{v} = (a, b, c)$. (763)

Equation of a Sphere Theorem The sphere with center (a, b, c) and radius r has equation $r^2 = (x - a)^2 + (y - b)^2 + (z - c)^2$. (750)

Equations for a Line in 3-Space Theorem A point $Q = (x, y, z)$ is on the line ℓ through $P = (x_0, y_0, z_0)$ parallel to $\vec{v} = (v_1, v_2, v_3)$ if and only if there is a real number t such that

a. $\overrightarrow{PQ} = t\vec{v}$, or equivalently $(x - x_0, y - y_0, z - z_0) = t(v_1, v_2, v_3)$ (**vector equation for ℓ**) or

b. $\begin{cases} x = x_0 + tv_1 \\ y = y_0 + tv_2 \\ z = z_0 + tv_3 \end{cases}$

(**parametric equations for ℓ**). (761)

equivalent equations Two or more equations with the same solutions. (163)

equivalent graphs Two graphs for which there is a 1-1 correspondence between their vertices and edges under which the edge-endpoint function of one corresponds to the edge-endpoint function of the other. (659)

essential discontinuity A discontinuity that cannot be removed by insertion of a single point. (303)

essential features of a counting problem Whether order makes a difference in the objects to be counted, and whether or not the objects can be repeated. (602)

Euler circles See *Venn diagram.*

Euler circuit On a graph, a circuit that contains every edge and every vertex of the graph. (679)

Euler Circuit Theorem If a graph has an Euler circuit, then every vertex of the graph has even degree. (680)

Euler's formula Let G be a connected graph with no crossings, and let V, E, and F be the number of vertices, edges, and faces of G. Then $V - E + F = 2$. (703)

Evaluation of a Finite Geometric Series Theorem If a is any real number and r is any real number other than 1, then for all integers $n \geq 1$, $a + ar + ar^2 + \ldots + ar^{n-1} = a\left(\frac{1 - r^n}{1 - r}\right)$. (436)

Evaluation of an Infinite Geometric Series Theorem If a is any real number and r is a real number with $0 < |r| < 1$, then $\sum_{k=0}^{\infty} ar^k = \frac{a}{1 - r}$. (438)

even function A function such that $\forall$ x in its domain, $f(-x) = f(x)$. (101)

exclusive *or* One or the other but not both. (22)

existential statement A statement of the form *There exists x in S such that p(x)*, or, symbolically, $\exists$ *x in S such that p(x)*. (10)

expanded form of a polynomial A polynomial written in the form $p(x) = a_n x^n + a_{n-1}x^{n-1} + \ldots + a_1 x + a_0$. (225)

expanded form of a sum The form in which $\sum_{i=m}^{n} a_i$ is rewritten as $a_m + a_{m+1} + \ldots + a_n$. (413)

explicit formula for a sequence An equation which gives the *n*th term of a sequence in terms of n. (124)

exponential function with base *b* Any function defined by $f: x \rightarrow ab^x$, $\forall$ x, where the base b is a positive real number, $b \neq 1$, and a (the **initial value** of f) is a nonzero real number. (117)

exponential sequence See *geometric sequence*.

faces of a planar graph The regions of the plane into which the edges of the graph divide the plane. (701)

factor Given integers n and d with $d \neq 0$, d is a factor (or **divisor**) of n if and only if there is an integer q such that $n = q \cdot d$. (224)

Factor of a Polynomial Sum Theorem For all polynomials $a(x)$, $b(x)$, and $c(x)$, if $a(x)$ is a factor of $b(x)$ and $a(x)$ is a factor of $c(x)$, then $a(x)$ is a factor of $b(x) + c(x)$. (227)

Factor of an Integer Product Theorem For all integers m, n, and p, if m is a factor of n, then m is a factor of $n \cdot p$. (229)

Factor of an Integer Sum Theorem For all integers a, b, and c, if a is a factor of b and a is a factor of c, then a is a factor of $b + c$. (226)

Factor Search Theorem If an integer n has no prime factors between 1 and $\sqrt{n}$ inclusive, then n is prime. (267)

Factor Theorem For all polynomials $p(x)$, $x - c$ is a factor of $p(x)$ if and only if $p(c) = 0$; that is, if and only if c is a zero of $p(x)$. (244)

factored form of a polynomial A polynomial written as the product of two or more polynomials of lesser degree. (225)

Fibonacci numbers The integers 1, 2, 3, 5, 8, 13, 21, . . . , which are terms of the Fibonacci sequence. (125)

Fibonacci sequence The sequence defined by

$$\begin{cases} F_1 = 1 \\ F_2 = 1 \\ F_{n+1} = F_n + F_{n-1} \text{ for all integers } n \geq \end{cases}$$

2.

(125, 410)

field of complex numbers The complex numbers together with the operations of addition and multiplication. (474)

field properties Addition and multiplication are closed, commutative, and associative. There is an identity for addition and a different identity for multiplication. Every number has an additive inverse and every number but the additive identity has a multiplicative inverse. Multiplication is distributive over addition. (474)

finite sequence A function whose domain is the interval of integers $[a, b]$. (124)

finite series The indicated sum of finitely many consecutive terms of a sequence. (435)

first derivative The derivative function or a value of that function. (578)

fixed point For a function f in a dynamical system, a value of x for which $f(x) = x$. (540)

force An influence that changes the velocity of an object. (727)

function A correspondence from a set A (the **domain**) to a set B in which each element in A corresponds to exactly one element of B. Also called *mapping*. (78)

Function Composition and Equality Property For any real functions f, g, and h, and values of x for which f, g, $h \circ f$, and $h \circ g$ are defined: If $f(x) = g(x)$, then $h(f(x)) = h(g(x))$. (164)

Function Inequality Theorem Suppose that f is a continuous real function. If f has zeros a and b and no zeros between a and b, then either $f(x) > 0$ for all x between a and b or $f(x) < 0$ for all x between a and b. (190)

functionally equivalent networks Two networks that produce the same output for each combination of input signals. (30)

fundamental period of a function The smallest positive number p such that $f(x + p) = f(x)$ for all x in the domain of f, if such a number exists. (113)

fundamental region See *tessellation*.

Fundamental Theorem of Algebra If $p(x)$ is any polynomial of degree $n \geq 1$, with real or complex coefficients, then $p(x)$ has at least one complex zero. (521)

Fundamental Theorem of Arithmetic Suppose that n is an integer and that $n > 1$. Then either n is a prime number or n has a prime factorization which is unique except for the order of the factors. (268)

Fundamental Theorem of Calculus Let f be a continuous function on the interval from a to b.

1. If g is a function whose derivative is f, then

$$\int_a^b f(x)\,dx = g(b) - g(a).$$

2. If $g(x) = \int_a^x f(t)\,dt$ for all x from a to b, then $g'(x) = f(x)$ for all such x. (827)

generating curve See *surface of revolution with axis ℓ*.

Geometric Addition Theorem Let $z = a + bi$ and $w = c + di$ be two complex numbers that are not collinear with (0, 0). Then the point representing $z + w$ is the fourth vertex of a parallelogram with consecutive vertices $z = a + bi$, 0, and $w = c + di$. (488)

GLOSSARY

Geometric Multiplication Theorem Let z and w be complex numbers. If $z = [r, \theta]$ and $w = [s, \phi]$, then $zw = [rs, \theta + \phi]$. That is, multiplying a complex number z by w applies to z the composite of a size change of magnitude s and a rotation of ϕ about the origin. (490)

Geometric *n*th Roots Theorem When graphed in the complex plane, the nth roots of any nonzero complex number z are the vertices of a regular n-gon whose center is at (0, 0). (515)

geometric sequence A sequence g in which $\forall\ n > 1$, $g_n = rg_{n-1}$, where r is a constant. That is, each term beyond the first is a constant r (the **constant ratio**) times the preceding term. Also called *exponential sequence.* (123)

geometric series The indicated sum of consecutive terms of a geometric sequence. (435)

Goldbach's conjecture A conjecture, originally made by Christian Goldbach in the middle of the 18th century, that every number greater than 2 can be written as the sum of two primes. (56)

graph A finite set of vertices, a finite set of edges, and a function (the **edge-endpoint function**) that maps each edge to a set of either one or two vertices (the **endpoints** of the edge). (666)

Graph Scale-Change Theorem In a relation described by a sentence in x and y, the following two processes yield the same graph: (1) replacing x by $\frac{x}{a}$ and y by $\frac{y}{b}$; (2) applying the scale change $S_{a,b}$: $(x, y) \rightarrow (ax, by)$ to the graph of the original relation. (196)

Graph-Standardization Theorem Suppose that G is the graph of a relation in x and y. Let h and k be any real numbers and let a and b be nonzero real numbers. Let G' be the image of G under the rubberband transformation T: $(x, y) \rightarrow (ax + h, by + k)$.
***x-y* form**: If G is described by a rule relating x and y, then a rule for G' is found by replacing x by $\frac{x-h}{a}$ and y by $\frac{y-k}{b}$.
parametric form:
If G is described by $\begin{cases} x = f(t) \\ y = g(t), \end{cases}$
then G' is described by $\begin{cases} x = af(t) + h \\ y = bg(t) + k. \end{cases}$
(198)

graph theory The study of graphs and their properties. (657)

Graph-Translation Theorem In a relation described by a sentence in x and y, the following two processes yield the same graph: (1) replacing x by $x - h$ and y by $y - k$;
(2) applying the translation $T_{h,k}$: $(x, y) \rightarrow (x + h, y + k)$ to the graph of the original relation. (195)

half-adder A network of logic gates that takes two binary digits as input and produces the two digits of their sum as output. (261)

half-angle identities For all real numbers x, $\cos\left(\frac{x}{2}\right) = \pm\sqrt{\frac{\cos x + 1}{2}}$ or $\sin\left(\frac{x}{2}\right) = \pm\sqrt{\frac{1 - \cos x}{2}}$. (380)

half-open interval, (*a*, *b*] or [*a*, *b*) See *interval.*

handshake problem Suppose n people are at a party. If each person shakes hands with every other person, how many handshakes are required? (673)

hexadecimal See *base 16.*

horizontal asymptote A horizontal line to which the graph of a function gets closer and closer as $x \rightarrow \infty$ or as $x \rightarrow -\infty$. (97)

horizontal component of a vector See *component representation.*

hypothesis p, in the conditional $p \Rightarrow q$. Also called *antecedent.* (35)

Identities for cos 2*x* Theorem For all real numbers x: $\cos 2x = \cos^2 x - \sin^2 x = 2\cos^2 x - 1 = 1 - 2\sin^2 x$. (377)

identity An equation that is true for all values of the variables for which both sides are defined. (285)

Identity for sin 2*x* Theorem For all real numbers x, $\sin 2x = 2 \sin x \cos x$. (378)

identity function, *I* A function that maps each element of its domain onto itself. (157)

if and only if *p if and only if q* is denoted by $p \Leftrightarrow q$ and is equivalent to (*if p then q*) *and* (*if q then p*), or symbolically, $p \Rightarrow q$ *and* $q \Rightarrow p$. $p \Leftrightarrow q$ is true only when p and q are both true or both false. (40)

imaginary axis See *complex plane.*

imaginary number A number of the form bi, where b is a real number and i is the imaginary unit. (473)

imaginary part of a complex number See *complex number.*

imaginary unit, *i* The complex number $i = \sqrt{-1}$. (473)

impedance The opposition to the flow of current caused by components called resistors, coils, and capacitors (measured in ohms). (476)

implies See *conditional statement.*

improper induction Concluding a universal statement from instances of it. (55)

inclusive *or* One or the other or both. (21)

increasing function A function f such that $\forall\ x_1$ and x_2 in its domain, if $x_1 < x_2$ then $f(x_1) < f(x_2)$. (92)

independent variable A variable representing domain values of a function. (78)

index A subscript in summation notation. (413)

inductive assumption In mathematical induction, the assumption that $S(k)$ is true for an arbitrarily chosen integer $k \geq 1$. (419)

inductive step See *Principle of Mathematical Induction.*

infinite sequence A function whose domain is the interval of integers $[a, \infty)$. (124)

infinite series The indicated sum of the terms of an infinite sequence. (435)

infinite sum, $\sum_{k=1}^{\infty} a_k$ The limit of the partial sums of a sequence as $n \rightarrow \infty$, provided this limit exists and is finite. (437)

Infinitude of Primes Theorem There are infinitely many prime numbers. (267)

initial conditions See *recursive definition for a sequence.*

initial value of an exponential function The value of the exponential function f: $x \rightarrow ab^x$ when $x = 0$. (117)

input-output table A table indicating what the output will be from any possible combination of input signals. (28)

instantaneous acceleration The instantaneous rate of change of an object's velocity with respect to time. (577)

instantaneous rate of change of *f* at *x* The derivative of f at x. (564)

instantaneous velocity at time *x* The limit as $\Delta x \to 0$ of the average velocity of the object between times x and Δx, provided this limit exists and is finite. (561)

integer division Division where the result is expressed as an integer quotient and an integer remainder. (232)

integer quotient See *Quotient-Remainder Theorem for Integers*.

integer remainder See *Quotient-Remainder Theorem for Integers*.

Integral of a Quadratic Function Theorem If $a > 0$, $\int_0^a x^2\,dx = \frac{a^3}{3}$. (814)

intermediate points for a Riemann sum, z_i See *Riemann sum of a function f over the interval from a to b*. (793)

Intermediate Value Theorem Suppose that f is a continuous function on the interval $[a, b]$. Then for every real number y_0 between $f(a)$ and $f(b)$, there is at least one real number x_0 between a and b such that $f(x_0) = y_0$. (170)

interval The set of numbers between two given numbers, or greater than a number, or less than a number, possibly including the given numbers (the **endpoints**). (81)

invalid argument An argument or argument form for which there exist instances in which the premises are true and the conclusion is false. (53)

inverse A relation formed by reversing the ordered pairs of a given relation. (156)

inverse cosine (Arccos) function, $\cos^{-1}$ The function that maps x onto the number or angle y whose cosine is x, for $0 \le y \le \pi$. (386)

inverse error An invalid argument of either of the following forms: (55)

Simple form	Universal form
If p then q.	$\forall x$, *if p(x) then q(x).*
not p	*not p(c) for a particular c.*
$\therefore$ *not q.*	$\therefore$ *not q(c).*

inverse functions, $f = g^{-1}$ Two functions f and g such that $f \circ g(x) = x$ for all x in the domain of g and $g \circ f(x) = x$ for all x in the domain of f. (156)

inverse of $p \Rightarrow q$ $\sim p \Rightarrow \sim q$. (40)

inverse sine (Arcsin) function, $\sin^{-1}$ The function that maps x onto the number or angle y whose sine is x, for $-\frac{\pi}{2} \le y \le \frac{\pi}{2}$. (386)

inverse tangent (Arctan) function, $\tan^{-1}$ The function that maps x onto the number or angle y whose tangent is x, for $-\frac{\pi}{2} < y < \frac{\pi}{2}$. (386)

irrational conjugates The real numbers $c + \sqrt{d}$ and $c - \sqrt{d}$, where c and d are rational numbers and $\sqrt{d}$ is not a rational number. (319)

irrational number A real number that cannot be written as a ratio of two integers. (315)

isolated vertex A vertex of a graph that is not the endpoint of any edge. (667)

iterate To repeat a process over and over. (452)

iterative algorithm An algorithm in which the same steps are repeated again and again. (452)

justification A generalization, such as a postulate, definition, theorem, or law of logic, used in a proof. (61)

Königsberg bridge problem In the city of Königsberg (now Kaliningrad), two branches of the Pregol'a River come together. In the 1700s, parts of Königsberg were on the banks of the river, another part was on a large island in the middle, and a final part was between the two branches of the river. Seven bridges connected these four parts of the city. Is it possible for a person to walk around the city crossing each bridge exactly once, starting and ending at the same point? (657)

Law of Detachment, *modus ponens* A valid argument of either of the following forms: (46)

Simple form	Universal form
If p then q.	$\forall x$, *if p(x) then q(x).*
p	*p(c), for a particular c.*
$\therefore$ *q.*	$\therefore$ *q(c).*

Law of Indirect Reasoning, *modus tollens* A valid argument of either of the following forms: (48)

Simple form	Universal form
If p then q.	$\forall x$, *if p(x) then q(x).*
not q	*not q(c) for a particular c.*
$\therefore$ *not p.*	$\therefore$ *not p(c).*

Law of Substitution A law of logic that states that if a universal statement is true for all elements of a given set, then it is true for each element of that set. (7)

Law of Transitivity A valid argument of either of the following forms: (47)

Simple form	Universal form
If p then q.	$\forall x$, *if p(x) then q(x).*
If q then r.	$\forall x$, *if q(x) then r(x).*
$\therefore$ *If p then r.*	$\therefore \forall x$, *if p(x) then r(x).*

leaf See *rose curve*.

leaves The ends of the branches in a tree. (608)

length of a walk The number of edges in the walk. (687)

limaçon The polar graph of an equation of the form $r = a + b\cos\theta$ or $r = a + b\sin\theta$, where a and b are nonzero real numbers. (495)

limit of a function *f* as $x \to \infty$ or as $x \to -\infty$, $\lim_{x\to\infty} f(x)$ or $\lim_{x\to\infty} f(x)$ The value that $f(x)$ approaches as x gets larger and larger without bound, or smaller and smaller without bound. (97)

limit of a sequence, $\lim_{x\to\infty} s_n$ A number L such that, for any positive number p, there is an integer N such that $|s_n - L| < p$ for all $n \ge N$. (204)

limited growth model See *logistic model*.

$\lim_{x\to a^+} f(x)$ The limit of the function f as x approaches a from the right. (296)

$\lim_{x\to a^-} f(x)$ The limit of the function f as x approaches a from the left. (296)

GLOSSARY

logarithm function with base *b* The function $\log_b$ defined by the rule $x \to \log_b x$, for all positive real numbers x. (131)

Logarithm of a Power Theorem $\log_b (u^s) = s \log_b u$. (132)

Logarithm of a Product Theorem $\log_b (u \cdot v) = \log_b u + \log_b v$. (132)

Logarithm of a Quotient Theorem $\log_b \left(\frac{u}{v}\right) = \log_b u - \log_b v$. (132)

logarithm of *x* to the base *b*, $\log_b x$ The power to which the **base** *b* must be raised to equal *x*; that is, the number *y* such that $b^y = x$. (130)

logarithmic scale An ordinary measurement scale which has been transformed by a logarithmic function so that constant differences correspond to constant ratios in the untransformed scale. (138)

logarithmic spiral The polar graph of $r = ab^\theta$, where $a > 0$ and $b > 1$. (504)

logical expression A formula in which variables representing statements are combined in an unambiguous way with *and, or, not,* or *if-then.* (22)

logically equivalent expressions, ≡ Two logical expressions with the same truth values for all substitutions of statements for their statement variables. (22)

logistic model A mathematical model of growth with a number which the growth cannot exceed. Also called a *limited growth model.* (127)

loop An edge of a graph whose endpoints are the same point. (666)

lower Riemann sum The Riemann sum of a function *f* where each $f(z_i)$ is the smallest value on the subinterval. (799)

lowest terms A fraction or rational expression in which the numerator and denominator have no common factor. (290)

magnitude of a vector The number *r* in the polar representation $[r, \theta]$ of a vector. (721)

main diagonal of a matrix For an $n \times n$ matrix, the diagonal consisting of all entries in the same row and the same column. (687)

mapping See *function.*

Markov chain Of a situation that can exist in only a finite number of states, when the probabilities of proceeding from one state to the next depend only on the first state. (44)

mathematical induction See *Principle of Mathematical Induction.*

mathematical proof A chain of logically valid deductions using agreed-upon assumptions, definitions, or previously proved statements. (61)

max-min problem A problem in which you need to find either the greatest or least value of a function. (86)

maximum value of a function *f* with domain *S* A number *m* such that $\exists\, x$ in *S* with $f(x) = m$ and $\forall\, x$ in *S*, $m \ge f(x)$. (88)

minimal spanning tree For a graph *G* in which each edge is labeled with a number, a spanning tree for *G* such that the sum of the labels on its edges has the smallest possible value. (707)

minimum value of a function *f* with domain *S* A number *m* such that $\exists\, x$ in *S* with $f(x) = m$ and $\forall\, x$ in *S*, $m \le f(x)$. (88)

modulus See *absolute value of a complex number.*

modulus, mod See *congruent modulo m.*

modus ponens See *Law of Detachment.*

modus tollens See *Law of Indirect Reasoning.*

multinomial coefficient A coefficient in the series expansion of $(a_1 + a_2 + \ldots + a_k)^n$. (645)

multiple Given integers *n* and *d* with $d \ne 0$, *n* is a multiple of *d* if and only if *d* is a factor of *n*. (224)

Multiplication Counting Principle Suppose that strings result from a procedure which consists of *k* successive steps and that:
the 1st step can be done in n_1 ways,
the 2nd step can be done in n_2 ways,
⋮
and the *k*th step can be done in n_k ways.

Then there are $n_1 n_2 \cdot \ldots \cdot n_k$ possible strings. (609)

Multiplication Properties of Inequality For any real expressions $f(x)$ and $g(x)$, if $f(x) < g(x)$: then $f(x) \cdot c < g(x) \cdot c$ if $c > 0$; and $f(x) \cdot c > g(x) \cdot c$ if $c < 0$. (175)

Multiplication Property of Equality For any real expressions $f(x)$ and $g(x)$, if $f(x) = g(x)$, then $f(x) \cdot c = g(x) \cdot c$. (161)

multiplicity of a zero For a zero *c* of a polynomial $p(x)$ of degree at least 1, the largest positive integer *m* such that $(x - c)^m$ is a factor of $p(x)$. (521)

natural logarithm, ln A logarithm with base *e*. (133)

necessary condition "*p* is a necessary condition for *q*" means $q \Rightarrow p$. (42)

negation The statement, denoted **not *p***, that, if true, exactly expresses what it would mean for *p* to be false. (14)

negation of $p \Rightarrow q$ *p and* (*not q*). (37)

negation of ∀ *x* in *S*, if *p(x)* then *q(x)* *∃ x in S such that p(x) and not q(x).* (38)

network of logic gates NOT, AND, and OR gates connected in such a way that the output signals from some of the gates become input signals for other gates. (29)

Newton's Method A recursive method for obtaining zeros of a continuous function *f* by (1) finding the tangent line to the graph of the function at an initial point, (2) determining the *x*-intercept of this tangent line, and (3) finding the tangent line to the graph of the function for this new value of *x*. Steps (2) and (3) are then repeated until the zero of the function has been estimated to the desired degree of accuracy. (592)

node A vertex in a tree; corresponds to a step in which several choices or results are possible. (608)

nonreversible step A reasoning step in solving an equation or inequality whose converse is not true for some values of the variables for which the expressions in the equation are defined. (163)

norm of a vector The length of the vector; denoted by $|\vec{u}|$. (723)

NOT gate An input-output device for which the output signal is 0 if the input signal is 1, and the output signal is 1 if the input signal is 0. Schematically, the NOT gate is represented by (28)

not *p* See *negation*.

***n*th root** Of a complex number *w*, a number *z* such that $z^n = w$. (514)

***n*th term of a sequence** The value of the sequence corresponding to the domain value *n*. (124)

Number of Zeros of a Polynomial Theorem A polynomial of degree *n* has at most *n* zeros. (246)

O(*d*) The orbit with initial point *d*. (535)

oblique asymptote An oblique line $y = mx + b$ which the graph of a function approaches as $x \to \infty$ or as $x \to -\infty$. (311)

octal See *base 8*.

odd function A function such that $\forall$ *x* in its domain, $f(-x) = -f(x)$. (101)

one-to-one function, 1-1 function A function *g* such that for all *u* and *v* in the domain of *g*, $g(u) = g(v) \Rightarrow u = v$. (157)

only if *p only if q* is equivalent to *if p then q*. (42)

open infinite interval, (*a*, ∞) or (-∞, *b*) The set of numbers greater than a given number (*a*), or the set of numbers less than a given number (*b*); $\{x: a < x\}$ or $\{x: x < b\}$. (81)

open interval, (*a*, *b*) The set of numbers greater than one number (*a*) and less than a second larger number (*b*); $\{x: a < x < b\}$. (81)

opposite of a vector, $-\vec{v}$ The vector with the same magnitude and direction opposite that of the given vector. (729)

optimization problem A problem in which the value of one variable is sought to obtain the most optimal, or desirable, value of another. (583)

OR gate An input-output device for which the output signal is 1 if one or both of the two input signals are 1. Otherwise, the output signal is 0. Schematically, the OR gate is represented by . (28)

orbit with initial point *d* For a set *D* and a function $f: D \to D$ constituting a discrete dynamical system, the sequence $a_0, a_1, a_2, \ldots$ defined by

$$\begin{cases} a_0 = d \\ a_{k+1} = f(a_k) \text{ for integers } k \geq 0 \end{cases}$$

(585)

ordinate The second coordinate *b* of the ordered pair (*a*, *b*). (150)

orthogonal vectors Vectors whose directions are perpendicular. (743)

P(*n*, *r*), $_nP_r$ The number of permutations of *n* elements taken *r* at a time. (617)

P(*n*, *r*) Calculation Theorem $P(n, r) = \frac{n!}{(n-r)!}$. (618)

parallel edges Two edges of a graph with both endpoints in common. (667)

parallel vectors Two vectors with the same or opposite directions. (733)

parameter An independent variable on which other variables (usually coordinates) depend. (103)

parametric equations A set of equations in which, in each equation, a different variable is expressed in terms of the same parameter. (103)

parametric form of an equation for a line A line through (x_0, y_0) that is parallel to the vector $\vec{v} = (v_1, v_2)$ has parametric equations $\begin{cases} x = x_0 + tv_1 \\ y = y_0 + tv_2 \end{cases}$ where *t* may be any real number. (735)

partial sum The sum of the first *n* terms of a sequence. (437)

Pascal's triangle A triangular array of binomial coefficients (equivalently, combinations) in which the *r*th element in row *n* is the sum of the $(r-1)$st and *r*th elements in row $n-1$. (628)

	Row
1	0
1 1	1
1 2 1	2
1 3 3 1	3
1 4 6 4 1	4
1 5 10 10 5 1	5
⋮	⋮

path A walk from one vertex to another in which no edge is repeated. (679)

perfect number A positive integer that is equal to the sum of its proper divisors. (230)

period of a function Any positive number *p* such that $f(x + p) = f(x)$ for all *x* in the domain of *f*. (113)

periodic function A real function *f* with the property that there is a positive number *p* such that $f(x + p) = f(x)$ for all *x* in the domain of *f*. (113)

permutation A string of all of the symbols $a_1, a_2, \ldots, a_n$ without repetition. (615)

permutation of *n* elements of the set *S* taken *r* at a time A string of *r* elements from *S* without repetition. (617)

Permutation Theorem There are *n*! permutations of *n* different elements. (616)

petal See *rose curve*.

phase shift The least positive or the greatest negative horizontal translation that maps $y = \cos x$ or $y = \sin x$ onto its translation image. (Previous course)

plane vector See *two-dimensional vector*.

polar axis A ray, usually horizontal and drawn to the right, through the pole of a polar coordinate system, from which rotations are measured. (480)

GLOSSARY

polar coordinate system A system in which a point is identified by a pair of numbers $[r, \theta]$, where $|r|$ is the distance of the point from a fixed point (the **pole**), and θ is a magnitude of rotation from the polar axis. (480)

polar coordinates, $[r, \theta]$ Description of a point in a polar coordinate system. (480)

polar form of a complex number The representation of the number in polar coordinates. (489)

polar grid A background of circles and rays emanating from the pole, of use in sketching graphs in a polar coordinate system. (482)

polar representation of a vector The representation of a two-dimensional vector with positive **magnitude** r and **direction** θ by the polar coordinates $[r, \theta]$. (721)

Polar-Rectangular Conversion Theorem If $[r, \theta]$ is a polar coordinate representation of a point P, then the rectangular coordinates (x, y) of P are given by $x = r \cos \theta$ and $y = r \sin \theta$. (483)

pole See *polar coordinate system.*

polynomial division Division of polynomials, analogous to integer division, where the result is expressed in terms of a quotient polynomial and a remainder polynomial. (234)

polynomial of degree n A function P for which there are numbers $a_0, a_1, \ldots, a_n$, with $a_n \neq 0$, such that $P(x) = a_nx^n + a_{n-1}x^{n-1} + \ldots + ax + a_0$ for all x in the domain of P. (224)

possibility tree A diagram used to display the possible outcomes of an experiment. (608)

power function A function with an equation of the form $y = ax^n$. (99)

premises See *argument.*

prime An integer $n > 1$ whose only positive integer factors are 1 and n. (265)

Prime Factor Theorem Every integer greater than 1 is either prime or has a prime factor. (265)

prime factorization A representation of a number as a product of primes. (268)

prime over the real numbers A polynomial $p(x)$ of degree ≥ 1 whose only factors with real coefficients and leading coefficient 1 are constants or constant multiples of $p(x)$. (269)

Principle of Mathematical Induction Suppose that for each positive integer n, $S(n)$ is a sentence in n. If

(1) $S(1)$ is true (the **basis step**), and

(2) for all integers $k \geq 1$, $S(k)$ is true $\Rightarrow S(k + 1)$ is true (the **inductive step**), then $S(n)$ is true for all positive integers n. (418)

Principle of Strong Mathematical Induction Suppose that for each positive integer n, $S(n)$ is a sentence in n. If

(1) $S(1)$ is true, and

(2) for all integers $k \geq 1$, the assumption that $S(1), S(2), \ldots, S(k-1), S(k)$ are all true implies that $S(k + 1)$ is also true, then $S(n)$ is true for all integers $n \geq 1$. (442)

probability tree A digraph in which each vertex represents an event, and the edge leading from vertex A to vertex B is labeled with the probability that event B occurs if A occurs. (662)

product of two functions For two real-valued functions f and g with domain S, the function $f \cdot g$ defined $\forall$ x in S by $(f \cdot g)(x) = f(x) \cdot g(x)$. (149)

proof by contradiction A proof in which, if s is the statement to be proved, one reasons from *not s* until a contradiction is deduced; from this it is concluded that *not s* is false, which means that s is true. (266)

Properties of Congruence (modular arithmetic) Let a, b, c, and d be any integers and let m be a positive integer. If $a \equiv b \pmod{m}$ and $c \equiv d \pmod{m}$, then

$a + c \equiv b + d \pmod{m}$
(Addition Property of Congruence)

$a - c \equiv b - d \pmod{m}$
(Subtraction Property of Congruence)

and $ac \equiv bd \pmod{m}$
(Multiplication Property of Congruence). (254)

Pythagorean Identity For all θ, $\cos^2 \theta + \sin^2 \theta = 1$. (113)

quantifier A phrase such as "for all" ($\forall$) or "there exists" ($\exists$) that is used to prefix a logical or mathematical sentence. (6)

Quicksort A particular recursive sorting algorithm whereby terms are divided into three sets and those sets are then sorted. (452)

Quicksort Theorem For each integer $n \geq 0$, the Quicksort Algorithm arranges any list of n distinct real numbers in increasing order. (454)

quotient The answer to a division problem. For integers n and d with $d \neq 0$, an integer q such that $n = q \cdot d$. (224)

quotient of two functions For two real-valued functions f and g with domain S, the function $\frac{f}{g}$ defined $\forall$ x in S by $\left(\frac{f}{g}\right)(x) = \frac{f(x)}{g(x)}$, provided $g(x) \neq 0$. (149)

Quotient-Remainder Theorem for Integers If n is an integer and d is a positive integer, then there exist unique integers q (the **integer quotient**) and r (the **integer remainder**) such that $n = q \cdot d + r$ and $0 \leq r < d$. (232)

Quotient-Remainder Theorem for Polynomials If $p(x)$ is a polynomial and $d(x)$ is a nonzero polynomial, then there exist unique polynomials $q(x)$ (the **quotient**) and $r(x)$ (the **remainder**) such that $p(x) = q(x) \cdot d(x) + r(x)$ and either degree of $r(x) <$ degree of $d(x)$ or $r(x) = 0$. (234)

radian A unit of measure of the magnitude of a rotation. 2π radians is equivalent to one revolution. (109)

range The set of possible values of the dependent variable of a function. Symbolically, for a function $f: A \rightarrow B$, the set of all elements y in B such that $\exists$ x in A with $f(x) = y$. (78)

rational equation An equation of the form $f(x) = g(x)$ where $f(x)$ and $g(x)$ are rational expressions. (329)

rational expression An algebraic expression of the form $\frac{p(x)}{q(x)}$, where $p(x)$ and $q(x)$ are polynomials with $q(x)$ not the zero polynomial. (289)

rational expression division Division of polynomials, analogous to rational division, where the result is expressed as a single rational expression. (234)

rational function A function f such that for all values of x in the domain of f, $f(x) = \frac{p(x)}{q(x)}$, where $p(x)$ and $q(x)$ are polynomials. (302)

rational number A real number such that there exist integers a and b ($b \neq 0$) such that $r = \frac{a}{b}$. (284)

rational number division Division where the quotient is expressed as a single rational number. (231)

Rational Zero Theorem Suppose that p is a polynomial function of degree n with integer coefficients: $p(x) = a_n x^n + a_{n-1}x^{n-1} + \ldots + a_1 x + a_0$, with $a_0 \neq 0$. If $r = \frac{m}{k}$ is a rational number in lowest terms that is a zero of p, then m is a factor of the constant coefficient a_0 and k is a factor of the leading coefficient a_n. (341)

rationalizing the denominator Multiplying the numerator and the denominator of a fraction by the irrational conjugate of the fraction's denominator in order to remove the square root from the denominator. (319)

real axis See *complex plane*.

real function A function whose independent and dependent variables have only real number values. (80)

real part of a complex number See *complex number*.

real-valued function A function whose range is a set of real numbers. (80)

recurrence relation See *recursive definition for a sequence*.

Recursion Principle Suppose that a recurrence relation defines a unique value of S_{n+1} in terms of S_n and n for all integers $n \geq 1$. Then there is exactly one sequence S satisfying this recurrence relation and the initial condition $S_1 = k$. (406)

recursive algorithm An algorithm that refers back to a smaller version of itself. (452)

recursive definition for a sequence A definition of a sequence consisting of one or more initial terms of the sequence (the **initial conditions**) and an equation that relates each of the other terms of the sequence to one or more of the previous terms (a **recurrence relation** or **difference equation**). (406)

recursive formula A formula for a sequence in which the first term or first few terms are given, and the nth term is expressed in terms of the preceding term(s). (124)

regular polygon A convex polygon whose sides are all the same length and whose angles are all the same measure. (334)

regular polyhedron (plural *polyhedra*) A convex polyhedron whose faces are all congruent regular polygons. (336)

relative maximum value for a function *f* with domain *S* A number m such that $\exists\, x$ in S with $f(x) = m$ and f is $\geq m$ on some open interval containing x. (93)

relative minimum value for a function *f* with domain *S* A number m such that $\exists\, x$ in S with $f(x) = m$ and f is $\leq m$ on some open interval containing x. (93)

remainder See *Quotient-Remainder Theorem for Integers* or *Quotient-Remainder Theorem for Polynomials*.

Remainder Theorem If a polynomial $p(x)$ of degree ≥ 1 is divided by $x - c$, then the remainder is the constant $p(c)$. That is, $p(x) = q(x)(x - c) + p(c)$. (240)

removable discontinuity at *x* For a function f, the existence of a hole in the graph of f at x such that it is possible to redefine f at x in a way that removes that hole. (303)

resultant force The combined effect of two or more forces. (728)

reversible step A reasoning step in solving an equation or inequality whose converse is true for all values of the variables for which the expressions in the equation are defined. (163)

Reversible Steps Theorem Let $f(x)$ and $g(x)$ be any real expressions. Then for all real expressions c and real functions h,
(1) $f(x) = g(x) \Leftrightarrow f(x) + c = g(x) + c$.
(2) $f(x) = g(x) \Leftrightarrow f(x) \cdot c = g(x) \cdot c$, provided $c \neq 0$.
(3) $f(x) = g(x) \Leftrightarrow h(f(x)) = h(g(x))$, provided h^{-1} exists. (165)

Reversible Steps Theorem for Inequalities For any real expressions $f(x)$, $g(x)$ and real function h, $f(x) < g(x) \Leftrightarrow h(f(x)) < h(g(x))$ if h is an increasing function, and $f(x) < g(x) \Leftrightarrow h(f(x)) > h(g(x))$ if h is a decreasing function. (179)

Riemann sum of a function *f* over the interval from *a* to *b* The sum $f(z_1)(x_1 - a) + f(z_2)(x_2 - x_1) + f(z_3)(x_3 - x_2) + \ldots + f(z_n)(b - x_{n-1})$, where f is a function defined over the interval from a to b and the interval is partitioned into n subintervals: the first from a to x_1, the second from x_1 to x_2, the third from x_2 to x_3, . . . , the nth from x_{n-1} to b and each z_i (the **intermediate points**) is a value in the ith subinterval. Letting $x_0 = a$ and $x_n = b$, this Riemann sum can be written as $\sum_{i=1}^{n} f(z_i)(x_i - x_{i-1})$. (793)

Ringel's Conjecture Consider any connected graph which has no circuits and all of whose vertices have degree 1 or 3. Let n be the number of edges in the graph. Then the edges of the graph can be numbered from 1 to n in such a way that the sum of the numbers on the edges leading into any vertex of degree 3 is a constant. (707)

rose curve The polar graphs of equations of the form

$r = a \cos(n\theta)$, $a > 0$, n a positive integer
or
$r = a \sin(n\theta)$, $a > 0$, n a positive integer.

Each loop of a rose curve is called a **leaf** or **petal**. (502)

rubberband transformation A transformation that is the composite of scale changes and translations. (196)

Russell's Paradox A self-contradictory statement that can arise in set theory when sets are allowed to include themselves as elements. (67)

GLOSSARY

scalar A real number (used in conjunction with vectors, matrices, and transformations). (733)

scalar multiple of a three-dimensional vector $\vec{u} = (u_1, u_2, u_3)$ by a real number k The vector $k\vec{u} = (ku_1, ku_2, ku_3)$. (753)

scalar multiplication The operation of multiplying a vector $\vec{v} = (v_1, v_2)$ by a real number k (the **scalar**) resulting in a **scalar multiple** $k \cdot \vec{v} = (kv_1, kv_2)$ of the original vector. (733)

secant line for the graph of a function A line passing through two distinct points on the graph of a continuous function. (553)

secant line to a circle A line that intersects the circle at two distinct points. (553)

Secant Method A method for obtaining zeros of a continuous function by splitting into successive intervals an interval which has the property that its endpoints produce function values with opposite signs. A zero will be between two such endpoints. At each step, the subinterval with this same property is split into two parts by the x-intercept of the secant line joining the two points on the graph of the function determined by the endpoints of the subinterval. By continuing to subdivide, the zero can be estimated to any degree of accuracy desired. (213)

secant of a real number x, sec x $\frac{1}{\cos x}$, $\forall$ x such that $\cos x \neq 0$. (322)

second derivative The derivative function of a derivative function. (578)

sequence A function whose domain is the set of integers greater than or equal to a fixed integer. (124)

series The indicated sum of consecutive terms of a sequence. (435)

set An unordered list of symbols with no repetitions. (604)

significant operations The number of major operations needed in a problem. (457)

simple graph A graph with no loops and no parallel edges. (668)

simple zero Of a polynomial, a zero that has multiplicity 1. (521)

Simpson's Paradox A situation in which the averages of data sets $A_1, A_2, \ldots, A_n$ are each greater than the averages of corresponding data sets $B_1, B_2, \ldots, B_n$, yet the overall average of the B data sets is greater than the overall average of the A data sets. (341)

Sine of a Difference Theorem For all real numbers α and β, $\sin(\alpha - \beta) = \sin\alpha\cos\beta - \cos\alpha\sin\beta$. (373)

sine of a real number x, sin x The second coordinate of the image of (1, 0) under a rotation of magnitude x about the origin. (110)

Sine of a Sum Theorem For all real numbers α and β, $\sin(\alpha + \beta) = \sin\alpha\cos\beta + \cos\alpha\sin\beta$. (372)

sinusoidal curve The image of the graph of a sine or cosine function under a rubberband transformation. (363)

size of a problem The number of operations needed to do a problem, or an estimate of that number. (457)

solid of revolution with axis ℓ The three-dimensional solid that results when a generating region is rotated around a given axis ℓ. (819)

solving the difference equation The process of developing an explicit formula for a sequence from a difference equation for that sequence. (127)

sorting algorithm An algorithm whose purpose is to arrange or sort a given list of items in some desired order. (450)

spanning tree Given a connected graph G, a tree consisting of a subset of the edges of G but all of the vertices of G. (707)

spiral of Archimedes The polar graphs of $r = a\theta + b$, where a is positive and b is nonnegative. (503)

standard normal distribution A distribution described by a bell-shaped curve whose equation is $y = \frac{1}{\sqrt{2\pi}}e^{-x^2/2}$. (122)

standard position An arrow for a vector whose initial point is at the origin or pole of the coordinate system. (721)

standard prime factorization The prime factorization of an integer $n > 1$ in which all like factors are combined using exponents, and the prime factors are arranged in increasing order of magnitude. (268)

statement A sentence that is either true or false and not both. (6)

stochastic matrix A matrix in which each element is nonnegative, and the entries in each row add to 1. (694)

string An ordered list of symbols. (603)

Structure of a Direct Proof of a Universal Conditional Express the statement to be proved in the form $\forall$ *x in S, if p(x) then q(x)*. Start the proof by assuming the antecedent $p(x)$. Use the Law of Detachment, the definitions of the terms that appear in $p(x)$, and known properties to make a chain of deductions ending in $q(x)$. Use the Law of Transitivity to conclude the universal conditional. (63)

sufficient condition "p is a sufficient condition for q" means $p \Rightarrow q$. (42)

Sufficient Condition for an Euler Circuit Theorem If a graph G is connected and every vertex of G has even degree, then G has an Euler circuit. (682)

Sum of Binomial Coefficients Theorem $\forall$ integers $n \geq 0$, $\binom{n}{0} + \binom{n}{1} + \binom{n}{2} + \cdots + \binom{n}{k} + \cdots + \binom{n}{n} = \sum_{k=0}^{n}\binom{n}{k} = 2^n$. (633)

Sum of the First n Powers Theorem If $r \neq 1$, then $1 + r + r^2 + \ldots + r^{n-1} = \frac{1 - r^n}{1 - r}$ $\forall$ integers $n \geq 1$. (435)

sum of three-dimensional vectors $\vec{u} = (u_1, u_2, u_3)$ and $\vec{v} = (v_1, v_2, v_3)$ The vector $\vec{u} + \vec{v} = (u_1 + v_1, u_2 + v_2, u_3 + v_3)$. (753)

sum of two functions For two real-valued functions f and g with domain S, the function $f + g$ defined $\forall$ x in S by $(f + g)(x) = f(x) + g(x)$. (149)

sum of two vectors, $\vec{u} + \vec{v}$ If $\vec{u} = (u_1, u_2)$ and $\vec{v} = (v_1, v_2)$, then $\vec{u} + \vec{v}$ is the vector $(u_1 + v_1, u_2 + v_2)$. (727)

Sum Property of Integrals Theorem If f and g are continuous functions on the interval from a to b, then $\int_a^b (f(x) + g(x))dx = \int_a^b f(x)\,dx + \int_a^b g(x)\,dx$. (808)

summation notation, $\sum_{i=m}^{n}$ Suppose m and n are integers with $m < n$. Then $\sum_{i=m}^{n} a_i = a_m + a_{m+1} + \ldots + a_n$. (413)

surface of revolution with axis ℓ The surface that results when a curve (the **generating curve**) is rotated around a given axis ℓ. (819)

symmetric matrix A matrix whose element in row i, column j equals its element in row j, column i $\forall$ i, j. (688)

tangent line to the graph of a function at the point (*x*, *f*(*x*)) A line that intersects the graph of a function at $(x, f(x))$ and whose slope equals $\lim_{\Delta x \to 0} \frac{f(x_1 + \Delta x) - f(x_1)}{\Delta x}$. (561)

Tangent of a Difference Theorem For all real numbers α and β such that $\tan \alpha$, $\tan \beta$, and $\tan(\alpha - \beta)$ are defined, $\tan(\alpha - \beta) = \frac{\tan \alpha - \tan \beta}{1 + \tan \alpha \tan \beta}$. (373)

tangent of a real number *x*, tan *x* $\frac{\sin x}{\cos x}$ $\forall$ x such that $\cos x \neq 0$. (111, 322)

Tangent of a Sum Theorem For all real numbers α and β such that $\tan \alpha$, $\tan \beta$, and $\tan(\alpha + \beta)$ are defined, $\tan(\alpha + \beta) = \frac{\tan \alpha + \tan \beta}{1 - \tan \alpha \tan \beta}$. (373)

terminating decimal A number of the form $a_n 10^n + \ldots + a_1 10 + a_0 + a_{-1}10^{-1} + a_{-2}10^{-2} + \ldots + a_{-m}10^{-m}$, where all the a_i are digits from 0 to 9. (317)

tessellation A covering of the plane with congruent copies of the same region (the **fundamental region**), with no holes and no overlaps. (334)

Test-Point Method for Solving Inequalities A method for solving inequalities in which the real line is split into intervals by the zeros of an appropriate function, a value is chosen in each of these intervals, and the interval is part of the solution to the inequality if and only if the value satisfies the inequality. (190)

three-dimensional space, 3-space A space in which three numbers are needed to determine the position of a point. (753)

total degree of a graph The sum of the degrees of all the vertices of the graph. (674)

Total Degree of a Graph Theorem The total degree of any graph equals twice the number of edges in the graph. (674)

transition probability A probability that one event will be followed by another. (694)

Transitive Property of Integer Factors Theorem For all integers a, b, and c, if a is a factor of b and b is a factor of c, then a is a factor of c. (226)

Transitive Property of Polynomial Factors Theorem For all polynomials $a(x)$, $b(x)$, and $c(x)$, if $a(x)$ is a factor of $b(x)$ and $b(x)$ is a factor of $c(x)$, then $a(x)$ is a factor of $c(x)$. (227)

Traveling Salesman problem Given a graph in which each edge is associated with a number, the problem of finding a route through all the vertices that minimizes the total length of the edges. (708)

tree A connected graph that has no circuits. (707)

trial A probabilistic situation that is repeated in an experiment. (635)

trigonometric form of a complex number The form $r(\cos \theta + i \sin \theta)$ of the complex number $[r, \theta]$. (489)

truth table A table that gives the truth values for a logical expression for all possible truth values of the statements in that expression. (14)

two-dimensional vector A vector that can be characterized by two numbers. (721)

Unique Factorization Theorem for Polynomials Suppose that $p(x)$ is a polynomial. Then either $p(x)$ is prime over the real numbers or $p(x)$ has a factorization into polynomials prime over the reals which is unique except for the order of the factors or multiplications by constants. (269)

unit circle The circle with center (0, 0) and radius 1. (109)

unit fraction A fraction of the form $\frac{1}{n}$, where n is a positive integer. (334)

unit vector A vector whose length is 1. (724)

universal statement A statement asserting that a certain property holds for all elements in some set. A statement of the form *For all x in S, p(x), or, symbolically,* $\forall$ *x in S, p(x).* (7)

upper Riemann sum The Riemann sum of a function f where each $f(z_i)$ is the largest value of the function on the subinterval. (799)

valid argument An argument with the property that no matter what conditions are substituted in place of $p(x)$ and $q(x)$ in the premises, if the premises are both true, then the conclusion is true. (45)

valid conclusion The conclusion of a valid argument. (45)

vector A quantity that can be characterized by its direction and its magnitude. (720)

vector equation for a line The set of all points Q on the line through P parallel to $\vec{v}$ is given by the equation $\overrightarrow{PQ} = t\vec{v}$, or equivalently, $(x - x_0, y - y_0) = t(v_1, v_2)$ for some real number t. (735)

Venn diagram A graph that employs circles (sometimes called **Euler circles**) or closed curves to represent relations among sets in a logical argument. (60)

vertex A point on a graph. Also called *node*. (658)

Vertex of a Parabola Theorem Let a, b, and c be real numbers with $a \neq 0$. Then the parabola that is the graph of $f(x) = ax^2 + bx + c$ has its vertex at the point where $x = -\frac{b}{2a}$. (582)

vertical asymptote A vertical line $x = a$ which the graph of a function approaches as x approaches a either from the right or from the left. (296)

vertical component of a vector See *component representation*.

voltage The electrical potential between two points in a circuit (measured in volts). (476)

GLOSSARY

walk An alternating sequence of adjacent vertices and edges from one vertex of a graph to another. (679)

***x*-component of a vector** See *component representation.*

***xy*-plane** The set of points in 3-space for which the z-coordinate is 0; it has the equation $z = 0$. (748)

***xz*-plane** The set of points in 3-space for which the y-coordinate is 0; it has the equation $y = 0$. (748)

***y*-component of a vector** See *component representation.*

***yz*-plane** The set of points in 3-space for which the x-coordinate is 0; it has the equation $x = 0$. (748)

Zeno's Paradox A paradox dealing with the impossibility of adding up an infinite number of quantities to achieve a finite sum. (413)

zero function The function defined by $p(x) = 0 \; \forall \; x$. (225)

zero of a polynomial For a given polynomial $p(x)$, a number c such that $p(c) = 0$. (244)

zero vector The vector with same initial point and endpoint; denoted by $\vec{0}$. (724)

Zero-Product Property Let f, g, and h be functions. If there exists c such that $h(c) = 0$ and $h = f \cdot g$, then either $f(c) = 0$ or $g(c) = 0$. (161)

MATHEMATICAL SYMBOLS

Algebra

$\approx$	is approximately equal to
$\pm$	positive or negative
e	the base of the natural logarithms $\approx 2.71828\ldots$
π	pi
∞	infinity
!	factorial
$\lvert x \rvert$	absolute value of x
$\sqrt{x}$	positive square root of x
$\sqrt[n]{x}$	nth root of x
$a + bi$	complex number
(a, b)	rectangular coordinates; rectangular form of a complex number
$[r, \theta]$	polar coordinates; polar form of a complex number
$r(\cos \theta + i \sin \theta)$	trigonometric form of a complex number
$\bar{z}$	complex conjugate of a complex number
$\lvert z \rvert$	modulus of a complex number
i	imaginary unit, $\sqrt{-1}$
$\aleph_0$	the cardinality of a countably infinite set
c	the cardinality of an uncountable set

Logic

$\Rightarrow$	if-then (conditional)
$\Leftrightarrow$	if and only if (biconditional)
$\forall$	for all
$\exists$	there exists
$\sim$	negation
$\equiv$	logically equivalent
$\therefore$	therefore

Coordinates and Vectors

(x, y)	ordered pair
(x, y, z)	ordered triple
$[r, \theta]$	polar coordinate
$\overrightarrow{AB}$ or $\vec{v}$ or v	vector
(v_1, v_2)	component representation of vector
$[r, \theta]$	polar representation of vector
$k\vec{v}$	scalar k times vector
$\lvert \vec{v} \rvert$	length of vector
$\vec{0}$	zero vector
$\vec{u} \cdot \vec{v}$	dot product of vectors
$\vec{u} \times \vec{v}$	cross product of vectors

Geometry

$\overleftrightarrow{AB}$	line through A and B
$\overrightarrow{AB}$	ray from A passing through B
$\overline{AB}$	segment with endpoints A and B
AB	distance from A to B
$\angle ABC$	angle ABC
$m\angle ABC$	measure of angle ABC
$\triangle ABC$	triangle with vertices A, B, and C
$ABCD$	polygon with vertices A, B, C, and D
$//$	is parallel to
$\cong$	is congruent to
$\sim$	is similar to
$T_{h,k}$	translation of h units horizontally and k units vertically
$S_{a,b}$	scale change with horizontal magnitude a and vertical magnitude b

Functions and Sequences

$\lim_{n \to \infty} a_n$	limit of sequence a as n approaches infinity
a_n	nth term of sequence a
$\sum_{i=1}^{n} x_i$	summation notation; the sum $x_1 + x_2 + \ldots + x_n$
S_∞	sum of the infinite series S
$\log x$	common logarithm of x
$\log_b x$	logarithm of x to the base b
$\ln x$	natural logarithm of x
$\lfloor x \rfloor$	greatest integer function of x, or floor function of x
$\lceil x \rceil$	ceiling function of x
f^{-1}	inverse function of f
$f \circ g$	composite of functions f and g
$x \to \infty$	x approaches infinity
$x \to a^-$	x approaches a from the left
$x \to a^+$	x approaches a from the right
$\lim_{x \to a} f(x)$	limit of function f as x approaches a
f'	first derivative of f
f''	second derivative of f
Δ	delta x, change in x
$\int_a^b f(x)\,dx$	definite integral of f from a to b

Combinatorics and Graphs

$P(n, r)$	permutations of n elements taken r at a time
${}_nP_r$	number of permutations of n elements taken r at a time
$C(n, r)$	combinations of n elements taken r at a time
${}_nC_r$ or $\binom{n}{r}$	number of combinations of n elements taken r at a time
deg (v)	degree of vertex v
e_i	the ith edge of a graph
v_i	the ith vertex of a graph
K_n	complete graph with n vertices
mod	modulo
$\equiv$	modular congruence
Rn	modulo class n

Acknowledgments

Unless otherwise acknowledged, all photographs are the property of Addison Wesley Educational Publishers, Inc. Page abbreviations are as follows: (t) top, (c) center, (b) bottom, (l) left, (r) right.

ix Nick Dolding/Tony Stone Images **vi(r)** Dwight Kuhn **vii(r)** Carl Vanderschuitt/FPG International Corp. **vii(l)** Superstock, Inc. **viii** D. & J. Heaton/Westlight **x** Bruce Hands/Tony Stone Images **4(b)** Superstock, Inc. **4(c)** Superstock, Inc. **4(tr)** Brandon D. Cole/ENP Images **4(tl)** Superstock, Inc. **5(b)** Superstock, Inc. **6** © Edgerton Foundation, 1997, courtesy of Palm Press, Inc. **11** Simon Milliken **15** Tony Freeman/PhotoEdit **18** Alinari/Art Resource **20(t)** Tony Freeman/PhotoEdit **21** W. Metzen/H. Armstrong Roberts, Inc. **23** Rare Books and Manuscript Library/Columbia University **25** Library of Congress **28** Pete Saloutos/Stock Market **31** Library of Congress **35** Everett Collection, Inc. **41** Richard Martin/Agence Vandystadt **42** NASA **44** Frank Herholdt/Tony Stone Images **48** Library of Congress **53** Novastock/Photo Researchers **57** James D. Watt/Animals Animals **58** Jan Kanter **60** National Portrait Gallery, Washington, D.C./Art Resource **61** Carl Corey/Westlight **64** Randy Well/Tony Stone Images **67(b)** Drawings by John Tenniel **67(t)** Sidney Harris **69(b)** Stephen Dunn/Allsport **69(t)** Stouffer Enterprises, Inc./Animals Animals **70** Adrienne T. Gibson/Earth Scenes **71** NASA **74** Doug Pencincer/Allsport **76** Paul & Lindamarie Ambrose/FPG International Corp. **76(b)** David Lorenz Winston/ENP Images **76(cr)** Dwight Kuhn **76(t)** Glen Allison/Tony Stone Images **77(b)** De Wys/IFA/Leo de Wys, Inc. **78** Orion Press/Westlight **81** Thomas Porett/Photo Researchers **86** Mike Powell/Allsport **92** Texas Collection, Baylor University, Waco, Texas **93** A. & L. Sinibaldi/Tony Stone Images **96** W. Geiersperger/Stock Market **100** Jonathan Daniel/Allsport **102** Center for Image Processing in Education **104** David Leah/Allsport **109** Cleo/PhotoEdit **114** Onne Van Der Wal/Stock Newport **120** Deborah Davis/PhotoEdit **122(b)** Randy Wells/Tony Stone Images **122(t)** Superstock, Inc. **123** John Scheiber/Stock Market **124** Zig Leszczynski/Animals Animals **126** Zig Leszczynski/Animals Animals **129** Susan Ley/Animals Animals **130** New York Public Library, Astor, Lenox and Tilden Foundations **132** Robert Landen/Westlight **135** Gerard Lacz/Animals Animals/Earth Scenes **137** Mark Scott/FPG International Corp. **146(br)** Superstock, Inc. **146(bl)** Superstock, Inc. **146(c)** R. Kord/H. Armstrong Roberts, Inc. **146(t)** Superstock, Inc. **147(t)** Superstock, Inc. **148** Larry Lefever/Grant Heilman Photography **151** Bachmann/PhotoEdit **153** Jean Gaumy/Magnum Photos **160** Ted Horowitz/Stock Market **168** Jose L. Pelaez/Stock Market **170** Chicago Tribune photo by Bill Hogan **174** Dennis Degnan/Westlight **175** Superstock, Inc. **186** Mark Lewis/Tony Stone Images **187** James Blank/Stock Market **194** Superstock, Inc. **206** Willie L. Hill., Jr./Stock Boston **208** Brad Whitmore/Francis Schweizer, STScI/NASA **212** Metropolitan Museum of Art, Gift of Thomas F. Ryan, 1910(11.173.9) **214** Frozen Images, Inc. **220** "Happy Industrial Park" screen from SimCity™ ©1996 Maxis, Inc. **220(t)** Mark Segal/Tony Stone Images **222(b)** Superstock, Inc. **222(c)** Scott Kohn/Stock Connection **222(tr)** Craig Aurness/Westlight **222(tl)** Carl Vanderschuitt/FPG International Corp. **223(b)** Larry Downing/Woodfin Camp & Associates **224** Myrleen Ferguson/PhotoEdit **226** Steve Hill Photo **231** Superstock, Inc. **236** Superstock, Inc. **237** Otto Rogge/Stock Market **251** Kunio Owaki/Stock Market **252** Corbis-Bettmann **257** Marine Art Posters, Hull, U.K. **258** Scott Burns **260** Superstock, Inc. **261** Moore School of Engineering **264** AP/Wide World **265** Courtesy, Cray Computer **267** Los Alamos National Laboratory **270** Barbara Gerlach/Visuals Unlimited **271** Cydney Conger/Westlight **277** Dennis O'Clair/Tony Stone Images **280** Amy C. Etra/PhotoEdit **281** Cameramann International, Ltd. **282(b)** Robert Landau/Westlight **282(c)** Dean Siracusa/FPG International Corp. **282(tr)** Lois Ellen Frank/Westlight **282(tl)** D. & J. Heaton/Westlight **283(b)** Gary Conner/PhotoEdit **294** Bob Daemmrich/Stock Boston **295** Superstock, Inc. **300** Courtesy, BMW **302** Courtesy, BMW **306** Courtesy, General Motors Corporation **307** NASA **315** Photo: Christa Kopperman, Staatliche Antikensammlungen und Glyptothek, Munich **326** Janice Burkhardt/Westlight **327** Mike Sedam Photography **328** Ron Watts/Westlight **330** Bachmann/PhotoEdit **331** Mike Fizer/Check Six **334** ©1998 M. C. Escher/Cordon Art-Baarn-Holland. All rights reserved. **335** Alon Reininger/Stock Market **340** Ron Kimball **348(t)** Superstock, Inc. **348(br)** Ron Watts/Westlight **348(bl)** Kevin Anderson/Tony Stone Images **348(c)** Gerben Oppermans/Tony Stone Images **349(t)** Superstock, Inc. **360** Frank Siteman/Stock Boston **361** Zig Leszczynski/Animals Animals **363** Leonard Lee Rue III/Animals Animals/Earth Scenes **371** Granger Collection **376** Arthur C. Smith III/Grant Heilman Photography **377** Globus, Holway & Lobel/Stock Market **379** Superstock, Inc. **383** Victoria McCormick/Earth Scenes **390** Joe Towers/Stock Market **391** Superstock, Inc. **398** Ken Reid/FPG International Corp. **402** Craig Aurness/Westlight **404(b)** Anne-Marie Weber/FPG International Corp. **404(cr)** Right Image/Stock Connection **404(cl)** Patrick Cocklin/Tony Stone Images **404(t)** Nourok/PhotoEdit **405(b)** W. Cody/Westlight **417** David Young-Wolff/PhotoEdit **431** Steve Chenn/Westlight **434** Gabe Palmer/Stock Market **436** Granger Collection **442** Jeff Mangiat/Stock Market **456** Tom McCarthy/PhotoEdit **461** Cary Wolinski/Stock Boston **462** Sidney Harris **463** Ron Kimball **470(b)** FourByFive/Superstock, Inc. **470(cr)** Frank Saragnese/FPG International Corp. **470(cl)** Mark Newman/Stock Connection **470(t)** Superstock, Inc. **471(t)** James L. Amos/Stock Connection **472** Adam Hart-Davis/SPL/Photo Researchers **473** Giraudon/Art Resource **474** Granger Collection **478** H.Schneebeli/SPL/Photo Researchers **480** Gregory G. Dimijian/Photo Researchers **485** Onne Van Der Wal/Stock Newport **486** Pekka Parviainen/SPL/Photo Researchers **488** W. Geiersperger/Stock Market **491** Tim Davis/Photo Researchers **495** Peter Weimann/Animals Animals **498** Frank Burek/Earth Scenes **501, 502** Patti Murray/Earth Scenes **505** Bruce Iverson **506** W. Gregory Brown/Animals Animals **507** Westlight **508** Granger Collection **510** Oxford Scientific Films/Animals Animals **526** Worldsat International Inc./Photo Researchers **534** Naoki Okamoto/Stock Market **539** Milt & Patti Putnam/Stock Market **540** Courtesy, Edward Lorenz **542(b)** Superstock, Inc. **542(c)** PhotoDisc, Inc. **542(t)** Japack/Leo de Wys, Inc. **543** PhotoDisc, Inc. **550(b)** CNRI/Phototake **550(c)** David Hanover/Tony Stone Images **550(tr)** Mark J. Barrett/Stock Connection **550(tl)** Jamie Squire/Allsport **551(c)** Japack/Leo de Wys, Inc. **552** Tom Van Sant/Geosphere Project, Santa Monica/SPL/Photo Researchers **554** NASA **558** G. McLaughlin/Stock Market **559** Tony Stone Images **560** Globus Brothers, Inc./Stock Market **562** Nancy Dudley/Stock Boston **567** Leo Mason/Sports Illustrated **569** Superstock, Inc. **576** NASA **579** Mendola Ltd./Stock Market **580** Robert E. Daemmrich/Tony Stone Images **583** Dale O'Dell/Stock Market **587** Superstock, Inc. **590(b)** Jim Steinberg/Photo Researchers **592** Superstock, Inc. **594** Grant Heilman/Grant Heilman Photography **600(br)** Randy Faris/Westlight **600(bl)** Miguel S. Salmeron/FPG International Corp. **600(c)** R. Fukuhara/Westlight **600(t)** Joe Sohm/Chromosohm/Stock Connection **601(c)** Nick Dolding/Tony Stone Images **602** Bob Daemmrich/Stock Boston **604** Superstock, Inc. **607** Don Mason/Stock Market **610** Secretary of State Office, Illinois **612** AP/Wide World **615** Fredric Y. Ichinose **618** Superstock, Inc. **627** Superstock, Inc. **631** Hand-colored by Cheryl Kucharzak **636** Robert E. Daemmrich/Tony Stone Images **647** Superstock, Inc. **648** Robin Smith/Tony Stone Images **650** L. Gervais/Westlight **650** Gary Buss/FPG International Corp. **654(b)** AP/Wide World **655** David M. Grossman/Photo Researchers **656(b&c)** Ron Chapple/FPG International Corp. **656(tr)** Bill Deering/FPG International Corp. **656(tl)** Richard Niebel/Stock Connection **657(b)** Superstock, Inc. **661** Bonnie Kamin/PhotoEdit **664** James Wells/Tony Stone Images **673** Bob Daemmrich/Stock Boston **677** Robert E. Daemmrich/Tony Stone Images **678** David R. Frazier/Tony Stone Images **679** Fritz Hoffmann/Image Works **687** Kartographischer Verlag, Innsbruck, Austria **691** Superstock, Inc. **693** Akira Fujii **696** Rich Iwasaki/Tony Stone Images **699** David Young-Wolff/PhotoEdit **700** Superstock, Inc. **706** Anthony Edgeworth, Inc./Stock Market **708** Adamsmith Productions/Westlight **711** Superstock, Inc. **712** Reprinted by permission of United Feature Syndicate **715** Jim Brown/Stock Market **716** Paul Merideth/Tony Stone Images **718(b)** Chuck O'Rear/Westlight **718(cr)** Superstock, Inc. **718(cl)** Anne-Marie Weber/FPG International Corp. **718(t)** Antony Nagelmann/FPG International Corp. **719(t)** Superstock, Inc. **720** Superstock, Inc. **721** Superstock, Inc. **726** Jeff Corwin/Tony Stone Images **728** Arthur Tilley/Tony Stone Images **731** Keith Wood/Tony Stone Images **732** Superstock, Inc. **733** Robert A. Mitchell/Tony Stone Images **736** Superstock, Inc. **744** NASA **751** Courtesy, Lear **752** NASA **754** Andrew Sacks/Tony Stone Images **771, 772** Superstock, Inc. **773** Adamsmith/FPG International Corp. **774** Warren Bolster/Tony Stone Images **777** Baron Wolman/Tony Stone Images **782(br)** David R. Frazier/Stock Solution **782(bl)** Superstock, Inc. **782(c)** H. D. Thoreau/Westlight **782(t)** Bruce Hands/Tony Stone Images **783(t)** Susan Benson/Stock Connection **784** Superstock, Inc. **788** Superstock, Inc. **789** Hans Halberstadt/Stock Market **792** Michael Newman/PhotoEdit **800** Ward/Corbis-Bettmann, Hand-colored by Cheryl Kucharzak **804** Henley & Savage/Stock Market **805** Grafton M. Smith/Stock Market **808** Joe Gator/Stock Market **810** Daniel J. Cox/Tony Stone Images **817** Dean Abramson/Stock Boston **818** Corbis-Bettmann, Hand-colored by Cheryl Kucharzak **819** Superstock, Inc. **820** Gary Wagner/Stock Boston **821** Eleanor Thompson/Stock Market **827** David Ulmer/Stock Boston **833(t)** PhotoDisc, Inc. **833(b)** Library of Congress **835** Craig Aurness/Westlight **837** Jim Foster/Stock Market **838** Superstock, Inc.

CHAPTER 2 PROJECT 5, p. 137

5. a. PROGRAM: FRACTAL (BASIC language)

```
10 CLS
20 FOR J = 1 TO 100
30 LET A = 1 – (8/9) ^ J
40 PRINT J, A
50 NEXT J
60 END
```

b.

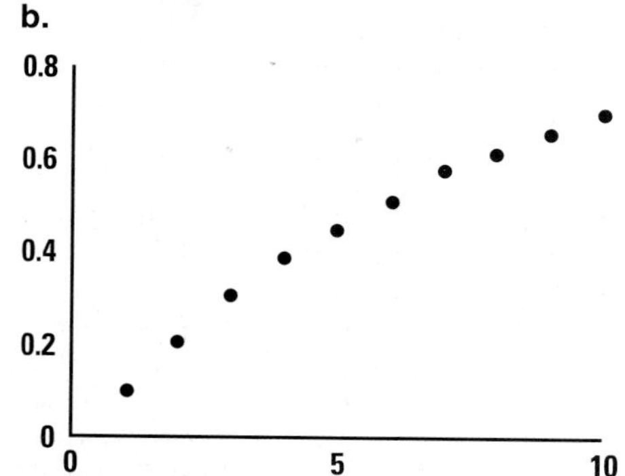

c. As $n \to \infty$, A_n approaches 1. This means it will seem as though there are no white squares.

d. $A_n = 1 - \frac{8^n}{9^n}$. As n becomes large, the term $\frac{8^n}{9^n}$ approaches zero and A_n approaches 1.

e. Sample:

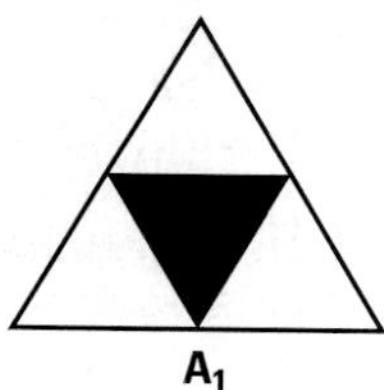

A_1

A_2

```
10 CLS
20 FOR J = 1 TO 100
30 LET A = 1 – (3/4) ^ J
40 PRINT J, A
50 NEXT J
60 END
```

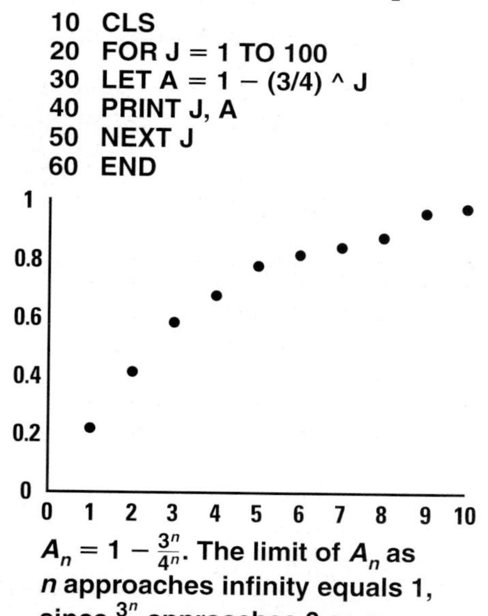

$A_n = 1 - \frac{3^n}{4^n}$. The limit of A_n as n approaches infinity equals 1, since $\frac{3^n}{4^n}$ approaches 0 as $n \to \infty$.

LESSON 5-1, p. 288

18. Suppose r and s are any two rational numbers. Then, there exist integers a, b, c, and d, where $b \neq 0$ and $d \neq 0$ such that $r = \frac{a}{b}$ and $s = \frac{c}{d}$.

$$\frac{r+s}{2} = \frac{\frac{a}{b} + \frac{c}{d}}{2}$$

$$= \frac{\frac{a}{b} \cdot \frac{d}{d} + \frac{c}{d} \cdot \frac{b}{b}}{2}$$

Mult. Prop. of 1

$$= \frac{\frac{ad}{bd} + \frac{bc}{bd}}{2}$$

Mult. of fractions

$$= \frac{\frac{ad + bc}{bd}}{2}$$

Distributive Prop.

$$= \frac{ad + cb}{bd} \cdot \frac{1}{2}$$

Def. of division of fractions

$$= \frac{ad + bc}{2bd}$$

Mult. of fractions

Because sums and products of integers are integers, $ad + bc$ and $2bd$ are integers. Therefore, $\frac{r+s}{2}$ is a rational number by definition.

19. Since the average of two rational numbers is rational, between any two numbers there exists a rational number. If r and s are both rational numbers where $r = \frac{a}{b}$ and $s = \frac{c}{d}$ with $b \neq 0$ and $d \neq 0$, then their average is $\frac{ad + bc}{2bd}$. If $r < s$, then $\frac{a}{b} < \frac{ad + bc}{2bd} < \frac{c}{d}$.

20. The sausage pizza is cut into $N + 2$ pieces, so each slice is $\frac{1}{N+2}$ of a pizza. The pepperoni pizza is still cut into $N - 2$ pieces, so each slice is $\frac{1}{N-2}$ of a pizza. Each student who has one slice from each pizza would have $\frac{1}{N-2} + \frac{1}{N+2} = \frac{2N}{N^2-4}$ of a whole pizza. The two students who have 2 slices of the popular pizza would have $\frac{1}{N+2} + \frac{1}{N+2} = \frac{2}{N+2}$ of a whole pizza.

23. $\frac{K}{K+1} = 1 - \frac{1}{K+1} = \frac{K+1}{K+1} - \frac{1}{K+1} = \frac{K}{K+1}$; Yes, both sides are equal for all values where both sides are defined.

24. $\frac{2A^2N}{N^2-9}$; Check: Let $N = 4$ and $A = 3$, then $\frac{a^2}{N+3} + \frac{A^2}{N-3} = \frac{9}{7} + 9 = \frac{72}{7}$ and $\frac{2A^2N}{(N+3)(N-3)} = \frac{2(9)(4)}{7(1)} = \frac{72}{7}$.

25. $\frac{K}{K+4}$; Check: Let $K = 5$, then $\frac{K}{K+1} \cdot \frac{K+1}{K+2} \cdot \frac{K+2}{K+3} \cdot \frac{K+3}{K+4} = \frac{5}{6} \cdot \frac{6}{7} \cdot \frac{7}{8} \cdot \frac{8}{9} = \frac{5}{9}$ and $\frac{K}{K+4} = \frac{5}{9}$

27. a. If n is not an even integer, then n^2 is not an even integer.

b. Suppose n is any odd integer. By definition, there exists an integer r such that $n = 2r + 1$. Then $n^2 = (2r + 1)^2 = 4r^2 + 4r + 1 = 2(2r^2 + 2r) + 1$. Since $2r^2 + 2r$ is an integer by closure properties, n^2 is not an even integer.

30. 5, 12, 13; 7, 24, 25; and 20, 21, 29

$$x^2 + (x+1)^2 = y^2$$
$$x^2 + x^2 + 2x + 1 = y^2$$
$$2x^2 + 2x + 1 = y^2$$
$$x^2 + y^2 = (x+1)^2$$
$$= x^2 + 2x + 1$$
$$y^2 = 2x + 1$$
$$y = \sqrt{2x+1} \text{ or}$$
$$x = \frac{y^2 - 1}{2}$$

for integer y

$\{y = 3, x = 4\}$: $3^2 + 4^2 = 5^2$

$\{y = 5\}$: $12^2 + 5^2 = 13^2$

$\{y = 7\}$: $24^2 + 7^2 = 25^2$

$\{y = 9\}$: $40^2 + 9^2 = 41^2$

LESSON 5-3, p. 498

4. a. The limit of $f(x)$ as x approaches 0 from the left is negative infinity. Sample:

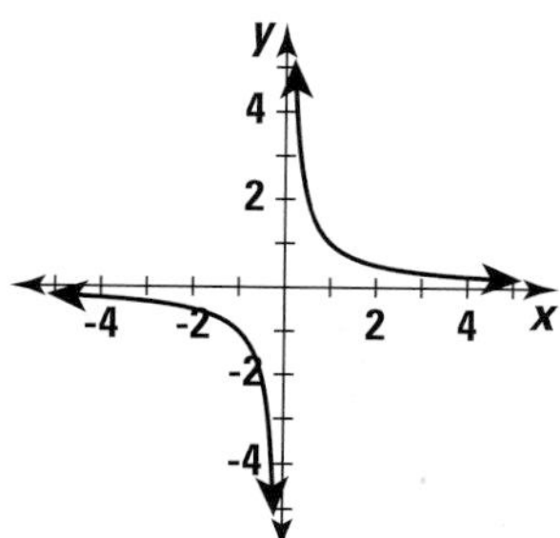

b. The limit of $f(x)$ as x approaches 0 from the left is positive infinity. Sample:

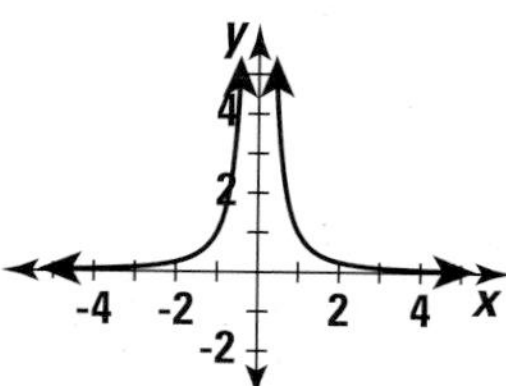

8. a. domain: $\{x: x \neq 0\}$; range: $\{y: y \neq 0\}$

b. decreasing over its entire domain as x goes from $-\infty$ to ∞

c. $\lim_{x \to \infty} f(x) = 0$ and $\lim_{x \to -\infty} f(x) = 0$

d. $\lim_{x \to 0^+} f(x) = \infty$ and $\lim_{x \to 0^-} f(x) = -\infty$

e. odd

f. 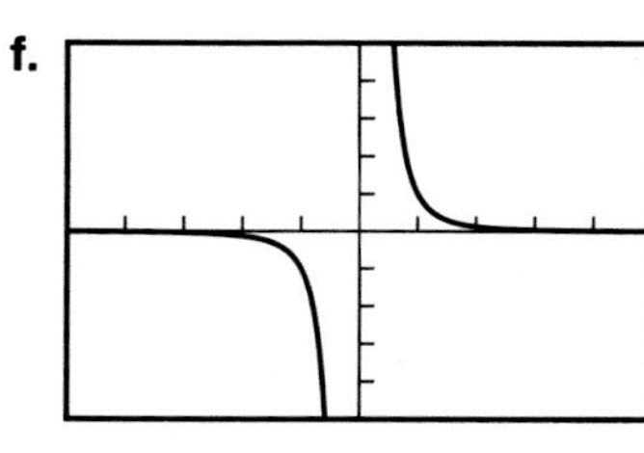

$-5 \le x \le 5$, x-scale = 1
$-5 \le y \le 5$, y-scale = 1

LESSON 5-3, p. 299

16. Suppose a, b, and c are any integers such that a is a factor of b and a is a factor of $b + c$. By definition, there exist integers r and s such that $b = a \cdot r$ and $b + c = a \cdot s$. Then, $c = (b + c) - b = a \cdot s - a \cdot r = a(s - r)$. Since $s - r$ is an integer by closure properties, a is a factor of c by definition.

19. a. $\lim\limits_{x \to -1^+} f(x) = -\infty$ and $\lim\limits_{x \to -1^-} f(x) = \infty$

b. Sample:

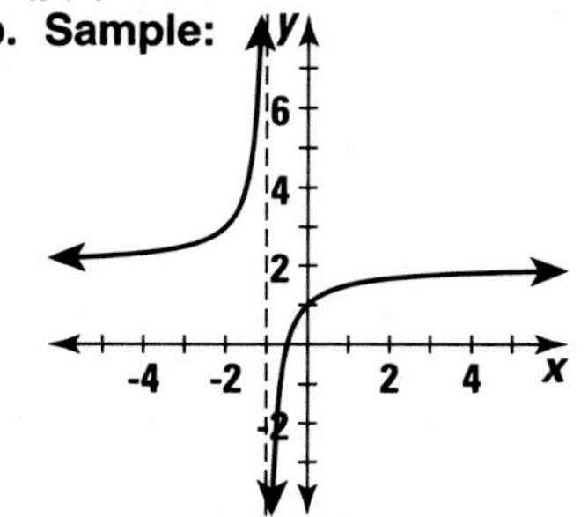

The above graph does not have the same problem, but graphs may vary.

x	y
-5	2.25
-4	2.30
-3	2.50
-2	3.00
-1	8.33
0	1.00
1	1.50
2	1.66
3	1.75
4	1.80
5	1.84

LESSON 5-4, p. 306

21. a. Let $d(x) = \cos x - 0.2x^2$. Since $d(1) > 0$, $d(1.5) < 0$, and $d(x)$ is continuous, the Intermediate Value Theorem ensures that there exists a zero of $d(x)$ in the interval from 1 to 1.5. Where $d(x) = 0$, $\cos x - 0.2x^2 = 0$, so $\cos x = 0.2x^2$, and hence there is a solution to the equation $\cos x = 0.2x^2$ in the interval from 1 to 1.5.

b. $1.25 \le x \le 1.26$

22. a. *The duplicating machine works, and it is not Sunday.*

b. *The car is not American made or it is an electric car.*

23. a. 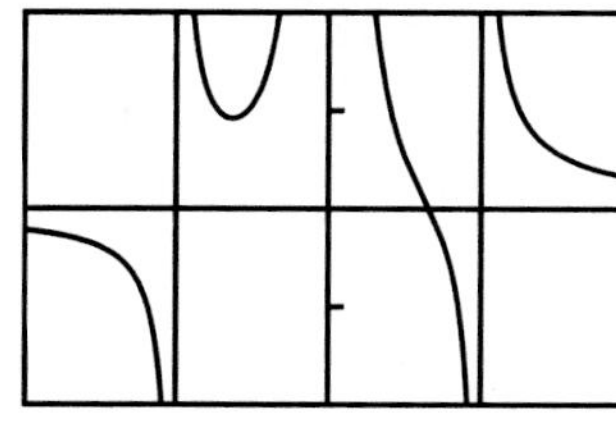

$-2 \le x \le 2$, x-scale = 1
$-10 \le y \le 10$, y-scale = 5

PROGRESS SELF-TEST, p. 343

9. a. $\lim\limits_{x \to 2^+} g(x) = \infty$

b. $\lim\limits_{x \to 2^-} g(x) = -\infty$

c. $\lim\limits_{x \to \infty} g(x) = 3$; $\lim\limits_{x \to -\infty} g(x) = 3$

d.

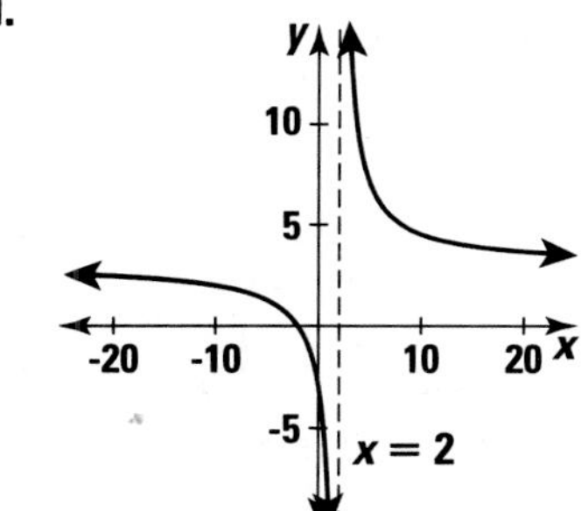

14.

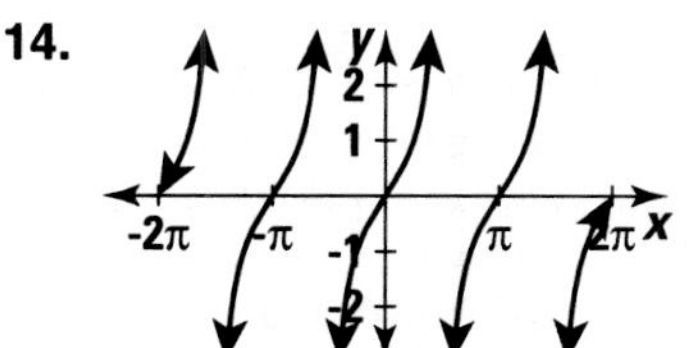

PROJECT ANSWERS, pp. 340–341

1. Students' reports may include the following events:

240 BC: Archimedes developed the classical method of computing π. He found it to be between $\frac{223}{71}$ and $\frac{22}{7}$.

150 AD: Ptolemy estimated π as $\frac{377}{120} \approx 3.1416$.

480: Tsu Ch'ung-chich estimated π as $\frac{355}{113} \approx 3.1415929$ (correct to six places).

1429: Al-Kashi computed π to 16 decimal places.

1610: Ludolph van Ceule computed π to 35 decimal places.

1699: Abraham Sharp found 71 correct decimal places.

1706: John Machin found 100 correct decimal places.

1841: William Rutherford computed π to 208 places (152 of which were correct).

1844: Zacharias Dase found π correct to 200 decimal places.

1853: Rutherford found π to 400 correct decimal places.

1873: William Shanks computed π to 707 places (528 correct).

1892: A writer announced a long lost secret that leads to 3.2 as the exact value of π.

1892: Ferdinand Lindenman gives the first proof that π is a transcendental number.

1897: Indiana State Legislature almost passed a bill stating, "It has been found that a circular area is to the square on a line equal to the quadrant of the circumference, as the area of an equilateral rectangle is to the square on one side.

1931: Another book purported to demonstrate that $\pi = 3\frac{13}{81}$.

1948: D. F. Ferguson and J. W. Wrench Jr. published π correct to 808 places.

1949: The ENIAC computer found π to 2,037 decimal places.

1959: Francois Genuys found π to 16,167 decimal places with an IBM 704.

1961: Wrench and Daniel Shanks found π to 100,265 places on an IBM 7090.

1966: M. Jean Guilloud approximated π to 250,000 places on a Stretch computer.

1967: M. Jean Guilloud approximated π to 500,000 places on a CDC 6600.

1974: M. Jean Guilloud approximated π to 1,000,000 places on a CDC 7600.

4. a. $p(x) = a_3x^3 + a_2x^2 + a_1x + a_0$

i. $p(\frac{m}{k}) = a_3(\frac{m}{k})^3 + a_2(\frac{m}{k})^2 + a_1(\frac{m}{k}) + a_0 = 0$
$a_3m^3 + a_2m^2k + a_1mk^2 + a_0k^3 = 0$
$a_3m^3 + a_2m^2k + a_1mk^2 = -a_0k^3$
$m[a_3m^3 + a_2mk + a_1k^2] = -a_0k^3$

ii. Since m is a factor on the left side, m is a factor on the right side. Since m and k have no common factor, m is a factor of a_0 rather than k^3.

iii. $p(\frac{m}{k}) = a_3(\frac{m}{k})^3 + a_2(\frac{m}{k})^2 + a_1(\frac{m}{k}) + a_0 = 0$
$a_3m^3 + a_2m^2k + a_1mk^2 + a_0k^3 = 0$
$a_3m^3 = -a_2m^2k - a_1mk^2 - a_0k^3 a_3m^3 = -k(a_2m^2 + a_1mk + a_0k^2)$

iv. Since k is a factor on the right side, k is a factor on the left side. Since m and k have no common factors, k is a factor of a_3 rather than m^3.

b. i. $p(x) = a_nx^n + a_{n-1}x^{n-1} + \ldots + a_1x + a_0$; $a_n \neq 0$
Replace x by the root $\frac{m}{k}$.
$p(\frac{m}{k}) = a_n(\frac{m}{k})^n + a_{n-1}(\frac{m}{k})^{n-1} + \ldots + a_1(\frac{m}{k}) + a_0 = 0$
Multiply both sides by k^n.
$a_nm^n + a_{n-1}m^{n-1}k + \ldots + a_1mk^{n-1} + a_0k^n = 0$
Factor m from the first n terms and subtract a_0k^n from both sides.
$m(a_nm^{n-1} + a_{n-1}m^{n-2}k + \ldots + a_1k^{n-1}) = -a_0k^n$
Factor k from the last n terms and subtract a_nm^n from both sides.
$k(a_{n-1}m^{n-1} + \ldots + a_1mk^{n-2} + a_0k^{n-1}) = -a_nm^n$
By the same arguments in ii and iv, substituting k^n for k^3 and m^n for m^3, m is a factor of a_0 and k is a factor of a_n.

ii. $\pm\frac{2}{3}, \pm\frac{1}{2}, \pm\frac{1}{3}$

iii. $\frac{2}{3}$ and $\frac{1}{2}$ are rational zeros.
The other roots are $+i\sqrt{6}$ and $-i\sqrt{6}$.

5. Sample:
The gas mileage for three popular cars was obtained:

Car	MPG City	MPG Highway	MPG Average
X	53	58	55.5
Y	24	34	29.0
Z	16	25	20.5

The price of gasoline was assumed to be a low $1.00 per gallon.
See detailed table at the top of columns 2–3.

Car	Miles per year	Yearly Cost of Fuel	If you drove … Car X	Car Y	Car Z
X	10,000	$ 180		lose $ 160	lose $ 308
	20,000	360		lose 330	lose 616
	30,000	540		lose 495	lose 924
Y	10,000	345	save $ 160		lose 143
	20,000	690	save 330		lose 286
	30,000	1,035	save 495		lose 429
Z	10,000	488	save 308	save 143	
	20,000	976	save 616	save 286	
	30,000	1,464	save 924	save 429	

6. a. player (1): .280, player (2): .248
b. first half: player (2)
second half: player (2)
entire season: player (1)
c. Consider two lawyers' percentage of wins in trials by jury and bench trials. (Lawyer (1) was appointed to more trials by jury than bench trials and lawyer (2) was appointed to more bench trials than trials by jury.)

LAWYER 1

Trial	Cases	Wins	Winning Percentage
Jury	40	30	75%
Bench	15	9	60%

LAWYER 2

Trial	Cases	Wins	Winning Percentage
Jury	15	12	80%
Bench	40	26	65%

Even though lawyer (2) has higher percentages of wins in both types of trial, his overall percentage of wins is only 69% while that of lawyer (1) is 71%.

d. Simpson's paradox is possible because the batting average for each player during the full season is a weighted average of the averages for the first and second halves, rather than a simple average. The data set is unbalanced for both players, with player (1) having more at-bats in the first half of the season and player (2) having more in the second half. While the second player has higher averages for both parts of the season, his seasonal average is more heavily weighted toward the second half of the season where he has more at-bats while the first player's seasonal average is more heavily weighted toward the first part of the season where he has more at-bats.

CHAPTER REVIEW, p. 345

43. Assume the negation is true, that $\sqrt{13}$ is rational. By definition, there exist integers a and b, with $b \neq 0$ such that $\sqrt{13} = \frac{a}{b}$, where $\frac{a}{b}$ is in lowest terms. Then, $13 = \frac{a^2}{b^2} \Rightarrow a^2 = 13b^2$. Thus, a^2 has a factor of 13, because if a is an integer and a^2 is divisible by a prime, then a is divisible by that prime. Therefore, let $a = 13k$ for some integer k. Then, $13b^2 = (13k)^2 \Rightarrow b^2 = 13k^2$. So b^2 and b have a factor of 13 by similar argument. Thus, a and b have a common factor of 13. This is a contradiction since $\frac{a}{b}$ is in lowest terms. Hence, the assumption must be false, and so $\sqrt{13}$ is irrational.
$b \neq 0$ and $d \neq 0$, then $\frac{a}{b} \cdot \frac{c}{d} = \frac{ac}{bd}$. ac and bd are both integers and $bd \neq 0$ since $b \neq 0$ and $d \neq 0$.

47. Assume the negation is true. Thus, the difference of a rational number p and an irrational number q is a rational number r. Then $p - q = r$. So $p - r = q$. However, by the closure property of rational numbers the difference between two rational numbers is another rational number. Hence, there is a contradiction, and so the assumption is false, which proves the original statement.

52. a. $t = 2$ and $t = -2$
b. $\lim_{x \to 2^-} f(t) = -\infty$;
$\lim_{t \to -2^+} f(t) = -\infty$;
$\lim_{t \to -2^-} f(t) = \infty$
c. $\lim_{t \to \infty} f(t) = 3$;
$\lim_{t \to -\infty} h(t) = 3$

d.

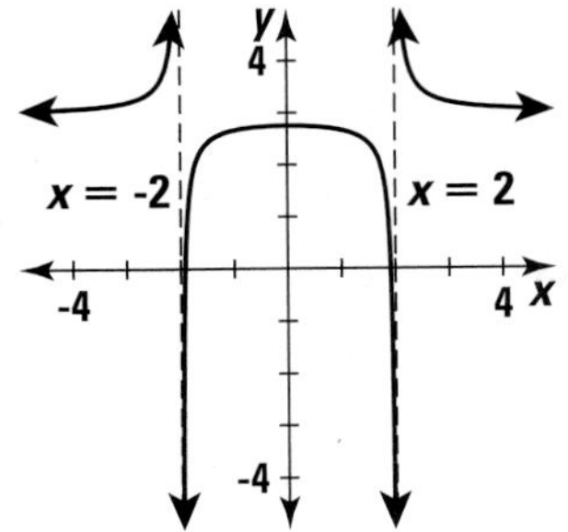

LESSON 6-1, p. 355

23. $(f+g)(t) = e^t + e^{-t}, \forall\, t$; $(f-g)(t) = e^t - e^{-t}, \forall\, t$; $(f \cdot g)(t) = 1, \forall\, t$; $\left(\frac{f}{g}\right)(t) = e^{2t}, \forall\, t$
24. $OC = OA$ and $OD = OB$, since these segments are radii of the same respective circles. So by SAS, $\triangle COD \cong \triangle AOB$. Therefore, $AB = CD$, since corresponding parts in congruent figures are congruent.
25. angles in Quandrant 2: $\frac{\pi}{2} < \theta < \pi$; angles in Quandrant 3: $\pi < \theta < \frac{3\pi}{2}$; angles in Quandrant 4: $\frac{3\pi}{2} < \theta < 2\pi$

LESSON 6-1, p. 355 # 26. a.

x	$\sin x$	$x - \frac{x^3}{6} + \frac{x^5}{120}$	$\left\lvert \sin x - \left(x - \frac{x^3}{6} + \frac{x^5}{120}\right)\right\rvert$
-3.0	-0.141	0.525	0.384
-2.5	-0.598	-0.710	0.111
-2.0	-0.909	-0.933	0.024
-1.5	-0.997	-1.001	0.003
-1.0	-0.841	-0.842	0.0002
-0.5	-0.479	-0.479	0.0000
0	0	0	0.0000
0.5	0.479	0.479	0.0000
1.0	0.841	0.842	0.0002
1.5	0.997	1.001	0.003
2.0	0.909	0.933	0.024
2.5	0.598	0.710	0.111
3.0	0.141	0.525	0.384

LESSON 6-2, p. 359

3. Technique 3:

	$\sin^2 x + \cos^2 x = 1$	Pythagorean Identity
$\Leftrightarrow$	$\frac{\cos^2 x}{\sin^2 x} + \frac{\sin^2 x}{\sin^2 x} = \frac{1}{\sin^2 x}$	$M_{\frac{1}{\sin^2 x}}$; provided $\sin x \neq 0$
$\Leftrightarrow$	$\cot^2 x + 1 = \csc^2 x$	definitions of cot and csc

$\therefore \cot^2 x + 1 = \csc^2 x$

4. a. $\{x \colon x \neq n\pi, \forall \text{ integers } n\}$

   b. (left side)

$\sin x \cot x = \sin x \cdot \frac{\cos x}{\sin x}$	definition of cot
$= \cos x$	simplification

   (right side)

   $\therefore \sin x \cot x = \cos x$ for all real numbers x for which both sides are defined.

5.

	$\cos x \tan x$	$\sin x$
definition of tan	$= \cos x \cdot \frac{\sin x}{\cos x}$	
simplification	$= \sin x$	

$\therefore \cos x \tan x = \sin x$

domain: $\{x \colon x \neq \frac{(2n+1)}{2}\pi, \forall \text{ integers } n\}$

6.

	$\tan x \cdot \cot x$	$\cos^2 x + \sin^2 x$
def. of tan and cot	$= \frac{\sin x}{\cos x} \cdot \frac{\cos x}{\sin x}$	$= 1$ Pythagorean Identity
simplification	$= 1$	

$\therefore \tan x \cdot \cot x = \cos^2 x + \sin^2 x$

domain: $\{x \colon x \neq \frac{n\pi}{2}, \forall \text{ integers } n\}$

7.

	$\csc^2 x \sin x$	$\frac{\sec^2 x - \tan^2 x}{\sin x}$	
def. of csc	$= \frac{1}{\sin^2 x} \cdot \sin x$	$= \frac{\frac{1}{\cos^2 x} - \frac{\sin^2 x}{\cos^2 x}}{\sin x}$	def. of sec and tan
simplification	$= \frac{1}{\sin x}$	$= \frac{1 - \sin^2 x}{\sin x \cos^2 x}$	simplification
		$= \frac{\cos^2 x}{\sin x \cos^2 x}$	Pythagorean Identity
		$= \frac{1}{\sin x}$	simplification

$\therefore \csc^2 x \sin x = \frac{\sec^2 x - \tan^2 x}{\sin x}$

domain: $\{x \colon x \neq \frac{n\pi}{2}, \forall \text{ integers } n\}$

8.

	$\tan x + \cot x$	$\sec x \cdot \csc x$	
def. of tan and cot	$= \frac{\sin x}{\cos x} + \frac{\cos x}{\sin x}$	$= \frac{1}{\cos x} \cdot \frac{1}{\sin x}$	def. of sec and csc
addition of fractions	$= \frac{\sin^2 x + \cos^2 x}{\sin x \cos x}$	$= \frac{1}{\sin x \cos x}$	multiplication of fractions
Pythagorean Identity	$= \frac{1}{\sin x \cos x}$		

$\therefore \tan x + \cot x = \sec x \cdot \csc x$

domain: $\{x \colon x \neq \frac{n\pi}{2}, \forall \text{ integers } n\}$

9. An identity:
(left side)

$\sin^2 x(\cot^2 x + 1) = \sin^2 x\left(\frac{\cos^2 x}{\sin^2 x} + 1\right)$ definition of cot

$= \frac{\sin^2 x \cos^2 x}{\sin^2 x} + \sin^2 x$ Distributive Property

$= \cos^2 x + \sin^2 x$ simplification

$= 1$ Pythgorean Identity

(right side)

LESSON 6-3, pp. 365–366

9. a. The average of the maximum and minimum fox populations: $20.5 = \frac{30 + 11}{2}$.
   b. Half the difference of the maximum and minimum fox populations: $9.5 = \frac{30 - 11}{2}$.
   c. to give function F the appropriate phase shift, since the fox population has maxima at years 2 and 6, but the function $y = \cos\left(\frac{\pi}{2}t\right)$ has maxima at 0 and 4.

11. a. amplitude: 5; period: $\frac{2\pi}{3}$; phase shift: $-\frac{\pi}{2}$
   b.

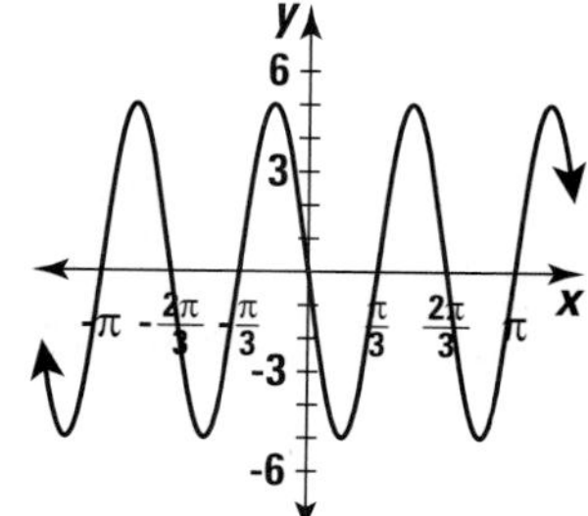

15. It is an identity. Proof:

$\cos x \cot x$	$\csc x - \sin x$
$\cos x \frac{\cos x}{\sin x}$	$\frac{1}{\sin x} - \sin x$
definition of cot	definition of csc
$\frac{\cos^2 x}{\sin x}$	$\frac{1 - \sin^2 x}{\sin x}$
simplification	simplification
	$\frac{\cos^2 x}{\sin x}$
	Pythagorean Identity

$\therefore \cos x \cot x = \csc x - \sin x$

16. a. $\frac{1}{1 + \sin x} + \frac{1}{1 - \sin x}$

$= \frac{1 - \sin x + 1 + \sin x}{1 - \sin^2 x}$ Addition of fractions

$= \frac{2}{1 - \sin^2 x}$ simplification

$= \frac{2}{\cos^2 x}$ Pyth. Identity

$= 2\sec^2 x$ def. of sec

$\therefore \frac{1}{1 + \sin x} + \frac{1}{1 - \sin x} = 2\sec^2 x$

   b. $\{x: x \neq \frac{(2n + 1)\pi}{2}, \forall \text{ integers } n\}$

18. a. $4 + \frac{11}{x^2 + 3}$
   b. $\lim_{x \to \infty} h(x) = 4$; $\lim_{x \to -\infty} h(x) = 4$
   c. h has no discontinuities.
   d.

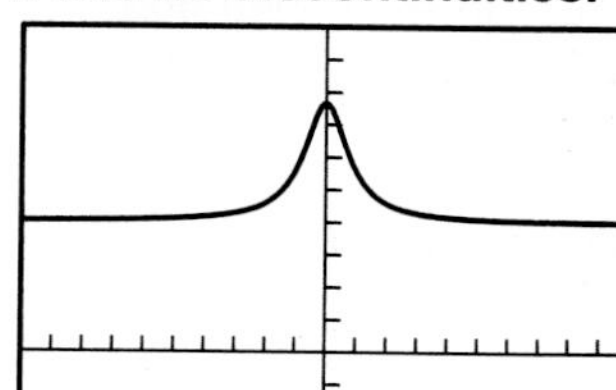

$-20 \le x \le 20$, x-scale $= 2$
$-2 \le y \le 10$, y-scale $= 1$

Yes. The graph asymptotically approaches $y = 4$ as $x \to \infty$ and $x \to -\infty$.

22. Sample: (Source: http://water.dnr.state.sc.us/climate/sercc/products/normals/317069_30yr_norm.html)

Average Monthly High Temperature Raleigh, NC

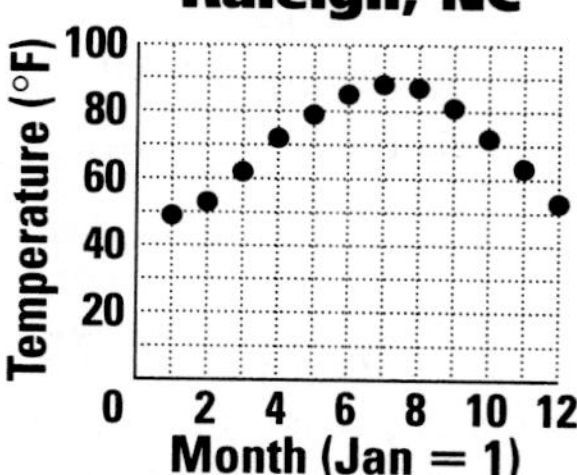

amplitude: 20°; period: 1 year

LESSON 6-4, pp. 370–371

8. $\cos\left(\frac{3\pi}{2} + x\right) = \cos\frac{3\pi}{2}\cos x - \sin\frac{3\pi}{2}\sin x = 0 - (-1)\sin x = \sin x$

9. $\cos(x - y) - \cos(x + y) = \cos x \cos y + \sin x \sin y - (\cos x \cos y - \sin x \sin y) = 2\sin x \sin y$

19. a.

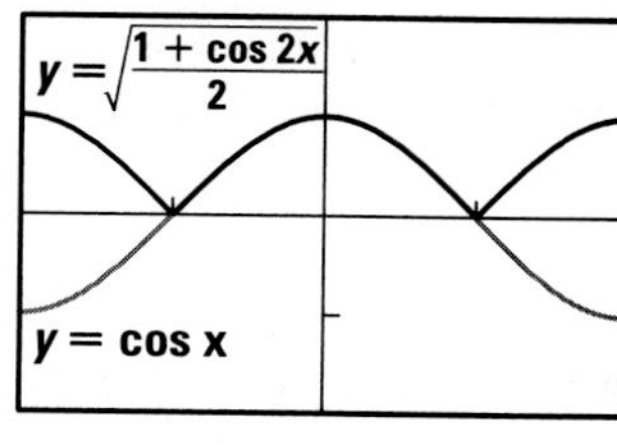

$-\pi \le x \le \pi$, x-scale $= \frac{\pi}{2}$
$-2 \le y \le 2$, y-scale $= 1$

   b. $-\frac{\pi}{2} \le x \le \frac{\pi}{2}$
   c. (i) $\sqrt{\frac{1 + \cos\left(2 \cdot \frac{\pi}{4}\right)}{2}} = \frac{\sqrt{2}}{2}$ and $\cos\frac{\pi}{4} = \frac{\sqrt{2}}{2}$

   (ii) $\sqrt{\frac{1 + \cos\left(2 \cdot \frac{3\pi}{4}\right)}{2}} = \frac{\sqrt{2}}{2}$ but $\cos\frac{3\pi}{4} = -\frac{\sqrt{2}}{2}$

   d. $\sqrt{\frac{1 + \cos 2x}{2}} = |\cos x|$

LESSON 6-5, p. 376

13. $R_{\theta + \phi} = \begin{bmatrix} \cos(\theta + \phi) & -\sin(\theta + \phi) \\ \sin(\theta + \phi) & \cos(\theta + \phi) \end{bmatrix}$;

$R_\theta \cdot R_\phi = \begin{bmatrix} \cos\theta & -\sin\theta \\ \sin\theta & \cos\theta \end{bmatrix}\begin{bmatrix} \cos\phi & -\sin\phi \\ \sin\phi & \cos\phi \end{bmatrix}$

$= \begin{bmatrix} \cos\theta\cos\phi - \sin\theta\sin\phi & -\cos\theta\sin\phi - \sin\theta\cos\phi \\ \sin\theta\cos\phi + \cos\theta\sin\phi & -\sin\theta\sin\phi + \cos\theta\cos\phi \end{bmatrix}$

15. a. $a^2 + b^2 + (c + k)^2 + (d + k)^2$
$= a^2 + b^2 + c^2 + 2ck + k^2 + d^2 + 2dk + k^2$ Multiplication
$= c^2 + d^2 + a^2 + b^2 + 2k(c + d) + 2k^2$ Factoring
$= c^2 + d^2 + a^2 + b^2 + 2k(a + b) + 2k^2$ $a + b = c + d$
$= c^2 + d^2 + a^2 + 2ak + k^2 + b^2 + 2kb + b^2$ Distributive property
$= c^2 + d^2 + (a + k)^2 + (b + k)^2$ Factoring

   b. Sample: For $k > 0$, sums of squares are equal to the sums of different squares. If $k = 2$, $1^2 + 4^2 + 4^2 + 5^2 = 2^2 + 3^2 + 3^2 + 6^2 = 58$

20. c. Proof: (Chunk $(\alpha + \beta)$ and apply cosine and sine of sum identities.)
$\cos[(\alpha + \beta) + \gamma] =$
$\cos(\alpha + \beta)\cos\gamma - \sin(\alpha + \beta)\sin\gamma$
$= (\cos\alpha\cos\beta - \sin\alpha\sin\beta)\cos\gamma - (\sin\alpha\cos\beta + \cos\alpha\sin\beta)\sin\gamma$
$= \cos\alpha\cos\beta\cos\gamma - \sin\alpha\sin\beta\cos\gamma - \sin\alpha\cos\beta\sin\gamma - \cos\alpha\sin\beta\sin\gamma$

$$\frac{\sin(\alpha+\beta)}{\cos\alpha \cdot \cos\beta} = \tan\alpha + \tan\beta$$

$$\frac{\sin\alpha \cdot \cos\beta + \sin\beta \cdot \cos\alpha}{\cos\alpha \cdot \cos\beta}$$

$$\frac{\sin\alpha \cdot \cos\beta}{\cos\alpha \cdot \cos\beta} + \frac{\sin\beta \cdot \cos\alpha}{\cos\alpha \cos\beta}$$

$$\frac{\sin\alpha}{\cos\alpha} + \frac{\sin\beta}{\cos\beta}$$

$$\tan\alpha + \tan\beta$$

$$\frac{\sin\alpha}{\cos\alpha} + \frac{\sin\beta}{\sin\beta}$$

LESSON 6-7, p. 390

3. a.

points on $y = \sin x$	$(-\frac{\pi}{2}, -1)$	$(-\frac{\pi}{3}, -\frac{\sqrt{3}}{2})$	$(-\frac{\pi}{4}, -\frac{\sqrt{2}}{2})$	$(-\frac{\pi}{6}, -\frac{1}{2})$	$(0, 0)$	$(\frac{\pi}{6}, \frac{1}{2})$	$(\frac{\pi}{4}, \frac{\sqrt{2}}{2})$	$(\frac{\pi}{3}, \frac{\sqrt{3}}{2})$	$(\frac{\pi}{2}, 1)$
corresponding points $y = \sin^{-1}x$	$(-1, -\frac{\pi}{2})$	$(-\frac{\sqrt{3}}{2}, -\frac{\pi}{3})$	$(-\frac{\sqrt{2}}{2}, -\frac{\pi}{4})$	$(-\frac{1}{2}, -\frac{\pi}{6})$	$(0, 0)$	$(\frac{1}{2}, \frac{\pi}{6})$	$(\frac{\sqrt{2}}{2}, \frac{\pi}{4})$	$(\frac{\sqrt{3}}{2}, \frac{\pi}{3})$	$(1, \frac{\pi}{2})$

23. a. Sample: Let $x = 0$.

Then $\sin(0 + \frac{\pi}{4}) + \sin(0 - \frac{\pi}{4})$

$= \sin 0 \cos\frac{\pi}{4} + \cos 0 \sin\frac{\pi}{4} + \sin 0 \cos\frac{\pi}{4} - \cos 0 \sin\frac{\pi}{4}$

$= 0 + \frac{\sqrt{2}}{2} + 0 - \frac{\sqrt{2}}{2} = 0 = \sin 0$

b. $\sin(x + \frac{\pi}{3}) + \sin(x - \frac{\pi}{3})$

$= \sin x \cos\frac{\pi}{3} + \sin\frac{\pi}{3}\cos x + \sin x \cos\frac{\pi}{3} - \sin\frac{\pi}{3}\cos x$

$= 2 \cdot \sin x \cdot \frac{1}{2} = \sin x$

25. a. Sample: 15, 26, 37, 48, 59, 70, 81, 92, 103, 114

b. Sample: $\frac{5\pi}{2}, \frac{7\pi}{2}, \frac{9\pi}{2}, \frac{11\pi}{2}, \frac{13\pi}{2}$

CHAPTER 6 PROJECTS, p. 398

2. c. iii. $\frac{\text{ptan } x + \text{ptan } y}{1 + \text{ptan } x \text{ ptan } y}$

$$= \frac{\frac{2^{2x}-1}{2^{2x}+1} + \frac{2^{2y}-1}{2^{2y}+1}}{1 + \frac{2^{2x}-1}{2^{2x}+1} \cdot \frac{2^{2y}-1}{2^{2y}+1}}$$

$$= \frac{\frac{(2^{2x}-1)(2^{2y}+1) + (2^{2y}-1)(2^{2x}+1)}{(2^{2x}+1)(2^{2y}+1)}}{\frac{(2^{2x}+1)(2^{2y}+1) + (2^{2x}-1)(2^{2y}-1)}{(2^{2x}+1)(2^{2y}+1)}}$$

$$= \frac{(2^{2x}-1)(2^{2y}+1) + (2^{2y}-1)(2^{2x}+1)}{(2^{2x}+1)(2^{2y}+1) + (2^{2x}-1)(2^{2y}-1)}$$

$$= \frac{2^{2x+2y} - 2^{2y} + 2^{2x} - 1 + 2^{2x+2y} - 2^{2x} + 2^{2y} - 1}{2^{2x+2y} + 2^{2x} + 2^{2y} + 1 + 2^{2x+2y} - 2^{2x} - 2^{2y} + 1}$$

$$= \frac{2^{2x+2y} - 1 + 2^{2x+2y} - 1}{2^{2x+2y} + 1 + 2^{2x+2y} + 1} = \frac{2(2^{2(x+y)} - 1)}{2(2^{2(x+y)} + 1)}$$

$$= \frac{2^{2(x+y)} - 1}{2^{2(x+y)} + 1} = \text{ptan}(x + y)$$

2. d. Samples:

psin x pcos y − pcos x psin y

$= (2^{x-1} - 2^{-x-1})(2^{y-1} + 2^{-y-1}) - (2^{x-1} + 2^{-x-1})(2^{y-1} - 2^{-y-1})$

$= 2^{x+y-2} + 2^{x-y-2} - 2^{-x+y-2} - 2^{-x-y-2} - 2^{x+y-2} + 2^{x-y-2} - 2^{-x+y-2} + 2^{-x-y-2}$

$= 2^{x-y-2} - 2^{-x+y-2} + 2^{x-y-2} - 2^{-x+y-2}$

$= 2^{(x-y)-1} - 2^{-(x-y)-1}$

$=$ psin$(x - y)$

pcos x pcos y − psin x psin y

$= (2^{x-1} + 2^{-x-1})(2^{y-1} + 2^{-y-1}) - (2^{x-1} - 2^{-x-1})(2^{y-1} - 2^{-y-1})$

$= 2^{x+y-2} + 2^{x-y-2} + 2^{-x+y-2} + 2^{-x-y-2} - 2^{x+y-2} + 2^{x-y-2} + 2^{-x+y-2} - 2^{-x-y-2}$

$= 2^{x-y-2} + 2^{-x+y-2} + 2^{x-y-2} + 2^{-x+y-2} = 2^{(x-y)-1} + 2^{-(x-y)-1} =$ pcos$(x - y)$

$$\frac{\text{ptan } x - \text{ptan } y}{1 - \text{ptan } x \text{ ptan } y} = \frac{\frac{2^{2x}-1}{2^{2x}+1} - \frac{2^{2y}-1}{2^{2y}+1}}{1 - \frac{2^{2x}-1}{2^{2x}+1} \cdot \frac{2^{2y}-1}{2^{2y}+1}} = \frac{\frac{(2^{2x}-1)(2^{2y}+1) - (2^{2y}-1)(2^{2x}+1)}{(2^{2x}+1)(2^{2y}+1)}}{\frac{(2^{2x}+1)(2^{2y}+1) - (2^{2x}-1)(2^{2y}-1)}{(2^{2x}+1)(2^{2y}+1)}}$$

$$= \frac{(2^{2x}-1)(2^{2y}+1) - (2^{2y}-1)(2^{2x}+1)}{(2^{2x}+1)(2^{2y}+1) - (2^{2x}-1)(2^{2y}-1)} = \frac{2^{2x+2y} - 2^{2y} + 2^{2x} - 1 - 2^{2x+2y} + 2^{2x} - 2^{2y} + 1}{2^{2x+2y} + 2^{2x} + 2^{2y} + 1 - 2^{2x+2y} + 2^{2x} + 2^{2y} - 1}$$

$$= \frac{-2^{2y} + 2^{2x} + 2^{2x} - 2^{2y}}{2^{2x} + 2^{2y} + 2^{2x} + 2^{2y}} = \frac{2^{2x+1} - 2^{2y+1}}{2^{2x+1} + 2^{2y+1}} = \frac{\frac{2^{2x+1}}{2^{2y+1}} - 1}{\frac{2^{2x+1}}{2^{2y+1}} + 1} = \frac{2^{2(x-y)} - 1}{2^{2(x-y)} + 1} = \text{ptan}(x - y)$$

CHAPTER 6 PROGRESS SELF-TEST, p. 400

9.

$\frac{\sin(\alpha + \beta)}{\cos\alpha\cos\beta}$	$\tan\alpha + \tan\beta$
Identity for $\sin(\alpha + \beta)$ $= \frac{\sin\alpha\cos\beta + \cos\alpha\sin\beta}{\cos\alpha\cos\beta}$	$= \frac{\sin\alpha}{\cos\alpha} + \frac{\sin\beta}{\cos\beta}$
simplifying $= \frac{\sin\alpha}{\cos\alpha} + \frac{\sin\beta}{\cos\beta}$	

$\therefore \frac{\sin(\alpha + \beta)}{\cos\alpha\cos\beta} = \tan\alpha + \tan\beta$

domain: $\alpha \neq (2n + 1)\frac{\pi}{2}$, $\beta \neq (2n + 1)\frac{\pi}{2}$, n an integer

CHAPTER 6 REVIEW, pp. 402–403

36.

$\sec x + \cot x \csc x$	$\sec x \csc^2 x$
Trig. def. $= \frac{1}{\cos x} + \frac{\cos x}{\sin^2 x}$	$= \frac{1}{\cos x \sin^2 x}$ Trig. def.
add. of fractions $= \frac{\sin^2 x + \cos^2 x}{\cos x \sin^2 x}$	
Pyth. Identity $= \frac{1}{\cos x \sin^2 x}$	

$\therefore \sec x + \cot x \csc x = \sec x \csc^2 x$; domain: $x \neq \frac{n\pi}{2}$, n an integer

37. (left side)

$= \cos 4x$

$= \cos^2 2x - \sin^2 2x$ — Identity for $\cos 2x$

$= (\cos^2 x - \sin^2 x)^2 - (2\cos x \sin x)^2$ — Identities for $\cos 2x$ and $\sin 2x$

$= \cos^4 x - 2\cos^2 x \sin^2 x + \sin^4 x - 4\cos^2 x \sin^2 x$ — Multiplication

(right side)

$\therefore \cos 4x = \cos^4 x - 6\cos^2 x \sin^2 x + \sin^4 x$

domain: all real numbers

51. an identity;

	$1 + \cot^2 x$	$\csc^2 x$
def. of cot	$= 1 + \frac{\cos^2 x}{\sin^2 x}$	$= \frac{1}{\sin^2 x}$ def. of cos
addition	$= \frac{\sin^2 x + \cos^2 x}{\sin^2 x}$	
Pythagorean Identity	$= \frac{1}{\sin^2 x}$	

$\therefore 1 + \cot^2 x = \csc^2 x$, $x \neq n\pi$, n an integer

53. an identity;
(left side)
$= \tan(\pi + \gamma)$
$= \frac{\sin(\pi + \gamma)}{\cos(\pi + \gamma)}$ def. of tan
$= \frac{\sin \pi \cos \gamma + \sin \gamma \cos \pi}{\cos \pi \cos \gamma - \sin \pi \sin \gamma}$ Identities for sine and cosine of a sum
$= \frac{-\sin \gamma}{-\cos \gamma}$ evaluating specific values of trig. functions
$= \tan \gamma$ def. tan
(right side)
$\therefore \tan \gamma = \tan(\pi + \gamma)$

54. Approximately $-2 \le x \le 2$
55. You can check various different cases by holding α constant and graphing the resulting functions in β. For example, when $\alpha = \frac{\pi}{3}$, you could graph $y = \sin(\frac{\pi}{3} + \beta)$ and $y = \sin \frac{\pi}{3} \cos \beta - \cos \frac{\pi}{3} \sin \beta$.
56. a.

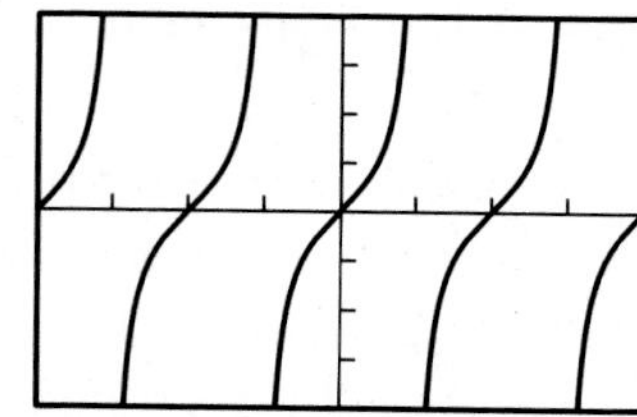

$-2\pi \le x \le 2\pi$, x-scale $= \frac{\pi}{2}$
$-4 \le y \le 4$, y-scale $= 1$

b. $y = \tan x$
c. $\sin x \sec x = \tan x$
57. a. $x \approx 1.1$ or $x \approx 3.6$
b. $0 \le x < 1.1$, $3.6 < x < 2\pi$
58. a. $x = \pm\frac{\pi}{4}, \pm\frac{3\pi}{4}, \pm\frac{5\pi}{4}, \pm\frac{7\pi}{4}$

INDEX

INDEX

NOTES

NOTES

NOTES

NOTES

NOTES

NOTES

NOTES

NOTES

NOTES